CUMULATIVE PROBABILITIES FOR THE STANDARD NORMAL DISTRIBUTION

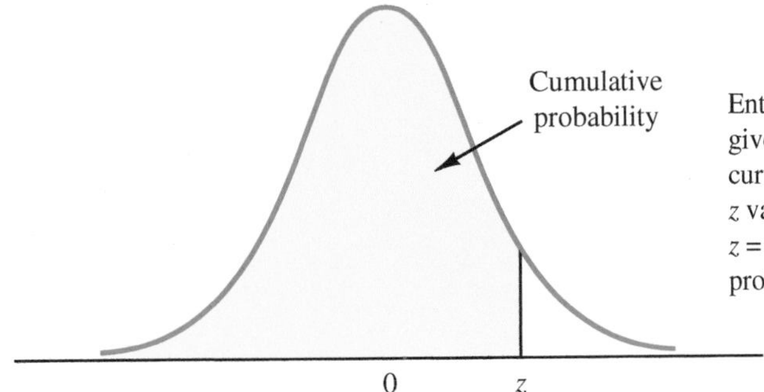

Entries in the table give the area under the curve to the left of the z value. For example, for $z = 1.25$, the cumulative probability is .8944.

z	.00	.01	.02	.03	.04	.05	.06	.07	.08	.09
.0	.5000	.5040	.5080	.5120	.5160	.5199	.5239	.5279	.5319	.5359
.1	.5398	.5438	.5478	.5517	.5557	.5596	.5636	.5675	.5714	.5753
.2	.5793	.5832	.5871	.5910	.5948	.5987	.6026	.6064	.6103	.6141
.3	.6179	.6217	.6255	.6293	.6331	.6368	.6406	.6443	.6480	.6517
.4	.6554	.6591	.6628	.6664	.6700	.6736	.6772	.6808	.6844	.6879
.5	.6915	.6950	.6985	.7019	.7054	.7088	.7123	.7157	.7190	.7224
.6	.7257	.7291	.7324	.7357	.7389	.7422	.7454	.7486	.7517	.7549
.7	.7580	.7611	.7642	.7673	.7704	.7734	.7764	.7794	.7823	.7852
.8	.7881	.7910	.7939	.7967	.7995	.8023	.8051	.8078	.8106	.8133
.9	.8159	.8186	.8212	.8238	.8264	.8289	.8315	.8340	.8365	.8389
1.0	.8413	.8438	.8461	.8485	.8508	.8531	.8554	.8577	.8599	.8621
1.1	.8643	.8665	.8686	.8708	.8729	.8749	.8770	.8790	.8810	.8830
1.2	.8849	.8869	.8888	.8907	.8925	.8944	.8962	.8980	.8997	.9015
1.3	.9032	.9049	.9066	.9082	.9099	.9115	.9131	.9147	.9162	.9177
1.4	.9192	.9207	.9222	.9236	.9251	.9265	.9279	.9292	.9306	.9319
1.5	.9332	.9345	.9357	.9370	.9382	.9394	.9406	.9418	.9429	.9441
1.6	.9452	.9463	.9474	.9484	.9495	.9505	.9515	.9525	.9535	.9545
1.7	.9554	.9564	.9573	.9582	.9591	.9599	.9608	.9616	.9625	.9633
1.8	.9641	.9649	.9656	.9664	.9671	.9678	.9686	.9693	.9699	.9706
1.9	.9713	.9719	.9726	.9732	.9738	.9744	.9750	.9756	.9761	.9767
2.0	.9772	.9778	.9783	.9788	.9793	.9798	.9803	.9808	.9812	.9817
2.1	.9821	.9826	.9830	.9834	.9838	.9842	.9846	.9850	.9854	.9857
2.2	.9861	.9864	.9868	.9871	.9875	.9878	.9881	.9884	.9887	.9890
2.3	.9893	.9896	.9898	.9901	.9904	.9906	.9909	.9911	.9913	.9916
2.4	.9918	.9920	.9922	.9925	.9927	.9929	.9931	.9932	.9934	.9936
2.5	.9938	.9940	.9941	.9943	.9945	.9946	.9948	.9949	.9951	.9952
2.6	.9953	.9955	.9956	.9957	.9959	.9960	.9961	.9962	.9963	.9964
2.7	.9965	.9966	.9967	.9968	.9969	.9970	.9971	.9972	.9973	.9974
2.8	.9974	.9975	.9976	.9977	.9977	.9978	.9979	.9979	.9980	.9981
2.9	.9981	.9982	.9982	.9983	.9984	.9984	.9985	.9985	.9986	.9986
3.0	.9987	.9987	.9987	.9988	.9988	.9989	.9989	.9989	.9990	.9990

Essentials of Business Statistics and Analytics

University of Toledo

Special Edition

Jeffrey D. Camm | James J. Cochran | Michael J. Fry | Jeffrey W. Ohlmann | David R. Anderson | Dennis J. Sweeney | Thomas A. Williams

CENGAGE Learning

Australia • Brazil • Japan • Korea • Mexico • Singapore • Spain • United Kingdom • United States

Essentials of Business Statistics and Analytics: University of Toledo, Special Edition

Essentials of Modern Business Statistics with Microsoft® Excel®, 6th Edition
David R. Anderson | Dennis J. Sweeney | Thomas A. Williams

Essentials of Business Analytics, 2nd Edition
Jeffrey D. Camm | James J. Cochran | Michael J. Fry | Jeffrey W. Ohlmann | David R. Anderson | Dennis J. Sweeney | Thomas A. Williams

ISBN: 978-1-337-05189-7

Printed in Mexico

Cengage Learning
20 Channel Center Street
Boston, MA 02210
USA

Cengage Learning is a leading provider of customized learning solutions with office locations around the globe, including Singapore, the United Kingdom, Australia, Mexico, Brazil, and Japan. Locate your local office at: **www.international.cengage.com/region.**

Cengage Learning products are represented in Canada by Nelson Education, Ltd.

For your lifelong learning solutions, visit **www.cengage.com/custom.**

Visit our corporate website at **www.cengage.com.**

Brief Contents

From:
Essentials of Modern Business Statistics with Microsoft® Excel®, 6th Edition
David R. Anderson | Dennis J. Sweeney | Thomas A. Williams

Chapter 1 Data and Statistics 1
Chapter 2 Descriptive Statistics: Tabular and Graphical Presentations 36
Chapter 3 Descriptive Statistics: Numerical Measures 106
Chapter 4 Introduction to Probability 178
Chapter 5 Discrete Probability Distributions 224
Chapter 6 Continuous Probability Distributions 268
Chapter 7 Sampling and Sampling Distributions 300
Chapter 8 Interval Estimation 341
Chapter 9 Hypothesis Tests 381
Chapter 10 Comparisons Involving Means, Experimental Design, and Analysis of Variance 428
Chapter 11 Comparisons Involving Proportions and a Test of Independence 489

From:
Essentials of Business Analytics, 2nd Edition
Jeffrey D. Camm | James J. Cochran | Michael J. Fry | Jeffrey W. Ohlmann |
David R. Anderson | Dennis J. Sweeney | Thomas A. Williams

Chapter 1 Introduction 1
Chapter 4 Descriptive Data Mining 137
Chapter 7 Linear Regression 295
Chapter 8 Time Series Analysis and Forecasting 380
Chapter 9 Predictive Data Mining 438
Chapter 10 Spreadsheet Models 508
Chapter 15 Decision Analysis 752
Appendix A Basics of Excel 810

From:
Essentials of Modern Business Statistics with Microsoft® Excel®, 6th Edition
David R. Anderson | Dennis J. Sweeney | Thomas A. Williams

Appendix B Tables B-1

From:
Essentials of Business Analytics, 2nd Edition
Jeffrey D. Camm | James J. Cochran | Michael J. Fry | Jeffrey W. Ohlmann |
David R. Anderson | Dennis J. Sweeney | Thomas A. Williams

Appendix C Solutions to Even-Numbered Questions (select chapters):
Chapter 4 Descriptive Data Mining 19
Chapter 7 Regression Analysis 40
Chapter 8 Time Series Analysis and Forecasting 75
Chapter 9 Predictive Data Mining 106
Chapter 10 Spreadsheet Models 119
Chapter 15 Decision Analysis 211

From:
Essentials of Modern Business Statistics with Microsoft® Excel®, 6th Edition
David R. Anderson | Dennis J. Sweeney | Thomas A. Williams

Appendix D Self-Test Solutions and Answers to Even-Numbered Exercises D-1
Appendix E Microsoft Excel 2013 and Tools for Statistical Analysis E-1

CHAPTER 1

Data and Statistics

CONTENTS

STATISTICS IN PRACTICE: *BLOOMBERG BUSINESSWEEK*

1.1 APPLICATIONS IN BUSINESS AND ECONOMICS
- Accounting
- Finance
- Marketing
- Production
- Economics
- Information Systems

1.2 DATA
- Elements, Variables, and Observations
- Scales of Measurement
- Categorical and Quantitative Data
- Cross-Sectional and Time Series Data

1.3 DATA SOURCES
- Existing Sources
- Observational Study
- Experiment
- Time and Cost Issues
- Data Acquisition Errors

1.4 DESCRIPTIVE STATISTICS

1.5 STATISTICAL INFERENCE

1.6 STATISTICAL ANALYSIS USING MICROSOFT EXCEL
- Data Sets and Excel Worksheets
- Using Excel for Statistical Analysis

1.7 DATA MINING

1.8 ETHICAL GUIDELINES FOR STATISTICAL PRACTICE

STATISTICS *in* PRACTICE

*BLOOMBERG BUSINESSWEEK**
NEW YORK, NEW YORK

With a global circulation of more than 1 million, *Bloomberg Businessweek* is one of the most widely read business magazines in the world. Bloomberg's 1700 reporters in 145 service bureaus around the world enable *Bloomberg Businessweek* to deliver a variety of articles of interest to the global business and economic community. Along with feature articles on current topics, the magazine contains articles on international business, economic analysis, information processing, and science and technology. Information in the feature articles and the regular sections helps readers stay abreast of current developments and assess the impact of those developments on business and economic conditions.

Most issues of *Bloomberg Businessweek,* formerly *BusinessWeek,* provide an in-depth report on a topic of current interest. Often, the in-depth reports contain statistical facts and summaries that help the reader understand the business and economic information. Examples of articles and reports include the impact of businesses moving important work to cloud computing, the crisis facing the U.S. Postal Service, and why the debt crisis is even worse than we think. In addition, *Bloomberg Businessweek* provides a variety of statistics about the state of the economy, including production indexes, stock prices, mutual funds, and interest rates.

Bloomberg Businessweek also uses statistics and statistical information in managing its own business. For example, an annual survey of subscribers helps the company learn about subscriber demographics, reading habits, likely purchases, lifestyles, and so on. *Bloomberg Businessweek* managers use statistical summaries from the survey to provide better services to subscribers and advertisers. One recent North American subscriber survey indicated that 90% of *Bloomberg Businessweek* subscribers use a personal computer at home and that 64% of *Bloomberg Businessweek* subscribers are involved with computer purchases at work. Such statistics alert *Bloomberg Businessweek* managers to subscriber interest in articles about new developments in computers. The results of the subscriber survey are also made available to potential advertisers. The high percentage of subscribers using personal computers at home and the high percentage of subscribers involved with computer purchases at work would be an incentive for a computer manufacturer to consider advertising in *Bloomberg Businessweek.*

Bloomberg Businessweek uses statistical facts and summaries in many of its articles. © Kyodo/Newscom

In this chapter, we discuss the types of data available for statistical analysis and describe how the data are obtained. We introduce descriptive statistics and statistical inference as ways of converting data into meaningful and easily interpreted statistical information.

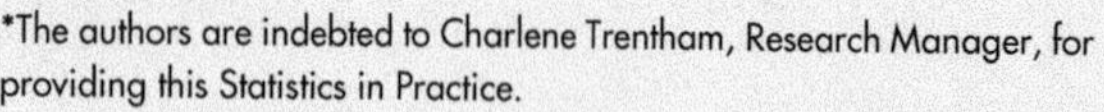
*The authors are indebted to Charlene Trentham, Research Manager, for providing this Statistics in Practice.

Frequently, we see the following types of statements in newspapers and magazines:

- In the first nine months of last year, Turkish Airlines' profit increased to about $482 million on sales of $6.2 billion (*Fortune*, February 25, 2013).
- A survey conducted by the Pew Research Center reported that 68% of Internet users believe current laws are not good enough in protecting people's privacy online (*The Wall Street Journal*, March 24, 2014).

- VW Group's U.S. sales continue to slide, with total sales off by 13% from last January, to 36,930 vehicles (*Panorama*, March 2014).
- A Yahoo! Finance survey reported 51% of workers say the key to getting ahead is internal politics, whereas 27% say the key to getting ahead is hard work (*USA Today*, September 29, 2012).
- The California State Teachers' Retirement System has $154.3 billion under management (*Bloomberg Businessweek*, January 21–January 27, 2013).
- At a Sotheby's art auction held on February 5, 2013, Pablo Picasso's painting *Woman Sitting Near a Window* sold for $45 million (*The Wall Street Journal*, February 15, 2013).
- Over the past three months, the industry average for sales incentives per vehicle by GM, Chrysler, Ford, Toyota, and Honda was $2336 (*The Wall Street Journal*, February 14, 2013).

The numerical facts in the preceding statements—$482 million, $6.2 billion, 68%, 13%, 36,930, 51%, 27%, $154.3 billion, $45 million, $2336—are called **statistics**. In this usage, the term *statistics* refers to numerical facts such as averages, medians, percentages, and maximums that help us understand a variety of business and economic situations. However, as you will see, the field, or subject, of statistics involves much more than numerical facts. In a broader sense, statistics is the art and science of collecting, analyzing, presenting, and interpreting data. Particularly in business and economics, the information provided by collecting, analyzing, presenting, and interpreting data gives managers and decision makers a better understanding of the business and economic environment and thus enables them to make more informed and better decisions. In this text, we emphasize the use of statistics for business and economic decision making.

Chapter 1 begins with some illustrations of the applications of statistics in business and economics. In Section 1.2 we define the term *data* and introduce the concept of a data set. This section also introduces key terms such as *variables* and *observations,* discusses the difference between quantitative and categorical data, and illustrates the uses of cross-sectional and time series data. Section 1.3 discusses how data can be obtained from existing sources or through survey and experimental studies designed to obtain new data. The important role that the Internet now plays in obtaining data is also highlighted. The uses of data in developing descriptive statistics and in making statistical inferences are described in Sections 1.4 and 1.5. The last three sections of Chapter 1 provide the role of the computer in statistical analysis, an introduction to data mining, and a discussion of ethical guidelines for statistical practice. A chapter-ending appendix includes an introduction to the add-in StatTools which can be used to extend the statistical options for users of Microsoft Excel.

1.1 Applications in Business and Economics

In today's global business and economic environment, anyone can access vast amounts of statistical information. The most successful managers and decision makers understand the information and know how to use it effectively. In this section, we provide examples that illustrate some of the uses of statistics in business and economics.

Accounting

Public accounting firms use statistical sampling procedures when conducting audits for their clients. For instance, suppose an accounting firm wants to determine whether the amount of accounts receivable shown on a client's balance sheet fairly represents the actual amount of accounts receivable. Usually the large number of individual accounts receivable makes reviewing and validating every account too time-consuming and expensive. As common practice in such situations, the audit staff selects a subset of the accounts called a sample. After reviewing the accuracy of the sampled accounts, the auditors draw a conclusion as to whether the accounts receivable amount shown on the client's balance sheet is acceptable.

Finance

Financial analysts use a variety of statistical information to guide their investment recommendations. In the case of stocks, analysts review financial data such as price/earnings ratios and dividend yields. By comparing the information for an individual stock with information about the stock market averages, an analyst can begin to draw a conclusion as to whether the stock is a good investment. For example, *The Wall Street Journal* (March 19, 2012) reported that the average dividend yield for the S&P 500 companies was 2.2%. Microsoft showed a dividend yield of 2.42%. In this case, the statistical information on dividend yield indicates a higher dividend yield for Microsoft than the average dividend yield for the S&P 500 companies. This and other information about Microsoft would help the analyst make an informed buy, sell, or hold recommendation for Microsoft stock.

Marketing

Electronic scanners at retail checkout counters collect data for a variety of marketing research applications. For example, data suppliers such as ACNielsen and Information Resources, Inc., purchase point-of-sale scanner data from grocery stores, process the data, and then sell statistical summaries of the data to manufacturers. Manufacturers spend hundreds of thousands of dollars per product category to obtain this type of scanner data. Manufacturers also purchase data and statistical summaries on promotional activities such as special pricing and the use of in-store displays. Brand managers can review the scanner statistics and the promotional activity statistics to gain a better understanding of the relationship between promotional activities and sales. Such analyses often prove helpful in establishing future marketing strategies for the various products.

Production

Today's emphasis on quality makes quality control an important application of statistics in production. A variety of statistical quality control charts are used to monitor the output of a production process. In particular, an x-bar chart can be used to monitor the average output. Suppose, for example, that a machine fills containers with 12 ounces of a soft drink. Periodically, a production worker selects a sample of containers and computes the average number of ounces in the sample. This average, or x-bar value, is plotted on an x-bar chart. A plotted value above the chart's upper control limit indicates overfilling, and a plotted value below the chart's lower control limit indicates underfilling. The process is termed "in control" and allowed to continue as long as the plotted x-bar values fall between the chart's upper and lower control limits. Properly interpreted, an x-bar chart can help determine when adjustments are necessary to correct a production process.

Economics

Economists frequently provide forecasts about the future of the economy or some aspect of it. They use a variety of statistical information in making such forecasts. For instance, in forecasting inflation rates, economists use statistical information on such indicators as the Producer Price Index, the unemployment rate, and manufacturing capacity utilization. Often these statistical indicators are entered into computerized forecasting models that predict inflation rates.

Information Systems

Information systems administrators are responsible for the day-to-day operation of an organization's computer networks. A variety of statistical information helps administrators assess the performance of computer networks, including local area networks (LANs), wide area networks (WANs), network segments, intranets, and other data communication systems. Statistics such as the mean number of users on the system, the proportion of time any component of the system is down, and the proportion of bandwidth utilized at various times of the day are examples of statistical information that help the system administrator better understand and manage the computer network.

Applications of statistics such as those described in this section are an integral part of this text. Such examples provide an overview of the breadth of statistical applications. To supplement these examples, practitioners in the fields of business and economics provided chapter-opening Statistics in Practice articles that introduce the material covered in each chapter. The Statistics in Practice applications show the importance of statistics in a wide variety of business and economic situations.

1.2 Data

Data are the facts and figures collected, analyzed, and summarized for presentation and interpretation. All the data collected in a particular study are referred to as the **data set** for the study. Table 1.1 shows a data set containing information for 60 nations that participate in the World Trade Organization. The World Trade Organization encourages the free flow of international trade and provides a forum for resolving trade disputes.

Elements, Variables, and Observations

Elements are the entities on which data are collected. Each nation listed in Table 1.1 is an element with the nation or element name shown in the first column. With 60 nations, the data set contains 60 elements.

A **variable** is a characteristic of interest for the elements. The data set in Table 1.1 includes the following five variables:

- WTO Status: The nation's membership status in the World Trade Organization; this can be either as a member or an observer.
- Per Capita GDP ($): The total market value ($) of all goods and services produced by the nation divided by the number of people in the nation; this is commonly used to compare economic productivity of the nations.
- Trade Deficit ($1000s): The difference between the total dollar value of the nation's imports and the total dollar value of the nation's exports.
- Fitch Rating: The nation's sovereign credit rating as appraised by the Fitch Group[1]; the credit ratings range from a high of AAA to a low of F and can be modified by + or −.
- Fitch Outlook: An indication of the direction the credit rating is likely to move over the upcoming two years; the outlook can be negative, stable, or positive.

Measurements collected on each variable for every element in a study provide the data. The set of measurements obtained for a particular element is called an **observation**. Referring to Table 1.1, we see that the first observation contains the following measurements:

[1]The Fitch Group is one of three nationally recognized statistical rating organizations designated by the U.S. Securities and Exchange Commission. The other two are Standard and Poor's and Moody's investor service.

Nations

Data sets such as Nations are available on the website for this text.

TABLE 1.1 DATA SET FOR 60 NATIONS IN THE WORLD TRADE ORGANIZATION

Nation	WTO Status	Per Capita GDP ($)	Trade Deficit ($1000s)	Fitch Rating	Fitch Outlook
Armenia	Member	5,400	2,673,359	BB−	Stable
Australia	Member	40,800	−33,304,157	AAA	Stable
Austria	Member	41,700	12,796,558	AAA	Stable
Azerbaijan	Observer	5,400	−16,747,320	BBB−	Positive
Bahrain	Member	27,300	3,102,665	BBB	Stable
Belgium	Member	37,600	−14,930,833	AA+	Negative
Brazil	Member	11,600	−29,796,166	BBB	Stable
Bulgaria	Member	13,500	4,049,237	BBB−	Positive
Canada	Member	40,300	−1,611,380	AAA	Stable
Cape Verde	Member	4,000	874,459	B+	Stable
Chile	Member	16,100	−14,558,218	A+	Stable
China	Member	8,400	−156,705,311	A+	Stable
Colombia	Member	10,100	−1,561,199	BBB−	Stable
Costa Rica	Member	11,500	5,807,509	BB+	Stable
Croatia	Member	18,300	8,108,103	BBB−	Negative
Cyprus	Member	29,100	6,623,337	BBB	Negative
Czech Republic	Member	25,900	−10,749,467	A+	Positive
Denmark	Member	40,200	−15,057,343	AAA	Stable
Ecuador	Member	8,300	1,993,819	B−	Stable
Egypt	Member	6,500	28,486,933	BB	Negative
El Salvador	Member	7,600	5,019,363	BB	Stable
Estonia	Member	20,200	802,234	A+	Stable
France	Member	35,000	118,841,542	AAA	Stable
Georgia	Member	5,400	4,398,153	B+	Positive
Germany	Member	37,900	−213,367,685	AAA	Stable
Hungary	Member	19,600	−9,421,301	BBB−	Negative
Iceland	Member	38,000	−504,939	BB+	Stable
Ireland	Member	39,500	−59,093,323	BBB+	Negative
Israel	Member	31,000	6,722,291	A	Stable
Italy	Member	30,100	33,568,668	A+	Negative
Japan	Member	34,300	31,675,424	AA	Negative
Kazakhstan	Observer	13,000	−33,220,437	BBB	Positive
Kenya	Member	1,700	9,174,198	B+	Stable
Latvia	Member	15,400	2,448,053	BBB−	Positive
Lebanon	Observer	15,600	13,715,550	B	Stable
Lithuania	Member	18,700	3,359,641	BBB	Positive
Malaysia	Member	15,600	−39,420,064	A−	Stable
Mexico	Member	15,100	1,288,112	BBB	Stable
Peru	Member	10,000	−7,888,993	BBB	Stable
Philippines	Member	4,100	15,667,209	BB+	Stable
Poland	Member	20,100	19,552,976	A−	Stable
Portugal	Member	23,200	21,060,508	BBB−	Negative
South Korea	Member	31,700	−37,509,141	A+	Stable
Romania	Member	12,300	13,323,709	BBB−	Stable
Russia	Observer	16,700	−151,400,000	BBB	Positive
Rwanda	Member	1,300	939,222	B	Stable
Serbia	Observer	10,700	8,275,693	BB−	Stable
Seychelles	Observer	24,700	666,026	B	Stable
Singapore	Member	59,900	−27,110,421	AAA	Stable
Slovakia	Member	23,400	−2,110,626	A+	Stable
Slovenia	Member	29,100	2,310,617	AA−	Negative

South Africa	Member	11,000	3,321,801	BBB+	Stable
Sweden	Member	40,600	−10,903,251	AAA	Stable
Switzerland	Member	43,400	−27,197,873	AAA	Stable
Thailand	Member	9,700	2,049,669	BBB	Stable
Turkey	Member	14,600	71,612,947	BB+	Positive
UK	Member	35,900	162,316,831	AAA	Negative
Uruguay	Member	15,400	2,662,628	BB	Positive
USA	Member	48,100	784,438,559	AAA	Stable
Zambia	Member	1,600	−1,805,198	B+	Stable

Member, 5,400, 2,673,359, BB−, and Stable. The second observation contains the following measurements: Member, 40,800, −33,304,157, AAA, Stable, and so on. A data set with 60 elements contains 60 observations.

Scales of Measurement

Data collection requires one of the following scales of measurement: nominal, ordinal, interval, or ratio. The scale of measurement determines the amount of information contained in the data and indicates the most appropriate data summarization and statistical analyses.

When the data for a variable consist of labels or names used to identify an attribute of the element, the scale of measurement is considered a **nominal scale**. For example, referring to the data in Table 1.1, the scale of measurement for the WTO Status variable is nominal because the data "member" and "observer" are labels used to identify the status category for the nation. In cases where the scale of measurement is nominal, a numerical code as well as a nonnumerical label may be used. For example, to facilitate data collection and to prepare the data for entry into a computer database, we might use a numerical code for the WTO Status variable by letting 1 denote a member nation in the World Trade Organization and 2 denote an observer nation. The scale of measurement is nominal even though the data appear as numerical values.

The scale of measurement for a variable is considered an **ordinal scale** if the data exhibit the properties of nominal data and in addition, the order or rank of the data is meaningful. For example, referring to the data in Table 1.1, the scale of measurement for the Fitch Rating is ordinal because the rating labels which range from AAA to F can be rank ordered from best credit rating AAA to poorest credit rating F. The rating letters provide the labels similar to nominal data, but in addition, the data can also be ranked or ordered based on the credit rating, which makes the measurement scale ordinal. Ordinal data can also be recorded by a numerical code, for example, your class rank in school.

The scale of measurement for a variable is an **interval scale** if the data have all the properties of ordinal data and the interval between values is expressed in terms of a fixed unit of measure. Interval data are always numeric. College admission SAT scores are an example of interval-scaled data. For example, three students with SAT math scores of 620, 550, and 470 can be ranked or ordered in terms of best performance to poorest performance in math. In addition, the differences between the scores are meaningful. For instance, student 1 scored $620 - 550 = 70$ points more than student 2, while student 2 scored $550 - 470 = 80$ points more than student 3.

The scale of measurement for a variable is a **ratio scale** if the data have all the properties of interval data and the ratio of two values is meaningful. Variables such as distance, height, weight, and time use the ratio scale of measurement. This scale requires that a zero value be included to indicate that nothing exists for the variable at the zero point. For example, consider the cost of an automobile. A zero value for the cost would indicate that the automobile has no cost and is free. In addition, if we compare the cost of $30,000 for one automobile to the cost of $15,000 for a second automobile, the ratio property shows that the first automobile is $30,000/$15,000 = 2 times, or twice, the cost of the second automobile.

Categorical and Quantitative Data

Data can be classified as either categorical or quantitative. Data that can be grouped by specific categories are referred to as **categorical data**. Categorical data use either the nominal or ordinal scale of measurement. Data that use numeric values to indicate how much or how many are referred to as **quantitative data**. Quantitative data are obtained using either the interval or ratio scale of measurement.

The statistical method appropriate for summarizing data depends upon whether the data are categorical or quantitative.

A **categorical variable** is a variable with categorical data, and a **quantitative variable** is a variable with quantitative data. The statistical analysis appropriate for a particular variable depends upon whether the variable is categorical or quantitative. If the variable is categorical, the statistical analysis is limited. We can summarize categorical data by counting the number of observations in each category or by computing the proportion of the observations in each category. However, even when the categorical data are identified by a numerical code, arithmetic operations such as addition, subtraction, multiplication, and division do not provide meaningful results. Section 2.1 discusses ways of summarizing categorical data.

Arithmetic operations provide meaningful results for quantitative variables. For example, quantitative data may be added and then divided by the number of observations to compute the average value. This average is usually meaningful and easily interpreted. In general, more alternatives for statistical analysis are possible when data are quantitative. Section 2.2 and Chapter 3 provide ways of summarizing quantitative data.

Cross-Sectional and Time Series Data

For purposes of statistical analysis, distinguishing between cross-sectional data and time series data is important. **Cross-sectional data** are data collected at the same or approximately the same point in time. The data in Table 1.1 are cross-sectional because they describe the five variables for the 60 World Trade Organization nations at the same point in time. **Time series data** are data collected over several time periods. For example, the time series in Figure 1.1 shows the U.S. average price per gallon of conventional regular gasoline between 2007 and 2014. Note that gasoline prices peaked in the summer of 2008 and then dropped sharply in the fall of 2008. Between January 2009 and May 2011, the average price per gallon continued to climb steadily. Since then prices have shown more fluctuation, reaching an average price per gallon of $3.31 in February 2014.

Graphs of time series data are frequently found in business and economic publications. Such graphs help analysts understand what happened in the past, identify any trends over time, and project future values for the time series. The graphs of time series data can take on a variety of forms, as shown in Figure 1.2. With a little study, these graphs are usually easy to understand and interpret. For example, Panel (A) in Figure 1.2 is a graph that shows the Dow Jones Industrial Average Index from 2002 to 2013. In April 2002, the popular stock market index was near 10,000. Over the next five years the index rose to slightly over 14,000 in October 2007. However, notice the sharp decline in the time series after the high in 2007. By March 2009, poor economic conditions had caused the Dow Jones Industrial Average Index to return to the 7000 level. This was a scary and discouraging period for investors. However, by late 2009, the index was showing a recovery by reaching 10,000. The index has climbed steadily since then and was above 15,000 in early 2013.

FIGURE 1.1 U.S. AVERAGE PRICE PER GALLON FOR CONVENTIONAL REGULAR GASOLINE

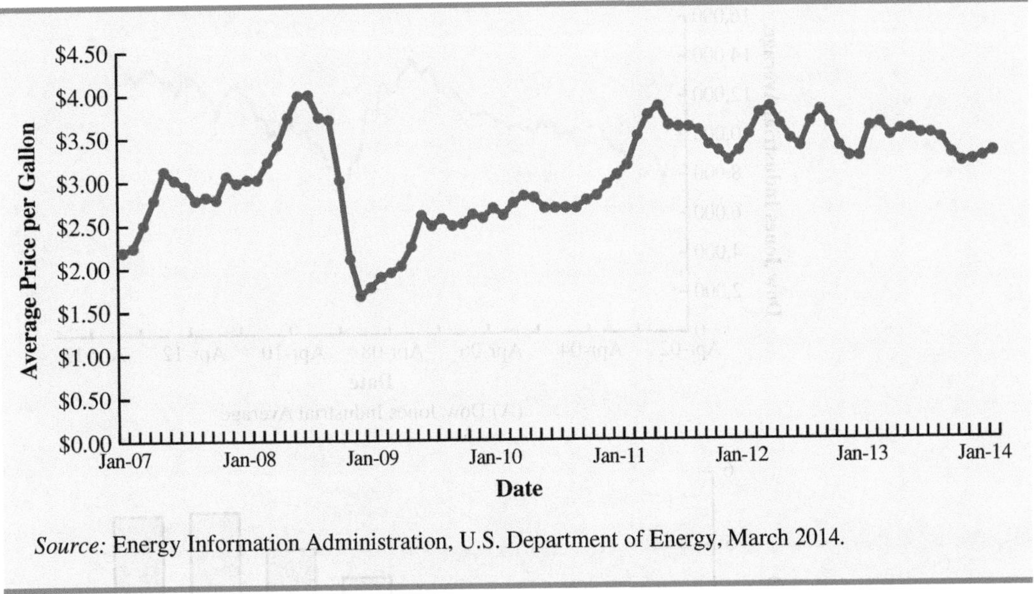

Source: Energy Information Administration, U.S. Department of Energy, March 2014.

The graph in Panel (B) shows the net income of McDonald's Inc. from 2005 to 2012. The declining economic conditions in 2008 and 2009 were actually beneficial to McDonald's as the company's net income rose to all-time highs. The growth in McDonald's net income showed that the company was thriving during the economic downturn as people were cutting back on the more expensive sit-down restaurants and seeking less-expensive alternatives offered by McDonald's. McDonald's net income continued to new all-time highs in 2010 and 2011, but decreased slightly in 2012.

Panel (C) shows the time series for the occupancy rate of hotels in South Florida over a one-year period. The highest occupancy rates, 95% and 98%, occur during the months of February and March when the climate of South Florida is attractive to tourists. In fact, January to April of each year is typically the high-occupancy season for South Florida hotels. On the other hand, note the low occupancy rates during the months of August to October, with the lowest occupancy rate of 50% occurring in September. High temperatures and the hurricane season are the primary reasons for the drop in hotel occupancy during this period.

NOTES AND COMMENTS

1. An observation is the set of measurements obtained for each element in a data set. Hence, the number of observations is always the same as the number of elements. The number of measurements obtained for each element equals the number of variables. Hence, the total number of data items can be determined by multiplying the number of observations by the number of variables.
2. Quantitative data may be discrete or continuous. Quantitative data that measure how many (e.g., number of calls received in 5 minutes) are discrete. Quantitative data that measure how much (e.g., weight or time) are continuous because no separation occurs between the possible data values.

FIGURE 1.2 A VARIETY OF GRAPHS OF TIME SERIES DATA

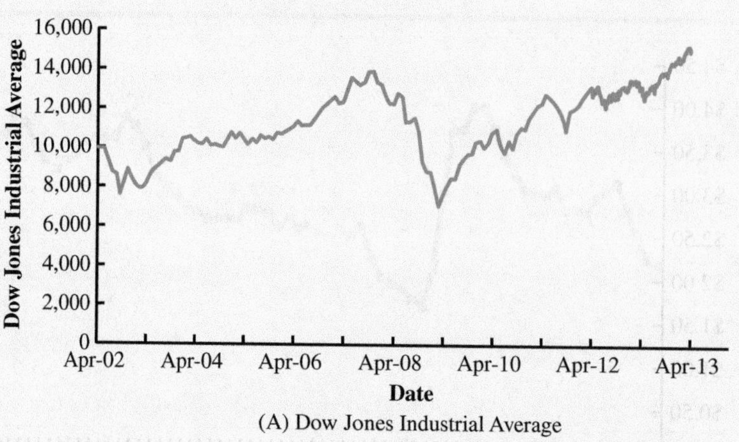

(A) Dow Jones Industrial Average

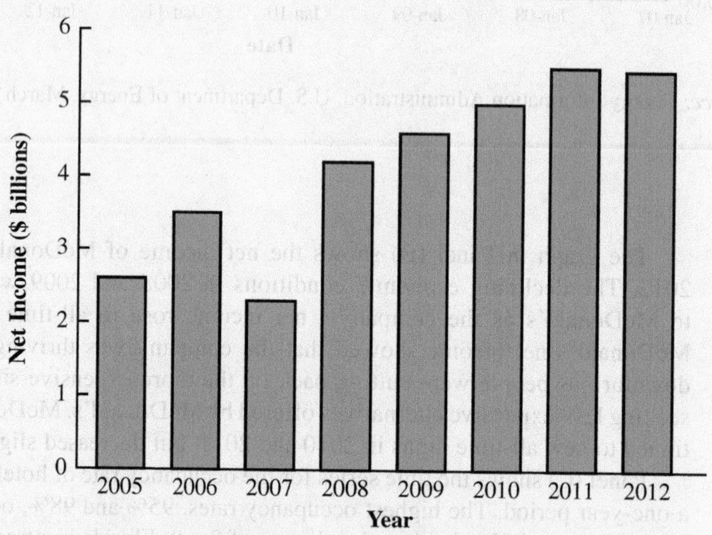

(B) Net Income for McDonald's Inc.

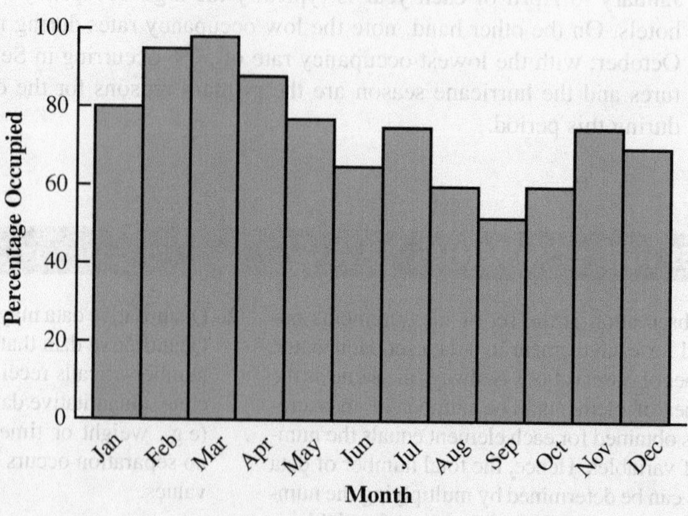

(C) Occupancy Rate of South Florida Hotels

Data Sources

Data can be obtained from existing sources, by conducting an observational study, or by conducting an experiment.

Existing Sources

In some cases, data needed for a particular application already exist. Companies maintain a variety of databases about their employees, customers, and business operations. Data on employee salaries, ages, and years of experience can usually be obtained from internal personnel records. Other internal records contain data on sales, advertising expenditures, distribution costs, inventory levels, and production quantities. Most companies also maintain detailed data about their customers. Table 1.2 shows some of the data commonly available from internal company records.

Organizations that specialize in collecting and maintaining data make available substantial amounts of business and economic data. Companies access these external data sources through leasing arrangements or by purchase. Dun & Bradstreet, Bloomberg, and Dow Jones & Company are three firms that provide extensive business database services to clients. ACNielsen and Information Resources, Inc., built successful businesses collecting and processing data that they sell to advertisers and product manufacturers.

Data are also available from a variety of industry associations and special interest organizations. The Travel Industry Association of America maintains travel-related information such as the number of tourists and travel expenditures by states. Such data would be of interest to firms and individuals in the travel industry. The Graduate Management Admission Council maintains data on test scores, student characteristics, and graduate management education programs. Most of the data from these types of sources are available to qualified users at a modest cost.

The Internet is an important source of data and statistical information. Almost all companies maintain websites that provide general information about the company as well as data on sales, number of employees, number of products, product prices, and product specifications. In addition, a number of companies now specialize in making information available over the Internet. As a result, one can obtain access to stock quotes, meal prices at restaurants, salary data, and an almost infinite variety of information.

TABLE 1.2 EXAMPLES OF DATA AVAILABLE FROM INTERNAL COMPANY RECORDS

Source	Some of the Data Typically Available
Employee records	Name, address, social security number, salary, number of vacation days, number of sick days, and bonus
Production records	Part or product number, quantity produced, direct labor cost, and materials cost
Inventory records	Part or product number, number of units on hand, reorder level, economic order quantity, and discount schedule
Sales records	Product number, sales volume, sales volume by region, and sales volume by customer type
Credit records	Customer name, address, phone number, credit limit, and accounts receivable balance
Customer profile	Age, gender, income level, household size, address, and preferences

TABLE 1.3 EXAMPLES OF DATA AVAILABLE FROM SELECTED GOVERNMENT AGENCIES

Government Agency	Some of the Data Available
Census Bureau	Population data, number of households, and household income
Federal Reserve Board	Data on the money supply, installment credit, exchange rates, and discount rates
Office of Management and Budget	Data on revenue, expenditures, and debt of the federal government
Department of Commerce	Data on business activity, value of shipments by industry, level of profits by industry, and growing and declining industries
Bureau of Labor Statistics	Consumer spending, hourly earnings, unemployment rate, safety records, and international statistics

Government agencies are another important source of existing data. For instance, the U.S. Department of Labor maintains considerable data on employment rates, wage rates, size of the labor force, and union membership. Table 1.3 lists selected governmental agencies and some of the data they provide. Most government agencies that collect and process data also make the results available through a website. Figure 1.3 shows the homepage for the U.S. Bureau of Labor Statistics website.

Observational Study

In an *observational study* we simply observe what is happening in a particular situation, record data on one or more variables of interest, and conduct a statistical analysis of

FIGURE 1.3 U.S. BUREAU OF LABOR STATISTICS HOMEPAGE

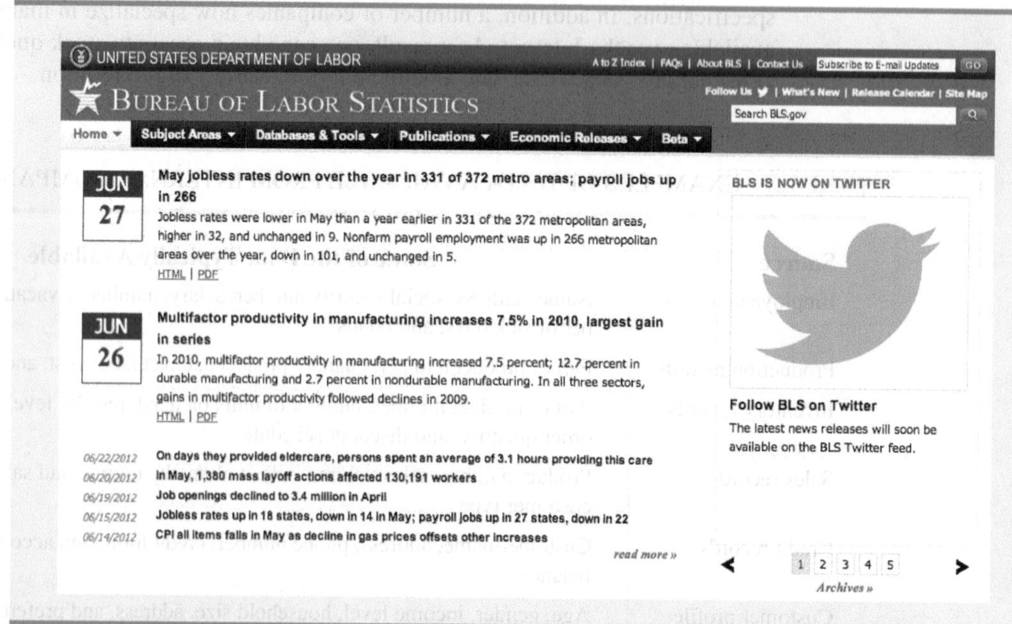

Studies of smokers and nonsmokers are observational studies because researchers do not determine or control who will smoke and who will not smoke.

the resulting data. For example, researchers might observe a randomly selected group of customers that enter a Walmart supercenter to collect data on variables such as the length of time the customer spends shopping, the gender of the customer, the amount spent, and so on. Statistical analysis of the data may help management determine how factors such as the length of time shopping and the gender of the customer affect the amount spent.

As another example of an observational study, suppose that researchers were interested in investigating the relationship between the gender of the CEO for a *Fortune* 500 company and the performance of the company as measured by the return on equity (ROE). To obtain data, the researchers selected a sample of companies and recorded the gender of the CEO and the ROE for each company. Statistical analysis of the data can help determine the relationship between performance of the company and the gender of the CEO. This example is an observational study because the researchers had no control over the gender of the CEO or the ROE at each of the companies that were sampled.

Surveys and public opinion polls are two other examples of commonly used observational studies. The data provided by these types of studies simply enable us to observe opinions of the respondents. For example, the New York State legislature commissioned a telephone survey in which residents were asked if they would support or oppose an increase in the state gasoline tax in order to provide funding for bridge and highway repairs. Statistical analysis of the survey results will assist the state legislature in determining if it should introduce a bill to increase gasoline taxes.

Experiment

The largest experimental statistical study ever conducted is believed to be the 1954 Public Health Service experiment for the Salk polio vaccine. Nearly 2 million children in grades 1, 2, and 3 were selected from throughout the United States.

The key difference between an observational study and an experiment is that an experiment is conducted under controlled conditions. As a result, the data obtained from a well-designed experiment can often provide more information as compared to the data obtained from existing sources or by conducting an observational study. For example, suppose a pharmaceutical company would like to learn about how a new drug it has developed affects blood pressure. To obtain data about how the new drug affects blood pressure, researchers selected a sample of individuals. Different groups of individuals are given different dosage levels of the new drug, and before and after data on blood pressure are collected for each group. Statistical analysis of the data can help determine how the new drug affects blood pressure.

The types of experiments we deal with in statistics often begin with the identification of a particular variable of interest. Then one or more other variables are identified and controlled so that data can be obtained about how the other variables influence the primary variable of interest. In Chapter 10 we discuss statistical methods appropriate for analyzing the data from an experiment.

Time and Cost Issues

Anyone wanting to use data and statistical analysis as aids to decision making must be aware of the time and cost required to obtain the data. The use of existing data sources is desirable when data must be obtained in a relatively short period of time. If important data are not readily available from an existing source, the additional time and cost involved in obtaining the data must be taken into account. In all cases, the decision maker should consider the contribution of the statistical analysis to the decision-making process. The cost of data acquisition and the subsequent statistical analysis should not exceed the savings generated by using the information to make a better decision.

Data Acquisition Errors

Managers should always be aware of the possibility of data errors in statistical studies. Using erroneous data can be worse than not using any data at all. An error in data acquisition occurs whenever the data value obtained is not equal to the true or actual value that would be obtained with a correct procedure. Such errors can occur in a number of ways. For example, an interviewer might make a recording error, such as a transposition in writing the age of a 24-year-old person as 42, or the person answering an interview question might misinterpret the question and provide an incorrect response.

Experienced data analysts take great care in collecting and recording data to ensure that errors are not made. Special procedures can be used to check for internal consistency of the data. For instance, such procedures would indicate that the analyst should review the accuracy of data for a respondent shown to be 22 years of age but reporting 20 years of work experience. Data analysts also review data with unusually large and small values, called outliers, which are candidates for possible data errors. In Chapter 3 we present some of the methods statisticians use to identify outliers.

Errors often occur during data acquisition. Blindly using any data that happen to be available or using data that were acquired with little care can result in misleading information and bad decisions. Thus, taking steps to acquire accurate data can help ensure reliable and valuable decision-making information.

1.4 Descriptive Statistics

Most of the statistical information in newspapers, magazines, company reports, and other publications consists of data that are summarized and presented in a form that is easy for the reader to understand. Such summaries of data, which may be tabular, graphical, or numerical, are referred to as **descriptive statistics**.

Refer to the data set in Table 1.1 showing data for 60 nations that participate in the World Trade Organization. Methods of descriptive statistics can be used to summarize these data. For example, consider the variable Fitch Outlook, which indicates the direction the nation's credit rating is likely to move over the next two years. The Fitch Outlook is recorded as being negative, stable, or positive. A tabular summary of the data showing the number of nations with each of the Fitch Outlook ratings is shown in Table 1.4. A graphical summary of the same data, called a bar chart, is shown in Figure 1.4. These types of summaries make the data easier to interpret. Referring to Table 1.4 and Figure 1.4, we can see that the majority of Fitch Outlook credit ratings are stable, with 65% of the nations having this rating. Negative and positive outlook credit ratings are similar, with slightly more nations having a negative outlook (18.3%) than a positive outlook (16.7%).

TABLE 1.4 FREQUENCIES AND PERCENT FREQUENCIES FOR THE FITCH CREDIT RATING OUTLOOK OF 60 NATIONS

Fitch Outlook	Frequency	Percent Frequency (%)
Positive	10	16.7
Stable	39	65.0
Negative	11	18.3

FIGURE 1.4 BAR CHART FOR THE FITCH CREDIT RATING OUTLOOK FOR 60 NATIONS

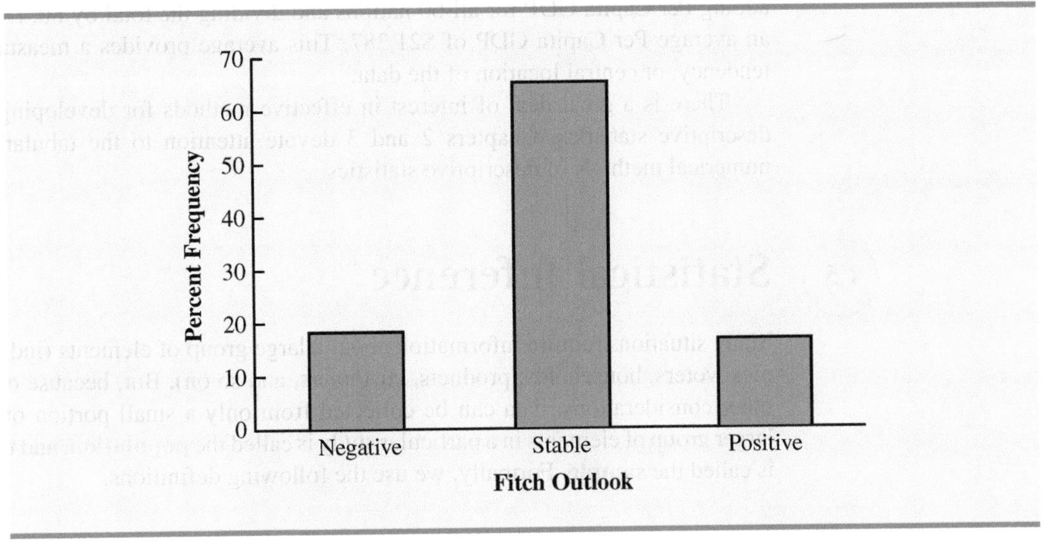

A graphical summary of the data for the quantitative variable Per Capita GDP in Table 1.1, called a histogram, is provided in Figure 1.5. Using the histogram, it is easy to see that Per Capita GDP for the 60 nations ranges from $0 to $60,000, with the highest concentration between $10,000 and $20,000. Only one nation had a Per Capita GDP exceeding $50,000.

In addition to tabular and graphical displays, numerical descriptive statistics are used to summarize data. The most common numerical measure is the average, or mean. Using

FIGURE 1.5 HISTOGRAM OF PER CAPITA GDP FOR 60 NATIONS

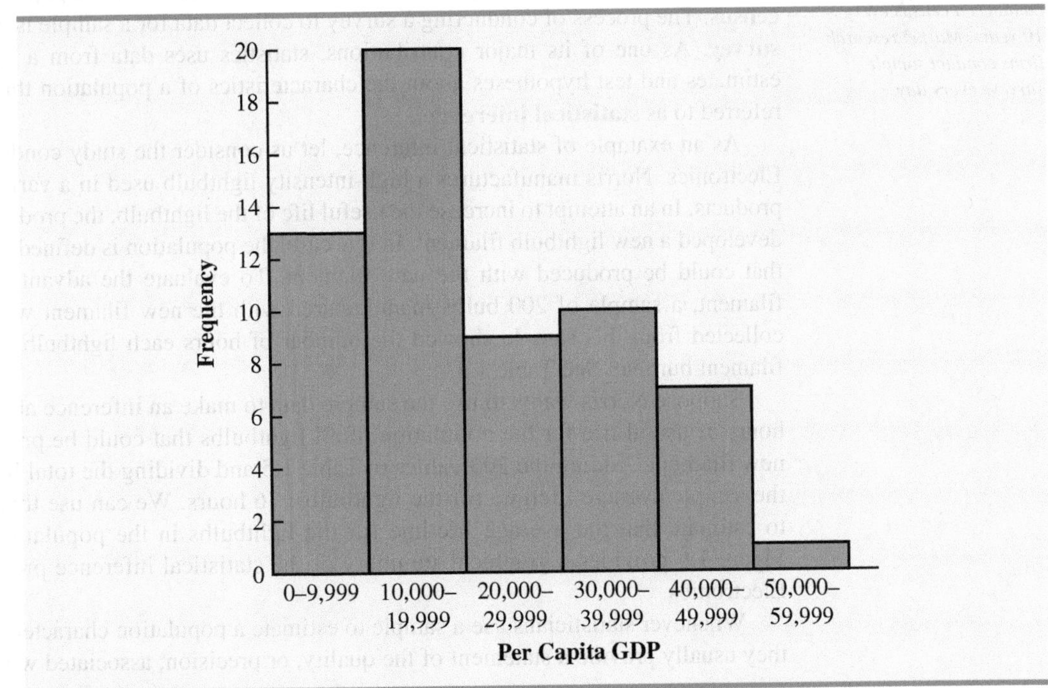

the data on Per Capita GDP for the 60 nations in Table 1.1, we can compute the average by adding Per Capita GDP for all 60 nations and dividing the total by 60. Doing so provides an average Per Capita GDP of $21,387. This average provides a measure of the central tendency, or central location of the data.

There is a great deal of interest in effective methods for developing and presenting descriptive statistics. Chapters 2 and 3 devote attention to the tabular, graphical, and numerical methods of descriptive statistics.

1.5 Statistical Inference

Many situations require information about a large group of elements (individuals, companies, voters, households, products, customers, and so on). But, because of time, cost, and other considerations, data can be collected from only a small portion of the group. The larger group of elements in a particular study is called the **population**, and the smaller group is called the **sample**. Formally, we use the following definitions.

POPULATION

A population is the set of all elements of interest in a particular study.

SAMPLE

A sample is a subset of the population.

The U.S. government conducts a census every 10 years. Market research firms conduct sample surveys every day.

The process of conducting a survey to collect data for the entire population is called a **census**. The process of conducting a survey to collect data for a sample is called a **sample survey**. As one of its major contributions, statistics uses data from a sample to make estimates and test hypotheses about the characteristics of a population through a process referred to as **statistical inference**.

As an example of statistical inference, let us consider the study conducted by Norris Electronics. Norris manufactures a high-intensity lightbulb used in a variety of electrical products. In an attempt to increase the useful life of the lightbulb, the product design group developed a new lightbulb filament. In this case, the population is defined as all lightbulbs that could be produced with the new filament. To evaluate the advantages of the new filament, a sample of 200 bulbs manufactured with the new filament were tested. Data collected from this sample showed the number of hours each lightbulb operated before filament burnout. See Table 1.5.

Suppose Norris wants to use the sample data to make an inference about the average hours of useful life for the population of all lightbulbs that could be produced with the new filament. Adding the 200 values in Table 1.5 and dividing the total by 200 provides the sample average lifetime for the lightbulbs: 76 hours. We can use this sample result to estimate that the average lifetime for the lightbulbs in the population is 76 hours. Figure 1.6 provides a graphical summary of the statistical inference process for Norris Electronics.

Whenever statisticians use a sample to estimate a population characteristic of interest, they usually provide a statement of the quality, or precision, associated with the estimate.

TABLE 1.5 HOURS UNTIL BURNOUT FOR A SAMPLE OF 200 LIGHTBULBS FOR THE NORRIS ELECTRONICS EXAMPLE

Norris

107	73	68	97	76	79	94	59	98	57
54	65	71	70	84	88	62	61	79	98
66	62	79	86	68	74	61	82	65	98
62	116	65	88	64	79	78	79	77	86
74	85	73	80	68	78	89	72	58	69
92	78	88	77	103	88	63	68	88	81
75	90	62	89	71	71	74	70	74	70
65	81	75	62	94	71	85	84	83	63
81	62	79	83	93	61	65	62	92	65
83	70	70	81	77	72	84	67	59	58
78	66	66	94	77	63	66	75	68	76
90	78	71	101	78	43	59	67	61	71
96	75	64	76	72	77	74	65	82	86
66	86	96	89	81	71	85	99	59	92
68	72	77	60	87	84	75	77	51	45
85	67	87	80	84	93	69	76	89	75
83	68	72	67	92	89	82	96	77	102
74	91	76	83	66	68	61	73	72	76
73	77	79	94	63	59	62	71	81	65
73	63	63	89	82	64	85	92	64	73

FIGURE 1.6 THE PROCESS OF STATISTICAL INFERENCE FOR THE NORRIS ELECTRONICS EXAMPLE

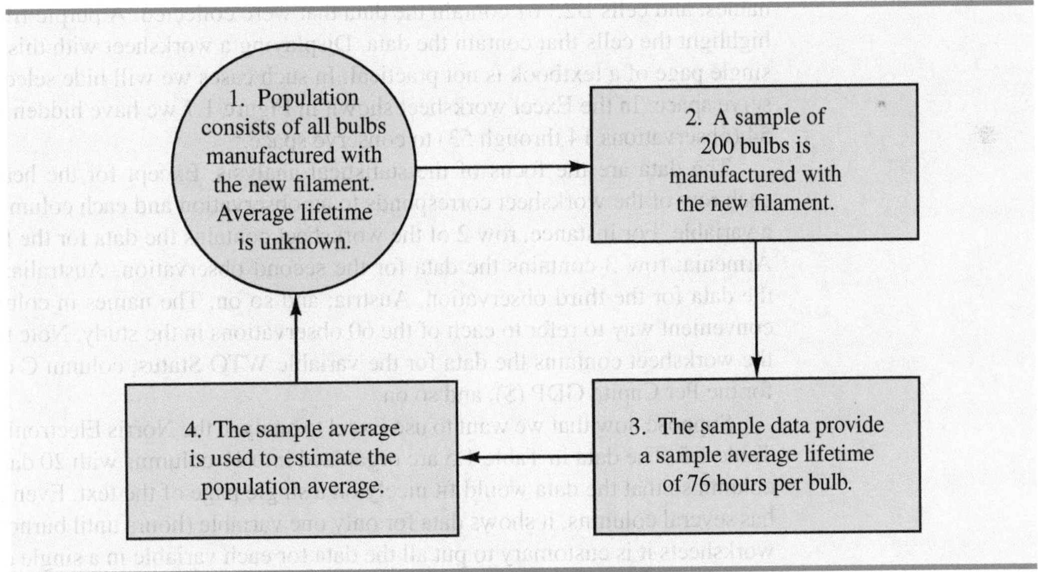

For the Norris example, the statistician might state that the point estimate of the average lifetime for the population of new lightbulbs is 76 hours with a margin of error of ±4 hours. Thus, an interval estimate of the average lifetime for all lightbulbs produced with the new filament is 72 hours to 80 hours. The statistician can also state how confident he or she is that the interval from 72 hours to 80 hours contains the population average.

Statistical Analysis Using Microsoft Excel

The appendix to Chapter 1 provides an introduction to StatTools.

Because statistical analysis typically involves working with large amounts of data, computer software is frequently used to conduct the analysis. In this book we show how statistical analysis can be performed using Microsoft Excel. In selected cases where Excel does not contain statistical analysis functions or data analysis tools that can be used to perform a statistical procedure discussed in the text, we have included a chapter appendix that shows how to use StatTools, an Excel add-in that provides an extended range of statistical and graphical options.

We want to emphasize that this book is about statistics; it is not a book about spreadsheets. Our focus is on showing the appropriate statistical procedures for collecting, analyzing, presenting, and interpreting data. Because Excel is widely available in business organizations, you can expect to put the knowledge gained here to use in the setting where you currently, or soon will, work. If, in the process of studying this material, you become more proficient with Excel, so much the better.

We begin most sections with an application scenario in which a statistical procedure is useful. After showing what the statistical procedure is and how it is used, we turn to showing how to implement the procedure using Excel. Thus, you should gain an understanding of what the procedure is, the situation in which it is useful, and how to implement it using the capabilities of Excel.

Data Sets and Excel Worksheets

Data sets are organized in Excel worksheets in much the same way as the data set for the 60 nations that participate in the World Trade Organization that appears in Table 1.1 is organized. Figure 1.7 shows an Excel worksheet for that data set. Note that row 1 and column A contain labels. Cells Bl:Fl contain the variable names; cells A2:A61 contain the observation names; and cells B2:F61 contain the data that were collected. A purple fill color is used to highlight the cells that contain the data. Displaying a worksheet with this many rows on a single page of a textbook is not practical. In such cases we will hide selected rows to conserve space. In the Excel worksheet shown in Figure 1.7 we have hidden rows 15 through 54 (observations 14 through 53) to conserve space.[2]

The data are the focus of the statistical analysis. Except for the headings in row 1, each row of the worksheet corresponds to an observation and each column corresponds to a variable. For instance, row 2 of the worksheet contains the data for the first observation, Armenia; row 3 contains the data for the second observation, Australia; row 4 contains the data for the third observation, Austria; and so on. The names in column A provide a convenient way to refer to each of the 60 observations in the study. Note that column B of the worksheet contains the data for the variable WTO Status, column C contains the data for the Per Capita GDP ($), and so on.

Suppose now that we want to use Excel to analyze the Norris Electronics data shown in Table 1.5. The data in Table 1.5 are organized into 10 columns with 20 data values in each column so that the data would fit nicely on a single page of the text. Even though the table has several columns, it shows data for only one variable (hours until burnout). In statistical worksheets it is customary to put all the data for each variable in a single column. Refer to the Excel worksheet shown in Figure 1.8. To make it easier to identify each observation in the data set, we entered the heading Observation into cell Al and the numbers 1–200 into cells A2:A201. The heading Hours until Burnout has been entered into cell B1, and the data for the 200 observations have been entered into cells B2:B201. Note that rows 7 through 195 have been hidden to conserve space.

[2]To hide rows 15 through 54 of the Excel worksheet, first select rows 15 through 54. Then, right-click and choose the Hide option. To redisplay rows 15 through 54, just select rows 15 through 54, right-click, and select the Unhide option.

FIGURE 1.7 EXCEL WORKSHEET FOR THE 60 NATIONS THAT PARTICIPATE IN THE WORLD TRADE ORGANIZATION

Note: Rows 15–54 are hidden.

	A	B	C	D	E	F	G
1	Nation	WTO Status	Per Capita GDP ($)	Trade Deficit ($1000s)	Fitch Rating	Fitch Outlook	
2	Armenia	Member	5,400	2,673,359	BB-	Stable	
3	Australia	Member	40,800	-33,304,157	AAA	Stable	
4	Austria	Member	41,700	12,796,558	AAA	Stable	
5	Azerbaijan	Observer	5,400	-16,747,320	BBB-	Positive	
6	Bahrain	Member	27,300	3,102,665	BBB	Stable	
7	Belgium	Member	37,600	-14,930,833	AA+	Negative	
8	Brazil	Member	11,600	-29,796,166	BBB	Stable	
9	Bulgaria	Member	13,500	4,049,237	BBB-	Positive	
10	Canada	Member	40,300	-1,611,380	AAA	Stable	
11	Cape Verde	Member	4,000	874,459	B+	Stable	
12	Chile	Member	16,100	-14,558,218	A+	Stable	
13	China	Member	8,400	-156,705,311	A+	Stable	
14	Colombia	Member	10,100	-1,561,199	BBB-	Stable	
55	Switzerland	Member	43,400	-27,197,873	AAA	Stable	
56	Thailand	Member	9,700	2,049,669	BBB	Stable	
57	Turkey	Member	14,600	71,612,947	BB+	Positive	
58	UK	Member	35,900	162,316,831	AAA	Negative	
59	Uruguay	Member	15,400	2,662,628	BB	Positive	
60	USA	Member	48,100	784,438,559	AAA	Stable	
61	Zambia	Member	1,600	-1,805,198	B+	Stable	
62							

FIGURE 1.8 EXCEL WORKSHEET FOR THE NORRIS ELECTRONICS DATA SET

Note: Rows 7–195 are hidden.

	A	B	C
1	Observation	Hours until Burnout	
2	1	107	
3	2	54	
4	3	66	
5	4	62	
6	5	74	
196	195	45	
197	196	75	
198	197	102	
199	198	76	
200	199	65	
201	200	73	
202			
203			

Using Excel for Statistical Analysis

To separate the discussion of a statistical procedure from the discussion of using Excel to implement the procedure, the material that discusses the use of Excel will usually be set apart in sections with headings such as Using Excel to Construct a Bar Chart and a Pie Chart, Using Excel to Construct a Frequency Distribution, and so on. In using Excel for statistical analysis, four tasks may be needed: Enter/Access Data; Enter Functions and Formulas; Apply Tools; and Editing Options.

Enter/Access Data: Select cell locations for the data and enter the data along with appropriate labels; or, open an existing Excel file such as one of the WEBfiles that accompany the text.

Enter Functions and Formulas: Select cell locations and enter Excel functions and formulas and provide descriptive labels to identify the results.

Apply Tools: Use Excel's tools for data analysis and presentation.

Editing Options: Edit the results to better identify the output or to create a different type of presentation. For example, when using Excel's chart tools, we can edit the chart that is created by adding, removing, or changing chart elements such as the title, legend, data labels, and so on.

Our approach will be to describe how these tasks are performed each time we use Excel to implement a statistical procedure. It will always be necessary to enter data or open an existing Excel file. But, depending on the complexity of the statistical analysis, only one of the second or third tasks may be needed.

To illustrate how the discussion of Excel will appear throughout the book, we will show how to use Excel's AVERAGE function to compute the average lifetime for the 200 burnout times in Table 1.5. Refer to Figure 1.9 as we describe the tasks involved. The worksheet

FIGURE 1.9 COMPUTING THE AVERAGE LIFETIME OF LIGHTBULBS FOR NORRIS ELECTRONICS USING EXCEL'S AVERAGE FUNCTION

	A	B	C	D	E	F
1	Observation	Hours until Burnout				
2	1	107		Average Lifetime	=AVERAGE(B2:B201)	
3	2	54				
4	3	66				
5	4	62				
6	5	74				
196	195	45				
197	196	75				
198	197	102				
199	198	76				
200	199	65				
201	200	73				
202						

	A	B	C	D	E	F
1	Observation	Hours until Burnout				
2	1	107		Average Lifetime	76	
3	2	54				
4	3	66				
5	4	62				
6	5	74				
196	195	45				
197	196	75				
198	197	102				
199	198	76				
200	199	65				
201	200	73				
202						

shown in the foreground of Figure 1.9 displays the data for the problem and shows the results of the analysis. It is called the *value worksheet*. The worksheet shown in the background displays the Excel formula used to compute the average lifetime and is called the *formula worksheet*. A purple fill color is used to highlight the cells that contain the data in both worksheets. In addition, a green fill color is used to highlight the cells containing the functions and formulas in the formula worksheet and the corresponding results in the value worksheet.

Enter/Access Data: Open the WEBfile named Norris. The data are in cells B2:B201 and labels are in colunm A and cell B1.

Enter Functions and Formulas: Excel's AVERAGE function can be used to compute the mean by entering the following formula into cell E2:

=AVERAGE(B2:B201)

Similarly, the formulas =MEDIAN(B2:B201) and =MODE.SNGL(B2:B201) could be entered into cells E3 and E4, respectively, to compute the median and the mode.

To identify the result, the label Average Lifetime is entered into cell D2. Note that for this illustration the Apply Tools and Editing Options tasks were not required. The value worksheet shows that the value computed using the AVERAGE function is 76 hours.

1.7 Data Mining

With the aid of magnetic card readers, bar code scanners, and point-of-sale terminals, most organizations obtain large amounts of data on a daily basis. And, even for a small local restaurant that uses touch screen monitors to enter orders and handle billing, the amount of data collected can be substantial. For large retail companies, the sheer volume of data collected is hard to conceptualize, and figuring out how to effectively use these data to improve profitability is a challenge. Mass retailers such as Walmart capture data on 20 to 30 million transactions every day, telecommunication companies such as France Telecom and AT&T generate over 300 million call records per day, and Visa processes 6800 payment transactions per second or approximately 600 million transactions per day. Storing and managing the transaction data is a substantial undertaking.

The term *data warehousing* is used to refer to the process of capturing, storing, and maintaining the data. Computing power and data collection tools have reached the point where it is now feasible to store and retrieve extremely large quantities of data in seconds. Analysis of the data in the warehouse may result in decisions that will lead to new strategies and higher profits for the organization.

The subject of **data mining** deals with methods for developing useful decision-making information from large databases. Using a combination of procedures from statistics, mathematics, and computer science, analysts "mine the data" in the warehouse to convert it into useful information, hence the name *data mining*. Dr. Kurt Thearling, a leading practitioner in the field, defines data mining as "the automated extraction of predictive information from (large) databases." The two key words in Dr. Thearling's definition are "automated" and "predictive." Data mining systems that are the most effective use automated procedures to extract information from the data using only the most general or even vague queries by the user. And data mining software automates the process of uncovering hidden predictive information that in the past required hands-on analysis.

The major applications of data mining have been made by companies with a strong consumer focus, such as retail businesses, financial organizations, and communication companies. Data mining has been successfully used to help retailers such as Amazon and Barnes & Noble determine one or more related products that customers who have already purchased a specific product are also likely to purchase. Then, when a customer logs on to the company's website and purchases a product, the website uses pop-ups to alert the customer about additional products that the customer is likely to purchase. In another application, data mining may be used to identify customers who are likely to spend more than $20 on a particular shopping trip. These customers may then be identified as the ones to receive special e-mail or regular mail discount offers to encourage them to make their next shopping trip before the discount termination date.

Statistical methods play an important role in data mining, both in terms of discovering relationships in the data and predicting future outcomes. However, a thorough coverage of data mining and the use of statistics in data mining is outside the scope of this text.

Data mining is a technology that relies heavily on statistical methodology such as multiple regression, logistic regression, and correlation. But it takes a creative integration of all these methods and computer science technologies involving artificial intelligence and machine learning to make data mining effective. A substantial investment in time and money is required to implement commercial data mining software packages developed by firms such as Oracle, Teradata, and SAS. The statistical concepts introduced in this text will be helpful in understanding the statistical methodology used by data mining software packages and enable you to better understand the statistical information that is developed.

Because statistical models play an important role in developing predictive models in data mining, many of the concerns that statisticians deal with in developing statistical models are also applicable. For instance, a concern in any statistical study involves the issue of model reliability. Finding a statistical model that works well for a particular sample of data does not necessarily mean that it can be reliably applied to other data. One of the common statistical approaches to evaluating model reliability is to divide the sample data set into two parts: a training data set and a test data set. If the model developed using the training data is able to accurately predict values in the test data, we say that the model is reliable. One advantage that data mining has over classical statistics is that the enormous amount of data available allows the data mining software to partition the data set so that a model developed for the training data set may be tested for reliability on other data. In this sense, the partitioning of the data set allows data mining to develop models and relationships and then quickly observe if they are repeatable and valid with new and different data. On the other hand, a warning for data mining applications is that with so much data available, there is a danger of overfitting the model to the point that misleading associations and cause/effect conclusions appear to exist. Careful interpretation of data mining results and additional testing will help avoid this pitfall.

1.8 Ethical Guidelines for Statistical Practice

Ethical behavior is something we should strive for in all that we do. Ethical issues arise in statistics because of the important role statistics plays in the collection, analysis, presentation, and interpretation of data. In a statistical study, unethical behavior can take a variety of forms including improper sampling, inappropriate analysis of the data, development of misleading graphs, use of inappropriate summary statistics, and/or a biased interpretation of the statistical results.

As you begin to do your own statistical work, we encourage you to be fair, thorough, objective, and neutral as you collect data, conduct analyses, make oral presentations, and present written reports containing information developed. As a consumer of statistics, you should also be aware of the possibility of unethical statistical behavior by others. When you see statistics in newspapers, on television, on the Internet, and so on, it is a good idea to view the information with some skepticism, always being aware of the source as well as the purpose and objectivity of the statistics provided.

The American Statistical Association, the nation's leading professional organization for statistics and statisticians, developed the report "Ethical Guidelines for

Statistical Practice"[3] to help statistical practitioners make and communicate ethical decisions and assist students in learning how to perform statistical work responsibly. The report contains 67 guidelines organized into eight topic areas: Professionalism; Responsibilities to Funders, Clients, and Employers; Responsibilities in Publications and Testimony; Responsibilities to Research Subjects; Responsibilities to Research Team Colleagues; Responsibilities to Other Statisticians or Statistical Practitioners; Responsibilities Regarding Allegations of Misconduct; and Responsibilities of Employers Including Organizations, Individuals, Attorneys, or Other Clients Employing Statistical Practitioners.

One of the ethical guidelines in the professionalism area addresses the issue of running multiple tests until a desired result is obtained. Let us consider an example. In Section 1.5 we discussed a statistical study conducted by Norris Electronics involving a sample of 200 high-intensity lightbulbs manufactured with a new filament. The average lifetime for the sample, 76 hours, provided an estimate of the average lifetime for all lightbulbs produced with the new filament. However, since Norris selected a sample of bulbs, it is reasonable to assume that another sample would have provided a different average lifetime.

Suppose Norris's management had hoped the sample results would enable them to claim that the average lifetime for the new lightbulbs was 80 hours or more. Suppose further that Norris's management decides to continue the study by manufacturing and testing repeated samples of 200 lightbulbs with the new filament until a sample mean of 80 hours or more is obtained. If the study is repeated enough times, a sample may eventually be obtained—by chance alone—that would provide the desired result and enable Norris to make such a claim. In this case, consumers would be misled into thinking the new product is better than it actually is. Clearly, this type of behavior is unethical and represents a gross misuse of statistics in practice.

Several ethical guidelines in the responsibilities and publications and testimony area deal with issues involving the handling of data. For instance, a statistician must account for all data considered in a study and explain the sample(s) actually used. In the Norris Electronics study the average lifetime for the 200 bulbs in the original sample is 76 hours; this is considerably less than the 80 hours or more that management hoped to obtain. Suppose now that after reviewing the results showing a 76 hour average lifetime, Norris discards all the observations with 70 or fewer hours until burnout, allegedly because these bulbs contain imperfections caused by startup problems in the manufacturing process. After discarding these lightbulbs, the average lifetime for the remaining lightbulbs in the sample turns out to be 82 hours. Would you be suspicious of Norris's claim that the lifetime for its lightbulbs is 82 hours?

If the Norris lightbulbs showing 70 or fewer hours until burnout were discarded to simply provide an average lifetime of 82 hours, there is no question that discarding the lightbulbs with 70 or fewer hours until burnout is unethical. But, even if the discarded lightbulbs contain imperfections due to startup problems in the manufacturing process—and, as a result, should not have been included in the analysis—the statistician who conducted the study must account for all the data that were considered and explain how the sample actually used was obtained. To do otherwise is potentially misleading and would constitute unethical behavior on the part of both the company and the statistician.

A guideline in the shared values section of the American Statistical Association report states that statistical practitioners should avoid any tendency to slant statistical work toward predetermined outcomes. This type of unethical practice is often observed when unrepresentative samples are used to make claims. For instance, in many areas of the country smoking is not permitted in restaurants. Suppose, however, a lobbyist for the tobacco industry

[3]American Statistical Association, "Ethical Guidelines for Statistical Practice," 1999.

interviews people in restaurants where smoking is permitted in order to estimate the percentage of people who are in favor of allowing smoking in restaurants. The sample results show that 90% of the people interviewed are in favor of allowing smoking in restaurants. Based upon these sample results, the lobbyist claims that 90% of all people who eat in restaurants are in favor of permitting smoking in restaurants. In this case we would argue that only sampling persons eating in restaurants that allow smoking has biased the results. If only the final results of such a study are reported, readers unfamiliar with the details of the study (i.e., that the sample was collected only in restaurants allowing smoking) can be misled.

The scope of the American Statistical Association's report is broad and includes ethical guidelines that are appropriate not only for a statistician, but also for consumers of statistical information. We encourage you to read the report to obtain a better perspective of ethical issues as you continue your study of statistics and to gain the background for determining how to ensure that ethical standards are met when you start to use statistics in practice.

Summary

Statistics is the art and science of collecting, analyzing, presenting, and interpreting data. Nearly every college student majoring in business or economics is required to take a course in statistics. We began the chapter by describing typical statistical applications for business and economics.

Data consist of the facts and figures that are collected and analyzed. Four scales of measurement used to obtain data on a particular variable include nominal, ordinal, interval, and ratio. The scale of measurement for a variable is nominal when the data are labels or names used to identify an attribute of an element. The scale is ordinal if the data demonstrate the properties of nominal data and the order or rank of the data is meaningful. The scale is interval if the data demonstrate the properties of ordinal data and the interval between values is expressed in terms of a fixed unit of measure. Finally, the scale of measurement is ratio if the data show all the properties of interval data and the ratio of two values is meaningful.

For purposes of statistical analysis, data can be classified as categorical or quantitative. Categorical data use labels or names to identify an attribute of each element. Categorical data use either the nominal or ordinal scale of measurement and may be nonnumeric or numeric. Quantitative data are numeric values that indicate how much or how many. Quantitative data use either the interval or ratio scale of measurement. Ordinary arithmetic operations are meaningful only if the data are quantitative. Therefore, statistical computations used for quantitative data are not always appropriate for categorical data.

In Sections 1.4 and 1.5 we introduced the topics of descriptive statistics and statistical inference. Descriptive statistics are the tabular, graphical, and numerical methods used to summarize data. The process of statistical inference uses data obtained from a sample to make estimates or test hypotheses about the characteristics of a population. The last three sections of the chapter provide information on the role of computers in statistical analysis, an introduction to the relatively new field of data mining, and a summary of ethical guidelines for statistical practice.

Glossary

Statistics The art and science of collecting, analyzing, presenting, and interpreting data.

Data The facts and figures collected, analyzed, and summarized for presentation and interpretation.

Data set All the data collected in a particular study.
Elements The entities on which data are collected.
Variable A characteristic of interest for the elements.
Observation The set of measurements obtained for a particular element.
Nominal scale The scale of measurement for a variable when the data are labels or names used to identify an attribute of an element. Nominal data may be nonnumeric or numeric.
Ordinal scale The scale of measurement for a variable if the data exhibit the properties of nominal data and the order or rank of the data is meaningful. Ordinal data may be nonnumeric or numeric.
Interval scale The scale of measurement for a variable if the data demonstrate the properties of ordinal data and the interval between values is expressed in terms of a fixed unit of measure. Interval data are always numeric.
Ratio scale The scale of measurement for a variable if the data demonstrate all the properties of interval data and the ratio of two values is meaningful. Ratio data are always numeric.
Categorical data Labels or names used to identify an attribute of each element. Categorical data use either the nominal or ordinal scale of measurement and may be nonnumeric or numeric.
Quantitative data Numeric values that indicate how much or how many of something. Quantitative data are obtained using either the interval or ratio scale of measurement.
Categorical variable A variable with categorical data.
Quantitative variable A variable with quantitative data.
Cross-sectional data Data collected at the same or approximately the same point in time.
Time series data Data collected over several time periods.
Descriptive statistics Tabular, graphical, and numerical summaries of data.
Population The set of all elements of interest in a particular study.
Sample A subset of the population.
Census A survey to collect data on the entire population.
Sample survey A survey to collect data on a sample.
Statistical inference The process of using data obtained from a sample to make estimates or test hypotheses about the characteristics of a population.
Data mining The process of using procedures from statistics and computer science to extract useful information from extremely large databases.

Supplementary Exercises

1. Discuss the differences between statistics as numerical facts and statistics as a discipline or field of study.

2. Tablet PC Comparison provides a wide variety of information about tablet computers. The company's website enables consumers to easily compare different tablets using factors such as cost, type of operating system, display size, battery life, and CPU manufacturer. A sample of 10 tablet computers is shown in Table 1.6 (Tablet PC Comparison website, February 28, 2013).
   a. How many elements are in this data set?
   b. How many variables are in this data set?
   c. Which variables are categorical and which variables are quantitative?
   d. What type of measurement scale is used for each of the variables?

3. Refer to Table 1.6.
   a. What is the average cost for the tablets?
   b. Compare the average cost of tablets with a Windows operating system to the average cost of tablets with an Android operating system.

TABLE 1.6 PRODUCT INFORMATION FOR 10 TABLET COMPUTERS

Tablet	Cost ($)	Operating System	Display Size (inches)	Battery Life (hours)	CPU Manufacturer
Acer Iconia W510	599	Windows	10.1	8.5	Intel
Amazon Kindle Fire HD	299	Android	8.9	9	TI OMAP
Apple iPad 4	499	iOS	9.7	11	Apple
HP Envy X2	860	Windows	11.6	8	Intel
Lenovo ThinkPad Tablet	668	Windows	10.1	10.5	Intel
Microsoft Surface Pro	899	Windows	10.6	4	Intel
Motorola Droid XYboard	530	Android	10.1	9	TI OMAP
Samsung Ativ Smart PC	590	Windows	11.6	7	Intel
Samsung Galaxy Tab	525	Android	10.1	10	Nvidia
Sony Tablet S	360	Android	9.4	8	Nvidia

c. What percentage of tablets use a CPU manufactured by TI OMAP?
d. What percentage of tablets use an Android operating system?

4. Table 1.7 shows data for eight cordless telephones (*Consumer Reports*, November 2012). The Overall Score, a measure of the overall quality for the cordless telephone, ranges from 0 to 100. Voice Quality has possible ratings of poor, fair, good, very good, and excellent. Talk Time is the manufacturer's claim of how long the handset can be used when it is fully charged.
   a. How many elements are in this data set?
   b. For the variables Price, Overall Score, Voice Quality, Handset on Base, and Talk Time, which variables are categorical and which variables are quantitative?
   c. What scale of measurement is used for each variable?

5. Refer to the data set in Table 1.7.
   a. What is the average price for the cordless telephones?
   b. What is the average talk time for the cordless telephones?
   c. What percentage of the cordless telephones have a voice quality of excellent?
   d. What percentage of the cordless telephones have a handset on the base?

6. J.D. Power and Associates surveys new automobile owners to learn about the quality of recently purchased vehicles. The following questions were asked in the J.D. Power Initial Quality Survey, May 2012.

TABLE 1.7 DATA FOR EIGHT CORDLESS TELEPHONES

Brand	Model	Price ($)	Overall Score	Voice Quality	Handset on Base	Talk Time (Hours)
AT&T	CL84100	60	73	Excellent	Yes	7
AT&T	TL92271	80	70	Very Good	No	7
Panasonic	4773B	100	78	Very Good	Yes	13
Panasonic	6592T	70	72	Very Good	No	13
Uniden	D2997	45	70	Very Good	No	10
Uniden	D1788	80	73	Very Good	Yes	7
Vtech	DS6521	60	72	Excellent	No	7
Vtech	CS6649	50	72	Very Good	Yes	7

a. Did you purchase or lease the vehicle?
b. What price did you pay?
c. What is the overall attractiveness of your vehicle's exterior? (Unacceptable, Average, Outstanding, or Truly Exceptional)
d. What is your average miles-per-gallon?
e. What is your overall rating of your new vehicle? (1- to 10-point scale with 1 Unacceptable and 10 Truly Exceptional)

Comment on whether each question provides categorical or quantitative data.

7. The Kroger Company is one of the largest grocery retailers in the United States, with over 2000 grocery stores across the country. Kroger uses an online customer opinion questionnaire to obtain performance data about its products and services and learn about what motivates its customers (Kroger website, April 2012). In the survey, Kroger customers were asked if they would be willing to pay more for products that had each of the following four characteristics. The four questions were: Would you pay more for

products that have a brand name?
products that are environmentally friendly?
products that are organic?
products that have been recommended by others?

For each question, the customers had the option of responding Yes if they would pay more or No if they would not pay more.
a. Are the data collected by Kroger in this example categorical or quantitative?
b. What measurement scale is used?

8. *The Tennessean*, an online newspaper located in Nashville, Tennessee, conducts a daily poll to obtain reader opinions on a variety of current issues. In a recent poll, 762 readers responded to the following question: "If a constitutional amendment to ban a state income tax is placed on the ballot in Tennessee, would you want it to pass?" Possible responses were Yes, No, or Not Sure (*The Tennessean* website, February 15, 2013).
a. What was the sample size for this poll?
b. Are the data categorical or quantitative?
c. Would it make more sense to use averages or percentages as a summary of the data for this question?
d. Of the respondents, 67% said Yes, they would want it to pass. How many individuals provided this response?

9. The Commerce Department reported receiving the following applications for the Malcolm Baldrige National Quality Award: 23 from large manufacturing firms, 18 from large service firms, and 30 from small businesses.
a. Is type of business a categorical or quantitative variable?
b. What percentage of the applications came from small businesses?

10. The Bureau of Transportation Statistics Omnibus Household Survey is conducted annually and serves as an information source for the U.S. Department of Transportation. In one part of the survey the person being interviewed was asked to respond to the following statement: "Drivers of motor vehicles should be allowed to talk on a hand-held cell phone while driving." Possible responses were strongly agree, somewhat agree, somewhat disagree, and strongly disagree. Forty-four respondents said that they strongly agree with this statement, 130 said that they somewhat agree, 165 said they somewhat disagree, and 741 said they strongly disagree with this statement (Bureau of Transportation website, August 2010).
a. Do the responses for this statement provide categorical or quantitative data?
b. Would it make more sense to use averages or percentages as a summary of the responses for this statement?

c. What percentage of respondents strongly agree with allowing drivers of motor vehicles to talk on a hand-held cell phone while driving?
d. Do the results indicate general support for or against allowing drivers of motor vehicles to talk on a hand-held cell phone while driving?

11. In a Gallup telephone survey conducted on April 9–10, 2013, the person being interviewed was asked if he would vote for a law in his state that would increase the gas tax up to 20 cents a gallon, with the new gas tax money going to improve roads and bridges and build more mass transportation in his state. Possible responses were vote for, vote against, and no opinion. Two hundred ninety five respondents said they would vote for the law, 672 said they would vote against the law, and 51 said they had no opinion (Gallup website, June 14, 2013).
    a. Do the responses for this question provide categorical or quantitative data?
    b. What was the sample size for this Gallup poll?
    c. What percentage of respondents would vote for a law increasing the gas tax?
    d. Do the results indicate general support for or against increasing the gas tax to improve roads and bridges and build more mass transportation?

12. The Hawaii Visitors Bureau collects data on visitors to Hawaii. The following questions were among 16 asked in a questionnaire handed out to passengers during incoming airline flights.
    - This trip to Hawaii is my: 1st, 2nd, 3rd, 4th, etc.
    - The primary reason for this trip is: (10 categories, including vacation, convention, honeymoon)
    - Where I plan to stay: (11 categories, including hotel, apartment, relatives, camping)
    - Total days in Hawaii

    a. What is the population being studied?
    b. Is the use of a questionnaire a good way to reach the population of passengers on incoming airline flights?
    c. Comment on each of the four questions in terms of whether it will provide categorical or quantitative data.

13. Figure 1.10 provides a bar chart showing the amount of federal spending in trillions of inflation adjusted dollars (2012) for the years 2004 to 2012 (The Heritage Foundation website, June 13, 2013).

FIGURE 1.10 FEDERAL SPENDING

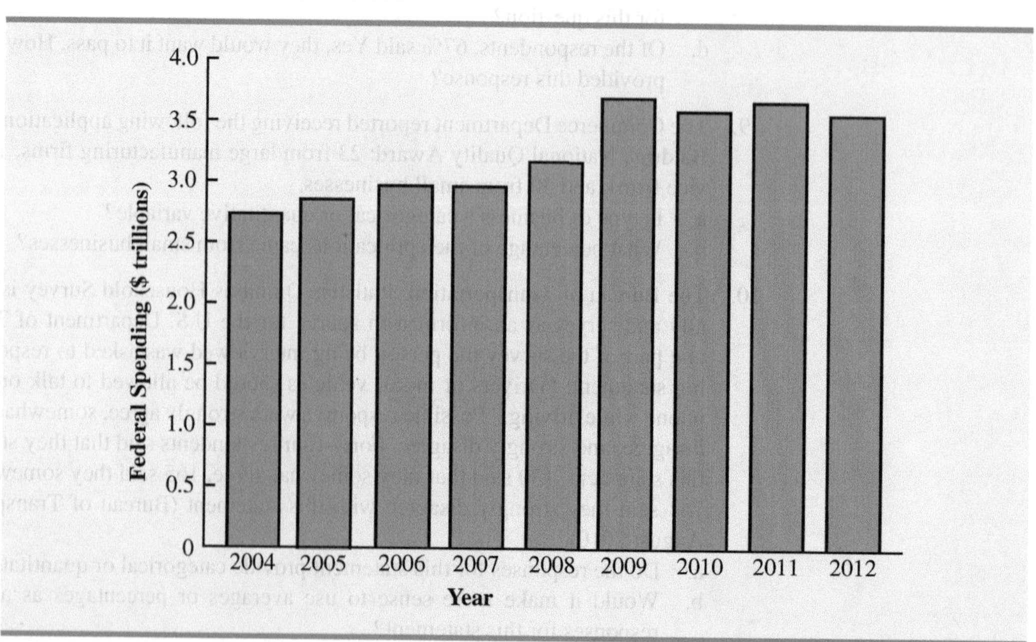

a. What is the variable of interest?
b. Are the data categorical or quantitative?
c. Are the data time series or cross-sectional?
d. Comment on the trend in federal spending over time.

14. The following data show the number of rental cars in service for three rental car companies: Hertz, Avis, and Dollar. The data are for the years 2007–2010 and are in thousands of vehicles (*Auto Rental News* website, May 15, 2011).

	Cars in Service (1000s)			
Company	**2007**	**2008**	**2009**	**2010**
Hertz	327	311	286	290
Dollar	167	140	106	108
Avis	204	220	300	270

a. Construct a time series graph for the years 2007 to 2010 showing the number of rental cars in service for each company. Show the time series for all three companies on the same graph.
b. Comment on who appears to be the market share leader and how the market shares are changing over time.
c. Construct a bar chart showing rental cars in service for 2010. Is this chart based on cross-sectional or time series data?

15. Every year, the U.S. Coast Guard collects data and compiles statistics on reported recreational boating accidents. These statistics are derived from accident reports that are filed by the owners/operators of recreational vessels involved in accidents. In 2009, 4730 recreational boating accident reports were filed. Figure 1.11 provides a bar chart summarizing the number of accident reports that were filed each month (U.S. Coast Guard's Boating Safety Division website, August 2010).
a. Are the data categorical or quantitative?
b. Are the data time series or cross-sectional?

FIGURE 1.11 NUMBER OF RECREATIONAL BOATING ACCIDENTS

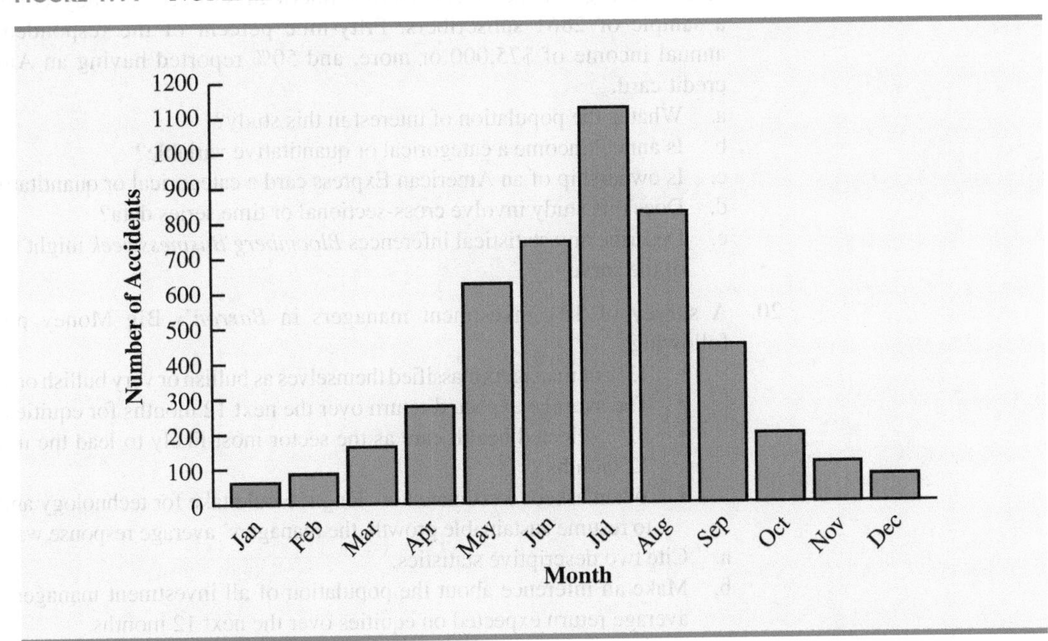

c. In what month were the most accident reports filed? Approximately how many?
d. There were 61 accident reports filed in January and 76 accident reports filed in December. What percentage of the total number of accident reports for the year were filed in these two months? Does this seem reasonable?
e. Comment on the overall shape of the bar graph.

16. The Energy Information Administration of the U.S. Department of Energy provided time series data for the U.S. average price per gallon of conventional regular gasoline between January 2007 and February 2014 (Energy Information Administration website, March 2014). Use the Internet to obtain the average price per gallon of conventional regular gasoline since February 2014.
    a. Extend the graph of the time series shown in Figure 1.1.
    b. What interpretations can you make about the average price per gallon of conventional regular gasoline since February 2014?
    c. Does the time series continue to show a summer increase in the average price per gallon? Explain.
17. A manager of a large corporation recommends a $10,000 raise be given to keep a valued subordinate from moving to another company. What internal and external sources of data might be used to decide whether such a salary increase is appropriate?
18. A random telephone survey of 1021 adults (aged 18 and older) was conducted by Opinion Research Corporation on behalf of CompleteTax, an online tax preparation and e-filing service. The survey results showed that 684 of those surveyed planned to file their taxes electronically (CompleteTax Tax Prep Survey 2010).
    a. Develop a descriptive statistic that can be used to estimate the percentage of all taxpayers who file electronically.
    b. The survey reported that the most frequently used method for preparing the tax return is to hire an accountant or professional tax preparer. If 60% of the people surveyed had their tax return prepared this way, how many people used an accountant or professional tax preparer?
    c. Other methods that the person filing the return often used include manual preparation, use of an online tax service, and use of a software tax program. Would the data for the method for preparing the tax return be considered categorical or quantitative?
19. A *Bloomberg Businessweek* North American subscriber study collected data from a sample of 2861 subscribers. Fifty-nine percent of the respondents indicated an annual income of $75,000 or more, and 50% reported having an American Express credit card.
    a. What is the population of interest in this study?
    b. Is annual income a categorical or quantitative variable?
    c. Is ownership of an American Express card a categorical or quantitative variable?
    d. Does this study involve cross-sectional or time series data?
    e. Describe any statistical inferences *Bloomberg Businessweek* might make on the basis of the survey.
20. A survey of 131 investment managers in *Barron's* Big Money poll revealed the following:
    - 43% of managers classified themselves as bullish or very bullish on the stock market.
    - The average expected return over the next 12 months for equities was 11.2%.
    - 21% selected health care as the sector most likely to lead the market in the next 12 months.
    - When asked to estimate how long it would take for technology and telecom stocks to resume sustainable growth, the managers' average response was 2.5 years.

    a. Cite two descriptive statistics.
    b. Make an inference about the population of all investment managers concerning the average return expected on equities over the next 12 months.

c. Make an inference about the length of time it will take for technology and telecom stocks to resume sustainable growth.

21. A seven-year medical research study reported that women whose mothers took the drug DES during pregnancy were twice as likely to develop tissue abnormalities that might lead to cancer as were women whose mothers did not take the drug.
    a. This study compared two populations. What were the populations?
    b. Do you suppose the data were obtained in a survey or an experiment?
    c. For the population of women whose mothers took the drug DES during pregnancy, a sample of 3980 women showed that 63 developed tissue abnormalities that might lead to cancer. Provide a descriptive statistic that could be used to estimate the number of women out of 1000 in this population who have tissue abnormalities.
    d. For the population of women whose mothers did not take the drug DES during pregnancy, what is the estimate of the number of women out of 1000 who would be expected to have tissue abnormalities?
    e. Medical studies often use a relatively large sample (in this case, 3980). Why?

22. A survey conducted by Better Homes and Gardens Real Estate LLC showed that one in five U.S. homeowners have either moved from their home or would like to move because their neighborhood or community isn't ideal for their lifestyle (Better Homes and Gardens Real Estate website, September 26, 2013). The top lifestyle priorities of respondents when searching for their next home include ease of commuting by car, access to health and safety services, family-friendly neighborhood, availability of retail stores, access to cultural activities, public transportation access, and nightlife and restaurant access. Suppose a real estate agency in Denver, Colorado, hired you to conduct a similar study to determine the top lifestyle priorities for clients that currently have a home listed for sale with the agency or have hired the agency to help them locate a new home.
    a. What is the population for the survey you will be conducting?
    b. How would you collect the data for this study?

23. Pew Research Center is a nonpartisan polling organization that provides information about issues, attitudes, and trends shaping America. In a poll, Pew researchers found that 47% of American adult respondents reported getting at least some local news on their cell phone or tablet computer (Pew Research website, May 14, 2011). Further findings showed that 42% of respondents who own cell phones or tablet computers use those devices to check local weather reports and 37% use the devices to find local restaurants or other businesses.
    a. One statistic concerned using cell phones or tablet computers for local news. What population is that finding applicable to?
    b. Another statistic concerned using cell phones or tablet computers to check local weather reports and to find local restaurants. What population is this finding applicable to?
    c. Do you think the Pew researchers conducted a census or a sample survey to obtain their results? Why?
    d. If you were a restaurant owner, would you find these results interesting? Why? How could you take advantage of this information?

24. A sample of midterm grades for five students showed the following results: 72, 65, 82, 90, 76. Which of the following statements are correct, and which should be challenged as being too generalized?
    a. The average midterm grade for the sample of five students is 77.
    b. The average midterm grade for all students who took the exam is 77.
    c. An estimate of the average midterm grade for all students who took the exam is 77.
    d. More than half of the students who take this exam will score between 70 and 85.
    e. If five other students are included in the sample, their grades will be between 65 and 90.

TABLE 1.8 DATA SET FOR 25 SHADOW STOCKS

Shadow02

Company	Exchange	Ticker Symbol	Market Cap ($ millions)	Price/ Earnings Ratio	Gross Profit Margin (%)
DeWolfe Companies	AMEX	DWL	36.4	8.4	36.7
North Coast Energy	OTC	NCEB	52.5	6.2	59.3
Hansen Natural Corp.	OTC	HANS	41.1	14.6	44.8
MarineMax, Inc.	NYSE	HZO	111.5	7.2	23.8
Nanometrics Incorporated	OTC	NANO	228.6	38.0	53.3
TeamStaff, Inc.	OTC	TSTF	92.1	33.5	4.1
Environmental Tectonics	AMEX	ETC	51.1	35.8	35.9
Measurement Specialties	AMEX	MSS	101.8	26.8	37.6
SEMCO Energy, Inc.	NYSE	SEN	193.4	18.7	23.6
Party City Corporation	OTC	PCTY	97.2	15.9	36.4
Embrex, Inc.	OTC	EMBX	136.5	18.9	59.5
Tech/Ops Sevcon, Inc.	AMEX	TO	23.2	20.7	35.7
ARCADIS NV	OTC	ARCAF	173.4	8.8	9.6
Qiao Xing Universal Tele.	OTC	XING	64.3	22.1	30.8
Energy West Incorporated	OTC	EWST	29.1	9.7	16.3
Barnwell Industries, Inc.	AMEX	BRN	27.3	7.4	73.4
Innodata Corporation	OTC	INOD	66.1	11.0	29.6
Medical Action Industries	OTC	MDCI	137.1	26.9	30.6
Instrumentarium Corp.	OTC	INMRY	240.9	3.6	52.1
Petroleum Development	OTC	PETD	95.9	6.1	19.4
Drexler Technology Corp.	OTC	DRXR	233.6	45.6	53.6
Gerber Childrenswear Inc.	NYSE	GCW	126.9	7.9	25.8
Gaiam, Inc.	OTC	GAIA	295.5	68.2	60.7
Artesian Resources Corp.	OTC	ARTNA	62.8	20.5	45.5
York Water Company	OTC	YORW	92.2	22.9	74.2

25. Table 1.8 shows a data set containing information for 25 of the shadow stocks tracked by the American Association of Individual Investors. Shadow stocks are common stocks of smaller companies that are not closely followed by Wall Street analysts. The data set is also on the website that accompanies the text in the WEBfile named Shadow02.
    a. How many variables are in the data set?
    b. Which of the variables are categorical and which are quantitative?
    c. For the Exchange variable, show the frequency and the percent frequency for AMEX, NYSE, and OTC. Construct a bar graph similar to Figure 1.4 for the Exchange variable.
    d. Show the frequency distribution for the Gross Profit Margin using the five intervals: 0–14.9, 15–29.9, 30–44.9, 45–59.9, and 60–74.9. Construct a histogram similar to Figure 1.5.
    e. What is the average price/earnings ratio?

CHAPTER 2

Descriptive Statistics: Tabular and Graphical Displays

CONTENTS

STATISTICS IN PRACTICE: COLGATE-PALMOLIVE COMPANY

2.1 SUMMARIZING DATA FOR A CATEGORICAL VARIABLE
- Frequency Distribution
- Relative Frequency and Percent Frequency Distributions
- Using Excel to Construct a Frequency Distribution, a Relative Frequency Distribution, and a Percent Frequency Distribution
- Bar Charts and Pie Charts
- Using Excel to Construct a Bar Chart and a Pie Chart

2.2 SUMMARIZING DATA FOR A QUANTITATIVE VARIABLE
- Frequency Distribution
- Relative Frequency and Percent Frequency Distributions
- Using Excel to Construct a Frequency Distribution
- Dot Plot
- Histogram
- Using Excel's Recommended Charts Tool to Construct a Histogram
- Cumulative Distributions
- Stem-and-Leaf Display

2.3 SUMMARIZING DATA FOR TWO VARIABLES USING TABLES
- Crosstabulation
- Using Excel's PivotTable Tool to Construct a Crosstabulation
- Simpson's Paradox

2.4 SUMMARIZING DATA FOR TWO VARIABLES USING GRAPHICAL DISPLAYS
- Scatter Diagram and Trendline
- Using Excel to Construct a Scatter Diagram and a Trendline
- Side-by-Side and Stacked Bar Charts
- Using Excel's Recommended Charts Tool to Construct Side-by-Side and Stacked Bar Charts

2.5 DATA VISUALIZATION: BEST PRACTICES IN CREATING EFFECTIVE GRAPHICAL DISPLAYS
- Creating Effective Graphical Displays
- Choosing the Type of Graphical Display
- Data Dashboards
- Data Visualization in Practice: Cincinnati Zoo and Botanical Garden

STATISTICS *in* PRACTICE

COLGATE-PALMOLIVE COMPANY*
NEW YORK, NEW YORK

The Colgate-Palmolive Company started as a small soap and candle shop in New York City in 1806. Today, Colgate-Palmolive employs more than 40,000 people working in more than 200 countries and territories around the world. Although best known for its brand names of Colgate, Palmolive, and Fab, the company also markets Mennen, Hill's Science Diet, and Hill's Prescription Diet products.

The Colgate-Palmolive Company uses statistics in its quality assurance program for home laundry detergent products. One concern is customer satisfaction with the quantity of detergent in a carton. Every carton in each size category is filled with the same amount of detergent by weight, but the volume of detergent is affected by the density of the detergent powder. For instance, if the powder density is on the heavy side, a smaller volume of detergent is needed to reach the carton's specified weight. As a result, the carton may appear to be underfilled when opened by the consumer.

To control the problem of heavy detergent powder, limits are placed on the acceptable range of powder density. Statistical samples are taken periodically, and the density of each powder sample is measured. Data summaries are then provided for operating personnel so that corrective action can be taken if necessary to keep the density within the desired quality specifications.

A frequency distribution for the densities of 150 samples taken over a one-week period and a histogram are shown in the accompanying table and figure. Density levels above .40 are unacceptably high. The frequency distribution and histogram show that the operation is meeting its quality guidelines with all of the densities less than or equal to .40. Managers viewing these statistical summaries would be pleased with the quality of the detergent production process.

In this chapter, you will learn about tabular and graphical methods of descriptive statistics such as frequency distributions, bar charts, histograms, stem-and-leaf displays, crosstabulations, and others. The goal of these methods is to summarize data so that the data can be easily understood and interpreted.

The Colgate-Palmolive Company uses statistical summaries to help maintain the quality of its products. © Kurt Brady/Alamy.

Frequency Distribution of Density Data

Density	Frequency
.29–.30	30
.31–.32	75
.33–.34	32
.35–.36	9
.37–.38	3
.39–.40	1
Total	150

Histogram of Density Data

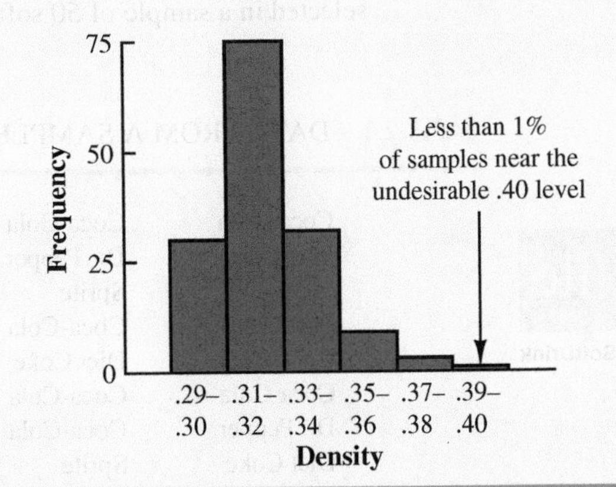

*The authors are indebted to William R. Fowle, Manager of Quality Assurance, Colgate-Palmolive Company, for providing this Statistics in Practice.

As indicated in Chapter 1, data can be classified as either categorical or quantitative. **Categorical data** use labels or names to identify categories of like items, and **quantitative data** are numerical values that indicate how much or how many. This chapter introduces the use of tabular and graphical displays for summarizing both categorical and quantitative data. Tabular and graphical displays can be found in annual reports, newspaper articles, and research studies. Everyone is exposed to these types of presentations. Hence, it is important to understand how they are constructed and how they should be interpreted.

We begin with a discussion of the use of tablular and graphical displays to summarize the data for a single variable. This is followed by a discussion of the use of tabular and graphical displays to summarize the data for two variables in a way that reveals the relationship between the two variables. **Data visualization** is a term often used to describe the use of graphical displays to summarize and present information about a data set. The last section of this chapter provides an introduction to data visualization and provides guidelines for creating effective graphical displays.

2.1 Summarizing Data for a Categorical Variable

Frequency Distribution

We begin the discussion of how tabular and graphical displays can be used to summarize categorical data with the definition of a **frequency distribution.**

FREQUENCY DISTRIBUTION

A frequency distribution is a tabular summary of data showing the number (frequency) of observations in each of several nonoverlapping categories or classes.

Let us use the following example to demonstrate the construction and interpretation of a frequency distribution for categorical data. Coca-Cola, Diet Coke, Dr. Pepper, Pepsi, and Sprite are five popular soft drinks. Assume that the data in Table 2.1 show the soft drink selected in a sample of 50 soft drink purchases.

SoftDrink

TABLE 2.1 DATA FROM A SAMPLE OF 50 SOFT DRINK PURCHASES

Coca-Cola	Coca-Cola	Coca-Cola	Sprite	Coca-Cola
Diet Coke	Dr. Pepper	Diet Coke	Dr. Pepper	Diet Coke
Pepsi	Sprite	Coca-Cola	Pepsi	Pepsi
Diet Coke	Coca-Cola	Sprite	Diet Coke	Pepsi
Coca-Cola	Diet Coke	Pepsi	Pepsi	Pepsi
Coca-Cola	Coca-Cola	Coca-Cola	Coca-Cola	Pepsi
Dr. Pepper	Coca-Cola	Coca-Cola	Coca-Cola	Coca-Cola
Diet Coke	Sprite	Coca-Cola	Coca-Cola	Dr. Pepper
Pepsi	Coca-Cola	Pepsi	Pepsi	Pepsi
Pepsi	Diet Coke	Coca-Cola	Dr. Pepper	Sprite

TABLE 2.2 FREQUENCY DISTRIBUTION OF SOFT DRINK PURCHASES

Soft Drink	Frequency
Coca-Cola	19
Diet Coke	8
Dr. Pepper	5
Pepsi	13
Sprite	5
Total	50

To develop a frequency distribution for these data, we count the number of times each soft drink appears in Table 2.1. Coca-Cola appears 19 times, Diet Coke appears 8 times, Dr. Pepper appears 5 times, Pepsi appears 13 times, and Sprite appears 5 times. These counts are summarized in the frequency distribution in Table 2.2.

This frequency distribution provides a summary of how the 50 soft drink purchases are distributed across the five soft drinks. This summary offers more insight than the original data shown in Table 2.1. Viewing the frequency distribution, we see that Coca-Cola is the leader, Pepsi is second, Diet Coke is third, and Sprite and Dr. Pepper are tied for fourth. The frequency distribution summarizes information about the popularity of the five soft drinks.

Relative Frequency and Percent Frequency Distributions

A frequency distribution shows the number (frequency) of observations in each of several nonoverlapping classes. However, we are often interested in the proportion, or percentage, of observations in each class. The *relative frequency* of a class equals the fraction or proportion of observations belonging to a class. For a data set with n observations, the relative frequency of each class can be determined as follows:

RELATIVE FREQUENCY

$$\text{Relative frequency of a class} = \frac{\text{Frequency of the class}}{n} \tag{2.1}$$

The *percent frequency* of a class is the relative frequency multiplied by 100.

A **relative frequency distribution** gives a tabular summary of data showing the relative frequency for each class. A **percent frequency distribution** summarizes the percent frequency of the data for each class. Table 2.3 shows a relative frequency distribution and a percent frequency distribution for the soft drink data. In Table 2.3 we see that the relative frequency for Coca-Cola is 19/50 = .38, the relative frequency for Diet Coke is 8/50 = .16, and so on. From the percent frequency distribution, we see that 38% of the purchases were Coca-Cola, 16% of the purchases were Diet Coke, and so on. We can also note that 38% + 26% + 16% = 80% of the purchases were for the top three soft drinks.

TABLE 2.3 RELATIVE FREQUENCY AND PERCENT FREQUENCY DISTRIBUTIONS OF SOFT DRINK PURCHASES

Soft Drink	Relative Frequency	Percent Frequency
Coca-Cola	.38	38
Diet Coke	.16	16
Dr. Pepper	.10	10
Pepsi	.26	26
Sprite	.10	10
Total	1.00	100

Using Excel to Construct a Frequency Distribution, a Relative Frequency Distribution, and a Percent Frequency Distribution

We can use Excel's Recommended PivotTables tool to construct a frequency distribution for the sample of 50 soft drink purchases. Two tasks are involved: Enter/Access Data and Apply Tools.

Enter/Access Data: Open the WEBfile named SoftDrink. The data are in cells A2:A51 and a label is in cell A1.

Apply Tools: The following steps describe how to use Excel's Recommended PivotTables tool to construct a frequency distribution for the sample of 50 soft drink purchases.

Every WEBfile in the text will open with the cursor in cell A1.

Step 1. Select any cell in the data set (cells A1:A51)
Step 2. Click **INSERT** on the Ribbon
Step 3. In the **Tables** group click **Recommended PivotTables**; a preview showing the frequency distribution appears
Step 4. Click **OK**; the frequency distribution will appear in a new worksheet

The worksheet in Figure 2.1 shows the frequency distribution for the 50 soft drink purchases created using these steps. Also shown is the PivotTable Fields dialog box, a key component of every PivotTable report. We will discuss the use of the PivotTable Fields dialog box later in the chapter.

FIGURE 2.1 FREQUENCY DISTRIBUTION OF SOFT DRINK PURCHASES CONSTRUCTED USING EXCEL'S RECOMMENDED PIVOTTABLES TOOL

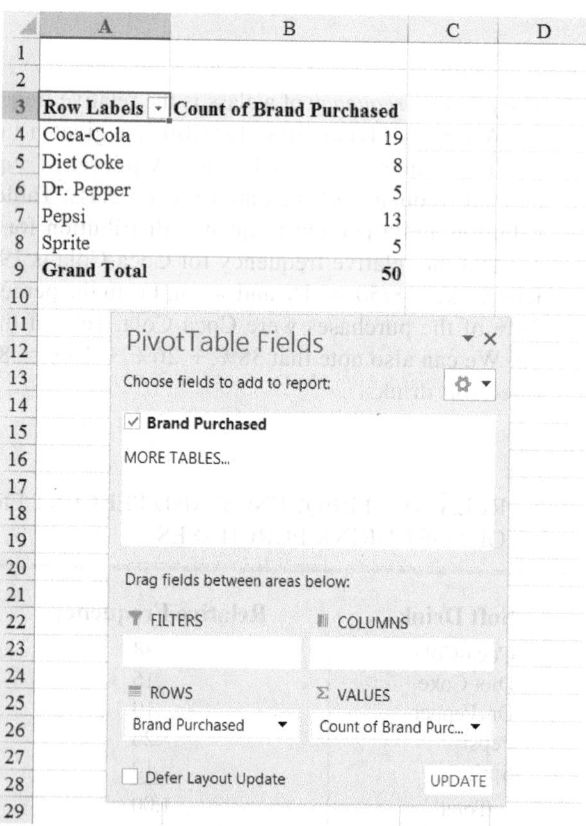

Row Labels	Count of Brand Purchased
Coca-Cola	19
Diet Coke	8
Dr. Pepper	5
Pepsi	13
Sprite	5
Grand Total	**50**

FIGURE 2.2 RELATIVE FREQUENCY AND PERCENT FREQUENCY DISTRIBUTIONS OF SOFT DRINK PURCHASES CONSTRUCTED USING EXCEL'S RECOMMENDED PIVOTTABLES TOOL

	A	B	C	D	E
1					
2					
3	**Soft Drink**	**Frequency**	**Relative Frequency**	**Percent Frequency**	
4	Coca-Cola	19	=B4/$B$9	=C4*100	
5	Diet Coke	8	=B5/$B$9	=C5*100	
6	Dr. Pepper	5	=B6/$B$9	=C6*100	
7	Pepsi	13	=B7/$B$9	=C7*100	
8	Sprite	5	=B8/$B$9	=C8*100	
9	**Total**	**50**	=SUM(C4:C8)	=SUM(D4:D8)	
10					
11					

	A	B	C	D	E
1					
2					
3	**Soft Drink**	**Frequency**	**Relative Frequency**	**Percent Frequency**	
4	Coca-Cola	19	0.38	38	
5	Diet Coke	8	0.16	16	
6	Dr. Pepper	5	0.1	10	
7	Pepsi	13	0.26	26	
8	Sprite	5	0.1	10	
9	**Total**	**50**	1	100	
10					

Editing Options: You can easily change the column headings in the frequency distribution output. For instance, to change the current heading in cell A3 (Row Labels) to "Soft Drink," click in cell A3 and type "Soft Drink"; to change the current heading in cell B3 (Count of Brand Purchased) to "Frequency," click in cell B3 and type "Frequency"; and to change the current heading in A9 (Grand Total) to "Total," click in cell A9 and type "Total." The foreground and background worksheets shown in Figure 2.2 contain the revised headings; in addition, the headings "Relative Frequency" and "Percent Frequency" were entered into cells C3 and D3. We will now show how to construct the relative frequency and percent frequency distributions.

Enter Functions and Formulas: Refer to Figure 2.2 as we describe how to create the relative and percent frequency distributions for the soft drink purchases. The formula worksheet is in the background and the value worksheet in the foreground. To compute the relative frequency for Coca-Cola using equation (2.1), we entered the formula =B4/$B$9 into cell C4; the result, 0.38, is the relative frequency for Coca-Cola. Copying cell C4 to cells C5:C8 computes the relative frequencies for each of the other soft drinks. To compute the percent frequency for Coca-Cola, we entered the formula =C4*100 into cell D4. The result, 38, indicates that 38% of the soft drink purchases were Coca-Cola. Copying cell D4 to cells D5:D8 computes the percent frequencies for each of the other soft drinks. To compute the total of the relative and percent frequencies we used Excel's SUM function in cells C9 and D9.

Bar Charts and Pie Charts

A **bar chart** is a graphical display for depicting categorical data summarized in a frequency, relative frequency, or percent frequency distribution. On one axis of the graph we specify the labels that are used for the classes (categories). A frequency, relative

FIGURE 2.3 BAR CHART OF SOFT DRINK PURCHASES

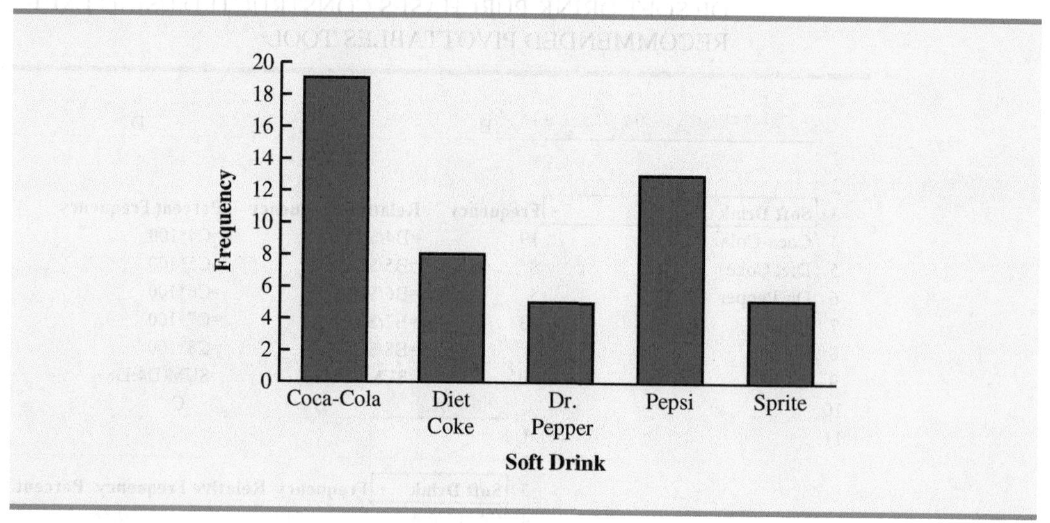

In quality control applications, bar charts are used to identify the most important causes of problems. When the bars are arranged in descending order of height from left to right with the most frequently occurring cause appearing first, the bar chart is called a Pareto diagram. *This diagram is named for its founder, Vilfredo Pareto, an Italian economist.*

frequency, or percent frequency scale can be used for the other axis of the chart. Then, using a bar of fixed width drawn above or next to each class label, we extend the length of the bar until we reach the frequency, relative frequency, or percent frequency of the class. For categorical data, the bars should be separated to emphasize the fact that each class is separate. Figure 2.3 shows a bar chart of the frequency distribution for the 50 soft drink purchases. Note how the graphical presentation shows Coca-Cola, Pepsi, and Diet Coke to be the most preferred brands.

In Figure 2.3 the horizontal axis was used to specify the labels for the categories; thus, the bars of the chart appear vertically in the display. In Excel, this type of display is referred to as a *column chart*. We could also display the bars for the chart horizontally by using the vertical axis to display the labels; Excel refers to this type of display as a *bar chart*. The choice of whether to display the bars vertically or horizontally depends upon what you want the final chart to look like. Throughout the text we will refer to either type of display as a bar chart.

The **pie chart** provides another graphical display for presenting relative frequency and percent frequency distributions for categorical data. To construct a pie chart, we first draw a circle to represent all the data. Then we use the relative frequencies to subdivide the circle into sectors, or parts, that correspond to the relative frequency for each class. For example, because a circle contains 360 degrees and Coca-Cola shows a relative frequency of .38, the sector of the pie chart labeled Coca-Cola consists of $.38(360) = 136.8$ degrees. The sector of the pie chart labeled Diet Coke consists of $.16(360) = 57.6$ degrees. Similar calculations for the other classes yield the pie chart in Figure 2.4. The numerical values shown for each sector can be frequencies, relative frequencies, or percent frequencies.

Numerous options involving the use of colors, shading, legends, text font, and three-dimensional perspectives are available to enhance the visual appearance of bar and pie charts. When used carefully, such options can provide a more effective display. But this is not always the case. For instance, consider the three-dimensional pie chart for the soft drink data shown in Figure 2.5. Compare it to the simpler presentation shown in Figure 2.4. The three-dimensional perspective adds no new understanding. In fact, because you have to view the three-dimensional pie chart in Figure 2.5 at an angle rather than straight overhead, it can be more difficult to visualize. The use of a legend in Figure 2.5 also forces your eyes to shift back and forth between the key and the chart. The simpler chart shown in Figure 2.4, which shows the percentages and classes directly on the pie, is more effective.

FIGURE 2.4 PIE CHART OF SOFT DRINK PURCHASES

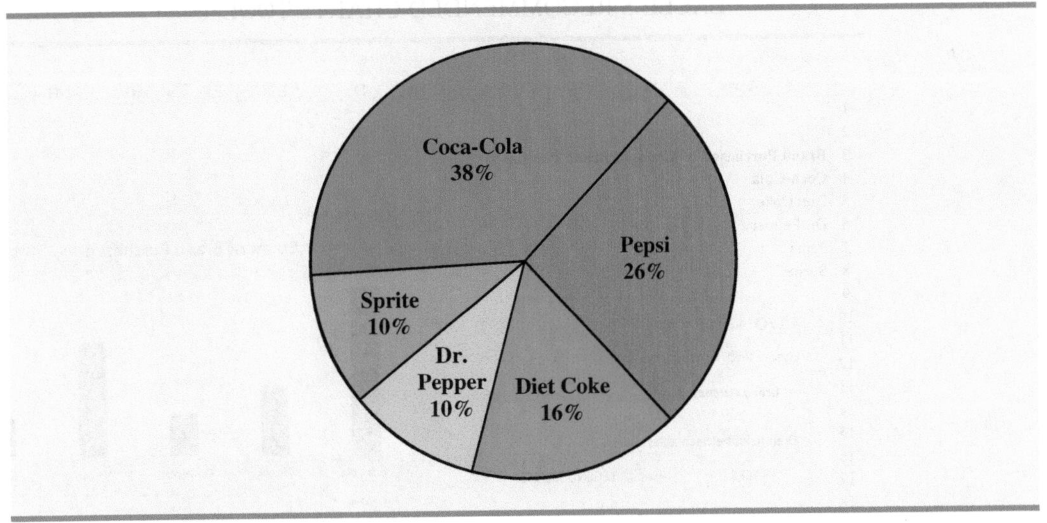

FIGURE 2.5 THREE-DIMENSIONAL PIE CHART OF SOFT DRINK PURCHASES

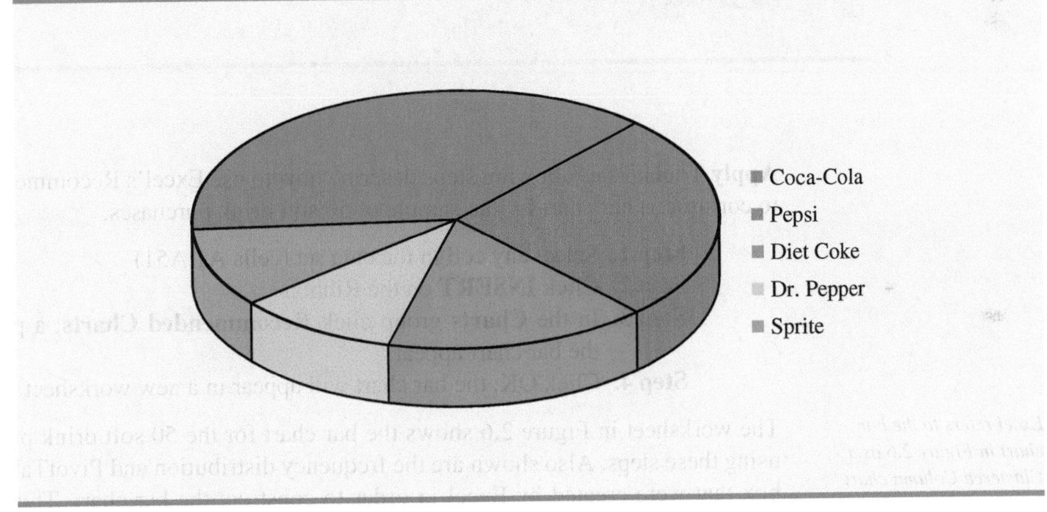

In general, pie charts are not the best way to present percentages for comparison. Research has shown that people are much better at accurately judging differences in length rather than differences in angles (or slices). When making such comparisons, we recommend you use a bar chart similar to Figure 2.3. In Section 2.5 we provide additional guidelines for creating effective visual displays.

Using Excel to Construct a Bar Chart and a Pie Chart

We can use Excel's Recommended Charts tool to construct a bar chart and a pie chart for the sample of 50 soft drink purchases. Two tasks are involved: Enter/Access Data and Apply Tools.

Enter/Access Data: Open the WEBfile named SoftDrink. The data are in cell A2:A51 and a label is in cell A1.

FIGURE 2.6 BAR CHART OF SOFT DRINK PURCHASES CONSTRUCTED USING EXCEL'S RECOMMENDED CHARTS TOOL

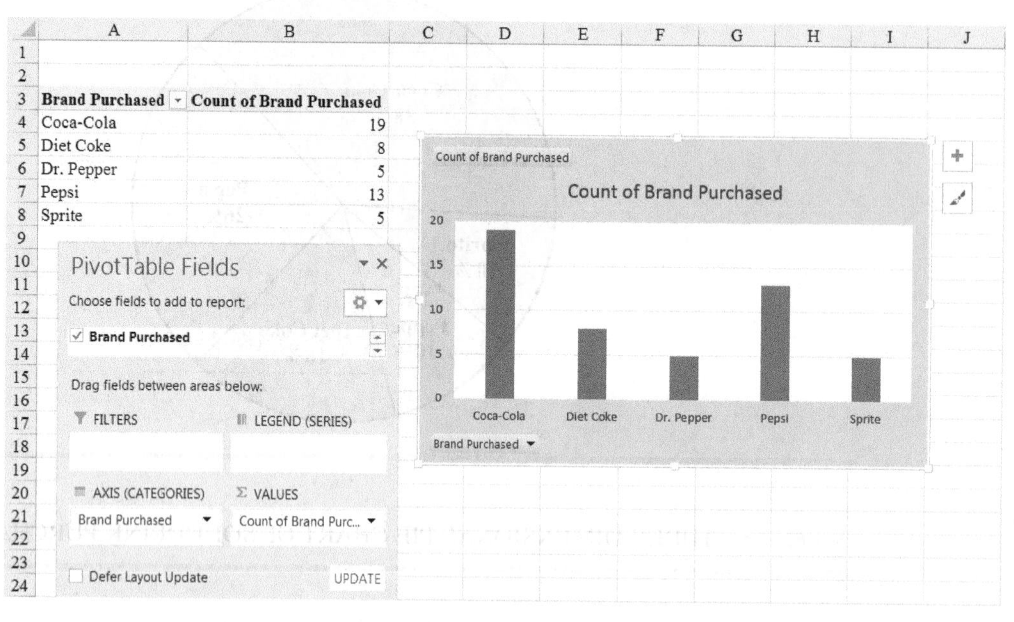

Apply Tools: The following steps describe how to use Excel's Recommended Charts tool to construct a bar chart for the sample of 50 soft drink purchases.

Step 1. Select any cell in the data set (cells A1:A51)
Step 2. Click **INSERT** on the Ribbon
Step 3. In the **Charts** group click **Recommended Charts**; a preview showing the bar chart appears
Step 4. Click OK; the bar chart will appear in a new worksheet

Excel refers to the bar chart in Figure 2.6 as a Clustered Column chart.

The worksheet in Figure 2.6 shows the bar chart for the 50 soft drink purchases created using these steps. Also shown are the frequency distribution and PivotTable Fields dialog box that were created by Excel in order to construct the bar chart. Thus, using Excel's Recommended Charts tool you can construct a bar chart and a frequency distribution at the same time.

Editing Options: You can easily edit the bar chart to display a different chart title and add axis titles. For instance, suppose you would like to use "Bar Chart of Soft Drink Purchases" as the chart title and insert "Soft Drink" for the horizontal axis title and "Frequency" for the vertical axis title.

Step 1. Click the **Chart Title** and replace it with **Bar Chart of Soft Drink Purchases**
Step 2. Click the **Chart Elements** button + (located next to the top right corner of the chart)
Step 3. When the list of chart elements appears:
Click **Axis Titles** (creates placeholders for the axis titles)
Step 4. Click the **Horizontal (Category) Axis Title** and replace it with **Soft Drink**
Step 5. Click the **Vertical (Value) Axis Title** and replace it with **Frequency**

The edited bar chart is shown in Figure 2.7.

FIGURE 2.7 EDITED BAR CHART OF SOFT DRINK PURCHASES CONSTRUCTED USING EXCEL'S RECOMMENDED CHARTS TOOL

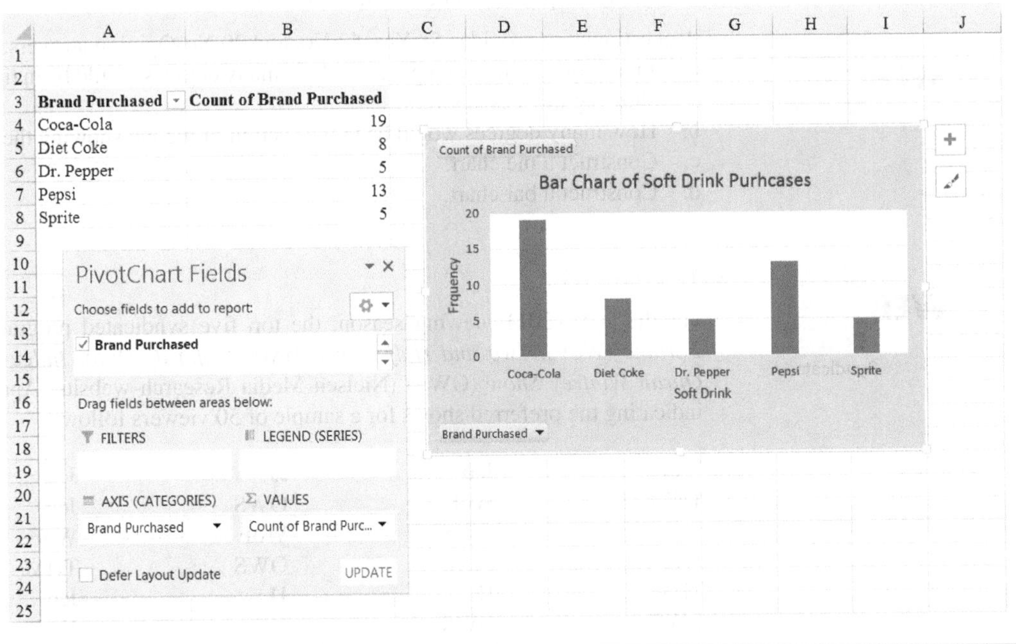

Creating a Pie Chart: To display a pie chart, select the bar chart (by clicking anywhere in the chart) to display three tabs (**Analyze**, **Design**, and **Format**) located on the Ribbon under the heading **PivotChart Tools**. Click the **Design Tab** and choose the **Change Chart Type** option to display the Change Chart Type dialog box. Click the **Pie** option and then **OK** to display a pie chart of the soft drink purchases.

Exercises

Methods

1. The response to a question has three alternatives: A, B, and C. A sample of 120 responses provides 60 A, 24 B, and 36 C. Show the frequency and relative frequency distributions.

2. A partial relative frequency distribution is given.

Class	Relative Frequency
A	.22
B	.18
C	.40
D	

a. What is the relative frequency of class D?
b. The total sample size is 200. What is the frequency of class D?
c. Show the frequency distribution.
d. Show the percent frequency distribution.

3. A questionnaire provides 58 Yes, 42 No, and 20 No-Opinion answers.
   a. In the construction of a pie chart, how many degrees would be in the section of the pie showing the Yes answers?
   b. How many degrees would be in the section of the pie showing the No answers?
   c. Construct a pie chart.
   d. Construct a bar chart.

Applications

Syndicated

4. For the 2010–2011 viewing season, the top five syndicated programs were *Wheel of Fortune* (WoF), *Two and Half Men* (THM), *Jeopardy* (Jep), *Judge Judy* (JJ), and the *Oprah Winfrey Show* (OWS) (Nielsen Media Research website, April 16, 2012). Data indicating the preferred shows for a sample of 50 viewers follow.

WoF	Jep	JJ	Jep	THM
THM	WoF	OWS	Jep	THM
Jep	OWS	WoF	WoF	WoF
WoF	THM	OWS	THM	WoF
THM	JJ	JJ	Jep	THM
OWS	OWS	JJ	JJ	Jep
JJ	WoF	THM	WoF	WoF
THM	THM	WoF	JJ	JJ
Jep	THM	WoF	Jep	Jep
WoF	THM	OWS	OWS	Jep

   a. Are these data categorical or quantitative?
   b. Provide frequency and percent frequency distributions.
   c. Construct a bar chart and a pie chart.
   d. On the basis of the sample, which television show has the largest viewing audience? Which one is second?

5. In alphabetical order, the six most common last names in the United States are Brown, Johnson, Jones, Miller, Smith, and Williams (*The World Almanac,* 2012). Assume that a sample of 50 individuals with one of these last names provided the following data.

2012Names

Brown	Williams	Williams	Williams	Brown
Smith	Jones	Smith	Johnson	Smith
Miller	Smith	Brown	Williams	Johnson
Johnson	Smith	Smith	Johnson	Brown
Williams	Miller	Johnson	Williams	Johnson
Williams	Johnson	Jones	Smith	Brown
Johnson	Smith	Smith	Brown	Jones
Jones	Jones	Smith	Smith	Miller
Miller	Jones	Williams	Miller	Smith
Jones	Johnson	Brown	Johnson	Miller

   Summarize the data by constructing the following:
   a. Relative and percent frequency distributions
   b. A bar chart
   c. A pie chart
   d. Based on these data, what are the three most common last names?

6. Nielsen Media Research provided the list of the 25 top-rated single shows in television history (*The World Almanac*, 2012). The following data show the television network that produced each of these 25 top-rated shows.

2012Networks

CBS	CBS	NBC	FOX	CBS
CBS	NBC	NBC	NBC	ABC
ABC	NBC	ABC	ABC	NBC
CBS	NBC	CBS	ABC	NBC
NBC	CBS	CBS	ABC	CBS

a. Construct a frequency distribution, percent frequency distribution, and bar chart for the data.
b. Which network or networks have done the best in terms of presenting top-rated television shows? Compare the performance of ABC, CBS, and NBC.

7. The Canmark Research Center Airport Customer Satisfaction Survey uses an online questionnaire to provide airlines and airports with customer satisfaction ratings for all aspects of the customers' flight experience (airportsurvey website, July, 2012). After completing a flight, customers receive an e-mail asking them to go to the website and rate a variety of factors, including the reservation process, the check-in process, luggage policy, cleanliness of gate area, service by flight attendants, food/beverage selection, on-time arrival, and so on. A five-point scale, with Excellent (E), Very Good (V), Good (G), Fair (F), and Poor (P), is used to record customer ratings. Assume that passengers on a Delta Airlines flight from Myrtle Beach, South Carolina, to Atlanta, Georgia, provided the following ratings for the question, "Please rate the airline based on your overall experience with this flight." The sample ratings are shown below.

AirSurvey

E	E	G	V	V	E	V	V	V	E
E	G	V	E	E	V	E	E	E	V
V	V	V	F	V	E	V	E	G	E
G	E	V	E	V	E	V	V	V	V
E	E	V	V	E	P	E	V	P	V

a. Use a percent frequency distribution and a bar chart to summarize these data. What do these summaries indicate about the overall customer satisfaction with the Delta flight?
b. The online survey questionnaire enabled respondents to explain any aspect of the flight that failed to meet expectations. Would this be helpful information to a manager looking for ways to improve the overall customer satisfaction on Delta flights? Explain.

8. Data for a sample of 55 members of the Baseball Hall of Fame in Cooperstown, New York, are shown here. Each observation indicates the primary position played by the Hall of Famers: pitcher (P), catcher (H), 1st base (1), 2nd base (2), 3rd base (3), shortstop (S), left field (L), center field (C), and right field (R).

BaseballHall

L	P	C	H	2	P	R	1	S	S	1	L	P	R	P
P	P	P	R	C	S	L	R	P	C	C	P	P	R	P
2	3	P	H	L	P	1	C	P	P	P	S	1	L	R
R	1	2	H	S	3	H	2	L	P					

a. Construct frequency and relative frequency distributions to summarize the data.
b. What position provides the most Hall of Famers?
c. What position provides the fewest Hall of Famers?
d. What outfield position (L, C, or R) provides the most Hall of Famers?
e. Compare infielders (1, 2, 3, and S) to outfielders (L, C, and R).

9. The Pew Research Center's Social & Demographic Trends project found that 46% of U.S. adults would rather live in a different type of community than the one where they are living now (Pew Research Center, January 29, 2009). The national survey of 2260 adults asked: "Where do you live now?" and "What do you consider to be the ideal community?" Response options were City (C), Suburb (S), Small Town (T), or Rural (R). A representative portion of this survey for a sample of 100 respondents is as follows.

LivingArea

Where do you live now?

S	T	R	C	R	R	T	C	S	T	C	S	C	S	T
S	S	C	S	S	T	T	C	C	S	T	C	S	T	C
T	R	S	S	T	C	S	C	T	C	T	C	T	C	R
C	C	R	T	C	S	S	T	S	C	C	C	R	S	C
S	S	C	C	S	C	R	T	T	T	C	R	T	C	R
C	T	R	R	C	T	C	C	R	T	T	R	S	R	T
T	S	S	S	S	S	C	C	R	T					

What do you consider to be the ideal community?

S	C	R	R	R	S	T	S	S	T	T	S	C	S	T
C	C	R	T	R	S	T	T	S	S	C	C	T	T	S
S	R	C	S	C	C	S	C	R	C	T	S	R	R	R
C	T	S	T	T	T	R	R	S	C	C	R	R	S	S
S	T	C	T	T	C	R	T	T	T	C	T	T	R	R
C	S	R	T	C	T	C	C	T	T	T	R	C	R	T
T	C	S	S	C	S	T	S	S	R					

a. Provide a percent frequency distribution for each question.
b. Construct a bar chart for each question.
c. Where are most adults living now?
d. What do most adults consider the ideal community?
e. What changes in living areas would you expect to see if people moved from where they currently live to their ideal community?

HotelRatings

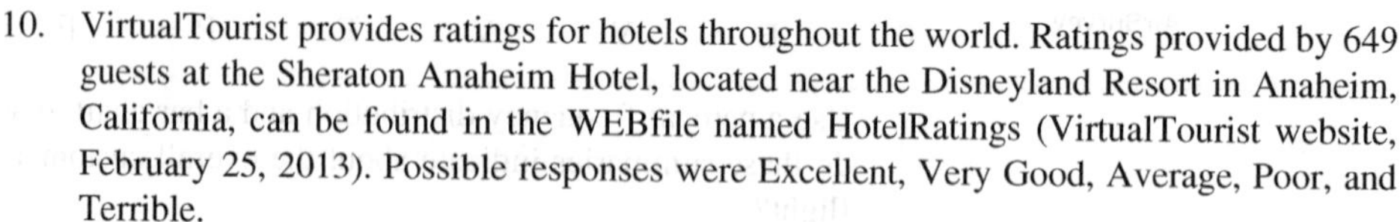

10. VirtualTourist provides ratings for hotels throughout the world. Ratings provided by 649 guests at the Sheraton Anaheim Hotel, located near the Disneyland Resort in Anaheim, California, can be found in the WEBfile named HotelRatings (VirtualTourist website, February 25, 2013). Possible responses were Excellent, Very Good, Average, Poor, and Terrible.

a. Construct a frequency distribution.
b Construct a percent frequency distribution.
c Construct a bar chart for the percent frequency distribution.
d Comment on how guests rate their stay at the Sheraton Anaheim Hotel.
e Results for 1679 guests who stayed at Disney's Grand Californian provided the following frequency distribution.

Rating	Frequency
Excellent	807
Very Good	521
Average	200
Poor	107
Terrible	44

Compare the ratings for Disney's Grand Californian with the results obtained for the Sheraton Anaheim Hotel.

2.2 Summarizing Data for a Quantitative Variable

Frequency Distribution

As defined in Section 2.1, a frequency distribution is a tabular summary of data showing the number (frequency) of observations in each of several nonoverlapping categories or classes. This definition holds for quantitative as well as categorical data. However, with quantitative data we must be more careful in defining the nonoverlapping classes to be used in the frequency distribution.

Audit

For example, consider the quantitative data in Table 2.4. These data show the time in days required to complete year-end audits for a sample of 20 clients of Sanderson and Clifford, a small public accounting firm. The three steps necessary to define the classes for a frequency distribution with quantitative data are

TABLE 2.4

YEAR-END AUDIT TIMES (IN DAYS)

12	14	19	18
15	15	18	17
20	27	22	23
22	21	33	28
14	18	16	13

1. Determine the number of nonoverlapping classes.
2. Determine the width of each class.
3. Determine the class limits.

Let us demonstrate these steps by developing a frequency distribution for the audit time data in Table 2.4.

Number of classes Classes are formed by specifying ranges that will be used to group the data. As a general guideline, we recommend using between 5 and 20 classes. For a small number of data items, as few as 5 or 6 classes may be used to summarize the data. For a larger number of data items, a larger number of classes is usually required. The goal is to use enough classes to show the variation in the data, but not so many classes that some contain only a few data items. Because the number of data items in Table 2.4 is relatively small ($n = 20$), we chose to develop a frequency distribution with five classes.

Making the classes the same width reduces the chance of inappropriate interpretations by the user.

Width of the classes The second step in constructing a frequency distribution for quantitative data is to choose a width for the classes. As a general guideline, we recommend that the width be the same for each class. Thus the choices of the number of classes and the width of classes are not independent decisions. A larger number of classes means a smaller class width, and vice versa. To determine an approximate class width, we begin by identifying the largest and smallest data values. Then, with the desired number of classes specified, we can use the following expression to determine the approximate class width.

$$\text{Approximate class width} = \frac{\text{Largest data value} - \text{Smallest data value}}{\text{Number of classes}} \tag{2.2}$$

The approximate class width given by equation (2.2) can be rounded to a more convenient value based on the preference of the person developing the frequency distribution. For example, an approximate class width of 9.28 might be rounded to 10 simply because 10 is a more convenient class width to use in presenting a frequency distribution.

No single frequency distribution is best for a data set. Different people may construct different, but equally acceptable, frequency distributions. The goal is to reveal the natural grouping and variation in the data.

For the data involving the year-end audit times, the largest data value is 33 and the smallest data value is 12. Because we decided to summarize the data with five classes, using equation (2.2) provides an approximate class width of $(33 - 12)/5 = 4.2$. We therefore decided to round up and use a class width of five days in the frequency distribution.

In practice, the number of classes and the appropriate class width are determined by trial and error. Once a possible number of classes is chosen, equation (2.2) is used to find the approximate class width. The process can be repeated for a different number of classes.

Ultimately, the analyst uses judgment to determine the combination of the number of classes and class width that provides the best frequency distribution for summarizing the data.

For the audit time data in Table 2.4, after deciding to use five classes, each with a width of five days, the next task is to specify the class limits for each of the classes.

Class limits Class limits must be chosen so that each data item belongs to one and only one class. The *lower class limit* identifies the smallest possible data value assigned to the class. The *upper class limit* identifies the largest possible data value assigned to the class. In developing frequency distributions for categorical data, we did not need to specify class limits because each data item naturally fell into a separate class. But with quantitative data, such as the audit times in Table 2.4, class limits are necessary to determine where each data value belongs.

TABLE 2.5

FREQUENCY DISTRIBUTION FOR THE AUDIT TIME DATA

Audit Time (days)	Frequency
10–14	4
15–19	8
20–24	5
25–29	2
30–34	1
Total	20

Using the audit time data in Table 2.4, we selected 10 days as the lower class limit and 14 days as the upper class limit for the first class. This class is denoted 10–14 in Table 2.5. The smallest data value, 12, is included in the 10–14 class. We then selected 15 days as the lower class limit and 19 days as the upper class limit of the next class. We continued defining the lower and upper class limits to obtain a total of five classes: 10–14, 15–19, 20–24, 25–29, and 30–34. The largest data value, 33, is included in the 30–34 class. The difference between the lower class limits of adjacent classes is the class width. Using the first two lower class limits of 10 and 15, we see that the class width is $15 - 10 = 5$.

With the number of classes, class width, and class limits determined, a frequency distribution can be obtained by counting the number of data values belonging to each class. For example, the data in Table 2.4 show that four values—12, 14, 14, and 13—belong to the 10–14 class. Thus, the frequency for the 10–14 class is 4. Continuing this counting process for the 15–19, 20–24, 25–29, and 30–34 classes provides the frequency distribution in Table 2.5. Using this frequency distribution, we can observe the following:

1. The most frequently occurring audit times are in the class of 15–19 days. Eight of the 20 audit times belong to this class.
2. Only one audit required 30 or more days.

Other conclusions are possible, depending on the interests of the person viewing the frequency distribution. The value of a frequency distribution is that it provides insights about the data that are not easily obtained by viewing the data in their original unorganized form.

Class midpoint In some applications, we want to know the midpoints of the classes in a frequency distribution for quantitative data. The **class midpoint** is the value halfway between the lower and upper class limits. For the audit time data, the five class midpoints are 12, 17, 22, 27, and 32.

Relative Frequency and Percent Frequency Distributions

We define the relative frequency and percent frequency distributions for quantitative data in the same manner as for categorical data. First, recall that the relative frequency is the proportion of the observations belonging to a class. With n observations,

$$\text{Relative frequency of class} = \frac{\text{Frequency of the class}}{n}$$

The percent frequency of a class is the relative frequency multiplied by 100.

Based on the class frequencies in Table 2.5 and with $n = 20$, Table 2.6 shows the relative frequency distribution and percent frequency distribution for the audit time data. Note that .40 of the audits, or 40%, required 15 to 19 days. Only .05 of the audits, or 5%, required 30 or more days. Again, additional interpretations and insights can be obtained by using Table 2.6.

TABLE 2.6 RELATIVE FREQUENCY AND PERCENT FREQUENCY DISTRIBUTIONS FOR THE AUDIT TIME DATA

Audit Time (days)	Relative Frequency	Percent Frequency
10–14	.20	20
15–19	.40	40
20–24	.25	25
25–29	.10	10
30–34	.05	5
Total	1.00	100

Using Excel to Construct a Frequency Distribution

We can use Excel's PivotTable tool to construct a frequency distribution for the audit time data. Two tasks are involved: Enter/Access Data and Apply Tools.

Enter/Access Data: Open the WEBfile named Audit. The data are in cells A2:A21 and a label is in cell A1.

Apply Tools: The following steps describe how to use Excel's PivotTable tool to construct a frequency distribution for the audit time data. When using Excel's PivotTable tool, each column of data is referred to as a field. Thus, for the audit time example, the data appearing in cells A2:A21 and the label in cell A1 are referred to as the Audit Time field.

Step 1. Select any cell in the data set (cells A1:A21)
Step 2. Click **INSERT** on the Ribbon
Step 3. In the **Tables** group click **PivotTable**
Step 4. When the Create PivotTable dialog box appears:
Click **OK**; a **PivotTable** and **PivotTable Fields** dialog box will appear in a new worksheet
Step 5. In the **PivotTable Fields** dialog box:
Drag **Audit Time** to the **Rows** area
Drag **Audit Time** to the **Values** area
Step 6. Click on **Sum of Audit Time** in the **Values** area
Step 7. Click **Value Field Settings** from the list of options that appears
Step 8. When the Value Field Settings dialog box appears:
Under **Summarize value field by**, choose **Count**
Click **OK**

Figure 2.8 shows the resulting PivotTable Fields Dialog and the corresponding PivotTable. To construct the frequency distribution shown in Table 2.5, we must group the rows containing the audit times. The following steps accomplish this.

Step 1. Right-click cell A4 in the PivotTable or any other cell containing an audit time.
Step 2. Choose **Group** from the list of options that appears
Step 3. When the Grouping dialog box appears:
Enter 10 in the **Starting at** box
Enter 34 in the **Ending at** box
Enter 5 in the **By** box
Click **OK**

Figure 2.9 shows the completed PivotTable Fields dialog box and the corresponding PivotTable. We see that with the exception of the column headings, the PivotTable provides the same information as the frequency distribution shown in Table 2.5.

FIGURE 2.8 PIVOTTABLE FIELDS DIALOG BOX AND INITIAL PIVOTTABLE USED TO CONSTRUCT A FREQUENCY DISTRIBUTION FOR THE AUDIT TIME DATA

	A	B	C	D	E	F	G	H
1								
2								
3	**Row Labels**	**Count of Audit Time**						
4	12	1						
5	13	1						
6	14	2						
7	15	2						
8	16	1						
9	17	1						
10	18	3						
11	19	1						
12	20	1						
13	21	1						
14	22	2						
15	23	1						
16	27	1						
17	28	1						
18	33	1						
19	**Grand Total**	**20**						
20								
21								
22								
23								

PivotTable Fields

Choose fields to add to report:

☑ Audit Time

MORE TABLES...

Drag fields between areas below:

FILTERS | COLUMNS

ROWS | Σ VALUES

Audit Time | Count of Audit Time

☐ Defer Layout Update | UPDATE

The same Excel procedures we followed in the previous section can now be used to develop relative and percent frequency distributions if desired.

Editing Options: You can easily change the labels in the PivotTable to match the labels in Table 2.5. For instance, to change the current heading in cell A3 (Row Labels) to "Audit Time (days)," click in cell A3 and type "Audit Time (days)"; to change the current heading in cell B3 (Count of Audit Time) to "Frequency," click in cell B3 and type "Frequency"; and to change the current heading in A9 (Grand Total) to "Total," click in cell A9 and type "Total."

In some cases the frequency distribution created using Excel's PivotTable tool can have class labels that appear to indicate overlapping classes. For instance, suppose that the audit time data in Table 2.4 had been recorded to the nearest tenth of a day as shown below:

12.1	15.4	20.4	22.4	14.0	14.3	15.0	27.4	21.4	18.3
19.4	18.0	21.9	33.2	16.4	17.6	17.2	23.4	28.1	13.2

We can use the same Excel procedure to construct a frequency distribution for this revised audit time data; a portion of the Excel PivotTable tool output for the revised audit time data follows.

Row Labels	Count of Revised Audit Time
10–15	4
15–20	8
20–25	5
25–30	2
30–35	1
Grand Total	**20**

FIGURE 2.9 FREQUENCY DISTRIBUTION FOR THE AUDIT TIME DATA CONSTRUCTED USING EXCEL'S PIVOTTABLE TOOL

	A	B
1		
2		
3	**Row Labels**	**Count of Audit Time**
4	10-14	4
5	15-19	8
6	20-24	5
7	25-29	2
8	30-34	1
9	**Grand Total**	**20**

PivotTable Fields

Choose fields to add to report:

☑ **Audit Time**

MORE TABLES...

Drag fields between areas below:

FILTERS | COLUMNS

ROWS: Audit Time | Σ VALUES: Count of Audit Time

☐ Defer Layout Update | UPDATE

The class labels, 10–15, 15–20, and so on, appear to indicate overlapping classes. For instance, the value of 15.0 in the revised audit time data appears to fall in both the first and second classes. However, using Excel's PivotTable tool, the 10–15 class includes all the data values that are *greater than or equal* to 10 but *less than* 15; the 15–20 class includes all the data values that are *greater than or equal* to 15 but *less than* 20; and so on. Thus, the value of 15.0 in the revised audit time data set is included in the second class. Any possible confusion caused by the class labels created by Excel's PivotTable tool can be avoided by changing the class labels 10–14.9, 15–19.9, 20–24.9, 25–29.9, and 30–34.9.

Dot Plot

One of the simplest graphical summaries of data is a **dot plot**. A horizontal axis shows the range for the data. Each data value is represented by a dot placed above the axis. Figure 2.10 is

FIGURE 2.10 DOT PLOT FOR THE AUDIT TIME DATA

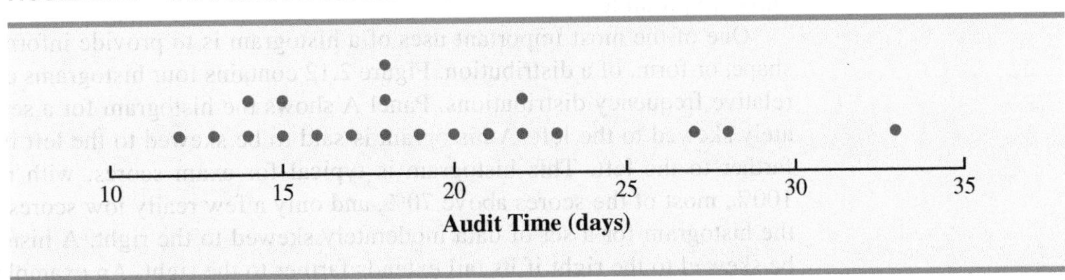

FIGURE 2.11 HISTOGRAM FOR THE AUDIT TIME DATA

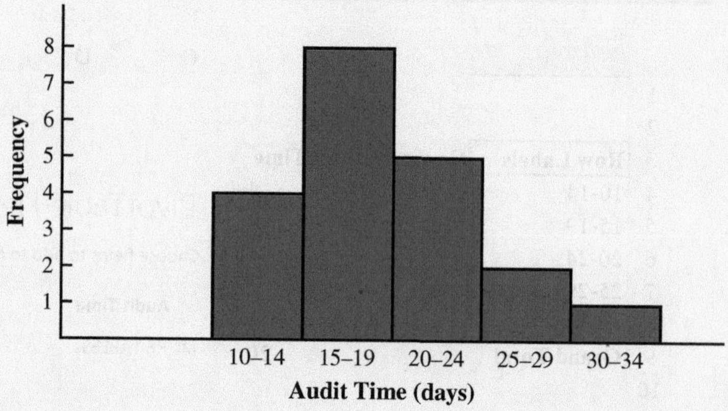

the dot plot for the audit time data in Table 2.4. The three dots located above 18 on the horizontal axis indicate that an audit time of 18 days occurred three times. Dot plots show the details of the data and are useful for comparing the distribution of the data for two or more variables.

Histogram

A common graphical display of quantitative data is a **histogram.** This graphical display can be prepared for data previously summarized in either a frequency, relative frequency, or percent frequency distribution. A histogram is constructed by placing the variable of interest on the horizontal axis and the frequency, relative frequency, or percent frequency on the vertical axis. The frequency, relative frequency, or percent frequency of each class is shown by drawing a rectangle whose base is determined by the class limits on the horizontal axis and whose height is the corresponding frequency, relative frequency, or percent frequency.

Figure 2.11 is a histogram for the audit time data. Note that the class with the greatest frequency is shown by the rectangle appearing above the class of 15–19 days. The height of the rectangle shows that the frequency of this class is 8. A histogram for the relative or percent frequency distribution of these data would look the same as the histogram in Figure 2.11 with the exception that the vertical axis would be labeled with relative or percent frequency values.

As Figure 2.11 shows, the adjacent rectangles of a histogram touch one another. Unlike a bar chart, a histogram contains no natural separation between the rectangles of adjacent classes. This format is the usual convention for histograms. Because the classes for the audit time data are stated as 10–14, 15–19, 20–24, 25–29, and 30–34, one-unit spaces of 14 to 15, 19 to 20, 24 to 25, and 29 to 30 would seem to be needed between the classes. These spaces are eliminated when constructing a histogram. Eliminating the spaces between classes in a histogram for the audit time data helps show that all values between the lower limit of the first class and the upper limit of the last class are possible.

One of the most important uses of a histogram is to provide information about the shape, or form, of a distribution. Figure 2.12 contains four histograms constructed from relative frequency distributions. Panel A shows the histogram for a set of data moderately skewed to the left. A histogram is said to be skewed to the left if its tail extends farther to the left. This histogram is typical for exam scores, with no scores above 100%, most of the scores above 70%, and only a few really low scores. Panel B shows the histogram for a set of data moderately skewed to the right. A histogram is said to be skewed to the right if its tail extends farther to the right. An example of this type of

FIGURE 2.12 HISTOGRAMS SHOWING DIFFERING LEVELS OF SKEWNESS

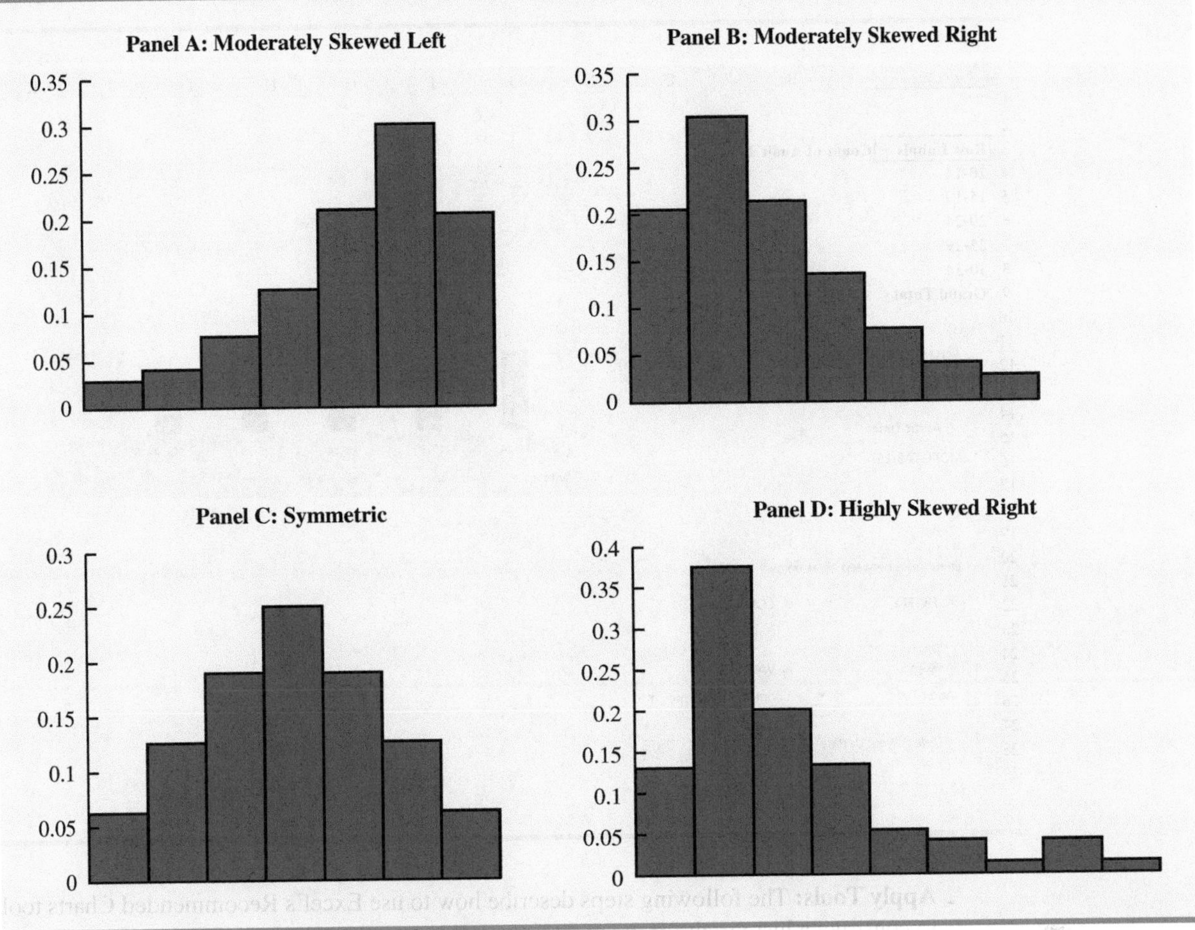

histogram would be for data such as housing prices; a few expensive houses create the skewness in the right tail.

Panel C shows a symmetric histogram. In a symmetric histogram, the left tail mirrors the shape of the right tail. Histograms for data found in applications are never perfectly symmetric, but the histogram for many applications may be roughly symmetric. Data for SAT scores, heights and weights of people, and so on lead to histograms that are roughly symmetric. Panel D shows a histogram highly skewed to the right. This histogram was constructed from data on the amount of customer purchases over one day at a women's apparel store. Data from applications in business and economics often lead to histograms that are skewed to the right. For instance, data on housing prices, salaries, purchase amounts, and so on often result in histograms skewed to the right.

Using Excel's Recommended Charts Tool to Construct a Histogram

In Figure 2.9 we showed the results of using Excel's PivotTable tool to construct a frequency distribution for the audit time data. We will use these results to illustrate how Excel's Recommended Charts tool can be used to construct a histogram for depicting quantitative data summarized in a frequency distribution. Refer to Figure 2.13 as we describe the steps involved.

FIGURE 2.13 INITIAL CHART USED TO CONSTRUCT A HISTOGRAM FOR THE AUDIT TIME DATA

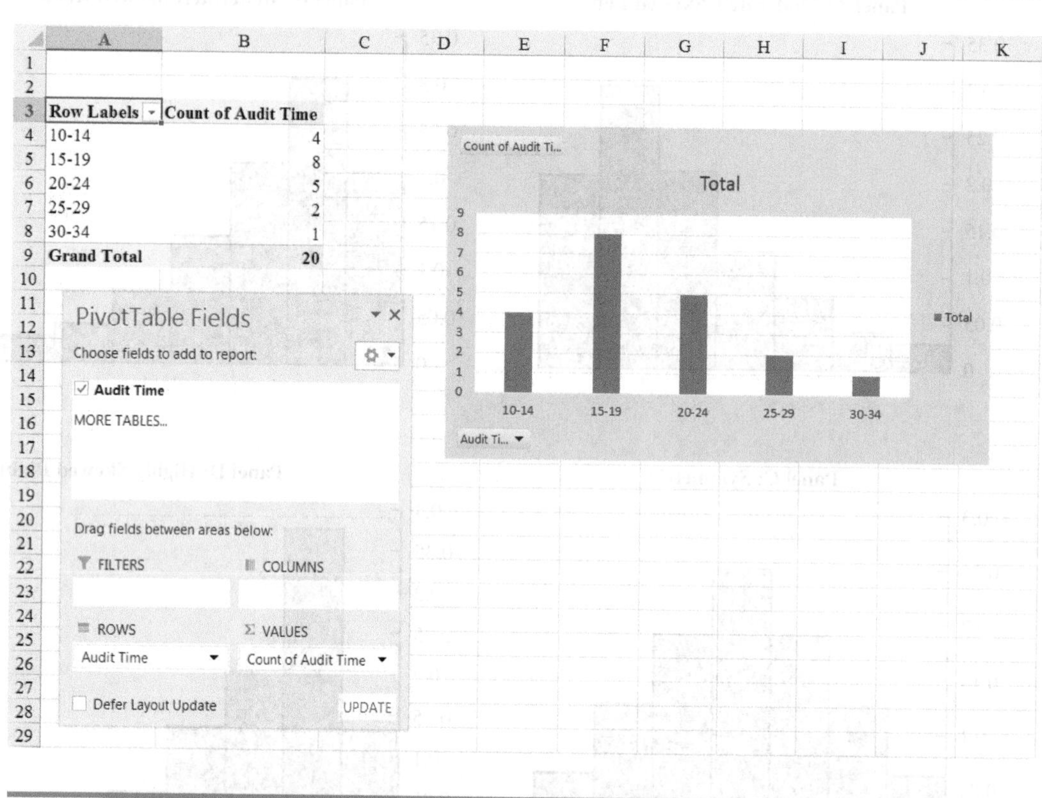

Apply Tools: The following steps describe how to use Excel's Recommended Charts tool to construct a histogram for the audit time data.

Step 1. Select any cell in the PivotTable report (cells A3:B9)
Step 2. Click **INSERT** on the Ribbon
Step 3. In the **Charts** group click **Recommended Charts**; a preview showing the recommended chart appears
Step 4. Click **OK**

Excel refers to the bar chart in Figure 2.13 as a Clustered Column chart.

The worksheet in Figure 2.13 shows the chart for the audit time data created using these steps. With the exception of the gaps separating the bars, this resembles the histogram for the audit time data shown in Figure 2.11. We can easily edit this chart to remove the gaps between the bars and enter more descriptive axis labels and a chart heading.

Editing Options: In addition to removing the gaps between the bars, suppose you would like to use "Histogram for Audit Time Data" as the chart title and insert "Audit Time (days)" for the horizontal axis title and "Frequency" for the vertical axis title.

Step 1. Right-click any bar in the chart and choose **Format Data Series** from the list of options that appears
Step 2. When the Format Data Series dialog box appears:
Go to the **Series Options** section
Set the **Gap Width** to 0
Click the **Close** button × at the top right of the dialog box
Step 3. Click the **Chart Title** and replace it with **Histogram for Audit Time Data**

FIGURE 2.14 HISTOGRAM FOR THE AUDIT TIME DATA CREATED USING EXCEL'S RECOMMENDED CHARTS TOOL

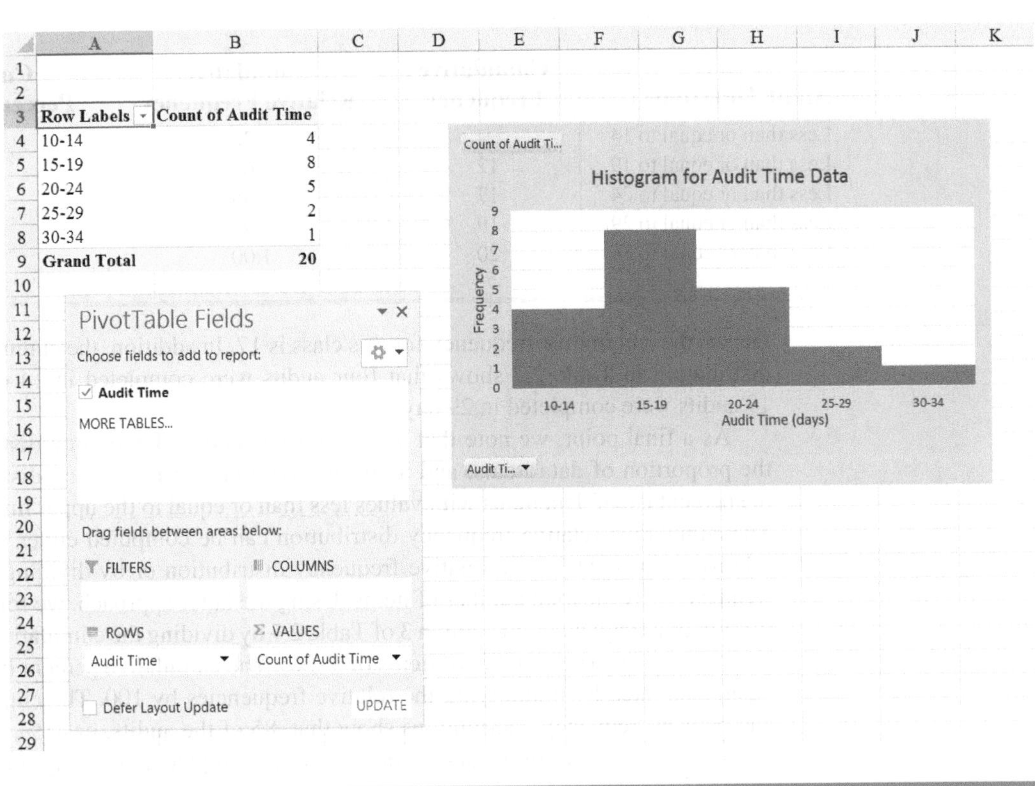

Step 4. Click the **Chart Elements** button + (located next to the top right corner of the chart)

Step 5. When the list of chart elements appears:

Click **Axis Titles** (creates placeholders for the axis titles)

Click **Legend** to remove the check in the Legend box

Step 6. Click the **Horizontal (Category) Axis Title** and replace it with **Audit Time (days)**

Step 7. Click the **Vertical (Value) Axis Title** and replace it with **Frequency**

The edited histogram for the audit time is shown in Figure 2.14.

Cumulative Distributions

A variation of the frequency distribution that provides another tabular summary of quantitative data is the **cumulative frequency distribution**. The cumulative frequency distribution uses the number of classes, class widths, and class limits developed for the frequency distribution. However, rather than showing the frequency of each class, the cumulative frequency distribution shows the number of data items with values *less than or equal to the upper class limit* of each class. The first two columns of Table 2.7 provide the cumulative frequency distribution for the audit time data.

To understand how the cumulative frequencies are determined, consider the class with the description "less than or equal to 24." The cumulative frequency for this class is simply the sum of the frequencies for all classes with data values less than or equal to 24. For the frequency distribution in Table 2.5, the sum of the frequencies for classes 10–14, 15–19, and 20–24 indicates that $4 + 8 + 5 = 17$ data values are less than or equal to 24.

TABLE 2.7 CUMULATIVE FREQUENCY, CUMULATIVE RELATIVE FREQUENCY, AND CUMULATIVE PERCENT FREQUENCY DISTRIBUTIONS FOR THE AUDIT TIME DATA

Audit Time (days)	Cumulative Frequency	Cumulative Relative Frequency	Cumulative Percent Frequency
Less than or equal to 14	4	.20	20
Less than or equal to 19	12	.60	60
Less than or equal to 24	17	.85	85
Less than or equal to 29	19	.95	95
Less than or equal to 34	20	1.00	100

Hence, the cumulative frequency for this class is 17. In addition, the cumulative frequency distribution in Table 2.7 shows that four audits were completed in 14 days or less and 19 audits were completed in 29 days or less.

As a final point, we note that a **cumulative relative frequency distribution** shows the proportion of data items, and a **cumulative percent frequency distribution** shows the percentage of data items with values less than or equal to the upper limit of each class. The cumulative relative frequency distribution can be computed either by summing the relative frequencies in the relative frequency distribution or by dividing the cumulative frequencies by the total number of items. Using the latter approach, we found the cumulative relative frequencies in column 3 of Table 2.7 by dividing the cumulative frequencies in column 2 by the total number of items ($n = 20$). The cumulative percent frequencies were again computed by multiplying the relative frequencies by 100. The cumulative relative and percent frequency distributions show that .85 of the audits, or 85%, were completed in 24 days or less, .95 of the audits, or 95%, were completed in 29 days or less, and so on.

Stem-and-Leaf Display

A **stem-and-leaf display** is a graphical display used to show simultaneously the rank order and shape of a distribution of data. To illustrate the use of a stem-and-leaf display, consider the data in Table 2.8. These data result from a 150-question aptitude test given to 50 individuals recently interviewed for a position at Haskens Manufacturing. The data indicate the number of questions answered correctly.

To develop a stem-and-leaf display, we first arrange the leading digits of each data value to the left of a vertical line. To the right of the vertical line, we record the last digit for each data value. Based on the top row of data in Table 2.8 (112, 72, 69, 97, and 107), the first

TABLE 2.8 NUMBER OF QUESTIONS ANSWERED CORRECTLY ON AN APTITUDE TEST

112	72	69	97	107
73	92	76	86	73
126	128	118	127	124
82	104	132	134	83
92	108	96	100	92
115	76	91	102	81
95	141	81	80	106
84	119	113	98	75
68	98	115	106	95
100	85	94	106	119

five entries in constructing a stem-and-leaf display would be as follows:

```
 6 | 9
 7 | 2
 8 |
 9 | 7
10 | 7
11 | 2
12 |
13 |
14 |
```

For example, the data value 112 shows the leading digits 11 to the left of the line and the last digit 2 to the right of the line. Similarly, the data value 72 shows the leading digit 7 to the left of the line and last digit 2 to the right of the line. Continuing to place the last digit of each data value on the line corresponding to its leading digit(s) provides the following:

```
 6 | 9 8
 7 | 2 3 6 3 6 5
 8 | 6 2 3 1 1 0 4 5
 9 | 7 2 2 6 2 1 5 8 8 5 4
10 | 7 4 8 0 2 6 6 0 6
11 | 2 8 5 9 3 5 9
12 | 6 8 7 4
13 | 2 4
14 | 1
```

With this organization of the data, sorting the digits on each line into rank order is simple. Doing so provides the stem-and-leaf display shown here.

```
 6 | 8 9
 7 | 2 3 3 5 6 6
 8 | 0 1 1 2 3 4 5 6
 9 | 1 2 2 2 4 5 5 6 7 8 8
10 | 0 0 2 4 6 6 6 7 8
11 | 2 3 5 5 8 9 9
12 | 4 6 7 8
13 | 2 4
14 | 1
```

The numbers to the left of the vertical line (6, 7, 8, 9, 10, 11, 12, 13, and 14) form the *stem*, and each digit to the right of the vertical line is a *leaf*. For example, consider the first row with a stem value of 6 and leaves of 8 and 9.

```
6 | 8 9
```

This row indicates that two data values have a first digit of six. The leaves show that the data values are 68 and 69. Similarly, the second row

```
7 | 2 3 3 5 6 6
```

indicates that six data values have a first digit of seven. The leaves show that the data values are 72, 73, 73, 75, 76, and 76.

To focus on the shape indicated by the stem-and-leaf display, let us use a rectangle to contain the leaves of each stem. Doing so, we obtain the following:

```
 6 | 8 9
 7 | 2 3 3 5 6 6
 8 | 0 1 1 2 3 4 5 6
 9 | 1 2 2 2 4 5 5 6 7 8 8
10 | 0 0 2 4 6 6 6 7 8
11 | 2 3 5 5 8 9 9
12 | 4 6 7 8
13 | 2 4
14 | 1
```

Rotating this page counterclockwise onto its side provides a picture of the data that is similar to a histogram with classes of 60–69, 70–79, 80–89, and so on.

Although the stem-and-leaf display may appear to offer the same information as a histogram, it has two primary advantages.

1. The stem-and-leaf display is easier to construct by hand.
2. Within a class interval, the stem-and-leaf display provides more information than the histogram because the stem-and-leaf shows the actual data.

Just as a frequency distribution or histogram has no absolute number of classes, neither does a stem-and-leaf display have an absolute number of rows or stems. If we believe that our original stem-and-leaf display condensed the data too much, we can easily stretch the display by using two or more stems for each leading digit. For example, to use two stems for each leading digit, we would place all data values ending in 0, 1, 2, 3, and 4 in one row and all values ending in 5, 6, 7, 8, and 9 in a second row. The following stretched stem-and-leaf display illustrates this approach.

In a stretched stem-and-leaf display, whenever a stem value is stated twice, the first value corresponds to leaf values of 0–4, and the second value corresponds to leaf values of 5–9.

```
 6 | 8 9
 7 | 2 3 3
 7 | 5 6 6
 8 | 0 1 1 2 3 4
 8 | 5 6
 9 | 1 2 2 2 4
 9 | 5 5 6 7 8 8
10 | 0 0 2 4
10 | 6 6 6 7 8
11 | 2 3
11 | 5 5 8 9 9
12 | 4
12 | 6 7 8
13 | 2 4
13 |
14 | 1
```

Note that values 72, 73, and 73 have leaves in the 0–4 range and are shown with the first stem value of 7. The values 75, 76, and 76 have leaves in the 5–9 range and are shown with the second stem value of 7. This stretched stem-and-leaf display is similar to a frequency distribution with intervals of 65–69, 70–74, 75–79, and so on.

The preceding example showed a stem-and-leaf display for data with as many as three digits. Stem-and-leaf displays for data with more than three digits are possible. For example, consider the following data on the number of hamburgers sold by a fast-food restaurant for each of 15 weeks.

1565	1852	1644	1766	1888	1912	2044	1812
1790	1679	2008	1852	1967	1954	1733	

A stem-and-leaf display of these data follows.

Leaf unit = 10

```
15 | 6
16 | 4 7
17 | 3 6 9
18 | 1 5 5 8
19 | 1 5 6
20 | 0 4
```

A single digit is used to define each leaf in a stem-and-leaf display. The leaf unit indicates how to multiply the stem-and-leaf numbers in order to approximate the original data. Leaf units may be 100, 10, 1, .1, and so on.

Note that a single digit is used to define each leaf and that only the first three digits of each data value have been used to construct the display. At the top of the display we have specified Leaf unit = 10. To illustrate how to interpret the values in the display, consider the first stem, 15, and its associated leaf, 6. Combining these numbers, we obtain 156. To reconstruct an approximation of the original data value, we must multiply this number by 10, the value of the *leaf unit*. Thus, $156 \times 10 = 1560$ is an approximation of the original data value used to construct the stem-and-leaf display. Although it is not possible to reconstruct the exact data value from this stem-and-leaf display, the convention of using a single digit for each leaf enables stem-and-leaf displays to be constructed for data having a large number of digits. For stem-and-leaf displays where the leaf unit is not shown, the leaf unit is assumed to equal 1.

NOTES AND COMMENTS

1. A bar chart and a histogram are essentially the same thing; both are graphical presentations of the data in a frequency distribution. A histogram is just a bar chart with no separation between bars. For some discrete quantitative data, a separation between bars is also appropriate. Consider, for example, the number of classes in which a college student is enrolled. The data may only assume integer values. Intermediate values such as 1.5, 2.73, and so on are not possible. With continuous quantitative data, however, such as the audit times in Table 2.4, a separation between bars is not appropriate.
2. The appropriate values for the class limits with quantitative data depend on the level of accuracy of the data. For instance, with the audit time data of Table 2.4 the limits used were integer values. If the data were rounded to the nearest tenth of a day (e.g., 12.3, 14.4, and so on), then the limits would be stated in tenths of days. For instance, the first class would be 10.0–14.9. If the data were recorded to the nearest hundredth of a day (e.g., 12.34, 14.45, and so on), the limits would be stated in hundredths of days. For instance, the first class would be 10.00–14.99.
3. An *open-end* class requires only a lower class limit or an upper class limit. For example, in the audit time data of Table 2.4, suppose two of the audits had taken 58 and 65 days. Rather than continue with the classes of width 5 with classes 35–39, 40–44, 45–49, and so on, we could simplify the frequency distribution to show an open-end class of "35 or more." This class would have a frequency of 2. Most often the open-end class appears at the upper end of the distribution. Sometimes an open-end class appears at the lower end of the distribution, and occasionally such classes appear at both ends.
4. The last entry in a cumulative frequency distribution always equals the total number of observations. The last entry in a cumulative relative frequency distribution always equals 1.00 and the last entry in a cumulative percent frequency distribution always equals 100.

Exercises

Methods

11. Consider the following data.

14	21	23	21	16
19	22	25	16	16
24	24	25	19	16
19	18	19	21	12
16	17	18	23	25
20	23	16	20	19
24	26	15	22	24
20	22	24	22	20

a. Develop a frequency distribution using classes of 12–14, 15–17, 18–20, 21–23, and 24–26.
b. Develop a relative frequency distribution and a percent frequency distribution using the classes in part (a).

12. Consider the following frequency distribution.

Class	Frequency
10–19	10
20–29	14
30–39	17
40–49	7
50–59	2

Construct a cumulative frequency distribution and a cumulative relative frequency distribution.

13. Construct a histogram for the data in exercise 12.
14. Consider the following data.

8.9	10.2	11.5	7.8	10.0	12.2	13.5	14.1	10.0	12.2
6.8	9.5	11.5	11.2	14.9	7.5	10.0	6.0	15.8	11.5

a. Construct a dot plot.
b. Construct a frequency distribution.
c. Construct a percent frequency distribution.

15. Construct a stem-and-leaf display for the following data.

11.3	9.6	10.4	7.5	8.3	10.5	10.0
9.3	8.1	7.7	7.5	8.4	6.3	8.8

16. Construct a stem-and-leaf display for the following data. Use a leaf unit of 10.

1161	1206	1478	1300	1604	1725	1361	1422
1221	1378	1623	1426	1557	1730	1706	1689

Applications

17. A doctor's office staff studied the waiting times for patients who arrive at the office with a request for emergency service. The following data with waiting times in minutes were collected over a one-month period.

2 5 10 12 4 4 5 17 11 8 9 8 12 21 6 8 7 13 18 3

Use classes of 0–4, 5–9, and so on in the following:

a. Show the frequency distribution.
b. Show the relative frequency distribution.
c. Show the cumulative frequency distribution.
d. Show the cumulative relative frequency distribution.
e. What proportion of patients needing emergency service wait 9 minutes or less?

18. CBSSports.com developed the Total Player Ratings system to rate players in the National Basketball Association (NBA) based upon various offensive and defensive statistics. The following data show the average number of points scored per game (PPG) for 50 players with the highest ratings for a portion of the 2012–2013 NBA season (CBSSports.com website, February 25, 2013).

NBAPlayerPts

27.0	28.8	26.4	27.1	22.9	28.4	19.2	21.0	20.8	17.6
21.1	19.2	21.2	15.5	17.2	16.7	17.6	18.5	18.3	18.3
23.3	16.4	18.9	16.5	17.0	11.7	15.7	18.0	17.7	14.6
15.7	17.2	18.2	17.5	13.6	16.3	16.2	13.6	17.1	16.7
17.0	17.3	17.5	14.0	16.9	16.3	15.1	12.3	18.7	14.6

Use classes starting at 10 and ending at 30 in increments of 2 for PPG in the following.

a. Show the frequency distribution.
b. Show the relative frequency distribution.
c. Show the cumulative percent frequency distribution.
d. Develop a histogram for the average number of points scored per game.
e. Do the data appear to be skewed? Explain.
f. What percentage of the players averaged at least 20 points per game?

19. Based on the tons handled in a year, the ports listed below are the 25 busiest ports in the United States (*The 2013 World Almanac*).

WEB file

Ports

Port	Tons Handled (Millions)	Port	Tons Handled (Millions)
Baltimore	39.6	Norfolk Harbor	41.6
Baton Rouge	55.5	Pascagoula	37.3
Beaumont	77.0	Philadelphia	34.0
Corpus Christi	73.7	Pittsburgh	33.8
Duluth-Superior	36.6	Plaquemines	55.8
Houston	227.1	Port Arthur	30.2
Huntington	61.5	Savannah	34.7
Lake Charles	54.6	South Louisiana	236.3
Long Beach	75.4	St. Louis	30.8
Los Angeles	62.4	Tampa	34.2
Mobile	55.7	Texas City	56.6
New Orleans	72.4	Valdez	31.9
New York	139.2		

a. What is the largest number of tons handled? What is the smallest number of tons handled?
b. Using a class width of 25, develop a frequency distribution of the data starting with 25–49.9, 50–74.9, 75–99.9, and so on.
c. Prepare a histogram. Interpret the histogram.

20. The London School of Economics and the Harvard Business School conducted a study of how chief executive officers (CEOs) spend their day. The study found that CEOs spend on average about 18 hours per week in meetings, not including conference

calls, business meals, and public events (*The Wall Street Journal,* February 14, 2012). Shown below is the time spent per week in meetings (hours) for a sample of 25 CEOs.

CEOTime

14	15	18	23	15
19	20	13	15	23
23	21	15	20	21
16	15	18	18	19
19	22	23	21	12

a. What is the least amount of time spent per week on meetings? The highest?
b. Use a class width of two hours to prepare a frequency distribution and a percent frequency distribution for the data.
c. Prepare a histogram and comment on the shape of the distribution.

21. *Fortune* provides a list of America's largest corporations based on annual revenue. Shown below are the 50 largest corporations, with annual revenue expressed in billions of dollars (*CNN Money* website, January 15, 2010).

LargeCorp

Corporation	Revenue	Corporation	Revenue
Amerisource Bergen	71	Lowe's	48
Archer Daniels Midland	70	Marathon Oil	74
AT&T	124	McKesson	102
Bank of America	113	Medco Health	51
Berkshire Hathaway	108	MetLife	55
Boeing	61	Microsoft	60
Cardinal Health	91	Morgan Stanley	62
Caterpillar	51	Pepsico	43
Chevron	263	Pfizer	48
Citigroup	112	Procter & Gamble	84
ConocoPhillips	231	Safeway	44
Costco Wholesale	72	Sears Holdings	47
CVS Caremark	87	State Farm Insurance	61
Dell	61	Sunoco	52
Dow Chemical	58	Target	65
ExxonMobil	443	Time Warner	47
Ford Motors	146	United Parcel Service	51
General Electric	149	United Technologies	59
Goldman Sachs	54	UnitedHealth Group	81
Hewlett-Packard	118	Valero Energy	118
Home Depot	71	Verizon	97
IBM	104	Walgreen	59
JPMorgan Chase	101	Walmart	406
Johnson & Johnson	64	WellPoint	61
Kroger	76	Wells Fargo	52

Summarize the data by constructing the following:

a. A frequency distribution (classes 0–49, 50–99, 100–149, and so on).
b. A relative frequency distribution.
c. A cumulative frequency distribution.
d. A cumulative relative frequency distribution.
e. What do these distributions tell you about the annual revenue of the largest corporations in America?
f. Show a histogram. Comment on the shape of the distribution.
g. What is the largest corporation in America and what is its annual revenue?

22. *Entrepreneur* magazine ranks franchises using performance measures such as growth rate, number of locations, startup costs, and financial stability. The number of locations for the top 20 U.S. franchises follow (*The World Almanac,* 2012).

Franchise

Franchise	No. U.S. Locations	Franchise	No. U.S. Locations
Hampton Inns	1864	Jan-Pro Franchising Intl. Inc.	12,394
ampm	3183	Hardee's	1901
McDonald's	32,805	Pizza Hut Inc.	13,281
7-Eleven Inc.	37,496	Kumon Math & Reading Centers	25,199
Supercuts	2130	Dunkin' Donuts	9947
Days Inn	1877	KFC Corp.	16,224
Vanguard Cleaning Systems	2155	Jazzercise Inc.	7683
Servpro	1572	Anytime Fitness	1618
Subway	34,871	Matco Tools	1431
Denny's Inc.	1668	Stratus Building Solutions	5018

Use classes 0–4999, 5000–9999, 10,000–14,999, and so forth to answer the following questions.

a. Construct a frequency distribution and a percent frequency distribution of the number of U.S. locations for these top-ranked franchises.
b. Construct a histogram of these data.
c. Comment on the shape of the distribution.

23. The following data show the year to date percent change (YTD % Change) for 30 stock-market indexes from around the word (*The Wall Street Journal*, August 26, 2013).

MarketIndexes

Country	Index	YTD % Change
Australia	S&P/ASX200	10.2
Belgium	Bel-20	12.6
Brazil	São Paulo Bovespa	−14.4
Canada	S&P/TSX Comp	2.6
Chile	Santiago IPSA	−16.3
China	Shanghai Composite	−9.3
Eurozone	EURO Stoxx	10.0
France	CAC 40	11.8
Germany	DAX	10.6
Hong Kong	Hang Seng	−3.5
India	S&P BSE Sensex	−4.7
Israel	Tel Aviv	1.3
Italy	FTSE MIB	6.6
Japan	Nikkei	31.4
Mexico	IPC All-Share	−6.4
Netherlands	AEX	9.3
Singapore	Straits Times	−2.5
South Korea	Kospi	−6.4
Spain	IBEX 35	6.4
Sweden	SX All Share	13.8
Switzerland	Swiss Market	17.4
Taiwan	Weighted	2.3
U.K.	FTSE 100	10.1
U.S.	S&P 500	16.6
U.S.	DJIA	14.5
U.S.	Dow Jones Utility	6.6
U.S.	Nasdaq 100	17.4
U.S.	Nasdaq Composite	21.1
World	DJ Global ex U.S.	4.2
World	DJ Global Index	9.9

a. What index has the largest positive YTD % Change?
b. Using a class width of 5 beginning with −20 and going to 40, develop a frequency distribution for the data.
c. Prepare a histogram. Interpret the histogram, including a discussion of the general shape of the histogram.
d. Use *The Wall Street Journal* or another media source to find the current percent changes for these stock market indexes in the current year. What index has had the largest percent increase? What index has had the smallest percent decrease? Prepare a summary of the data.

24. *Money* magazine listed top career opportunities for work that is enjoyable, pays well, and will still be around 10 years from now (*Money*, November 2009). Shown below are 20 top career opportunities, with the median pay and top pay for workers with two to seven years of experience in the field. Data are shown in thousands of dollars.

Careers

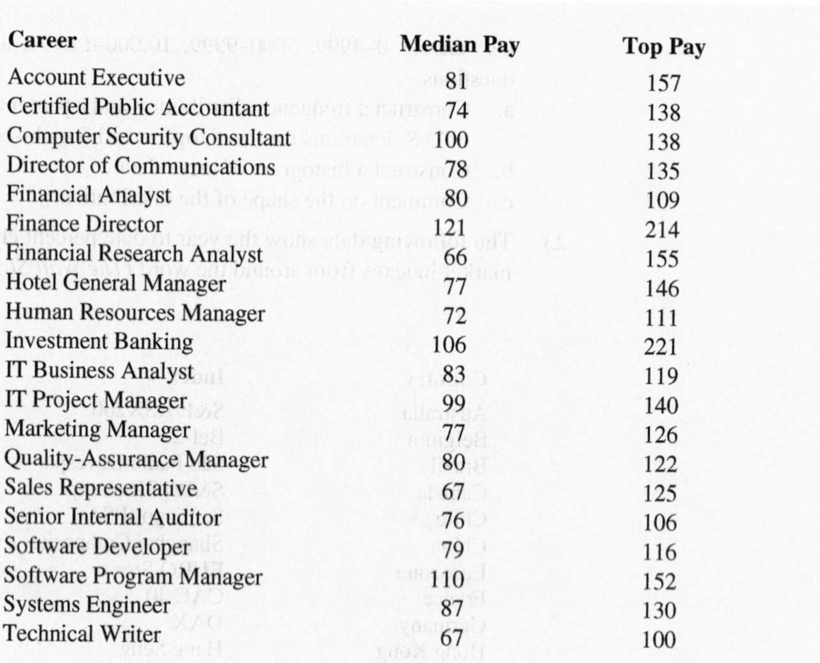
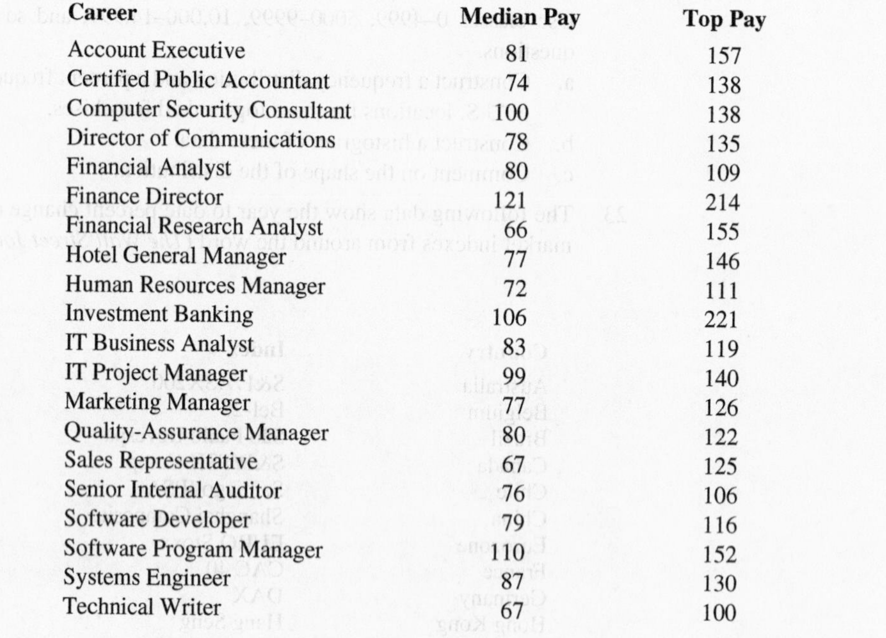

Career	Median Pay	Top Pay
Account Executive	81	157
Certified Public Accountant	74	138
Computer Security Consultant	100	138
Director of Communications	78	135
Financial Analyst	80	109
Finance Director	121	214
Financial Research Analyst	66	155
Hotel General Manager	77	146
Human Resources Manager	72	111
Investment Banking	106	221
IT Business Analyst	83	119
IT Project Manager	99	140
Marketing Manager	77	126
Quality-Assurance Manager	80	122
Sales Representative	67	125
Senior Internal Auditor	76	106
Software Developer	79	116
Software Program Manager	110	152
Systems Engineer	87	130
Technical Writer	67	100

Develop a stem-and-leaf display for both the median pay and the top pay. Comment on what you learn about the pay for these careers.

25. Each year America.EDU ranks the best paying college degrees in America. The following data show the median starting salary, the mid-career salary, and the percentage increase from starting salary to mid-career salary for the 20 college degrees with the highest mid-career salary (America.EDU website, August 29, 2013).

Degree	Starting Salary	Mid-Career Salary	% Increase
Aerospace engineering	59,400	108,000	82
Applied mathematics	56,400	101,000	79
Biomedical engineering	54,800	101,000	84
Chemical engineering	64,800	108,000	67
Civil engineering	53,500	93,400	75
Computer engineering	61,200	87,700	43
Computer science	56,200	97,700	74

BestPayingDegrees

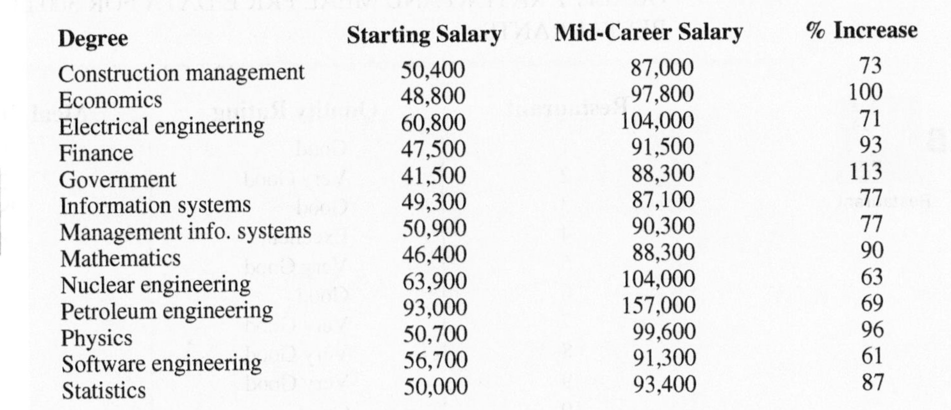

Degree	Starting Salary	Mid-Career Salary	% Increase
Construction management	50,400	87,000	73
Economics	48,800	97,800	100
Electrical engineering	60,800	104,000	71
Finance	47,500	91,500	93
Government	41,500	88,300	113
Information systems	49,300	87,100	77
Management info. systems	50,900	90,300	77
Mathematics	46,400	88,300	90
Nuclear engineering	63,900	104,000	63
Petroleum engineering	93,000	157,000	69
Physics	50,700	99,600	96
Software engineering	56,700	91,300	61
Statistics	50,000	93,400	87

a. Using a class width of 10, construct a histogram for the percentage increase in the starting salary.
b. Comment on the shape of the distribution.
c. Develop a stem-and-leaf display for the percentage increase in the starting salary.
d. What are the primary advantages of the stem-and-leaf display as compared to the histogram?

26. The 2011 Cincinnati Flying Pig Half-Marathon (13.1 miles) had 10,897 finishers (Cincinnati Flying Pig Marathon website). The following data show the ages for a sample of 40 half-marathoners.

Marathon

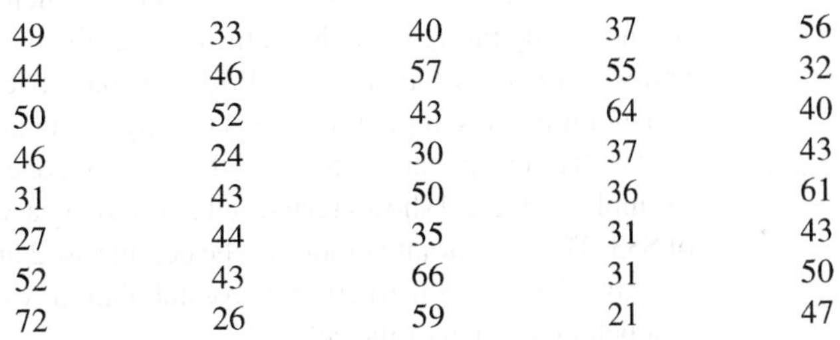

49	33	40	37	56
44	46	57	55	32
50	52	43	64	40
46	24	30	37	43
31	43	50	36	61
27	44	35	31	43
52	43	66	31	50
72	26	59	21	47

a. Construct a stretched stem-and-leaf display.
b. What age group had the largest number of runners?
c. What age occurred most frequently?

Summarizing Data for Two Variables Using Tables

Thus far in this chapter, we have focused on using tabular and graphical displays to summarize the data for a single categorical or quantitative variable. Often a manager or decision maker needs to summarize the data for two variables in order to reveal the relationship—if any—between the variables. In this section, we show how to construct a tabular summary of the data for two variables.

Crosstabulation

A **crosstabulation** is a tabular summary of data for two variables. Although both variables can be either categorical or quantitative, crosstabulations in which one variable is categorical and the other variable is quantitative are just as common. We will illustrate this latter case by considering the following application based on data from Zagat's Restaurant

TABLE 2.9 QUALITY RATING AND MEAL PRICE DATA FOR 300 LOS ANGELES RESTAURANTS

Restaurant

Restaurant	Quality Rating	Meal Price ($)
1	Good	18
2	Very Good	22
3	Good	28
4	Excellent	38
5	Very Good	33
6	Good	28
7	Very Good	19
8	Very Good	11
9	Very Good	23
10	Good	13
.	.	.
.	.	.
.	.	.

Review. Data showing the quality rating and the typical meal price were collected for a sample of 300 restaurants in the Los Angeles area. Table 2.9 shows the data for the first 10 restaurants. Quality rating is a categorical variable with rating categories of Good, Very Good, and Excellent. Meal Price is a quantitative variable that ranges from $10 to $49.

Grouping the data for a quantitative variable enables us to treat the quantitative variable as if it were a categorical variable when creating a crosstabulation.

A crosstabulation of the data for this application is shown in Table 2.10. The labels shown in the margins of the table define the categories (classes) for the two variables. In the left margin, the row labels (Good, Very Good, and Excellent) correspond to the three rating categories for the quality rating variable. In the top margin, the column labels ($10–19, $20–29, $30–39, and $40–49) show that the Meal Price data have been grouped into four classes. Because each restaurant in the sample provides a quality rating and a meal price, each restaurant is associated with a cell appearing in one of the rows and one of the columns of the crosstabulation. For example, Table 2.9 shows restaurant 5 as having a Very Good quality rating and a Meal Price of $33. This restaurant belongs to the cell in row 2 and column 3 of the crosstabulation shown in Table 2.10. In constructing a crosstabulation, we simply count the number of restaurants that belong to each of the cells.

Although four classes of the Meal Price variable were used to construct the crosstabulation shown in Table 2.10, the crosstabulation of quality rating and meal price could have been developed using fewer or more classes for the meal price variable. The issues involved in deciding how to group the data for a quantitative variable in a crosstabulation are similar to the issues involved in deciding the number of classes to use when constructing a frequency distribution for a quantitative variable. For this application, four classes of meal price were considered a reasonable number of classes to reveal any relationship between quality rating and meal price.

TABLE 2.10 CROSSTABULATION OF QUALITY RATING AND MEAL PRICE DATA FOR 300 LOS ANGELES RESTAURANTS

	Meal Price				
Quality Rating	**$10–19**	**$20–29**	**$30–39**	**$40–49**	**Total**
Good	42	40	2	0	84
Very Good	34	64	46	6	150
Excellent	2	14	28	22	66
Total	78	118	76	28	300

In reviewing Table 2.10, we see that the greatest number of restaurants in the sample (64) have a very good rating and a meal price in the \$20–29 range. Only two restaurants have an excellent rating and a meal price in the \$10–19 range. Similar interpretations of the other frequencies can be made. In addition, note that the right and bottom margins of the crosstabulation provide the frequency distributions for quality rating and meal price separately. From the frequency distribution in the right margin, we see that data on quality ratings show 84 restaurants with a good quality rating, 150 restaurants with a very good quality rating, and 66 restaurants with an excellent quality rating. Similarly, the bottom margin shows the frequency distribution for the meal price variable.

Dividing the totals in the right margin of the crosstabulation by the total for that column provides a relative and percent frequency distribution for the quality rating variable.

Quality Rating	Relative Frequency	Percent Frequency
Good	.28	28
Very Good	.50	50
Excellent	.22	22
Total	1.00	100

From the percent frequency distribution we see that 28% of the restaurants were rated good, 50% were rated very good, and 22% were rated excellent.

Dividing the totals in the bottom row of the crosstabulation by the total for that row provides a relative and percent frequency distribution for the meal price variable.

Meal Price	Relative Frequency	Percent Frequency
\$10–19	.26	26
\$20–29	.39	39
\$30–39	.25	25
\$40–49	.09	9
Total	1.00	100

Note that the sum of the values in the relative frequency column does not add exactly to 1.00 and the sum of the values in the percent frequency distribution does not add exactly to 100; the reason is that the values being summed are rounded. From the percent frequency distribution we see that 26% of the meal prices are in the lowest price class (\$10–19), 39% are in the next higher class, and so on.

The frequency and relative frequency distributions constructed from the margins of a crosstabulation provide information about each of the variables individually, but they do not shed any light on the relationship between the variables. The primary value of a crosstabulation lies in the insight it offers about the relationship between the variables. A review of the crosstabulation in Table 2.10 reveals that restaurants with higher meal prices received higher quality ratings than restaurants with lower meal prices.

Converting the entries in a crosstabulation into row percentages or column percentages can provide more insight into the relationship between the two variables. For row percentages, the results of dividing each frequency in Table 2.10 by its corresponding row total are shown in Table 2.11. Each row of Table 2.11 is a percent frequency distribution of meal price for one of the quality rating categories. Of the restaurants with the lowest quality rating (good), we see that the greatest percentages are for the less expensive restaurants (50% have \$10–19 meal prices and 47.6% have \$20–29 meal prices). Of the restaurants with the highest quality rating (excellent), we see that the greatest percentages are for the more expensive restaurants

TABLE 2.11 ROW PERCENTAGES FOR EACH QUALITY RATING CATEGORY

	Meal Price				
Quality Rating	**$10–19**	**$20–29**	**$30–39**	**$40–49**	**Total**
Good	50.0	47.6	2.4	0.0	100
Very Good	22.7	42.7	30.6	4.0	100
Excellent	3.0	21.2	42.4	33.4	100

(42.4% have $30–39 meal prices and 33.4% have $40–49 meal prices). Thus, we continue to see that restaurants with higher meal prices received higher quality ratings.

Crosstabulations are widely used to investigate the relationship between two variables. In practice, the final reports for many statistical studies include a large number of crosstabulations. In the Los Angeles restaurant survey, the crosstabulation is based on one categorical variable (Quality Rating) and one quantitative variable (Meal Price). Crosstabulations can also be developed when both variables are categorical and when both variables are quantitative. When quantitative variables are used, however, we must first create classes for the values of the variable. For instance, in the restaurant example we grouped the meal prices into four classes ($10–19, $20–29, $30–39, and $40–49).

Using Excel's PivotTable Tool to Construct a Crosstabulation

Excel's PivotTable tool can be used to summarize the data for two or more variables simultaneously. We will illustrate the use of Excel's PivotTable tool by showing how to develop a crosstabulation of quality ratings and meal prices for the sample of 300 restaurants located in the Los Angeles area.

Enter/Access Data: Open the WEBfile named Restaurant. The data are in cells B2:C301 and labels are in column A and cells B1:C1.

Apply Tools: Each of the three columns in the Restaurant data set [labeled Restaurant, Quality Rating, and Meal Price ($)] is considered a field by Excel. Fields may be chosen to represent rows, columns, or values in the PivotTable. The following steps describe how to use Excel's PivotTable tool to construct a crosstabulation of quality ratings and meal prices.

Step 1. Select cell A1 or any cell in the data set
Step 2. Click **INSERT** on the Ribbon
Step 3. In the **Tables** group click **PivotTable**
Step 4. When the Create PivotTable dialog box appears:
  Click **OK**; a **PivotTable** and **PivotTable Fields** dialog box will appear in a new worksheet
Step 5. In the **PivotTable Fields** dialog box:
  Drag **Quality Rating** to the **Rows** area
  Drag **Meal Price** to the **Columns** area
  Drag **Restaurant** to the **Values** area
Step 6. Click on **Sum of Restaurant** in the **Values** area
Step 7. Click **Value Field Settings** from the list of options that appears
Step 8. When the Value Field Settings dialog box appears:
  Under **Summarize value field by**, choose **Count**
  Click **OK**

FIGURE 2.15 INITIAL PIVOTTABLE FIELDS DIALOG BOX AND PIVOTTABLE FOR THE RESTAURANT DATA

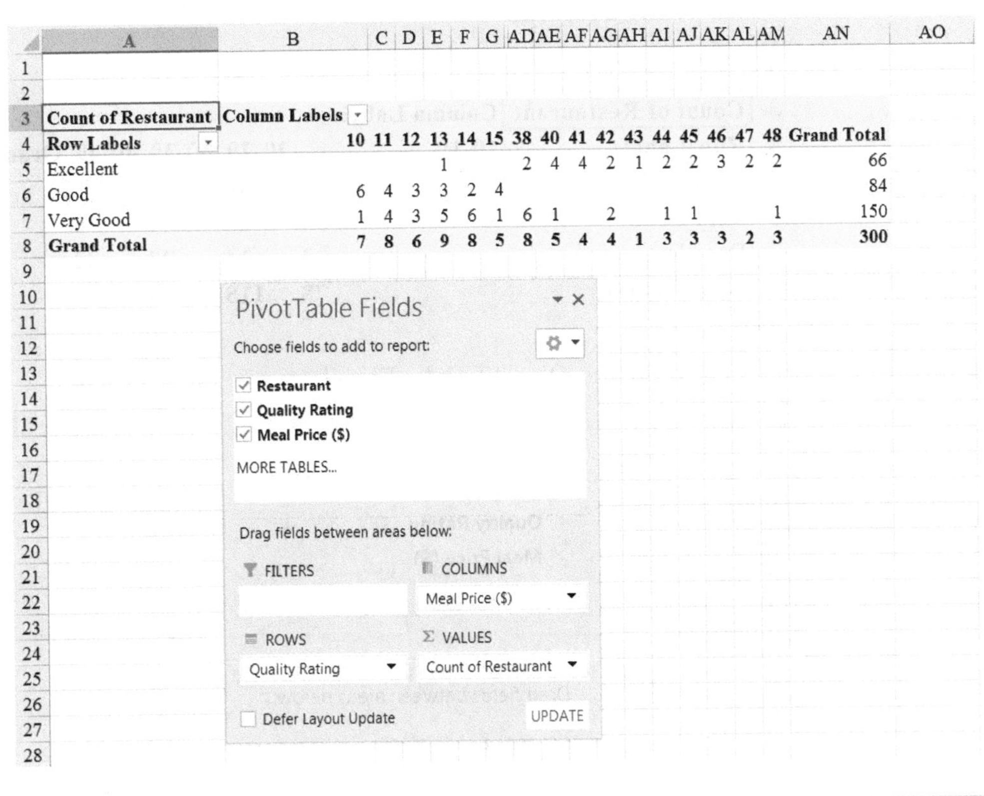

Count of Restaurant	Column Labels																
Row Labels	10	11	12	13	14	15	38	40	41	42	43	44	45	46	47	48	Grand Total
Excellent				1			2	4	4	2	1	2	2	3	2	2	66
Good	6	4	3	3	2	4											84
Very Good	1	4	3	5	6	1	6	1		2		1	1			1	150
Grand Total	7	8	6	9	8	5	8	5	4	4	1	3	3	3	2	3	300

Figure 2.15 shows the PivotTable Fields dialog box and the corresponding PivotTable created following the above steps. For readability, columns H:AC have been hidden.

Editing Options: To complete the PivotTable we need to group the rows containing the meal prices and place the rows for quality rating in the proper order. The following steps accomplish this.

Step 1. Right-click cell B4 in the PivotTable or any other cell containing meal prices
Step 2. Choose **Group** from the list of options that appears
Step 3. When the Grouping dialog box appears:
  Enter 10 in the **Starting at** box
  Enter 49 in the **Ending at** box
  Enter 10 in the **By** box
  Click **OK**
Step 4. Right-click on **Excellent** in cell A5
Step 5. Choose Move and click Move "Excellent" to End

The final PivotTable is shown in Figure 2.16. Note that it provides the same information as the crosstabulation shown in Table 2.10.

Simpson's Paradox

The data in two or more crosstabulations are often combined or aggregated to produce a summary crosstabulation showing how two variables are related. In such cases, conclusions

FIGURE 2.16 FINAL PIVOTTABLE FOR THE RESTAURANT DATA

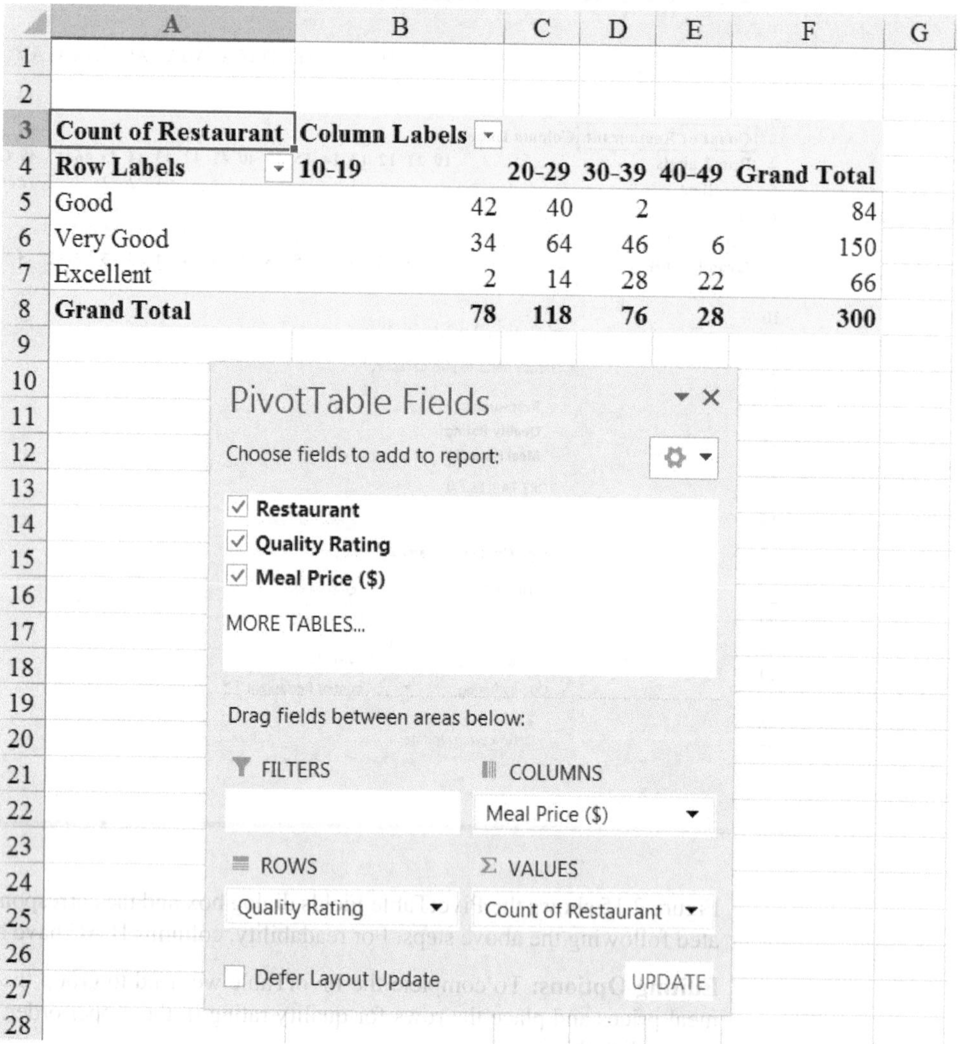

	A	B	C	D	E	F
1						
2						
3	**Count of Restaurant**	**Column Labels**				
4	**Row Labels**	**10-19**	**20-29**	**30-39**	**40-49**	**Grand Total**
5	Good	42	40	2		84
6	Very Good	34	64	46	6	150
7	Excellent	2	14	28	22	66
8	**Grand Total**	**78**	**118**	**76**	**28**	**300**

PivotTable Fields

Choose fields to add to report:

- ☑ **Restaurant**
- ☑ **Quality Rating**
- ☑ **Meal Price ($)**

MORE TABLES...

Drag fields between areas below:

FILTERS	COLUMNS
	Meal Price ($)
ROWS	**VALUES**
Quality Rating	Count of Restaurant

☐ Defer Layout Update   UPDATE

drawn from two or more separate crosstabulations can be reversed when the data are aggregated into a single crosstabulation. The reversal of conclusions based on aggregate and unaggregated data is called **Simpson's paradox**. To provide an illustration of Simpson's paradox we consider an example involving the analysis of verdicts for two judges in two different courts.

Judges Ron Luckett and Dennis Kendall presided over cases in Common Pleas Court and Municipal Court during the past three years. Some of the verdicts they rendered were appealed. In most of these cases the appeals court upheld the original verdicts, but in some cases those verdicts were reversed. For each judge a crosstabulation was developed based upon two variables: Verdict (upheld or reversed) and Type of Court (Common Pleas and Municipal). Suppose that the two crosstabulations were then combined by aggregating the type of court data. The resulting aggregated crosstabulation contains two variables: Verdict (upheld or reversed) and Judge (Luckett or Kendall). This crosstabulation shows the number of appeals in which the verdict was upheld and the number in which the verdict was reversed for both judges. The following crosstabulation shows these results along with the column percentages in parentheses next to each value.

	Judge		
Verdict	**Luckett**	**Kendall**	**Total**
Upheld	129 (86%)	110 (88%)	239
Reversed	21 (14%)	15 (12%)	36
Total (%)	150 (100%)	125 (100%)	275

A review of the column percentages shows that 86% of the verdicts were upheld for Judge Luckett, whereas 88% of the verdicts were upheld for Judge Kendall. From this aggregated crosstabulation, we conclude that Judge Kendall is doing the better job because a greater percentage of Judge Kendall's verdicts are being upheld.

The following unaggregated crosstabulations show the cases tried by Judge Luckett and Judge Kendall in each court; column percentages are shown in parentheses next to each value.

	Judge Luckett		
Verdict	**Common Pleas**	**Municipal Court**	**Total**
Upheld	29 (91%)	100 (85%)	129
Reversed	3 (9%)	18 (15%)	21
Total (%)	32 (100%)	118 (100%)	150

	Judge Kendall		
Verdict	**Common Pleas**	**Municipal Court**	**Total**
Upheld	90 (90%)	20 (80%)	110
Reversed	10 (10%)	5 (20%)	15
Total (%)	100 (100%)	25 (100%)	125

From the crosstabulation and column percentages for Judge Luckett, we see that the verdicts were upheld in 91% of the Common Pleas Court cases and in 85% of the Municipal Court cases. From the crosstabulation and column percentages for Judge Kendall, we see that the verdicts were upheld in 90% of the Common Pleas Court cases and in 80% of the Municipal Court cases. Thus, when we unaggregate the data, we see that Judge Luckett has a better record because a greater percentage of Judge Luckett's verdicts are being upheld in both courts. This result contradicts the conclusion we reached with the aggregated data crosstabulation that showed Judge Kendall had the better record. This reversal of conclusions based on aggregated and unaggregated data illustrates Simpson's paradox.

The original crosstabulation was obtained by aggregating the data in the separate crosstabulations for the two courts. Note that for both judges the percentage of appeals that resulted in reversals was much higher in Municipal Court than in Common Pleas Court. Because Judge Luckett tried a much higher percentage of his cases in Municipal Court, the aggregated data favored Judge Kendall. When we look at the crosstabulations for the two courts separately, however, Judge Luckett shows the better record. Thus, for the original crosstabulation, we see that the *type of court* is a hidden variable that cannot be ignored when evaluating the records of the two judges.

Because of the possibility of Simpson's paradox, realize that the conclusion or interpretation may be reversed depending upon whether you are viewing unaggregated or aggregate crosstabulation data. Before drawing a conclusion, you may want to investigate whether the aggregate or unaggregate form of the crosstabulation provides the better insight and conclusion. Especially when the crosstabulation involves aggregated data, you should investigate whether a hidden variable could affect the results such that separate or unaggregated crosstabulations provide a different and possibly better insight and conclusion.

Exercises

Methods

27. The following data are for 30 observations involving two categorical variables, x and y. The categories for x are A, B, and C; the categories for y are 1 and 2.

Observation	x	y	Observation	x	y
1	A	1	16	B	2
2	B	1	17	C	1
3	B	1	18	B	1
4	C	2	19	C	1
5	B	1	20	B	1
6	C	2	21	C	2
7	B	1	22	B	1
8	C	2	23	C	2
9	A	1	24	A	1
10	B	1	25	B	1
11	A	1	26	C	2
12	B	1	27	C	2
13	C	2	28	A	1
14	C	2	29	B	1
15	C	2	30	B	2

a. Develop a crosstabulation for the data, with x as the row variable and y as the column variable.
b. Compute the row percentages.
c. Compute the column percentages.
d. What is the relationship, if any, between x and y?

28. The following observations are for two quantitative variables, x and y.

Observation	x	y	Observation	x	y
1	28	72	11	13	98
2	17	99	12	84	21
3	52	58	13	59	32
4	79	34	14	17	81
5	37	60	15	70	34
6	71	22	16	47	64
7	37	77	17	35	68
8	27	85	18	62	67
9	64	45	19	30	39
10	53	47	20	43	28

a. Develop a crosstabulation for the data, with x as the row variable and y as the column variable. For x use classes of 10–29, 30–49, and so on; for y use classes of 40–59, 60–79, and so on.
b. Compute the row percentages.
c. Compute the column percentages.
d. What is the relationship, if any, between x and y?

Applications

29. The Daytona 500 is a 500-mile automobile race held annually at the Daytona International Speedway in Daytona Beach, Florida. The following crosstabulation shows the automobile make by average speed of the 25 winners from 1988 to 2012 (*The 2013 World Almanac*).

	Average Speed in Miles per Hour					
Make	**130–139.9**	**140–149.9**	**150–159.9**	**160–169.9**	**170–179.9**	**Total**
Buick	1					1
Chevrolet	3	5	4	3	1	16
Dodge		2				2
Ford	2	1	2	1		6
Total	6	8	6	4	1	25

a. Compute the row percentages.
b. What percentage of winners driving a Chevrolet won with an average speed of at least 150 miles per hour?
c. Compute the column percentages.
d. What percentage of winning average speeds 160–169.9 miles per hour were Chevrolets?

30. The following crosstabulation shows the average speed of the 25 winners by year of the Daytona 500 automobile race (*The 2013 World Almanac*).

	Year					
Average Speed	**1988–1992**	**1993–1997**	**1998–2002**	**2003–2007**	**2008–2012**	**Total**
130–139.9	1			2	3	6
140–149.9	2	2	1	2	1	8
150–159.9		3	1	1	1	6
160–169.9	2		2			4
170–179.9			1			1
Total	5	5	5	5	5	25

a. Calculate the row percentages.
b. What is the apparent relationship between average winning speed and year? What might be the cause of this apparent relationship?

31. Recently, management at Oak Tree Golf Course received a few complaints about the condition of the greens. Several players complained that the greens are too fast. Rather than react to the comments of just a few, the Golf Association conducted a survey of 100 male and 100 female golfers. The survey results are summarized here.

Male Golfers

	Greens Condition	
Handicap	**Too Fast**	**Fine**
Under 15	10	40
15 or more	25	25

Female Golfers

	Greens Condition	
Handicap	**Too Fast**	**Fine**
Under 15	1	9
15 or more	39	51

a. Combine these two crosstabulations into one with Male and Female as the row labels and Too Fast and Fine as the column labels. Which group shows the highest percentage saying that the greens are too fast?

b. Refer to the initial crosstabulations. For those players with low handicaps (better players), which group (male or female) shows the highest percentage saying the greens are too fast?
c. Refer to the initial crosstabulations. For those players with higher handicaps, which group (male or female) shows the highest percentage saying the greens are too fast?
d. What conclusions can you draw about the preferences of men and women concerning the speed of the greens? Are the conclusions you draw from part (a) as compared with parts (b) and (c) consistent? Explain any apparent inconsistencies.

32. The following crosstabulation shows the number of households (1000s) in each of the four regions of the United States and the number of households at each income level (U.S. Census Bureau website, August 2013).

	Income Level of Household							
Region	**Under $15,000**	**$15,000 to $24,999**	**$25,000 to $34,999**	**$35,000 to $49,999**	**$50,000 to $74,999**	**$75,000 to $99,999**	**$100,000 and over**	**Number of Households (1000s)**
Northeast	2733	2244	2264	2807	3699	2486	5246	21,479
Midwest	3273	3326	3056	3767	5044	3183	4742	26,391
South	6235	5657	5038	6476	7730	4813	7660	43,609
West	3086	2796	2644	3557	4804	3066	6104	26,057
Total	15,327	14,023	13,002	16,607	21,277	13,548	23,752	117,536

a. Compute the row percentages and identify the percent frequency distributions of income for households in each region.
b. What percentage of households in the West region have an income level of $50,000 or more? What percentage of households in the South region have an income level of $50,000 or more?
c. Construct percent frequency histograms for each region of households. Do any relationships between regions and income level appear to be evident in your findings?
d. Compute the column percentages. What information do the column percentages provide?
e. What percent of households with a household income of $100,000 and over are from the South region? What percentage of households from the South region have a household income of $100,000 and over? Why are these two percentages different?

33. Each year Forbes ranks the world's most valuable brands. A portion of the data for 82 of the brands in the 2013 Forbes list is shown in Table 2.12 (Forbes website, February 4, 2014). The data set includes the following variables:

Brand: The name of the brand.

Industry: The type of industry associated with the brand, labeled Automotive & Luxury, Consumer Packaged Goods, Financial Services, Other, Technology.

Brand Value ($ billions): A measure of the brand's value in billions of dollars developed by Forbes based on a variety of financial information about the brand.

1-Yr Value Change (%): The percentage change in the value of the brand over the previous year.

Brand Revenue ($ billions): The total revenue in billions of dollars for the brand.

a. Prepare a crosstabulation of the data on Industry (rows) and Brand Value ($ billions). Use classes of 0–10, 10–20, 20–30, 30–40, 40–50, and 50–60 for Brand Value ($ billions).
b. Prepare a frequency distribution for the data on Industry.
c. Prepare a frequency distribution for the data on Brand Value ($ billions).

TABLE 2.12 DATA FOR 82 OF THE MOST VALUABLE BRANDS

Brand	Industry	Brand Value ($ billions)	1-Yr Value Change (%)	Brand Revenue ($ billions)
Accenture	Other	9.7	10	30.4
Adidas	Other	8.4	23	14.5
Allianz	Financial Services	6.9	5	130.8
Amazon.Com	Technology	14.7	44	60.6
⋮	⋮	⋮	⋮	⋮
Heinz	Consumer Packaged Goods	5.6	2	4.4
Hermès	Automotive & Luxury	9.3	20	4.5
⋮	⋮	⋮	⋮	⋮
Wells Fargo	Financial Services	9	−14	91.2
Zara	Other	9.4	11	13.5

Source: Data from Forbes, 2014

d. How has the crosstabulation helped in preparing the frequency distributions in parts (b) and (c)?

e. What conclusions can you draw about the type of industry and the brand value?

34. Refer to Table 2.12.

a. Prepare a crosstabulation of the data on Industry (rows) and Brand Revenue ($ billions). Use class intervals of 25 starting at 0 for Brand Revenue ($ billions).

b. Prepare a frequency distribution for the data on Brand Revenue ($ billions).

c. What conclusions can you draw about the type of industry and the brand revenue?

d. Prepare a crosstabulation of the data on Industry (rows) and the 1-Yr Value Change (%). Use class intervals of 20 starting at −60 for 1-Yr Value Change (%).

e. Prepare a frequency distribution for the data on 1-Yr Value Change (%).

f. What conclusions can you draw about the type of industry and the 1-year change in value?

35. The U.S. Department of Energy's Fuel Economy Guide provides fuel efficiency data for cars and trucks (Fuel Economy website, September 8, 2012). A portion of the data for 149 compact, midsize, and large cars is shown in Table 2.13. The data set contains the following variables:

Size: Compact, Midsize, and Large

Displacement: Engine size in liters

Cylinders: Number of cylinders in the engine

Drive: All wheel (A), front wheel (F), and rear wheel (R)

Fuel Type: Premium (P) or regular (R) fuel

City MPG: Fuel efficiency rating for city driving in terms of miles per gallon

Hwy MPG: Fuel efficiency rating for highway driving in terms of miles per gallon

The complete data set is contained in the file named FuelData2012.

a. Prepare a crosstabulation of the data on Size (rows) and Hwy MPG (columns). Use classes of 15–19, 20–24, 25–29, 30–34, 35–39, and 40–44 for Hwy MPG.

b. Comment on the relationship beween Size and Hwy MPG.

c. Prepare a crosstabulation of the data on Drive (rows) and City MPG (columns). Use classes of 10–14, 15–19, 20–24, 25–29, 30–34, and 35–39, and 40–44 for City MPG.

d. Comment on the relationship between Drive and City MPG.

e. Prepare a crosstabulation of the data on Fuel Type (rows) and City MPG (columns). Use classes of 10–14, 15–19, 20–24, 25–29, 30–34, 35–39, and 40–44 for City MPG.

f. Comment on the relationship between Fuel Type and City MPG.

TABLE 2.13 FUEL EFFICIENCY DATA

FuelData2012

Car	Size	Displacement	Cylinders	Drive	Fuel Type	City MPG	Hwy MPG
1	Compact	2.0	4	F	P	22	30
2	Compact	2.0	4	A	P	21	29
3	Compact	2.0	4	A	P	21	31
•	•	•	•	•	•	•	•
•	•	•	•	•	•	•	•
•	•	•	•	•	•	•	•
94	Midsize	3.5	6	A	R	17	25
95	Midsize	2.5	4	F	R	23	33
•	•	•	•	•	•	•	•
•	•	•	•	•	•	•	•
•	•	•	•	•	•	•	•
148	Large	6.7	12	R	P	11	18
149	Large	6.7	12	R	P	11	18

2.4 Summarizing Data for Two Variables Using Graphical Displays

In the previous section we showed how a crosstabulation can be used to summarize the data for two variables and help reveal the relationship between the variables. In most cases, a graphical display is more useful for recognizing patterns and trends in the data.

In this section, we introduce a variety of graphical displays for exploring the relationships between two variables. Displaying data in creative ways can lead to powerful insights and allow us to make "common-sense inferences" based on our ability to visually compare, contrast, and recognize patterns. We begin with a discussion of scatter diagrams and trendlines.

Scatter Diagram and Trendline

A **scatter diagram** is a graphical display of the relationship between two quantitative variables, and a **trendline** is a line that provides an approximation of the relationship. As an illustration, consider the advertising/sales relationship for a stereo and sound equipment store in San Francisco. On 10 occasions during the past three months, the store used weekend television commercials to promote sales at its stores. The managers want to investigate whether a relationship exists between the number of commercials shown and sales at the store during the following week. Sample data for the 10 weeks with sales in hundreds of dollars are shown in Table 2.14.

Figure 2.17 shows the scatter diagram and the trendline[1] for the data in Table 2.14. The number of commercials (x) is shown on the horizontal axis and the sales (y) are shown on the vertical axis. For week 1, $x = 2$ and $y = 50$. A point with those coordinates is plotted on the scatter diagram. Similar points are plotted for the other nine weeks. Note that during two of the weeks one commercial was shown, during two of the weeks two commercials were shown, and so on.

The scatter diagram in Figure 2.17 indicates a positive relationship between the number of commercials and sales. Higher sales are associated with a higher number of commercials. The relationship is not perfect in that all points are not on a straight line.

[1]The equation of the trendline is $y = 36.15 + 4.95x$. The slope of the trendline is 4.95 and the y-intercept (the point where the trendline intersects the y-axis) is 36.15. We will discuss in detail the interpretation of the slope and y-intercept for a linear trendline in Chapter 14 when we study simple linear regression.

TABLE 2.14 SAMPLE DATA FOR THE STEREO AND SOUND EQUIPMENT STORE

WEB file
Stereo

Week	Number of Commercials x	Sales ($100s) y
1	2	50
2	5	57
3	1	41
4	3	54
5	4	54
6	1	38
7	5	63
8	3	48
9	4	59
10	2	46

However, the general pattern of the points and the trendline suggest that the overall relationship is positive.

Some general scatter diagram patterns and the types of relationships they suggest are shown in Figure 2.18. The top left panel depicts a positive relationship similar to the one for the number of commercials and sales example. In the top right panel, the scatter diagram shows no apparent relationship between the variables. The bottom panel depicts a negative relationship where y tends to decrease as x increases.

Using Excel to Construct a Scatter Diagram and a Trendline

We can use Excel to construct a scatter diagram and a trendline for the stereo and sound equipment store data.

Enter/Access Data: Open the WEBfile named Stereo. The data are in cells B2:C11 and labels are in column A and cells B1:C1.

FIGURE 2.17 SCATTER DIAGRAM AND TRENDLINE FOR THE STEREO AND SOUND EQUIPMENT STORE

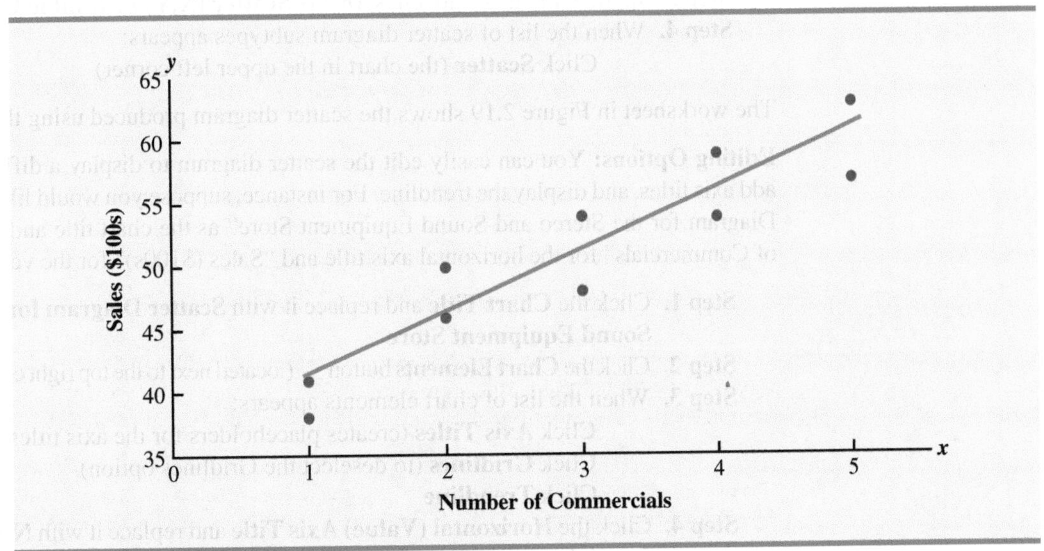

FIGURE 2.18 TYPES OF RELATIONSHIPS DEPICTED BY SCATTER DIAGRAMS

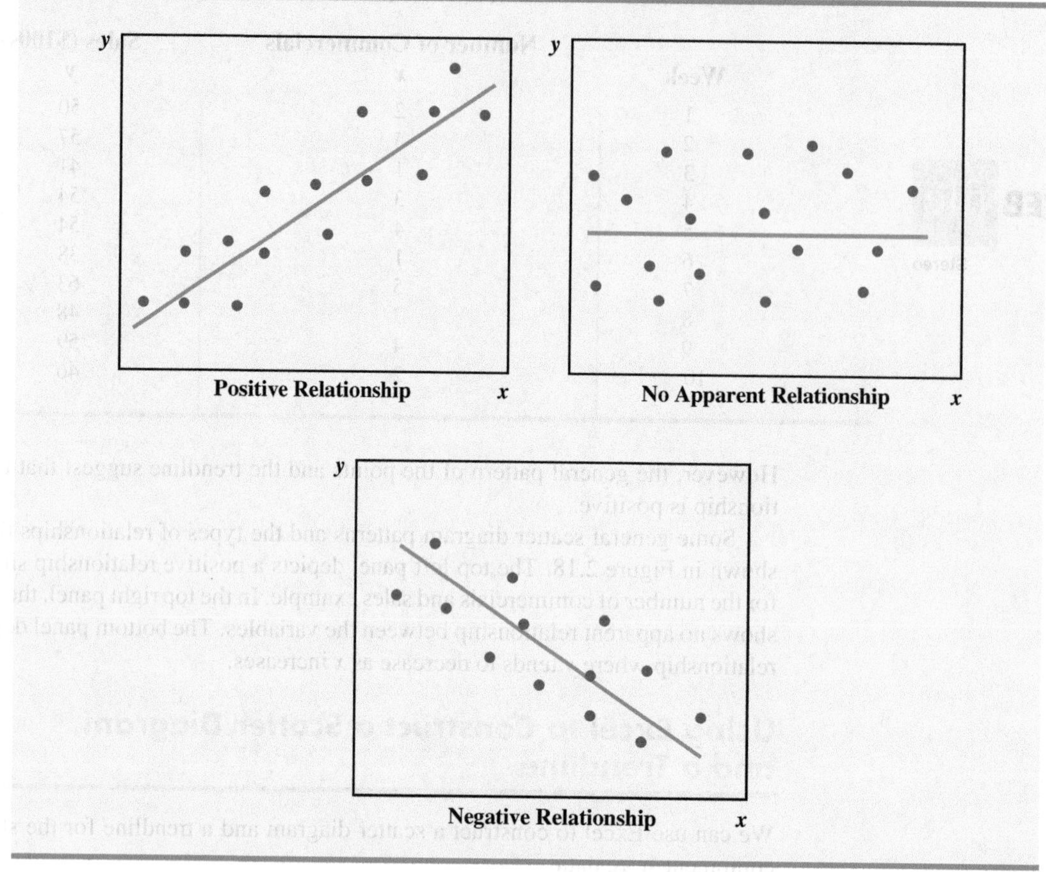

Apply Tools: The following steps describe how to use Excel to construct a scatter diagram from the data in the worksheet.

Step 1. Select cells B1:C11
Step 2. Click the **INSERT** tab on the Ribbon
Step 3. In the **Charts** group, click **Insert Scatter (X,Y) or Bubble Chart**
Step 4. When the list of scatter diagram subtypes appears:
Click **Scatter** (the chart in the upper left corner)

The worksheet in Figure 2.19 shows the scatter diagram produced using these steps.

Editing Options: You can easily edit the scatter diagram to display a different chart title, add axis titles, and display the trendline. For instance, suppose you would like to use "Scatter Diagram for the Stereo and Sound Equipment Store" as the chart title and insert "Number of Commercials" for the horizontal axis title and "Sales ($100s)" for the vertical axis title.

Step 1. Click the **Chart Title** and replace it with **Scatter Diagram for the Stereo and Sound Equipment Store**
Step 2. Click the **Chart Elements** button (located next to the top right corner of the chart)
Step 3. When the list of chart elements appears:
Click **Axis Titles** (creates placeholders for the axis titles)
Click **Gridlines** (to deselect the Gridlines option)
Click **Trendline**
Step 4. Click the **Horizontal (Value) Axis Title** and replace it with **Number of Commercials**

FIGURE 2.19 INITIAL SCATTER DIAGRAM FOR THE STEREO AND SOUND EQUIPMENT STORE USING EXCEL'S RECOMMENDED CHARTS TOOL

	A	B	C
1	Week	No. of Commercials	Sales ($100s)
2	1	2	50
3	2	5	57
4	3	1	41
5	4	3	54
6	5	4	54
7	6	1	38
8	7	5	63
9	8	3	48
10	9	4	59
11	10	2	46

Sales ($100s)

Step 5. Click the **Vertical (Value) Axis Title** and replace it with **Sales ($100s)**

Step 6. To change the trendline from a dashed line to a solid line, right-click on the trendline and choose the **Format Trendline** option

Step 7. When the Format Trendline dialog box appears:

Select the **Fill & Line** option

In the **Dash type** box, select **Solid**

Close the Format Trendline dialog box

The edited scatter diagram and trendline are shown in Figure 2.20.

FIGURE 2.20 EDITED SCATTER DIAGRAM AND TRENDLINE FOR THE STEREO AND SOUND EQUIPMENT STORE USING EXCEL'S RECOMMENDED CHARTS TOOL

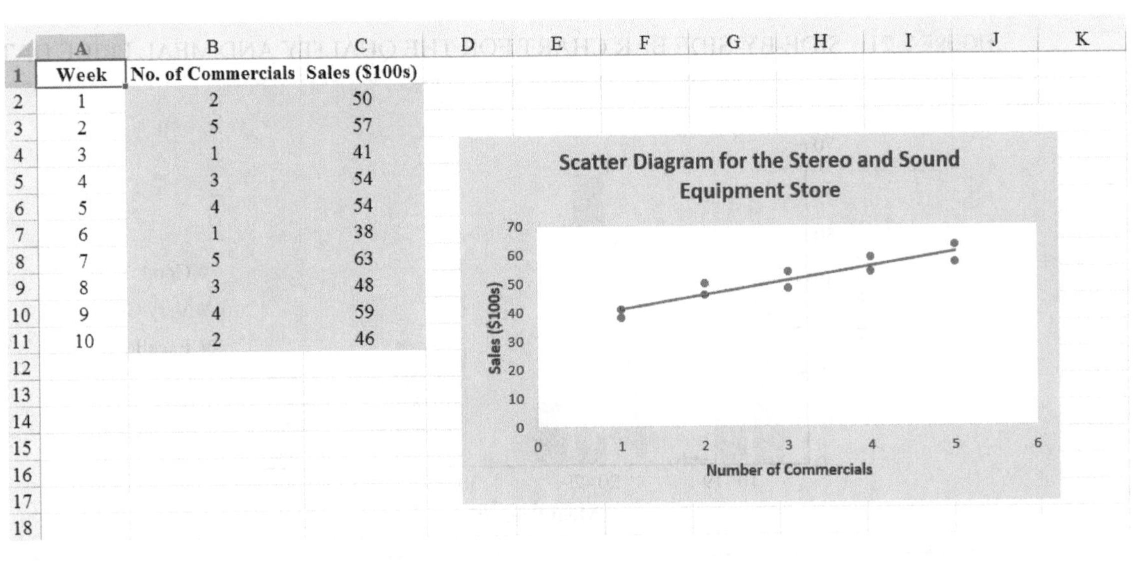

	A	B	C
1	Week	No. of Commercials	Sales ($100s)
2	1	2	50
3	2	5	57
4	3	1	41
5	4	3	54
6	5	4	54
7	6	1	38
8	7	5	63
9	8	3	48
10	9	4	59
11	10	2	46

Side-by-Side and Stacked Bar Charts

In Section 2.1 we said that a bar chart is a graphical display for depicting categorical data summarized in a frequency, relative frequency, or percent frequency distribution. Side-by-side bar charts and stacked bar charts are extensions of basic bar charts that are used to display and compare two variables. By displaying two variables on the same chart, we may better understand the relationship between the variables.

A **side-by-side bar chart** is a graphical display for depicting multiple bar charts on the same display. To illustrate the construction of a side-by-side chart, recall the application involving the quality rating and meal price data for a sample of 300 restaurants located in the Los Angeles area. Quality rating is a categorical variable with rating categories of Good, Very Good, and Excellent. Meal Price is a quantitative variable that ranges from \$10 to \$49. The crosstabulation displayed in Table 2.10 shows that the data for meal price were grouped into four classes: \$10–19, \$20–29, \$30–39, and \$40–49. We will use these classes to construct a side-by-side bar chart.

Figure 2.21 shows a side-by-side chart for the restaurant data. The color of each bar indicates the quality rating (blue = good, red = very good, and green = excellent). Each bar is constructed by extending the bar to the point on the vertical axis that represents the frequency with which that quality rating occurred for each of the meal price categories. Placing each meal price category's quality rating frequency adjacent to one another allows us to quickly determine how a particular meal price category is rated. We see that the lowest meal price category (\$10–\$19) received mostly good and very good ratings, but very few excellent ratings. The highest price category (\$40–49), however, shows a much different result. This meal price category received mostly excellent ratings, some very good ratings, but no good ratings.

Figure 2.21 also provides a good sense of the relationship between meal price and quality rating. Notice that as the price increases (left to right), the height of the blue bars decreases and the height of the green bars generally increases. This indicates that as price increases, the quality rating tends to be better. The very good rating, as expected, tends to be more prominent in the middle price categories as indicated by the dominance of the red bars in the middle of the chart.

Stacked bar charts are another way to display and compare two variables on the same display. A **stacked bar chart** is a bar chart in which each bar is broken into rectangular segments of a different color showing the relative frequency of each class in a manner similar

FIGURE 2.21 SIDE-BY-SIDE BAR CHART FOR THE QUALITY AND MEAL PRICE DATA

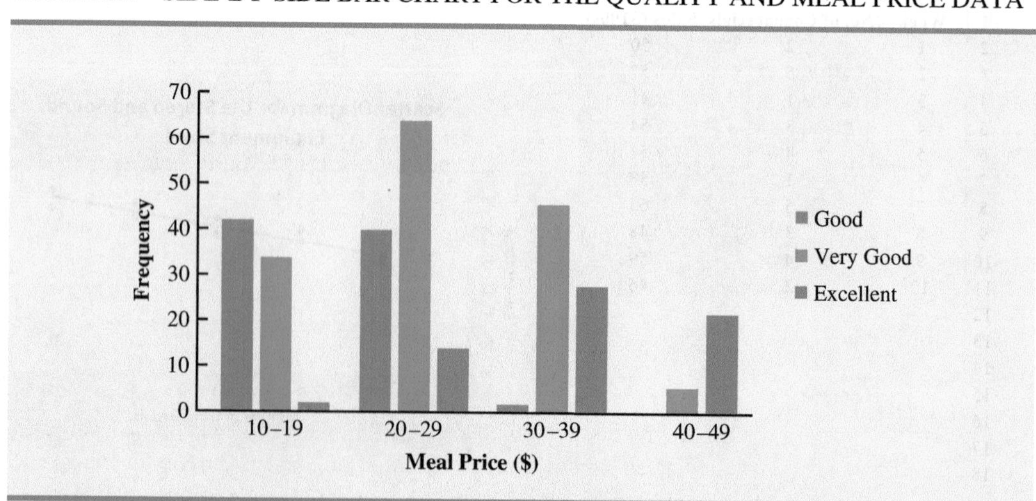

TABLE 2.15 COLUMN PERCENTAGES FOR EACH MEAL PRICE CATEGORY

	Meal Price			
Quality Rating	$10–19	$20–29	$30–39	$40–49
Good	53.8%	33.9%	2.6%	0.0%
Very Good	43.6	54.2	60.5	21.4
Excellent	2.6	11.9	36.8	78.6
Total	100.0%	100.0%	100.0%	100.0%

FIGURE 2.22 STACKED BAR CHART FOR THE QUALITY RATING AND MEAL PRICE DATA

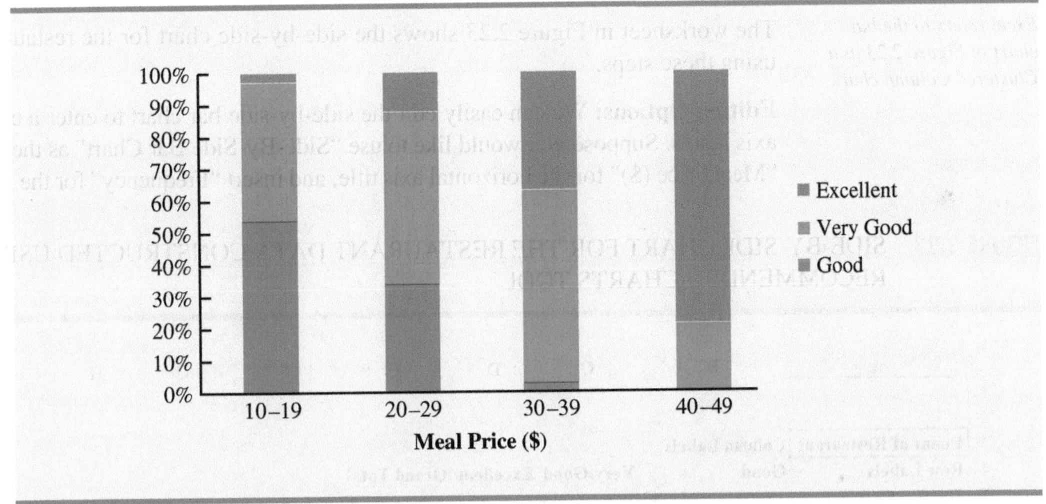

to a pie chart. To illustrate a stacked bar chart we will use the quality rating and meal price data summarized in the crosstabulation shown in Table 2.10.

We can convert the frequency data in Table 2.10 into column percentages by dividing each element in a particular column by the total for that column. For instance, 42 of the 78 restaurants with a meal price in the $10–19 range had a good quality rating. In other words, (42/78)100 or 53.8% of the 78 restaurants had a good rating. Table 2.15 shows the column percentages for each meal price category. Using the data in Table 2.15 we constructed the stacked bar chart shown in Figure 2.22. Because the stacked bar chart is based on percentages, Figure 2.22 shows even more clearly than Figure 2.21 the relationship between the variables. As we move from the low price category ($10–19) to the high price category ($40–49), the length of the blue bars decreases and the length of the green bars increases.

Using Excel's Recommended Charts Tool to Construct Side-by-Side and Stacked Bar Charts

In Figure 2.16 we showed the results of using Excel's PivotTable tool to construct a frequency distribution for the sample of 300 restaurants in the Los Angeles area. We will use these results to illustrate how Excel's Recommended Charts tool can be used to construct side-by-side and stacked bar charts for the restaurant data using the PivotTable output.

Apply Tools: The following steps describe how to use Excel's Recommended Charts tool to construct a side-by-side bar chart for the restaurant data using the PivotTable tool output shown in Figure 2.16.

Step 1. Select any cell in the PivotTable report (cells A3:F8)
Step 2. Click **INSERT** on the Ribbon.
Step 3. In the **Charts** group click **Recommended Charts**; a preview showing a bar chart with quality rating on the horizontal axis appears
Step 4. Click **OK**
Step 5. Click **DESIGN** on the Ribbon (located below the **PIVOTCHART TOOLS** heading)
Step 6. In the **Data** group click **Switch Row/Column**; a side-by-side bar chart with meal price on the horizontal axis appears

Excel refers to the bar chart in Figure 2.23 as a Clustered Column chart.

The worksheet in Figure 2.23 shows the side-by-side chart for the restaurant data created using these steps.

Editing Options: We can easily edit the side-by-side bar chart to enter a chart heading and axis labels. Suppose you would like to use "Side-By-Side Bar Chart" as the chart title, insert "Meal Price ($)" for the horizontal axis title, and insert "Frequency" for the vertical axis title.

FIGURE 2.23 SIDE-BY-SIDE CHART FOR THE RESTAURANT DATA CONSTRUCTED USING EXCEL'S RECOMMENDED CHARTS TOOL

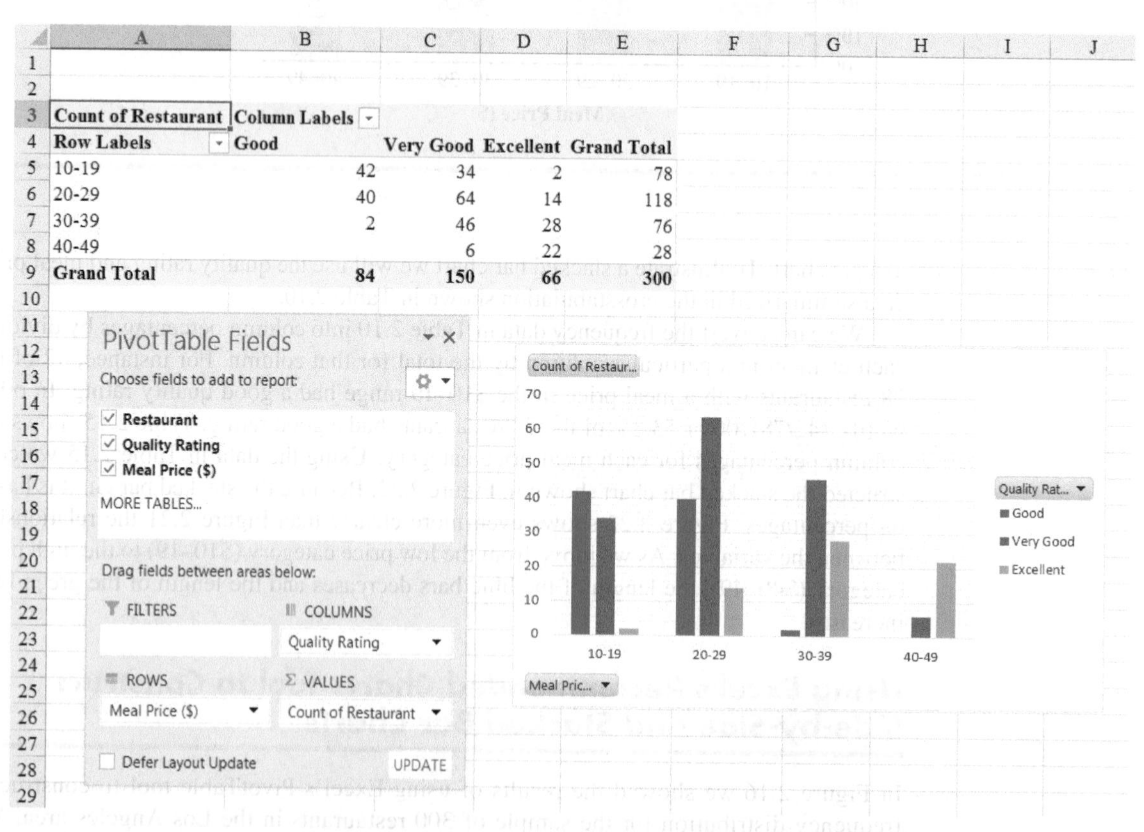

FIGURE 2.24 EDITED SIDE-BY-SIDE CHART FOR THE RESTAURANT DATA CONSTRUCTED USING EXCEL'S RECOMMENDED CHARTS TOOL

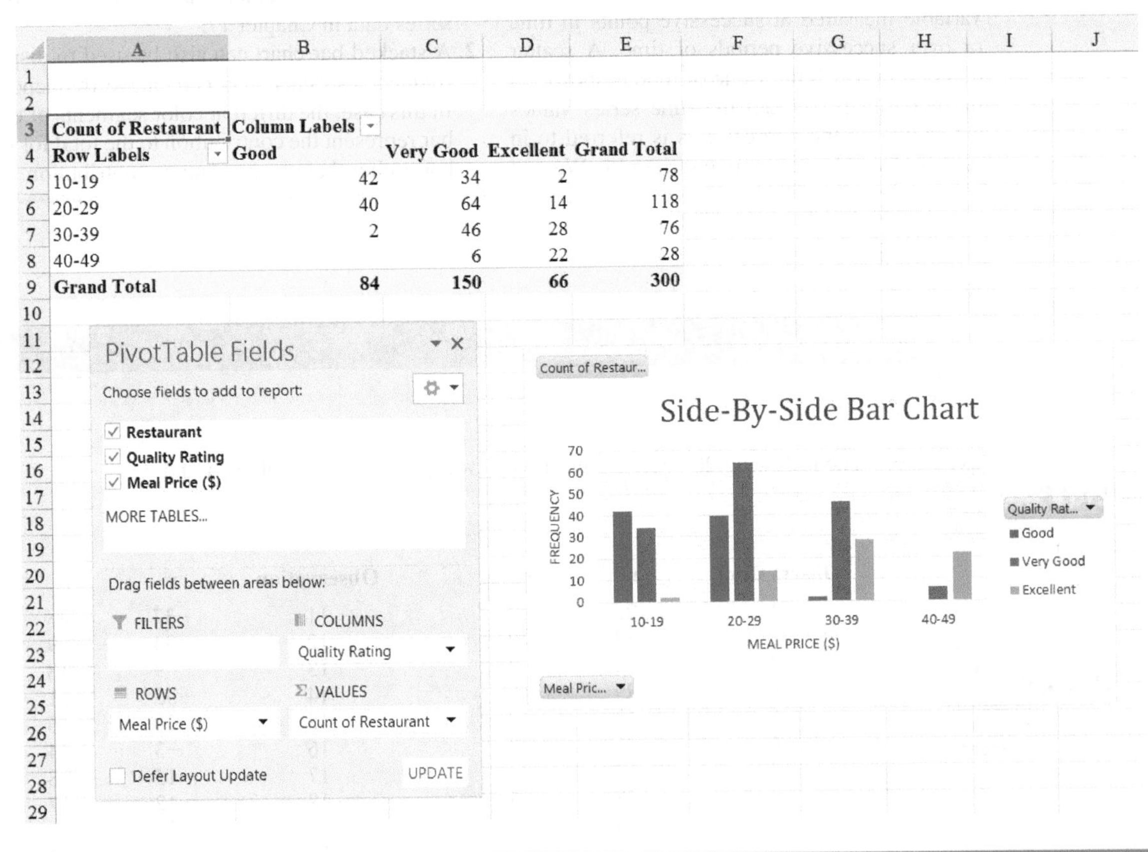

Count of Restaurant	Column Labels			
Row Labels	Good	Very Good	Excellent	Grand Total
10-19	42	34	2	78
20-29	40	64	14	118
30-39	2	46	28	76
40-49		6	22	28
Grand Total	**84**	**150**	**66**	**300**

Step 1. Click the **Chart Elements** button (located next to the top right corner of the chart)

Step 2. When the list of chart elements appears:
Click **Chart title** (creates placeholder for the chart title)
Click **Axis Titles** (creates placeholder for the axis titles)

Step 3. Click the **Chart Title** and replace it with **Side-By-Side Bar Chart**

Step 4. Click the **Horizontal (Category) Axis Title** and replace it with **Meal Price ($)**

Step 5. Click the **Vertical (Value) Axis Title** and replace it with **Frequency**

The edited side-by-side chart is shown in Figure 2.24.

You can easily change the side-by-side bar chart to a stacked bar chart using the following steps.

Step 6. In the **Type** group click **Change Chart Type**

Step 7. When the Change Chart Type dialog box appears:
Select the **Stacked Columns** option
Click **OK**

Once you have created a side-by-side bar chart or a stacked bar chart, you can easily switch back and forth between the two chart types by reapplying steps 6 and 7.

NOTES AND COMMENTS

1. A time series is a sequence of observations on a variable measured at successive points in time or over successive periods of time. A scatter diagram in which the value of time is shown on the horizontal axis and the time series values are shown on the vertical axis is referred to in time series analysis as a time series plot. We will discuss time series plots and how to analyze time series data in Chapter 17.
2. A stacked bar chart can also be used to display frequencies rather than percentage frequencies. In this case, the different color segments of each bar represent the contribution to the total for that bar, rather than the percentage contribution.

Exercises

Methods

36. The following 20 observations are for two quantitative variables, x and y.

Scatter

Observation	x	y	Observation	x	y
1	−22	22	11	−37	48
2	−33	49	12	34	−29
3	2	8	13	9	−18
4	29	−16	14	−33	31
5	−13	10	15	20	−16
6	21	−28	16	−3	14
7	−13	27	17	−15	18
8	−23	35	18	12	17
9	14	−5	19	−20	−11
10	3	−3	20	−7	−22

a. Develop a scatter diagram for the relationship between x and y.
b. What is the relationship, if any, between x and y?

37. Consider the following data on two categorical variables. The first variable, x, can take on values A, B, C, or D. The second variable, y, can take on values I or II. The following table gives the frequency with which each combination occurs.

x \ y	I	II
A	143	857
B	200	800
C	321	679
D	420	580

a. Construct a side-by-side bar chart with x on the horizontal axis.
b. Comment on the relationship between x and y.

38. The following crosstabulation summarizes the data for two categorical variables, x and y. The variable x can take on values Low, Medium, or High and the variable y can take on values Yes or No.

x	y Yes	No	Total
Low	20	10	30
Medium	15	35	50
High	20	5	25
Total	55	50	105

a. Compute the row percentages.
b. Construct a stacked percent frequency bar chart with x on the horizontal axis.

Applications

39. A study on driving speed (miles per hour) and fuel efficiency (miles per gallon) for midsize automobiles resulted in the following data:

MPG

Driving Speed	30	50	40	55	30	25	60	25	50	55
Fuel Efficiency	28	25	25	23	30	32	21	35	26	25

a. Construct a scatter diagram with driving speed on the horizontal axis and fuel efficiency on the vertical axis.
b. Comment on any apparent relationship between these two variables.

Snow

40. The Current Results website lists the average annual high and low temperatures (degrees Fahrenheit) and average annual snowfall (inches) for 51 major U.S. cities, based on data from 1981 to 2010. The data are contained in the WEBfile named Snow. For example, the average low temperature for Columbus, Ohio, is 44 degrees and the average annual snowfall is 27.5 inches.
    a. Construct a scatter diagram with the average annual low temperature on the horizontal axis and the average annual snowfall on the vertical axis.
    b. Does there appear to be any relationship between these two variables?
    c. Based on the scatter diagram, comment on any data points that seem to be unusual.
41. People often wait until middle age to worry about having a healthy heart. However, recent studies have shown that earlier monitoring of risk factors such as blood pressure can be very beneficial (*The Wall Street Journal,* January 10, 2012). Having higher than normal blood pressure, a condition known as hypertension, is a major risk factor for heart disease. Suppose a large sample of individuals of various ages and gender was selected and that each individual's blood pressure was measured to determine if they have hypertension. For the sample data, the following table shows the percentage of individuals with hypertension.

Hypertension

Age	Male	Female
20–34	11.00%	9.00%
35–44	24.00%	19.00%
45–54	39.00%	37.00%
55–64	57.00%	56.00%
65–74	62.00%	64.00%
75+	73.30%	79.00%

a. Develop a side-by-side bar chart with age on the horizontal axis, the percentage of individuals with hypertension on the vertical axis, and side-by-side bars based on gender.
b. What does the display you developed in part (a), indicate about hypertension and age?
c. Comment on differences by gender.

42. Smartphones are advanced mobile phones with Internet, photo, music, and video capability (The Pew Research Center, Internet & American Life Project, 2011). The following survey results show smartphone ownership by age.

Smartphones

Age Category	Smartphone (%)	Other Cell Phone (%)	No Cell Phone (%)
18–24	49	46	5
25–34	58	35	7
35–44	44	45	11
45–54	28	58	14
55–64	22	59	19
65+	11	45	44

a. Construct a stacked bar chart to display the above survey data on type of mobile phone ownership. Use age category as the variable on the horizontal axis.
b. Comment on the relationship between age and smartphone ownership.
c. How would you expect the results of this survey to be different if conducted in 2021?

43. The Northwest regional manager of an outdoor equipment retailer conducted a study to determine how managers at three store locations are using their time. A summary of the results is shown in the following table.

ManagerTime

	Percentage of Manager's Work Week Spent on			
Store Location	Meetings	Reports	Customers	Idle
Bend	18	11	52	19
Portland	52	11	24	13
Seattle	32	17	37	14

a. Create a stacked bar chart with store location on the horizontal axis and percentage of time spent on each task on the vertical axis.
b. Create a side-by-side bar chart with store location on the horizontal axis and side-by-side bars of the percentage of time spent on each task.
c. Which type of bar chart (stacked or side-by-side) do you prefer for these data? Why?

2.5 Data Visualization: Best Practices in Creating Effective Graphical Displays

Data visualization is a term used to describe the use of graphical displays to summarize and present information about a data set. The goal of data visualization is to communicate as effectively and clearly as possible the key information about the data. In this section, we provide guidelines for creating an effective graphical display, discuss how to select an appropriate type of display given the purpose of the study, illustrate the use of data dashboards, and show how the Cincinnati Zoo and Botanical Garden uses data visualization techniques to improve decision making.

Creating Effective Graphical Displays

The data presented in Table 2.16 show the forecasted or planned value of sales ($1000s) and the actual value of sales ($1000s) by sales region in the United States for Gustin Chemical for the past year. Note that there are two quantitative variables (planned sales and actual

TABLE 2.16 PLANNED AND ACTUAL SALES BY SALES REGION ($1000s)

Sales Region	Planned Sales ($1000s)	Actual Sales ($1000s)
Northeast	540	447
Northwest	420	447
Southeast	575	556
Southwest	360	341

sales) and one categorical variable (sales region). Suppose we would like to develop a graphical display that would enable management of Gustin Chemical to visualize how each sales region did relative to planned sales and simultaneously enable management to visualize sales performance across regions.

Figure 2.25 shows a side-by-side bar chart of the planned versus actual sales data. Note how this bar chart makes it very easy to compare the planned versus actual sales in a region, as well as across regions. This graphical display is simple, contains a title, is well labeled, and uses distinct colors to represent the two types of sales. Note also that the scale of the vertical axis begins at zero. The four sales regions are separated by space so that it is clear that they are distinct, whereas the planned versus actual sales values are side-by-side for easy comparison within each region. The side-by-side bar chart in Figure 2.25 makes it easy to see that the Southwest region is the lowest in both planned and actual sales and that the Northwest region slightly exceeded its planned sales.

Creating an effective graphical display is as much art as it is science. By following the general guidelines listed below you can increase the likelihood that your display will effectively convey the key information in the data.

- Give the display a clear and concise title.
- Keep the display simple. Do not use three dimensions when two dimensions are sufficient.
- Clearly label each axis and provide the units of measure.
- If color is used to distinguish categories, make sure the colors are distinct.
- If multiple colors or line types are used, use a legend to define how they are used and place the legend close to the representation of the data.

FIGURE 2.25 SIDE-BY-SIDE BAR CHART FOR PLANNED VERSUS ACTUAL SALES

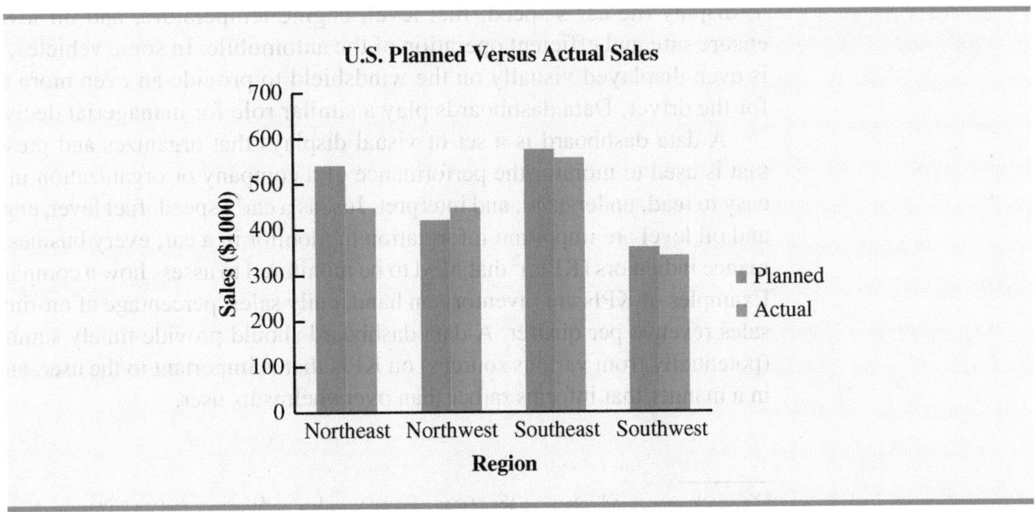

Choosing the Type of Graphical Display

In this chapter we discussed a variety of graphical displays, including bar charts, pie charts, dot plots, histograms, stem-and-leaf plots, scatter diagrams, side-by-side bar charts, and stacked bar charts. Each of these types of displays was developed for a specific purpose. In order to provide guidelines for choosing the appropriate type of graphical display, we now provide a summary of the types of graphical displays categorized by their purpose. We note that some types of graphical displays may be used effectively for multiple purposes.

Displays Used to Show the Distribution of Data

- Bar Chart—Used to show the frequency distribution and relative frequency distribution for categorical data
- Pie Chart—Used to show the relative frequency and percent frequency for categorical data
- Dot Plot—Used to show the distribution for quantitative data over the entire range of the data
- Histogram—Used to show the frequency distribution for quantitative data over a set of class intervals
- Stem-and-Leaf Display—Used to show both the rank order and shape of the distribution for quantitative data

Displays Used to Make Comparisons

- Side-by-Side Bar Chart—Used to compare two variables
- Stacked Bar Charts—Used to compare the relative frequency or percent frequency of two categorical variables

Displays Used to Show Relationships

- Scatter diagram—Used to show the relationship between two quantitative variables
- Trendline—Used to approximate the relationship of data in a scatter diagram

Data Dashboards

Data dashboards are also referred to as digital dashboards.

One of the most widely used data visualization tools is a **data dashboard**. If you drive a car, you are already familiar with the concept of a data dashboard. In an automobile, the car's dashboard contains gauges and other visual displays that provide the key information that is important when operating the vehicle. For example, the gauges used to display the car's speed, fuel level, engine temperature, and oil level are critical to ensure safe and efficient operation of the automobile. In some vehicles, this information is even displayed visually on the windshield to provide an even more effective display for the driver. Data dashboards play a similar role for managerial decision making.

A data dashboard is a set of visual displays that organizes and presents information that is used to monitor the performance of a company or organization in a manner that is easy to read, understand, and interpret. Just as a car's speed, fuel level, engine temperature, and oil level are important information to monitor in a car, every business has key performance indicators (KPIs)[2] that need to be monitored to assess how a company is performing. Examples of KPIs are inventory on hand, daily sales, percentage of on-time deliveries, and sales revenue per quarter. A data dashboard should provide timely summary information (potentially from various sources) on KPIs that is important to the user, and it should do so in a manner that informs rather than overwhelms its user.

[2] Key performance indicators are sometimes referred to as key performance metrics (KPMs).

FIGURE 2.26 GROGAN OIL INFORMATION TECHNOLOGY CALL CENTER DATA DASHBOARD

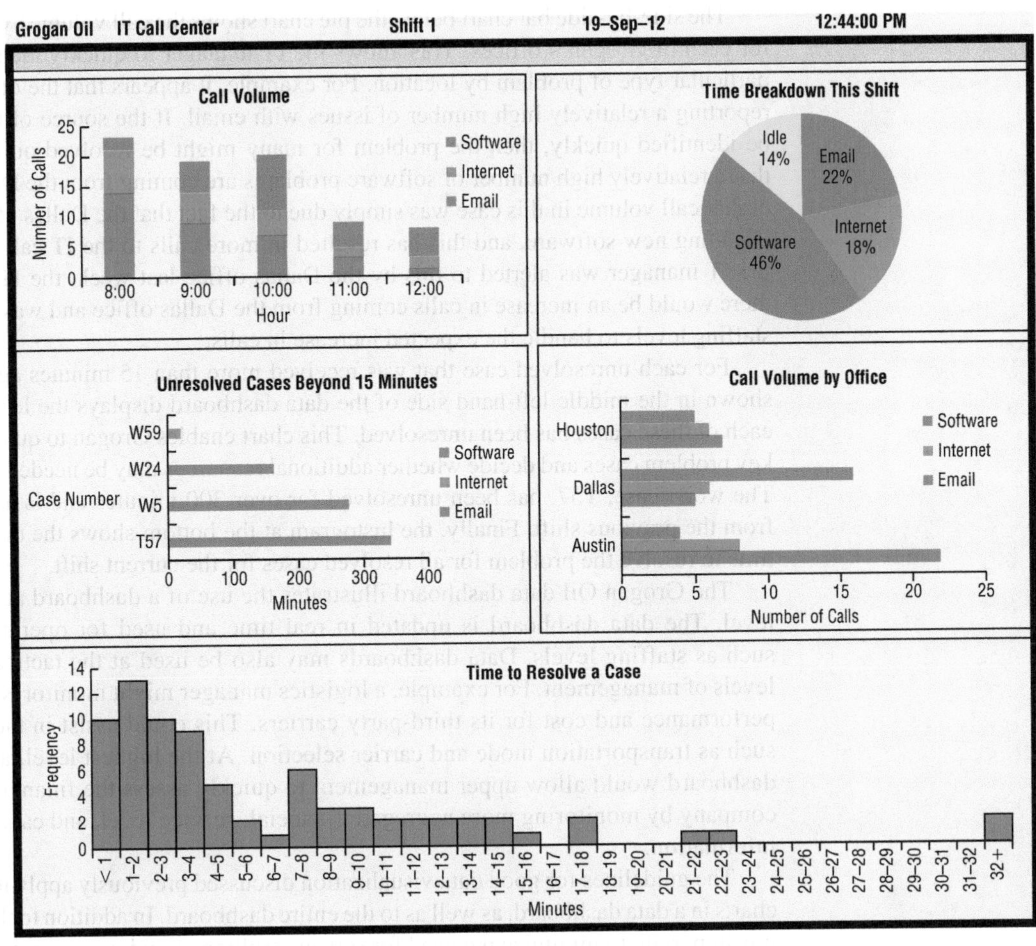

To illustrate the use of a data dashboard in decision making, we will discuss an application involving the Grogan Oil Company. Grogan has offices located in three cities in Texas: Austin (its headquarters), Houston, and Dallas. Grogan's Information Technology (IT) call center, located in the Austin office, handles calls from employees regarding computer-related problems involving software, Internet, and email issues. For example, if a Grogan employee in Dallas has a computer software problem, the employee can call the IT call center for assistance.

The data dashboard shown in Figure 2.26 was developed to monitor the performance of the call center. This data dashboard combines several displays to monitor the call center's KPIs. The data presented are for the current shift, which started at 8:00 A.M. The stacked bar chart in the upper left-hand corner shows the call volume for each type of problem (software, Internet, or email) over time. This chart shows that call volume is heavier during the first few hours of the shift, calls concerning email issues appear to decrease over time, and volume of calls regarding software issues are highest at midmorning. The pie chart in the upper right-hand corner of the dashboard shows the percentage of time that call-center employees spent on each type of problem or not working on a call (idle). Both of these charts are important displays in determining optimal staffing levels. For instance, knowing the call mix and how stressed the system is—as measured by percentage of idle time—can help the IT manager make sure there are enough call center employees available with the right level of expertise.

The side-by-side bar chart below the pie chart shows the call volume by type of problem for each of Grogan's offices. This allows the IT manager to quickly identify if there is a particular type of problem by location. For example, it appears that the office in Austin is reporting a relatively high number of issues with email. If the source of the problem can be identified quickly, then the problem for many might be resolved quickly. Also, note that a relatively high number of software problems are coming from the Dallas office. The higher call volume in this case was simply due to the fact that the Dallas office is currently installing new software, and this has resulted in more calls to the IT call center. Because the IT manager was alerted to this by the Dallas office last week, the IT manager knew there would be an increase in calls coming from the Dallas office and was able to increase staffing levels to handle the expected increase in calls.

For each unresolved case that was received more than 15 minutes ago, the bar chart shown in the middle left-hand side of the data dashboard displays the length of time that each of these cases has been unresolved. This chart enables Grogan to quickly monitor the key problem cases and decide whether additional resources may be needed to resolve them. The worst case, T57, has been unresolved for over 300 minutes and is actually left over from the previous shift. Finally, the histogram at the bottom shows the distribution of the time to resolve the problem for all resolved cases for the current shift.

The Grogan Oil data dashboard illustrates the use of a dashboard at the operational level. The data dashboard is updated in real time and used for operational decisions such as staffing levels. Data dashboards may also be used at the tactical and strategic levels of management. For example, a logistics manager might monitor KPIs for on-time performance and cost for its third-party carriers. This could assist in tactical decisions such as transportation mode and carrier selection. At the highest level, a more strategic dashboard would allow upper management to quickly assess the financial health of the company by monitoring more aggregate financial, service level, and capacity utilization information.

The guidelines for good data visualization discussed previously apply to the individual charts in a data dashboard, as well as to the entire dashboard. In addition to those guidelines, it is important to minimize the need for screen scrolling, avoid unnecessary use of color or three-dimensional displays, and use borders between charts to improve readability. As with individual charts, simpler is almost always better.

Data Visualization in Practice: Cincinnati Zoo and Botanical Garden[3]

The Cincinnati Zoo and Botanical Garden, located in Cincinnati, Ohio, is the second oldest zoo in the world. In order to improve decision making by becoming more data-driven, management decided they needed to link together the different facets of their business and provide nontechnical managers and executives with an intuitive way to better understand their data. A complicating factor is that when the zoo is busy, managers are expected to be on the grounds interacting with guests, checking on operations, and anticipating issues as they arise or before they become an issue. Therefore, being able to monitor what is happening on a real-time basis was a key factor in deciding what to do. Zoo management concluded that a data visualization strategy was needed to address the problem.

[3] The authors are indebted to John Lucas of the Cincinnati Zoo and Botanical Garden for providing this application.

FIGURE 2.27 DATA DASHBOARD FOR THE CINCINNATI ZOO

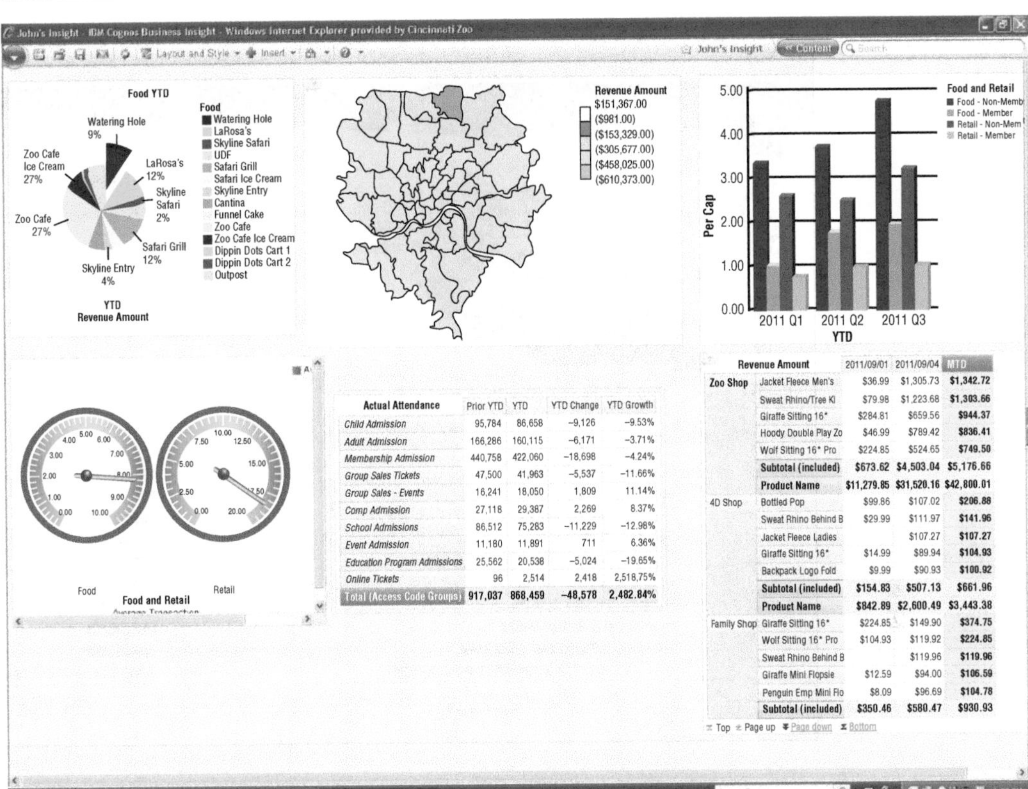

Because of its ease of use, real-time updating capability, and iPad compatibility, the Cincinnati Zoo decided to implement its data visualization strategy using IBM's Cognos advanced data visualization software. Using this software, the Cincinnati Zoo developed the data dashboard shown in Figure 2.27 to enable zoo management to track the following key performance indicators:

- Item Analysis (sales volumes and sales dollars by location within the zoo)
- Geo Analytics (using maps and displays of where the day's visitors are spending their time at the zoo)
- Customer Spending
- Cashier Sales Performance
- Sales and Attendance Data versus Weather Patterns
- Performance of the Zoo's Loyalty Rewards Program

An iPad mobile application was also developed to enable the zoo's managers to be out on the grounds and still see and anticipate what is occurring on a real-time basis. The Cincinnati Zoo's iPad data dashboard, shown in Figure 2.28, provides managers with access to the following information:

- Real-time attendance data, including what "types" of guests are coming to the zoo
- Real-time analysis showing which items are selling the fastest inside the zoo
- Real-time geographical representation of where the zoo's visitors live

FIGURE 2.28 THE CINCINNATI ZOO iPAD DATA DASHBOARD

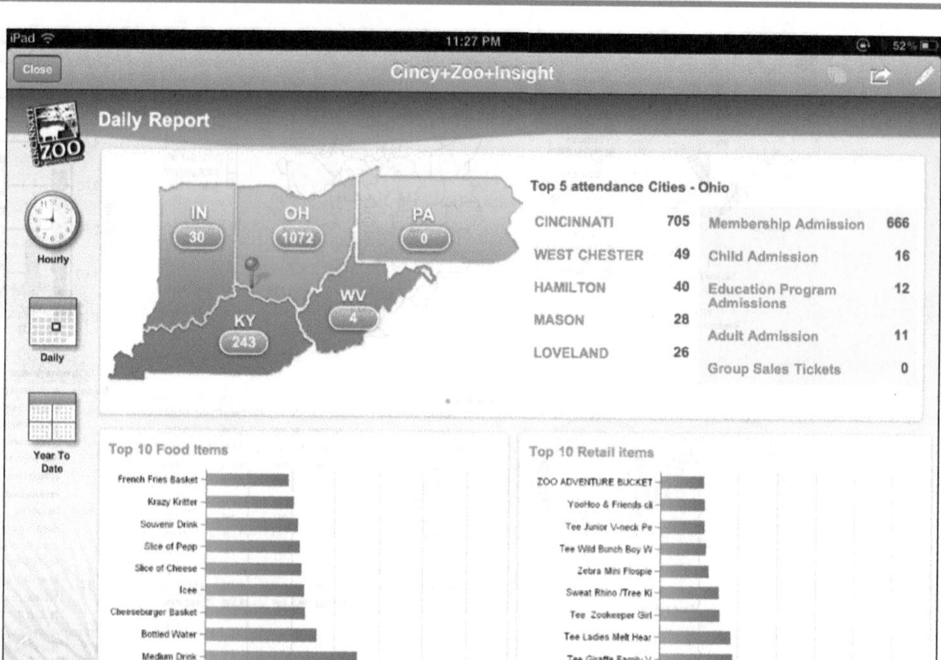

Having access to the data shown in Figures 2.27 and 2.28 allows the zoo managers to make better decisions on staffing levels within the zoo, which items to stock based upon weather and other conditions, and how to better target its advertising based on geodemographics.

The impact that data visualization has had on the zoo has been significant. Within the first year of use, the system has been directly responsible for revenue growth of over $500,000, increased visitation to the zoo, enhanced customer service, and reduced marketing costs.

NOTES AND COMMENTS

1. A variety of software is available for data visualization. Among the more popular packages are Cognos, JMP, Spotfire, and Tableau.
2. Radar charts and bubble charts are two other commonly used charts for displaying relationships between multiple variables. However, many experts in data visualization recommend against using these charts because they can be overcomplicated. Instead, the use of simpler displays such as bar charts and scatter diagrams is recommended.
3. A very powerful tool for visualizing geographic data is a Geographic Information System (GIS). A GIS uses color, symbols, and text on a map to help you understand how variables are distributed geographically. For example, a company interested in trying to locate a new distribution center might wish to better understand how the demand for its product varies throughout the United States. A GIS can be used to map the demand where red regions indicate high demand, blue lower demand, and no color for regions where the product is not sold. Locations closer to red high-demand regions might be good candidate sites for further consideration.

Summary

A set of data, even if modest in size, is often difficult to interpret directly in the form in which it is gathered. Tabular and graphical displays can be used to summarize and present data so that patterns are revealed and the data are more easily interpreted. Frequency distributions, relative frequency distributions, percent frequency distributions, bar charts, and pie charts were presented as tabular and graphical displays for summarizing the data for a single categorical variable. Frequency distributions, relative frequency distributions, percent frequency distributions, histograms, cumulative frequency distributions, cumulative relative frequency distributions, cumulative percent frequency distributions, and stem-and-leaf displays were presented as ways of summarizing the data for a single quantitative variable.

A crosstabulation was presented as a tabular display for summarizing the data for two variables and a scatter diagram was introduced as a graphical display for summarizing the data for two quantitative variables. We also showed that side-by-side bar charts and stacked bar charts are just extensions of basic bar charts that can be used to display and compare two categorical variables. Guidelines for creating effective graphical displays and how to choose the most appropriate type of display were discussed. Data dashboards were introduced to illustrate how a set of visual displays can be developed that organizes and presents information that is used to monitor a company's performance in a manner that is easy to read, understand, and interpret. Figure 2.29 provides a summary of the tabular and graphical methods presented in this chapter.

FIGURE 2.29 TABULAR AND GRAPHICAL DISPLAYS FOR SUMMARIZING DATA

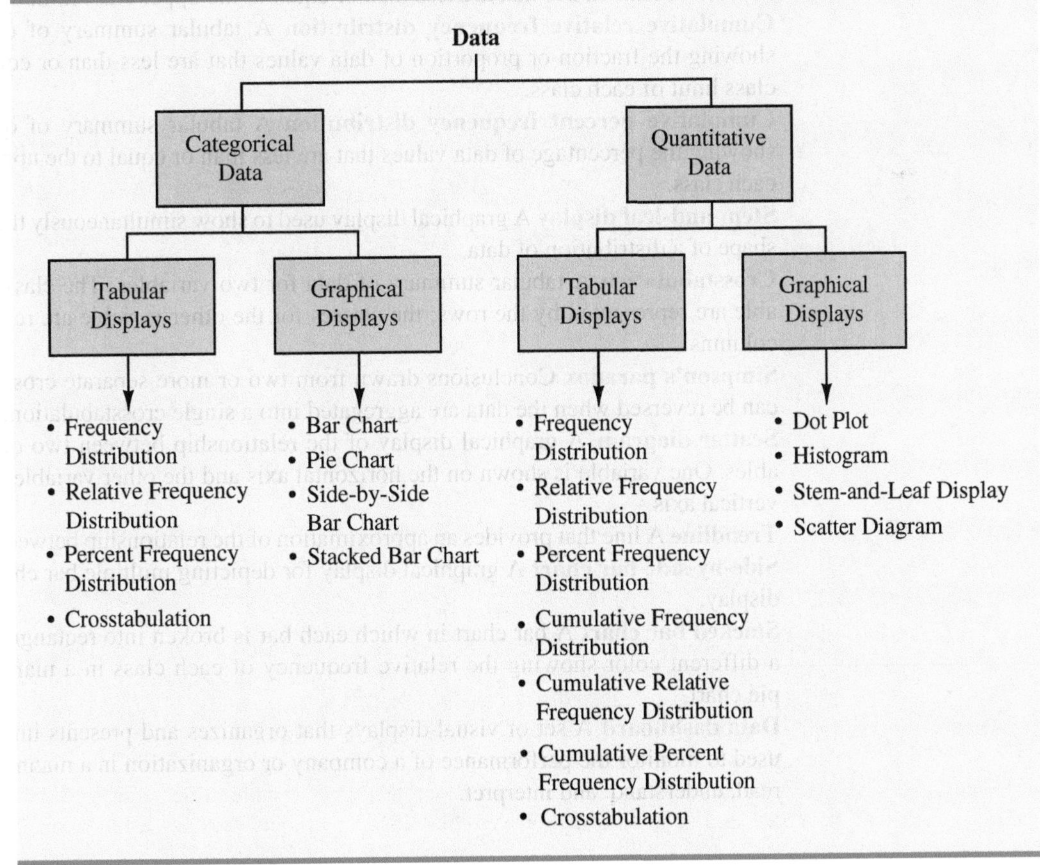

Glossary

Categorical data Labels or names used to identify categories of like items.

Quantitative data Numerical values that indicate how much or how many.

Data visualization A term used to describe the use of graphical displays to summarize and present information about a data set.

Frequency distribution A tabular summary of data showing the number (frequency) of observations in each of several nonoverlapping categories or classes.

Relative frequency distribution A tabular summary of data showing the fraction or proportion of observations in each of several nonoverlapping categories or classes.

Percent frequency distribution A tabular summary of data showing the percentage of observations in each of several nonoverlapping classes.

Bar chart A graphical device for depicting categorical data that have been summarized in a frequency, relative frequency, or percent frequency distribution.

Pie chart A graphical device for presenting data summaries based on subdivision of a circle into sectors that correspond to the relative frequency for each class.

Class midpoint The value halfway between the lower and upper class limits.

Dot plot A graphical device that summarizes data by the number of dots above each data value on the horizontal axis.

Histogram A graphical display of a frequency distribution, relative frequency distribution, or percent frequency distribution of quantitative data constructed by placing the class intervals on the horizontal axis and the frequencies, relative frequencies, or percent frequencies on the vertical axis.

Cumulative frequency distribution A tabular summary of quantitative data showing the number of data values that are less than or equal to the upper class limit of each class.

Cumulative relative frequency distribution A tabular summary of quantitative data showing the fraction or proportion of data values that are less than or equal to the upper class limit of each class.

Cumulative percent frequency distribution A tabular summary of quantitative data showing the percentage of data values that are less than or equal to the upper class limit of each class.

Stem-and-leaf display A graphical display used to show simultaneously the rank order and shape of a distribution of data.

Crosstabulation A tabular summary of data for two variables. The classes for one variable are represented by the rows; the classes for the other variable are represented by the columns.

Simpson's paradox Conclusions drawn from two or more separate crosstabulations that can be reversed when the data are aggregated into a single crosstabulation.

Scatter diagram A graphical display of the relationship between two quantitative variables. One variable is shown on the horizontal axis and the other variable is shown on the vertical axis.

Trendline A line that provides an approximation of the relationship between two variables.

Side-by-side bar chart A graphical display for depicting multiple bar charts on the same display.

Stacked bar chart A bar chart in which each bar is broken into rectangular segments of a different color showing the relative frequency of each class in a manner similar to a pie chart.

Data dashboard A set of visual displays that organizes and presents information that is used to monitor the performance of a company or organization in a manner that is easy to read, understand, and interpret.

Key Formulas

Relative Frequency

$$\frac{\text{Frequency of the class}}{n} \tag{2.1}$$

Approximate Class Width

$$\frac{\text{Largest data value} - \text{Smallest data value}}{\text{Number of classes}} \tag{2.2}$$

Supplementary Exercises

44. Approximately 1.5 million high school students take the SAT each year and nearly 80% of the college and universities without open admissions policies use SAT scores in making admission decisions (College Board, March 2009). The current version of the SAT includes three parts: reading comprehension, mathematics, and writing. A perfect combined score for all three parts is 2400. A sample of SAT scores for the combined three-part SAT is as follows.

NewSAT

1665	1525	1355	1645	1780
1275	2135	1280	1060	1585
1650	1560	1150	1485	1990
1590	1880	1420	1755	1375
1475	1680	1440	1260	1730
1490	1560	940	1390	1175

a. Show a frequency distribution and histogram. Begin with the first class starting at 800 and use a class width of 200.
b. Comment on the shape of the distribution.
c. What other observations can be made about the SAT scores based on the tabular and graphical summaries?

45. The Pittsburgh Steelers defeated the Arizona Cardinals 27 to 23 in professional football's 43rd Super Bowl. With this win, its sixth championship, the Pittsburgh Steelers became the team with the most wins in the 43-year history of the event (*Tampa Tribune,* February 2, 2009). The Super Bowl has been played in eight different states: Arizona (AZ), California (CA),

SuperBowl

Super Bowl	State	Won By Points	Super Bowl	State	Won By Points	Super Bowl	State	Won By Points
1	CA	25	16	MI	5	31	LA	14
2	FL	19	17	CA	10	32	CA	7
3	FL	9	18	FL	19	33	FL	15
4	LA	16	19	CA	22	34	GA	7
5	FL	3	20	LA	36	35	FL	27
6	FL	21	21	CA	19	36	LA	3
7	CA	7	22	CA	32	37	CA	27
8	TX	17	23	FL	4	38	TX	3
9	LA	10	24	LA	45	39	FL	3
10	FL	4	25	FL	1	40	MI	11
11	CA	18	26	MN	13	41	FL	12
12	LA	17	27	CA	35	42	AZ	3
13	FL	4	28	GA	17	43	FL	4
14	CA	12	29	FL	23			
15	LA	17	30	AZ	10			

Florida (FL), Georgia (GA), Louisiana (LA), Michigan (MI), Minnesota (MN), and Texas (TX). Data in the table show the state where the Super Bowls were played and the point margin of victory for the winning team.

a. Show a frequency distribution and bar chart for the state where the Super Bowl was played.
b. What conclusions can you draw from your summary in part (a)? What percentage of Super Bowls were played in the states of Florida or California? What percentage of Super Bowls were played in northern or cold-weather states?
c. Show a stretched stem-and-leaf display for the point margin of victory for the winning team. Show a histogram.
d. What conclusions can you draw from your summary in part (c)? What percentage of Super Bowls have been close games with the margin of victory less than 5 points? What percentage of Super Bowls have been won by 20 or more points?
e. The closest Super Bowl occurred when the New York Giants beat the Buffalo Bills. Where was this game played and what was the winning margin of victory? The biggest point margin in Super Bowl history occurred when the San Francisco 49ers beat the Denver Broncos. Where was this game played and what was the winning margin of victory?

46. Data showing the population by state in millions of people follow (*The World Almanac,* 2012).

2012Population

State	Population	State	Population	State	Population
Alabama	4.8	Louisiana	4.5	Ohio	11.5
Alaska	0.7	Maine	1.3	Oklahoma	3.8
Arizona	6.4	Maryland	5.8	Oregon	4.3
Arkansas	2.9	Massachusetts	6.5	Pennsylvania	12.7
California	37.3	Michigan	9.9	Rhode Island	1.0
Colorado	5.0	Minnesota	5.3	South Carolina	4.6
Connecticut	3.6	Mississippi	3.0	South Dakota	0.8
Delaware	0.9	Missouri	6.0	Tennessee	6.3
Florida	18.8	Montana	0.9	Texas	25.1
Georgia	9.7	Nebraska	1.8	Utah	2.8
Hawaii	1.4	Nevada	2.7	Vermont	0.6
Idaho	1.6	New Hampshire	1.3	Virginia	8.0
Illinois	12.8	New Jersey	8.8	Washington	6.7
Indiana	6.5	New Mexico	2.0	West Virginia	1.9
Iowa	3.0	New York	19.4	Wisconsin	5.7
Kansas	2.9	North Carolina	9.5	Wyoming	0.6
Kentucky	4.3	North Dakota	0.7		

a. Develop a frequency distribution, a percent frequency distribution, and a histogram. Use a class width of 2.5 million.
b. Does there appear to be any skewness in the distribution? Explain.
c. What observations can you make about the population of the 50 states?

47. A startup company's ability to gain funding is a key to success. The funds raised (in millions of dollars) by 50 startup companies follow (*The Wall Street Journal,* March 10, 2011).

StartUps

81	61	103	166	168
80	51	130	77	78
69	119	81	60	20
73	50	110	21	60
192	18	54	49	63
91	272	58	54	40
47	24	57	78	78
154	72	38	131	52
48	118	40	49	55
54	112	129	156	31

a. Construct a stem-and-leaf display.
b. Comment on the display.

48. Consumer complaints are frequently reported to the Better Business Bureau. In 2011, the industries with the most complaints to the Better Business Bureau were banks; cable and satellite television companies; collection agencies; cellular phone providers; and new car dealerships (*USA Today,* April 16, 2012). The results for a sample of 200 complaints are contained in the WEBfile named BBB.
    a. Show the frequency and percent frequency of complaints by industry.
    b. Construct a bar chart of the percent frequency distribution.
    c. Which industry had the highest number of complaints?
    d. Comment on the percentage frequency distribution for complaints.

49. Dividend yield is the annual dividend paid by a company expressed as a percentage of the price of the stock (Dividend/Stock price × 100). The dividend yield for the Dow Jones Industrial Average companies is shown in Table 2.17 (*The Wall Street Journal,* June 8, 2009).
    a. Construct a frequency distribution and percent frequency distribution.
    b. Construct a histogram.
    c. Comment on the shape of the distribution.
    d. What do the tabular and graphical summaries indicate about the dividend yields among the Dow Jones Industrial Average companies?
    e. What company has the highest dividend yield? If the stock for this company currently sells for $14 per share and you purchase 500 shares, how much dividend income will this investment generate in one year?

TABLE 2.17 DIVIDEND YIELD FOR DOW JONES INDUSTRIAL AVERAGE COMPANIES

Company	Dividend Yield %	Company	Dividend Yield %
3M	3.6	IBM	2.1
Alcoa	1.3	Intel	3.4
American Express	2.9	J.P. Morgan Chase	0.5
AT&T	6.6	Johnson & Johnson	3.6
Bank of America	0.4	Kraft Foods	4.4
Boeing	3.8	McDonald's	3.4
Caterpillar	4.7	Merck	5.5
Chevron	3.9	Microsoft	2.5
Cisco Systems	0.0	Pfizer	4.2
Coca-Cola	3.3	Procter & Gamble	3.4
DuPont	5.8	Travelers	3.0
ExxonMobil	2.4	United Technologies	2.9
General Electric	9.2	Verizon	6.3
Hewlett-Packard	0.9	Wal-Mart Stores	2.2
Home Depot	3.9	Walt Disney	1.5

50. The U.S. Census Bureau serves as the leading source of quantitative data about the nation's people and economy. The following crosstabulation shows the number of households (1000s) and the household income by the level of education for heads of household having received a high school degree or more education (U.S. Census Bureau website, 2013).

	Household Income				
Level of Education	**Under $25,000**	**$25,000 to $49,999**	**$50,000 to $99,999**	**$100,000 and Over**	**Total**
High school graduate	9880	9970	9441	3482	32,773
Bachelor's degree	2484	4164	7666	7817	22,131
Master's degree	685	1205	3019	4094	9003
Doctoral degree	79	160	422	1076	1737
Total	13,128	15,499	20,548	16,469	65,644

a. Construct a percent frequency distribution for the level of education variable. What percentage of heads of households have a master's or doctoral degree?

b. Construct a percent frequency distribution for the household income variable. What percentage of households have an income of $50,000 or more?

c. Convert the entries in the crosstabulation into column percentages. Compare the level of education of households with a household income of under $25,000 to the level of education of households with a household income of $100,000 or more. Comment on any other items of interest when reviewing the crosstabulation showing column percentages.

51. Western University has only one women's softball scholarship remaining for the coming year. The final two players that Western is considering are Allison Fealey and Emily Janson. The coaching staff has concluded that the speed and defensive skills are virtually identical for the two players, and that the final decision will be based on which player has the best batting average. Crosstabulations of each player's batting performance in their junior and senior years of high school are as follows:

	Allison Fealey	
Outcome	**Junior**	**Senior**
Hit	15	75
No Hit	25	175
Total At-Bats	40	250

	Emily Janson	
Outcome	**Junior**	**Senior**
Hit	70	35
No Hit	130	85
Total At-Bats	200	120

A player's batting average is computed by dividing the number of hits a player has by the total number of at-bats. Batting averages are represented as a decimal number with three places after the decimal.

a. Calculate the batting average for each player in her junior year. Then calculate the batting average of each player in her senior year. Using this analysis, which player should be awarded the scholarship? Explain.

b. Combine or aggregate the data for the junior and senior years into one crosstabulation as follows:

	Player	
Outcome	**Fealey**	**Janson**
Hit		
No Hit		
Total At-Bats		

Calculate each player's batting average for the combined two years. Using this analysis, which player should be awarded the scholarship? Explain.

c. Are the recommendations you made in parts (a) and (b) consistent? Explain any apparent inconsistencies.

FortuneBest100

52. *Fortune* magazine publishes an annual survey of the 100 best companies to work for. The data in the WEBfile named FortuneBest100 shows the rank, company name, the size of the company, and the percentage job growth for full-time employees for 98 of the *Fortune* 100 companies for which percentage job growth data were available (*Fortune* magazine website, February 25, 2013). The column labeled Rank shows the rank of the company in the *Fortune* 100 list; the column labeled Size indicates whether the company is a small company (less than 2500 employees), a midsized company (2500 to 10,000 employees), or a large company (more than 10,000 employees); and the column labeled Growth Rate (%) shows the percentage growth rate for full-time employees.
    a. Construct a crosstabulation with Job Growth (%) as the row variable and Size as the column variable. Use classes starting at −10 and ending at 70 in increments of 10 for Growth Rate (%).
    b. Show the frequency distribution for Job Growth (%) and the frequency distribution for Size.
    c. Using the crosstabulation constructed in part (a), develop a crosstabulation showing column percentages.
    d. Using the crosstabulation constructed in part (a), develop a crosstabulation showing row percentages.
    e. Comment on the relationship between the percentage job growth for full-time employees and the size of the company.

53. Table 2.18 shows a portion of the data for a sample of 103 private colleges and universities. The complete data set is contained in the WEBfile named Colleges. The data include the name of the college or university, the year the institution was founded, the tuition and fees (not including room and board) for the most recent academic year, and the percentage of full time, first-time bachelor's degree-seeking undergraduate students who obtain their degree in six years or less (*The World Almanac*, 2012).
    a. Construct a crosstabulation with Year Founded as the row variable and Tuition & Fees as the column variable. Use classes starting with 1600 and ending with 2000 in increments of 50 for Year Founded. For Tuition & Fees, use classes starting with 1 and ending 45000 in increments of 5000.
    b. Compute the row percentages for the crosstabulation in part (a).
    c. What relationship, if any, do you notice between Year Founded and Tuition & Fees?

54. Refer to the data set in Table 2.18.
    a. Construct a crosstabulation with Year Founded as the row variable and % Graduate as the column variable. Use classes starting with 1600 and ending with 2000 in increments of 50 for Year Founded. For % Graduate, use classes starting with 35% and ending with 100% in increments of 5%.
    b. Compute the row percentages for your crosstabulation in part (a).
    c. Comment on any relationship between the variables.

TABLE 2.18 DATA FOR A SAMPLE OF PRIVATE COLLEGES AND UNIVERSITIES

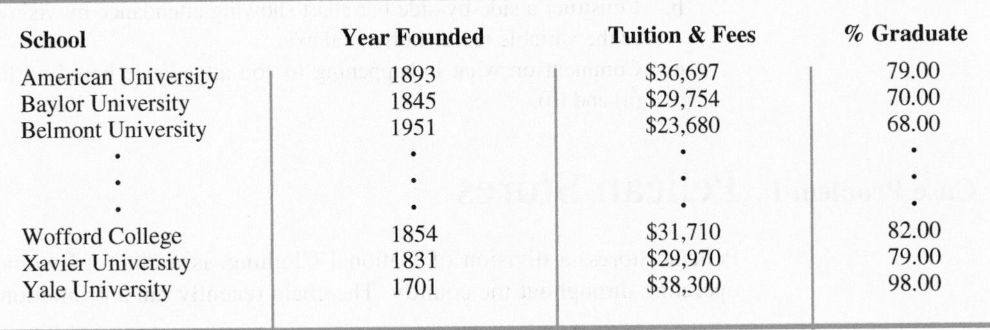

School	Year Founded	Tuition & Fees	% Graduate
American University	1893	$36,697	79.00
Baylor University	1845	$29,754	70.00
Belmont University	1951	$23,680	68.00
•	•	•	•
•	•	•	•
•	•	•	•
Wofford College	1854	$31,710	82.00
Xavier University	1831	$29,970	79.00
Yale University	1701	$38,300	98.00

Colleges

55. Refer to the data set in Table 2.18.
   a. Construct a scatter diagram to show the relationship between Year Founded and Tuition & Fees.
   b. Comment on any relationship between the variables.
56. Refer to the data set in Table 2.18.
   a. Prepare a scatter diagram to show the relationship between Tuition & Fees and % Graduate.
   b. Comment on any relationship between the variables.
57. Google has changed its strategy with regard to how much and over which media it invests in advertising. The following table shows Google's marketing budget in millions of dollars for 2008 and 2011 (*The Wall Street Journal,* March 27, 2012).

	2008	2011
Internet	26.0	123.3
Newspaper, etc.	4.0	20.7
Television	0.0	69.3

   a. Construct a side-by-side bar chart with year as the variable on the horizontal axis. Comment on any trend in the display.
   b. Convert the above table to percentage allocation for each year. Construct a stacked bar chart with year as the variable on the horizontal axis.
   c. Is the display in part (a) or part (b) more insightful? Explain.
58. A zoo has categorized its visitors into three categories: member, school, and general. The member category refers to visitors who pay an annual fee to support the zoo. Members receive certain benefits such as discounts on merchandise and trips planned by the zoo. The school category includes faculty and students from day care and elementary and secondary schools; these visitors generally receive a discounted rate. The general category includes all other visitors. The zoo has been concerned about a recent drop in attendance. To help better understand attendance and membership, a zoo staff member has collected the following data:

Zoo

	Attendance			
Visitor Category	**2011**	**2012**	**2013**	**2014**
General	153,713	158,704	163,433	169,106
Member	115,523	104,795	98,437	81,217
School	82,885	79,876	81,970	81,290
Total	352,121	343,375	343,840	331,613

   a. Construct a bar chart of total attendance over time. Comment on any trend in the data.
   b. Construct a side-by-side bar chart showing attendance by visitor category with year as the variable on the horizontal axis.
   c. Comment on what is happening to zoo attendance based on the charts from parts (a) and (b).

Case Problem 1 Pelican Stores

Pelican Stores, a division of National Clothing, is a chain of women's apparel stores operating throughout the country. The chain recently ran a promotion in which discount

PelicanStores

TABLE 2.19 DATA FOR A SAMPLE OF 100 CREDIT CARD PURCHASES AT PELICAN STORES

Customer	Type of Customer	Items	Net Sales	Method of Payment	Gender	Marital Status	Age
1	Regular	1	39.50	Discover	Male	Married	32
2	Promotional	1	102.40	Proprietary Card	Female	Married	36
3	Regular	1	22.50	Proprietary Card	Female	Married	32
4	Promotional	5	100.40	Proprietary Card	Female	Married	28
5	Regular	2	54.00	MasterCard	Female	Married	34
•	•	•	•	•	•	•	•
•	•	•	•	•	•	•	•
•	•	•	•	•	•	•	•
96	Regular	1	39.50	MasterCard	Female	Married	44
97	Promotional	9	253.00	Proprietary Card	Female	Married	30
98	Promotional	10	287.59	Proprietary Card	Female	Married	52
99	Promotional	2	47.60	Proprietary Card	Female	Married	30
100	Promotional	1	28.44	Proprietary Card	Female	Married	44

coupons were sent to customers of other National Clothing stores. Data collected for a sample of 100 in-store credit card transactions at Pelican Stores during one day while the promotion was running are contained in the WEBfile named PelicanStores. Table 2.19 shows a portion of the data set. The Proprietary Card method of payment refers to charges made using a National Clothing charge card. Customers who made a purchase using a discount coupon are referred to as promotional customers and customers who made a purchase but did not use a discount coupon are referred to as regular customers. Because the promotional coupons were not sent to regular Pelican Stores customers, management considers the sales made to people presenting the promotional coupons as sales it would not otherwise make. Of course, Pelican also hopes that the promotional customers will continue to shop at its stores.

Most of the variables shown in Table 2.19 are self-explanatory, but two of the variables require some clarification.

Items	The total number of items purchased
Net Sales	The total amount ($) charged to the credit card

Pelican's management would like to use this sample data to learn about its customer base and to evaluate the promotion involving discount coupons.

Managerial Report

Use the tabular and graphical methods of descriptive statistics to help management develop a customer profile and to evaluate the promotional campaign. At a minimum, your report should include the following:

1. Percent frequency distribution for key variables.
2. A bar chart or pie chart showing the number of customer purchases attributable to the method of payment.
3. A crosstabulation of type of customer (regular or promotional) versus net sales. Comment on any similarities or differences present.
4. A scatter diagram to explore the relationship between net sales and customer age.

Case Problem 2 Motion Picture Industry

The motion picture industry is a competitive business. More than 50 studios produce a total of 300 to 400 new motion pictures each year, and the financial success of each motion picture varies considerably. The opening weekend gross sales ($millions), the total gross sales ($millions), the number of theaters the movie was shown in, and the number of weeks the motion picture was in release are common variables used to measure the success of a motion picture. Data collected for the top 100 motion pictures produced in 2011 are contained in the WEBfile named 2011Movies (Box Office Mojo, March 17, 2012). Table 2.20 shows the data for the first 10 motion pictures in this file.

Managerial Report

Use the tabular and graphical methods of descriptive statistics to learn how these variables contribute to the success of a motion picture. Include the following in your report.

1. Tabular and graphical summaries for each of the four variables along with a discussion of what each summary tells us about the motion picture industry.
2. A scatter diagram to explore the relationship between Total Gross Sales and Opening Weekend Gross Sales. Discuss.
3. A scatter diagram to explore the relationship between Total Gross Sales and Number of Theaters. Discuss.
4. A scatter diagram to explore the relationship between Total Gross Sales and Number of Weeks in Release. Discuss.

TABLE 2.20 PERFORMANCE DATA FOR 10 MOTION PICTURES

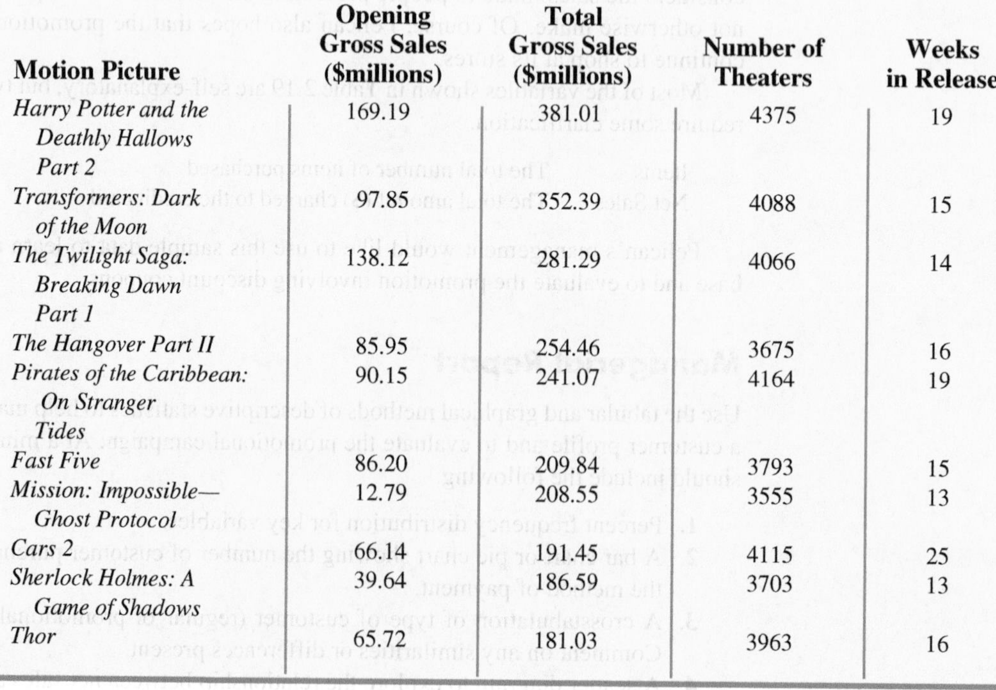

Motion Picture	Opening Gross Sales ($millions)	Total Gross Sales ($millions)	Number of Theaters	Weeks in Release
Harry Potter and the Deathly Hallows Part 2	169.19	381.01	4375	19
Transformers: Dark of the Moon	97.85	352.39	4088	15
The Twilight Saga: Breaking Dawn Part 1	138.12	281.29	4066	14
The Hangover Part II	85.95	254.46	3675	16
Pirates of the Caribbean: On Stranger Tides	90.15	241.07	4164	19
Fast Five	86.20	209.84	3793	15
Mission: Impossible—Ghost Protocol	12.79	208.55	3555	13
Cars 2	66.14	191.45	4115	25
Sherlock Holmes: A Game of Shadows	39.64	186.59	3703	13
Thor	65.72	181.03	3963	16

2011Movies

CHAPTER 3

Descriptive Statistics: Numerical Measures

CONTENTS

STATISTICS IN PRACTICE: SMALL FRY DESIGN

3.1 MEASURES OF LOCATION
- Mean
- Median
- Mode
- Using Excel to Compute the Mean, Median, and Mode
- Weighted Mean
- Geometric Mean
- Using Excel to Compute Geometric Mean
- Percentiles
- Quartiles
- Using Excel to Compute Percentiles and Quartiles

3.2 MEASURES OF VARIABILITY
- Range
- Interquartile Range
- Variance
- Standard Deviation
- Using Excel to Compute the Sample Variance and Sample Standard Deviation
- Coefficient of Variation
- Using Excel's Descriptive Statistics Tool

3.3 MEASURES OF DISTRIBUTION SHAPE, RELATIVE LOCATION, AND DETECTING OUTLIERS
- Distribution Shape
- *z*-Scores
- Chebyshev's Theorem
- Empirical Rule
- Detecting Outliers

3.4 FIVE-NUMBER SUMMARIES AND BOX PLOTS
- Five-Number Summary
- Box Plot
- Comparative Analysis Using Box Plots

3.5 MEASURES OF ASSOCIATION BETWEEN TWO VARIABLES
- Covariance
- Interpretation of the Covariance
- Correlation Coefficient
- Interpretation of the Correlation Coefficient
- Using Excel to Compute the Sample Covariance and Sample Correlation Coefficient

3.6 DATA DASHBOARDS: ADDING NUMERICAL MEASURES TO IMPROVE EFFECTIVENESS

STATISTICS *in* PRACTICE

SMALL FRY DESIGN*
SANTA ANA, CALIFORNIA

Founded in 1997, Small Fry Design is a toy and accessory company that designs and imports products for infants. The company's product line includes teddy bears, mobiles, musical toys, rattles, and security blankets and features high-quality soft toy designs with an emphasis on color, texture, and sound. The products are designed in the United States and manufactured in China.

Small Fry Design uses independent representatives to sell the products to infant furnishing retailers, children's accessory and apparel stores, gift shops, upscale department stores, and major catalog companies. Currently, Small Fry Design products are distributed in more than 1000 retail outlets throughout the United States.

Cash flow management is one of the most critical activities in the day-to-day operation of this company. Ensuring sufficient incoming cash to meet both current and ongoing debt obligations can mean the difference between business success and failure. A critical factor in cash flow management is the analysis and control of accounts receivable. By measuring the average age and dollar value of outstanding invoices, management can predict cash availability and monitor changes in the status of accounts receivable. The company set the following goals: The average age for outstanding invoices should not exceed 45 days, and the dollar value of invoices more than 60 days old should not exceed 5% of the dollar value of all accounts receivable.

In a recent summary of accounts receivable status, the following descriptive statistics were provided for the age of outstanding invoices:

Mean	40 days
Median	35 days
Mode	31 days

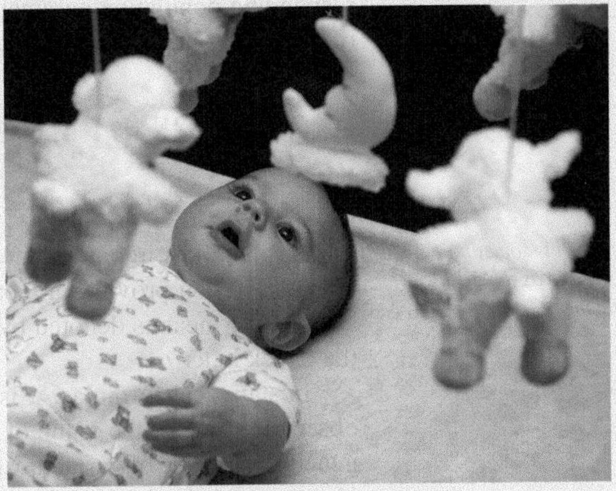

Small Fry Design uses descriptive statistics to monitor its accounts receivable and incoming cash flow. © Robert Dant/Alamy.

Interpretation of these statistics shows that the mean or average age of an invoice is 40 days. The median shows that half of the invoices remain outstanding 35 days or more. The mode of 31 days, the most frequent invoice age, indicates that the most common length of time an invoice is outstanding is 31 days. The statistical summary also showed that only 3% of the dollar value of all accounts receivable was more than 60 days old. Based on the statistical information, management was satisfied that accounts receivable and incoming cash flow were under control.

In this chapter, you will learn how to compute and interpret some of the statistical measures used by Small Fry Design. In addition to the mean, median, and mode, you will learn about other descriptive statistics such as the range, variance, standard deviation, percentiles, and correlation. These numerical measures will assist in the understanding and interpretation of data.

*The authors are indebted to John A. McCarthy, President of Small Fry Design, for providing this Statistics in Practice.

In Chapter 2 we discussed tabular and graphical presentations used to summarize data. In this chapter, we present several numerical measures that provide additional alternatives for summarizing data.

We start by developing numerical summary measures for data sets consisting of a single variable. When a data set contains more than one variable, the same numerical measures can be computed separately for each variable. However, in the two-variable case, we will also develop measures of the relationship between the variables.

Numerical measures of location, dispersion, shape, and association are introduced. If the measures are computed for data from a sample, they are called **sample statistics**. If the measures are computed for data from a population, they are called **population parameters**. In statistical inference, a sample statistic is referred to as the **point estimator** of the corresponding population parameter. In Chapter 7 we will discuss in more detail the process of point estimation.

3.1 Measures of Location

Mean

The mean is sometimes referred to as the arithmetic mean.

Perhaps the most important measure of location is the **mean**, or average value, for a variable. The mean provides a measure of central location for the data. If the data are for a sample, the mean is denoted by $\bar{x}$; if the data are for a population, the mean is denoted by the Greek letter μ.

In statistical formulas, it is customary to denote the value of variable x for the first observation by x_1, the value of variable x for the second observation by x_2, and so on. In general, the value of variable x for the ith observation is denoted by x_i. For a sample with n observations, the formula for the sample mean is as follows.

The sample mean $\bar{x}$ is a sample statistic.

SAMPLE MEAN

$$\bar{x} = \frac{\Sigma x_i}{n} \tag{3.1}$$

In the preceding formula, the numerator is the sum of the values of the n observations. That is,

$$\Sigma x_i = x_1 + x_2 + \cdots + x_n$$

The Greek letter Σ is the summation sign.

To illustrate the computation of a sample mean, let us consider the following class size data for a sample of five college classes.

46 54 42 46 32

We use the notation x_1, x_2, x_3, x_4, x_5 to represent the number of students in each of the five classes.

$$x_1 = 46 \qquad x_2 = 54 \qquad x_3 = 42 \qquad x_4 = 46 \qquad x_5 = 32$$

Hence, to compute the sample mean, we can write

$$\bar{x} = \frac{\Sigma x_i}{n} = \frac{x_1 + x_2 + x_3 + x_4 + x_5}{5} = \frac{46 + 54 + 42 + 46 + 32}{5} = 44$$

The sample mean class size is 44 students.

To provide a visual perspective of the mean and to show how it can be influenced by extreme values, consider the dot plot for the class size data shown in Figure 3.1. Treating the horizontal axis used to create the dot plot as a long narrow board in which each of the dots has the same fixed weight, the mean is the point at which we would place a fulcrum

FIGURE 3.1 THE MEAN AS THE CENTER OF BALANCE FOR THE DOT PLOT OF THE CLASSROOM SIZE DATA

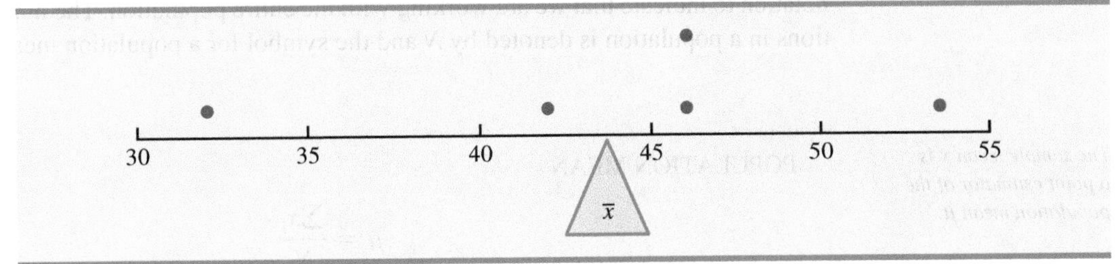

or pivot point under the board in order to balance the dot plot. This is the same principle by which a see-saw on a playground works, the only difference being that the see-saw is pivoted in the middle so that as one end goes up, the other end goes down. In the dot plot we are locating the pivot point based upon the location of the dots. Now consider what happens to the balance if we increase the largest value from 54 to 114. We will have to move the fulcrum under the new dot plot in a positive direction in order to reestablish balance. To determine how far we would have to shift the fulcrum, we simply compute the sample mean for the revised class size data.

$$\bar{x} = \frac{\Sigma x_i}{n} = \frac{x_1 + x_2 + x_3 + x_4 + x_5}{5} = \frac{46 + 114 + 42 + 46 + 32}{5} = \frac{280}{5} = 56$$

Thus, the mean for the revised class size data is 56, an increase of 12 students. In other words, we have to shift the balance point 12 units to the right to establish balance under the new dot plot.

Another illustration of the computation of a sample mean is given in the following situation. Suppose that a college placement office sent a questionnaire to a sample of business school graduates requesting information on monthly starting salaries. Table 3.1 shows the collected data. The mean monthly starting salary for the sample of 12 business college graduates is computed as

$$\bar{x} = \frac{\Sigma x_i}{n} = \frac{x_1 + x_2 + \cdots + x_{12}}{12}$$
$$= \frac{3850 + 3950 + \cdots + 3880}{12}$$
$$= \frac{47{,}280}{12} = 3940$$

TABLE 3.1 MONTHLY STARTING SALARIES FOR A SAMPLE OF 12 BUSINESS SCHOOL GRADUATES

2012StartSalary

Graduate	Monthly Starting Salary ($)	Graduate	Monthly Starting Salary ($)
1	3850	7	3890
2	3950	8	4130
3	4050	9	3940
4	3880	10	4325
5	3755	11	3920
6	3710	12	3880

Equation (3.1) shows how the mean is computed for a sample with n observations. The formula for computing the mean of a population remains the same, but we use different notation to indicate that we are working with the entire population. The number of observations in a population is denoted by N and the symbol for a population mean is μ.

The sample mean $\bar{x}$ is a point estimator of the population mean μ.

POPULATION MEAN

$$\mu = \frac{\Sigma x_i}{N} \tag{3.2}$$

Median

The **median** is another measure of central location. The median is the value in the middle when the data are arranged in ascending order (smallest value to largest value). With an odd number of observations, the median is the middle value. An even number of observations has no single middle value. In this case, we follow convention and define the median as the average of the values for the middle two observations. For convenience the definition of the median is restated as follows.

MEDIAN

Arrange the data in ascending order (smallest value to largest value).

(a) For an odd number of observations, the median is the middle value.
(b) For an even number of observations, the median is the average of the two middle values.

Let us apply this definition to compute the median class size for the sample of five college classes. Arranging the data in ascending order provides the following list.

32 42 46 46 54

Because $n = 5$ is odd, the median is the middle value. Thus the median class size is 46 students. Even though this data set contains two observations with values of 46, each observation is treated separately when we arrange the data in ascending order.

Suppose we also compute the median starting salary for the 12 business college graduates in Table 3.1. We first arrange the data in ascending order.

3710 3755 3850 3880 3880 3890 3920 3940 3950 4050 4130 4325

(3890 3920: Middle Two Values)

Because $n = 12$ is even, we identify the middle two values: 3890 and 3920. The median is the average of these values.

$$\text{Median} = \frac{3890 + 3920}{2} = 3905$$

The procedure we used to compute the median depends upon whether there is an odd number of observations or an even number of observations. Let us now describe a more conceptual and visual approach using the monthly starting salary for the 12 business college graduates. As before, we begin by arranging the data in ascending order.

3710 3755 3850 3880 3880 3890 3920 3940 3950 4050 4130 4325

Once the data are in ascending order, we trim pairs of extreme high and low values until no further pairs of values can be trimmed without completely eliminating all the data. For instance, after trimming the lowest observation (3710) and the highest observation (4325) we obtain a new data set with 10 observations.

~~3710~~ 3755 3850 3880 3880 3890 3920 3940 3950 4050 4130 ~~4325~~

We then trim the next lowest remaining value (3755) and the next highest remaining value (4130) to produce a new data set with eight observations.

~~3710~~ ~~3755~~ 3850 3880 3880 3890 3920 3940 3950 4050 ~~4130~~ ~~4325~~

Continuing this process we obtain the following results.

~~3710~~ ~~3755~~ ~~3850~~ 3880 3880 3890 3920 3940 3950 ~~4050~~ ~~4130~~ ~~4325~~

~~3710~~ ~~3755~~ ~~3850~~ ~~3880~~ 3880 3890 3920 3940 ~~3950~~ ~~4050~~ ~~4130~~ ~~4325~~

~~3710~~ ~~3755~~ ~~3850~~ ~~3880~~ ~~3880~~ 3890 3920 ~~3940~~ ~~3950~~ ~~4050~~ ~~4130~~ ~~4325~~

At this point no further trimming is possible without eliminating all the data. So, the median is just the average of the remaining two values. When there is an even number of observations, the trimming process will always result in two remaining values, and the average of these values will be the median. When there is an odd number of observations, the trimming process will always result in one final value, and this value will be the median. Thus, this method works whether the number of observations is odd or even.

The median is the measure of location most often reported for annual income and property value data because a few extremely large incomes or property values can inflate the mean. In such cases, the median is the preferred measure of central location.

Although the mean is the more commonly used measure of central location, in some situations the median is preferred. The mean is influenced by extremely small and large data values. For instance, suppose that the highest paid graduate (see Table 3.1) had a starting salary of $10,000 per month (maybe the individual's family owns the company). If we change the highest monthly starting salary in Table 3.1 from $4325 to $10,000 and recompute the mean, the sample mean changes from $3940 to $4413. The median of $3905, however, is unchanged, because $3890 and $3920 are still the middle two values. With the extremely high starting salary included, the median provides a better measure of central location than the mean. We can generalize to say that whenever a data set contains extreme values, the median is often the preferred measure of central location.

Mode

Another measure of location is the **mode**. The mode is defined as follows.

> MODE
>
> The mode is the value that occurs with greatest frequency.

To illustrate the identification of the mode, consider the sample of five class sizes. The only value that occurs more than once is 46. Because this value, occurring with a frequency of 2, has the greatest frequency, it is the mode. As another illustration, consider the sample of starting salaries for the business school graduates. The only monthly starting salary that occurs more than once is $3880. Because this value has the greatest frequency, it is the mode.

Situations can arise for which the greatest frequency occurs at two or more different values. In these instances more than one mode exists. If the data contain exactly two modes, we say that the data are *bimodal*. If data contain more than two modes, we say that the data are *multimodal*. In multimodal cases the mode is almost never reported because listing three or more modes would not be particularly helpful in describing a location for the data.

Using Excel to Compute the Mean, Median, and Mode

Excel provides functions for computing the mean, median, and mode. We illustrate the use of these functions by computing the mean, median, and mode for the starting salary data in Table 3.1. Refer to Figure 3.2 as we describe the tasks involved. The formula worksheet is in the background; the value worksheet is in the foreground.

Enter/Access Data: Open the WEBfile named 2012StartSalary. The data are in cells B2:B13 and labels are in column A and cell B1.

Enter Functions and Formulas: Excel's AVERAGE function can be used to compute the mean by entering the following formula into cell E2:

=AVERAGE(B2:B13)

Similarly, the formulas =MEDIAN(B2:B13) and =MODE.SNGL(B2:B13) are entered into cells E3 and E4, respectively, to compute the median and the mode.

The formulas in cells E2:E4 are displayed in the background worksheet of Figure 3.2 and the values computed using the Excel functions are displayed in the foreground worksheet. Labels were also entered into cell D2:D4 to identify the output. Note that the mean (3940), median (3905), and mode (3880) are the same as we computed earlier.

FIGURE 3.2 EXCEL WORKSHEET USED TO COMPUTE THE MEAN, MEDIAN, AND MODE FOR THE STARTING SALARY DATA

	A	B	C	D	E	F
1	Graduate	Monthly Starting Salary ($)				
2	1	3850		Mean	=AVERAGE(B2:B13)	
3	2	3950		Median	=MEDIAN(B2:B13)	
4	3	4050		Mode	=MODE.SNGL(B2:B13)	
5	4	3880				
6	5	3755				
7	6	3710				
8	7	3890				
9	8	4130				
10	9	3940				
11	10	4325				
12	11	3920				
13	12	3880				
14						

	A	B	C	D	E	F
1	Graduate	Monthly Starting Salary ($)				
2	1	3850		Mean	3940	
3	2	3950		Median	3905	
4	3	4050		Mode	3880	
5	4	3880				
6	5	3755				
7	6	3710				
8	7	3890				
9	8	4130				
10	9	3940				
11	10	4325				
12	11	3920				
13	12	3880				
14						

Weighted Mean

In the formulas for the sample mean and population mean, each x_i is given equal importance or weight. For instance, the formula for the sample mean can be written as follows:

$$\bar{x} = \frac{\Sigma x_i}{n} = \frac{1}{n}\left(\sum x_i\right) = \frac{1}{n}(x_1 + x_2 + \cdots + x_n) = \frac{1}{n}(x_1) + \frac{1}{n}(x_2) + \cdots + \frac{1}{n}(x_n)$$

This shows that each observation in the sample is given a weight of $1/n$. Although this practice is most common, in some instances the mean is computed by giving each observation a weight that reflects its relative importance. A mean computed in this manner is referred to as a **weighted mean**. The weighted mean is computed as follows:

WEIGHTED MEAN

$$\bar{x} = \frac{\Sigma w_i x_i}{\Sigma w_i} \tag{3.3}$$

where

w_i = weight for observation i

When the data are from a sample, equation (3.3) provides the weighted sample mean. If the data are from a population, μ replaces $\bar{x}$ and equation (3.3) provides the weighted population mean.

As an example of the need for a weighted mean, consider the following sample of five purchases of a raw material over the past three months.

Purchase	Cost per Pound ($)	Number of Pounds
1	3.00	1200
2	3.40	500
3	2.80	2750
4	2.90	1000
5	3.25	800

Note that the cost per pound varies from $2.80 to $3.40, and the quantity purchased varies from 500 to 2750 pounds. Suppose that a manager wanted to know the mean cost per pound of the raw material. Because the quantities ordered vary, we must use the formula for a weighted mean. The five cost-per-pound data values are $x_1 = 3.00$, $x_2 = 3.40$, $x_3 = 2.80$, $x_4 = 2.90$, and $x_5 = 3.25$. The weighted mean cost per pound is found by weighting each cost by its corresponding quantity. For this example, the weights are $w_1 = 1200$, $w_2 = 500$, $w_3 = 2750$, $w_4 = 1000$, and $w_5 = 800$. Based on equation (3.3), the weighted mean is calculated as follows:

$$\bar{x} = \frac{1200(3.00) + 500(3.40) + 2750(2.80) + 1000(2.90) + 800(3.25)}{1200 + 500 + 2750 + 1000 + 800}$$

$$= \frac{18{,}500}{6250} = 2.96$$

Thus, the weighted mean computation shows that the mean cost per pound for the raw material is $2.96. Note that using equation (3.1) rather than the weighted mean formula in equation (3.3) would provide misleading results. In this case, the sample mean of the five cost-per-pound values is (3.00 + 3.40 + 2.80 + 2.90 + 3.25)/5 = 15.35/5 = $3.07, which overstates the actual mean cost per pound purchased.

The choice of weights for a particular weighted mean computation depends upon the application. An example that is well known to college students is the computation of a grade point average (GPA). In this computation, the data values generally used are 4 for an A grade, 3 for a B grade, 2 for a C grade, 1 for a D grade, and 0 for an F grade. The weights are the number of credit hours earned for each grade. Exercise 16 at the end of this section provides an example of this weighted mean computation. In other weighted mean computations, quantities such as pounds, dollars, or volume are frequently used as weights. In any case, when observations vary in importance, the analyst must choose the weight that best reflects the importance of each observation in the determination of the mean.

Geometric Mean

The **geometric mean** is a measure of location that is calculated by finding the nth root of the product of n values. The general formula for the geometric mean, denoted $\bar{x}_g$, follows.

GEOMETRIC MEAN

$$\bar{x}_g = \sqrt[n]{(x_1)(x_2)\cdots(x_n)} = [(x_1)(x_2)\cdots(x_n)]^{1/n} \tag{3.4}$$

The geometric mean is often used in analyzing growth rates in financial data. In these types of situations the arithmetic mean or average value will provide misleading results.

To illustrate the use of the geometric mean, consider Table 3.2, which shows the percentage annual returns, or growth rates, for a mutual fund over the past 10 years. Suppose we want to compute how much $100 invested in the fund at the beginning of year 1 would be worth at the end of year 10. Let's start by computing the balance in the fund at the end

TABLE 3.2 PERCENTAGE ANNUAL RETURNS AND GROWTH FACTORS FOR THE MUTUAL FUND DATA

Year	Return (%)	Growth Factor
1	−22.1	0.779
2	28.7	1.287
3	10.9	1.109
4	4.9	1.049
5	15.8	1.158
6	5.5	1.055
7	−37.0	0.630
8	26.5	1.265
9	15.1	1.151
10	2.1	1.021

of year 1. Because the percentage annual return for year 1 was −22.1%, the balance in the fund at the end of year 1 would be

$$\$100 - .221(\$100) = \$100(1 - .221) = \$100(.779) = \$77.90$$

The growth factor for each year is 1 plus .01 times the percentage return. A growth factor less than 1 indicates negative growth, while a growth factor greater than 1 indicates positive growth. The growth factor cannot be less than zero.

Note that .779 is identified as the growth factor for year 1 in Table 3.2. This result shows that we can compute the balance at the end of year 1 by multiplying the value invested in the fund at the beginning of year 1 times the growth factor for year 1.

The balance in the fund at the end of year 1, \$77.90, now becomes the beginning balance in year 2. So, with a percentage annual return for year 2 of 28.7%, the balance at the end of year 2 would be

$$\$77.90 + .287(\$77.90) = \$77.90(1 + .287) = \$77.90(1.287) = \$100.2573$$

Note that 1.287 is the growth factor for year 2. And, by substituting \$100(.779) for \$77.90, we see that the balance in the fund at the end of year 2 is

$$\$100(.779)(1.287) = \$100.2573$$

In other words, the balance at the end of year 2 is just the initial investment at the beginning of year 1 times the product of the first two growth factors. This result can be generalized to show that the balance at the end of year 10 is the initial investment times the product of all 10 growth factors.

$$\$100[(.779)(1.287)(1.109)(1.049)(1.158)(1.055)(.630)(1.265)(1.151)(1.021)] =$$
$$\$100(1.334493) = \$133.4493$$

The nth root can be computed using most calculators or by using the POWER function in Excel. For instance, using Excel, the 10th root of 1.334493 = POWER (1.334493,1/10) or 1.029275.

So, a \$100 investment in the fund at the beginning of year 1 would be worth \$133.4493 at the end of year 10. Note that the product of the 10 growth factors is 1.334493. Thus, we can compute the balance at the end of year 10 for any amount of money invested at the beginning of year 1 by multiplying the value of the initial investment times 1.334493. For instance, an initial investment of \$2500 at the beginning of year 1 would be worth \$2500(1.334493) or approximately \$3336 at the end of year 10.

But what was the mean percentage annual return or mean rate of growth for this investment over the 10-year period? Let us see how the geometric mean of the 10 growth factors can be used to answer to this question. Because the product of the 10 growth factors is 1.334493, the geometric mean is the 10th root of 1.334493 or

$$\bar{x}_g = \sqrt[10]{1.334493} = 1.029275$$

The geometric mean tells us that annual returns grew at an average annual rate of (1.029275 − 1)100% or 2.9275%. In other words, with an average annual growth rate of 2.9275%, a \$100 investment in the fund at the beginning of year 1 would grow to $\$100(1.029275)^{10} = \$133.4493$ at the end of 10 years.

It is important to understand that the arithmetic mean of the percentage annual returns does not provide the mean annual growth rate for this investment. The sum of the 10 annual percentage returns in Table 3.2 is 50.4. Thus, the arithmetic mean of the 10 percentage annual returns is 50.4/10 = 5.04%. A broker might try to convince you to invest in this fund by stating that the mean annual percentage return was 5.04%. Such a statement is not only misleading, it is also inaccurate. A mean annual percentage return of 5.04% corresponds to an average growth factor of 1.0504. So, if the average growth factor were really 1.0504, \$100 invested in the fund at the beginning of year 1 would have grown to $\$100(1.0504)^{10} = \$163.51$ at the end of 10 years. But, using the 10 annual percentage returns in Table 3.2, we showed that an initial \$100 investment is worth \$133.45 at the end of 10 years. The broker's claim that the mean annual percentage return is 5.04% grossly overstates the true growth for this mutual fund. The problem is that the sample mean is only appropriate for an additive process. For a multiplicative process, such as applications involving growth rates, the geometric mean is the appropriate measure of location.

While the applications of the geometric mean to problems in finance, investments, and banking are particularly common, the geometric mean should be applied any time you want to determine the mean rate of change over several successive periods. Other common applications include changes in populations of species, crop yields, pollution levels, and birth and death rates. Also note that the geometric mean can be applied to changes that occur over any number of successive periods of any length. In addition to annual changes, the geometric mean is often applied to find the mean rate of change over quarters, months, weeks, and even days.

Using Excel to Compute the Geometric Mean

Excel's GEOMEAN function can be used to compute the geometric mean for the mutual fund data in Table 3.2. Refer to Figure 3.3 as we describe the tasks involved. The formula worksheet is in the background; the value worksheet is in the foreground.

Enter/Access Data: Open the WEBfile named MutualFund. The data are in cells B2:B11 and labels are in column A and cell B2.

Enter Functions and Formulas: To compute the growth factor for the percentage return in cell B2 (−22.1) we entered the following formula into cell C2:

=1+.01*B2

To compute the growth factors for the other percentage returns we copied the same formula into cells C3:C11. Excel's GEOMEAN function can now be used to compute the geometric mean for the growth factors in cells C2:C11 by entering the following formula into cell F2:

=GEOMEAN(C2:C11)

The labels Growth Factor and Geometric Mean were entered into cells C1 and E2, respectively, to identify the output. Note that the geometric mean (1.029275) is the same value as we computed earlier.

FIGURE 3.3 USING EXCEL TO COMPUTE THE GEOMETRIC MEAN FOR THE MUTUAL FUND DATA

	A	B	C	D	E	F	G
1	Year	Return (%)	Growth Factor				
2	1	-22.1	=1+0.01*B2		Geometric Mean	=GEOMEAN(C2:C11)	
3	2	28.7	=1+0.01*B3				
4	3	10.9	=1+0.01*B4				
5	4	4.9	=1+0.01*B5				
6	5	15.8	=1+0.01*B6				
7	6	5.5	=1+0.01*B7				
8	7	-37	=1+0.01*B8				
9	8	26.5	=1+0.01*B9				
10	9	15.1	=1+0.01*B10				
11	10	2.1	=1+0.01*B11				
12							

	A	B	C	D	E	F	G
1	Year	Return (%)	Growth Factor				
2	1	-22.1	0.779		Geometric Mean	1.029275	
3	2	28.7	1.287				
4	3	10.9	1.109				
5	4	4.9	1.049				
6	5	15.8	1.158				
7	6	5.5	1.055				
8	7	-37	0.63				
9	8	26.5	1.265				
10	9	15.1	1.151				
11	10	2.1	1.021				
12							

Percentiles

A **percentile** provides information about how the data are spread over the interval from the smallest value to the largest value. For a data set containing n observations, the **pth percentile** divides the data into two parts: Approximately p% of the observations are less than the pth percentile, and approximately $(100 - p)$% of the observations are greater than the pth percentile.

Colleges and universities frequently report admission test scores in terms of percentiles. For instance, suppose an applicant obtains a score of 630 on the math portion of an admissions test. How this applicant performed in relation to others taking the same test may not be readily apparent. However, if the score of 630 corresponds to the 82nd percentile, we know that approximately that 82% of the applicants scored lower than this individual and approximately 18% of the applicants scored higher than this individual.

To calculate the pth percentile for a data set containing n observations, we must first arrange the data in ascending order (smallest value to largest value). The smallest value is in position 1, the next smallest value is in position 2, and so on. The location of the pth percentile, denoted L_p, is computed using the following equation.

Several procedures can be used to compute the location of the pth percentile using sample data. All provide similar values, especially for large data sets. The procedure we show here is the procedure used by Excel's PERCENTILE.EXC function as well as several other statistical software packages.

LOCATION OF THE pth PERCENTILE

$$L_p = \frac{p}{100}(n + 1) \tag{3.5}$$

To illustrate the computation of the pth percentile, let us compute the 80th percentile for the starting salary data in Table 3.1. We begin by arranging the sample of 12 starting salaries in ascending order.

	3710	3755	3850	3880	3880	3890	3920	3940	3950	4050	4130	4325
Position	1	2	3	4	5	6	7	8	9	10	11	12

The position of each observation in the sorted data is shown directly below its value. For instance, the smallest value (3710) is in position 1, the next smallest value (3755) is in position 2, and so on. Using equation (3.5) with $p = 80$ and $n = 12$, the location of the 80th percentile is

$$L_{80} = \frac{p}{100}(n + 1) = \left(\frac{80}{100}\right)(12 + 1) = 10.4$$

The interpretation of $L_{80} = 10.4$ is that the 80th percentile is 40% of the way between the value in position 10 and the value in position 11. In other words, the 80th percentile is the value in position 10 (4050) plus .4 times the difference between the value in position 11 (4130) and the value in position 10 (4050). Thus,

$$\text{80th percentile} = 4050 + .4(4130 - 4050) = 4050 + .4(80) = 4082$$

Let us now compute the 50th percentile for the starting salary data. With $p = 50$ and $n = 12$, the location of the 50th percentile is

$$L_{50} = \frac{p}{100}(n + 1) = \left(\frac{50}{100}\right)(12 + 1) = 6.5$$

With $L_{50} = 6.5$, we see that the 50th percentile is 50% of the way between the value in position 6 (3890) and the value in position 7 (3920). Thus,

$$\text{50th percentile} = 3890 + .5(3920 - 3890) = 3890 + .5(30) = 3905$$

Note that the *50th percentile is also the median.*

Quartiles

Quartiles are just specific percentiles; thus, the steps for computing percentiles can be applied directly in the computation of quartiles.

It is often desirable to divide a data set into four parts, with each part containing approximately one-fourth, or 25%, of the observations. These division points are referred to as the **quartiles** and are defined as follows.

Q_1 = first quartile, or 25th percentile

Q_2 = second quartile, or 50th percentile (also the median)

Q_3 = third quartile, or 75th percentile

Because quartiles are just specific percentiles, the procedure for computing percentiles can be used to compute the quartiles.

To illustrate the computation of the quartiles for a data set consisting of n observations, we will compute the quartiles for the starting salary data in Table 3.1. Previously we showed that the 50th percentile for the starting salary data is 3905; thus, the second quartile (median) is $Q_2 = 3905$. To compute the first and third quartiles we must find the 25th and 75th percentiles. The calculations follow.

For Q_1,

$$L_{25} = \frac{p}{100}(n + 1) = \left(\frac{25}{100}\right)(12 + 1) = 3.25$$

The first quartile, or 25th percentile, is .25 of the way between the value in position 3 (3850) and the value in position 4 (3880). Thus,

$$Q_1 = 3850 + .25(3880 - 3850) = 3850 + .25(30) = 3857.5$$

For Q_3,

$$L_{75} = \frac{p}{100}(n + 1) = \left(\frac{75}{100}\right)(12 + 1) = 9.75$$

The third quartile, or 75th percentile, is .75 of the way between the value in position 9 (3950) and the value in position 10 (4050). Thus,

$$Q_3 = 3950 + .75(4050 - 3950) = 3950 + .75(100) = 4025$$

We defined the quartiles as the 25th, 50th, and 75th percentiles. Thus, we computed the quartiles in the same way as percentiles. However, other conventions are sometimes used to compute quartiles, and the actual values reported for quartiles may vary slightly depending on the convention used. Nevertheless, the objective of all procedures for computing quartiles is to divide the data into four equal parts.

Using Excel to Compute Percentiles and Quartiles

Excel provides functions for computing percentiles and quartiles. We will illustrate the use of these functions by showing how to compute the pth percentile and the quartiles for the starting salary data in Table 3.1. Refer to Figure 3.4 as we describe the tasks involved. The formula worksheet is in the background; the value worksheet is in the foreground.

Enter/Access Data: Open the WEBfile named 2012StartSalary. The data are in cells B2:B13 and labels are in column A and cell B1.

Enter Functions and Formulas: Excel's PERCENTILE.EXC function can be used to compute the pth percentile. For the starting salary data the general form of this function is

=PERCENTILE.EXC(B2:B13,*p*/100)

FIGURE 3.4 USING EXCEL TO COMPUTE PERCENTILES AND QUARTILES

	A	B	C	D	E	F
1	Graduate	Monthly Starting Salary ($)		Percentile		
2	1	3850		80	=PERCENTILE.EXC(B2:B13,0.8)	
3	2	3950				
4	3	4050		Quartile	Value	
5	4	3880		1	=QUARTILE.EXC($B$2:$B$13,D5)	
6	5	3755		2	=QUARTILE.EXC($B$2:$B$13,D6)	
7	6	3710		3	=QUARTILE.EXC($B$2:$B$13,D7)	
8	7	3890				
9	8	4130				
10	9	3940				
11	10	4325				
12	11	3920				
13	12	3880				
14						

	A	B	C	D	E	F
1	Graduate	Monthly Starting Salary ($)		Percentile		
2	1	3850		80	4082.0	
3	2	3950				
4	3	4050		Quartile	Value	
5	4	3880		1	3857.5	
6	5	3755		2	3905.0	
7	6	3710		3	4025.0	
8	7	3890				
9	8	4130				
10	9	3940				
11	10	4325				
12	11	3920				
13	12	3880				
14						

If we wanted to compute the 80th percentile for the starting salary data we could enter the formula

=PERCENTILE.EXC(B2:B13,.8)

into cell E2.

Because the quartiles are just the 25th, 50th, and 75th percentiles, we could compute the quartiles for the starting salary data by using Excel's PERCENTILE.EXC function as described above. But we can also use Excel's QUARTILE.EXC function to compute the quartiles. For the starting salary data, the general form of this function is

=QUARTILE.EXC(B2:B13,Quart)

where Quart = 1 for the first quartile, 2 for the second quartile, and 3 for the third quartile. To illustrate the use of this function for computing the quartiles we entered the values 1, 2, and 3 into cells D5:D7 of the worksheet. To compute the first quartile we entered the following function into cell E5:

=QUARTILE.EXC($B$2:$B$13,D5)

To compute the second and third quartiles we copied the formula in cell E5 into cells E6 and E7. Labels were entered into cells D4 and E4 to identify the output. Note that the three quartiles (3857.5, 3905, and 4025) are the same values as computed previously.

NOTES AND COMMENTS

1. It is better to use the median than the mean as a measure of central location when a data set contains extreme values. Another measure that is sometimes used when extreme values are present is the trimmed mean. The trimmed mean is obtained by deleting a percentage of the smallest and largest values from a data set and then computing the mean of the remaining values. For example, the 5% trimmed mean is obtained by removing the smallest 5% and the largest 5% of the data values and then computing the mean of the remaining values. Using the sample with n = 12 starting salaries, 0.05(12) = 0.6. Rounding this value to 1 indicates that the 5% trimmed mean is obtained by removing the smallest data value and the largest data value and then computing the mean of the remaining 10 values. For the starting salary data, the 5% trimmed mean is 3924.50.
2. Other commonly used percentiles are the quintiles (the 20th, 40th, 60th, and 80th percentiles) and the deciles (the 10th, 20th, 30th, 40th, 50th, 60th, 70th, 80th, and 90th percentiles).

Exercises

Methods

1. Consider a sample with data values of 10, 20, 12, 17, and 16. Compute the mean and median.
2. Consider a sample with data values of 10, 20, 21, 17, 16, and 12. Compute the mean and median.
3. Consider the following data and corresponding weights.

x_i	Weight (w_i)
3.2	6
2.0	3
2.5	2
5.0	8

   a. Compute the weighted mean.
   b. Compute the sample mean of the four data values without weighting. Note the difference in the results provided by the two computations.
4. Consider the following data.

Period	Rate of Return (%)
1	−6.0
2	−8.0
3	−4.0
4	2.0
5	5.4

   What is the mean growth rate over these five periods?
5. Consider a sample with data values of 27, 25, 20, 15, 30, 34, 28, and 25. Compute the 20th, 25th, 65th, and 75th percentiles.

6. Consider a sample with data values of 53, 55, 70, 58, 64, 57, 53, 69, 57, 68, and 53. Compute the mean, median, and mode.

Applications

7. The average number of minutes Americans commute to work is 27.7 minutes (*Sterling's Best Places*, April 13, 2012). The average commute time in minutes for 48 cities are as follows:

CommuteTime

Albuquerque	23.3	Jacksonville	26.2	Phoenix	28.3
Atlanta	28.3	Kansas City	23.4	Pittsburgh	25.0
Austin	24.6	Las Vegas	28.4	Portland	26.4
Baltimore	32.1	Little Rock	20.1	Providence	23.6
Boston	31.7	Los Angeles	32.2	Richmond	23.4
Charlotte	25.8	Louisville	21.4	Sacramento	25.8
Chicago	38.1	Memphis	23.8	Salt Lake City	20.2
Cincinnati	24.9	Miami	30.7	San Antonio	26.1
Cleveland	26.8	Milwaukee	24.8	San Diego	24.8
Columbus	23.4	Minneapolis	23.6	San Francisco	32.6
Dallas	28.5	Nashville	25.3	San Jose	28.5
Denver	28.1	New Orleans	31.7	Seattle	27.3
Detroit	29.3	New York	43.8	St. Louis	26.8
El Paso	24.4	Oklahoma City	22.0	Tucson	24.0
Fresno	23.0	Orlando	27.1	Tulsa	20.1
Indianapolis	24.8	Philadelphia	34.2	Washington, D.C.	32.8

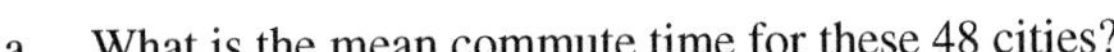

a. What is the mean commute time for these 48 cities?
b. Compute the median commute time.
c. Compute the mode.
d. Compute the third quartile.

8. *The Wall Street Journal* reported that the median salary for middle-level manager jobs was approximately $85,000 (*The Wall Street Journal*, August 6, 2013). Suppose that an independent study of middle-level managers employed at companies located in Atlanta, Georgia, was conducted to compare the salaries of managers working at firms in Atlanta to the national average. The following data show the salary, in thousands of dollars, for a sample of 15 middle-level managers.

108 83 106 73 53 85 80 63 67 75 124 55 93 118 77

a. Compute the median salary for the sample of 15 middle-level managers. How does the median for this group compare to the median reported by *The Wall Street Journal*?
b. Compute the mean annual salary and discuss how and why it differs from the median computed in part (a).
c. Compute the first and third quartiles.

9. Endowment income is a critical part of the annual budgets at colleges and universities. A study by the National Association of College and University Business Officers reported that the 435 colleges and universities surveyed held a total of $413 billion in endowments. The 10 wealthiest universities are shown below (*The Wall Street Journal*, January 27, 2009). Amounts are in billion of dollars.

University	Endowment ($billion)	University	Endowment ($billion)
Columbia	7.2	Princeton	16.4
Harvard	36.6	Stanford	17.2
M.I.T.	10.1	Texas	16.1
Michigan	7.6	Texas A&M	6.7
Northwestern	7.2	Yale	22.9

a. What is the mean endowment for these universities?
b. What is the median endowment?

c. What is the mode endowment?
d. Compute the first and third quartiles.
e. What is the total endowment at these 10 universities? These universities represent 2.3% of the 435 colleges and universities surveyed. What percentage of the total $413 billion in endowments is held by these 10 universities?
f. *The Wall Street Journal* reported that over a recent five-month period, a downturn in the economy has caused endowments to decline 23%. What is the estimate of the dollar amount of the decline in the total endowments held by these 10 universities? Given this situation, what are some of the steps you would expect university administrators to be considering?

JacketRatings

10. Over a nine-month period, OutdoorGearLab tested hardshell jackets designed for ice climbing, mountaineering, and backpacking. Based on the breathability, durability, versatility, features, mobility, and weight of each jacket, an overall rating ranging from 0 (lowest) to 100 (highest) was assigned to each jacket tested. The following data show the results for 20 top-of-the-line jackets (OutdoorGearLab website, February 27, 2013).

42	66	67	71	78	62	61	76	71	67
61	64	61	54	83	63	68	69	81	53

a. Compute the mean, median, and mode.
b. Compute the first and third quartiles.
c. Compute and interpret the 90th percentile.

11. According to the National Education Association (NEA), teachers generally spend more than 40 hours each week working on instructional duties (NEA website, April 2012). The following data show the number of hours worked per week for a sample of 13 high school science teachers and a sample of 11 high school English teachers.

High School Science Teachers: 53 56 54 54 55 58 49 61 54 54 52 53 54
High School English Teachers: 52 47 50 46 47 48 49 46 55 44 47

a. What is the median number of hours worked per week for the sample of 13 high school science teachers?
b. What is the median number of hours worked per week for the sample of 11 high school English teachers?
c. Which group has the highest median number of hours worked per week? What is the difference between the median number of hours worked per week?

BigBangTheory

12. *The Big Bang Theory*, a situation comedy featuring Johnny Galecki, Jim Parsons, and Kaley Cuoco, is one of the most watched programs on network television. The first two episodes for the 2011–2012 season premiered on September 22, 2011; the first episode attracted 14.1 million viewers and the second episode attracted 14.7 million viewers. The following table shows the number of viewers in millions for the first 21 episodes of the 2011–2012 season (*The Big Bang Theory* website, April 17, 2012).

Air Date	Viewers (millions)	Air Date	Viewers (millions)
September 22, 2011	14.1	January 12, 2012	16.1
September 22, 2011	14.7	January 19, 2012	15.8
September 29, 2011	14.6	January 26, 2012	16.1
October 6, 2011	13.6	February 2, 2012	16.5
October 13, 2011	13.6	February 9, 2012	16.2
October 20, 2011	14.9	February 16, 2012	15.7
October 27, 2011	14.5	February 23, 2012	16.2
November 3, 2011	16.0	March 8, 2012	15.0
November 10, 2011	15.9	March 29, 2012	14.0
November 17, 2011	15.1	April 5, 2012	13.3
December 8, 2011	14.0		

a. Compute the minimum and maximum number of viewers.
b. Compute the mean, median, and mode.
c. Compute the first and third quartiles.
d. Has viewership grown or declined over the 2011–2012 season? Discuss.

13. In automobile mileage and gasoline-consumption testing, 13 automobiles were road tested for 300 miles in both city and highway driving conditions. The following data were recorded for miles-per-gallon performance.

City:	16.2	16.7	15.9	14.4	13.2	15.3	16.8	16.0	16.1	15.3	15.2	15.3	16.2
Highway:	19.4	20.6	18.3	18.6	19.2	17.4	17.2	18.6	19.0	21.1	19.4	18.5	18.7

Use the mean, median, and mode to make a statement about the difference in performance for city and highway driving.

WEB file
StateUnemp

14. The data contained in the WEBfile named StateUnemp show the unemployment rate in March 2011 and the unemployment rate in March 2012 for every state and the District of Columbia (Bureau of Labor Statistics website, April 20, 2012). To compare unemployment rates in March 2011 with unemployment rates in March 2012, compute the first quartile, the median, and the third quartile for the March 2011 unemployment data and the March 2012 unemployment data. What do these statistics suggest about the change in unemployment rates across the states?

15. Martinez Auto Supplies has retail stores located in eight cities in California. The price they charge for a particular product in each city varies because of differing competitive conditions. For instance, the price they charge for a case of a popular brand of motor oil in each city follows. Also shown are the number of cases that Martinez Auto sold last quarter in each city.

City	Price ($)	Sales (cases)
Bakersfield	34.99	501
Los Angeles	38.99	1425
Modesto	36.00	294
Oakland	33.59	882
Sacramento	40.99	715
San Diego	38.59	1088
San Francisco	39.59	1644
San Jose	37.99	819

Compute the average sales price per case for this product during the last quarter.

16. The grade point average for college students is based on a weighted mean computation. For most colleges, the grades are given the following data values: A (4), B (3), C (2), D (1), and F (0). After 60 credit hours of course work, a student at State University earned 9 credit hours of A, 15 credit hours of B, 33 credit hours of C, and 3 credit hours of D.
a. Compute the student's grade point average.
b. Students at State University must maintain a 2.5 grade point average for their first 60 credit hours of course work in order to be admitted to the business college. Will this student be admitted?

17. The following table shows the total return and the number of funds for four categories of mutual funds.

Type of Fund	Number of Funds	Total Return (%)
Domestic Equity	9191	4.65
International Equity	2621	18.15
Specialty Stock	1419	11.36
Hybrid	2900	6.75

a. Using the number of funds as weights, compute the weighted average total return for these mutual funds.

b. Is there any difficulty associated with using the "number of funds" as the weights in computing the weighted average total return in part (a)? Discuss. What else might be used for weights?

c. Suppose you invested $10,000 in this group of mutual funds and diversified the investment by placing $2000 in Domestic Equity funds, $4000 in International Equity funds, $3000 in Specialty Stock funds, and $1000 in Hybrid funds. What is the expected return on the portfolio?

18. Based on a survey of 425 master's programs in business administration, *U.S. News & World Report* ranked the Indiana University Kelley Business School as the 20th best business program in the country (*America's Best Graduate Schools,* 2009). The ranking was based in part on surveys of business school deans and corporate recruiters. Each survey respondent was asked to rate the overall academic quality of the master's program on a scale from 1 "marginal" to 5 "outstanding." Use the sample of responses shown in the following table to compute the weighted mean score for the business school deans and the corporate recruiters. Discuss.

Quality Assessment	Business School Deans	Corporate Recruiters
5	44	31
4	66	34
3	60	43
2	10	12
1	0	0

19. Annual revenue for Corning Supplies grew by 5.5% in 2010; 1.1% in 2011; −3.5% in 2012; −1.1% in 2013; and 1.8% in 2014. What is the mean growth annual rate over this period?

20. Suppose that at the beginning of 2004 you invested $10,000 in the Stivers mutual fund and $5000 in the Trippi mutual fund. The value of each investment at the end of each subsequent year is provided in the table below. Which mutual fund performed better?

Year	Stivers	Trippi
2004	11,000	5600
2005	12,000	6300
2006	13,000	6900
2007	14,000	7600
2008	15,000	8500
2009	16,000	9200
2010	17,000	9900
2011	18,000	10,600

21. If an asset declines in value from \$5000 to \$3500 over nine years, what is the mean annual growth rate in the asset's value over these nine years?

22. The current value of a company is \$25 million. If the value of the company six years ago was \$10 million, what is the company's mean annual growth rate over the past six years?

3.2 Measures of Variability

The variability in the delivery time creates uncertainty for production scheduling. Methods in this section help measure and understand variability.

In addition to measures of location, it is often desirable to consider measures of variability, or dispersion. For example, suppose that you are a purchasing agent for a large manufacturing firm and that you regularly place orders with two different suppliers. After several months of operation, you find that the mean number of days required to fill orders is 10 days for both of the suppliers. The histograms summarizing the number of working days required to fill orders from the suppliers are shown in Figure 3.5. Although the mean number of days is 10 for both suppliers, do the two suppliers demonstrate the same degree of reliability in terms of making deliveries on schedule? Note the dispersion, or variability, in delivery times indicated by the histograms. Which supplier would you prefer?

For most firms, receiving materials and supplies on schedule is important. The 7- or 8-day deliveries shown for J.C. Clark Distributors might be viewed favorably; however, a few of the slow 13- to 15-day deliveries could be disastrous in terms of keeping a workforce busy and production on schedule. This example illustrates a situation in which the variability in the delivery times may be an overriding consideration in selecting a supplier. For most purchasing agents, the lower variability shown for Dawson Supply, Inc., would make Dawson the preferred supplier.

We turn now to a discussion of some commonly used measures of variability.

Range

The simplest measure of variability is the **range**.

RANGE

$$\text{Range} = \text{Largest value} - \text{Smallest value}$$

FIGURE 3.5 HISTORICAL DATA SHOWING THE NUMBER OF DAYS REQUIRED TO FILL ORDERS

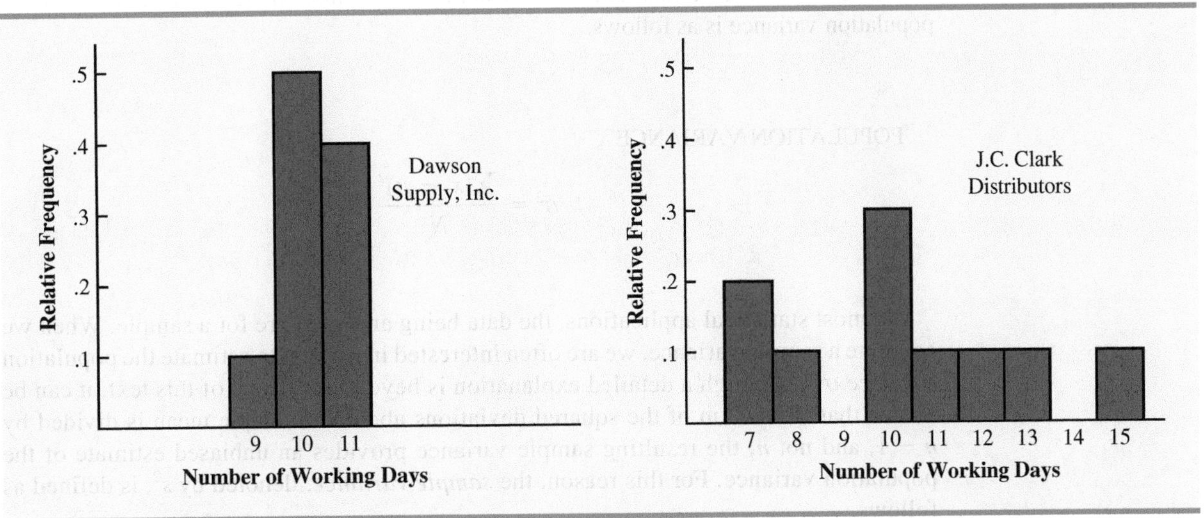

Let us refer to the data on starting salaries for business school graduates in Table 3.1. The largest starting salary is 4325 and the smallest is 3710. The range is 4325 − 3710 = 615.

Although the range is the easiest of the measures of variability to compute, it is seldom used as the only measure. The reason is that the range is based on only two of the observations and thus is highly influenced by extreme values. Suppose the highest paid graduate received a starting salary of $10,000 per month. In this case, the range would be 10,000 − 3710 = 6290 rather than 615. This large value for the range would not be especially descriptive of the variability in the data because 11 of the 12 starting salaries are closely grouped between 3710 and 4130.

Interquartile Range

A measure of variability that overcomes the dependency on extreme values is the **interquartile range (IQR)**. This measure of variability is the difference between the third quartile, Q_3, and the first quartile, Q_1. In other words, the interquartile range is the range for the middle 50% of the data.

INTERQUARTILE RANGE

$$\text{IQR} = Q_3 - Q_1 \tag{3.6}$$

For the data on monthly starting salaries, the quartiles are $Q_3 = 4025$ and $Q_1 = 3857.5$. Thus, the interquartile range is 4025 − 3857.5 = 167.5.

Variance

The **variance** is a measure of variability that utilizes all the data. The variance is based on the difference between the value of each observation (x_i) and the mean. The difference between each x_i and the mean ($\bar{x}$ for a sample, μ for a population) is called a *deviation about the mean.* For a sample, a deviation about the mean is written $(x_i - \bar{x})$; for a population, it is written $(x_i - \mu)$. In the computation of the variance, the deviations about the mean are *squared.*

If the data are for a population, the average of the squared deviations is called the *population variance.* The population variance is denoted by the Greek symbol σ^2. For a population of N observations and with μ denoting the population mean, the definition of the population variance is as follows.

POPULATION VARIANCE

$$\sigma^2 = \frac{\Sigma(x_i - \mu)^2}{N} \tag{3.7}$$

In most statistical applications, the data being analyzed are for a sample. When we compute a sample variance, we are often interested in using it to estimate the population variance σ^2. Although a detailed explanation is beyond the scope of this text, it can be shown that if the sum of the squared deviations about the sample mean is divided by $n - 1$, and not n, the resulting sample variance provides an unbiased estimate of the population variance. For this reason, the *sample variance,* denoted by s^2, is defined as follows.

The sample variance s^2 is a point estimator of the population variance σ^2.

SAMPLE VARIANCE

$$s^2 = \frac{\Sigma(x_i - \bar{x})^2}{n - 1} \tag{3.8}$$

To illustrate the computation of the sample variance, we will use the data on class size for the sample of five college classes as presented in Section 3.1. A summary of the data, including the computation of the deviations about the mean and the squared deviations about the mean, is shown in Table 3.3. The sum of squared deviations about the mean is $\Sigma(x_i - \bar{x})^2 = 256$. Hence, with $n - 1 = 4$, the sample variance is

$$s^2 = \frac{\Sigma(x_i - \bar{x})^2}{n - 1} = \frac{256}{4} = 64$$

Before moving on, let us note that the units associated with the sample variance often cause confusion. Because the values being summed in the variance calculation, $(x_i - \bar{x})^2$, are squared, the units associated with the sample variance are also *squared.* For instance, the sample variance for the class size data is $s^2 = 64$ (students)^2. The squared units associated with variance make it difficult to develop an intuitive understanding and interpretation of the numerical value of the variance. We recommend that you think of the variance as a measure useful in comparing the amount of variability for two or more variables. In a comparison of the variables, the one with the largest variance shows the most variability. Further interpretation of the value of the variance may not be necessary.

The variance is useful in comparing the variability of two or more variables.

As another illustration of computing a sample variance, consider the starting salaries listed in Table 3.1 for the 12 business school graduates. In Section 3.1, we showed that the sample mean starting salary was 3940. The computation of the sample variance ($s^2 = 27{,}440.91$) is shown in Table 3.4.

In Tables 3.3 and 3.4 we show both the sum of the deviations about the mean and the sum of the squared deviations about the mean. For any data set, the sum of the deviations about the mean will *always equal zero.* Note that in Tables 3.3 and 3.4, $\Sigma(x_i - \bar{x}) = 0$. The positive deviations and negative deviations cancel each other, causing the sum of the deviations about the mean to equal zero.

TABLE 3.3 COMPUTATION OF DEVIATIONS AND SQUARED DEVIATIONS ABOUT THE MEAN FOR THE CLASS SIZE DATA

Number of Students in Class (x_i)	Mean Class Size ($\bar{x}$)	Deviation About the Mean ($x_i - \bar{x}$)	Squared Deviation About the Mean $(x_i - \bar{x})^2$
46	44	2	4
54	44	10	100
42	44	−2	4
46	44	2	4
32	44	−12	144
		0	256
		$\Sigma(x_i - \bar{x})$	$\Sigma(x_i - \bar{x})^2$

TABLE 3.4 COMPUTATION OF THE SAMPLE VARIANCE FOR THE STARTING SALARY DATA

Monthly Salary (x_i)	Sample Mean ($\bar{x}$)	Deviation About the Mean ($x_i - \bar{x}$)	Squared Deviation About the Mean ($(x_i - \bar{x})^2$)
3850	3940	−90	8100
3950	3940	10	100
4050	3940	110	12,100
3880	3940	−60	3600
3755	3940	−185	34,225
3710	3940	−230	52,900
3890	3940	−50	2500
4130	3940	190	36,100
3940	3940	0	0
4325	3940	385	148,225
3920	3940	−20	400
3880	3940	−60	3600
		0	301,850
		$\Sigma(x_i - \bar{x})$	$\Sigma(x_i - \bar{x})^2$

Using equation (3.8),

$$s^2 = \frac{\Sigma(x_i - \bar{x})^2}{n - 1} = \frac{301,850}{11} = 27,440.91$$

Standard Deviation

The **standard deviation** is defined to be the positive square root of the variance. Following the notation we adopted for a sample variance and a population variance, we use s to denote the sample standard deviation and σ to denote the population standard deviation. The standard deviation is derived from the variance in the following way.

The sample standard deviation s is a point estimator of the population standard deviation σ.

STANDARD DEVIATION

$$\text{Sample standard deviation} = s = \sqrt{s^2} \tag{3.9}$$

$$\text{Population standard deviation} = \sigma = \sqrt{\sigma^2} \tag{3.10}$$

Recall that the sample variance for the sample of class sizes in five college classes is $s^2 = 64$. Thus, the sample standard deviation is $s = \sqrt{64} = 8$. For the data on starting salaries, the sample standard deviation is $s = \sqrt{27,440.91} = 165.65$.

The standard deviation is easier to interpret than the variance because the standard deviation is measured in the same units as the data.

What is gained by converting the variance to its corresponding standard deviation? Recall that the units associated with the variance are squared. For example, the sample variance for the starting salary data of business school graduates is $s^2 = 27,440.91$ (dollars)^2. Because the standard deviation is the square root of the variance, the units of the variance, dollars squared, are converted to dollars in the standard deviation. Thus, the standard deviation of the starting salary data is \$165.65. In other words, the standard deviation is measured in the same units as the original data. For this reason the standard deviation is more easily compared to the mean and other statistics that are measured in the same units as the original data.

Using Excel to Compute the Sample Variance and Sample Standard Deviation

Excel provides functions for computing the sample variance and sample standard deviation. We illustrate the use of these functions by computing the sample variance and sample standard deviation for the starting salary data in Table 3.1. Refer to Figure 3.6 as we describe the tasks involved. Figure 3.6 is an extension of Figure 3.2, where we showed how to use Excel functions to compute the mean, median, and mode. The formula worksheet is in the background; the value worksheet is in the foreground.

Enter/Access Data: Open the WEBfile named 2012StartSalary. The data are in cells B2:B13 and labels appear in column A and cell B1.

Enter Functions and Formulas: Excel's AVERAGE, MEDIAN, and MODE.SNGL functions were entered into cells E2:E4 as described earlier. Excel's VAR.S function can be used to compute the sample variance by entering the following formula into cell E5:

=VAR.S(B2:B13)

Similarly, the formula =STDEV.S(B2:B13) is entered into cell E6 to compute the sample standard deviation.

The labels in cells D2:D6 identify the output. Note that the sample variance (27440.91) and the sample standard deviation (165.65) are the same as we computed earlier using the definitions.

FIGURE 3.6 EXCEL WORKSHEET USED TO COMPUTE THE SAMPLE VARIANCE AND THE SAMPLE STANDARD DEVIATION FOR THE STARTING SALARY DATA

	A	B	C	D	E	F
1	Graduate	Monthly Starting Salary ($)				
2	1	3850		Mean	=AVERAGE(B2:B13)	
3	2	3950		Median	=MEDIAN(B2:B13)	
4	3	4050		Mode	=MODE.SNGL(B2:B13)	
5	4	3880		Variance	=VAR.S(B2:B13)	
6	5	3755		Standard Deviation	=STDEV.S(B2:B13)	
7	6	3710				
8	7	3890				
9	8	4130				
10	9	3940				
11	10	4325				
12	11	3920				
13	12	3880				
14						

	A	B	C	D	E	F
1	Graduate	Monthly Starting Salary ($)				
2	1	3850		Mean	3940	
3	2	3950		Median	3905	
4	3	4050		Mode	3880	
5	4	3880		Variance	27440.91	
6	5	3755		Standard Deviation	165.65	
7	6	3710				
8	7	3890				
9	8	4130				
10	9	3940				
11	10	4325				
12	11	3920				
13	12	3880				
14						

Coefficient of Variation

The coefficient of variation is a relative measure of variability; it measures the standard deviation relative to the mean.

In some situations we may be interested in a descriptive statistic that indicates how large the standard deviation is relative to the mean. This measure is called the **coefficient of variation** and is usually expressed as a percentage.

COEFFICIENT OF VARIATION

$$\left(\frac{\text{Standard deviation}}{\text{Mean}} \times 100\right)\% \tag{3.11}$$

For the class size data, we found a sample mean of 44 and a sample standard deviation of 8. The coefficient of variation is $[(8/44) \times 100]\% = 18.2\%$. In words, the coefficient of variation tells us that the sample standard deviation is 18.2% of the value of the sample mean. For the starting salary data with a sample mean of 3940 and a sample standard deviation of 165.65, the coefficient of variation, $[(165.65/3940) \times 100]\% = 4.2\%$, tells us the sample standard deviation is only 4.2% of the value of the sample mean. In general, the coefficient of variation is a useful statistic for comparing the variability of variables that have different standard deviations and different means.

Using Excel's Descriptive Statistics Tool

As we have seen, Excel provides statistical functions to compute descriptive statistics for a data set. These functions can be used to compute one statistic at a time (e.g., mean, variance, etc.). Excel also provides a variety of data analysis tools. One of these, called Descriptive Statistics, allows the user to compute a variety of descriptive statistics at once. We will now show how Excel's Descriptive Statistics tool can be used for the starting salary data in Table 3.1. Refer to Figure 3.7 as we describe the tasks involved.

Enter/Access Data: Open the WEBfile named 2012StartSalary. The data are in cells B2:B13 and labels appear in column A and in cell B1.

Apply Tools: The following steps describe how to use Excel's Descriptive Statistics tool for these data.

Step 1. Click the **DATA** tab on the Ribbon
Step 2. In the **Analysis** group, click **Data Analysis**
Step 3. Choose **Descriptive Statistics** from the list of **Analysis Tools**
Step 4. When the Descriptive Statistics dialog box appears (see Figure 3.7):
Enter B1:B13 in the **Input Range** box
Select **Grouped By Columns**
Select **Labels in First Row**
Select **Output Range**
Enter D1 in the **Output Range** box (to identify the upper left corner of the section of the worksheet where the descriptive statistics will appear)
Select **Summary Statistics**
Click **OK**

Cells D1:D15 of Figure 3.8 show the descriptive statistics provided by Excel. A gold screen is used to highlight the results. The boldfaced entries are the descriptive statistics that we have already covered. The descriptive statistics that are not boldfaced are either covered subsequently in the text or discussed in more advanced texts.

FIGURE 3.7 DIALOG BOX FOR EXCEL'S DESCRIPTIVE STATISTICS TOOL

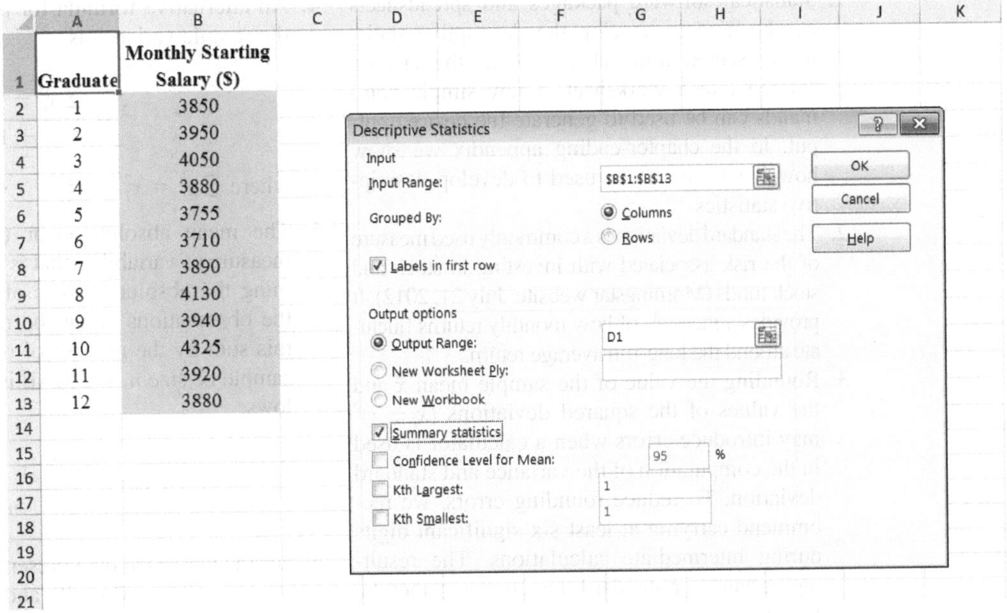

	A	B	C	D	E	F	G	H	I	J	K
1	Graduate	Monthly Starting Salary ($)									
2	1	3850									
3	2	3950									
4	3	4050									
5	4	3880									
6	5	3755									
7	6	3710									
8	7	3890									
9	8	4130									
10	9	3940									
11	10	4325									
12	11	3920									
13	12	3880									
14											
15											
16											
17											
18											
19											
20											
21											

Descriptive Statistics

Input

Input Range: $B$1:$B$13

Grouped By: (●) Columns ( ) Rows

[✓] Labels in first row

Output options

(●) Output Range: D1

( ) New Worksheet Ply:

( ) New Workbook

[✓] Summary statistics

[ ] Confidence Level for Mean: 95 %

[ ] Kth Largest: 1

[ ] Kth Smallest: 1

OK | Cancel | Help

FIGURE 3.8 DESCRIPTIVE STATISTICS PROVIDED BY EXCEL FOR THE STARTING SALARY DATA

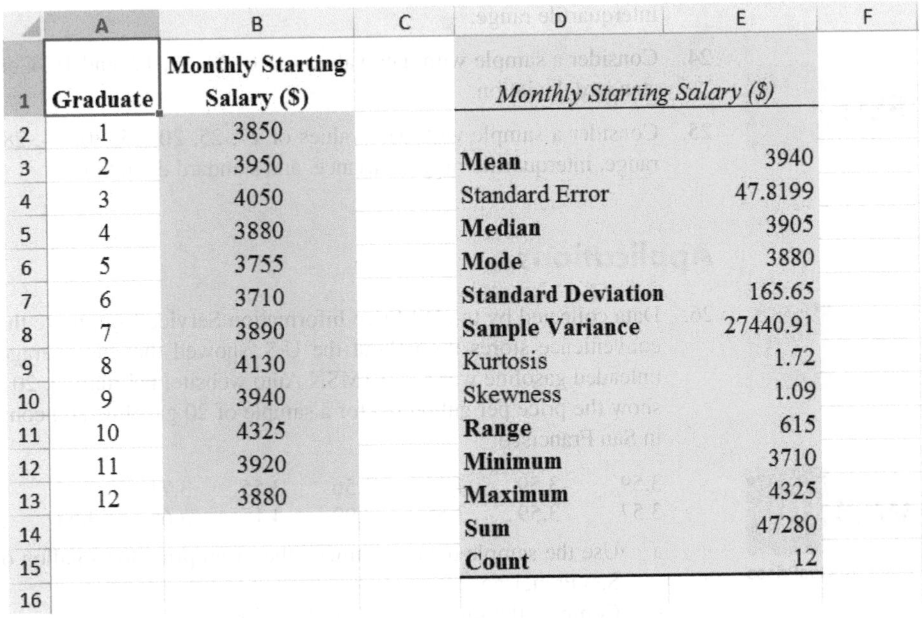

	A	B	C	D	E	F
1	Graduate	Monthly Starting Salary ($)		*Monthly Starting Salary ($)*		
2	1	3850				
3	2	3950		Mean	3940	
4	3	4050		Standard Error	47.8199	
5	4	3880		Median	3905	
6	5	3755		Mode	3880	
7	6	3710		Standard Deviation	165.65	
8	7	3890		Sample Variance	27440.91	
9	8	4130		Kurtosis	1.72	
10	9	3940		Skewness	1.09	
11	10	4325		Range	615	
12	11	3920		Minimum	3710	
13	12	3880		Maximum	4325	
14				Sum	47280	
15				Count	12	
16						

NOTES AND COMMENTS

1. Statistical software packages and spreadsheets can be used to develop the descriptive statistics presented in this chapter. After the data are entered into a worksheet, a few simple commands can be used to generate the desired output. In the chapter-ending appendix we show how StatTools can be used to develop descriptive statistics.
2. The standard deviation is a commonly used measure of the risk associated with investing in stock and stock funds (Morningstar website, July 21, 2012). It provides a measure of how monthly returns fluctuate around the long-run average return.
3. Rounding the value of the sample mean $\bar{x}$ and the values of the squared deviations $(x_i - \bar{x})^2$ may introduce errors when a calculator is used in the computation of the variance and standard deviation. To reduce rounding errors, we recommend carrying at least six significant digits during intermediate calculations. The resulting variance or standard deviation can then be rounded to fewer digits.
4. An alternative formula for the computation of the sample variance is

$$s^2 = \frac{\sum x_i^2 - n\bar{x}^2}{n - 1}$$

where $\sum x_i^2 = x_1^2 + x_2^2 + \cdots + x_n^2$.

5. The mean absolute error (MAE) is another measure of variability that is computed by summing the absolute values of the deviations of the observations about the mean and dividing this sum by the number of observations. For a sample of size n, the MAE is computed as follows:

$$\text{MAE} = \frac{\sum |x_i - \bar{x}|}{n}$$

For the class size data presented in Section 3.1, $\bar{x} = 44$, $\sum |x_i - \bar{x}| = 28$, and the MAE $= 28/5 = 5.6$.

Exercises

Methods

23. Consider a sample with data values of 10, 20, 12, 17, and 16. Compute the range and interquartile range.

24. Consider a sample with data values of 10, 20, 12, 17, and 16. Compute the variance and standard deviation.

25. Consider a sample with data values of 27, 25, 20, 15, 30, 34, 28, and 25. Compute the range, interquartile range, variance, and standard deviation.

Applications

26. Data collected by the Oil Price Information Service from more than 90,000 gasoline and convenience stores throughout the U.S. showed that the average price for a gallon of unleaded gasoline was $3.28 (MSN Auto website, February 2, 2014). The following data show the price per gallon ($) for a sample of 20 gasoline and convenience stores located in San Francisco.

SFGasPrices

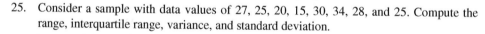

3.59	3.59	4.79	3.56	3.55	3.71	3.65	3.60	3.75	3.56
3.57	3.59	3.55	3.99	4.15	3.66	3.63	3.73	3.61	3.57

a. Use the sample data to estimate the mean price for a gallon of unleaded gasoline in San Francisco.
b. Compute the sample standard deviation.
c. Compare the mean price per gallon for the sample data to the national average price. What conclusions can you draw about the cost living in San Francisco?

27. The results of a search to find the least expensive round-trip flights to Atlanta and Salt Lake City from 14 major U.S. cities are shown in the following table. The departure date was June 20, 2012, and the return date was June 27, 2012.

Flights

	Round-Trip Cost ($)	
Departure City	**Atlanta**	**Salt Lake City**
Cincinnati	340.10	570.10
New York	321.60	354.60
Chicago	291.60	465.60
Denver	339.60	219.60
Los Angeles	359.60	311.60
Seattle	384.60	297.60
Detroit	309.60	471.60
Philadelphia	415.60	618.40
Washington, D.C.	293.60	513.60
Miami	249.60	523.20
San Francisco	539.60	381.60
Las Vegas	455.60	159.60
Phoenix	359.60	267.60
Dallas	333.90	458.60

a. Compute the mean price for a round-trip flight into Atlanta and the mean price for a round-trip flight into Salt Lake City. Is Atlanta less expensive to fly into than Salt Lake City? If so, what could explain this difference?

b. Compute the range, variance, and standard deviation for the two samples. What does this information tell you about the prices for flights into these two cities?

28. The Australian Open is the first of the four Grand Slam professional tennis events held each year. Victoria Azarenka beat Maria Sharapova to win the 2012 Australian Open women's title (*Washington Post,* January 27, 2012). During the tournament Ms. Azarenka's serve reached 178 kilometers per hour. A list of the 20 Women's Singles serve speed leaders for the 2012 Australian Open is provided in the following table.

AustralianOpen

Player	Serve Speed (km/h)	Player	Serve Speed (km/h)
S. Williams	191	G. Arn	179
S. Lisicki	190	V. Azarenka	178
M. Keys	187	A. Ivanovic	178
L. Hradecka	187	P. Kvitova	178
J. Gajdosova	187	M. Krajicek	178
J. Hampton	181	V. Dushevina	178
B. Mattek-Sands	181	S. Stosur	178
F. Schiavone	179	S. Cirstea	177
P. Parmentier	179	M. Barthel	177
N. Petrova	179	P. Ormaechea	177

a. Compute the mean, variance, and standard deviation for the serve speeds.

b. A similar sample of the 20 Women's Singles serve speed leaders for the 2011 Wimbledon tournament showed a sample mean serve speed of 182.5 kilometers per hour. The variance and standard deviation were 33.3 and 5.77, respectively. Discuss any difference between the serve speeds in the Australian Open and the Wimbledon women's tournaments.

29. The *Los Angeles Times* regularly reports the air quality index for various areas of Southern California. A sample of air quality index values for Pomona provided the following data: 28, 42, 58, 48, 45, 55, 60, 49, and 50.
    a. Compute the range and interquartile range.
    b. Compute the sample variance and sample standard deviation.
    c. A sample of air quality index readings for Anaheim provided a sample mean of 48.5, a sample variance of 136, and a sample standard deviation of 11.66. What comparisons can you make between the air quality in Pomona and that in Anaheim on the basis of these descriptive statistics?

30. The following data were used to construct the histograms of the number of days required to fill orders for Dawson Supply, Inc., and J.C. Clark Distributors (see Figure 3.5).

Dawson Supply Days for Delivery:	11	10	9	10	11	11	10	11	10	10
Clark Distributors Days for Delivery:	8	10	13	7	10	11	10	7	15	12

Use the range and standard deviation to support the previous observation that Dawson Supply provides the more consistent and reliable delivery times.

31. The results of Accounting Principals' latest Workonomix survey indicate the average American worker spends $1092 on coffee annually (*The Consumerist,* January 20, 2012). To determine if there are any differences in coffee expenditures by age group, samples of 10 consumers were selected for three age groups (18–34, 35–44, and 45 and Older). The dollar amount each consumer in the sample spent last year on coffee is provided below.

18–34	35–44	45 and Older
1355	969	1135
115	434	956
1456	1792	400
2045	1500	1374
1621	1277	1244
994	1056	825
1937	1922	763
1200	1350	1192
1567	1586	1305
1390	1415	1510

a. Compute the mean, variance, and standard deviation for each of these three samples.
b. What observations can be made based on these data?

32. *Advertising Age* annually compiles a list of the 100 companies that spend the most on advertising. Consumer-goods company Procter & Gamble has often topped the list, spending billions of dollars annually (*Advertising Age* website, March 12, 2013). Consider the data found in the file Advertising. It contains annual advertising expenditures for a sample of 20 companies in the automotive sector and 20 companies in the department store sector.
    a. What is the mean advertising spent for each sector?
    b. What is the standard deviation for each sector?
    c. What is the range of advertising spent for each sector?
    d. What is the interquartile range for each sector?
    e. Based on this sample and your answers to parts (a) to (d), comment on any differences in the advertising spending in the automotive companies versus the department store companies.

33. Scores turned in by an amateur golfer at the Bonita Fairways Golf Course in Bonita Springs, Florida, during 2011 and 2012 are as follows:

2011 Season:	74	78	79	77	75	73	75	77
2012 Season:	71	70	75	77	85	80	71	79

a. Use the mean and standard deviation to evaluate the golfer's performance over the two-year period.
b. What is the primary difference in performance between 2011 and 2012? What improvement, if any, can be seen in the 2012 scores?

34. The following times were recorded by the quarter-mile and mile runners of a university track team (times are in minutes).

Quarter-Mile Times:	.92	.98	1.04	.90	.99
Mile Times:	4.52	4.35	4.60	4.70	4.50

After viewing this sample of running times, one of the coaches commented that the quarter-milers turned in the more consistent times. Use the standard deviation and the coefficient of variation to summarize the variability in the data. Does the use of the coefficient of variation indicate that the coach's statement should be qualified?

3.3 Measures of Distribution Shape, Relative Location, and Detecting Outliers

We have described several measures of location and variability for data. In addition, it is often important to have a measure of the shape of a distribution. In Chapter 2 we noted that a histogram provides a graphical display showing the shape of a distribution. An important numerical measure of the shape of a distribution is called **skewness**.

Distribution Shape

Figure 3.9 shows four histograms constructed from relative frequency distributions. The histograms in Panels A and B are moderately skewed. The one in Panel A is skewed to the left; its skewness is −.85. The histogram in Panel B is skewed to the right; its skewness is +.85. The histogram in Panel C is symmetric; its skewness is zero. The histogram in Panel D is highly skewed to the right; its skewness is 1.62. The formula used to compute skewness is somewhat complex.[1] However, the skewness can easily be computed using statistical software. For data skewed to the left, the skewness is negative; for data skewed to the right, the skewness is positive. If the data are symmetric, the skewness is zero.

For a symmetric distribution, the mean and the median are equal. When the data are positively skewed, the mean will usually be greater than the median; when the data are negatively skewed, the mean will usually be less than the median. The data used to construct

[1]The formula for the skewness of sample data:

$$\text{Skewness} = \frac{n}{(n-1)(n-2)} \sum \left(\frac{x_i - \bar{x}}{s} \right)^3$$

FIGURE 3.9 HISTOGRAMS SHOWING THE SKEWNESS FOR FOUR DISTRIBUTIONS

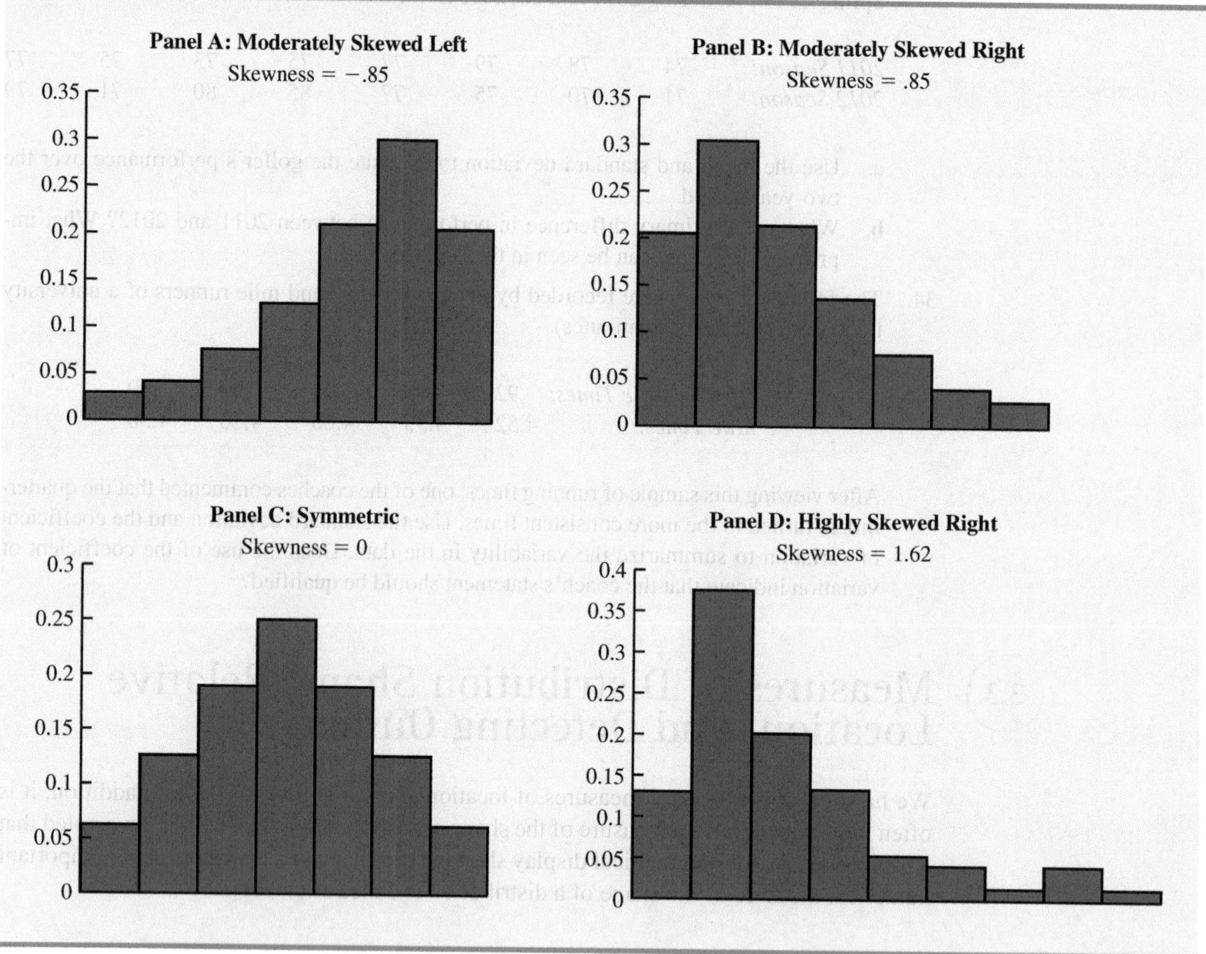

the histogram in Panel D are customer purchases at a women's apparel store. The mean purchase amount is \$77.60 and the median purchase amount is \$59.70. The relatively few large purchase amounts tend to increase the mean, whereas the median remains unaffected by the large purchase amounts. The median provides the preferred measure of location when the data are highly skewed.

z-Scores

In addition to measures of location, variability, and shape, we are also interested in the relative location of values within a data set. Measures of relative location help us determine how far a particular value is from the mean.

By using both the mean and standard deviation, we can determine the relative location of any observation. Suppose we have a sample of n observations, with the values denoted by $x_1, x_2, \ldots, x_n$. In addition, assume that the sample mean, $\bar{x}$, and the sample standard deviation, s, are already computed. Associated with each value, x_i, is another value called its **z-score**. Equation (3.12) shows how the z-score is computed for each x_i.

The z-score is often called the *standardized value*. The z-score, z_i, can be interpreted as the *number of standard deviations x_i is from the mean $\bar{x}$*. For example, $z_1 = 1.2$ would

z-SCORE

$$z_i = \frac{x_i - \bar{x}}{s} \tag{3.12}$$

where

z_i = the z-score for x_i
$\bar{x}$ = the sample mean
s = the sample standard deviation

indicate that x_1 is 1.2 standard deviations greater than the sample mean. Similarly, $z_2 = -.5$ would indicate that x_2 is .5, or 1/2, standard deviation less than the sample mean. A z-score greater than zero occurs for observations with a value greater than the mean, and a z-score less than zero occurs for observations with a value less than the mean. A z-score of zero indicates that the value of the observation is equal to the mean.

The z-score for any observation can be interpreted as a measure of the relative location of the observation in a data set. Thus, observations in two different data sets with the same z-score can be said to have the same relative location in terms of being the same number of standard deviations from the mean.

The process of converting a value for a variable to a z-score is often referred to as a z transformation.

The z-scores for the class size data from Section 3.1 are computed in Table 3.5. Recall the previously computed sample mean, $\bar{x} = 44$, and sample standard deviation, $s = 8$. The z-score of -1.50 for the fifth observation shows it is farthest from the mean; it is 1.50 standard deviations below the mean. Figure 3.10 provides a dot plot of the class size data with a graphical representation of the associated z-scores on the axis below.

Chebyshev's Theorem

Chebyshev's theorem enables us to make statements about the proportion of data values that must be within a specified number of standard deviations of the mean.

CHEBYSHEV'S THEOREM

At least $(1 - 1/z^2)$ of the data values must be within z standard deviations of the mean, where z is any value greater than 1.

TABLE 3.5 z-SCORES FOR THE CLASS SIZE DATA

Number of Students in Class (x_i)	Deviation About the Mean ($x_i - \bar{x}$)	z-Score $\left(\frac{x_i - \bar{x}}{s}\right)$
46	2	2/8 = .25
54	10	10/8 = 1.25
42	−2	−2/8 = −.25
46	2	2/8 = .25
32	−12	−12/8 = −1.50

FIGURE 3.10 DOT PLOT SHOWING CLASS SIZE DATA AND z-SCORES

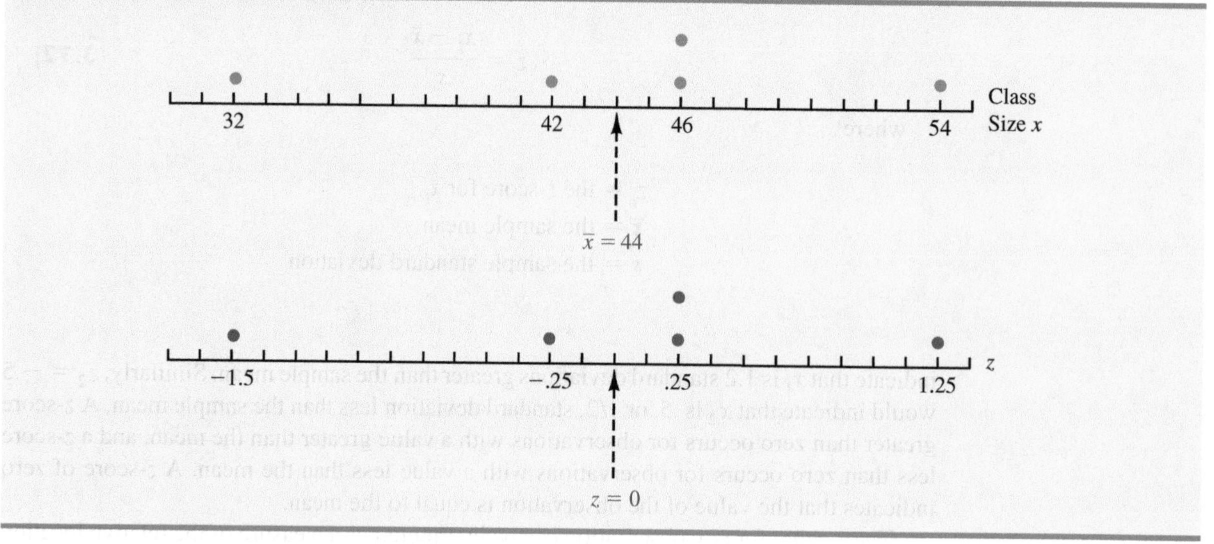

Some of the implications of this theorem, with $z = 2$, 3, and 4 standard deviations, follow.

- At least .75, or 75%, of the data values must be within $z = 2$ standard deviations of the mean.
- At least .89, or 89%, of the data values must be within $z = 3$ standard deviations of the mean.
- At least .94, or 94%, of the data values must be within $z = 4$ standard deviations of the mean.

For an example using Chebyshev's theorem, suppose that the midterm test scores for 100 students in a college business statistics course had a mean of 70 and a standard deviation of 5. How many students had test scores between 60 and 80? How many students had test scores between 58 and 82?

For the test scores between 60 and 80, we note that 60 is two standard deviations below the mean and 80 is two standard deviations above the mean. Using Chebyshev's theorem, we see that at least .75, or at least 75%, of the observations must have values within two standard deviations of the mean. Thus, at least 75% of the students must have scored between 60 and 80.

Chebyshev's theorem requires $z > 1$, but z need not be an integer.

For the test scores between 58 and 82, we see that $(58 - 70)/5 = -2.4$ indicates 58 is 2.4 standard deviations below the mean and that $(82 - 70)/5 = +2.4$ indicates 82 is 2.4 standard deviations above the mean. Applying Chebyshev's theorem with $z = 2.4$, we have

$$\left(1 - \frac{1}{z^2}\right) = \left(1 - \frac{1}{(2.4)^2}\right) = .826$$

At least 82.6% of the students must have test scores between 58 and 82.

The empirical rule is based on the normal probability distribution, which will be discussed in Chapter 6. The normal distribution is used extensively throughout the text.

Empirical Rule

One of the advantages of Chebyshev's theorem is that it applies to any data set regardless of the shape of the distribution of the data. Indeed, it could be used with any of the distributions in Figure 3.9. In many practical applications, however, data sets exhibit a symmetric

FIGURE 3.11 A SYMMETRIC MOUND-SHAPED OR BELL-SHAPED DISTRIBUTION

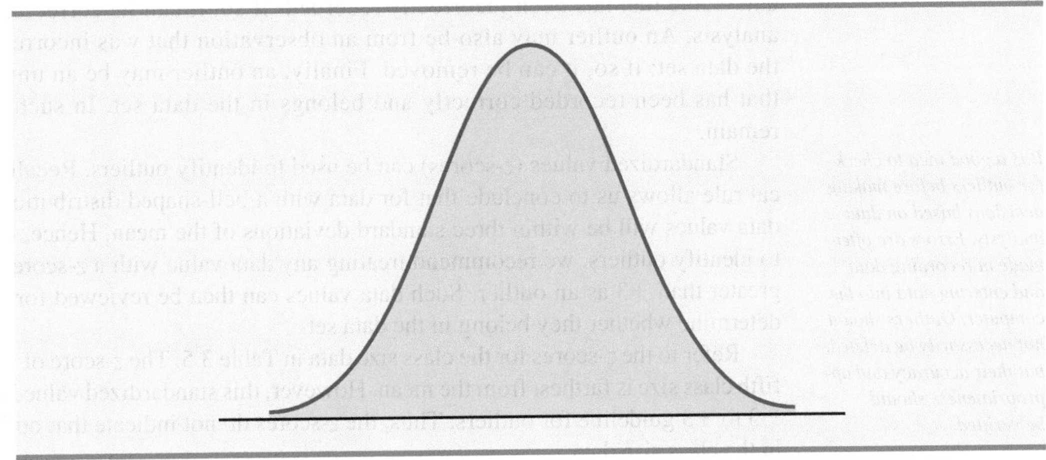

mound-shaped or bell-shaped distribution like the one shown in Figure 3.11. When the data are believed to approximate this distribution, the **empirical rule** can be used to determine the percentage of data values that must be within a specified number of standard deviations of the mean.

EMPIRICAL RULE

For data having a bell-shaped distribution:

- **Approximately 68% of the data values will be within one standard deviation of the mean.**
- **Approximately 95% of the data values will be within two standard deviations of the mean.**
- **Almost all of the data values will be within three standard deviations of the mean.**

For example, liquid detergent cartons are filled automatically on a production line. Filling weights frequently have a bell-shaped distribution. If the mean filling weight is 16 ounces and the standard deviation is .25 ounces, we can use the empirical rule to draw the following conclusions.

- Approximately 68% of the filled cartons will have weights between 15.75 and 16.25 ounces (within one standard deviation of the mean).
- Approximately 95% of the filled cartons will have weights between 15.50 and 16.50 ounces (within two standard deviations of the mean).
- Almost all filled cartons will have weights between 15.25 and 16.75 ounces (within three standard deviations of the mean).

Detecting Outliers

Sometimes a data set will have one or more observations with unusually large or unusually small values. These extreme values are called **outliers**. Experienced statisticians take steps to identify outliers and then review each one carefully. An outlier may be a data value that has been incorrectly recorded. If so, it can be corrected before further analysis. An outlier may also be from an observation that was incorrectly included in the data set; if so, it can be removed. Finally, an outlier may be an unusual data value that has been recorded correctly and belongs in the data set. In such cases it should remain.

It is a good idea to check for outliers before making decisions based on data analysis. Errors are often made in recording data and entering data into the computer. Outliers should not necessarily be deleted, but their accuracy and appropriateness should be verified.

Standardized values (z-scores) can be used to identify outliers. Recall that the empirical rule allows us to conclude that for data with a bell-shaped distribution, almost all the data values will be within three standard deviations of the mean. Hence, in using z-scores to identify outliers, we recommend treating any data value with a z-score less than -3 or greater than $+3$ as an outlier. Such data values can then be reviewed for accuracy and to determine whether they belong in the data set.

Refer to the z-scores for the class size data in Table 3.5. The z-score of -1.50 shows the fifth class size is farthest from the mean. However, this standardized value is well within the -3 to $+3$ guideline for outliers. Thus, the z-scores do not indicate that outliers are present in the class size data.

Another approach to identifying outliers is based upon the values of the first and third quartiles (Q_1 and Q_3) and the interquartile range (IQR). Using this method, we first compute the following lower and upper limits:

$$\text{Lower Limit} = Q_1 - 1.5(\text{IQR})$$

$$\text{Upper Limit} = Q_3 + 1.5(\text{IQR})$$

The approach that uses the first and third quartiles and the IQR to identify outliers does not necessarily provide the same results as the approach based upon a z-score less than −3 or greater than +3. Either or both procedures may be used.

An observation is classified as an outlier if its value is less than the lower limit or greater than the upper limit. For the monthly starting salary data shown in Table 3.1, $Q_1 = 3857.5$, $Q_3 = 4025$, IQR $= 167.5$, and the lower and upper limits are

$$\text{Lower Limit} = Q_1 - 1.5(\text{IQR}) = 3857.5 - 1.5(167.5) = 3606.25$$

$$\text{Upper Limit} = Q_3 + 1.5(\text{IQR}) = 4025 + 1.5(167.5) = 4276.25$$

Looking at the data in Table 3.1 we see that there are no observations with a starting salary less than the lower limit of 3606.25. But there is one starting salary, 4325, that is greater than the upper limit of 4276.25. Thus, 4325 is considered to be an outlier using this alternate approach to identifying outliers.

NOTES AND COMMENTS

1. Chebyshev's theorem is applicable for any data set and can be used to state the minimum number of data values that will be within a certain number of standard deviations of the mean. If the data are known to be approximately bell-shaped, more can be said. For instance, the empirical rule allows us to say that *approximately* 95% of the data values will be within two standard deviations of the mean; Chebyshev's theorem allows us to conclude only that at least 75% of the data values will be in that interval.
2. Before analyzing a data set, statisticians usually make a variety of checks to ensure the validity of data. In a large study it is not uncommon for errors to be made in recording data values or in entering the values into a computer. Identifying outliers is one tool used to check the validity of the data.

Exercises

Methods

35. Consider a sample with data values of 10, 20, 12, 17, and 16. Compute the z-score for each of the five observations.

36. Consider a sample with a mean of 500 and a standard deviation of 100. What are the z-scores for the following data values: 520, 650, 500, 450, and 280?

SELF test

37. Consider a sample with a mean of 30 and a standard deviation of 5. Use Chebyshev's theorem to determine the percentage of the data within each of the following ranges:
    a. 20 to 40
    b. 15 to 45
    c. 22 to 38
    d. 18 to 42
    e. 12 to 48

38. Suppose the data have a bell-shaped distribution with a mean of 30 and a standard deviation of 5. Use the empirical rule to determine the percentage of data within each of the following ranges:
    a. 20 to 40
    b. 15 to 45
    c. 25 to 35

Applications

SELF test

39. The results of a national survey showed that on average, adults sleep 6.9 hours per night. Suppose that the standard deviation is 1.2 hours.
    a. Use Chebyshev's theorem to calculate the percentage of individuals who sleep between 4.5 and 9.3 hours.
    b. Use Chebyshev's theorem to calculate the percentage of individuals who sleep between 3.9 and 9.9 hours.
    c. Assume that the number of hours of sleep follows a bell-shaped distribution. Use the empirical rule to calculate the percentage of individuals who sleep between 4.5 and 9.3 hours per day. How does this result compare to the value that you obtained using Chebyshev's theorem in part (a)?

40. The Energy Information Administration reported that the mean retail price per gallon of regular grade gasoline was $3.43 (Energy Information Administration, July 2012). Suppose that the standard deviation was $.10 and that the retail price per gallon has a bell-shaped distribution.
    a. What percentage of regular grade gasoline sold between $3.33 and $3.53 per gallon?
    b. What percentage of regular grade gasoline sold between $3.33 and $3.63 per gallon?
    c. What percentage of regular grade gasoline sold for more than $3.63 per gallon?

41. The national average for the math portion of the College Board's SAT test is 515 (*The World Almanac,* 2009). The College Board periodically rescales the test scores such that the standard deviation is approximately 100. Answer the following questions using a bell-shaped distribution and the empirical rule for the math test scores.
    a. What percentage of students have an SAT math score greater than 615?
    b. What percentage of students have an SAT math score greater than 715?
    c. What percentage of students have an SAT math score between 415 and 515?
    d. What percentage of students have an SAT math score between 315 and 615?

42. Many families in California are using backyard structures for home offices, art studios, and hobby areas as well as for additional storage. Suppose that the mean price for a customized wooden, shingled backyard structure is $3100. Assume that the standard deviation is $1200.

a. What is the z-score for a backyard structure costing $2300?
b. What is the z-score for a backyard structure costing $4900?
c. Interpret the z-scores in parts (a) and (b). Comment on whether either should be considered an outlier.
d. If the cost for a backyard shed-office combination built in Albany, California, is $13,000, should this structure be considered an outlier? Explain.

43. According to a *Los Angeles Times* study of more than 1 million medical dispatches from 2007 to 2012, the 911 response time for medical aid varies dramatically across Los Angeles (*LA Times* website, November 2012). Under national standards adopted by the Los Angeles Fire Department, rescuers are supposed to arrive within six minutes to almost all medical emergencies. But the *Times* analysis found that in affluent hillside communities stretching from Griffith Park to Pacific Palisades, firefighters failed to hit that mark nearly 85% of the time.

The following data show the response times, in minutes, for 10 emergency calls in the Griffith Park neighborhood.

11.8 10.3 10.7 10.6 11.5 8.3 10.5 10.9 10.7 11.2

Based on this sample of ten response times, compute the descriptive statistics in parts (a) and (b) and then answer the questions in parts (c) and (d):
a. Mean, median, and mode
b. Range and standard deviation
c. Should the response time of 8.3 minutes be considered an outlier in comparison to the other response times?
d. Do the response times indicate that the city is meeting the national standards? Should the city consider making changes to its response strategies? Would adding more stations to areas in the city be a practical solution? Discuss.

44. A sample of 10 NCAA college basketball game scores provided the following data.

Winning Team	Points	Losing Team	Points	Winning Margin
Arizona	90	Oregon	66	24
Duke	85	Georgetown	66	19
Florida State	75	Wake Forest	70	5
Kansas	78	Colorado	57	21
Kentucky	71	Notre Dame	63	8
Louisville	65	Tennessee	62	3
Oklahoma State	72	Texas	66	6
Purdue	76	Michigan State	70	6
Stanford	77	Southern Cal	67	10
Wisconsin	76	Illinois	56	20

a. Compute the mean and standard deviation for the points scored by the winning team.
b. Assume that the points scored by the winning teams for all NCAA games follow a bell-shaped distribution. Using the mean and standard deviation found in part (a), estimate the percentage of all NCAA games in which the winning team scores 84 or more points. Estimate the percentage of NCAA games in which the winning team scores more than 90 points.
c. Compute the mean and standard deviation for the winning margin. Do the data contain outliers? Explain.

45. *The Wall Street Journal* reported that Walmart Stores Inc. is planning to lay off 2300 employees at its Sam's Club warehouse unit. Approximately half of the layoffs will be hourly employees (*The Wall Street Journal*, January 25–26, 2014). Suppose the following data represent the percentage of hourly employees laid off for 15 Sam's Club stores.

55 56 44 43 44 56 60 62 57 45 36 38 50 69 65

a. Compute the mean and median percentage of hourly employees being laid off at these stores.
b. Compute the first and third quartiles.
c. Compute the range and interquartile range.
d. Compute the variance and standard deviation.
e. Do the data contain any outliers?
f. Based on the sample data, does it appear that Walmart is meeting its goal for reducing the number of hourly employees?

3.4 Five-Number Summaries and Box Plots

Summary statistics and easy-to-draw graphs based on summary statistics can be used to quickly summarize large quantities of data. In this section we show how five-number summaries and box plots can be developed to identify several characteristics of a data set.

Five-Number Summary

In a **five-number summary**, five numbers are used to summarize the data:

1. Smallest value
2. First quartile (Q_1)
3. Median (Q_2)
4. Third quartile (Q_3)
5. Largest value

To illustrate the development of a five-number summary, we will use the monthly starting salary data in Table 3.1. Arranging the data in ascending order, we obtain the following results.

3710 3755 3850 3880 3880 3890 3920 3940 3950 4050 4130 4325

The smallest value is 3710 and the largest value is 4325. We showed how to compute the quartiles ($Q_1 = 3857.5$; $Q_2 = 3905$; and $Q_3 = 4025$) in Section 3.1. Thus, the five-number summary for the monthly starting salary data is

3710 3857.5 3905 4025 4325

The five-number summary indicates that the starting salaries in the sample are between 3710 and 4325 and that the median or middle value is 3905; and, the first and third quartiles show that approximately 50% of the starting salaries are between 3857.5 and 4025.

Box Plot

A **box plot** is a graphical display of data based on a five-number summary. A key to the development of a box plot is the computation of the interquartile range, IQR $= Q_3 - Q_1$.

FIGURE 3.12 BOX PLOT OF THE MONTHLY STARTING SALARY DATA WITH LINES SHOWING THE LOWER AND UPPER LIMITS

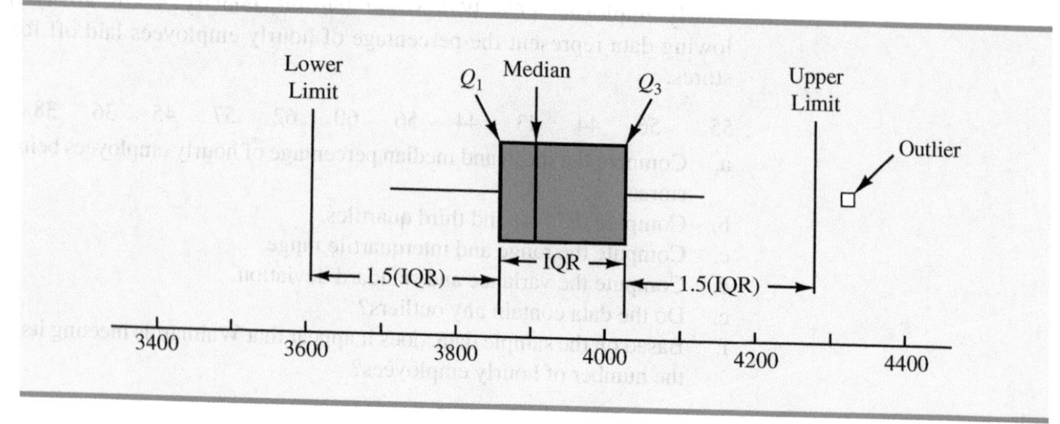

Figure 3.12 shows a box plot for the monthly starting salary data. The steps used to construct the box plot follow.

1. A box is drawn with the ends of the box located at the first and third quartiles. For the salary data, $Q_1 = 3857.5$ and $Q_3 = 4025$. This box contains the middle 50% of the data.
2. A vertical line is drawn in the box at the location of the median (3905 for the salary data).
3. By using the interquartile range, $\text{IQR} = Q_3 - Q_1$, *limits* are located at 1.5(IQR) below Q_1, and 1.5(IQR) above Q_3. For the salary data, $\text{IQR} = Q_3 - Q_1 = 4025 - 3857.5 = 167.5$. Thus, the limits are $3857.5 - 1.5(167.5) = 3606.25$ and $4025 + 1.5(167.5) = 4276.25$. Data outside these limits are considered *outliers*.
4. The horizontal lines extending from each end of the box in Figure 3.12 are called *whiskers*. The whiskers are drawn from the ends of the box to the smallest and largest values *inside the limits* computed in step 3. Thus, the whiskers end at salary values of 3710 and 4130.
5. Finally, the location of each outlier is shown with a small square-shaped symbol. In Figure 3.12 we see one outlier, 4325.

Box plots provide another way to identify outliers, but they do not necessarily identify the same values as those with a z-score less than −3 or greater than +3. Either or both procedures may be used.

In Figure 3.12 we included lines showing the location of the upper and lower limits. These lines were drawn to show how the limits are computed and where they are located. Although the limits are always computed, generally they are not drawn on the box plots. Figure 3.13 shows the usual appearance of a box plot for the starting salary data.

Comparative Analysis Using Box Plots

Box plots can also be used to provide a graphical summary of two or more groups and facilitate visual comparisons among the groups. For example, suppose the placement office decided to conduct a follow-up study to compare monthly starting salaries by the graduate's major: accounting, finance, information systems, management, and marketing. The major and starting salary data for a new sample of 111 recent business school graduates are shown in the WEBfile named 2012MajorSalary, and Figure 3.14 shows the box plots corresponding to each major. Note that major is shown on the horizontal axis and each box plot is shown vertically above the corresponding major. Displaying box plots in this manner is an excellent graphical technique for making comparisons among two or more groups.

2012MajorSalary

FIGURE 3.13 BOX PLOT OF THE MONTHLY STARTING SALARY DATA

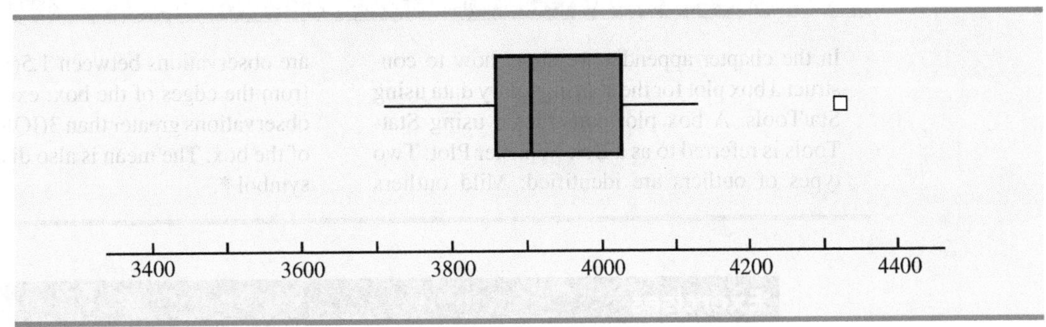

What interpretations can you make from the box plots in Figure 3.14? Specifically, we note the following:

- The higher salaries are in accounting; the lower salaries are in management and marketing.
- Based on the medians, accounting and information systems have similar and higher median salaries. Finance is next, with marketing and management showing lower median salaries.
- High salary outliers exist for accounting, finance, and marketing majors.

Perhaps you can see additional interpretations based on these box plots.

FIGURE 3.14 BOX PLOTS OF MONTHLY STARTING SALARY BY MAJOR

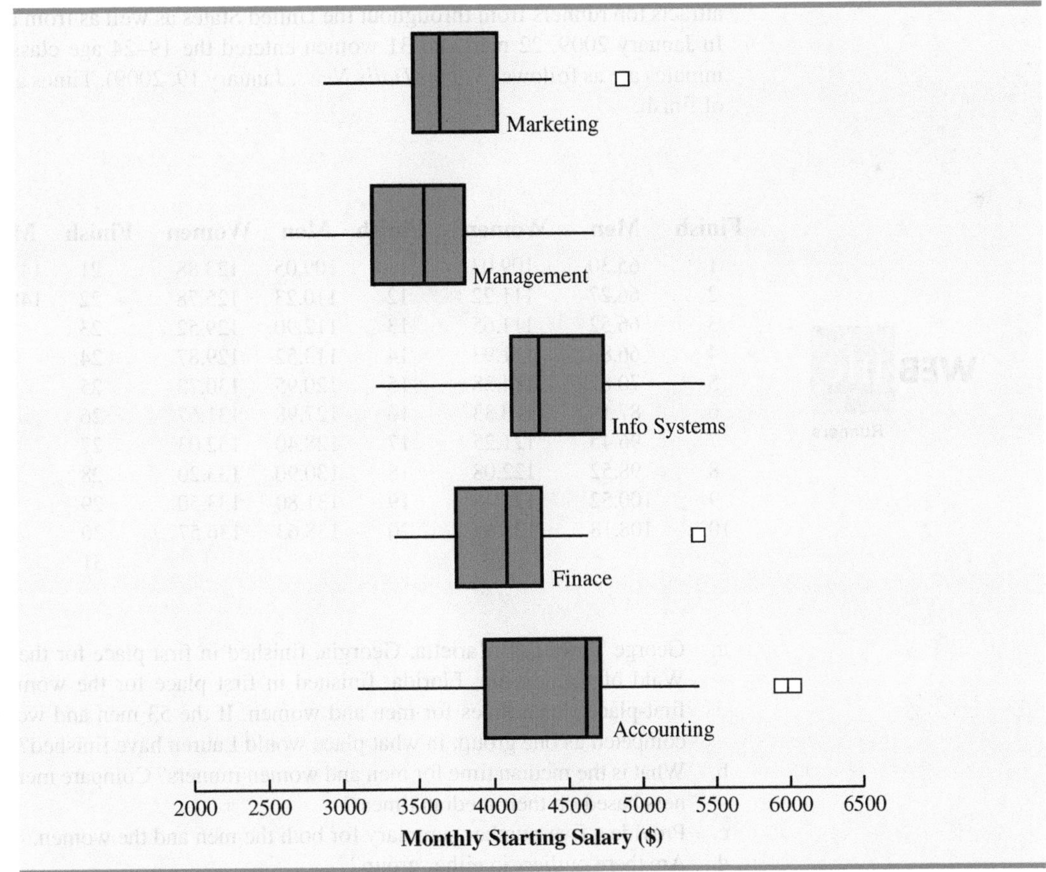

NOTE AND COMMENT

In the chapter appendix we show how to construct a box plot for the starting salary data using StatTools. A box plot constructed using StatTools is referred to as a Box-Whisker Plot. Two types of outliers are identified: Mild outliers are observations between 1.5(IQR) and 3(IQR) from the edges of the box; extreme outliers are observations greater than 3(IQR) from the edges of the box. The mean is also displayed using the symbol *.

Exercises

Methods

46. Consider a sample with data values of 27, 25, 20, 15, 30, 34, 28, and 25. Provide the five-number summary for the data.
47. Show the box plot for the data in exercise 46.

SELF test

48. Show the five-number summary and the box plot for the following data: 5, 15, 18, 10, 8, 12, 16, 10, 6.
49. A data set has a first quartile of 42 and a third quartile of 50. Compute the lower and upper limits for the corresponding box plot. Should a data value of 65 be considered an outlier?

Applications

50. Naples, Florida, hosts a half-marathon (13.1-mile race) in January each year. The event attracts top runners from throughout the United States as well as from around the world. In January 2009, 22 men and 31 women entered the 19–24 age class. Finish times in minutes are as follows (*Naples Daily News,* January 19, 2009). Times are shown in order of finish.

Finish	Men	Women	Finish	Men	Women	Finish	Men	Women
1	65.30	109.03	11	109.05	123.88	21	143.83	136.75
2	66.27	111.22	12	110.23	125.78	22	148.70	138.20
3	66.52	111.65	13	112.90	129.52	23		139.00
4	66.85	111.93	14	113.52	129.87	24		147.18
5	70.87	114.38	15	120.95	130.72	25		147.35
6	87.18	118.33	16	127.98	131.67	26		147.50
7	96.45	121.25	17	128.40	132.03	27		147.75
8	98.52	122.08	18	130.90	133.20	28		153.88
9	100.52	122.48	19	131.80	133.50	29		154.83
10	108.18	122.62	20	138.63	136.57	30		189.27
						31		189.28

a. George Towett of Marietta, Georgia, finished in first place for the men and Lauren Wald of Gainesville, Florida, finished in first place for the women. Compare the first-place finish times for men and women. If the 53 men and women runners had competed as one group, in what place would Lauren have finished?
b. What is the median time for men and women runners? Compare men and women runners based on their median times.
c. Provide a five-number summary for both the men and the women.
d. Are there outliers in either group?

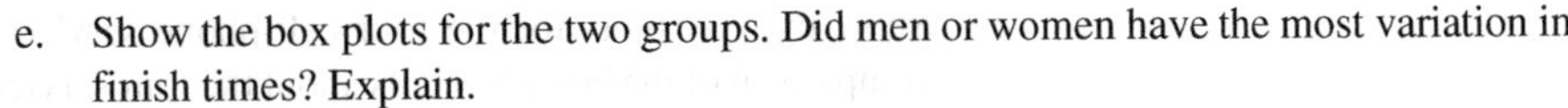

e. Show the box plots for the two groups. Did men or women have the most variation in finish times? Explain.

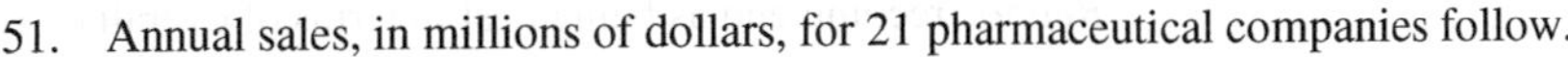

51. Annual sales, in millions of dollars, for 21 pharmaceutical companies follow.

SELF test

8408	1374	1872	8879	2459	11413
608	14138	6452	1850	2818	1356
10498	7478	4019	4341	739	2127
3653	5794	8305			

WEB file

PharmacySales

a. Provide a five-number summary.
b. Compute the lower and upper limits.
c. Do the data contain any outliers?
d. Johnson & Johnson's sales are the largest on the list at $14,138 million. Suppose a data entry error (a transposition) had been made and the sales had been entered as $41,138 million. Would the method of detecting outliers in part (c) identify this problem and allow for correction of the data entry error?
e. Show a box plot.

52. *Consumer Reports* provided overall customer satisfaction scores for AT&T, Sprint, T-Mobile, and Verizon cell-phone services in major metropolitan areas throughout the United States. The rating for each service reflects the overall customer satisfaction considering a variety of factors such as cost, connectivity problems, dropped calls, static interference, and customer support. A satisfaction scale from 0 to 100 was used with 0 indicating completely dissatisfied and 100 indicating completely satisfied. The ratings for the four cell-phone services in 20 metropolitan areas are as shown (*Consumer Reports,* January 2009).

CellService

Metropolitan Area	AT&T	Sprint	T-Mobile	Verizon
Atlanta	70	66	71	79
Boston	69	64	74	76
Chicago	71	65	70	77
Dallas	75	65	74	78
Denver	71	67	73	77
Detroit	73	65	77	79
Jacksonville	73	64	75	81
Las Vegas	72	68	74	81
Los Angeles	66	65	68	78
Miami	68	69	73	80
Minneapolis	68	66	75	77
Philadelphia	72	66	71	78
Phoenix	68	66	76	81
San Antonio	75	65	75	80
San Diego	69	68	72	79
San Francisco	66	69	73	75
Seattle	68	67	74	77
St. Louis	74	66	74	79
Tampa	73	63	73	79
Washington	72	68	71	76

a. Consider T-Mobile first. What is the median rating?
b. Develop a five-number summary for the T-Mobile service.
c. Are there outliers for T-Mobile? Explain.
d. Repeat parts (b) and (c) for the other three cell-phone services.

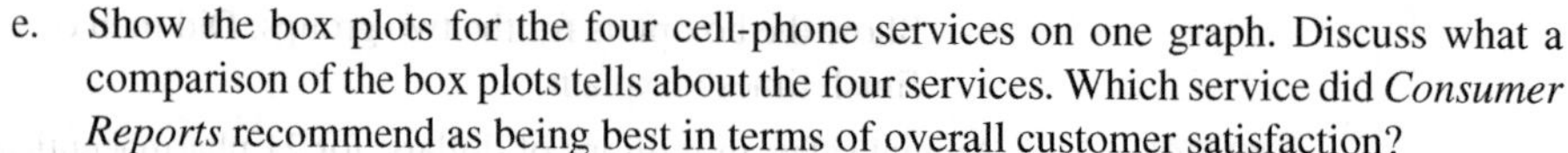

e. Show the box plots for the four cell-phone services on one graph. Discuss what a comparison of the box plots tells about the four services. Which service did *Consumer Reports* recommend as being best in terms of overall customer satisfaction?

AdmiredCompanies

53. *Fortune* magazine's list of the world's most admired companies for 2014 is provided the data contained in the WEBfile named AdmiredCompanies (*Fortune*, March 17, 2014). The data in the column labelled Return shows the one-year total return (%) for the top ranked 50 companies. For the same time period the S&P average return was 18.4%.
   a. Compute the median return for the top ranked 50 companies.
   b. What percentage of the top-ranked 50 companies had a one-year return greater than the S&P average return?
   c. Develop the five-number summary for the data.
   d. Are there any outliers?
   e. Develop a box plot for the one-year total return.

BorderCrossings

54. The Bureau of Transportation Statistics keeps track of all border crossings through ports of entry along the U.S.-Canadian and U.S.-Mexican borders. The data contained in the WEBfile named BorderCrossings show the most recently published figures for the number of personal vehicle crossings (rounded to the nearest 1000) at the 50 busiest ports of entry during the month of August (U.S. Department of Transportation website, February 28, 2013).
   a. What are the mean and median number of crossings for these ports of entry?
   b. What are the first and third quartiles?
   c. Provide a five-number summary.
   d. Do the data contain any outliers? Show a box plot.

3.5 Measures of Association Between Two Variables

Thus far we have examined numerical methods used to summarize the data for *one variable at a time.* Often a manager or decision maker is interested in the *relationship between two variables.* In this section we present covariance and correlation as descriptive measures of the relationship between two variables.

We begin by reconsidering the application concerning a stereo and sound equipment store in San Francisco as presented in Section 2.4. The store's manager wants to determine the relationship between the number of weekend television commercials shown and the sales at the store during the following week. Sample data with sales expressed in hundreds of dollars are provided in Table 3.6, which shows 10 observations ($n = 10$), one for each week. The scatter diagram in Figure 3.15 shows a positive relationship, with higher sales (y) associated with a greater number of commercials (x). In fact, the scatter diagram suggests that a straight line could be used as an approximation of the relationship. In the following discussion, we introduce **covariance** as a descriptive measure of the linear association between two variables.

Covariance

For a sample of size n with the observations (x_1, y_1), (x_2, y_2), and so on, the sample covariance is defined as follows:

SAMPLE COVARIANCE

$$s_{xy} = \frac{\Sigma(x_i - \bar{x})(y_i - \bar{y})}{n - 1} \tag{3.13}$$

TABLE 3.6 SAMPLE DATA FOR THE STEREO AND SOUND EQUIPMENT STORE

WEB file
Stereo

Week	Number of Commercials x	Sales ($100s) y
1	2	50
2	5	57
3	1	41
4	3	54
5	4	54
6	1	38
7	5	63
8	3	48
9	4	59
10	2	46

FIGURE 3.15 SCATTER DIAGRAM FOR THE STEREO AND SOUND EQUIPMENT STORE

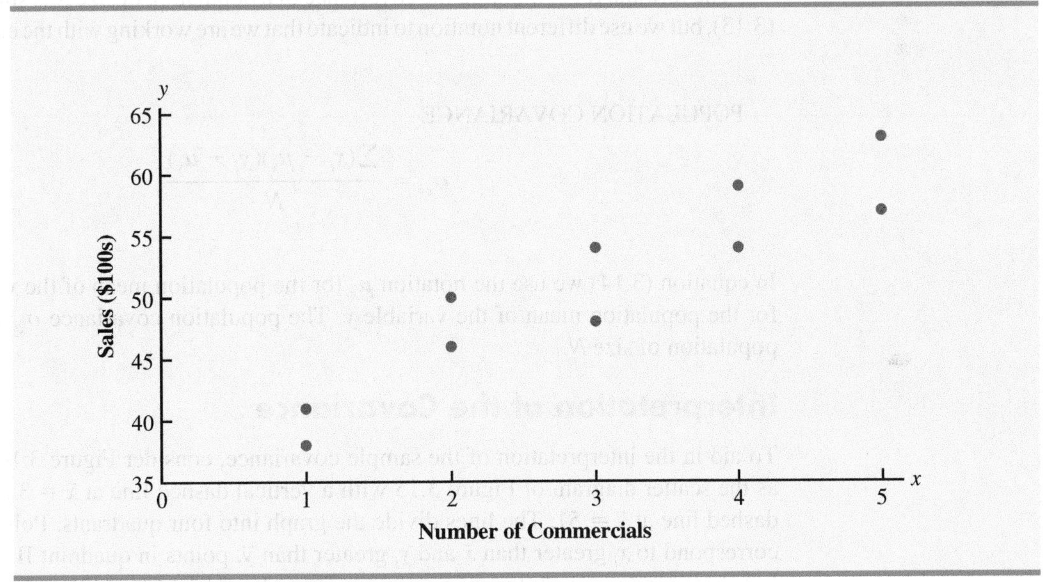

This formula pairs each x_i with a y_i. We then sum the products obtained by multiplying the deviation of each x_i from its sample mean $\bar{x}$ by the deviation of the corresponding y_i from its sample mean $\bar{y}$; this sum is then divided by $n - 1$.

To measure the strength of the linear relationship between the number of commercials x and the sales volume y in the stereo and sound equipment store problem, we use equation (3.13) to compute the sample covariance. The calculations in Table 3.7 show the computation of $\Sigma(x_i - \bar{x})(y_i - \bar{y})$. Note that $\bar{x} = 30/10 = 3$ and $\bar{y} = 510/10 = 51$. Using equation (3.13), we obtain a sample covariance of

$$s_{xy} = \frac{\Sigma(x_i - \bar{x})(y_i - \bar{y})}{n - 1} = \frac{99}{9} = 11$$

TABLE 3.7 CALCULATIONS FOR THE SAMPLE COVARIANCE

	x_i	y_i	$x_i - \bar{x}$	$y_i - \bar{y}$	$(x_i - \bar{x})(y_i - \bar{y})$
	2	50	−1	−1	1
	5	57	2	6	12
	1	41	−2	−10	20
	3	54	0	3	0
	4	54	1	3	3
	1	38	−2	−13	26
	5	63	2	12	24
	3	48	0	−3	0
	4	59	1	8	8
	2	46	−1	−5	5
Totals	30	510	0	0	99

$$s_{xy} = \frac{\Sigma(x_i - \bar{x})(y_i - \bar{y})}{n - 1} = \frac{99}{10 - 1} = 11$$

The formula for computing the covariance of a population of size N is similar to equation (3.13), but we use different notation to indicate that we are working with the entire population.

POPULATION COVARIANCE

$$\sigma_{xy} = \frac{\Sigma(x_i - \mu_x)(y_i - \mu_y)}{N} \tag{3.14}$$

In equation (3.14) we use the notation μ_x for the population mean of the variable x and μ_y for the population mean of the variable y. The population covariance σ_{xy} is defined for a population of size N.

Interpretation of the Covariance

To aid in the interpretation of the sample covariance, consider Figure 3.16. It is the same as the scatter diagram of Figure 3.15 with a vertical dashed line at $\bar{x} = 3$ and a horizontal dashed line at $\bar{y} = 51$. The lines divide the graph into four quadrants. Points in quadrant I correspond to x_i greater than $\bar{x}$ and y_i greater than $\bar{y}$, points in quadrant II correspond to x_i less than $\bar{x}$ and y_i greater than $\bar{y}$, and so on. Thus, the value of $(x_i - \bar{x})(y_i - \bar{y})$ must be positive for points in quadrant I, negative for points in quadrant II, positive for points in quadrant III, and negative for points in quadrant IV.

The covariance is a measure of the linear association between two variables.

If the value of s_{xy} is positive, the points with the greatest influence on s_{xy} must be in quadrants I and III. Hence, a positive value for s_{xy} indicates a positive linear association between x and y; that is, as the value of x increases, the value of y increases. If the value of s_{xy} is negative, however, the points with the greatest influence on s_{xy} are in quadrants II and IV. Hence, a negative value for s_{xy} indicates a negative linear association between x and y; that is, as the value of x increases, the value of y decreases. Finally, if the points are evenly distributed across all four quadrants, the value of s_{xy} will be close to zero, indicating no linear association between x and y. Figure 3.17 shows the values of s_{xy} that can be expected with three different types of scatter diagrams.

Referring again to Figure 3.16, we see that the scatter diagram for the stereo and sound equipment store follows the pattern in the top panel of Figure 3.17. As we should expect, the value of the sample covariance indicates a positive linear relationship with $s_{xy} = 11$.

FIGURE 3.16 PARTITIONED SCATTER DIAGRAM FOR THE STEREO AND SOUND EQUIPMENT STORE

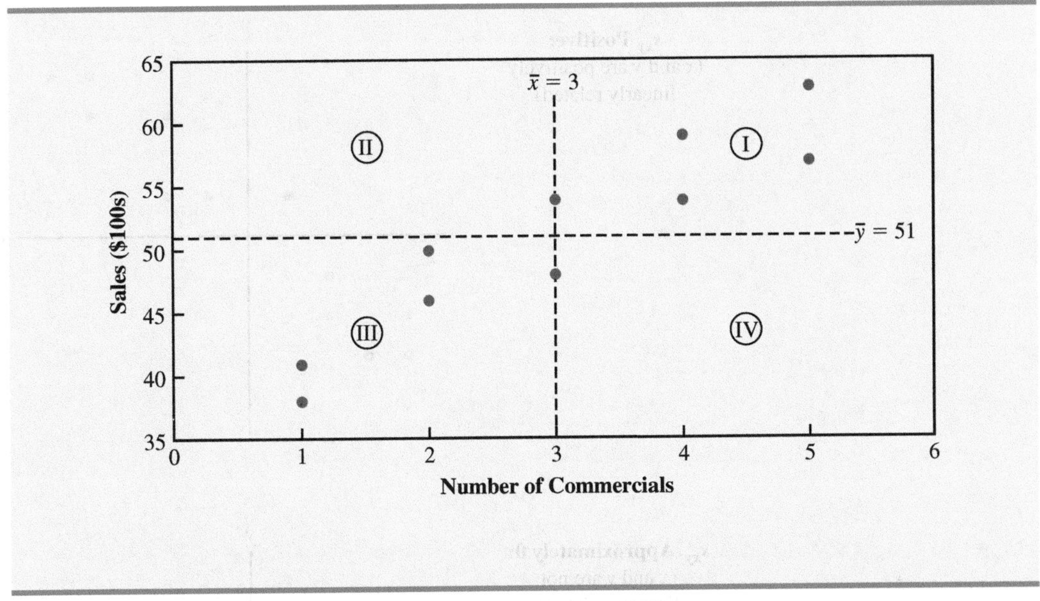

From the preceding discussion, it might appear that a large positive value for the covariance indicates a strong positive linear relationship and that a large negative value indicates a strong negative linear relationship. However, one problem with using covariance as a measure of the strength of the linear relationship is that the value of the covariance depends on the units of measurement for x and y. For example, suppose we are interested in the relationship between height x and weight y for individuals. Clearly the strength of the relationship should be the same whether we measure height in feet or inches. Measuring the height in inches, however, gives us much larger numerical values for $(x_i - \bar{x})$ than when we measure height in feet. Thus, with height measured in inches, we would obtain a larger value for the numerator $\Sigma(x_i - \bar{x})(y_i - \bar{y})$ in equation (3.13)—and hence a larger covariance—when in fact the relationship does not change. A measure of the relationship between two variables that is not affected by the units of measurement for x and y is the **correlation coefficient**.

Correlation Coefficient

For sample data, the Pearson product moment correlation coefficient is defined as follows.

PEARSON PRODUCT MOMENT CORRELATION COEFFICIENT: SAMPLE DATA

$$r_{xy} = \frac{s_{xy}}{s_x s_y} \tag{3.15}$$

where

r_{xy} = sample correlation coefficient
s_{xy} = sample covariance
s_x = sample standard deviation of x
s_y = sample standard deviation of y

FIGURE 3.17 INTERPRETATION OF SAMPLE COVARIANCE

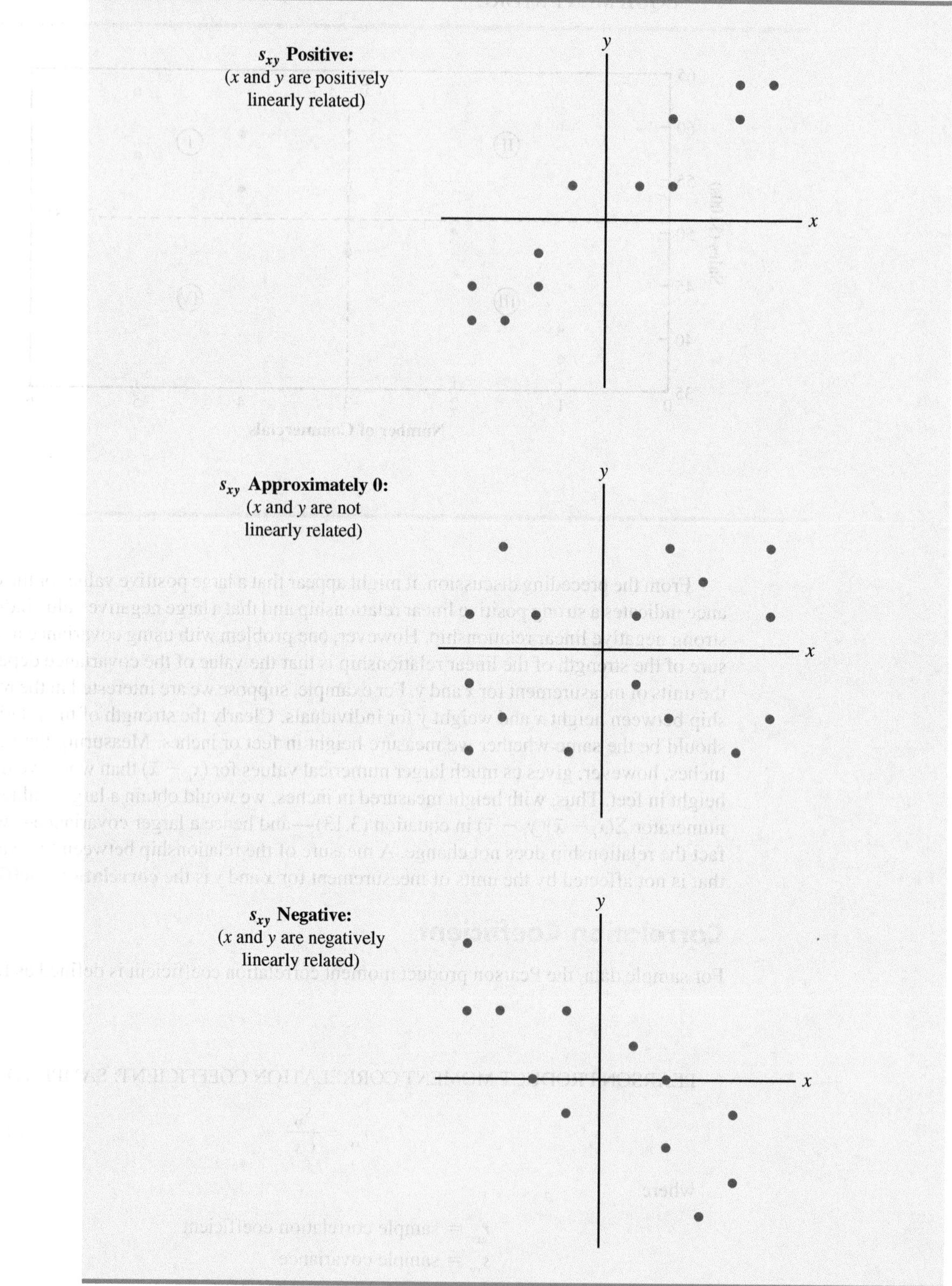

Equation (3.15) shows that the Pearson product moment correlation coefficient for sample data (commonly referred to more simply as the *sample correlation coefficient*) is computed by dividing the sample covariance by the product of the sample standard deviation of x and the sample standard deviation of y.

Let us now compute the sample correlation coefficient for the stereo and sound equipment store. Using the data in Table 3.6, we can compute the sample standard deviations for the two variables:

$$s_x = \sqrt{\frac{\Sigma(x_i - \bar{x})^2}{n - 1}} = \sqrt{\frac{20}{9}} = 1.49$$

$$s_y = \sqrt{\frac{\Sigma(y_i - \bar{y})^2}{n - 1}} = \sqrt{\frac{566}{9}} = 7.93$$

Now, because $s_{xy} = 11$, the sample correlation coefficient equals

$$r_{xy} = \frac{s_{xy}}{s_x s_y} = \frac{11}{(1.49)(7.93)} = .93$$

The formula for computing the correlation coefficient for a population, denoted by the Greek letter ρ_{xy} (rho, pronounced "row"), follows.

The sample correlation coefficient r_{xy} is a point estimator of the population correlation coefficient ρ_{xy}.

PEARSON PRODUCT MOMENT CORRELATION COEFFICIENT: POPULATION DATA

$$\rho_{xy} = \frac{\sigma_{xy}}{\sigma_x \sigma_y} \qquad \textbf{(3.16)}$$

where

ρ_{xy} = population correlation coefficient
σ_{xy} = population covariance
σ_x = population standard deviation for x
σ_y = population standard deviation for y

The sample correlation coefficient r_{xy} provides an estimate of the population correlation coefficient ρ_{xy}.

Interpretation of the Correlation Coefficient

First let us consider a simple example that illustrates the concept of a perfect positive linear relationship. The scatter diagram in Figure 3.18 depicts the relationship between x and y based on the following sample data.

x_i	y_i
5	10
10	30
15	50

FIGURE 3.18 SCATTER DIAGRAM DEPICTING A PERFECT POSITIVE LINEAR RELATIONSHIP

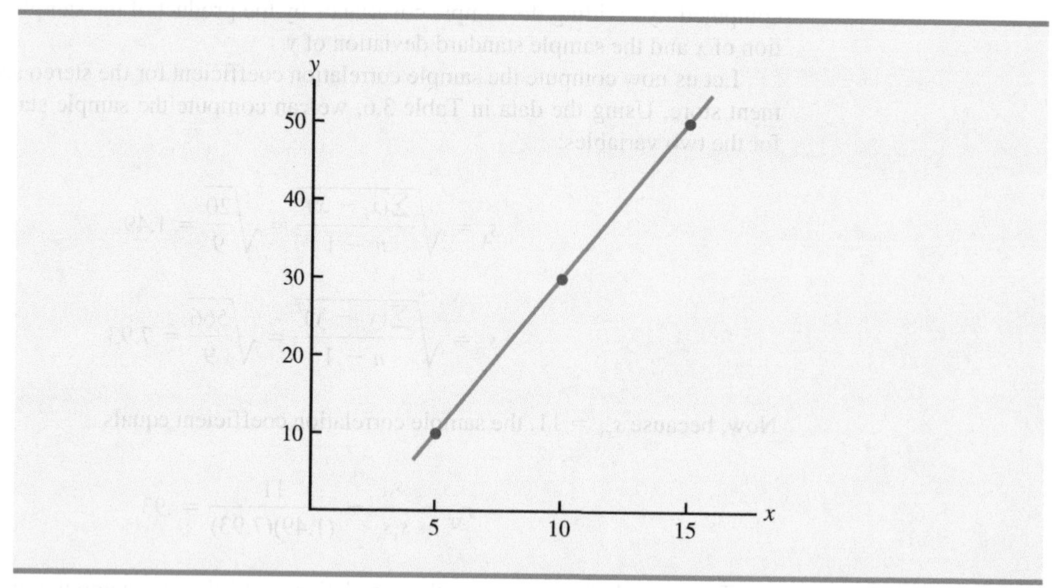

The straight line drawn through each of the three points shows a perfect linear relationship between x and y. In order to apply equation (3.15) to compute the sample correlation we must first compute s_{xy}, s_x, and s_y. Some of the computations are shown in Table 3.8. Using the results in this table, we find

$$s_{xy} = \frac{\Sigma(x_i - \bar{x})(y_i - \bar{y})}{n - 1} = \frac{200}{2} = 100$$

$$s_x = \sqrt{\frac{\Sigma(x_i - \bar{x})^2}{n - 1}} = \sqrt{\frac{50}{2}} = 5$$

$$s_y = \sqrt{\frac{\Sigma(y_i - \bar{y})^2}{n - 1}} = \sqrt{\frac{800}{2}} = 20$$

$$r_{xy} = \frac{s_{xy}}{s_x s_y} = \frac{100}{5(20)} = 1$$

Thus, we see that the value of the sample correlation coefficient is 1.

TABLE 3.8 COMPUTATIONS USED IN CALCULATING THE SAMPLE CORRELATION COEFFICIENT

	x_i	y_i	$x_i - \bar{x}$	$(x_i - \bar{x})^2$	$y_i - \bar{y}$	$(y_i - \bar{y})^2$	$(x_i - \bar{x})(y_i - \bar{y})$
	5	10	−5	25	−20	400	100
	10	30	0	0	0	0	0
	15	50	5	25	20	400	100
Totals	30	90	0	50	0	800	200

$\bar{x} = 10$ $\bar{y} = 30$

The correlation coefficient ranges from −1 to +1. Values close to −1 or +1 indicate a strong linear relationship. The closer the correlation is to zero, the weaker the relationship.

In general, it can be shown that if all the points in a data set fall on a positively sloped straight line, the value of the sample correlation coefficient is +1; that is, a sample correlation coefficient of +1 corresponds to a perfect positive linear relationship between x and y. Moreover, if the points in the data set fall on a straight line having negative slope, the value of the sample correlation coefficient is −1; that is, a sample correlation coefficient of −1 corresponds to a perfect negative linear relationship between x and y.

Let us now suppose that a certain data set indicates a positive linear relationship between x and y but that the relationship is not perfect. The value of r_{xy} will be less than 1, indicating that the points in the scatter diagram are not all on a straight line. As the points deviate more and more from a perfect positive linear relationship, the value of r_{xy} becomes smaller and smaller. A value of r_{xy} equal to zero indicates no linear relationship between x and y, and values of r_{xy} near zero indicate a weak linear relationship.

For the data involving the stereo and sound equipment store, $r_{xy} = .93$. Therefore, we conclude that a strong positive linear relationship occurs between the number of commercials and sales. More specifically, an increase in the number of commercials is associated with an increase in sales.

In closing, we note that correlation provides a measure of linear association and not necessarily causation. A high correlation between two variables does not mean that changes in one variable will cause changes in the other variable. For example, we may find that the quality rating and the typical meal price of restaurants are positively correlated. However, simply increasing the meal price at a restaurant will not cause the quality rating to increase.

Using Excel to Compute the Sample Covariance and Sample Correlation Coefficient

Excel provides functions that can be used to compute the covariance and correlation coefficient. We illustrate the use of these functions by computing the sample covariance and the sample correlation coefficient for the stereo and sound equipment store data in Table 3.6. Refer to Figure 3.19 as we describe the tasks involved. The formula worksheet is in the background; the value worksheet is in the foreground.

Enter/Access Data: Open the WEBfile named Stereo. The data are in cells B2:C11 and labels are in column A and cells B1:C1.

FIGURE 3.19 USING EXCEL TO COMPUTE THE COVARIANCE AND CORRELATION COEFFICIENT

	A	B	C	D	E	F	G
1	Week	No. of Commercials	Sales ($100s)				
2	1	2	50		Sample Covariance	=COVARIANCE.S(B2:B11,C2:C11)	
3	2	5	57		Sample Correlation	=CORREL(B2:B11,C2:C11)	
4	3	1	41				
5	4	3	54				
6	5	4	54				
7	6	1	38				
8	7	5	63				
9	8	3	48				
10	9	4	59				
11	10	2	46				
12							

	A	B	C	D	E	F	G
1	Week	No. of Commercials	Sales ($100s)				
2	1	2	50		Sample Covariance	11	
3	2	5	57		Sample Correlation	0.93	
4	3	1	41				
5	4	3	54				
6	5	4	54				
7	6	1	38				
8	7	5	63				
9	8	3	48				
10	9	4	59				
11	10	2	46				
12							

Enter Functions and Formulas: Excel's COVARIANCE.S function can be used to compute the sample covariance by entering the following formula into cell F2:

=COVARIANCE.S(B2:B11,C2:C11)

Similarly, the formula =CORREL(B2:B11,C2:C11) is entered into cell F3 to compute the sample correlation coefficient.

The labels in cells E2:E3 identify the output. Note that the sample covariance (11) and the sample correlation coefficient (.93) are the same as we computed earlier using the definitions.

NOTE AND COMMENT

Because the correlation coefficient measures only the strength of the linear relationship between two quantitative variables, it is possible for the correlation coefficient to be near zero, suggesting no linear relationship, when the relationship between the two variables is nonlinear. For example, the following scatter diagram shows the relationship between the amount spent by a small retail store for environmental control (heating and cooling) and the daily high outside temperature over 100 days.

The sample correlation coefficient for these data is $r_{xy} = -.007$ and indicates there is no linear relationship between the two variables. However, the scatter diagram provides strong visual evidence of a nonlinear relationship. That is, we can see that as the daily high outside temperature increases, the money spent on environmental control first decreases as less heating is required and then increases as greater cooling is required.

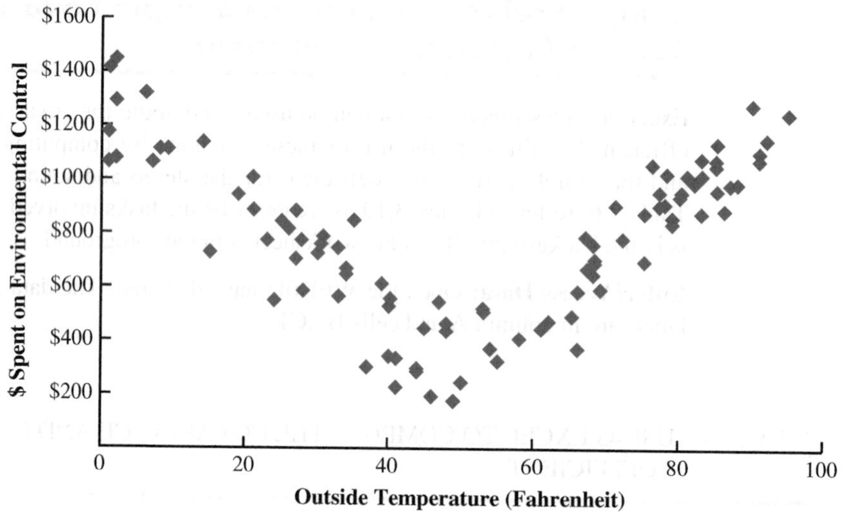

Exercises

Methods

55. Five observations taken for two variables follow.

x_i	4	6	11	3	16
y_i	50	50	40	60	30

a. Develop a scatter diagram with x on the horizontal axis.
b. What does the scatter diagram developed in part (a) indicate about the relationship between the two variables?

c. Compute and interpret the sample covariance.
d. Compute and interpret the sample correlation coefficient.

56. Five observations taken for two variables follow.

x_i	6	11	15	21	27
y_i	6	9	6	17	12

a. Develop a scatter diagram for these data.
b. What does the scatter diagram indicate about a relationship between x and y?
c. Compute and interpret the sample covariance.
d. Compute and interpret the sample correlation coefficient.

Applications

57. Ten major college football bowl games were played in January 2010, with the University of Alabama beating the University of Texas 37 to 21 to become the national champion of college football. The results of the 10 bowl games follow (*USA Today,* January 8, 2010).

BowlGames

Bowl Game	Score	Predicted Point Margin	Actual Point Margin
Outback	Auburn 38 Northwestern 35	5	3
Gator	Florida State 33 West Virginia 21	1	12
Capital One	Penn State 19 LSU 17	3	2
Rose	Ohio State 26 Oregon 17	−2	9
Sugar	Florida 51 Cincinnati 24	14	27
Cotton	Mississippi State 21 Oklahoma State 7	3	14
Alamo	Texas Tech 41 Michigan State 31	9	10
Fiesta	Boise State 17 TCU 10	−4	7
Orange	Iowa 24 Georgia Tech 14	−3	10
Championship	Alabama 37 Texas 21	4	16

The predicted winning point margin was based on Las Vegas betting odds approximately one week before the bowl games were played. For example, Auburn was predicted to beat Northwestern in the Outback Bowl by five points. The actual winning point margin for Auburn was three points. A negative predicted winning point margin means that the team that won the bowl game was an underdog and expected to lose. For example, in the Rose Bowl, Ohio State was a two-point underdog to Oregon and ended up winning by nine points.

a. Develop a scatter diagram with predicted point margin on the horizontal axis.
b. What is the relationship between predicted and actual point margins?
c. Compute and interpret the sample covariance.
d. Compute the sample correlation coefficient. What does this value indicate about the relationship between the Las Vegas predicted point margin and the actual point margin in college football bowl games?

58. A department of transportation's study on driving speed and miles per gallon for midsize automobiles resulted in the following data:

Speed (Miles per Hour)	30	50	40	55	30	25	60	25	50	55
Miles per Gallon	28	25	25	23	30	32	21	35	26	25

Compute and interpret the sample correlation coefficient.

59. At the beginning of 2009, the economic downturn resulted in the loss of jobs and an increase in delinquent loans for housing. The national unemployment rate was 6.5% and the percentage of delinquent loans was 6.12% (*The Wall Street Journal,* January 27, 2009). In projecting where the real estate market was headed in the coming year, economists studied the relationship between the jobless rate and the percentage of delinquent loans. The expectation was that if the jobless rate continued to increase, there would also be an increase in the percentage of delinquent loans. The data below show the jobless rate and the delinquent loan percentage for 27 major real estate markets.

Housing

Metro Area	Jobless Rate (%)	Delinquent Loan (%)	Metro Area	Jobless Rate (%)	Delinquent Loan (%)
Atlanta	7.1	7.02	New York	6.2	5.78
Boston	5.2	5.31	Orange County	6.3	6.08
Charlotte	7.8	5.38	Orlando	7.0	10.05
Chicago	7.8	5.40	Philadelphia	6.2	4.75
Dallas	5.8	5.00	Phoenix	5.5	7.22
Denver	5.8	4.07	Portland	6.5	3.79
Detroit	9.3	6.53	Raleigh	6.0	3.62
Houston	5.7	5.57	Sacramento	8.3	9.24
Jacksonville	7.3	6.99	St. Louis	7.5	4.40
Las Vegas	7.6	11.12	San Diego	7.1	6.91
Los Angeles	8.2	7.56	San Francisco	6.8	5.57
Miami	7.1	12.11	Seattle	5.5	3.87
Minneapolis	6.3	4.39	Tampa	7.5	8.42
Nashville	6.6	4.78			

a. Compute the correlation coefficient. Is there a positive correlation between the jobless rate and the percentage of delinquent housing loans? What is your interpretation?

b. Show a scatter diagram of the relationship between jobless rate and the percentage of delinquent housing loans.

Russell

60. The Russell 1000 is a stock market index consisting of the largest U.S. companies. The Dow Jones Industrial Average is based on 30 large companies. The file Russell gives the annual percentage returns for each of these stock indexes for the years 1988 to 2012 (1stock1 website).

a. Plot these percentage returns using a scatter plot.

b. Compute the sample mean and standard deviation for each index.

c. Compute the sample correlation.

d. Discuss similarities and differences in these two indexes.

BestPrivateColleges

61. A random sample of 30 colleges from Kiplinger's list of the best values in private college provided the data shown in the WEBfile named BestPrivateColleges (Kiplinger, October 2013). The variable named Admit Rate (%) shows the percentage of students that applied to the college and were admitted, and the variable named 4-yr Grad. Rate (%) shows the percentage of students that were admitted and graduated in four years.

a. Develop a scatter diagram with Admit Rate (%) as the independent variable. What does the scatter diagram indicate about the relationship between the two variables?

b. Compute the sample correlation coefficient. What does the value of the sample correlation coefficient indicate about the relationship between the Admit Rate (%) and the 4-yr Grad. Rate (%)?

Data Dashboards: Adding Numerical Measures to Improve Effectiveness

In Section 2.5 we provided an introduction to data visualization, a term used to describe the use of graphical displays to summarize and present information about a data set. The goal of data visualization is to communicate key information about the data as effectively and clearly as possible. One of the most widely used data visualization tools is a data dashboard, a set of visual displays that organizes and presents information that is used to monitor the performance of a company or organization in a manner that is easy to read, understand, and interpret. In this section we extend the discussion of data dashboards to show how the addition of numerical measures can improve the overall effectiveness of the display.

The addition of numerical measures, such as the mean and standard deviation of key performance indicators (KPIs), to a data dashboard is critical because numerical measures often provide benchmarks or goals by which KPIs are evaluated. In addition, graphical displays that include numerical measures as components of the display are also frequently included in data dashboards. We must keep in mind that the purpose of a data dashboard is to provide information on the KPIs in a manner that is easy to read, understand, and interpret. Adding numerical measures and graphs that utilize numerical measures can help us accomplish these objectives.

To illustrate the use of numerical measures in a data dashboard, recall the Grogan Oil Company application that we used in Section 2.5 to introduce the concept of a data dashboard. Grogan Oil has offices located in three cities in Texas: Austin (its headquarters), Houston, and Dallas. Grogan's Information Technology (IT) call center, located in the Austin office, handles calls regarding computer-related problems (software, Internet, and email) from employees in the three offices. Figure 3.20 shows the data dashboard that Grogan developed to monitor the performance of the call center. The key components of this dashboard are as follows:

- The stacked bar chart in the upper left corner of the dashboard shows the call volume for each type of problem (software, Internet, or email) over time.
- The pie chart in the upper right corner of the dashboard shows the percentage of time that call center employees spent on each type of problem or not working on a call (idle).
- For each unresolved case that was received more than 15 minutes ago, the bar chart shown in the middle left portion of the dashboard shows the length of time that each of these cases has been unresolved.
- The bar chart in the middle right portion of the dashboard shows the call volume by office (Houston, Dallas, Austin) for each type of problem.
- The histogram at the bottom of the dashboard shows the distribution of the time to resolve a case for all resolved cases for the current shift.

In order to gain additional insight into the performance of the call center, Grogan's IT manager has decided to expand the current dashboard by adding box plots for the time required to resolve calls received for each type of problem (email, Internet, and software). In addition, a graph showing the time to resolve individual cases has been added in the lower left portion of the dashboard. Finally, the IT manager added a display of summary statistics for each type of problem and summary statistics for each of the first few hours of the shift. The updated dashboard is shown in Figure 3.21.

The IT call center has set a target performance level or benchmark of 10 minutes for the mean time to resolve a case. Furthermore, the center has decided it is undesirable for the time to resolve a case to exceed 15 minutes. To reflect these benchmarks, a black

FIGURE 3.20 INITIAL GROGAN OIL INFORMATION TECHNOLOGY CALL CENTER DATA DASHBOARD

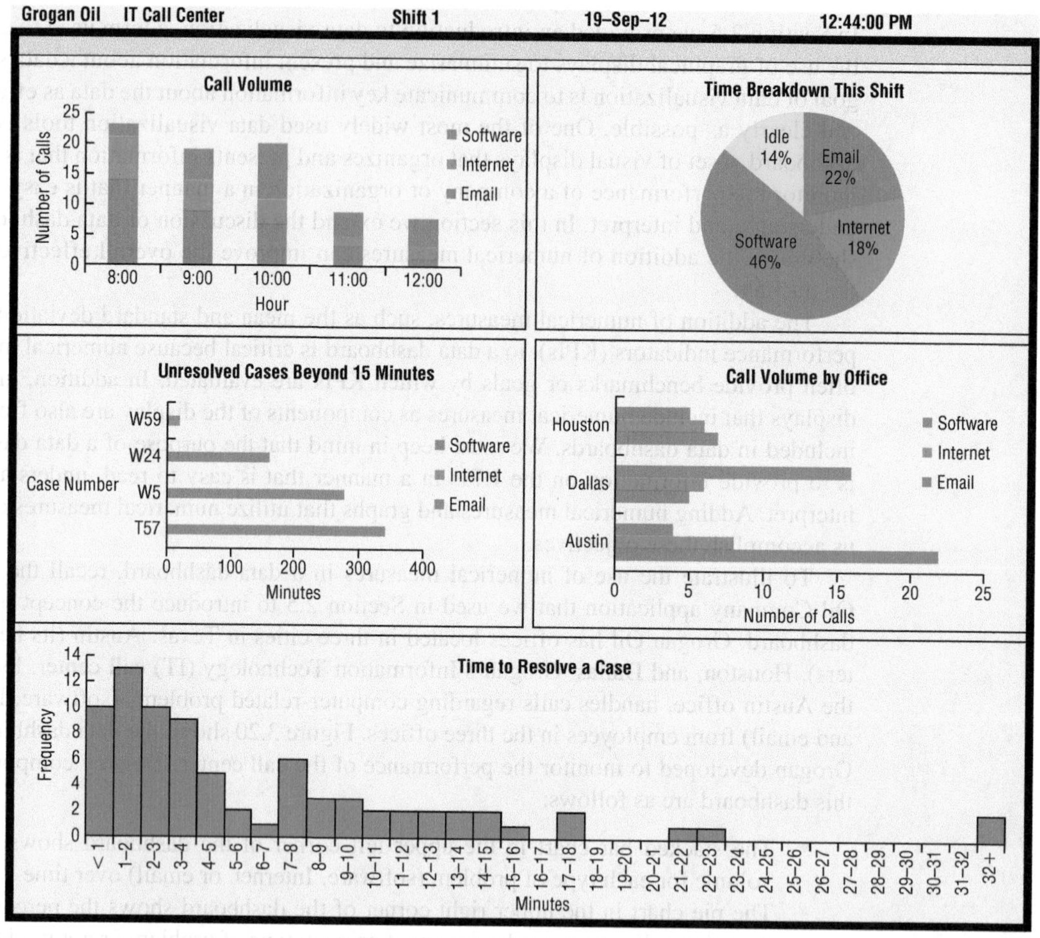

horizontal line at the mean target value of 10 minutes and a red horizontal line at the maximum acceptable level of 15 minutes have been added to both the graph showing the time to resolve cases and the box plots of the time required to resolve calls received for each type of problem.

The summary statistics in the dashboard in Figure 3.21 show that the mean time to resolve an email case is 5.8 minutes, the mean time to resolve an Internet case is 3.0 minutes, and the mean time to resolve a software case is 5.4 minutes. Thus, the mean time to resolve each type of case is better than the target mean (10 minutes).

Reviewing the box plots, we see that the box associated with the email cases is "larger" than the boxes associated with the other two types of cases. The summary statistics also show that the standard deviation of the time to resolve email cases is larger than the standard deviations of the times to resolve the other types of cases. This leads us to take a closer look at the email cases in the two new graphs. The box plot for the email cases has a whisker that extends beyond 15 minutes and an outlier well beyond 15 minutes. The graph of the time to resolve individual cases (in the lower left position

FIGURE 3.21 UPDATED GROGAN OIL INFORMATION TECHNOLOGY CALL CENTER DATA DASHBOARD

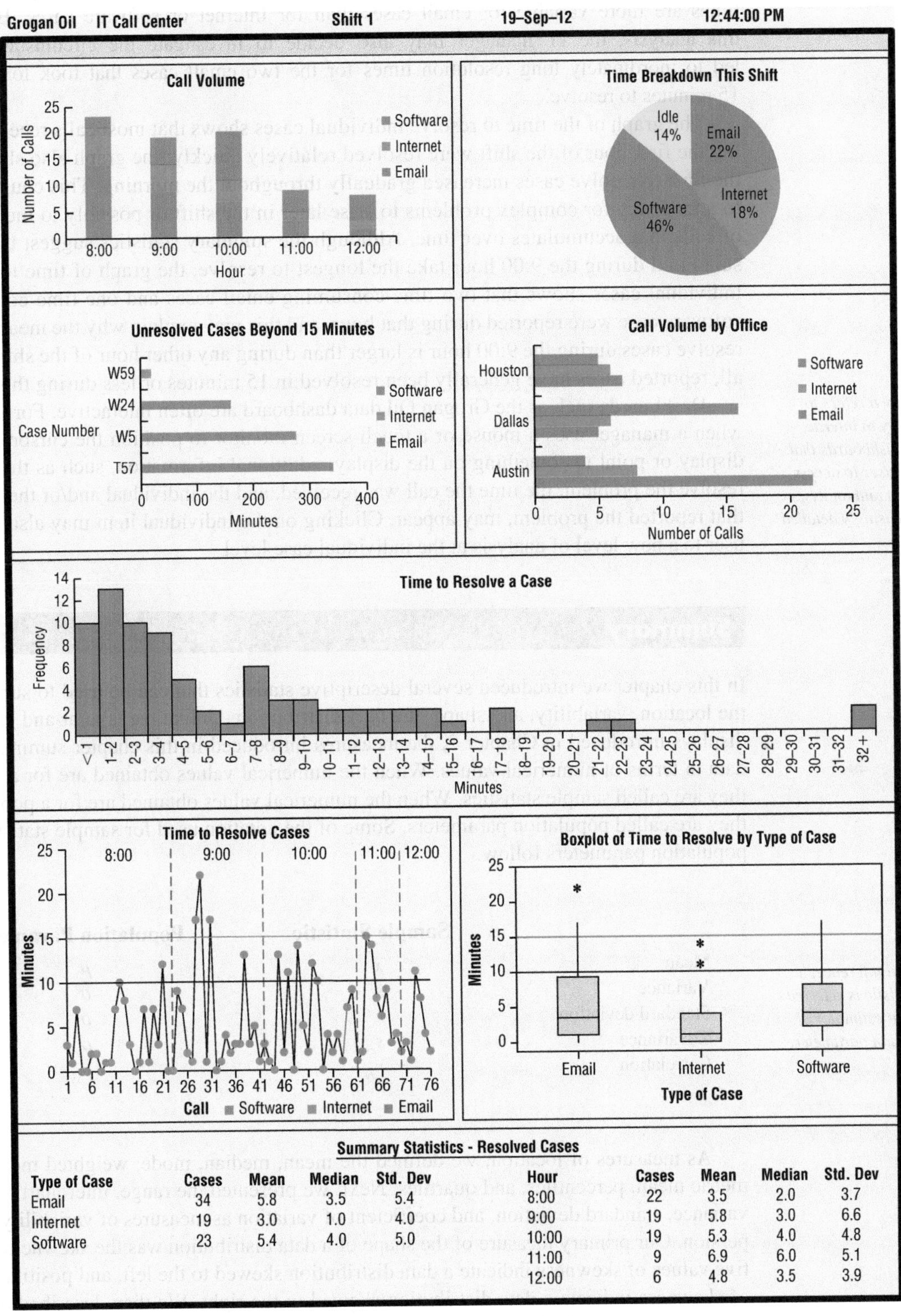

Type of Case	Cases	Mean	Median	Std. Dev
Email	34	5.8	3.5	5.4
Internet	19	3.0	1.0	4.0
Software	23	5.4	4.0	5.0

Hour	Cases	Mean	Median	Std. Dev
8:00	22	3.5	2.0	3.7
9:00	19	5.8	3.0	6.6
10:00	19	5.3	4.0	4.8
11:00	9	6.9	6.0	5.1
12:00	6	4.8	3.5	3.9

of the dashboard) shows that this is because of two calls on email cases during the 9:00 hour that took longer than the target maximum time (15 minutes) to resolve. This analysis may lead the IT call center manager to further investigate why resolution times are more variable for email cases than for Internet or software cases. Based on this analysis, the IT manager may also decide to investigate the circumstances that led to inordinately long resolution times for the two email cases that took longer than 15 minutes to resolve.

The graph of the time to resolve individual cases shows that most calls received during the first hour of the shift were resolved relatively quickly; the graph also shows that the time to resolve cases increased gradually throughout the morning. This could be due to a tendency for complex problems to arise later in the shift or possibly to the backlog of calls that accumulates over time. Although the summary statistics suggest that cases submitted during the 9:00 hour take the longest to resolve, the graph of time to resolve individual cases shows that two time-consuming email cases and one time-consuming software case were reported during that hour, and this may explain why the mean time to resolve cases during the 9:00 hour is larger than during any other hour of the shift. Overall, reported cases have generally been resolved in 15 minutes or less during this shift.

Drilling down refers to functionality in interactive data dashboards that allows the user to access information and analyses at an increasingly detailed level.

Dashboards such as the Grogan Oil data dashboard are often interactive. For instance, when a manager uses a mouse or a touch screen monitor to position the cursor over the display or point to something on the display, additional information, such as the time to resolve the problem, the time the call was received, and the individual and/or the location that reported the problem, may appear. Clicking on the individual item may also take the user to a new level of analysis at the individual case level.

Summary

In this chapter we introduced several descriptive statistics that can be used to summarize the location, variability, and shape of a data distribution. Unlike the tabular and graphical displays introduced in Chapter 2, the measures introduced in this chapter summarize the data in terms of numerical values. When the numerical values obtained are for a sample, they are called sample statistics. When the numerical values obtained are for a population, they are called population parameters. Some of the notation used for sample statistics and population parameters follow.

In statistical inference, a sample statistic is referred to as a point estimator of the population parameter.

	Sample Statistic	Population Parameter
Mean	$\bar{x}$	μ
Variance	s^2	σ^2
Standard deviation	s	σ
Covariance	s_{xy}	σ_{xy}
Correlation	r_{xy}	ρ_{xy}

As measures of location, we defined the mean, median, mode, weighted mean, geometric mean, percentiles, and quartiles. Next, we presented the range, interquartile range, variance, standard deviation, and coefficient of variation as measures of variability or dispersion. Our primary measure of the shape of a data distribution was the skewness. Negative values of skewness indicate a data distribution skewed to the left, and positive values of skewness indicate a data distribution skewed to the right. We then described how the mean and standard deviation could be used, applying Chebyshev's theorem and the empirical rule, to provide more information about the distribution of data and to identify outliers.

In Section 3.4 we showed how to develop a five-number summary and a box plot to provide simultaneous information about the location, variability, and shape of the distribution. In Section 3.5 we introduced covariance and the correlation coefficient as measures of association between two variables. In the final section, we showed how adding numerical measures can improve the effectiveness of data dashboards.

The descriptive statistics we discussed can be developed using statistical software packages and spreadsheets. In the chapter-ending appendixes we show how to use StatTools to develop the descriptive statistics introduced in this chapter.

Glossary

Sample statistic A numerical value used as a summary measure for a sample (e.g., the sample mean, $\bar{x}$, the sample variance, s^2, and the sample standard deviation, s).

Population parameter A numerical value used as a summary measure for a population (e.g., the population mean, μ, the population variance, σ^2, and the population standard deviation, σ).

Point estimator A sample statistic, such as $\bar{x}$, s^2, and s, used to estimate the corresponding population parameter.

Mean A measure of central location computed by summing the data values and dividing by the number of observations.

Median A measure of central location provided by the value in the middle when the data are arranged in ascending order.

Mode A measure of location, defined as the value that occurs with greatest frequency.

Weighted mean The mean obtained by assigning each observation a weight that reflects its importance.

Geometric mean A measure of location that is calculated by finding the nth root of the product of n values.

Percentile A value that provides information about how the data are spread over the interval from the smallest to the largest value.

***p*th percentile** For a data set containing n observations, the pth percentile divides the data into two parts: Approximately $p\%$ of the observations are less than the pth percentile and approximately $(100 - p)\%$ of the observations are greater than the pth percentile.

Quartiles The 25th, 50th, and 75th percentiles, referred to as the first quartile, the second quartile (median), and third quartile, respectively. The quartiles can be used to divide a data set into four parts, with each part containing approximately 25% of the data.

Range A measure of variability, defined to be the largest value minus the smallest value.

Interquartile range (IQR) A measure of variability, defined to be the difference between the third and first quartiles.

Variance A measure of variability based on the squared deviations of the data values about the mean.

Standard deviation A measure of variability computed by taking the positive square root of the variance.

Coefficient of variation A measure of relative variability computed by dividing the standard deviation by the mean and multiplying by 100.

Skewness A measure of the shape of a data distribution. Data skewed to the left result in negative skewness; a symmetric data distribution results in zero skewness; and data skewed to the right result in positive skewness.

***z*-score** A value computed by dividing the deviation about the mean $(x_i - \bar{x})$ by the standard deviation s. A z-score is referred to as a standardized value and denotes the number of standard deviations x_i is from the mean.

Chebyshev's theorem A theorem that can be used to make statements about the proportion of data values that must be within a specified number of standard deviations of the mean.

Empirical rule A rule that can be used to compute the percentage of data values that must be within one, two, and three standard deviations of the mean for data that exhibit a bell-shaped distribution.

Outlier An unusually small or unusually large data value.

Five-number summary A technique that uses five numbers to summarize the data: smallest value, first quartile, median, third quartile, and largest value.

Box plot A graphical summary of data based on a five-number summary.

Covariance A measure of linear association between two variables. Positive values indicate a positive relationship; negative values indicate a negative relationship.

Correlation coefficient A measure of linear association between two variables that takes on values between −1 and +1. Values near +1 indicate a strong positive linear relationship; values near −1 indicate a strong negative linear relationship; and values near zero indicate the lack of a linear relationship.

Key Formulas

Sample Mean

$$\bar{x} = \frac{\Sigma x_i}{n} \tag{3.1}$$

Population Mean

$$\mu = \frac{\Sigma x_i}{N} \tag{3.2}$$

Weighted Mean

$$\bar{x} = \frac{\Sigma w_i x_i}{\Sigma w_i} \tag{3.3}$$

Geometric Mean

$$\bar{x}_g = \sqrt[n]{(x_1)(x_2)\cdots(x_n)} = [(x_1)(x_2)\cdots(x_n)]^{1/n} \tag{3.4}$$

Location of the *p*th Percentile

$$L_p = \frac{p}{100}(n + 1) \tag{3.5}$$

Interquartile Range

$$\text{IQR} = Q_3 - Q_1 \tag{3.6}$$

Population Variance

$$\sigma^2 = \frac{\Sigma(x_i - \mu)^2}{N} \tag{3.7}$$

Sample Variance

$$s^2 = \frac{\Sigma(x_i - \bar{x})^2}{n - 1} \tag{3.8}$$

Standard Deviation

$$\text{Sample standard deviation} = s = \sqrt{s^2} \tag{3.9}$$

$$\text{Population standard deviation} = \sigma = \sqrt{\sigma^2} \tag{3.10}$$

Coefficient of Variation

$$\left(\frac{\text{Standard deviation}}{\text{Mean}} \times 100\right)\% \tag{3.11}$$

***z*-Score**

$$z_i = \frac{x_i - \bar{x}}{s} \tag{3.12}$$

Sample Covariance

$$s_{xy} = \frac{\Sigma(x_i - \bar{x})(y_i - \bar{y})}{n - 1} \tag{3.13}$$

Population Covariance

$$\sigma_{xy} = \frac{\Sigma(x_i - \mu_x)(y_i - \mu_y)}{N} \tag{3.14}$$

Pearson Product Moment Correlation Coefficient: Sample Data

$$r_{xy} = \frac{s_{xy}}{s_x s_y} \tag{3.15}$$

Pearson Product Moment Correlation Coefficient: Population Data

$$\rho_{xy} = \frac{\sigma_{xy}}{\sigma_x \sigma_y} \tag{3.16}$$

Supplementary Exercises

62. The average number of times Americans dine out in a week fell from 4.0 in 2008 to 3.8 in 2012 (Zagat.com, April 1, 2012). The number of times a sample of 20 families dined out last week provides the following data.

6	1	5	3	7	3	0	3	1	3
4	1	2	4	1	0	5	6	3	1

a. Compute the mean and median.
b. Compute the first and third quartiles.
c. Compute the range and interquartile range.
d. Compute the variance and standard deviation.
e. The skewness measure for these data is 0.34. Comment on the shape of this distribution. Is it the shape you would expect? Why or why not?
f. Do the data contain outliers?

Coaches

63. *USA Today* reports that NCAA colleges and universities are paying higher salaries to a newly recruited football coach compared to what they paid their previous football coach. (*USA Today*, February 12, 2013). The annual base salaries for the previous head football coach and the new head football coach at 23 schools are given in the file Coaches.
   a. Determine the median annual salary for a previous head football coach and a new head football coach.
   b. Compute the range for salaries for both previous and new head football coaches.
   c. Compute the standard deviation for salaries for both previous and new head football coaches.
   d. Based on your answers to (a) to (c), comment on any differences between the annual base salary a school pays a new head football coach compared to what it paid its pervious head football coach.

64. The average waiting time for a patient at an El Paso physician's office is just over 29 minutes, well above the national average of 21 minutes. In fact, El Paso has the longest physician's office waiting times in the United States (*El Paso Times*, January 8, 2012). In order to address the issue of long patient wait times, some physicians' offices are using wait tracking systems to notify patients of expected wait times. Patients can adjust their arrival times based on this information and spend less time in waiting rooms. The following data show wait times (minutes) for a sample of patients at offices that do not have an office tracking system and wait times for a sample of patients at offices with an office tracking system.

WaitTracking

Without Wait Tracking System	With Wait Tracking System
24	31
67	11
17	14
20	18
31	12
44	37
12	9
23	13
16	12
37	15

   a. What are the mean and median patient wait times for offices with a wait tracking system? What are the mean and median patient wait times for offices without a wait tracking system?
   b. What are the variance and standard deviation of patient wait times for offices with a wait tracking system? What are the variance and standard deviation of patient wait times for visits to offices without a wait tracking system?
   c. Do offices with a wait tracking system have shorter patient wait times than offices without a wait tracking system? Explain.
   d. Considering only offices without a wait tracking system, what is the z-score for the tenth patient in the sample?
   e. Considering only offices with a wait tracking system, what is the z-score for the sixth patient in the sample? How does this z-score compare with the z-score you calculated for part (d)?
   f. Based on z-scores, do the data for offices without a wait tracking system contain any outliers? Based on z-scores, do the data for offices with a wait tracking system contain any outliers?

Sleep

65. U.S. companies lose $63.2 billion per year from workers with insomnia. Workers lose an average of 7.8 days of productivity per year due to lack of sleep (*Wall Street Journal*, January 23, 2013). The following data show the number of hours of sleep attained during a recent night for a sample of 20 workers.

6	5	10	5	6	9	9	5	9	5
8	7	8	6	9	8	9	6	10	8

a. What is the mean number of hours of sleep for this sample?
b. What is the variance? Standard deviation?

Smartphone

66. A study of smartphone users shows that 68% of smartphone use occurs at home and a user spends an average of 410 minutes per month using a smartphone to interact with other people (*Harvard Business Review*, January–February 2013). Consider the following data indicating the number of minutes in a month spent interacting with others via a smartphone for a sample of 50 smartphone users.

353	458	404	394	416
437	430	369	448	430
431	469	446	387	445
354	468	422	402	360
444	424	441	357	435
461	407	470	413	351
464	374	417	460	352
445	387	468	368	430
384	367	436	390	464
405	372	401	388	367

a. What is the mean number of minutes spent interacting with others for this sample? How does it compare to the mean reported in the study?
b. What is the standard deviation for this sample?
c. Are there any outliers in this sample?

67. Public transportation and the automobile are two methods an employee can use to get to work each day. Samples of times recorded for each method are shown. Times are in minutes.

Transportation

Public Transportation:	28	29	32	37	33	25	29	32	41	34
Automobile:	29	31	33	32	34	30	31	32	35	33

a. Compute the sample mean time to get to work for each method.
b. Compute the sample standard deviation for each method.
c. On the basis of your results from parts (a) and (b), which method of transportation should be preferred? Explain.
d. Develop a box plot for each method. Does a comparison of the box plots support your conclusion in part (c)?

68. In 2007 the *New York Times* reported that the median annual household income in the United States was $55,500 (*New York Times* website, August, 21, 2013). Answer the following questions based on the following sample of 14 household incomes for 2013 ($1000s).

49.4	52.4	53.4	51.3	52.1	48.7	52.1
52.2	64.5	51.6	46.5	52.9	52.5	51.2

a. What is the median household income for the sample data for 2013?
b. Based on the sample data, estimate the percentage change in the median household income from 2007 to 2013.
c. Compute the first and third quartiles.
d. Provide a five-number summary.
e. Using the z-score approach, do the data contain any outliers? Does the approach that uses the values of the first and third quartiles and the interquartile range to detect outliers provide the same results?

FoodIndustry

69. The data contained in the WEBfile named FoodIndustry show the company/chain name, the average sales per store ($1000s), and the food segment industry for 47 restaurant chains (*Quick Service Restaurant Magazine* website, August 2013).
    a. What was the mean U.S. sales per store for the 47 restaurant chains?
    b. What are the first and third quartiles? What is your interpretation of the quartiles?
    c. Show a box plot for the level of sales and discuss if there are any outliers in terms of sales that would skew the results.
    d. Develop a frequency distribution showing the average sales per store for each segment. Comment on the results obtained.
70. *Travel + Leisure* magazine presented its annual list of the 500 best hotels in the world (*Travel + Leisure,* January 2009). The magazine provides a rating for each hotel along with a brief description that includes the size of the hotel, amenities, and the cost per night for a double room. A sample of 12 of the top-rated hotels in the United States follows.

Travel

Hotel	Location	Rooms	Cost/Night
Boulders Resort & Spa	Phoenix, AZ	220	499
Disney's Wilderness Lodge	Orlando, FL	727	340
Four Seasons Hotel Beverly Hills	Los Angeles, CA	285	585
Four Seasons Hotel	Boston, MA	273	495
Hay-Adams	Washington, DC	145	495
Inn on Biltmore Estate	Asheville, NC	213	279
Loews Ventana Canyon Resort	Phoenix, AZ	398	279
Mauna Lani Bay Hotel	Island of Hawaii	343	455
Montage Laguna Beach	Laguna Beach, CA	250	595
Sofitel Water Tower	Chicago, IL	414	367
St. Regis Monarch Beach	Dana Point, CA	400	675
The Broadmoor	Colorado Springs, CO	700	420

    a. What is the mean number of rooms?
    b. What is the mean cost per night for a double room?
    c. Develop a scatter diagram with the number of rooms on the horizontal axis and the cost per night on the vertical axis. Does there appear to be a relationship between the number of rooms and the cost per night? Discuss.
    d. What is the sample correlation coefficient? What does it tell you about the relationship between the number of rooms and the cost per night for a double room? Does this appear reasonable? Discuss.
71. The 32 teams in the National Football League (NFL) are worth, on average, $1.17 billion, 5% more than last year. The following data show the annual revenue ($ millions) and the estimated team value ($ millions) for the 32 NFL teams (*Forbes* website, February 28, 2014).

NFLTeamValue

Team	Revenue ($ millions)	Current Value ($ millions)
Arizona Cardinals	253	961
Atlanta Falcons	252	933
Baltimore Ravens	292	1227
Buffalo Bills	256	870
Carolina Panthers	271	1057
Chicago Bears	298	1252
Cincinnati Bengals	250	924
Cleveland Browns	264	1005
Dallas Cowboys	539	2300
Denver Broncos	283	1161
Detroit Lions	248	900
Green Bay Packers	282	1183
Houston Texans	320	1450
Indianapolis Colts	276	1200
Jacksonville Jaguars	260	840
Kansas City Chiefs	245	1009
Miami Dolphins	268	1074
Minnesota Vikings	234	1007
New England Patriots	408	1800
New Orleans Saints	276	1004
New York Giants	338	1550
New York Jets	321	1380
Oakland Raiders	229	825
Philadelphia Eagles	306	1314
Pittsburgh Steelers	266	1118
San Diego Chargers	250	949
San Francisco 49ers	255	1224
Seattle Seahawks	270	1081
St. Louis Rams	239	875
Tampa Bay Buccaneers	267	1067
Tennessee Titans	270	1055
Washington Redskins	381	1700

a. Develop a scatter diagram with Revenue on the horizontal axis and Value on the vertical axis. Does there appear that there are any relationship between the two variables?
b. What is the sample correlation coefficient? What can you say about the strength of the relationship between Revenue and Value?

72. Does a major league baseball team's record during spring training indicate how the team will play during the regular season? Over the last six years, the correlation coefficient between a team's winning percentage in spring training and its winning percentage in the regular season is .18 (*The Wall Street Journal,* March 30, 2009).

SpringTraining

Team	Spring Training	Regular Season	Team	Spring Training	Regular Season
Baltimore Orioles	.407	.422	Minnesota Twins	.500	.540
Boston Red Sox	.429	.586	New York Yankees	.577	.549
Chicago White Sox	.417	.546	Oakland A's	.692	.466
Cleveland Indians	.569	.500	Seattle Mariners	.500	.377
Detroit Tigers	.569	.457	Tampa Bay Rays	.731	.599
Kansas City Royals	.533	.463	Texas Rangers	.643	.488
Los Angeles Angels	.724	.617	Toronto Blue Jays	.448	.531

Shown are the winning percentages for the 14 American League teams during the 2008 season.

a. What is the correlation coefficient between the spring training and the regular season winning percentages?
b. What is your conclusion about a team's record during spring training indicating how the team will play during the regular season? What are some of the reasons why this occurs? Discuss.

73. The days to maturity for a sample of five money market funds are shown here. The dollar amounts invested in the funds are provided. Use the weighted mean to determine the mean number of days to maturity for dollars invested in these five money market funds.

Days to Maturity	Dollar Value ($millions)
20	20
12	30
7	10
5	15
6	10

74. Automobiles traveling on a road with a posted speed limit of 55 miles per hour are checked for speed by a state police radar system. Following is a frequency distribution of speeds.

Speed (miles per hour)	Frequency
47	10
52	40
57	150
62	175
67	75
72	15
77	10
Total	475

a. What is the mean speed of the automobiles traveling on this road?
b. Compute the variance and the standard deviation.

75. The Panama Railroad Company was established in 1850 to construct a railroad across the isthmus that would allow fast and easy access between the Atlantic and Pacific Oceans. The following table provides annual returns for Panama Railroad stock from 1853 through 1880 (*The Big Ditch*, Mauer and Yu, 2011).

a. Create a graph of the annual returns on the stock. The New York Stock Exchange earned an annual average return of 8.4% from 1853 through 1880. Can you tell from the graph if the Panama Railroad Company stock outperformed the New York Stock Exchange?
b. Calculate the mean annual return on Panama Railroad Company stock from 1853 through 1880. Did the stock outperform the New York Stock Exchange over the same period?

PanamaRailroad

Year	Return on Panama Railroad Company Stock (%)
1853	−1
1854	−9
1855	19
1856	2
1857	3
1858	36
1859	21
1860	16
1861	−5
1862	43
1863	44
1864	48
1865	7
1866	11
1867	23
1868	20
1869	−11
1870	−51
1871	−42
1872	39
1873	42
1874	12
1875	26
1876	9
1877	−6
1878	25
1879	31
1880	30

Case Problem 1 Pelican Stores

Pelican Stores, a division of National Clothing, is a chain of women's apparel stores operating throughout the country. The chain recently ran a promotion in which discount coupons were sent to customers of other National Clothing stores. Data collected for a sample of 100 in-store credit card transactions at Pelican Stores during one day while the promotion was running are contained in the file named PelicanStores. Table 3.9 shows a portion of the data set. The proprietary card method of payment refers to charges made using a National Clothing charge card. Customers who made a purchase using a discount coupon are referred to as promotional customers and customers who made a purchase but did not use a discount coupon are referred to as regular customers. Because the promotional coupons were not sent to regular Pelican Stores customers, management considers the sales made to people presenting the promotional coupons as sales it would not otherwise make. Of course, Pelican also hopes that the promotional customers will continue to shop at its stores.

Most of the variables shown in Table 3.9 are self-explanatory, but two of the variables require some clarification.

Items	The total number of items purchased
Net Sales	The total amount ($) charged to the credit card

Pelican's management would like to use this sample data to learn about its customer base and to evaluate the promotion involving discount coupons.

TABLE 3.9 SAMPLE OF 100 CREDIT CARD PURCHASES AT PELICAN STORES

PelicanStores

Customer	Type of Customer	Items	Net Sales	Method of Payment	Gender	Marital Status	Age
1	Regular	1	39.50	Discover	Male	Married	32
2	Promotional	1	102.40	Proprietary Card	Female	Married	36
3	Regular	1	22.50	Proprietary Card	Female	Married	32
4	Promotional	5	100.40	Proprietary Card	Female	Married	28
5	Regular	2	54.00	MasterCard	Female	Married	34
6	Regular	1	44.50	MasterCard	Female	Married	44
7	Promotional	2	78.00	Proprietary Card	Female	Married	30
8	Regular	1	22.50	Visa	Female	Married	40
9	Promotional	2	56.52	Proprietary Card	Female	Married	46
10	Regular	1	44.50	Proprietary Card	Female	Married	36
⋮	⋮	⋮	⋮	⋮	⋮	⋮	⋮
96	Regular	1	39.50	MasterCard	Female	Married	44
97	Promotional	9	253.00	Proprietary Card	Female	Married	30
98	Promotional	10	287.59	Proprietary Card	Female	Married	52
99	Promotional	2	47.60	Proprietary Card	Female	Married	30
100	Promotional	1	28.44	Proprietary Card	Female	Married	44

Managerial Report

Use the methods of descriptive statistics presented in this chapter to summarize the data and comment on your findings. At a minimum, your report should include the following:

1. Descriptive statistics on net sales and descriptive statistics on net sales by various classifications of customers.
2. Descriptive statistics concerning the relationship between age and net sales.

Case Problem 2 Motion Picture Industry

The motion picture industry is a competitive business. More than 50 studios produce several hundred new motion pictures each year, and the financial success of the motion pictures varies considerably. The opening weekend gross sales, the total gross sales, the number of theaters the movie was shown in, and the number of weeks the motion picture was in release are common variables used to measure the success of a motion picture. Data on the top 100 grossing motion pictures released in 2011 (Box Office Mojo website, March 17, 2012) are contained in a file named 2011Movies. Table 3.10 shows the data for the first 10 motion pictures in this file. Note that some movies, such as *War Horse*, were released late in 2011 and continued to run in 2012.

Managerial Report

Use the numerical methods of descriptive statistics presented in this chapter to learn how these variables contribute to the success of a motion picture. Include the following in your report:

1. Descriptive statistics for each of the four variables along with a discussion of what the descriptive statistics tell us about the motion picture industry.

TABLE 3.10 PERFORMANCE DATA FOR 10 MOTION PICTURES

2011Movies

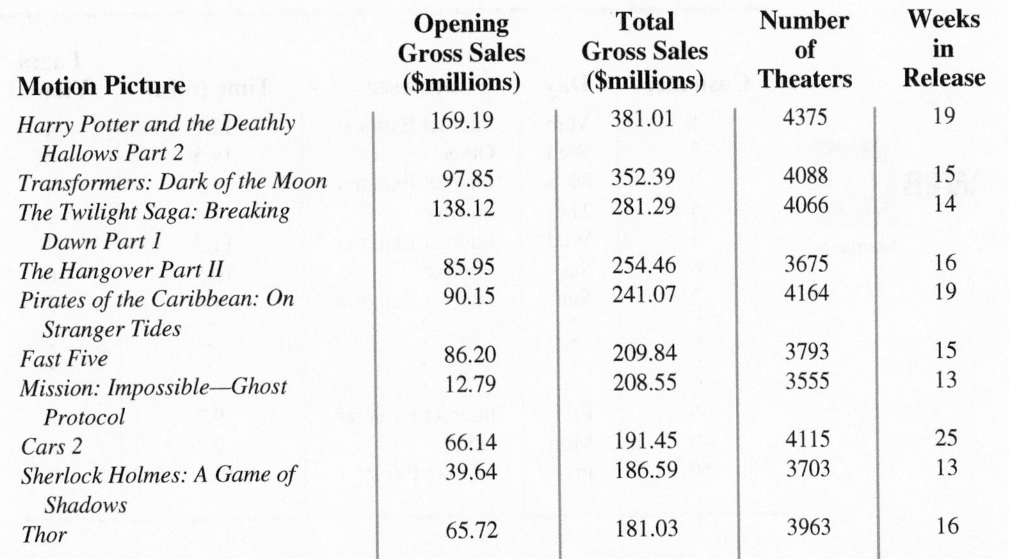

Motion Picture	Opening Gross Sales ($millions)	Total Gross Sales ($millions)	Number of Theaters	Weeks in Release
Harry Potter and the Deathly Hallows Part 2	169.19	381.01	4375	19
Transformers: Dark of the Moon	97.85	352.39	4088	15
The Twilight Saga: Breaking Dawn Part 1	138.12	281.29	4066	14
The Hangover Part II	85.95	254.46	3675	16
Pirates of the Caribbean: On Stranger Tides	90.15	241.07	4164	19
Fast Five	86.20	209.84	3793	15
Mission: Impossible—Ghost Protocol	12.79	208.55	3555	13
Cars 2	66.14	191.45	4115	25
Sherlock Holmes: A Game of Shadows	39.64	186.59	3703	13
Thor	65.72	181.03	3963	16

2. What motion pictures, if any, should be considered high-performance outliers? Explain.
3. Descriptive statistics showing the relationship between total gross sales and each of the other variables. Discuss.

Case Problem 3 Heavenly Chocolates Website Transactions

Heavenly Chocolates manufactures and sells quality chocolate products at its plant and retail store located in Saratoga Springs, New York. Two years ago the company developed a website and began selling its products over the Internet. Website sales have exceeded the company's expectations, and mangement is now considering stragegies to increase sales even further. To learn more about the website customers, a sample of 50 Heavenly Chocolate transactions was selected from the previous month's sales. Data showing the day of the week each transaction was made, the type of browser the customer used, the time spent on the website, the number of website pages viewed, and the amount spent by each of the 50 customers are contained in the file named Shoppers. A portion of the data is shown in Table 3.11.

Heavenly Chocolates would like to use the sample data to determine if online shoppers who spend more time and view more pages also spend more money during their visit to the website. The company would also like to investigate the effect that the day of the week and the type of browser have on sales.

Managerial Report

Use the methods of descriptive statistics to learn about the customers who visit the Heavenly Chocolates website. Include the following in your report.

1. Graphical and numerical summaries for the length of time the shopper spends on the website, the number of pages viewed, and the mean amount spent per transaction.

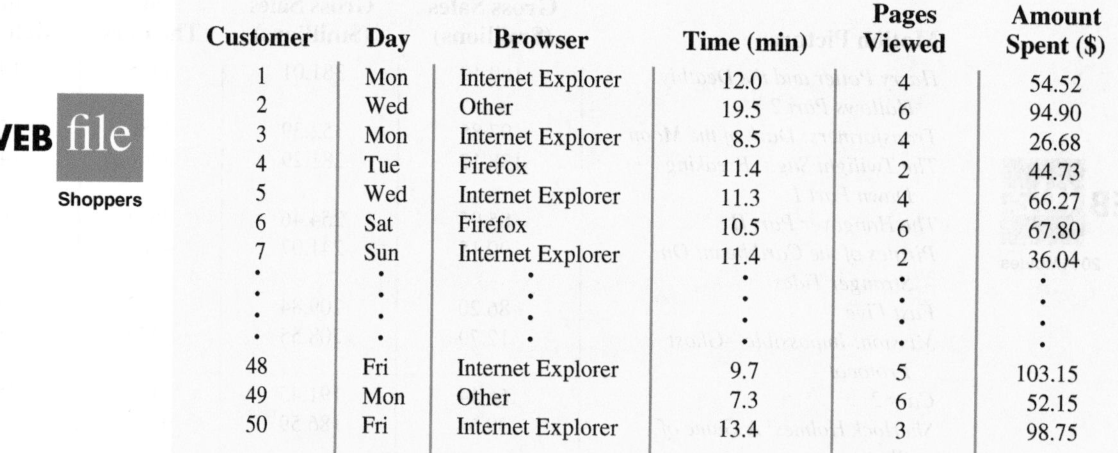

WEB file

Shoppers

TABLE 3.11 A SAMPLE OF 50 HEAVENLY CHOCOLATES WEBSITE TRANSACTIONS

Customer	Day	Browser	Time (min)	Pages Viewed	Amount Spent ($)
1	Mon	Internet Explorer	12.0	4	54.52
2	Wed	Other	19.5	6	94.90
3	Mon	Internet Explorer	8.5	4	26.68
4	Tue	Firefox	11.4	2	44.73
5	Wed	Internet Explorer	11.3	4	66.27
6	Sat	Firefox	10.5	6	67.80
7	Sun	Internet Explorer	11.4	2	36.04
•	•	•	•	•	•
•	•	•	•	•	•
•	•	•	•	•	•
48	Fri	Internet Explorer	9.7	5	103.15
49	Mon	Other	7.3	6	52.15
50	Fri	Internet Explorer	13.4	3	98.75

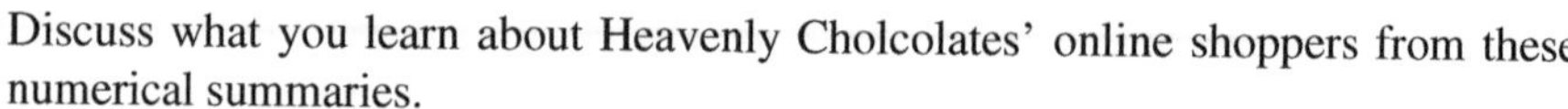

Discuss what you learn about Heavenly Cholcolates' online shoppers from these numerical summaries.

2. Summarize the frequency, the total dollars spent, and the mean amount spent per transaction for each day of week. What observations can you make about Heavenly Chocolates' business based on the day of the week? Discuss.
3. Summarize the frequency, the total dollars spent, and the mean amount spent per transaction for each type of browser. What observations can you make about Heavenly Chocolates' business based on the type of browser? Discuss.
4. Develop a scatter diagram and compute the sample correlation coefficient to explore the relationship between the time spent on the website and the dollar amount spent. Use the horizontal axis for the time spent on the website. Discuss.
5. Develop a scatter diagram and compute the sample correlation coefficient to explore the relationship between the the number of website pages viewed and the amount spent. Use the horizontal axis for the number of website pages viewed. Discuss.
6. Develop a scatter diagram and compute the sample correlation coefficient to explore the relationship between the time spent on the website and the number of pages viewed. Use the horizontal axis to represent the number of pages viewed. Discuss.

Case Problem 4 African Elephant Populations

Although millions of elephants once roamed across Africa, by the mid-1980s elephant populations in African nations had been devastated by poaching. Elephants are important to African ecosystems. In tropical forests, elephants create clearings in the canopy that encourage new tree growth. In savannas, elephants reduce bush cover to create an environment that is favorable to browsing and grazing animals. In addition, the seeds of many plant species depend on passing through an elephant's digestive tract before germination.

The status of the elephant now varies greatly across the continent; in some nations, strong measures have been taken to effectively protect elephant populations, while in other nations

TABLE 3.12 ELEPHANT POPULATIONS FOR SEVERAL AFRICAN NATIONS IN 1979, 1989, AND 2007

AfricanElephants

	Elephant population		
Country	**1979**	**1989**	**2007**
Angola	12,400	12,400	2530
Botswana	20,000	51,000	175,487
Cameroon	16,200	21,200	15,387
Cen African Rep	63,000	19,000	3334
Chad	15,000	3100	6435
Congo	10,800	70,000	22,102
Dem Rep of Congo	377,700	85,000	23,714
Gabon	13,400	76,000	70,637
Kenya	65,000	19,000	31,636
Mozambique	54,800	18,600	26,088
Somalia	24,300	6000	70
Sudan	134,000	4000	300
Tanzania	316,300	80,000	167,003
Zambia	150,000	41,000	29,231
Zimbabwe	30,000	43,000	99,107

the elephant populations remain in danger due to poaching for meat and ivory, loss of habitat, and conflict with humans. Table 3.12 shows elephant populations for several African nations in 1979, 1989, and 2007 (Lemieux and Clarke, "The International Ban on Ivory Sales and Its Effects on Elephant Poaching in Africa," *British Journal of Criminology,* 49(4), 2009).

The David Sheldrick Wildlife Trust was established in 1977 to honor the memory of naturalist David Leslie William Sheldrick, who founded Warden of Tsavo East National Park in Kenya and headed the Planning Unit of the Wildlife Conservation and Management Department in that country. Management of the Sheldrick Trust would like to know what these data indicate about elephant populations in various African countries since 1979.

Managerial Report

Use methods of descriptive statistics to summarize the data and comment on changes in elephant populations in African nations since 1979. At a minimum your report should include the following.

1. The mean annual change in elephant population for each country in the 10 years from 1979 to 1989, and a discussion of which countries saw the largest changes in elephant population over this 10-year period.
2. The mean annual change in elephant population for each country from 1989 to 2007, and a discussion of which countries saw the largest changes in elephant population over this 18-year period.
3. A comparison of your results from parts 1 and 2, and a discussion of the conclusions you can draw from this comparison.

CHAPTER 4

Introduction to Probability

CONTENTS

STATISTICS IN PRACTICE: NATIONAL AERONAUTICS AND SPACE ADMINISTRATION

4.1 RANDOM EXPERIMENTS, COUNTING RULES, AND ASSIGNING PROBABILITIES
Counting Rules, Combinations, and Permutations
Assigning Probabilities
Probabilities for the KP&L Project

4.2 EVENTS AND THEIR PROBABILITIES

4.3 SOME BASIC RELATIONSHIPS OF PROBABILITY
Complement of an Event
Addition Law

4.4 CONDITIONAL PROBABILITY
Independent Events
Multiplication Law

4.5 BAYES' THEOREM
Tabular Approach

STATISTICS *in* PRACTICE

NATIONAL AERONAUTICS AND SPACE ADMINISTRATION*
WASHINGTON, D.C.

The National Aeronautics and Space Administration (NASA) is the agency of the United States government that is responsible for the U.S. civilian space program and aeronautics and aerospace research. NASA is best known for its manned space exploration; its mission statement is to "pioneer the future in space exploration, scientific discovery and aeronautics research." NASA, with its 18,800 employees, is currently working on the design of a new Space Launch System that will take the astronauts farther into space than ever before and provide the cornerstone for future human space exploration.

Although NASA's primary mission is space exploration, its expertise has been called upon to assist countries and organizations throughout the world. In one such situation, the San José copper and gold mine in Copiapó, Chile, caved in, trapping 33 men more than 2000 feet underground. While it was important to bring the men safely to the surface as quickly as possible, it was imperative that the rescue effort be carefully designed and implemented to save as many miners as possible. The Chilean government asked NASA to provide assistance in developing a rescue method. In response, NASA sent a four-person team consisting of an engineer, two physicians, and a psychologist with expertise in vehicle design and issues of long-term confinement.

The probability of success and failure of various rescue methods was prominent in the thoughts of everyone involved. Since there were no historical data available that applied to this unique rescue situation, NASA scientists developed subjective probability estimates for the success and failure of various rescue methods based on similar circumstances experienced by astronauts returning from short- and long-term space missions. The probability estimates provided by NASA guided officials in the selection of a rescue method and provided insight as to how the miners would survive the ascent in a rescue cage.

NASA scientists based probabilities on similar circumstances experienced during space flights.

The rescue method designed by the Chilean officials in consultation with the NASA team resulted in the construction of 13-foot-long, 924-pound steel rescue capsule that would be used to bring up the miners one at a time. All miners were rescued, with the last miner emerging 68 days after the cave-in occurred.

In this chapter you will learn about probability as well as how to compute and interpret probabilities for a variety of situations. In addition to subjective probabilities, you will learn about classical and relative frequency methods for assigning probabilities. The basic relationships of probability, conditional probability, and Bayes' theorem will be covered.

*The authors are indebted to Dr. Michael Duncan and Clinton Cragg at NASA for providing this Statistics in Practice.

Managers often base their decisions on an analysis of uncertainties such as the following:

1. What are the chances that sales will decrease if we increase prices?
2. What is the likelihood that a new assembly method will increase productivity?
3. How likely is it that the project will be finished on time?
4. What is the chance that a new investment will be profitable?

Some of the earliest work on probability originated in a series of letters between Pierre de Fermat and Blaise Pascal in the 1650s.

Probability is a numerical measure of the likelihood that an event will occur. Thus, probabilities can be used as measures of the degree of uncertainty associated with the

FIGURE 4.1 PROBABILITY AS A NUMERICAL MEASURE OF THE LIKELIHOOD OF AN EVENT OCCURRING

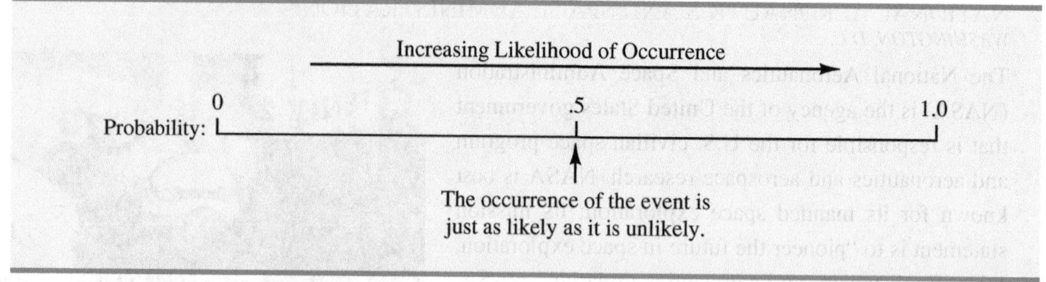

four events previously listed. If probabilities are available, we can determine the likelihood of each event occurring.

Probability values are always assigned on a scale from 0 to 1. A probability near zero indicates an event is unlikely to occur; a probability near 1 indicates an event is almost certain to occur. Other probabilities between 0 and 1 represent degrees of likelihood that an event will occur. For example, if we consider the event "rain tomorrow," we understand that when the weather report indicates "a near-zero probability of rain," it means almost no chance of rain. However, if a .90 probability of rain is reported, we know that rain is likely to occur. A .50 probability indicates that rain is just as likely to occur as not. Figure 4.1 depicts the view of probability as a numerical measure of the likelihood of an event occurring.

4.1 Random Experiments, Counting Rules, and Assigning Probabilities

In discussing probability, we deal with experiments that have the following characteristics:

1. The experimental outcomes are well defined, and in many cases can even be listed prior to conducting the experiment.
2. On any single repetition or *trial* of the experiment, one and only one of the possible experimental outcomes will occur.
3. The experimental outcome that occurs on any trial is determined solely by chance.

We refer to these types of experiments as **random experiments.**

RANDOM EXPERIMENT

A random experiment is a process that generates well-defined experimental outcomes. On any single repetition or trial, the outcome that occurs is determined completely by chance.

To illustrate the key features associated with a random experiment, consider the process of tossing a coin. Referring to one face of the coin as the head and to the other face as the tail, after tossing the coin the upward face will be either a head or a tail. Thus, there are two possible experimental outcomes: head or tail. On an any single repetition or *trial* of this experiment, only one of the two possible experimental outcomes will occur; in other words, each time we toss the coin we will either observe a head or a tail. And the outcome that occurs on any trial is determined solely by chance or random variability. As a result, the process of tossing a coin is considered a random experiment.

By specifying all the possible experimental outcomes, we identify the **sample space** for a random experiment.

SAMPLE SPACE

The sample space for a random experiment is the set of all experimental outcomes.

Experimental outcomes are also called sample points.

An experimental outcome is also called a **sample point** to identify it as an element of the sample space.

Consider the random experiment of tossing a coin. If we let S denote the sample space, we can use the following notation to describe the sample space.

$$S = \{\text{Head, Tail}\}$$

The random experiment of tossing a coin has two experimental outcomes (sample points). As an illustration of a random experiment with more than two experimental outcomes, consider the process of rolling a die. The possible experimental outcomes, defined as the number of dots appearing on the face of the die, results in six sample points. And, the sample space for this random experiment can be described as follows:

$$S = \{1, 2, 3, 4, 5, 6\}$$

Counting Rules, Combinations, and Permutations

Being able to identify and count the experimental outcomes is a necessary step in assigning probabilities. We now discuss three useful counting rules.

Multiple-step random experiments The first counting rule applies to **multiple-step random experiments**. Consider the experiment of tossing two coins. Let the experimental outcomes be defined in terms of the pattern of heads and tails appearing on the upward faces of the two coins. How many experimental outcomes are possible for this experiment? The experiment of tossing two coins can be thought of as a two-step random experiment in which step 1 is the tossing of the first coin and step 2 is the tossing of the second coin. If we use H to denote a head and T to denote a tail, (H, H) indicates the experimental outcome with a head on the first coin and a head on the second coin. Continuing this notation, we can describe the sample space (S) for this coin-tossing random experiment as follows:

$$S = \{(H, H), (H, T), (T, H), (T, T)\}$$

Thus, we see that four experimental outcomes are possible. In this case, we can easily list all the experimental outcomes.

The counting rule for multiple-step random experiments makes it possible to determine the number of experimental outcomes without listing them.

COUNTING RULE FOR MULTIPLE-STEP RANDOM EXPERIMENTS

If a random experiment can be described as a sequence of k steps with n_1 possible outcomes on the first step, n_2 possible outcomes on the second step, and so on, then the total number of experimental outcomes is given by $(n_1)\,(n_2) \cdots (n_k)$.

Viewing the random experiment of tossing two coins as a sequence of first tossing one coin ($n_1 = 2$) and then tossing the other coin ($n_2 = 2$), we can see from the counting rule that $(2)(2) = 4$ distinct experimental outcomes are possible. As shown, they are $S = \{(H, H),$

FIGURE 4.2 TREE DIAGRAM FOR THE RANDOM EXPERIMENT OF TOSSING TWO COINS

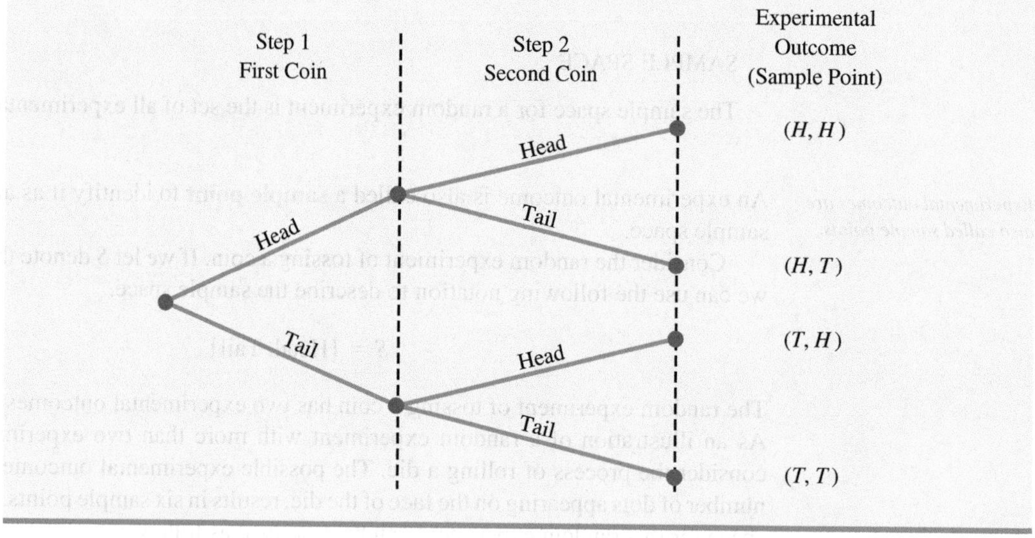

$(H, T), (T, H), (T, T)\}$. The number of experimental outcomes in a random experiment involving tossing six coins is $(2)(2)(2)(2)(2)(2) = 64$.

Without the tree diagram, one might think only three experimental outcomes are possible for two tosses of a coin: 0 heads, 1 head, and 2 heads.

A **tree diagram** is a graphical representation that helps in visualizing a multiple-step random experiment. Figure 4.2 shows a tree diagram for the random experiment of tossing two coins. The sequence of steps moves from left to right through the tree. Step 1 corresponds to tossing the first coin, and step 2 corresponds to tossing the second coin. For each step, the two possible outcomes are head or tail. Note that for each possible outcome at step 1 two branches correspond to the two possible outcomes at step 2. Each of the points on the right end of the tree corresponds to an experimental outcome. Each path through the tree from the leftmost node to one of the nodes at the right side of the tree corresponds to a unique sequence of outcomes.

Let us now see how the counting rule for multiple-step random experiments can be used in the analysis of a capacity expansion project for the Kentucky Power & Light Company (KP&L). KP&L is starting a project designed to increase the generating capacity of one of its plants in northern Kentucky. The project is divided into two sequential stages or steps: stage 1 (design) and stage 2 (construction). Even though each stage will be scheduled and controlled as closely as possible, management cannot predict beforehand the exact time required to complete each stage of the project. An analysis of similar construction projects revealed possible completion times for the design stage of 2, 3, or 4 months and possible completion times for the construction stage of 6, 7, or 8 months. In addition, because of the critical need for additional electrical power, management set a goal of 10 months for the completion of the entire project.

Because this project has three possible completion times for the design stage (step 1) and three possible completion times for the construction stage (step 2), the counting rule for multiple-step random experiments can be applied here to determine a total of $(3)(3) = 9$ experimental outcomes. To describe the experimental outcomes, we use a two-number notation; for instance, (2, 6) indicates that the design stage is completed in 2 months and the construction stage is completed in 6 months. This experimental outcome results in a total of $2 + 6 = 8$ months to complete the entire project. Table 4.1 summarizes the nine experimental outcomes for the KP&L problem. The tree diagram in Figure 4.3 shows how the nine outcomes (sample points) occur.

TABLE 4.1 EXPERIMENTAL OUTCOMES (SAMPLE POINTS) FOR THE KP&L PROJECT

Completion Time (months)			
Stage 1 Design	**Stage 2 Construction**	**Notation for Experimental Outcome**	**Total Project Completion Time (months)**
2	6	(2, 6)	8
2	7	(2, 7)	9
2	8	(2, 8)	10
3	6	(3, 6)	9
3	7	(3, 7)	10
3	8	(3, 8)	11
4	6	(4, 6)	10
4	7	(4, 7)	11
4	8	(4, 8)	12

FIGURE 4.3 TREE DIAGRAM FOR THE KP&L PROJECT

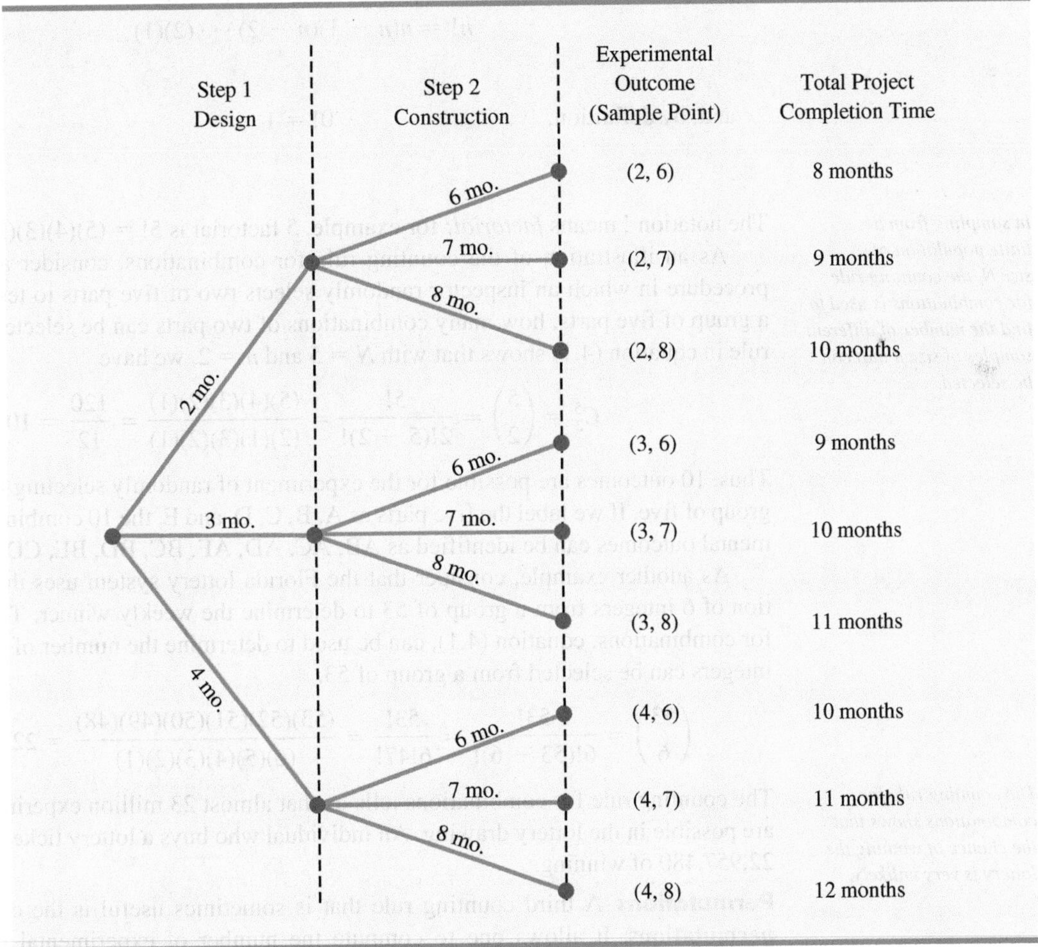

The counting rule and tree diagram help the project manager identify the experimental outcomes and determine the possible project completion times. From the information in Figure 4.3, we see that the project will be completed in 8 to 12 months, with six of the nine experimental outcomes providing the desired completion time of 10 months or less. Even though identifying the experimental outcomes may be helpful, we need to consider how probability values can be assigned to the experimental outcomes before making an assessment of the probability that the project will be completed within the desired 10 months.

Combinations A second useful counting rule allows one to count the number of experimental outcomes when the random experiment involves selecting n objects from a set of N objects. It is called the counting rule for **combinations**.

COUNTING RULE FOR COMBINATIONS

The number of combinations of N objects taken n at a time is

$$C_n^N = \binom{N}{n} = \frac{N!}{n!(N-n)!} \tag{4.1}$$

where

$$N! = N(N-1)(N-2)\cdots(2)(1)$$
$$n! = n(n-1)(n-2)\cdots(2)(1)$$

and, by definition,

$$0! = 1$$

In sampling from a finite population of size N, the counting rule for combinations is used to find the number of different samples of size n that can be selected.

The notation ! means *factorial;* for example, 5 factorial is $5! = (5)(4)(3)(2)(1) = 120$.

As an illustration of the counting rule for combinations, consider a quality control procedure in which an inspector randomly selects two of five parts to test for defects. In a group of five parts, how many combinations of two parts can be selected? The counting rule in equation (4.1) shows that with $N = 5$ and $n = 2$, we have

$$C_2^5 = \binom{5}{2} = \frac{5!}{2!(5-2)!} = \frac{(5)(4)(3)(2)(1)}{(2)(1)(3)(2)(1)} = \frac{120}{12} = 10$$

Thus, 10 outcomes are possible for the experiment of randomly selecting two parts from a group of five. If we label the five parts as A, B, C, D, and E, the 10 combinations or experimental outcomes can be identified as AB, AC, AD, AE, BC, BD, BE, CD, CE, and DE.

As another example, consider that the Florida lottery system uses the random selection of 6 integers from a group of 53 to determine the weekly winner. The counting rule for combinations, equation (4.1), can be used to determine the number of ways 6 different integers can be selected from a group of 53.

$$\binom{53}{6} = \frac{53!}{6!(53-6)!} = \frac{53!}{6!47!} = \frac{(53)(52)(51)(50)(49)(48)}{(6)(5)(4)(3)(2)(1)} = 22{,}957{,}480$$

The counting rule for combinations shows that the chance of winning the lottery is very unlikely.

The counting rule for combinations tells us that almost 23 million experimental outcomes are possible in the lottery drawing. An individual who buys a lottery ticket has 1 chance in 22,957,480 of winning.

Permutations A third counting rule that is sometimes useful is the counting rule for **permutations**. It allows one to compute the number of experimental outcomes when n objects are to be selected from a set of N objects where the order of selection is important. The same n objects selected in a different order are considered a different experimental outcome.

COUNTING RULE FOR PERMUTATIONS

The number of permutations of N objects taken n at a time is given by

$$P_n^N = n!\binom{N}{n} = \frac{N!}{(N-n)!} \tag{4.2}$$

The counting rule for permutations closely relates to the one for combinations; however, a random experiment involving permutations results in more experimental outcomes because every selection of n objects can be ordered in $n!$ different ways.

As an example, consider again the quality control process in which an inspector selects two of five parts to inspect for defects. How many permutations may be selected? The counting rule in equation (4.2) shows that with $N = 5$ and $n = 2$, we have

$$P_2^5 = \frac{5!}{(5-2)!} = \frac{5!}{3!} = \frac{(5)(4)(3)(2)(1)}{(3)(2)(1)} = \frac{120}{6} = 20$$

Thus, 20 outcomes are possible for the random experiment of randomly selecting two parts from a group of five when the order of selection must be taken into account. If we label the parts A, B, C, D, and E, the 20 permutations are AB, BA, AC, CA, AD, DA, AE, EA, BC, CB, BD, DB, BE, EB, CD, DC, CE, EC, DE, and ED.

Assigning Probabilities

Now let us see how probabilities can be assigned to experimental outcomes. The three approaches most frequently used are the classical, relative frequency, and subjective methods. Regardless of the method used, two **basic requirements for assigning probabilities** must be met.

BASIC REQUIREMENTS FOR ASSIGNING PROBABILITIES

1. **The probability assigned to each experimental outcome must be between 0 and 1, inclusively. If we let E_i denote the ith experimental outcome and $P(E_i)$ its probability, then this requirement can be written as**

$$0 \le P(E_i) \le 1 \text{ for all } i \tag{4.3}$$

2. **The sum of the probabilities for all the experimental outcomes must equal 1.0. For n experimental outcomes, this requirement can be written as**

$$P(E_1) + P(E_2) + \cdots + P(E_n) = 1 \tag{4.4}$$

The **classical method** of assigning probabilities is appropriate when all the experimental outcomes are equally likely. If n experimental outcomes are possible, a probability of $1/n$ is assigned to each experimental outcome. When using this approach, the two basic requirements for assigning probabilities are automatically satisfied.

For an example, consider the random experiment of tossing a fair coin; the two experimental outcomes—head and tail—are equally likely. Because one of the two equally likely outcomes is a head, the probability of observing a head is 1/2, or .50. Similarly, the probability of observing a tail is also 1/2, or .50.

As another example, consider the random experiment of rolling a die. It would seem reasonable to conclude that the six possible outcomes are equally likely, and hence each outcome is assigned a probability of 1/6. If $P(1)$ denotes the probability that one dot appears on the upward face of the die, then $P(1) = 1/6$. Similarly, $P(2) = 1/6$, $P(3) = 1/6$, $P(4) = 1/6$, $P(5) = 1/6$, and $P(6) = 1/6$. Note that these probabilities satisfy the two basic requirements of equations (4.3) and (4.4) because each of the probabilities is greater than or equal to zero and they sum to 1.0.

The **relative frequency method** of assigning probabilities is appropriate when data are available to estimate the proportion of the time the experimental outcome will occur if the random experiment is repeated a large number of times. As an example, consider a study of waiting times in the X-ray department for a local hospital. A clerk recorded the number of patients waiting for service at 9:00 A.M. on 20 successive days and obtained the following results.

Number Waiting	Number of Days Outcome Occurred
0	2
1	5
2	6
3	4
4	3
Total	20

These data show that on 2 of the 20 days, zero patients were waiting for service; on 5 of the days, one patient was waiting for service; and so on. Using the relative frequency method, we would assign a probability of 2/20 = .10 to the experimental outcome of zero patients waiting for service, 5/20 = .25 to the experimental outcome of one patient waiting, 6/20 = .30 to two patients waiting, 4/20 = .20 to three patients waiting, and 3/20 = .15 to four patients waiting. As with the classical method, using the relative frequency method automatically satisfies the two basic requirements of equations (4.3) and (4.4).

The **subjective method** of assigning probabilities is most appropriate when one cannot realistically assume that the experimental outcomes are equally likely and when little relevant data are available. When the subjective method is used to assign probabilities to the experimental outcomes, we may use any information available, such as our experience or intuition. After considering all available information, a probability value that expresses our *degree of belief* (on a scale from 0 to 1) that the experimental outcome will occur is specified. Because subjective probability expresses a person's degree of belief, it is personal. Using the subjective method, different people can be expected to assign different probabilities to the same experimental outcome.

The subjective method requires extra care to ensure that the two basic requirements of equations (4.3) and (4.4) are satisfied. Regardless of a person's degree of belief, the probability value assigned to each experimental outcome must be between 0 and 1, inclusive, and the sum of all the probabilities for the experimental outcomes must equal 1.0.

Consider the case in which Tom and Judy Elsbernd make an offer to purchase a house. Two outcomes are possible:

$$E_1 = \text{their offer is accepted}$$
$$E_2 = \text{their offer is rejected}$$

Judy believes that the probability their offer will be accepted is .8; thus, Judy would set $P(E_1) = .8$ and $P(E_2) = .2$. Tom, however, believes that the probability that their offer will be accepted is .6; hence, Tom would set $P(E_1) = .6$ and $P(E_2) = .4$. Note that Tom's probability estimate for E_1 reflects a greater pessimism that their offer will be accepted.

Bayes' theorem (see Section 4.5) provides a means for combining subjectively determined prior probabilities with probabilities obtained by other means to obtain revised, or posterior, probabilities.

Both Judy and Tom assigned probabilities that satisfy the two basic requirements. The fact that their probability estimates are different emphasizes the personal nature of the subjective method.

Even in business situations where either the classical or the relative frequency approach can be applied, managers may want to provide subjective probability estimates. In such cases, the best probability estimates often are obtained by combining the estimates from the classical or relative frequency approach with subjective probability estimates.

Probabilities for the KP&L Project

To perform further analysis on the KP&L project, we must develop probabilities for each of the nine experimental outcomes listed in Table 4.1. On the basis of experience and judgment, management concluded that the experimental outcomes were not equally likely. Hence, the classical method of assigning probabilities could not be used. Management then decided to conduct a study of the completion times for similar projects undertaken by KP&L over the past three years. The results of a study of 40 similar projects are summarized in Table 4.2.

After reviewing the results of the study, management decided to employ the relative frequency method of assigning probabilities. Management could have provided subjective probability estimates but felt that the current project was quite similar to the 40 previous projects. Thus, the relative frequency method was judged best.

In using the data in Table 4.2 to compute probabilities, we note that outcome (2, 6)—stage 1 completed in 2 months and stage 2 completed in 6 months—occurred six times in the 40 projects. We can use the relative frequency method to assign a probability of 6/40 = .15 to this outcome. Similarly, outcome (2, 7) also occurred in six of the 40 projects, providing a 6/40 = .15 probability. Continuing in this manner, we obtain the probability assignments for the sample points of the KP&L project shown in Table 4.3. Note that $P(2, 6)$ represents the probability of the sample point (2, 6), $P(2, 7)$ represents the probability of the sample point (2, 7), and so on.

TABLE 4.2 COMPLETION RESULTS FOR 40 KP&L PROJECTS

Completion Time (months)			
Stage 1 Design	Stage 2 Construction	Sample Point	Number of Past Projects Having These Completion Times
2	6	(2, 6)	6
2	7	(2, 7)	6
2	8	(2, 8)	2
3	6	(3, 6)	4
3	7	(3, 7)	8
3	8	(3, 8)	2
4	6	(4, 6)	2
4	7	(4, 7)	4
4	8	(4, 8)	6
		Total	40

TABLE 4.3 PROBABILITY ASSIGNMENTS FOR THE KP&L PROJECT BASED ON THE RELATIVE FREQUENCY METHOD

Sample Point	Project Completion Time	Probability of Sample Point
(2, 6)	8 months	$P(2, 6) = 6/40 = .15$
(2, 7)	9 months	$P(2, 7) = 6/40 = .15$
(2, 8)	10 months	$P(2, 8) = 2/40 = .05$
(3, 6)	9 months	$P(3, 6) = 4/40 = .10$
(3, 7)	10 months	$P(3, 7) = 8/40 = .20$
(3, 8)	11 months	$P(3, 8) = 2/40 = .05$
(4, 6)	10 months	$P(4, 6) = 2/40 = .05$
(4, 7)	11 months	$P(4, 7) = 4/40 = .10$
(4, 8)	12 months	$P(4, 8) = 6/40 = .15$
		Total 1.00

Exercises

Methods

1. A random experiment has three steps with three outcomes possible for the first step, two outcomes possible for the second step, and four outcomes possible for the third step. How many experimental outcomes exist for the entire experiment?

2. How many ways can three items be selected from a group of six items? Use the letters A, B, C, D, E, and F to identify the items, and list each of the different combinations of three items.
3. How many permutations of three items can be selected from a group of six? Use the letters A, B, C, D, E, and F to identify the items, and list each of the permutations of items B, D, and F.
4. Consider the random experiment of tossing a coin three times.
   a. Develop a tree diagram for the experiment.
   b. List the experimental outcomes.
   c. What is the probability for each experimental outcome?
5. Suppose a random experiment has five equally likely outcomes: E_1, E_2, E_3, E_4, E_5. Assign probabilities to each outcome and show that the requirements in equations (4.3) and (4.4) are satisfied. What method did you use?

6. A random experiment with three outcomes has been repeated 50 times, and it was learned that E_1 occurred 20 times, E_2 occurred 13 times, and E_3 occurred 17 times. Assign probabilities to the outcomes. What method did you use?
7. A decision maker subjectively assigned the following probabilities to the four outcomes of a random experiment: $P(E_1) = .10$, $P(E_2) = .15$, $P(E_3) = .40$, and $P(E_4) = .20$. Are these probability assignments valid? Explain.

Applications

8. In the city of Milford, applications for zoning changes go through a two-step process: a review by the planning commission and a final decision by the city council. At step 1 the planning commission reviews the zoning change request and makes a positive or negative recommendation concerning the change. At step 2 the city council reviews the planning commission's recommendation and then votes to approve or to disapprove the zoning change. Suppose the developer of an apartment complex submits an application for a zoning change. Consider the application process as a random experiment.

a. How many sample points are there for this experiment? List the sample points.
b. Construct a tree diagram for the experiment.

SELF test

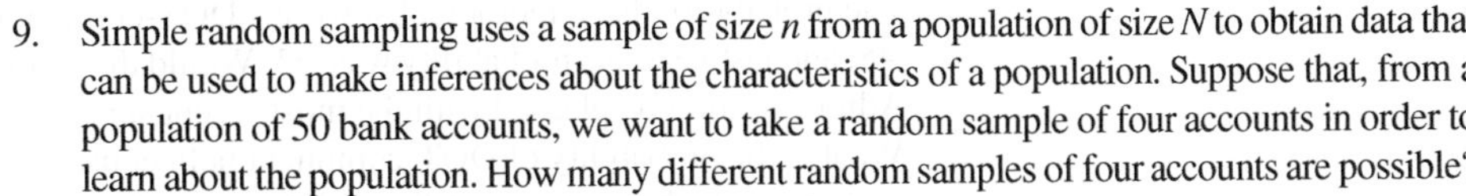

9. Simple random sampling uses a sample of size n from a population of size N to obtain data that can be used to make inferences about the characteristics of a population. Suppose that, from a population of 50 bank accounts, we want to take a random sample of four accounts in order to learn about the population. How many different random samples of four accounts are possible?

10. The following table shows the percentage of on-time arrivals, the number of mishandled baggage reports per 1000 passengers, and the number of customer complaints per 1000 passengers for ten airlines (*Forbes* website, February 12, 2014).

Airline	On-Time Arrivals (%)	Mishandled Baggage per 1000 Passengers	Customer Complaints per 1000 Passengers
Virgin America	83.5	0.87	1.50
JetBlue	79.1	1.88	0.79
AirTran Airways	87.1	1.58	0.91
Delta Air Lines	86.5	2.10	0.73
Alaska Airlines	87.5	2.93	0.51
Frontier Airlines	77.9	2.22	1.05
Southwest Airlines	83.1	3.08	0.25
US Airways	85.9	2.14	1.74
American Airlines	76.9	2.92	1.80
United Airlines	77.4	3.87	4.24

a. If you randomly choose a Delta Air Lines flight, what is the probability that this individual flight has an on-time arrival?
b. If you randomly choose one of the ten airlines for a follow-up study on airline quality ratings, what is the probability that you will choose an airline with less than two mishandled baggage reports per 1000 passengers?
c. If you randomly choose one of the ten airlines for a follow-up study on airline quality ratings, what is the probability that you will choose an airline with more than one customer complaint per 1000 passengers?
d. What is the probability that a randomly selected AirTran Airways flight will not arrive on time?

11. The National Occupant Protection Use Survey (NOPUS) was conducted to provide probability-based data on motorcycle helmet use in the United States. The survey was conducted by sending observers to randomly selected roadway sites where they collected data on motorcycle helmet use, including the number of motorcyclists wearing a Department of Transportation (DOT)-compliant helmet (National Highway Traffic Safety Administration website, January 7, 2010). Sample data consistent with the most recent NOPUS are shown below.

	Type of Helmet	
Region	DOT-Compliant	Noncompliant
Northeast	96	62
Midwest	86	43
South	92	49
West	76	16
Total	350	170

a. Use the data to compute the probability that a motorcyclist wears a DOT-compliant helmet.
b. The probability that a motorcyclist wore a DOT-compliant helmet five years ago was .48, and last year this probability was .63. Would the National Highway Traffic Safety Administration be pleased with the most recent survey results?
c. What is the probability of DOT-compliant helmet use by region of the country? What region has the highest probability of DOT-compliant helmet use?

12. The Powerball lottery is played twice each week in 31 states, the District of Columbia, and the Virgin Islands. To play Powerball, a participant must purchase a $2 ticket, select five numbers from the digits 1 through 59, and then select a Powerball number from the digits 1 through 35. To determine the winning numbers for each game, lottery officials draw 5 white balls out a drum of 59 white balls numbered 1 through 59 and 1 red ball out of a drum of 35 red balls numbered 1 through 35. To win the Powerball jackpot, a participant's numbers must match the numbers on the 5 white balls in any order and must also match the number on the red Powerball. The numbers 5–16–22–23–29 with a Powerball number of 6 provided the record jackpot of $580 million (Powerball website, November 29, 2012).
   a. How many Powerball lottery outcomes are possible? (*Hint:* Consider this a two-step random experiment. Select the 5 white ball numbers and then select the 1 red Powerball number.)
   b. What is the probability that a $2 lottery ticket wins the Powerball lottery?

13. A company that manufactures toothpaste is studying five different package designs. Assuming that one design is just as likely to be selected by a consumer as any other design, what selection probability would you assign to each of the package designs? In an actual study, 100 consumers were asked to pick the design they preferred. The following data were obtained. Do the data confirm the belief that one design is just as likely to be selected as another? Explain.

Design	Number of Times Preferred
1	5
2	15
3	30
4	40
5	10

4.2 Events and Their Probabilities

In the introduction to this chapter we used the term *event* much as it would be used in everyday language. Then, in Section 4.1 we introduced the concept of a random experiment and its associated experimental outcomes or sample points. Sample points and events provide the foundation for the study of probability. As a result, we must now introduce the formal definition of an **event** as it relates to sample points. Doing so will provide the basis for determining the probability of an event.

EVENT

An event is a collection of sample points.

For an example, let us return to the KP&L project and assume that the project manager is interested in the event that the entire project can be completed in 10 months or less.

Referring to Table 4.3, we see that six sample points—(2, 6), (2, 7), (2, 8), (3, 6), (3, 7), and (4, 6)—provide a project completion time of 10 months or less. Let C denote the event that the project is completed in 10 months or less; we write

$$C = \{(2, 6), (2, 7), (2, 8), (3, 6), (3, 7), (4, 6)\}$$

Event C is said to occur if *any one* of these six sample points appears as the experimental outcome.

Other events that might be of interest to KP&L management include the following.

L = The event that the project is completed in *less* than 10 months

M = The event that the project is completed in *more* than 10 months

Using the information in Table 4.3, we see that these events consist of the following sample points.

$$L = \{(2, 6), (2, 7), (3, 6)\}$$
$$M = \{(3, 8), (4, 7), (4, 8)\}$$

A variety of additional events can be defined for the KP&L project, but in each case the event must be identified as a collection of sample points for the random experiment.

Given the probabilities of the sample points shown in Table 4.3, we can use the following definition to compute the probability of any event that KP&L management might want to consider.

PROBABILITY OF AN EVENT

The probability of any event is equal to the sum of the probabilities of the sample points in the event.

Using this definition, we calculate the probability of a particular event by adding the probabilities of the sample points (experimental outcomes) that make up the event. We can now compute the probability that the project will take 10 months or less to complete. Because this event is given by $C = \{(2, 6), (2, 7), (2, 8), (3, 6), (3, 7), (4, 6)\}$, the probability of event C, denoted $P(C)$, is given by

$$P(C) = P(2, 6) + P(2, 7) + P(2, 8) + P(3, 6) + P(3, 7) + P(4, 6)$$

Refer to the sample point probabilities in Table 4.3; we have

$$P(C) = .15 + .15 + .05 + .10 + .20 + .05 = .70$$

Similarly, because the event that the project is completed in less than 10 months is given by $L = \{(2, 6), (2, 7), (3, 6)\}$, the probability of this event is given by

$$\begin{aligned} P(L) &= P(2, 6) + P(2, 7) + P(3, 6) \\ &= .15 + .15 + .10 = .40 \end{aligned}$$

Finally, for the event that the project is completed in more than 10 months, we have $M = \{(3, 8), (4, 7), (4, 8)\}$ and thus

$$\begin{aligned} P(M) &= P(3, 8) + P(4, 7) + P(4, 8) \\ &= .05 + .10 + .15 = .30 \end{aligned}$$

Using these probability results, we can now tell KP&L management that there is a .70 probability that the project will be completed in 10 months or less, a .40 probability that the project will be completed in less than 10 months, and a .30 probability that the project will be completed in more than 10 months. This procedure of computing event probabilities can be repeated for any event of interest to the KP&L management.

Any time that we can identify all the sample points of a random experiment and assign probabilities to each, we can compute the probability of an event using the definition. However, in many experiments the large number of sample points makes the identification of the sample points, as well as the determination of their associated probabilities, extremely cumbersome, if not impossible. In the remaining sections of this chapter, we present some basic probability relationships that can be used to compute the probability of an event without knowledge of all the sample point probabilities.

NOTES AND COMMENTS

1. The sample space, S, is an event. Because it contains all the experimental outcomes, it has a probability of 1; that is, $P(S) = 1$.
2. When the classical method is used to assign probabilities, the assumption is that the experimental outcomes are equally likely. In such cases, the probability of an event can be computed by counting the number of experimental outcomes in the event and dividing the result by the total number of experimental outcomes.

Exercises

Methods

14. A random experiment has four equally likely outcomes: E_1, E_2, E_3, and E_4.
    a. What is the probability that E_2 occurs?
    b. What is the probability that any two of the outcomes occur (e.g., E_1 or E_3)?
    c. What is the probability that any three of the outcomes occur (e.g., E_1 or E_2 or E_4)?

15. Consider the random experiment of selecting a playing card from a deck of 52 playing cards. Each card corresponds to a sample point with a 1/52 probability.
    a. List the sample points in the event an ace is selected.
    b. List the sample points in the event a club is selected.
    c. List the sample points in the event a face card (jack, queen, or king) is selected.
    d. Find the probabilities associated with each of the events in parts (a), (b), and (c).
16. Consider the random experiment of rolling a pair of dice. Suppose that we are interested in the sum of the face values showing on the dice.
    a. How many sample points are possible? (*Hint:* Use the counting rule for multiple-step random experiments.)
    b. List the sample points.
    c. What is the probability of obtaining a value of 7?
    d. What is the probability of obtaining a value of 9 or greater?
    e. Because each roll has six possible even values (2, 4, 6, 8, 10, and 12) and only five possible odd values (3, 5, 7, 9, and 11), the dice should show even values more often than odd values. Do you agree with this statement? Explain.
    f. What method did you use to assign the probabilities requested?

Applications

17. Refer to the KP&L sample points and sample point probabilities in Tables 4.2 and 4.3.
    a. The design stage (stage 1) will run over budget if it takes 4 months to complete. List the sample points in the event the design stage is over budget.
    b. What is the probability that the design stage is over budget?
    c. The construction stage (stage 2) will run over budget if it takes 8 months to complete. List the sample points in the event the construction stage is over budget.
    d. What is the probability that the construction stage is over budget?
    e. What is the probability that both stages are over budget?

18. *Fortune* magazine publishes an annual list of the 500 largest companies in the United States. The corporate headquarters for the 500 companies are located in 38 different states The following table shows the 8 states with the largest number of *Fortune* 500 companies (*Money*/CNN website, May 12, 2012).

State	Number of Companies	State	Number of Companies
California	53	Ohio	28
Illinois	32	Pennsylvania	23
New Jersey	21	Texas	52
New York	50	Virginia	24

Suppose one of the 500 companies is selected at random for a follow-up questionnaire.
    a. What is the probability that the company selected has its corporate headquarters in California?
    b. What is the probability that the company selected has its corporate headquarters in California, New York, or Texas?
    c. What is the probability that the company selected has its corporate headquarters in one of the 8 states listed above?

19. Do you think the government protects investors adequately? This question was part of an online survey of investors under age 65 living in the United States and Great Britain (*Financial Times*/Harris Poll, October 1, 2009). The numbers of investors from the United States and Great Britain who answered Yes, No, or Unsure to this question are provided below.

Response	United States	Great Britain
Yes	187	197
No	334	411
Unsure	256	213

    a. Estimate the probability that an investor in the United States thinks the government is not protecting investors adequately.
    b. Estimate the probability that an investor in Great Britain thinks the government is not protecting investors adequately or is unsure the government is protecting investors adequately.
    c. For a randomly selected investor from these two countries, estimate the probability that the investor thinks the government is not protecting investors adequately.
    d. Based on the survey results, does there appear to be much difference between the perceptions of investors in the United States and investors in Great Britain regarding the issue of the government protecting investors adequately?

20. Junior Achievement USA and the Allstate Foundation surveyed teenagers aged 14 to 18 and asked at what age they think that they will become financially independent (*USA Today*, April 30, 2012). The responses of 944 teenagers who answered this survey question are as follows.

Age Financially Independent	Number of Responces
16 to 20	191
21 to 24	467
25 to 27	244
28 or older	42

Consider the experiment of randomly selecting a teenager from the population of teenagers aged 14 to 18.

a. Compute the probability of being financially independent for each of the four age categories.
b. What is the probability of being financially independent before the age of 25?
c. What is the probability of a being financially independent after the age of 24?
d. Do the probabilities suggest that the teenagers may be somewhat unrealistic in their expectations about when they will become financially independent?

21. Data on U.S. work-related fatalities by cause follow (*The World Almanac*, 2012).

Cause of Fatality	Number of Fatalities
Transportation incidents	1795
Assaults and violent acts	837
Contact with objects and equipment	741
Falls	645
Exposure to harmful substances or environments	404
Fires and explosions	113

Assume that a fatality will be randomly chosen from this population.

a. What is the probability the fatality resulted from a fall?
b. What is the probability the fatality resulted from a transportation incident?
c. What cause of fatality is least likely to occur? What is the probability the fatality resulted from this cause?

4.3 Some Basic Relationships of Probability

Complement of an Event

Given an event A, the **complement of A** is defined to be the event consisting of all sample points that are *not* in A. The complement of A is denoted by A^c. Figure 4.4 is a diagram, known as a **Venn diagram**, which illustrates the concept of a complement. The rectangular area represents the sample space for the random experiment and as such contains all possible sample points. The circle represents event A and contains only the sample points that belong to A. The shaded region of the rectangle contains all sample points not in event A and is by definition the complement of A.

In any probability application, either event A or its complement A^c must occur. Therefore, we have

$$P(A) + P(A^c) = 1$$

FIGURE 4.4 COMPLEMENT OF EVENT A IS SHADED

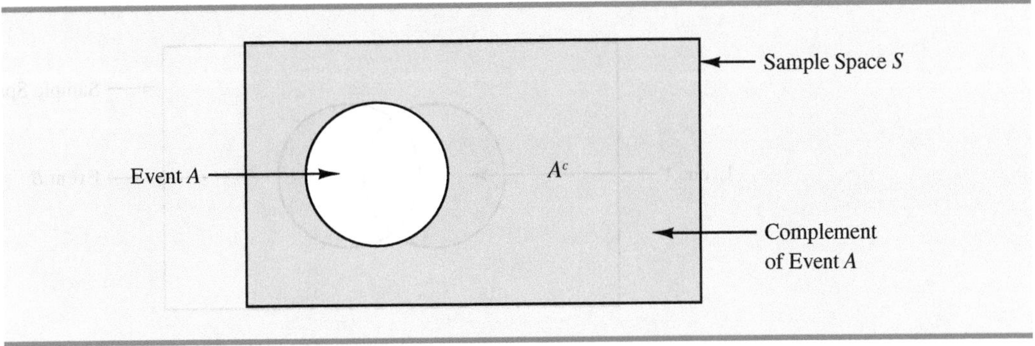

Solving for $P(A)$, we obtain the following result.

COMPUTING PROBABILITY USING THE COMPLEMENT

$$P(A) = 1 - P(A^c) \tag{4.5}$$

Equation (4.5) shows that the probability of an event A can be computed easily if the probability of its complement, $P(A^c)$, is known.

As an example, consider the case of a sales manager who, after reviewing sales reports, states that 80% of new customer contacts result in no sale. By allowing A to denote the event of a sale and A^c to denote the event of no sale, the manager is stating that $P(A^c) = .80$. Using equation (4.5), we see that

$$P(A) = 1 - P(A^c) = 1 - .80 = .20$$

We can conclude that a new customer contact has a .20 probability of resulting in a sale.

In another example, a purchasing agent states a .90 probability that a supplier will send a shipment that is free of defective parts. Using the complement, we can conclude that there is a $1 - .90 = .10$ probability that the shipment will contain defective parts.

Addition Law

The addition law is helpful when we are interested in knowing the probability that at least one of two events occurs. That is, with events A and B we are interested in knowing the probability that event A or event B or both occur.

Before we present the addition law, we need to discuss two concepts related to the combination of events: the *union* of events and the *intersection* of events. Given two events A and B, the **union of A and B** is defined as follows.

UNION OF TWO EVENTS

The *union* of A and B is the event containing *all* sample points belonging to A *or* B *or both.* The union is denoted by $A \cup B$.

The Venn diagram in Figure 4.5 depicts the union of events A and B. Note that the two circles contain all the sample points in event A as well as all the sample points in event B.

FIGURE 4.5 UNION OF EVENTS *A* AND *B* IS SHADED

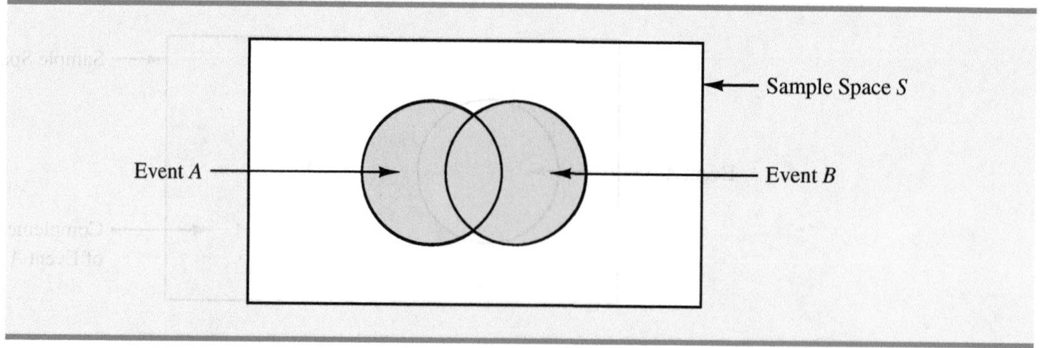

The fact that the circles overlap indicates that some sample points are contained in both *A* and *B*.

The definition of the **intersection of *A* and *B*** follows.

INTERSECTION OF TWO EVENTS

Given two events *A* and *B*, the *intersection* of *A* and *B* is the event containing the sample points belonging to *both A and B*. The intersection is denoted by $A \cap B$.

The Venn diagram depicting the intersection of events *A* and *B* is shown in Figure 4.6. The area where the two circles overlap is the intersection; it contains the sample points that are in both *A* and *B*.

Let us now continue with a discussion of the addition law. The **addition law** provides a way to compute the probability that event *A* or event *B* or both occur. In other words, the addition law is used to compute the probability of the union of two events. The addition law is written as follows.

ADDITION LAW

$$P(A \cup B) = P(A) + P(B) - P(A \cap B) \quad (4.6)$$

FIGURE 4.6 INTERSECTION OF EVENTS *A* AND *B* IS SHADED

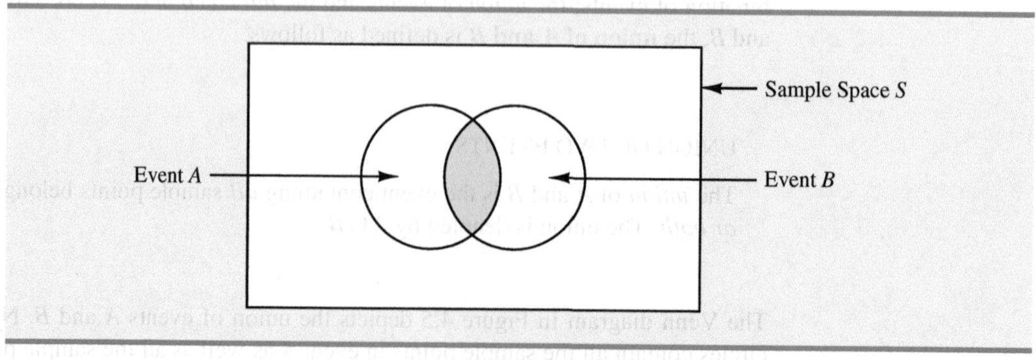

To understand the addition law intuitively, note that the first two terms in the addition law, $P(A) + P(B)$, account for all the sample points in $A \cup B$. However, because the sample points in the intersection $A \cap B$ are in both A and B, when we compute $P(A) + P(B)$, we are in effect counting each of the sample points in $A \cap B$ twice. We correct for this overcounting by subtracting $P(A \cap B)$.

As an example of an application of the addition law, let us consider the case of a small assembly plant with 50 employees. Each worker is expected to complete work assignments on time and in such a way that the assembled product will pass a final inspection. On occasion, some of the workers fail to meet the performance standards by completing work late or assembling a defective product. At the end of a performance evaluation period, the production manager found that 5 of the 50 workers completed work late, 6 of the 50 workers assembled a defective product, and 2 of the 50 workers both completed work late *and* assembled a defective product.

Let

$$L = \text{the event that the work is completed late}$$
$$D = \text{the event that the assembled product is defective}$$

The relative frequency information leads to the following probabilities.

$$P(L) = \frac{5}{50} = .10$$

$$P(D) = \frac{6}{50} = .12$$

$$P(L \cap D) = \frac{2}{50} = .04$$

After reviewing the performance data, the production manager decided to assign a poor performance rating to any employee whose work was either late or defective; thus the event of interest is $L \cup D$. What is the probability that the production manager assigned an employee a poor performance rating?

Note that the probability question is about the union of two events. Specifically, we want to know $P(L \cup D)$. Using equation (4.6), we have

$$P(L \cup D) = P(L) + P(D) - P(L \cap D)$$

Knowing values for the three probabilities on the right side of this expression, we can write

$$P(L \cup D) = .10 + .12 - .04 = .18$$

This calculation tells us that there is a .18 probability that a randomly selected employee received a poor performance rating.

As another example of the addition law, consider a recent study conducted by the personnel manager of a major computer software company. The study showed that 30% of the employees who left the firm within two years did so primarily because they were dissatisfied with their salary, 20% left because they were dissatisfied with their work assignments, and 12% of the former employees indicated dissatisfaction with *both* their salary and their work assignments. What is the probability that an employee who leaves within two years does so because of dissatisfaction with salary, dissatisfaction with the work assignment, or both?

Let

S = the event that the employee leaves because of salary
W = the event that the employee leaves because of work assignment

We have $P(S) = .30$, $P(W) = .20$, and $P(S \cap W) = .12$. Using equation (4.6), the addition law, we have

$$P(S \cup W) = P(S) + P(W) - P(S \cap W) = .30 + .20 - .12 = .38$$

We find a .38 probability that an employee leaves for salary or work assignment reasons.

Before we conclude our discussion of the addition law, let us consider a special case that arises for **mutually exclusive events.**

MUTUALLY EXCLUSIVE EVENTS

Two events are said to be mutually exclusive if the events have no sample points in common.

Events A and B are mutually exclusive if, when one event occurs, the other cannot occur. Thus, a requirement for A and B to be mutually exclusive is that their intersection must contain no sample points. The Venn diagram depicting two mutually exclusive events A and B is shown in Figure 4.7. In this case $P(A \cap B) = 0$ and the addition law can be written as follows.

ADDITION LAW FOR MUTUALLY EXCLUSIVE EVENTS

$$P(A \cup B) = P(A) + P(B)$$

FIGURE 4.7 MUTUALLY EXCLUSIVE EVENTS

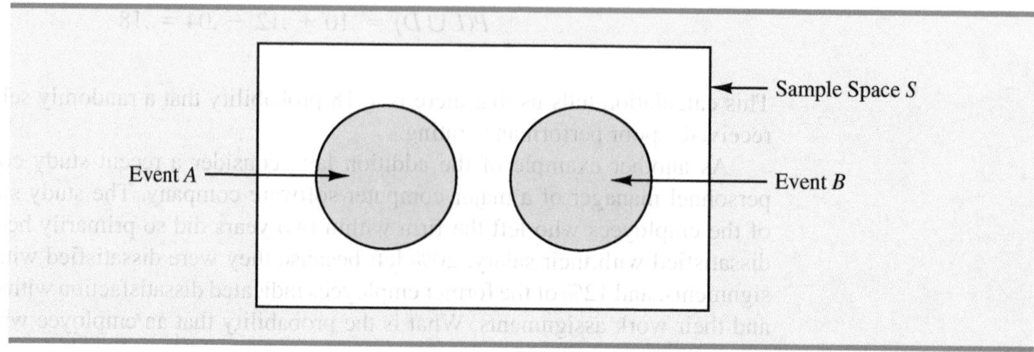

Exercises

Methods

22. Suppose that we have a sample space with five equally likely experimental outcomes: E_1, E_2, E_3, E_4, E_5. Let

$$A = \{E_1, E_2\}$$
$$B = \{E_3, E_4\}$$
$$C = \{E_2, E_3, E_5\}$$

   a. Find $P(A)$, $P(B)$, and $P(C)$.
   b. Find $P(A \cup B)$. Are A and B mutually exclusive?
   c. Find A^c, C^c, $P(A^c)$, and $P(C^c)$.
   d. Find $A \cup B^c$ and $P(A \cup B^c)$.
   e. Find $P(B \cup C)$.

23. Suppose that we have a sample space $S = \{E_1, E_2, E_3, E_4, E_5, E_6, E_7\}$, where $E_1, E_2, \ldots, E_7$ denote the sample points. The following probability assignments apply: $P(E_1) = .05$, $P(E_2) = .20$, $P(E_3) = .20$, $P(E_4) = .25$, $P(E_5) = .15$, $P(E_6) = .10$, and $P(E_7) = .05$. Let

$$A = \{E_1, E_4, E_6\}$$
$$B = \{E_2, E_4, E_7\}$$
$$C = \{E_2, E_3, E_5, E_7\}$$

   a. Find $P(A)$, $P(B)$, and $P(C)$.
   b. Find $A \cup B$ and $P(A \cup B)$.
   c. Find $A \cap B$ and $P(A \cap B)$.
   d. Are events A and C mutually exclusive?
   e. Find B^c and $P(B^c)$.

Applications

24. Clarkson University surveyed alumni to learn more about what they think of Clarkson. One part of the survey asked respondents to indicate whether their overall experience at Clarkson fell short of expectations, met expectations, or surpassed expectations. The results showed that 4% of the respondents did not provide a response, 26% said that their experience fell short of expectations, and 65% of the respondents said that their experience met expectations.
   a. If we chose an alumnus at random, what is the probability that the alumnus would say her experience *surpassed* expectations?
   b. If we chose an alumnus at random, what is the probability that the alumnus would say her experience met or surpassed expectations?

25. The Eco Pulse survey from the marketing communications firm Shelton Group asked individuals to indicate things they do that make them feel guilty (*Los Angeles Times*, August 15, 2012). Based on the survey results, there is a .39 probability that a randomly selected person will feel guilty about wasting food and a .27 probability that a randomly selected person will feel guilty about leaving lights on when not in a room. Moreover, there is a .12 probability that a randomly selected person will feel guilty for both of these reasons.
   a. What is the probability that a randomly selected person will feel guilty for either wasting food or leaving lights on when not in a room?
   b. What is the probability that a randomly selected person will not feel guilty for either of these reasons?

26. Information about mutual funds provided by Morningstar includes the type of mutual fund (Domestic Equity, International Equity, or Fixed Income) and the Morningstar rating for

the fund. The rating is expressed from 1-star (lowest rating) to 5-star (highest rating). Suppose a sample of 25 mutual funds provided the following counts:

- Sixteen mutual funds were Domestic Equity funds.
- Thirteen mutual funds were rated 3-star or less.
- Seven of the Domestic Equity funds were rated 4-star.
- Two of the Domestic Equity funds were rated 5-star.

Assume that one of these 25 mutual funds will be randomly selected in order to learn more about the mutual fund and its investment strategy.

a. What is the probability of selecting a Domestic Equity fund?
b. What is the probability of selecting a fund with a 4-star or 5-star rating?
c. What is the probability of selecting a fund that is both a Domestic Equity fund *and* a fund with a 4-star or 5-star rating?
d. What is the probability of selecting a fund that is a Domestic Equity fund *or* a fund with a 4-star or 5-star rating?

27. What NCAA college basketball conferences have the higher probability of having a team play in college basketball's national championship game? Over the last 20 years, the Atlantic Coast Conference (ACC) ranks first by having a team in the championship game 10 times. The Southeastern Conference (SEC) ranks second by having a team in the championship game 8 times. However, these two conferences have both had teams in the championship game only one time, when Arkansas (SEC) beat Duke (ACC) 76–70 in 1994 (NCAA website, April 2009). Use these data to estimate the following probabilities.
    a. What is the probability the ACC will have a team in the championship game?
    b. What is the probability the SEC will have team in the championship game?
    c. What is the probability the ACC and SEC will both have teams in the championship game?
    d. What is the probability at least one team from these two conferences will be in the championship game? That is, what is the probability a team from the ACC or SEC will play in the championship game?
    e. What is the probability that the championship game will not a have team from one of these two conferences?

28. A survey of magazine subscribers showed that 45.8% rented a car during the past 12 months for business reasons, 54% rented a car during the past 12 months for personal reasons, and 30% rented a car during the past 12 months for both business and personal reasons.
    a. What is the probability that a subscriber rented a car during the past 12 months for business or personal reasons?
    b. What is the probability that a subscriber did not rent a car during the past 12 months for either business or personal reasons?

29. High school seniors with strong academic records apply to the nation's most selective colleges in greater numbers each year. Because the number of slots remains relatively stable, some colleges reject more early applicants. Suppose that for a recent admissions class, an Ivy League college received 2851 applications for early admission. Of this group, it admitted 1033 students early, rejected 854 outright, and deferred 964 to the regular admission pool for further consideration. In the past, this school has admitted 18% of the deferred early admission applicants during the regular admission process. Counting the students admitted early and the students admitted during the regular admission process, the total class size was 2375. Let E, R, and D represent the events that a student who applies for early admission is admitted early, rejected outright, or deferred to the regular admissions pool.
    a. Use the data to estimate $P(E)$, $P(R)$, and $P(D)$.
    b. Are events E and D mutually exclusive? Find $P(E \cap D)$.
    c. For the 2375 students who were admitted, what is the probability that a randomly selected student was accepted during early admission?

d. Suppose a student applies for early admission. What is the probability that the student will be admitted for early admission or be deferred and later admitted during the regular admission process?

4.4 Conditional Probability

Often, the probability of an event is influenced by whether a related event already occurred. Suppose we have an event A with probability $P(A)$. If we obtain new information and learn that a related event, denoted by B, already occurred, we will want to take advantage of this information by calculating a new probability for event A. This new probability of event A is called a **conditional probability** and is written $P(A \mid B)$. We use the notation $\mid$ to indicate that we are considering the probability of event A *given* the condition that event B has occurred. Hence, the notation $P(A \mid B)$ reads "the probability of A given B."

As an illustration of the application of conditional probability, consider the situation of the promotion status of male and female officers of a major metropolitan police force in the eastern United States. The police force consists of 1200 officers, 960 men and 240 women. Over the past two years, 324 officers on the police force received promotions. The specific breakdown of promotions for male and female officers is shown in Table 4.4.

After reviewing the promotion record, a committee of female officers raised a discrimination case on the basis that 288 male officers had received promotions, but only 36 female officers had received promotions. The police administration argued that the relatively low number of promotions for female officers was due not to discrimination, but to the fact that relatively few females are members of the police force. Let us show how conditional probability could be used to analyze the discrimination charge.

Let

$$M = \text{event an officer is a man}$$
$$W = \text{event an officer is a woman}$$
$$A = \text{event an officer is promoted}$$
$$A^c = \text{event an officer is not promoted}$$

Dividing the data values in Table 4.4 by the total of 1200 officers enables us to summarize the available information with the following probability values.

$$P(M \cap A) = 288/1200 = .24 \text{ probability that a randomly selected officer is a man } \textit{and} \text{ is promoted}$$

$$P(M \cap A^c) = 672/1200 = .56 \text{ probability that a randomly selected officer is a man } \textit{and} \text{ is not promoted}$$

TABLE 4.4 PROMOTION STATUS OF POLICE OFFICERS OVER THE PAST TWO YEARS

	Men	Women	Total
Promoted	288	36	324
Not Promoted	672	204	876
Total	960	240	1200

TABLE 4.5 JOINT PROBABILITY TABLE FOR PROMOTIONS

Joint probabilities appear in the body of the table.

	Men (M)	Women (W)	Total
Promoted (A)	.24	.03	.27
Not Promoted (A^c)	.56	.17	.73
Total	.80	.20	1.00

Marginal probabilities appear in the margins of the table.

$P(W \cap A) = 36/1200 = .03$ probability that a randomly selected officer is a woman *and* is promoted

$P(W \cap A^c) = 204/1200 = .17$ probability that a randomly selected officer is a woman *and* is not promoted

Because each of these values gives the probability of the intersection of two events, the probabilities are called **joint probabilities**. Table 4.5, which provides a summary of the probability information for the police officer promotion situation, is referred to as a *joint probability table*.

The values in the margins of the joint probability table provide the probabilities of each event separately. That is, $P(M) = .80$, $P(W) = .20$, $P(A) = .27$, and $P(A^c) = .73$. These probabilities are referred to as **marginal probabilities** because of their location in the margins of the joint probability table. We note that the marginal probabilities are found by summing the joint probabilities in the corresponding row or column of the joint probability table. For instance, the marginal probability of being promoted is $P(A) = P(M \cap A) + P(W \cap A) = .24 + .03 = .27$. From the marginal probabilities, we see that 80% of the force is male, 20% of the force is female, 27% of all officers received promotions, and 73% were not promoted.

Let us begin the conditional probability analysis by computing the probability that an officer is promoted given that the officer is a man. In conditional probability notation, we are attempting to determine $P(A \mid M)$. To calculate $P(A \mid M)$, we first realize that this notation simply means that we are considering the probability of the event A (promotion) given that the condition designated as event M (the officer is a man) is known to exist. Thus $P(A \mid M)$ tells us that we are now concerned only with the promotion status of the 960 male officers. Because 288 of the 960 male officers received promotions, the probability of being promoted given that the officer is a man is $288/960 = .30$. In other words, given that an officer is a man, that officer had a 30% chance of receiving a promotion over the past two years.

This procedure was easy to apply because the values in Table 4.4 show the number of officers in each category. We now want to demonstrate how conditional probabilities such as $P(A \mid M)$ can be computed directly from related event probabilities rather than the frequency data of Table 4.4.

We have shown that $P(A \mid M) = 288/960 = .30$. Let us now divide both the numerator and denominator of this fraction by 1200, the total number of officers in the study.

$$P(A \mid M) = \frac{288}{960} = \frac{288/1200}{960/1200} = \frac{.24}{.80} = .30$$

We now see that the conditional probability $P(A \mid M)$ can be computed as .24/.80. Refer to the joint probability table (Table 4.5). Note in particular that .24 is the joint probability of A and M; that is, $P(A \cap M) = .24$. Also note that .80 is the marginal probability that a randomly selected officer is a man; that is, $P(M) = .80$. Thus, the conditional probability $P(A \mid M)$ can be computed as the ratio of the joint probability $P(A \cap M)$ to the marginal probability $P(M)$.

$$P(A \mid M) = \frac{P(A \cap M)}{P(M)} = \frac{.24}{.80} = .30$$

The fact that conditional probabilities can be computed as the ratio of a joint probability to a marginal probability provides the following general formula for conditional probability calculations for two events A and B.

CONDITIONAL PROBABILITY

$$P(A \mid B) = \frac{P(A \cap B)}{P(B)} \tag{4.7}$$

or

$$P(B \mid A) = \frac{P(A \cap B)}{P(A)} \tag{4.8}$$

The Venn diagram in Figure 4.8 is helpful in obtaining an intuitive understanding of conditional probability. The circle on the right shows that event B has occurred; the portion of the circle that overlaps with event A denotes the event $(A \cap B)$. We know that once event B has occurred, the only way that we can also observe event A is for the event $(A \cap B)$ to occur. Thus, the ratio $P(A \cap B)/P(B)$ provides the conditional probability that we will observe event A given that event B has already occurred.

Let us return to the issue of discrimination against the female officers. The marginal probability in row 1 of Table 4.5 shows that the probability of promotion of an officer is $P(A) = .27$ (regardless of whether that officer is male or female). However, the critical issue in the discrimination case involves the two conditional probabilities $P(A \mid M)$ and $P(A \mid W)$. That is, what is the probability of a promotion *given* that the officer is a man, and what is the probability of a promotion *given* that the officer is a woman? If these two probabilities are equal, a discrimination argument has no basis because the chances of a promotion are the same for male and female officers. However, a difference in the two conditional probabilities will support the position that male and female officers are treated differently in promotion decisions.

FIGURE 4.8 CONDITIONAL PROBABILITY $P(A \mid B) = P(A \cap B)/P(B)$

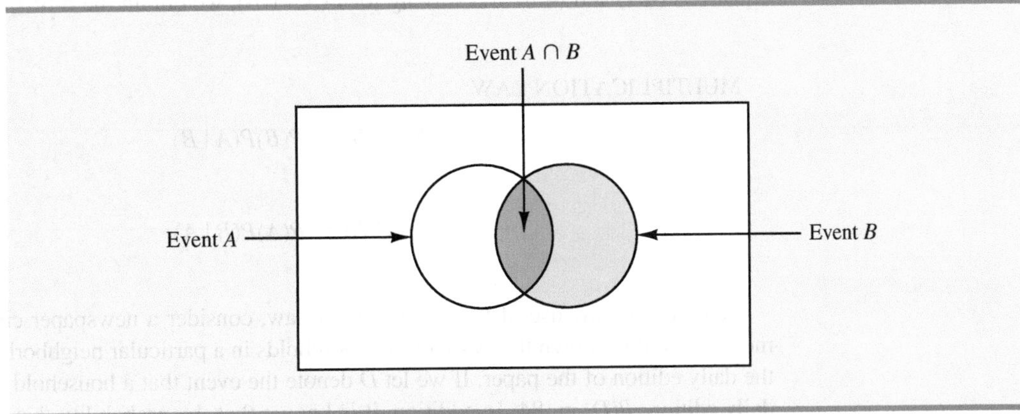

We already determined that $P(A \mid M) = .30$. Let us now use the probability values in Table 4.5 and the basic relationship of conditional probability in equation (4.7) to compute the probability that an officer is promoted given that the officer is a woman; that is, $P(A \mid W)$. Using equation (4.7), with W replacing B, we obtain

$$P(A \mid W) = \frac{P(A \cap W)}{P(W)} = \frac{.03}{.20} = .15$$

What conclusion do you draw? The probability of a promotion given that the officer is a man is .30, twice the .15 probability of a promotion given that the officer is a woman. Although the use of conditional probability does not in itself prove that discrimination exists in this case, the conditional probability values support the argument presented by the female officers.

Independent Events

In the preceding illustration, $P(A) = .27$, $P(A \mid M) = .30$, and $P(A \mid W) = .15$. We see that the probability of a promotion (event A) is affected or influenced by whether the officer is a man or a woman. Particularly, because $P(A \mid M) \neq P(A)$, we would say that events A and M are dependent events. That is, the probability of event A (promotion) is altered or affected by knowing that event M (the officer is a man) exists. Similarly, with $P(A \mid W) \neq P(A)$, we would say that events A and W are dependent events. However, if the probability of event A is not changed by the existence of event M—that is, $P(A \mid M) = P(A)$—we would say that events A and M are **independent events**. This situation leads to the following definition of the independence of two events.

INDEPENDENT EVENTS

Two events A and B are independent if

$$P(A \mid B) = P(A) \tag{4.9}$$

or

$$P(B \mid A) = P(B) \tag{4.10}$$

Otherwise, the events are dependent.

Multiplication Law

Whereas the addition law of probability is used to compute the probability of a union of two events, the multiplication law is used to compute the probability of the intersection of two events. The multiplication law is based on the definition of conditional probability. Using equations (4.7) and (4.8) and solving for $P(A \cap B)$, we obtain the **multiplication law**.

MULTIPLICATION LAW

$$P(A \cap B) = P(B)P(A \mid B) \tag{4.11}$$

or

$$P(A \cap B) = P(A)P(B \mid A) \tag{4.12}$$

To illustrate the use of the multiplication law, consider a newspaper circulation department where it is known that 84% of the households in a particular neighborhood subscribe to the daily edition of the paper. If we let D denote the event that a household subscribes to the daily edition, $P(D) = .84$. In addition, it is known that the probability that a household that already holds a daily subscription also subscribes to the Sunday edition (event S) is .75; that is, $P(S \mid D) = .75$. What is the probability that a household subscribes to both the Sunday and daily editions of the newspaper? Using the multiplication law, we compute the desired $P(S \cap D)$ as

$$P(S \cap D) = P(D)P(S \mid D) = .84(.75) = .63$$

We now know that 63% of the households subscribe to both the Sunday and daily editions.

Before concluding this section, let us consider the special case of the multiplication law when the events involved are independent. Recall that events A and B are independent whenever $P(A \mid B) = P(A)$ or $P(B \mid A) = P(B)$. Hence, using equations (4.11) and (4.12) for the special case of independent events, we obtain the following multiplication law.

MULTIPLICATION LAW FOR INDEPENDENT EVENTS

$$P(A \cap B) = P(A)P(B) \tag{4.13}$$

To compute the probability of the intersection of two independent events, we simply multiply the corresponding probabilities. Note that the multiplication law for independent events provides another way to determine whether A and B are independent. That is, if $P(A \cap B) = P(A)P(B)$, then A and B are independent; if $P(A \cap B) \neq P(A)P(B)$, then A and B are dependent.

As an application of the multiplication law for independent events, consider the situation of a service station manager who knows from past experience that 80% of the customers use a credit card when they purchase gasoline. What is the probability that the next two customers purchasing gasoline will each use a credit card? If we let

A = the event that the first customer uses a credit card

B = the event that the second customer uses a credit card

then the event of interest is $A \cap B$. Given no other information, we can reasonably assume that A and B are independent events. Thus,

$$P(A \cap B) = P(A)P(B) = (.80)(.80) = .64$$

To summarize this section, we note that our interest in conditional probability is motivated by the fact that events are often related. In such cases, we say the events are dependent and the conditional probability formulas in equations (4.7) and (4.8) must be used to compute the event probabilities. If two events are not related, they are independent; in this case neither event's probability is affected by whether the other event occurred.

NOTE AND COMMENT

Do not confuse the notion of mutually exclusive events with that of independent events. Two events with nonzero probabilities cannot be both mutually exclusive and independent. If one mutually exclusive event is known to occur, the other cannot occur; thus, the probability of the other event occurring is reduced to zero. They are therefore dependent.

Exercises

Methods

30. Suppose that we have two events, A and B, with $P(A) = .50$, $P(B) = .60$, and $P(A \cap B) = .40$.
    a. Find $P(A \mid B)$.
    b. Find $P(B \mid A)$.
    c. Are A and B independent? Why or why not?

31. Assume that we have two events, A and B, that are mutually exclusive. Assume further that we know $P(A) = .30$ and $P(B) = .40$.
    a. What is $P(A \cap B)$?
    b. What is $P(A \mid B)$?
    c. A student in statistics argues that the concepts of mutually exclusive events and independent events are really the same, and that if events are mutually exclusive they must be independent. Do you agree with this statement? Use the probability information in this problem to justify your answer.
    d. What general conclusion would you make about mutually exclusive and independent events given the results of this problem?

Applications

32. The automobile industry sold 657,000 vehicles in the United States during January 2009 (*The Wall Street Journal,* February 4, 2009). This volume was down 37% from January 2008 as economic conditions continued to decline. The Big Three U.S. automakers—General Motors, Ford, and Chrysler—sold 280,500 vehicles, down 48% from January 2008. A summary of sales by automobile manufacturer and type of vehicle sold is shown in the following table. Data are in thousands of vehicles. The non-U.S. manufacturers are led by Toyota, Honda, and Nissan. The category Light Truck includes pickup, minivan, SUV, and crossover models.

		Type of Vehicle	
		Car	Light Truck
Manufacturer	U.S.	87.4	193.1
	Non-U.S.	228.5	148.0

    a. Develop a joint probability table for these data and use the table to answer the remaining questions.
    b. What are the marginal probabilities? What do they tell you about the probabilities associated with the manufacturer and the type of vehicle sold?
    c. If a vehicle was manufactured by one of the U.S. automakers, what is the probability that the vehicle was a car? What is the probability it was a light truck?
    d. If a vehicle was not manufactured by one of the U.S. automakers, what is the probability that the vehicle was a car? What is the probability it was a light truck?
    e. If the vehicle was a light truck, what is the probability that it was manufactured by one of the U.S. automakers?
    f. What does the probability information tell you about sales?

33. Students taking the Graduate Management Admissions Test (GMAT) were asked about their undergraduate major and intent to pursue their MBA as a full-time or part-time student. A summary of their responses follows.

		Undergraduate Major			
		Business	Engineering	Other	Totals
Intended Enrollment Status	Full-Time	352	197	251	800
	Part-Time	150	161	194	505
	Totals	502	358	445	1305

    a. Develop a joint probability table for these data.
    b. Use the marginal probabilities of undergraduate major (business, engineering, or other) to comment on which undergraduate major produces the most potential MBA students.

c. If a student intends to attend classes full-time in pursuit of an MBA degree, what is the probability that the student was an undergraduate engineering major?
d. If a student was an undergraduate business major, what is the probability that the student intends to attend classes full-time in pursuit of an MBA degree?
e. Let F denote the event that the student intends to attend classes full-time in pursuit of an MBA degree, and let B denote the event that the student was an undergraduate business major. Are events F and B independent? Justify your answer.

34. The Bureau of Transportation Statistics reports on-time performance for airlines at major U.S. airports. JetBlue, United, and US Airways share terminal C at Boston's Logan Airport. The percentage of on-time flights reported for August 2012 was 76.8% for JetBlue, 71.5% for United, and 82.2% for US Airways (Bureau of Transportation Statistics website, October 2012). Assume that 30% of the flights arriving at terminal C are JetBlue flights, 32% are United flights, and 38% are US Airways flights.
    a. Develop a joint probability table with three rows (the airlines) and two columns (on-time and late).
    b. An announcement is made that Flight 1382 will be arriving at gate 20 of terminal C. What is the probability that Flight 1382 will arrive on time?
    c. What is the most likely airline for Flight 1382? What is the probability that Flight 1382 is by this airline?
    d. Suppose that an announcement is made saying that Flight 1382 will now be arriving late. What is the most likely airline for this flight? What is the probability that Flight 1382 is by this airline?

35. According to the Ameriprise Financial Money Across Generations study, 9 out of 10 parents with adult children ages 20 to 35 have helped their adult children with some type of financial assistance ranging from college to a car, rent, utilities, credit-card debt, and/or down payments for houses (*Money,* January 2009). The following table, constructed using sample data consistent with the study, shows the number of times parents have given their adult children financial assistance to buy a car and to pay rent.

		Pay Rent	
		Yes	**No**
Buy a Car	**Yes**	56	52
	No	14	78

    a. Develop a joint probability table and use it to answer the remaining questions.
    b. Using the marginal probabilities for buy a car and pay rent, are parents more likely to assist their adult children with buying a car or paying rent? What is your interpretation of the marginal probabilities?
    c. If parents provided financial assistance to buy a car, what is the probability that the parents assisted with paying rent?
    d. If parents did not provide financial assistance to buy a car, what is the probability the parents assisted with paying rent?
    e. Is financial assistance to buy a car independent of financial assistance to pay rent? Use probabilities to justify your answer.
    f. What is the probability that parents provided financial assistance for their adult children by either helping buy a car or pay rent?

36. Jamal Crawford of the National Basketball Association's Portland Trail Blazers is the best free-throw shooter on the team, making 93% of his shots (ESPN website, April 5, 2012). Assume that late in a basketball game, Jamal Crawford is fouled and is awarded two shots.
    a. What is the probability that he will make both shots?
    b. What is the probability that he will make at least one shot?
    c. What is the probability that he will miss both shots?

d. Late in a basketball game, a team often intentionally fouls an opposing player in order to stop the game clock. The usual strategy is to intentionally foul the other team's worst free-throw shooter. Assume that the Portland Trail Blazers' center makes 58% of his free-throw shots. Calculate the probabilities for the center as shown in parts (a), (b), and (c), and show that intentionally fouling the Portland Trail Blazers' center is a better strategy than intentionally fouling Jamal Crawford. Assume as in parts (a), (b), and (c) that two shots will be awarded.

37. A joint survey by *Parade* magazine and Yahoo! found that 59% of American workers say that if they could do it all over again, they would choose a different career (*USA Today*, September 24, 2012). The survey also found that 33% of American workers say they plan to retire early and 67% say they plan to wait and retire at age 65 or older. Assume that the following joint probability table applies.

		Retire Early		
		Yes	**No**	
Career	**Same**	.20	.21	.41
	Different	.13	.46	.59
		.33	.67	

a. What is the probability a worker would select the same career?
b. What is the probability a worker who would select the same career plans to retire early?
c. What is the probability a worker who would select a different career plans to retire early?
d. What do the conditional probabilities in parts (b) and (c) suggest about the reasons workers say they would select the same career?

38. The Institute for Higher Education Policy, a Washington, D.C.-based research firm, studied the payback of student loans for 1.8 million college students who had student loans that began to become due six years ago (*The Wall Street Journal*, November 27, 2012). The study found that 50% of the student loans were being paid back in a satisfactory fashion, whereas 50% of the student loans were delinquent. The following joint probability table shows the probabilities of the student loan status and whether or not the student had received a college degree.

		College Degree		
		Yes	**No**	
Loan Status	**Satisfactory**	.26	.24	.50
	Delinquent	.16	.34	.50
		.42	.58	

a. What is the probability that a student with a student loan had received a college degree?
b. What is the probability that a student with a student loan had not received a college degree?
c. Given the student had received a college degree, what is the probability that the student has a delinquent loan?
d. Given the student had not received a college degree, what is the probability that the student has a delinquent loan?
e. What is the impact of dropping out of college without a degree for students who have a student loan?

4.5 Bayes' Theorem

In the discussion of conditional probability, we indicated that revising probabilities when new information is obtained is an important phase of probability analysis. Often, we begin the analysis with initial or **prior probability** estimates for specific events of interest. Then, from sources such as a sample, a special report, or a product test, we obtain additional information about the events. Given this new information, we update the prior probability values by calculating revised probabilities, referred to as **posterior probabilities. Bayes' theorem** provides a means for making these probability calculations. The steps in this probability revision process are shown in Figure 4.9.

As an application of Bayes' theorem, consider a manufacturing firm that receives shipments of parts from two different suppliers. Let A_1 denote the event that a part is from supplier 1 and A_2 denote the event that a part is from supplier 2. Currently, 65% of the parts purchased by the company are from supplier 1 and the remaining 35% are from supplier 2. Hence, if a part is selected at random, we would assign the prior probabilities $P(A_1) = .65$ and $P(A_2) = .35$.

The quality of the purchased parts varies with the source of supply. Historical data suggest that the quality ratings of the two suppliers are as shown in Table 4.6. If we let G denote the event that a part is good and B denote the event that a part is bad, the information in Table 4.6 provides the following conditional probability values.

$$P(G \mid A_1) = .98 \quad P(B \mid A_1) = .02$$
$$P(G \mid A_2) = .95 \quad P(B \mid A_2) = .05$$

The tree diagram in Figure 4.10 depicts the process of the firm receiving a part from one of the two suppliers and then discovering that the part is good or bad as a two-step random experiment. We see that four experimental outcomes are possible; two correspond to the part being good and two correspond to the part being bad.

Each of the experimental outcomes is the intersection of two events, so we can use the multiplication rule to compute the probabilities. For instance,

$$P(A_1, G) = P(A_1 \cap G) = P(A_1)P(G \mid A_1)$$

FIGURE 4.9 PROBABILITY REVISION USING BAYES' THEOREM

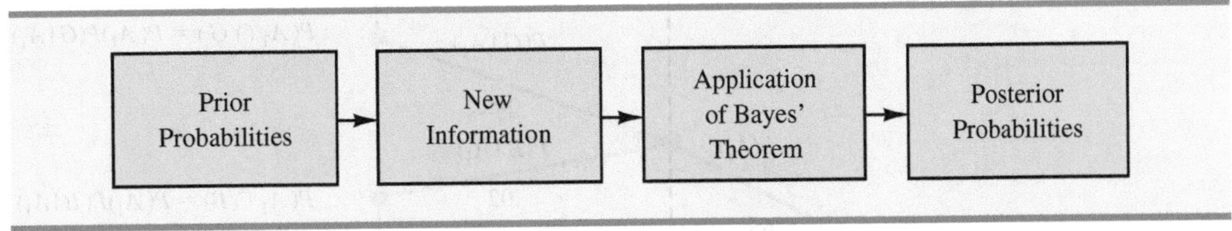

TABLE 4.6 HISTORICAL QUALITY LEVELS OF TWO SUPPLIERS

	Percentage Good Parts	Percentage Bad Parts
Supplier 1	98	2
Supplier 2	95	5

FIGURE 4.10 TREE DIAGRAM FOR TWO-SUPPLIER EXAMPLE

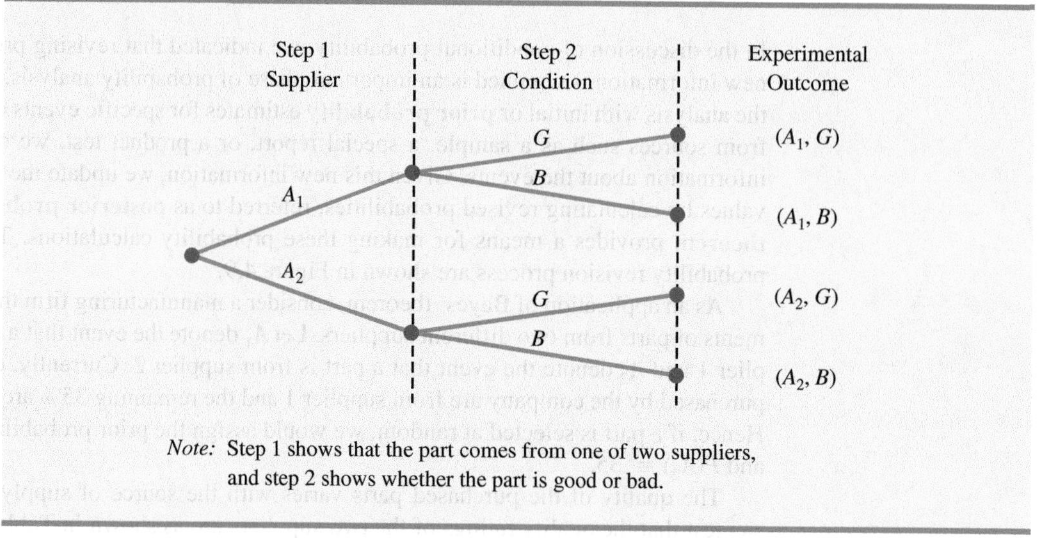

The process of computing these joint probabilities can be depicted in what is called a probability tree (see Figure 4.11). From left to right through the tree, the probabilities for each branch at step 1 are prior probabilities and the probabilities for each branch at step 2 are conditional probabilities. To find the probabilities of each experimental outcome, we simply multiply the probabilities on the branches leading to the outcome. Each of these joint probabilities is shown in Figure 4.11 along with the known probabilities for each branch.

Suppose now that the parts from the two suppliers are used in the firm's manufacturing process and that a machine breaks down because it attempts to process a bad part. Given the information that the part is bad, what is the probability that it came from supplier 1 and what is the probability that it came from supplier 2? With the information in the probability tree (Figure 4.11), Bayes' theorem can be used to answer these questions.

FIGURE 4.11 PROBABILITY TREE FOR TWO-SUPPLIER EXAMPLE

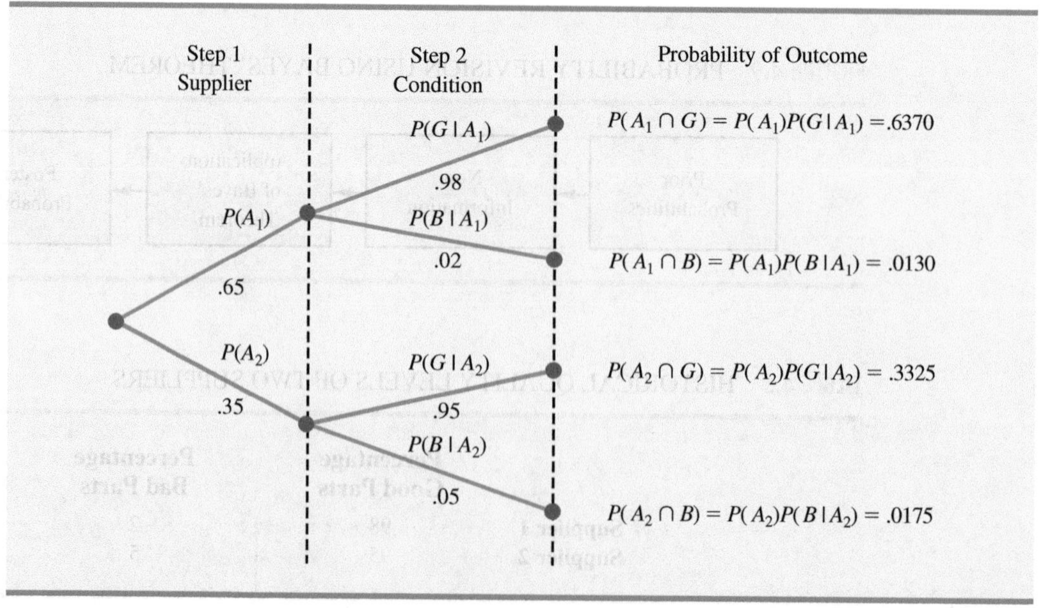

Letting B denote the event that the part is bad, we are looking for the posterior probabilities $P(A_1 \mid B)$ and $P(A_2 \mid B)$. From the law of conditional probability, we know that

$$P(A_1 \mid B) = \frac{P(A_1 \cap B)}{P(B)} \tag{4.14}$$

Referring to the probability tree, we see that

$$P(A_1 \cap B) = P(A_1)P(B \mid A_1) \tag{4.15}$$

To find $P(B)$, we note that event B can occur in only two ways: $(A_1 \cap B)$ and $(A_2 \cap B)$. Therefore, we have

$$\begin{aligned} P(B) &= P(A_1 \cap B) + P(A_2 \cap B) \\ &= P(A_1)P(B \mid A_1) + P(A_2)P(B \mid A_2) \end{aligned} \tag{4.16}$$

Substituting from equations (4.15) and (4.16) into equation (4.14) and writing a similar result for $P(A_2 \mid B)$, we obtain Bayes' theorem for the case of two events.

The Reverend Thomas Bayes (1702–1761), a Presbyterian minister, is credited with the original work leading to the version of Bayes' theorem in use today.

BAYES' THEOREM (TWO-EVENT CASE)

$$P(A_1 \mid B) = \frac{P(A_1)P(B \mid A_1)}{P(A_1)P(B \mid A_1) + P(A_2)P(B \mid A_2)} \tag{4.17}$$

$$P(A_2 \mid B) = \frac{P(A_2)P(B \mid A_2)}{P(A_1)P(B \mid A_1) + P(A_2)P(B \mid A_2)} \tag{4.18}$$

Using equation (4.17) and the probability values provided in the example, we have

$$\begin{aligned} P(A_1 \mid B) &= \frac{P(A_1)P(B \mid A_1)}{P(A_1)P(B \mid A_1) + P(A_2)P(B \mid A_2)} \\ &= \frac{(.65)(.02)}{(.65)(.02) + (.35)(.05)} = \frac{.0130}{.0130 + .0175} \\ &= \frac{.0130}{.0305} = .4262 \end{aligned}$$

In addition, using equation (4.18), we find $P(A_2 \mid B)$.

$$\begin{aligned} P(A_2 \mid B) &= \frac{(.35)(.05)}{(.65)(.02) + (.35)(.05)} \\ &= \frac{.0175}{.0130 + .0175} = \frac{.0175}{.0305} = .5738 \end{aligned}$$

Note that in this application we started with a probability of .65 that a part selected at random was from supplier 1. However, given information that the part is bad, the probability that the part is from supplier 1 drops to .4262. In fact, if the part is bad, it has better than a 50–50 chance that it came from supplier 2; that is, $P(A_2 \mid B) = .5738$.

Bayes' theorem is applicable when the events for which we want to compute posterior probabilities are mutually exclusive and their union is the entire sample space.[1] For the case of n mutually exclusive events $A_1, A_2, \ldots, A_n$, whose union is the entire sample space, Bayes' theorem can be used to compute any posterior probability $P(A_i \mid B)$ as shown here.

BAYES' THEOREM

$$P(A_i \mid B) = \frac{P(A_i)P(B \mid A_i)}{P(A_1)P(B \mid A_1) + P(A_2)P(B \mid A_2) + \cdots + P(A_n)P(B \mid A_n)} \quad (4.19)$$

With prior probabilities $P(A_1), P(A_2), \ldots, P(A_n)$ and the appropriate conditional probabilities $P(B \mid A_1), P(B \mid A_2), \ldots, P(B \mid A_n)$, equation (4.19) can be used to compute the posterior probability of the events $A_1, A_2, \ldots, A_n$.

Tabular Approach

A tabular approach is helpful in conducting the Bayes' theorem calculations. Such an approach is shown in Table 4.7 for the parts supplier problem. The computations shown there are done in the following steps.

Step 1. Prepare the following three columns:
Column 1—The mutually exclusive events A_i for which posterior probabilities are desired
Column 2—The prior probabilities $P(A_i)$ for the events
Column 3—The conditional probabilities $P(B \mid A_i)$ of the new information B given each event

Step 2. In column 4, compute the joint probabilities $P(A_i \cap B)$ for each event and the new information B by using the multiplication law. These joint probabilities are found by multiplying the prior probabilities in column 2 by the corresponding conditional probabilities in column 3; that is, $P(A_i \cap B) = P(A_i)P(B \mid A_i)$.

Step 3. Sum the joint probabilities in column 4. The sum is the probability of the new information, $P(B)$. Thus we see in Table 4.7 that there is a .0130 probability that the part came from supplier 1 and is bad and a .0175 probability that the part came from supplier 2 and is bad. Because these are the only two ways in which a bad part can be obtained, the sum .0130 + .0175 shows an overall probability of .0305 of finding a bad part from the combined shipments of the two suppliers.

TABLE 4.7 TABULAR APPROACH TO BAYES' THEOREM CALCULATIONS FOR THE TWO-SUPPLIER PROBLEM

(1) Events A_i	(2) Prior Probabilities $P(A_i)$	(3) Conditional Probabilities $P(B \mid A_i)$	(4) Joint Probabilities $P(A_i \cap B)$	(5) Posterior Probabilities $P(A_i \mid B)$
A_1	.65	.02	.0130	.0130/.0305 = .4262
A_2	.35	.05	.0175	.0175/.0305 = .5738
	1.00		$P(B)$ = .0305	1.0000

[1]If the union of events is the entire sample space, the events are said to be collectively exhaustive.

Step 4. In column 5, compute the posterior probabilities using the basic relationship of conditional probability.

$$P(A_i \mid B) = \frac{P(A_i \cap B)}{P(B)}$$

Note that the joint probabilities $P(A_i \cap B)$ are in column 4 and the probability $P(B)$ is the sum of column 4.

NOTES AND COMMENTS

1. Bayes' theorem is used extensively in decision analysis. The prior probabilities are often subjective estimates provided by a decision maker. Sample information is obtained and posterior probabilities are computed for use in choosing the best decision.
2. An event and its complement are mutually exclusive, and their union is the entire sample space. Thus, Bayes' theorem is always applicable for computing posterior probabilities of an event and its complement.

Exercises

Methods

39. The prior probabilities for events A_1 and A_2 are $P(A_1) = .40$ and $P(A_2) = .60$. It is also known that $P(A_1 \cap A_2) = 0$. Suppose $P(B \mid A_1) = .20$ and $P(B \mid A_2) = .05$.
    a. Are A_1 and A_2 mutually exclusive? Explain.
    b. Compute $P(A_1 \cap B)$ and $P(A_2 \cap B)$.
    c. Compute $P(B)$.
    d. Apply Bayes' theorem to compute $P(A_1 \mid B)$ and $P(A_2 \mid B)$.
40. The prior probabilities for events A_1, A_2, and A_3 are $P(A_1) = .20$, $P(A_2) = .50$, and $P(A_3) = .30$. The conditional probabilities of event B given A_1, A_2, and A_3 are $P(B \mid A_1) = .50$, $P(B \mid A_2) = .40$, and $P(B \mid A_3) = .30$.
    a. Compute $P(B \cap A_1)$, $P(B \cap A_2)$, and $P(B \cap A_3)$.
    b. Apply Bayes' theorem, equation (4.19), to compute the posterior probability $P(A_2 \mid B)$.
    c. Use the tabular approach to applying Bayes' theorem to compute $P(A_1 \mid B)$, $P(A_2 \mid B)$, and $P(A_3 \mid B)$.

Applications

41. A consulting firm submitted a bid for a large research project. The firm's management initially felt they had a 50–50 chance of getting the project. However, the agency to which the bid was submitted subsequently requested additional information on the bid. Past experience indicates that for 75% of the successful bids and 40% of the unsuccessful bids the agency requested additional information.
    a. What is the prior probability of the bid being successful (that is, prior to the request for additional information)?
    b. What is the conditional probability of a request for additional information given that the bid will ultimately be successful?
    c. Compute the posterior probability that the bid will be successful given a request for additional information.

42. A local bank reviewed its credit card policy with the intention of recalling some of its credit cards. In the past approximately 5% of cardholders defaulted, leaving the bank

unable to collect the outstanding balance. Hence, management established a prior probability of .05 that any particular cardholder will default. The bank also found that the probability of missing a monthly payment is .20 for customers who do not default. Of course, the probability of missing a monthly payment for those who default is 1.

a. Given a customer missed a monthly payment, compute the posterior probability that the customer will default.
b. The bank would like to recall its credit card if the probability that a customer will default is greater than .20. Should the bank recall its credit card if the customer misses a monthly payment? Why or why not?

43. In August 2012, tropical storm Isaac formed in the Caribbean and was headed for the Gulf of Mexico. There was an initial probability of .69 that Isaac would become a hurricane by the time it reached the Gulf of Mexico (National Hurricane Center website, August 21, 2012).
    a. What was the probability that Isaac would not become a hurricane but remain a tropical storm when it reached the Gulf of Mexico?
    b. Two days later, the National Hurricane Center projected the path of Isaac would pass directly over Cuba before reaching the Gulf of Mexico. How did passing over Cuba alter the probability that Isaac would become a hurricane by the time it reached the Gulf of Mexico? Use the following probabilities to answer this question. Hurricanes that reach the Gulf of Mexico have a .08 probability of having passed over Cuba. Tropical storms that reach the Gulf of Mexico have a .20 probability of having passed over Cuba.
    c. What happens to the probability of becoming a hurricane when a tropical storm passes over a landmass such as Cuba?
44. ParFore created a website to market golf equipment and golf apparel. Management would like a special pop-up offer to appear for female website visitors and a different special pop-up offer to appear for male website visitors. From a sample of past website visitors, ParFore's management learned that 60% of the visitors are male and 40% are female.
    a. What is the probability that a current visitor to the website is female?
    b. Suppose 30% of ParFore's female visitors previously visited the Dillard's Department Store website and 10% of ParFore's male visitors previously visited the Dillard's Department Store website. If the current visitor to ParFore's website previously visited the Dillard's website, what is the revised probability that the current visitor is female? Should the ParFore's website display the special offer that appeals to female visitors or the special offer that appeals to male visitors?
45. Two Wharton School professors at the University of Pennsylvania analyzed 1,613,234 putts by golfers on the Professional Golfers' Association (PGA) Tour and found that 983,764 putts were made and 629,470 putts were missed (*Is Tiger Woods Loss Averse? Persistent Bias in the Face of Experience, Competition, and High Stakes*, June 2009).
    a. What is the probability that a PGA Tour player makes a putt? What is the probability that a PGA Tour player misses a putt?
    b. Suppose that a PGA Tour player has a par putt. It is known that of putts made, 64.0% were for par whereas for putts missed, 20.3% were for par. What is the revised probability of making a putt given the PGA Tour player has a par putt?
    c. A birdie occurs when a player makes a putt in one stroke less than par. Suppose that a PGA Tour player has a birdie putt. It is known that of putts made, 18.8% were for birdie, whereas for putts missed, 73.4% were for birdie. What is the revised probability of making a putt given the PGA Tour player has a birdie putt?
    d. Comment on the differences in the probabilities computed in parts (b) and (c).

Summary

In this chapter we introduced basic probability concepts and illustrated how probability analysis can be used to provide helpful information for decision making. We described how probability can be interpreted as a numerical measure of the likelihood that an event will occur. In addition, we saw that the probability of an event can be computed either by summing the probabilities of the experimental outcomes (sample points) comprising the event or by using the relationships established by the addition, conditional probability, and multiplication laws of probability. For cases in which additional information is available, we showed how Bayes' theorem can be used to obtain revised or posterior probabilities.

Glossary

Probability A numerical measure of the likelihood that an event will occur.
Random experiment A random experiment is a process that generates well-defined experimental outcomes. On any single repetition or trial, the outcome that occurs is determined completely by chance.
Sample space The set of all experimental outcomes.
Sample point An element of the sample space. A sample point represents an experimental outcome.
Multiple-step random experiment A random experiment that can be described as a sequence of steps. If a multiple-step random experiment has k steps with n_1 possible outcomes on the first step, n_2 possible outcomes on the second step, and so on, the total number of experimental outcomes is given by $(n_1)(n_2) \ldots (n_k)$.
Tree diagram A graphical representation that helps in visualizing a multiple-step random experiment.
Combination In a random experiment we may be interested in determining the number of ways n objects may be selected from among N objects without regard to the *order in which the n objects are selected*. Each selection of n objects is called a combination and the total number of combinations of N objects taken n at a time is $C_n^N = \binom{N}{n} = \frac{N!}{n!(N-n)!}$ for $n = 0, 1, 2, \ldots, N$.
Permutation In a random experiment we may be interested in determining the number of ways n objects may be selected from among N objects when the *order in which the n objects are selected* is important. Each ordering of n objects is called a permutation and the total number of permutations of N objects taken n at a time is $P_n^N = n!\binom{N}{n} = \frac{N!}{(N-n)!}$ for $n = 0, 1, 2, \ldots, N$.
Basic requirements for assigning probabilities Two requirements that restrict the manner in which probability assignments can be made: (1) For each experimental outcome E_i we must have $0 \leq P(E_i) \leq 1$; (2) considering all experimental outcomes, we must have $P(E_1) + P(E_2) + \cdots + P(E_n) = 1.0$.
Classical method A method of assigning probabilities that is appropriate when all the experimental outcomes are equally likely.
Relative frequency method A method of assigning probabilities that is appropriate when data are available to estimate the proportion of the time the experimental outcome will occur if the random experiment is repeated a large number of times.
Subjective method A method of assigning probabilities on the basis of judgment.
Event A collection of sample points.
Complement of A The event consisting of all sample points that are not in A.
Venn diagram A graphical representation for showing symbolically the sample space and operations involving events in which the sample space is represented by a rectangle and events are represented as circles within the sample space.
Union of A and B The event containing all sample points belonging to A or B or both. The union is denoted $A \cup B$.
Intersection of A and B The event containing the sample points belonging to both A and B. The intersection is denoted $A \cap B$.

Addition law A probability law used to compute the probability of the union of two events. It is $P(A \cup B) = P(A) + P(B) - P(A \cap B)$. For mutually exclusive events, $P(A \cap B) = 0$; in this case the addition law reduces to $P(A \cup B) = P(A) + P(B)$.

Mutually exclusive events Events that have no sample points in common; that is, $A \cap B$ is empty and $P(A \cap B) = 0$.

Conditional probability The probability of an event given that another event already occurred. The conditional probability of A given B is $P(A \mid B) = P(A \cap B)/P(B)$.

Joint probability The probability of two events both occurring; that is, the probability of the intersection of two events.

Marginal probability The values in the margins of a joint probability table that provide the probabilities of each event separately.

Independent events Two events A and B where $P(A \mid B) = P(A)$ or $P(B \mid A) = P(B)$; that is, the events have no influence on each other.

Multiplication law A probability law used to compute the probability of the intersection of two events. It is $P(A \cap B) = P(B)P(A \mid B)$ or $P(A \cap B) = P(A)P(B \mid A)$. For independent events it reduces to $P(A \cap B) = P(A)P(B)$.

Prior probabilities Initial estimates of the probabilities of events.

Posterior probabilities Revised probabilities of events based on additional information.

Bayes' theorem A method used to compute posterior probabilities.

Key Formulas

Counting Rule for Combinations

$$C_n^N = \binom{N}{n} = \frac{N!}{n!(N-n)!} \tag{4.1}$$

Counting Rule for Permutations

$$P_n^N = n!\binom{N}{n} = \frac{N!}{(N-n)!} \tag{4.2}$$

Computing Probability Using the Complement

$$P(A) = 1 - P(A^c) \tag{4.5}$$

Addition Law

$$P(A \cup B) = P(A) + P(B) - P(A \cap B) \tag{4.6}$$

Conditional Probability

$$P(A \mid B) = \frac{P(A \cap B)}{P(B)} \tag{4.7}$$

$$P(B \mid A) = \frac{P(A \cap B)}{P(A)} \tag{4.8}$$

Multiplication Law

$$P(A \cap B) = P(B)P(A \mid B) \tag{4.11}$$

$$P(A \cap B) = P(A)P(B \mid A) \tag{4.12}$$

Multiplication Law for Independent Events

$$P(A \cap B) = P(A)P(B) \tag{4.13}$$

Bayes' Theorem

$$P(A_i \mid B) = \frac{P(A_i)P(B \mid A_i)}{P(A_1)P(B \mid A_1) + P(A_2)P(B \mid A_2) + \cdots + P(A_n)P(B \mid A_n)} \quad (4.19)$$

Supplementary Exercises

46. A survey of adults aged 18 and older conducted by Princess Cruises asked how many days into your vacation does it take until you feel truly relaxed (*USA Today*, August 24, 2011). The responses were as follows: 422—a day or less; 181—2 days; 80—3 days; 121—4 or more days; and 201—never feel relaxed.
    a. How many adults participated in the Princess Cruises survey?
    b. What response has the highest probability? What is the probability of this response?
    c. What is the probability a respondent never feels truly relaxed on a vacation?
    d. What is the probability it takes a respondent 2 or more days to feel truly relaxed?
47. A financial manager made two new investments—one in the oil industry and one in municipal bonds. After a one-year period, each of the investments will be classified as either successful or unsuccessful. Consider the making of the two investments as a random experiment.
    a. How many sample points exist for this experiment?
    b. Show a tree diagram and list the sample points.
    c. Let O = the event that the oil industry investment is successful and M = the event that the municipal bond investment is successful. List the sample points in O and in M.
    d. List the sample points in the union of the events $(O \cup M)$.
    e. List the sample points in the intersection of the events $(O \cap M)$.
    f. Are events O and M mutually exclusive? Explain.
48. Forty-three percent of Americans use social media and other websites to voice their opinions about television programs (*The Huffington Post,* November 23, 2011). Below are the results of a survey of 1364 individuals who were asked if they use social media and other websites to voice their opinions about television programs.

	Uses Social Media and Other Websites to Voice Opinions About Television Programs	Doesn't Use Social Media and Other Websites to Voice Opinions About Television Programs
Female	395	291
Male	323	355

    a. Show a joint probability table.
    b. What is the probability a respondent is female?
    c. What is the conditional probability a respondent uses social media and other websites to voice opinions about television programs given the respondent is female?
    d. Let F denote the event that the respondent is female and A denote the event that the respondent uses social media and other websites to voice opinions about television programs. Are events F and A independent?
49. A study of 31,000 hospital admissions in New York State found that 4% of the admissions led to treatment-caused injuries. One-seventh of these treatment-caused injuries resulted in death, and one-fourth were caused by negligence. Malpractice claims were filed in one out of 7.5 cases involving negligence, and payments were made in one out of every two claims.
    a. What is the probability a person admitted to the hospital will suffer a treatment-caused injury due to negligence?
    b. What is the probability a person admitted to the hospital will die from a treatment-caused injury?

c. In the case of a negligent treatment-caused injury, what is the probability a malpractice claim will be paid?

50. A telephone survey to determine viewer response to a new television show obtained the following data.

Rating	Frequency
Poor	4
Below average	8
Average	11
Above average	14
Excellent	13

a. What is the probability that a randomly selected viewer will rate the new show as average or better?
b. What is the probability that a randomly selected viewer will rate the new show below average or worse?

51. The U.S. Census Bureau serves as the leading source of quantitative data about the nation's people and economy. The following crosstabulation shows the number of households (1000s) and the household income by the highest level of education for the head of household (U.S. Census Bureau website, 2013). Only households in which the head has a high school diploma or more are included.

	Household Income				
Highest Level of Education	**Under $25,000**	**$25,000 to $49,999**	**$50,000 to $99,999**	**$100,000 and Over**	**Total**
High school graduate	9880	9970	9441	3482	32,773
Bachelor's degree	2484	4164	7666	7817	22,131
Master's degree	685	1205	3019	4094	9003
Doctoral degree	79	160	422	1076	1737
Total	13,128	15,499	20,548	16,469	65,644

a. Develop a joint probability table.
b. What is the probability of the head of one of these household having a master's degree or more education?
c. What is the probability of a household headed by someone with a high school diploma earning $100,000 or more?
d. What is the probability of one of these households having an income below $25,000?
e. What is the probability of a household headed by someone with a bachelor's degree earning less than $25,000?
f. Is household income independent of educational level?

52. An MBA new-matriculants survey provided the following data for 2018 students.

		Applied to More Than One School	
		Yes	**No**
Age Group	**23 and under**	207	201
	24–26	299	379
	27–30	185	268
	31–35	66	193
	36 and over	51	169

a. For a randomly selected MBA student, prepare a joint probability table for the random experiment consisting of observing the student's age and whether the student applied to one or more schools.
b. What is the probability that a randomly selected applicant is 23 or under?
c. What is the probability that a randomly selected applicant is older than 26?
d. What is the probability that a randomly selected applicant applied to more than one school?

53. Refer again to the data from the MBA new-matriculants survey in exercise 52.
a. Given that a person applied to more than one school, what is the probability that the person is 24–26 years old?
b. Given that a person is in the 36-and-over age group, what is the probability that the person applied to more than one school?
c. What is the probability that a person is 24–26 years old or applied to more than one school?
d. Suppose a person is known to have applied to only one school. What is the probability that the person is 31 or more years old?
e. Is the number of schools applied to independent of age? Explain.

54. In February 2012, the Pew Internet & American Life project conducted a survey that included several questions about how Internet users feel about search engines and other websites collecting information about them and using this information either to shape search results or target advertising to them (Pew Research Center, March 9, 2012). In one question, participants were asked, "If a search engine kept track of what you search for, and then used that information to personalize your future search results, how would you feel about that?" Respondents could indicate either "Would *not* be okay with it because you feel it is an invasion of your privacy" or "Would be *okay* with it, even if it means they are gathering information about you." Joint probabilities of responses and age groups are summarized in the following table.

Age	Not Okay	Okay
18–29	.1485	.0604
30–49	.2273	.0907
50+	.4008	.0723

a. What is the probability a respondent will *not be okay* with this practice?
b. Given a respondent is 30–49 years old, what is the probability the respondent will *be okay* with this practice?
c. Given a respondent is *not okay* with this practice, what is the probability the respondent is 50+ years old?
d. Is the attitude about this practice independent of the age of the respondent? Why or why not?
e. Do attitudes toward this practice for respondents who are 18–29 years old and respondents who are 50+ years old differ?

55. A large consumer goods company ran a television advertisement for one of its soap products. On the basis of a survey that was conducted, probabilities were assigned to the following events.

B = individual purchased the product
S = individual recalls seeing the advertisement
$B \cap S$ = individual purchased the product and recalls seeing the advertisement

The probabilities assigned were $P(B) = .20$, $P(S) = .40$, and $P(B \cap S) = .12$.
a. What is the probability of an individual's purchasing the product given that the individual recalls seeing the advertisement? Does seeing the advertisement increase

the probability that the individual will purchase the product? As a decision maker, would you recommend continuing the advertisement (assuming that the cost is reasonable)?

b. Assume that individuals who do not purchase the company's soap product buy from its competitors. What would be your estimate of the company's market share? Would you expect that continuing the advertisement will increase the company's market share? Why or why not?

c. The company also tested another advertisement and assigned it values of $P(S) = .30$ and $P(B \cap S) = .10$. What is $P(B \mid S)$ for this other advertisement? Which advertisement seems to have had the bigger effect on customer purchases?

56. Cooper Realty is a small real estate company located in Albany, New York, specializing primarily in residential listings. The company recently became interested in determining the likelihood of one of its listings being sold within a certain number of days. An analysis of company sales of 800 homes in previous years produced the following data.

		Days Listed Until Sold			
		Under 30	31–90	Over 90	Total
Initial Asking Price	Under $150,000	50	40	10	100
	$150,000–$199,999	20	150	80	250
	$200,000–$250,000	20	280	100	400
	Over $250,000	10	30	10	50
	Total	100	500	200	800

a. If A is defined as the event that a home is listed for more than 90 days before being sold, estimate the probability of A.

b. If B is defined as the event that the initial asking price is under $150,000, estimate the probability of B.

c. What is the probability of $A \cap B$?

d. Assuming that a contract was just signed to list a home with an initial asking price of less than $150,000, what is the probability that the home will take Cooper Realty more than 90 days to sell?

e. Are events A and B independent?

57. A company studied the number of lost-time accidents occurring at its Brownsville, Texas, plant. Historical records show that 6% of the employees suffered lost-time accidents last year. Management believes that a special safety program will reduce such accidents to 5% during the current year. In addition, it estimates that 15% of employees who had lost-time accidents last year will experience a lost-time accident during the current year.

a. What percentage of the employees will experience lost-time accidents in both years?

b. What percentage of the employees will suffer at least one lost-time accident over the two-year period?

58. According to the Open Doors Report, 9.5% of all full-time U.S. undergraduate students study abroad (Institute of International Education, November 14, 2011). Assume that 60% of the undergraduate students who study abroad are female and that 49% of the undergraduate students who do not study abroad are female.

a. Given a female undergraduate student, what is the probability that she studies abroad?

b. Given a male undergraduate student, what is the probability that he studies abroad?

c. What is the overall percentage of full-time female undergraduate students? What is the overall percentage of full-time male undergraduate students?

59. An oil company purchased an option on land in Alaska. Preliminary geologic studies assigned the following prior probabilities.

$$P(\text{high-quality oil}) = .50$$
$$P(\text{medium-quality oil}) = .20$$
$$P(\text{no oil}) = .30$$

a. What is the probability of finding oil?
b. After 200 feet of drilling on the first well, a soil test is taken. The probabilities of finding the particular type of soil identified by the test follow.

$$P(\text{soil} \mid \text{high-quality oil}) = .20$$
$$P(\text{soil} \mid \text{medium-quality oil}) = .80$$
$$P(\text{soil} \mid \text{no oil}) = .20$$

How should the firm interpret the soil test? What are the revised probabilities, and what is the new probability of finding oil?

60. The five most common words appearing in spam emails are *shipping!*, *today!*, *here!*, *available*, and *fingertips!* (Andy Greenberg, "The Most Common Words in Spam Email," *Forbes* website, March 17, 2010). Many spam filters separate spam from ham (email not considered to be spam) through application of Bayes' theorem. Suppose that for one email account, 1 in every 10 messages is spam and the proportions of spam messages that have the five most common words in spam email are given below.

shipping!	.051
today!	.045
here!	.034
available	.014
fingertips!	.014

Also suppose that the proportions of ham messages that have these words are

shipping!	.0015
today!	.0022
here!	.0022
available	.0041
fingertips!	.0011

a. If a message includes the word *shipping!*, what is the probability the message is spam? If a message includes the word *shipping!*, what is the probability the message is ham? Should messages that include the word *shipping!* be flagged as spam?
b. If a message includes the word *today!*, what is the probability the message is spam? If a message includes the word *here!*, what is the probability the message is spam? Which of these two words is a stronger indicator that a message is spam? Why?
c. If a message includes the word *available*, what is the probability the message is spam? If a message includes the word *fingertips!*, what is the probability the message is spam? Which of these two words is a stronger indicator that a message is spam? Why?
d. What insights do the results of parts (b) and (c) yield about what enables a spam filter that uses Bayes' theorem to work effectively?

Case Problem Hamilton County Judges

Hamilton County judges try thousands of cases per year. In an overwhelming majority of the cases disposed, the verdict stands as rendered. However, some cases are appealed, and of those appealed, some of the cases are reversed. Kristen DelGuzzi of *The Cincinnati Enquirer* conducted a study of cases handled by Hamilton County judges over a three-year period. Shown in Table 4.8 are the results for 182,908 cases handled (disposed) by

TABLE 4.8 TOTAL CASES DISPOSED, APPEALED, AND REVERSED IN HAMILTON COUNTY COURTS

WEB file Judge

Common Pleas Court

Judge	Total Cases Disposed	Appealed Cases	Reversed Cases
Fred Cartolano	3037	137	12
Thomas Crush	3372	119	10
Patrick Dinkelacker	1258	44	8
Timothy Hogan	1954	60	7
Robert Kraft	3138	127	7
William Mathews	2264	91	18
William Morrissey	3032	121	22
Norbert Nadel	2959	131	20
Arthur Ney, Jr.	3219	125	14
Richard Niehaus	3353	137	16
Thomas Nurre	3000	121	6
John O'Connor	2969	129	12
Robert Ruehlman	3205	145	18
J. Howard Sundermann	955	60	10
Ann Marie Tracey	3141	127	13
Ralph Winkler	3089	88	6
Total	43,945	1762	199

Domestic Relations Court

Judge	Total Cases Disposed	Appealed Cases	Reversed Cases
Penelope Cunningham	2729	7	1
Patrick Dinkelacker	6001	19	4
Deborah Gaines	8799	48	9
Ronald Panioto	12,970	32	3
Total	30,499	106	17

Municipal Court

Judge	Total Cases Disposed	Appealed Cases	Reversed Cases
Mike Allen	6149	43	4
Nadine Allen	7812	34	6
Timothy Black	7954	41	6
David Davis	7736	43	5
Leslie Isaiah Gaines	5282	35	13
Karla Grady	5253	6	0
Deidra Hair	2532	5	0
Dennis Helmick	7900	29	5
Timothy Hogan	2308	13	2
James Patrick Kenney	2798	6	1
Joseph Luebbers	4698	25	8
William Mallory	8277	38	9
Melba Marsh	8219	34	7
Beth Mattingly	2971	13	1
Albert Mestemaker	4975	28	9
Mark Painter	2239	7	3
Jack Rosen	7790	41	13
Mark Schweikert	5403	33	6
David Stockdale	5371	22	4
John A. West	2797	4	2
Total	108,464	500	104

38 judges in Common Pleas Court, Domestic Relations Court, and Municipal Court. Two of the judges (Dinkelacker and Hogan) did not serve in the same court for the entire three-year period.

The purpose of the newspaper's study was to evaluate the performance of the judges. Appeals are often the result of mistakes made by judges, and the newspaper wanted to know which judges were doing a good job and which were making too many mistakes. You are called in to assist in the data analysis. Use your knowledge of probability and conditional probability to help with the ranking of the judges. You also may be able to analyze the likelihood of appeal and reversal for cases handled by different courts.

Managerial Report

Prepare a report with your rankings of the judges. Also, include an analysis of the likelihood of appeal and case reversal in the three courts. At a minimum, your report should include the following:

1. The probability of cases being appealed and reversed in the three different courts.
2. The probability of a case being appealed for each judge.
3. The probability of a case being reversed for each judge.
4. The probability of reversal given an appeal for each judge.
5. Rank the judges within each court. State the criteria you used and provide a rationale for your choice.

CHAPTER 5

Discrete Probability Distributions

CONTENTS

STATISTICS IN PRACTICE: CITIBANK

5.1 RANDOM VARIABLES
Discrete Random Variables
Continuous Random Variables

5.2 DEVELOPING DISCRETE PROBABILITY DISTRIBUTIONS

5.3 EXPECTED VALUE AND VARIANCE
Expected Value
Variance
Using Excel to Compute the Expected Value, Variance, and Standard Deviation

5.4 BINOMIAL PROBABILITY DISTRIBUTION
A Binomial Experiment
Martin Clothing Store Problem
Using Excel to Compute Binomial Probabilities
Expected Value and Variance for the Binomial Distribution

5.5 POISSON PROBABILITY DISTRIBUTION
An Example Involving Time Intervals
An Example Involving Length or Distance Intervals
Using Excel to Compute Poisson Probabilities

5.6 HYPERGEOMETRIC PROBABILITY DISTRIBUTION
Using Excel to Compute Hypergeometric Probabilities

STATISTICS *in* PRACTICE

CITIBANK*

LONG ISLAND CITY, NEW YORK

Citibank, the retail banking division of Citigroup, offers a wide range of financial services including checking and saving accounts, loans and mortgages, insurance, and investment services. It delivers these services through a unique system referred to as Citibanking.

Citibank was one of the first banks in the United States to introduce automatic teller machines (ATMs). Citibank's ATMs, located in Citicard Banking Centers (CBCs), let customers do all of their banking in one place with the touch of a finger, 24 hours a day, 7 days a week. More than 150 different banking functions—from deposits to managing investments—can be performed with ease. Citibank customers use ATMs for 80% of their transactions.

Each Citibank CBC operates as a waiting line system with randomly arriving customers seeking service at one of the ATMs. If all ATMs are busy, the arriving customers wait in line. Periodic CBC capacity studies are used to analyze customer waiting times and to determine whether additional ATMs are needed.

Data collected by Citibank showed that the random customer arrivals followed a probability distribution known as the Poisson distribution. Using the Poisson distribution, Citibank can compute probabilities for the number of customers arriving at a CBC during any time period and make decisions concerning the number of ATMs needed. For example, let x = the number of customers arriving during a one-minute period. Assuming that a particular CBC has a mean arrival rate of two customers per minute, the following table shows the probabilities for the number of customers arriving during a one-minute period.

*The authors are indebted to Ms. Stacey Karter, Citibank, for providing this Statistics in Practice.

Each Citicard Banking Center operates as a waiting line system with randomly arriving customers seeking service at an ATM. © Chris Pancewicz/Alamy.

x	Probability
0	.1353
1	.2707
2	.2707
3	.1804
4	.0902
5 or more	.0527

Discrete probability distributions, such as the one used by Citibank, are the topic of this chapter. In addition to the Poisson distribution, you will learn about the binomial and hypergeometric distributions and how they can be used to provide helpful probability information.

In this chapter we extend the study of probability by introducing the concepts of random variables and probability distributions. Random variables and probability distributions are models for populations of data. The focus of this chapter is on probability distributions for discrete data, that is, discrete probability distributions.

We will introduce two types of discrete probability distributions. The first type is a table with one column for the values of the random variable and a second column for the associated probabilities. We will see that the rules for assigning probabilities to experimental outcomes introduced in Chapter 4 are used to assign probabilities for such a distribution. The second type of discrete probability distribution uses a special mathematical function to compute the probabilities for each value of the random variable. We present three probability distributions of this type that are widely used in practice: the binomial, Poisson, and hypergeometric distributions.

5.1 Random Variables

In Chapter 4 we defined the concept of a random experiment and its associated experimental outcomes. A random variable provides a means for describing experimental outcomes using numerical values. Random variables must assume numerical values.

Random variables must assume numerical values.

RANDOM VARIABLE

A **random variable** is a numerical description of the outcome of a random experiment.

In effect, a random variable associates a numerical value with each possible experimental outcome. The particular numerical value of the random variable depends on the outcome of the experiment. A random variable can be classified as being either *discrete* or *continuous* depending on the numerical values it assumes.

Discrete Random Variables

A random variable that may assume either a finite number of values or an infinite sequence of values such as 0, 1, 2, . . . is referred to as a **discrete random variable**. For example, consider the random experiment of an accountant taking the certified public accountant (CPA) examination. The examination has four parts. We can define a random variable as x = the number of parts of the CPA examination passed. It is a discrete random variable because it may assume the finite number of values 0, 1, 2, 3, or 4.

As another example of a discrete random variable, consider the random experiment of cars arriving at a tollbooth. The random variable of interest is x = the number of cars arriving during a one-day period. The possible values for x come from the sequence of integers 0, 1, 2, and so on. Hence, x is a discrete random variable assuming one of the values in this infinite sequence.

Although the outcomes of many random experiments can naturally be described by numerical values, others cannot. For example, a survey question might ask an individual to recall the message in a recent television commercial. This random experiment would have two possible outcomes: The individual cannot recall the message and the individual can recall the message. We can still describe these experimental outcomes numerically by defining the discrete random variable x as follows: Let $x = 0$ if the individual cannot recall the message and $x = 1$ if the individual can recall the message. The numerical values for this random variable are arbitrary (we could use 5 and 10), but they are acceptable in terms of the definition of a random variable—namely, x is a random variable because it provides a numerical description of the outcome of the random experiment.

Table 5.1 provides some additional examples of discrete random variables. Note that in each example the discrete random variable assumes a finite number of values or an infinite sequence of values such as 0, 1, 2, ... These types of discrete random variables are discussed in detail in this chapter.

Continuous Random Variables

A random variable that may assume any numerical value in an interval or collection of intervals is called a **continuous random variable**. Experimental outcomes based on

TABLE 5.1 EXAMPLES OF DISCRETE RANDOM VARIABLES

Random Experiment	Random Variable (x)	Possible Values for the Random Variable
Contact five customers	Number of customers who place an order	0, 1, 2, 3, 4, 5
Inspect a shipment of 50 radios	Number of defective radios	0, 1, 2, . . . , 49, 50
Operate a restaurant for one day	Number of customers	0, 1, 2, 3, . . .
Sell an automobile	Gender of the customer	0 if male; 1 if female

measurement scales such as time, weight, distance, and temperature can be described by continuous random variables. For example, consider a random experiment of monitoring incoming telephone calls to the claims office of a major insurance company. Suppose the random variable of interest is x = the time between consecutive incoming calls in minutes. This random variable may assume any value in the interval $x \geq 0$. Actually, an infinite number of values are possible for x, including values such as 1.26 minutes, 2.751 minutes, 4.3333 minutes, and so on. As another example, consider a 90-mile section of interstate highway I-75 north of Atlanta, Georgia. For an emergency ambulance service located in Atlanta, we might define the random variable as x = number of miles to the location of the next traffic accident along this section of I-75. In this case, x would be a continuous random variable assuming any value in the interval $0 \leq x \leq 90$. Additional examples of continuous random variables are listed in Table 5.2. Note that each example describes a random variable that may assume any value in an interval of values. Continuous random variables and their probability distributions will be the topic of Chapter 6.

TABLE 5.2 EXAMPLES OF CONTINUOUS RANDOM VARIABLES

Random Experiment	Random Variable (x)	Possible Values for the Random Variable
Operate a bank	Time between customer arrivals in minutes	$x \geq 0$
Fill a soft drink can (max = 12.1 ounces)	Number of ounces	$0 \leq x \leq 12.1$
Construct a new library	Percentage of project complete after six months	$0 \leq x \leq 100$
Test a new chemical process	Temperature when the desired reaction takes place (min 150° F; max 212° F)	$150 \leq x \leq 212$

NOTE AND COMMENT

One way to determine whether a random variable is discrete or continuous is to think of the values of the random variable as points on a line segment. Choose two points representing values of the random variable. If the entire line segment between the two points also represents possible values for the random variable, then the random variable is continuous.

Exercises

Methods

1. Consider the random experiment of tossing a coin twice.
   a. List the experimental outcomes.
   b. Define a random variable that represents the number of heads occurring on the two tosses.
   c. Show what value the random variable would assume for each of the experimental outcomes.
   d. Is this random variable discrete or continuous?
2. Consider the random experiment of a worker assembling a product.
   a. Define a random variable that represents the time in minutes required to assemble the product.
   b. What values may the random variable assume?
   c. Is the random variable discrete or continuous?

Applications

3. Three students scheduled interviews for summer employment at the Brookwood Institute. In each case the interview results in either an offer for a position or no offer. Experimental outcomes are defined in terms of the results of the three interviews.
   a. List the experimental outcomes.
   b. Define a random variable that represents the number of offers made. Is the random variable continuous?
   c. Show the value of the random variable for each of the experimental outcomes.
4. In January the U.S. unemployment rate dropped to 8.3% (U.S. Department of Labor website, February 10, 2012). The Census Bureau includes nine states in the Northeast region. Assume that the random variable of interest is the number of Northeastern states with an unemployment rate in January that was less than 8.3%. What values may this random variable assume?
5. To perform a certain type of blood analysis, lab technicians must perform two procedures. The first procedure requires either one or two separate steps, and the second procedure requires either one, two, or three steps.
   a. List the experimental outcomes associated with performing the blood analysis.
   b. If the random variable of interest is the total number of steps required to do the complete analysis (both procedures), show what value the random variable will assume for each of the experimental outcomes.
6. Listed is a series of random experiments and associated random variables. In each case, identify the values that the random variable can assume and state whether the random variable is discrete or continuous.

Random Experiment	Random Variable (x)
a. Take a 20-question examination	Number of questions answered correctly
b. Observe cars arriving at a tollbooth for 1 hour	Number of cars arriving at tollbooth
c. Audit 50 tax returns	Number of returns containing errors
d. Observe an employee's work	Number of nonproductive hours in an eight-hour workday
e. Weigh a shipment of goods	Number of pounds

Developing Discrete Probability Distributions

The **probability distribution** for a random variable describes how probabilities are distributed over the values of the random variable. For a discrete random variable x, a **probability function**, denoted by $f(x)$, provides the probability for each value of the random variable. As such, you might suppose that the classical, subjective, and relative frequency methods of assigning probabilities introduced in Chapter 4 would be useful in developing discrete probability distributions. They are, and in this section we show how. Application of this methodology leads to what we call tabular discrete probability distributions, that is, probability distributions that are presented in a table.

The classical method of assigning probabilities to values of a random variable is applicable when the experimental outcomes generate values of the random variable that are equally likely. For instance, consider the random experiment of rolling a die and observing the number on the upward face. It must be one of the numbers 1, 2, 3, 4, 5, or 6 and each of these outcomes is equally likely. Thus, if we let x = number obtained on one roll of a die and $f(x)$ = the probability of x, the probability distribution of x is given in Table 5.3.

The subjective method of assigning probabilities can also lead to a table of values of the random variable together with the associated probabilities. With the subjective method the individual developing the probability distribution uses their best judgment to assign each probability. So, unlike probability distributions developed using the classical method, different people can be expected to obtain different probability distributions.

The relative frequency method of assigning probabilities to values of a random variable is applicable when reasonably large amounts of data are available. We then treat the data as if they were the population and use the relative frequency method to assign probabilities to the experimental outcomes. The use of the relative frequency method to develop discrete probability distributions leads to what is called an **empirical discrete distribution**. With the large amounts of data available today (e.g., scanner data, credit card data), this type of probability distribution is becoming more widely used in practice. Let us illustrate by considering the sale of automobiles at a dealership.

We will use the relative frequency method to develop a probability distribution for the number of cars sold per day at DiCarlo Motors in Saratoga, New York. Over the past 300 days, DiCarlo has experienced 54 days with no automobiles sold, 117 days with 1 automobile sold, 72 days with 2 automobiles sold, 42 days with 3 automobiles sold, 12 days with 4 automobiles sold, and 3 days with 5 automobiles sold. Suppose we consider the experiment of observing a day of operations at DiCarlo Motors and define the random variable of interest as x = the number of automobiles sold during a day. Using the relative frequencies to assign probabilities to the values of the random variable x, we can develop the probability distribution for x.

TABLE 5.3 PROBABILITY DISTRIBUTION FOR NUMBER OBTAINED ON ONE ROLL OF A DIE

Number Obtained x	Probability of x $f(x)$
1	1/6
2	1/6
3	1/6
4	1/6
5	1/6
6	1/6

TABLE 5.4 PROBABILITY DISTRIBUTION FOR THE NUMBER OF AUTOMOBILES SOLD DURING A DAY AT DICARLO MOTORS

x	$f(x)$
0	.18
1	.39
2	.24
3	.14
4	.04
5	.01
Total	1.00

In probability function notation, $f(0)$ provides the probability of 0 automobiles sold, $f(1)$ provides the probability of 1 automobile sold, and so on. Because historical data show 54 of 300 days with 0 automobiles sold, we assign the relative frequency $54/300 = .18$ to $f(0)$, indicating that the probability of 0 automobiles being sold during a day is .18. Similarly, because 117 of 300 days had 1 automobile sold, we assign the relative frequency $117/300 = .39$ to $f(1)$, indicating that the probability of exactly 1 automobile being sold during a day is .39. Continuing in this way for the other values of the random variable, we compute the values for $f(2)$, $f(3)$, $f(4)$, and $f(5)$ as shown in Table 5.4.

A primary advantage of defining a random variable and its probability distribution is that once the probability distribution is known, it is relatively easy to determine the probability of a variety of events that may be of interest to a decision maker. For example, using the probability distribution for DiCarlo Motors as shown in Table 5.4, we see that the most probable number of automobiles sold during a day is 1 with a probability of $f(1) = .39$. In addition, the probability of selling 3 or more automobiles during a day is $f(3) + f(4) + f(5) = .14 + .04 + .01 = .19$. These probabilities, plus others the decision maker may ask about, provide information that can help the decision maker understand the process of selling automobiles at DiCarlo Motors.

In the development of a probability function for any discrete random variable, the following two conditions must be satisfied.

These conditions are the analogs to the two basic requirements for assigning probabilities to experimental outcomes presented in Chapter 4.

REQUIRED CONDITIONS FOR A DISCRETE PROBABILITY FUNCTION

$$f(x) \geq 0 \tag{5.1}$$

$$\Sigma f(x) = 1 \tag{5.2}$$

Table 5.4 shows that the probabilities for the random variable x satisfy equation (5.1); $f(x)$ is greater than or equal to 0 for all values of x. In addition, because the probabilities sum to 1, equation (5.2) is satisfied. Thus, the DiCarlo Motors probability function is a valid discrete probability function.

We can also show the DiCarlo Motors probability distribution graphically. In Figure 5.1 the values of the random variable x for DiCarlo Motors are shown on the horizontal axis and the probability associated with these values is shown on the vertical axis.

In addition to the probability distributions shown in tables, a formula that gives the probability function, $f(x)$, for every value of x is often used to describe probability

FIGURE 5.1 GRAPHICAL REPRESENTATION OF THE PROBABILITY DISTRIBUTION FOR THE NUMBER OF AUTOMOBILES SOLD DURING A DAY AT DICARLO MOTORS

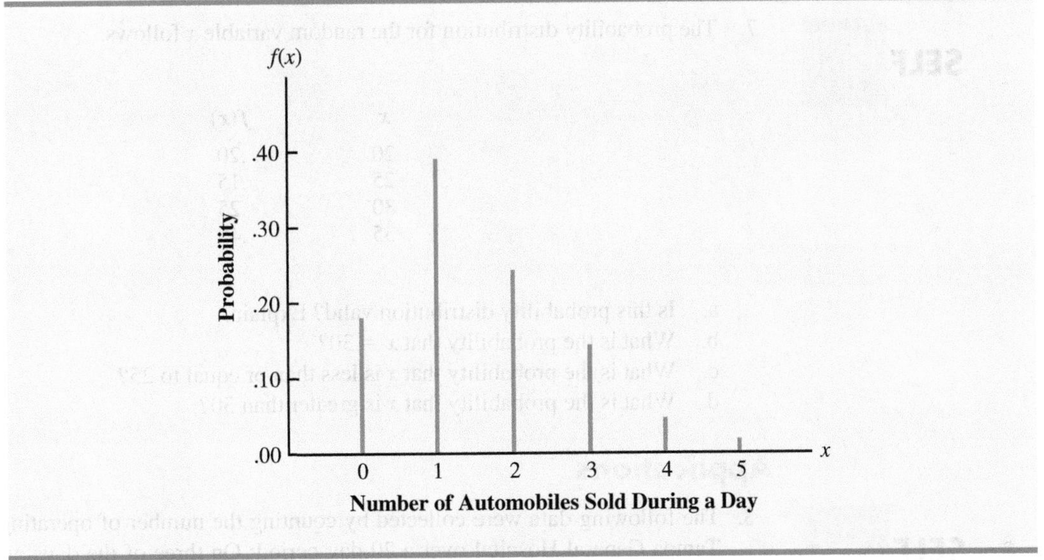

distributions. The simplest example of a discrete probability distribution given by a formula is the **discrete uniform probability distribution.** Its probability function is defined by equation (5.3).

DISCRETE UNIFORM PROBABILITY FUNCTION

$$f(x) = 1/n \tag{5.3}$$

where

$n =$ the number of values the random variable may assume

For example, consider again the experiment of rolling a die. We define the random variable x to be the number of dots on the upward face. For this experiment, $n = 6$ values are possible for the random variable; $x = 1, 2, 3, 4, 5, 6$. We showed earlier how the probability distribution for this experiment can be expressed as a table. Since the probabilities are equally likely, the discrete uniform probability function can also be used. The probability function for this discrete uniform random variable is

$$f(x) = 1/6 \quad x = 1, 2, 3, 4, 5, 6$$

Several widely used discrete probability distributions are specified by formulas. Three important cases are the binomial, Poisson, and hypergeometric distributions; these distributions are discussed later in the chapter.

Exercises

Methods

7. The probability distribution for the random variable x follows.

x	$f(x)$
20	.20
25	.15
30	.25
35	.40

   a. Is this probability distribution valid? Explain.
   b. What is the probability that $x = 30$?
   c. What is the probability that x is less than or equal to 25?
   d. What is the probability that x is greater than 30?

Applications

8. The following data were collected by counting the number of operating rooms in use at Tampa General Hospital over a 20-day period: On three of the days only one operating room was used, on five of the days two were used, on eight of the days three were used, and on four days all four of the hospital's operating rooms were used.
   a. Use the relative frequency approach to construct an empirical discrete probability distribution for the number of operating rooms in use on any given day.
   b. Draw a graph of the probability distribution.
   c. Show that your probability distribution satisfies the required conditions for a valid discrete probability distribution.

9. For unemployed persons in the United States, the average number of months of unemployment at the end of December 2009 was approximately seven months (Bureau of Labor Statistics, January 2010). Suppose the following data are for a particular region in upstate New York. The values in the first column show the number of months unemployed and the values in the second column show the corresponding number of unemployed persons.

Months Unemployed	Number Unemployed
1	1029
2	1686
3	2269
4	2675
5	3487
6	4652
7	4145
8	3587
9	2325
10	1120

   Let x be a random variable indicating the number of months a randomly selected person is unemployed.
   a. Use the data to develop an empirical discrete probability distribution for x.
   b. Show that your probability distribution satisfies the conditions for a valid discrete probability distribution.

c. What is the probability that a person is unemployed for two months or less? Unemployed for more than two months?
d. What is the probability that a person is unemployed for more than six months?

10. The percent frequency distributions of job satisfaction scores for a sample of information systems (IS) senior executives and middle managers are as follows. The scores range from a low of 1 (very dissatisfied) to a high of 5 (very satisfied).

Job Satisfaction Score	IS Senior Executives (%)	IS Middle Managers (%)
1	5	4
2	9	10
3	3	12
4	42	46
5	41	28

a. Develop a probability distribution for the job satisfaction score of a randomly selected senior executive.
b. Develop a probability distribution for the job satisfaction score of a randomly selected middle manager.
c. What is the probability a randomly selected senior executive will report a job satisfaction score of 4 or 5?
d. What is the probability a randomly selected middle manager is very satisfied?
e. Compare the overall job satisfaction of senior executives and middle managers.

11. A technician services mailing machines at companies in the Phoenix area. Depending on the type of malfunction, the service call can take 1, 2, 3, or 4 hours. The different types of malfunctions occur at about the same frequency.
a. Develop a probability distribution for the duration of a service call.
b. Draw a graph of the probability distribution.
c. Show that your probability distribution satisfies the conditions required for a discrete probability function.
d. What is the probability a randomly selected service call will take three hours?
e. A service call has just come in, but the type of malfunction is unknown. It is 3:00 P.M. and service technicians usually get off at 5:00 P.M. What is the probability the service technician will have to work overtime to fix the machine today?

12. Time Warner Cable provides television and Internet service to over 15 million people (Time Warner Cable website, October 24, 2012). Suppose that the management of Time Warner Cable subjectively assesses a probability distribution for the number of new subscribers next year in the state of New York as follows.

x	$f(x)$
100,000	.10
200,000	.20
300,000	.25
400,000	.30
500,000	.10
600,000	.05

a. Is this probability distribution valid? Explain.
b. What is the probability Time Warner will obtain more than 400,000 new subscribers?
c. What is the probability Time Warner will obtain fewer than 200,000 new subscribers?

13. A psychologist determined that the number of sessions required to obtain the trust of a new patient is either 1, 2, or 3. Let x be a random variable indicating the number of

sessions required to gain the patient's trust. The following probability function has been proposed.

$$f(x) = \frac{x}{6} \qquad \text{for } x = 1, 2, \text{ or } 3$$

a. Is this probability function valid? Explain.
b. What is the probability that it takes exactly 2 sessions to gain the patient's trust?
c. What is the probability that it takes at least 2 sessions to gain the patient's trust?

14. The following table is a partial probability distribution for the MRA Company's projected profits (x = profit in \$1000s) for the first year of operation (the negative value denotes a loss).

x	$f(x)$
−100	.10
0	.20
50	.30
100	.25
150	.10
200	

a. What is the proper value for $f(200)$? What is your interpretation of this value?
b. What is the probability that MRA will be profitable?
c. What is the probability that MRA will make at least \$100,000?

5.3 Expected Value and Variance

Expected Value

The **expected value**, or mean, of a random variable is a measure of the central location for the random variable. The formula for the expected value of a discrete random variable x follows.

The expected value is a weighted average of the values of the random variable where the weights are the probabilities.

EXPECTED VALUE OF A DISCRETE RANDOM VARIABLE

$$E(x) = \mu = \Sigma x f(x) \tag{5.4}$$

Both the notations $E(x)$ and μ are used to denote the expected value of a random variable.

Equation (5.4) shows that to compute the expected value of a discrete random variable, we must multiply each value of the random variable by the corresponding probability $f(x)$ and then add the resulting products. Using the DiCarlo Motors automobile sales example from Section 5.2, we show the calculation of the expected value for the number of automobiles sold during a day in Table 5.5. The sum of the entries in the $xf(x)$ column shows that the expected value is 1.50 automobiles per day. We therefore know that although sales of 0, 1, 2, 3, 4, or 5 automobiles are possible on any one day, over time DiCarlo can anticipate selling an average of 1.50 automobiles per day. Assuming 30 days of operation during a month, we can use the expected value of 1.50 to forecast average monthly sales of 30(1.50) = 45 automobiles.

The expected value does not have to be a value the random variable can assume.

Variance

The expected value provides a measure of central tendency for a random variable, but we often also want a measure of variability, or dispersion. Just as we used the variance in Chapter 3 to summarize the variability in data, we now use **variance** to summarize the variability in the values of a random variable. The formula for the variance of a discrete random variable follows.

TABLE 5.5 CALCULATION OF THE EXPECTED VALUE FOR THE NUMBER OF AUTOMOBILES SOLD DURING A DAY AT DICARLO MOTORS

x	$f(x)$	$xf(x)$
0	.18	0(.18) = .00
1	.39	1(.39) = .39
2	.24	2(.24) = .48
3	.14	3(.14) = .42
4	.04	4(.04) = .16
5	.01	5(.01) = .05
		1.50

$E(x) = \mu = \Sigma xf(x)$

The variance is a weighted average of the squared deviations of a random variable from its mean. The weights are the probabilities.

VARIANCE OF A DISCRETE RANDOM VARIABLE

$$Var(x) = \sigma^2 = \Sigma(x - \mu)^2 f(x) \tag{5.5}$$

As equation (5.5) shows, an essential part of the variance formula is the deviation, $x - \mu$, which measures how far a particular value of the random variable is from the expected value, or mean, μ. In computing the variance of a random variable, the deviations are squared and then weighted by the corresponding value of the probability function. The sum of these weighted squared deviations for all values of the random variable is referred to as the *variance.* The notations $Var(x)$ and σ^2 are both used to denote the variance of a random variable.

The calculation of the variance for the probability distribution of the number of automobiles sold during a day at DiCarlo Motors is summarized in Table 5.6. We see that the variance is 1.25. The **standard deviation,** σ, is defined as the positive square root of the variance. Thus, the standard deviation for the number of automobiles sold during a day is

$$\sigma = \sqrt{1.25} = 1.118$$

The standard deviation is measured in the same units as the random variable ($\sigma = 1.118$ automobiles) and therefore is often preferred in describing the variability of a random variable. The variance σ^2 is measured in squared units and is thus more difficult to interpret.

TABLE 5.6 CALCULATION OF THE VARIANCE FOR THE NUMBER OF AUTOMOBILES SOLD DURING A DAY AT DICARLO MOTORS

x	$x - \mu$	$(x - \mu)^2$	$f(x)$	$(x - \mu)^2 f(x)$
0	0 − 1.50 = −1.50	2.25	.18	2.25(.18) = .4050
1	1 − 1.50 = −.50	.25	.39	.25(.39) = .0975
2	2 − 1.50 = .50	.25	.24	.25(.24) = .0600
3	3 − 1.50 = 1.50	2.25	.14	2.25(.14) = .3150
4	4 − 1.50 = 2.50	6.25	.04	6.25(.04) = .2500
5	5 − 1.50 = 3.50	12.25	.01	12.25(.01) = .1225
				1.2500

$\sigma^2 = \Sigma(x - \mu)^2 f(x)$

Using Excel to Compute the Expected Value, Variance, and Standard Deviation

The calculations involved in computing the expected value and variance for a discrete random variable can easily be made in an Excel worksheet. One approach is to enter the formulas necessary to make the calculations in Tables 5.4 and 5.5. An easier way, however, is to make use of Excel's SUMPRODUCT function. In this subsection we show how to use the SUMPRODUCT function to compute the expected value and variance for daily automobile sales at DiCarlo Motors. Refer to Figure 5.2 as we describe the tasks involved. The formula worksheet is in the background; the value worksheet is in the foreground.

Enter/Access Data: The data needed are the values for the random variable and the corresponding probabilities. Labels, values for the random variable, and the corresponding probabilities are entered in cells A1:B7.

Enter Functions and Formulas: The SUMPRODUCT function multiplies each value in one range by the corresponding value in another range and sums the products. To use the SUMPRODUCT function to compute the expected value of daily automobile sales at DiCarlo Motors, we entered the following formula into cell B9:

=SUMPRODUCT(A2:A7,B2:B7)

Note that the first range, A2:A7, contains the values for the random variable, daily automobile sales. The second range, B2:B7, contains the corresponding probabilities. Thus, the SUMPRODUCT function in cell B9 is computing A2*B2 + A3*B3 + A4*B4 + A5*B5 + A6*B6 + A7*B7; hence, it is applying the formula in equation (5.4) to compute the expected value. The result, shown in cell B9 of the value worksheet, is 1.5.

FIGURE 5.2 EXCEL WORKSHEET FOR EXPECTED VALUE, VARIANCE, AND STANDARD DEVIATION

	A	B	C	D
1	Sales	Probability	Sq Dev from Mean	
2	0	0.18	=(A2-$B$9)^2	
3	1	0.39	=(A3-$B$9)^2	
4	2	0.24	=(A4-$B$9)^2	
5	3	0.14	=(A5-$B$9)^2	
6	4	0.04	=(A6-$B$9)^2	
7	5	0.01	=(A7-$B$9)^2	
8				
9	Mean	=SUMPRODUCT(A2:A7,B2:B7)		
10				
11	Variance	=SUMPRODUCT(C2:C7,B2:B7)		
12				
13	Std Deviation	=SQRT(B11)		
14				

	A	B	C	D
1	Sales	Probability	Sq Dev from Mean	
2	0	0.18	2.25	
3	1	0.39	0.25	
4	2	0.24	0.25	
5	3	0.14	2.25	
6	4	0.04	6.25	
7	5	0.01	12.25	
8				
9	Mean	1.5		
10				
11	Variance	1.25		
12				
13	Std Deviation	1.118		
14				

The formulas in cells C2:C7 are used to compute the squared deviations from the expected value or mean of 1.5 (the mean is in cell B9). The results, shown in the value worksheet, are the same as the results shown in Table 5.5. The formula necessary to compute the variance for daily automobile sales was entered into cell B11. It uses the SUMPRODUCT function to multiply each value in the range C2:C7 by each corresponding value in the range B2:B7 and sums the products. The result, shown in the value worksheet, is 1.25. Because the standard deviation is the square root of the variance, we entered the formula =SQRT(B11) into cell B13 to compute the standard deviation for daily automobile sales. The result, shown in the value worksheet, is 1.118.

Exercises

Methods

15. The following table provides a probability distribution for the random variable x.

x	$f(x)$
3	.25
6	.50
9	.25

a. Compute $E(x)$, the expected value of x.
b. Compute σ^2, the variance of x.
c. Compute σ, the standard deviation of x.

16. The following table provides a probability distribution for the random variable y.

y	$f(y)$
2	.20
4	.30
7	.40
8	.10

a. Compute $E(y)$.
b. Compute $Var(y)$ and σ.

Applications

17. The number of students taking the SAT has risen to an all-time high of more than 1.5 million (College Board, August 26, 2008). Students are allowed to repeat the test in hopes of improving the score that is sent to college and university admission offices. The number of times the SAT was taken and the number of students are as follows.

Number of Times	Number of Students
1	721,769
2	601,325
3	166,736
4	22,299
5	6,730

a. Let x be a random variable indicating the number of times a student takes the SAT. Show the probability distribution for this random variable.
b. What is the probability that a student takes the SAT more than one time?
c. What is the probability that a student takes the SAT three or more times?
d. What is the expected value of the number of times the SAT is taken? What is your interpretation of the expected value?
e. What is the variance and standard deviation for the number of times the SAT is taken?

18. The American Housing Survey reported the following data on the number of times that owner-occupied and renter-occupied units had a water supply stoppage lasting 6 or more hours in the past 3 months (U.S. Census Bureau website, October 2012).

	Number of Units (1000s)	
Number of Times	**Owner Occupied**	**Renter Occupied**
0	439	394
1	1100	760
2	249	221
3	98	92
4 times or more	120	111

a. Define a random variable x = number of times that owner-occupied units had a water supply stoppage lasting 6 or more hours in the past 3 months and develop a probability distribution for the random variable. (Let $x = 4$ represent 4 or more times.)
b. Compute the expected value and variance for x.
c. Define a random variable y = number of times that renter-occupied units had a water supply stoppage lasting 6 or more hours in the past 3 months and develop a probability distribution for the random variable. (Let $y = 4$ represent 4 or more times.)
d. Compute the expected value and variance for y.
e. What observations can you make from a comparison of the number of water supply stoppages reported by owner-occupied units versus renter-occupied units?

19. West Virginia has one of the highest divorce rates in the nation, with an annual rate of approximately 5 divorces per 1000 people (Centers for Disease Control and Prevention website, January 12, 2012). The Marital Counseling Center, Inc. (MCC) thinks that the high divorce rate in the state may require them to hire additional staff. Working with a consultant, the management of MCC has developed the following probability distribution for x = the number of new clients for marriage counseling for the next year.

x	$f(x)$
10	.05
20	.10
30	.10
40	.20
50	.35
60	.20

a. Is this probability distribution valid? Explain.
b. What is the probability MCC will obtain more than 30 new clients?
c. What is the probability MCC will obtain fewer than 20 new clients?
d. Compute the expected value and variance of x.

20. The probability distribution for damage claims paid by the Newton Automobile Insurance Company on collision insurance follows.

Payment ($)	Probability
0	.85
500	.04
1000	.04
3000	.03
5000	.02
8000	.01
10000	.01

a. Use the expected collision payment to determine the collision insurance premium that would enable the company to break even.

b. The insurance company charges an annual rate of $520 for the collision coverage. What is the expected value of the collision policy for a policyholder? (*Hint:* It is the expected payments from the company minus the cost of coverage.) Why does the policyholder purchase a collision policy with this expected value?

21. The following probability distributions of job satisfaction scores for a sample of information systems (IS) senior executives and middle managers range from a low of 1 (very dissatisfied) to a high of 5 (very satisfied).

	Probability	
Job Satisfaction Score	IS Senior Executives	IS Middle Managers
1	.05	.04
2	.09	.10
3	.03	.12
4	.42	.46
5	.41	.28

a. What is the expected value of the job satisfaction score for senior executives?

b. What is the expected value of the job satisfaction score for middle managers?

c. Compute the variance of job satisfaction scores for executives and middle managers.

d. Compute the standard deviation of job satisfaction scores for both probability distributions.

e. Compare the overall job satisfaction of senior executives and middle managers.

22. The demand for a product of Carolina Industries varies greatly from month to month. The probability distribution in the following table, based on the past two years of data, shows the company's monthly demand.

Unit Demand	Probability
300	.20
400	.30
500	.35
600	.15

a. If the company bases monthly orders on the expected value of the monthly demand, what should Carolina's monthly order quantity be for this product?

b. Assume that each unit demanded generates $70 in revenue and that each unit ordered costs $50. How much will the company gain or lose in a month if it places an order based on your answer to part (a) and the actual demand for the item is 300 units?

23. In Gallup's Annual Consumption Habits Poll, telephone interviews were conducted for a random sample of 1014 adults aged 18 and over. One of the questions was, "How many cups of coffee, if any, do you drink on an average day?" The following table shows the results obtained (Gallup website, August 6, 2012).

Number of Cups per Day	Number of Responses
0	365
1	264
2	193
3	91
4 or more	101

Define a random variable x = number of cups of coffee consumed on an average day. Let $x = 4$ represent four or more cups.

a. Develop a probability distribution for x.
b. Compute the expected value of x.
c. Compute the variance of x.
d. Suppose we are only interested in adults who drink at least one cup of coffee on an average day. For this group, let y = the number of cups of coffee consumed on an average day. Compute the expected value of y and compare it to the expected value of x.

24. The J. R. Ryland Computer Company is considering a plant expansion to enable the company to begin production of a new computer product. The company's president must determine whether to make the expansion a medium- or large-scale project. Demand for the new product is uncertain, which for planning purposes may be low demand, medium demand, or high demand. The probability estimates for demand are .20, .50, and .30, respectively. Letting x and y indicate the annual profit in thousands of dollars, the firm's planners developed the following profit forecasts for the medium- and large-scale expansion projects.

		Medium-Scale Expansion Profit		Large-Scale Expansion Profit	
		x	$f(x)$	y	$f(y)$
Demand	Low	50	.20	0	.20
	Medium	150	.50	100	.50
	High	200	.30	300	.30

a. Compute the expected value for the profit associated with the two expansion alternatives. Which decision is preferred for the objective of maximizing the expected profit?
b. Compute the variance for the profit associated with the two expansion alternatives. Which decision is preferred for the objective of minimizing the risk or uncertainty?

5.4 Binomial Probability Distribution

The binomial probability distribution is a discrete probability distribution that has many applications. It is associated with a multiple-step experiment that we call the binomial experiment.

A Binomial Experiment

A **binomial experiment** exhibits the following four properties.

PROPERTIES OF A BINOMIAL EXPERIMENT

1. The experiment consists of a sequence of n identical trials.
2. Two outcomes are possible on each trial. We refer to one outcome as a *success* and the other outcome as a *failure.*
3. The probability of a success, denoted by p, does not change from trial to trial. Consequently, the probability of a failure, denoted by $1 - p$, does not change from trial to trial.
4. The trials are independent.

Jakob Bernoulli (1654–1705), the first of the Bernoulli family of Swiss mathematicians, published a treatise on probability that contained the theory of permutations and combinations, as well as the binomial theorem.

If properties 2, 3, and 4 are present, we say the trials are generated by a Bernoulli process. If, in addition, property 1 is present, we say we have a binomial experiment. Figure 5.3 depicts one possible sequence of successes and failures for a binomial experiment involving eight trials.

In a binomial experiment, our interest is in the *number of successes occurring in the n trials*. If we let x denote the number of successes occurring in the n trials, we see that x can assume the values of 0, 1, 2, 3, . . . , n. Because the number of values is finite, x is a *discrete* random variable. The probability distribution associated with this random variable is called the **binomial probability distribution**. For example, consider the experiment of tossing a coin five times and on each toss observing whether the coin lands with a head or a tail on its upward face. Suppose we want to count the number of heads appearing over the five tosses. Does this experiment show the properties of a binomial experiment? What is the random variable of interest? Note that

1. The experiment consists of five identical trials; each trial involves the tossing of one coin.
2. Two outcomes are possible for each trial: a head or a tail. We can designate head a success and tail a failure.
3. The probability of a head and the probability of a tail are the same for each trial, with $p = .5$ and $1 - p = .5$.
4. The trials or tosses are independent because the outcome on any one trial is not affected by what happens on other trials or tosses.

FIGURE 5.3 ONE POSSIBLE SEQUENCE OF SUCCESSES AND FAILURES FOR AN EIGHT-TRIAL BINOMIAL EXPERIMENT

Property 1: The experiment consists of $n = 8$ identical trials.

Property 2: Each trial results in either success (S) or failure (F).

Trials →	1	2	3	4	5	6	7	8
Outcomes →	S	F	F	S	S	F	S	S

Thus, the properties of a binomial experiment are satisfied. The random variable of interest is x = the number of heads appearing in the five trials. In this case, x can assume the values of 0, 1, 2, 3, 4, or 5.

As another example, consider an insurance salesperson who visits 10 randomly selected families. The outcome associated with each visit is classified as a success if the family purchases an insurance policy and a failure if the family does not. From past experience, the salesperson knows the probability that a randomly selected family will purchase an insurance policy is .10. Checking the properties of a binomial experiment, we observe that

1. The experiment consists of 10 identical trials; each trial involves contacting one family.
2. Two outcomes are possible on each trial: the family purchases a policy (success) or the family does not purchase a policy (failure).
3. The probabilities of a purchase and a nonpurchase are assumed to be the same for each sales call, with $p = .10$ and $1 - p = .90$.
4. The trials are independent because the families are randomly selected.

Because the four assumptions are satisfied, this example is a binomial experiment. The random variable of interest is the number of sales obtained in contacting the 10 families. In this case, x can assume the values of 0, 1, 2, 3, 4, 5, 6, 7, 8, 9, and 10.

Property 3 of the binomial experiment is called the *stationarity assumption* and is sometimes confused with property 4, independence of trials. To see how they differ, consider again the case of the salesperson calling on families to sell insurance policies. If, as the day wore on, the salesperson got tired and lost enthusiasm, the probability of success (selling a policy) might drop to .05, for example, by the tenth call. In such a case, property 3 (stationarity) would not be satisfied, and we would not have a binomial experiment. Even if property 4 held—that is, the purchase decisions of each family were made independently—it would not be a binomial experiment if property 3 was not satisfied.

In applications involving binomial experiments, a special mathematical formula, called the *binomial probability function,* can be used to compute the probability of x successes in the n trials. Using probability concepts introduced in Chapter 4, we will show in the context of an illustrative problem how the formula can be developed.

Martin Clothing Store Problem

Let us consider the purchase decisions of the next three customers who enter the Martin Clothing Store. On the basis of past experience, the store manager estimates the probability that any one customer will make a purchase is .30. What is the probability that two of the next three customers will make a purchase?

Using a tree diagram (Figure 5.4), we can see that the experiment of observing the three customers each making a purchase decision has eight possible outcomes. Using S to denote success (a purchase) and F to denote failure (no purchase), we are interested in experimental outcomes involving two successes in the three trials (purchase decisions). Next, let us verify that the experiment involving the sequence of three purchase decisions can be viewed as a binomial experiment. Checking the four requirements for a binomial experiment, we note that

1. The experiment can be described as a sequence of three identical trials, one trial for each of the three customers who will enter the store.
2. Two outcomes—the customer makes a purchase (success) or the customer does not make a purchase (failure)—are possible for each trial.
3. The probability that the customer will make a purchase (.30) or will not make a purchase (.70) is assumed to be the same for all customers.
4. The purchase decision of each customer is independent of the decisions of the other customers.

FIGURE 5.4 TREE DIAGRAM FOR THE MARTIN CLOTHING STORE PROBLEM

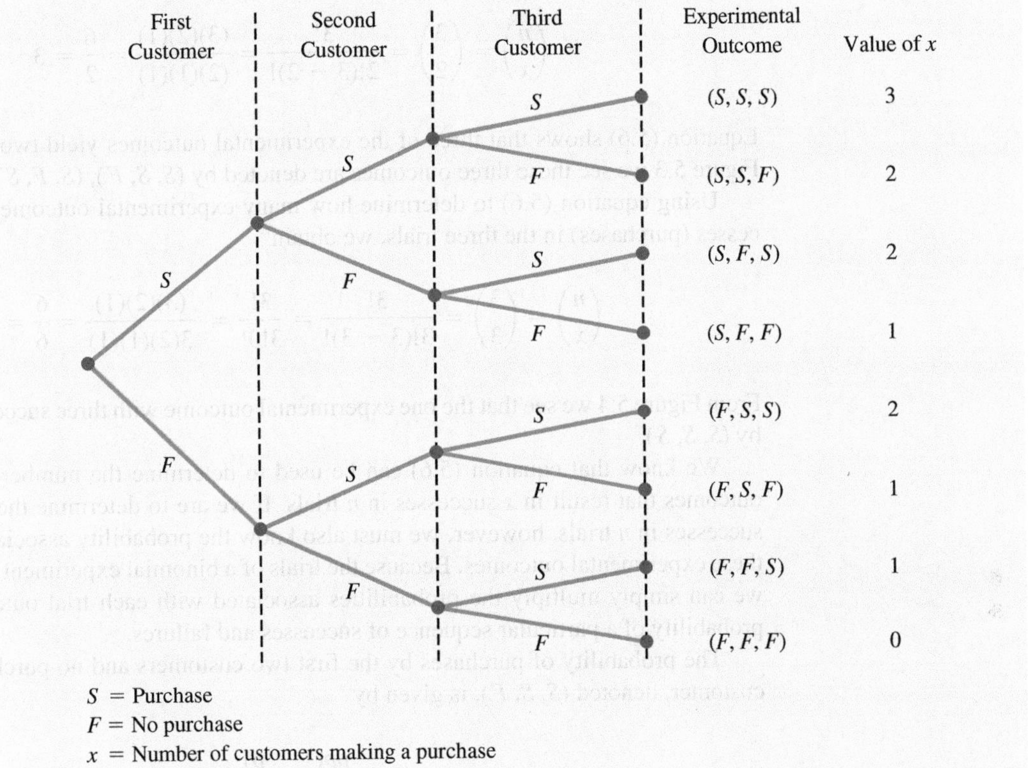

First Customer	Second Customer	Third Customer	Experimental Outcome	Value of x
S	S	S	(S, S, S)	3
		F	(S, S, F)	2
	F	S	(S, F, S)	2
		F	(S, F, F)	1
F	S	S	(F, S, S)	2
		F	(F, S, F)	1
	F	S	(F, F, S)	1
		F	(F, F, F)	0

S = Purchase
F = No purchase
x = Number of customers making a purchase

Hence, the properties of a binomial experiment are present.

The number of experimental outcomes resulting in exactly x successes in n trials can be computed using the following formula.[1]

NUMBER OF EXPERIMENTAL OUTCOMES PROVIDING EXACTLY x SUCCESSES IN n TRIALS

$$\binom{n}{x} = \frac{n!}{x!(n-x)!} \tag{5.6}$$

where

$$n! = n(n-1)(n-2)\cdots(2)(1)$$

and, by definition,

$$0! = 1$$

Now let us return to the Martin Clothing Store experiment involving three customer purchase decisions. Equation (5.6) can be used to determine the number of experimental

[1]This formula, introduced in Chapter 4, determines the number of combinations of n objects selected x at a time. For the binomial experiment, this combinatorial formula provides the number of experimental outcomes (sequences of n trials) resulting in x successes.

outcomes involving two purchases; that is, the number of ways of obtaining $x = 2$ successes in the $n = 3$ trials. From equation (5.6) we have

$$\binom{n}{x} = \binom{3}{2} = \frac{3!}{2!(3-2)!} = \frac{(3)(2)(1)}{(2)(1)(1)} = \frac{6}{2} = 3$$

Equation (5.6) shows that three of the experimental outcomes yield two successes. From Figure 5.3 we see these three outcomes are denoted by (S, S, F), (S, F, S), and (F, S, S).

Using equation (5.6) to determine how many experimental outcomes have three successes (purchases) in the three trials, we obtain

$$\binom{n}{x} = \binom{3}{3} = \frac{3!}{3!(3-3)!} = \frac{3!}{3!0!} = \frac{(3)(2)(1)}{3(2)(1)(1)} = \frac{6}{6} = 1$$

From Figure 5.4 we see that the one experimental outcome with three successes is identified by (S, S, S).

We know that equation (5.6) can be used to determine the number of experimental outcomes that result in x successes in n trials. If we are to determine the probability of x successes in n trials, however, we must also know the probability associated with each of these experimental outcomes. Because the trials of a binomial experiment are independent, we can simply multiply the probabilities associated with each trial outcome to find the probability of a particular sequence of successes and failures.

The probability of purchases by the first two customers and no purchase by the third customer, denoted (S, S, F), is given by

$$pp(1-p)$$

With a .30 probability of a purchase on any one trial, the probability of a purchase on the first two trials and no purchase on the third is given by

$$(.30)(.30)(.70) = (.30)^2(.70) = .063$$

Two other experimental outcomes also result in two successes and one failure. The probabilities for all three experimental outcomes involving two successes follow.

Trial Outcomes				
1st Customer	2nd Customer	3rd Customer	Experimental Outcome	Probability of Experimental Outcome
Purchase	Purchase	No purchase	(S, S, F)	$pp(1-p) = p^2(1-p)$ $= (.30)^2(.70) = .063$
Purchase	No purchase	Purchase	(S, F, S)	$p(1-p)p = p^2(1-p)$ $= (.30)^2(.70) = .063$
No purchase	Purchase	Purchase	(F, S, S)	$(1-p)pp = p^2(1-p)$ $= (.30)^2(.70) = .063$

Observe that all three experimental outcomes with two successes have exactly the same probability. This observation holds in general. In any binomial experiment, all sequences of trial outcomes yielding x successes in n trials have the *same probability* of occurrence. The probability of each sequence of trials yielding x successes in n trials follows.

$$\text{Probability of a particular sequence of trial outcomes with } x \text{ successes in } n \text{ trials} = p^x(1-p)^{(n-x)} \tag{5.7}$$

For the Martin Clothing Store, this formula shows that any experimental outcome with two successes has a probability of $p^2(1-p)^{(3-2)} = p^2(1-p)^1 = (.30)^2(.70)^1 = .063$.

Because equation (5.6) shows the number of outcomes in a binomial experiment with x successes and equation (5.7) gives the probability for each sequence involving x successes, we combine equations (5.6) and (5.7) to obtain the following **binomial probability function.**

BINOMIAL PROBABILITY FUNCTION

$$f(x) = \binom{n}{x} p^x(1-p)^{(n-x)} \tag{5.8}$$

where

$$x = \text{the number of successes}$$
$$p = \text{the probability of a success on one trial}$$
$$n = \text{the number of trials}$$
$$f(x) = \text{the probability of } x \text{ successes in } n \text{ trials}$$
$$\binom{n}{x} = \frac{n!}{x!(n-x)!}$$

For the binomial probability distribution, x is a discrete random variable with the probability function $f(x)$ applicable for values of $x = 0, 1, 2, \ldots, n$.

In the Martin Clothing Store example, let us use equation (5.8) to compute the probability that no customer makes a purchase, exactly one customer makes a purchase, exactly two customers make a purchase, and all three customers make a purchase. The calculations are summarized in Table 5.7, which gives the probability distribution of the number of customers making a purchase. Figure 5.5 is a graph of this probability distribution.

TABLE 5.7 PROBABILITY DISTRIBUTION FOR THE NUMBER OF CUSTOMERS MAKING A PURCHASE

x	$f(x)$
0	$\frac{3!}{0!3!}(.30)^0(.70)^3 = .343$
1	$\frac{3!}{1!2!}(.30)^1(.70)^2 = .441$
2	$\frac{3!}{2!1!}(.30)^2(.70)^1 = .189$
3	$\frac{3!}{3!0!}(.30)^3(.70)^0 = .027$
	1.000

FIGURE 5.5 GRAPHICAL REPRESENTATION OF THE PROBABILITY DISTRIBUTION FOR THE NUMBER OF CUSTOMERS MAKING A PURCHASE

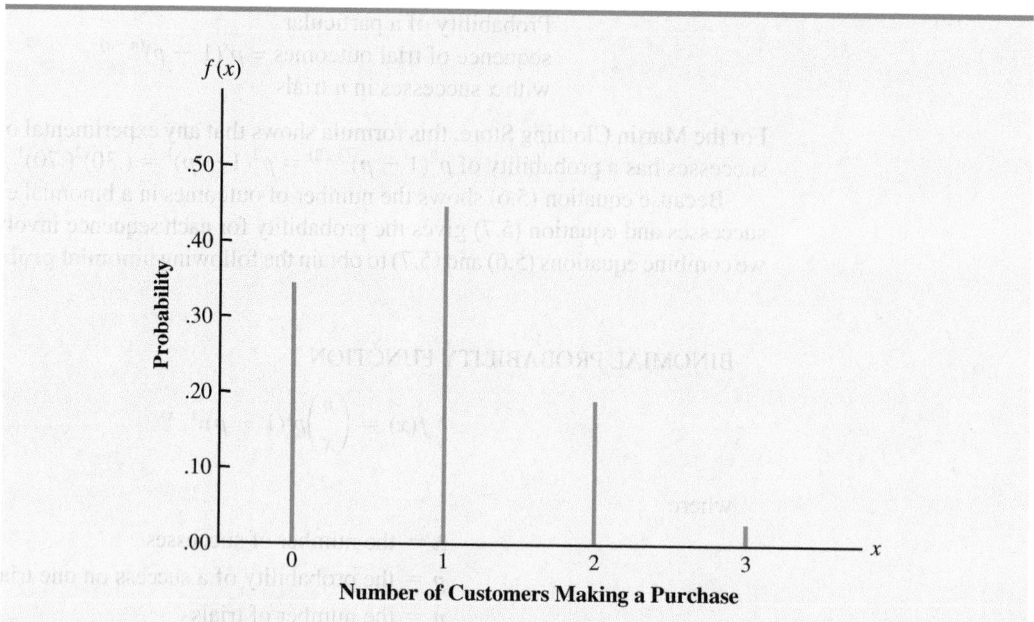

The binomial probability function can be applied to *any* binomial experiment. If we are satisfied that a situation demonstrates the properties of a binomial experiment and if we know the values of n and p, we can use equation (5.8) to compute the probability of x successes in the n trials.

If we consider variations of the Martin experiment, such as 10 customers rather than 3 entering the store, the binomial probability function given by equation (5.8) is still applicable. Suppose we have a binomial experiment with $n = 10$, $x = 4$, and $p = .30$. The probability of making exactly four sales to 10 customers entering the store is

$$f(4) = \frac{10!}{4!6!}(.30)^4(.70)^6 = .2001$$

Using Excel to Compute Binomial Probabilities

For many probability functions that can be specified as formulas, Excel provides functions for computing probabilities and cumulative probabilities. In this section, we show how Excel's BINOM.DIST function can be used to compute binomial probabilities and cumulative binomial probabilities. We begin by showing how to compute the binomial probabilities for the Martin Clothing Store example shown in Table 5.7. Refer to Figure 5.6 as we describe the tasks involved. The formula worksheet is in the background; the value worksheet is in the foreground.

Enter/Access Data: In order to compute a binomial probability we must know the number of trials (n), the probability of success (p), and the value of the random variable (x). For the Martin Clothing Store example, the number of trials is 3; this value has been entered into cell D1. The probability of success is .3; this value has been entered into cell D2. Because we want to compute the probability for $x = 0, 1, 2,$ and 3, these values were entered into cells B5:B8.

FIGURE 5.6 EXCEL WORKSHEET FOR COMPUTING BINOMIAL PROBABILITIES OF NUMBER OF CUSTOMERS MAKING A PURCHASE

	A	B	C	D	E
1			**Number of Trials (n)**	3	
2			**Probability of Success (p)**	0.3	
3					
4		x	$f(x)$		
5		0	=BINOM.DIST(B5,$D$1,$D$2,FALSE)		
6		1	=BINOM.DIST(B6,$D$1,$D$2,FALSE)		
7		2	=BINOM.DIST(B7,$D$1,$D$2,FALSE)		
8		3	=BINOM.DIST(B8,$D$1,$D$2,FALSE)		
9					

	A	B	C	D	E
1			**Number of Trials (n)**	3	
2			**Probability of Success (p)**	0.3	
3					
4		x	$f(x)$		
5		0	0.343		
6		1	0.441		
7		2	0.189		
8		3	0.027		
9					

Enter Functions and Formulas: The BINOM.DIST function has four inputs: The first is the value of x, the second is the value of n, the third is the value of p, and the fourth is FALSE or TRUE. We choose FALSE for the fourth input if a probability is desired and TRUE if a cumulative probability is desired. The formula =BINOM.DIST(B5,$D$1,$D$2,FALSE) has been entered into cell C5 to compute the probability of 0 successes in 3 trials. Note in the value worksheet that the probability computed for $f(0)$, .343, is the same as that shown in Table 5.7. The formula in cell C5 is copied to cells C6:C8 to compute the probabilities for $x = 1$, 2, and 3 successes, respectively.

We can also compute cumulative probabilities using Excel's BINOM.DIST function. To illustrate, let us consider the case of 10 customers entering the Martin Clothing Store and compute the probabilities and cumulative probabilities for the number of customers making a purchase. Recall that the cumulative probability for $x = 1$ is the probability of 1 or fewer purchases, the cumulative probability for $x = 2$ is the probability of 2 or fewer purchases, and so on. So, the cumulative probability for $x = 10$ is 1. Refer to Figure 5.7 as

FIGURE 5.7 EXCEL WORKSHEET FOR COMPUTING PROBABILITIES AND CUMULATIVE PROBABILITIES FOR NUMBER OF PURCHASES WITH 10 CUSTOMERS

	A	B	C	D	E
1			**Number of Trials (n)**	10	
2			**Probability of Success (p)**	0.3	
3					
4		x	$f(x)$	**Cum Prob**	
5		0	=BINOM.DIST(B5,$D$1,$D$2,FALSE)	=BINOM.DIST(B5,$D$1,$D$2,TRUE)	
6		1	=BINOM.DIST(B6,$D$1,$D$2,FALSE)	=BINOM.DIST(B6,$D$1,$D$2,TRUE)	
7		2	=BINOM.DIST(B7,$D$1,$D$2,FALSE)	=BINOM.DIST(B7,$D$1,$D$2,TRUE)	
8		3	=BINOM.DIST(B8,$D$1,$D$2,FALSE)	=BINOM.DIST(B8,$D$1,$D$2,TRUE)	
9		4	=BINOM.DIST(B9,$D$1,$D$2,FALSE)	=BINOM.DIST(B9,$D$1,$D$2,TRUE)	
10		5	=BINOM.DIST(B10,$D$1,$D$2,FALSE)	=BINOM.DIST(B10,$D$1,$D$2,TRUE)	
11		6	=BINOM.DIST(B11,$D$1,$D$2,FALSE)	=BINOM.DIST(B11,$D$1,$D$2,TRUE)	
12		7	=BINOM.DIST(B12,$D$1,$D$2,FALSE)	=BINOM.DIST(B12,$D$1,$D$2,TRUE)	
13		8	=BINOM.DIST(B13,$D$1,$D$2,FALSE)	=BINOM.DIST(B13,$D$1,$D$2,TRUE)	
14		9	=BINOM.DIST(B14,$D$1,$D$2,FALSE)	=BINOM.DIST(B14,$D$1,$D$2,TRUE)	
15		10	=BINOM.DIST(B15,$D$1,$D$2,FALSE)	=BINOM.DIST(B15,$D$1,$D$2,TRUE)	
16					

	A	B	C	D	E
1			**Number of Trials (n)**	10	
2			**Probability of Success (p)**	0.3	
3					
4		x	$f(x)$	**Cum Prob**	
5		0	0.0282	0.0282	
6		1	0.1211	0.1493	
7		2	0.2335	0.3828	
8		3	0.2668	0.6496	
9		4	0.2001	0.8497	
10		5	0.1029	0.9527	
11		6	0.0368	0.9894	
12		7	0.0090	0.9984	
13		8	0.0014	0.9999	
14		9	0.0001	1.0000	
15		10	0.0000	1.0000	
16					

we describe the tasks involved in computing these cumulative probabilities. The formula worksheet is in the background; the value worksheet is in the foreground.

Enter/Access Data: We entered the number of trials (10) into cell D1, the probability of success (.3) into cell D2, and the values for the random variable into cells B5:B15.

Enter Functions and Formulas: The binomial probabilities for each value of the random variable are computed in column C and the cumulative probabilities are computed in column D. We entered the formula =BINOM.DIST(B5,$D$1,$D$2,FALSE) into cell C5 to compute the probability of 0 successes in 10 trials. Note that we used FALSE as the fourth input in the BINOM.DIST function. The probability (.0282) is shown in cell C5 of the value worksheet. The formula in cell C5 is simply copied to cells C6:C15 to compute the remaining probabilities.

To compute the cumulative probabilities we start by entering the formula =BINOM.DIST(B5,$D$1,$D$2,TRUE) into cell D5. Note that we used TRUE as the fourth input in the BINOM.DIST function. The formula in cell D5 is then copied to cells D6:D15 to compute the remaining cumulative probabilities. In cell D5 of the value worksheet we see that the cumulative probability for $x = 0$ is the same as the probability for $x = 0$. Each of the remaining cumulative probabilities is the sum of the previous cumulative probability and the individual probability in column C. For instance, the cumulative probability for $x = 4$ is given by $.6496 + .2001 = .8497$. Note also that the cumulative probability for $x = 10$ is 1. The cumulative probability of $x = 9$ is also 1 because the probability of $x = 10$ is zero (to four decimal places of accuracy).

Expected Value and Variance for the Binomial Distribution

In Section 5.3 we provided formulas for computing the expected value and variance of a discrete random variable. In the special case where the random variable has a binomial distribution with a known number of trials n and a known probability of success p, the general formulas for the expected value and variance can be simplified. The results follow.

EXPECTED VALUE AND VARIANCE FOR THE BINOMIAL DISTRIBUTION

$$E(x) = \mu = np \tag{5.9}$$

$$Var(x) = \sigma^2 = np(1 - p) \tag{5.10}$$

For the Martin Clothing Store problem with three customers, we can use equation (5.9) to compute the expected number of customers who will make a purchase.

$$E(x) = np = 3(.30) = .9$$

Suppose that for the next month the Martin Clothing Store forecasts 1000 customers will enter the store. What is the expected number of customers who will make a purchase? The answer is $\mu = np = (1000)(.3) = 300$. Thus, to increase the expected number of purchases, Martin's must induce more customers to enter the store and/or somehow increase the probability that any individual customer will make a purchase after entering.

For the Martin Clothing Store problem with three customers, we see that the variance and standard deviation for the number of customers who will make a purchase are

$$\sigma^2 = np(1 - p) = 3(.3)(.7) = .63$$
$$\sigma = \sqrt{.63} = .79$$

For the next 1000 customers entering the store, the variance and standard deviation for the number of customers who will make a purchase are

$$\sigma^2 = np(1 - p) = 1000(.3)(.7) = 210$$
$$\sigma = \sqrt{210} = 14.49$$

Exercises

Methods

25. Consider a binomial experiment with two trials and $p = .4$.
    a. Draw a tree diagram for this experiment (see Figure 5.3).
    b. Compute the probability of one success, $f(1)$.
    c. Compute $f(0)$.
    d. Compute $f(2)$.
    e. Compute the probability of at least one success.
    f. Compute the expected value, variance, and standard deviation.
26. Consider a binomial experiment with $n = 10$ and $p = .10$.
    a. Compute $f(0)$.
    b. Compute $f(2)$.
    c. Compute $P(x \leq 2)$.
    d. Compute $P(x \geq 1)$.
    e. Compute $E(x)$.
    f. Compute $Var(x)$ and σ.
27. Consider a binomial experiment with $n = 20$ and $p = .70$.
    a. Compute $f(12)$.
    b. Compute $f(16)$.
    c. Compute $P(x \geq 16)$.
    d. Compute $P(x \leq 15)$.
    e. Compute $E(x)$.
    f. Compute $Var(x)$ and σ.

Applications

28. For its Music 360 survey, Nielsen Co. asked teenagers and adults how each group has listened to music in the past 12 months. Nearly two-thirds of U.S. teenagers under the age of 18 say they use Google Inc.'s video-sharing site to listen to music and 35% of the teenagers said they use Pandora Media Inc.'s custom online radio service (*The Wall Street Journal*, August 14, 2012). Suppose 10 teenagers are selected randomly to be interviewed about how they listen to music.
    a. Is randomly selecting 10 teenagers and asking whether or not they use Pandora Media Inc.'s online service a binomial experiment?
    b. What is the probability that none of the 10 teenagers use Pandora Media Inc.'s online radio service?
    c. What is the probability that 4 of the 10 teenagers use Pandora Media Inc.'s online radio service?
    d. What is the probability that at least 2 of the 10 teenagers use Pandora Media Inc.'s online radio service?

29. The Center for Medicare and Medical Services reported that there were 295,000 appeals for hospitalization and other Part A Medicare service. For this group, 40% of first-round appeals were successful (*The Wall Street Journal*, October 22, 2012). Suppose 10 first-round appeals have just been received by a Medicare appeals office.
    a. Compute the probability that none of the appeals will be successful.
    b. Compute the probability that exactly one of the appeals will be successful.
    c. What is the probability that at least two of the appeals will be successful?
    d. What is the probability that more than half of the appeals will be successful?

30. When a new machine is functioning properly, only 3% of the items produced are defective. Assume that we will randomly select two parts produced on the machine and that we are interested in the number of defective parts found.
    a. Describe the conditions under which this situation would be a binomial experiment.
    b. Draw a tree diagram similar to Figure 5.4 showing this problem as a two-trial experiment.
    c. How many experimental outcomes result in exactly one defect being found?
    d. Compute the probabilities associated with finding no defects, exactly one defect, and two defects.
31. A Randstad/Harris interactive survey reported that 25% of employees said their company is loyal to them (*USA Today,* November 11, 2009). Suppose 10 employees are selected randomly and will be interviewed about company loyalty.
    a. Is the selection of 10 employees a binomial experiment? Explain.
    b. What is the probability that none of the 10 employees will say their company is loyal to them?
    c. What is the probability that 4 of the 10 employees will say their company is loyal to them?
    d. What is the probability that at least 2 of the 10 employees will say their company is loyal to them?
32. Military radar and missile detection systems are designed to warn a country of an enemy attack. A reliability question is whether a detection system will be able to identify an attack and issue a warning. Assume that a particular detection system has a .90 probability of detecting a missile attack. Use the binomial probability distribution to answer the following questions.
    a. What is the probability that a single detection system will detect an attack?
    b. If two detection systems are installed in the same area and operate independently, what is the probability that at least one of the systems will detect the attack?
    c. If three systems are installed, what is the probability that at least one of the systems will detect the attack?
    d. Would you recommend that multiple detection systems be used? Explain.
33. Twelve of the top 20 finishers in the 2009 PGA Championship at Hazeltine National Golf Club in Chaska, Minnesota, used a Titleist brand golf ball (GolfBallTest website, November 12, 2009). Suppose these results are representative of the probability that a randomly selected PGA Tour player uses a Titleist brand golf ball. For a sample of 15 PGA Tour players, make the following calculations.
    a. Compute the probability that exactly 10 of the 15 PGA Tour players use a Titleist brand golf ball.
    b. Compute the probability that more than 10 of the 15 PGA Tour players use a Titleist brand golf ball.
    c. For a sample of 15 PGA Tour players, compute the expected number of players who use a Titleist brand golf ball.
    d. For a sample of 15 PGA Tour players, compute the variance and standard deviation of the number of players who use a Titleist brand golf ball.
34. A study conducted by the Pew Research Center showed that 75% of 18- to 34-year-olds living with their parents say they contribute to household expenses (*The Wall Street*

Journal, October 22, 2012). Suppose that a random sample of fifteen 18- to 34-year-olds living with their parents is selected and asked if they contribute to household expenses.

a. Is the selection of the fifteen 18- to 34-year-olds living with their parents a binomial experiment? Explain.
b. If the sample shows that none of the fifteen 18- to 34-year-olds living with their parents contribute to household expenses, would you question the results of the Pew Research Study? Explain.
c. What is the probability that at least 10 of the fifteen 18- to 34-year-olds living with their parents contribute to household expenses?

35. A university found that 20% of its students withdraw without completing the introductory statistics course. Assume that 20 students registered for the course.
    a. Compute the probability that 2 or fewer will withdraw.
    b. Compute the probability that exactly 4 will withdraw.
    c. Compute the probability that more than 3 will withdraw.
    d. Compute the expected number of withdrawals.
36. A Gallup Poll showed that 30% of Americans are satisfied with the way things are going in the United States (Gallup website, September 12, 2012). Suppose a sample of 20 Americans is selected as part of a study of the state of the nation.
    a. Compute the probability that exactly 4 of the 20 Americans surveyed are satisfied with the way things are going in the United States.
    b. Compute the probability that at least 2 of the Americans surveyed are satisfied with the way things are going in the United States.
    c. For the sample of 20 Americans, compute the expected number of Americans who are satisfied with the way things are going in the United States.
    d. For the sample of 20 Americans, compute the variance and standard deviation of the number of Americans who are satisfied with the way things are going in the United States.
37. Twenty-three percent of automobiles are not covered by insurance (CNN, February 23, 2006). On a particular weekend, 35 automobiles are involved in traffic accidents.
    a. What is the expected number of these automobiles that are not covered by insurance?
    b. What are the variance and standard deviation?

5.5 Poisson Probability Distribution

The Poisson probability distribution is often used to model random arrivals in waiting line situations.

In this section we consider a discrete random variable that is often useful in estimating the number of occurrences over a specified interval of time or space. For example, the random variable of interest might be the number of arrivals at a car wash in one hour, the number of repairs needed in 10 miles of highway, or the number of leaks in 100 miles of pipeline. If the following two properties are satisfied, the number of occurrences is a random variable described by the **Poisson probability distribution**.

PROPERTIES OF A POISSON EXPERIMENT

1. **The probability of an occurrence is the same for any two intervals of equal length.**
2. **The occurrence or nonoccurrence in any interval is independent of the occurrence or nonoccurrence in any other interval.**

The **Poisson probability function** is defined by equation (5.11).

Siméon Poisson taught mathematics at the Ecole Polytechnique in Paris from 1802 to 1808. In 1837, he published a work entitled "Researches on the Probability of Criminal and Civil Verdicts," which includes a discussion of what later became known as the Poisson distribution.

POISSON PROBABILITY FUNCTION

$$f(x) = \frac{\mu^x e^{-\mu}}{x!} \quad (5.11)$$

where

$f(x)$ = the probability of x occurrences in an interval
μ = expected value or mean number of occurrences in an interval
e = 2.71828

For the Poisson probability distribution, x is a discrete random variable indicating the number of occurrences in the interval. Since there is no stated upper limit for the number of occurrences, the probability function $f(x)$ is applicable for values $x = 0, 1, 2, \ldots$ without limit. In practical applications, x will eventually become large enough so that $f(x)$ is approximately zero and the probability of any larger values of x becomes negligible.

An Example Involving Time Intervals

Bell Labs used the Poisson distribution to model the arrival of telephone calls.

Suppose that we are interested in the number of arrivals at the drive-up teller window of a bank during a 15-minute period on weekday mornings. If we can assume that the probability of a car arriving is the same for any two time periods of equal length and that the arrival or nonarrival of a car in any time period is independent of the arrival or nonarrival in any other time period, the Poisson probability function is applicable. Suppose these assumptions are satisfied and an analysis of historical data shows that the average number of cars arriving in a 15-minute period of time is 10; in this case, the following probability function applies.

$$f(x) = \frac{10^x e^{-10}}{x!}$$

The random variable here is x = number of cars arriving in any 15-minute period.

If management wanted to know the probability of exactly five arrivals in 15 minutes, we would set $x = 5$ and thus obtain

$$\text{Probability of exactly 5 arrivals in 15 minutes} = f(5) = \frac{10^5 e^{-10}}{5!} = .0378$$

The probability of five arrivals in 15 minutes was obtained by using a calculator to evaluate the probability function. Excel also provides a function called POISSON.DIST for computing Poisson probabilities and cumulative probabilities. This function is easier to use when numerous probabilities and cumulative probabilities are desired. At the end of this section, we show how to compute these probabilities with Excel.

A property of the Poisson distribution is that the mean and variance are equal.

In the preceding example, the mean of the Poisson distribution is $\mu = 10$ arrivals per 15-minute period. A property of the Poisson distribution is that the mean of the distribution and the variance of the distribution are *equal.* Thus, the variance for the number of arrivals during 15-minute periods is $\sigma^2 = 10$. The standard deviation is $\sigma = \sqrt{10} = 3.16$.

Our illustration involves a 15-minute period, but other time periods can be used. Suppose we want to compute the probability of one arrival in a 3-minute period. Because 10 is the expected number of arrivals in a 15-minute period, we see that $10/15 = 2/3$ is the expected number of arrivals in a 1-minute period and that $(2/3)(3 \text{ minutes}) = 2$ is the expected number of arrivals in a 3-minute period. Thus, the probability of

x arrivals in a 3-minute time period with $\mu = 2$ is given by the following Poisson probability function.

$$f(x) = \frac{2^x e^{-2}}{x!}$$

The probability of one arrival in a 3-minute period is calculated as follows:

$$\text{Probability of exactly 1 arrival in 3 minutes} = f(1) = \frac{2^1 e^{-2}}{1!} = .2707$$

Earlier we computed the probability of five arrivals in a 15-minute period; it was .0378. Note that the probability of one arrival in a three-minute period (.2707) is not the same. When computing a Poisson probability for a different time interval, we must first convert the mean arrival rate to the time period of interest and then compute the probability.

An Example Involving Length or Distance Intervals

Let us illustrate an application not involving time intervals in which the Poisson distribution is useful. Suppose we are concerned with the occurrence of major defects in a highway one month after resurfacing. We will assume that the probability of a defect is the same for any two highway intervals of equal length and that the occurrence or nonoccurrence of a defect in any one interval is independent of the occurrence or nonoccurrence of a defect in any other interval. Hence, the Poisson distribution can be applied.

Suppose we learn that major defects one month after resurfacing occur at the average rate of two per mile. Let us find the probability of no major defects in a particular 3-mile section of the highway. Because we are interested in an interval with a length of 3 miles, $\mu = (2 \text{ defects/mile})(3 \text{ miles}) = 6$ represents the expected number of major defects over the 3-mile section of highway. Using equation (5.7), the probability of no major defects is $f(0) = 6^0 e^{-6}/0! = .0025$. Thus, it is unlikely that no major defects will occur in the 3-mile section. In fact, this example indicates a $1 - .0025 = .9975$ probability of at least one major defect in the 3-mile highway section.

Using Excel to Compute Poisson Probabilities

The Excel function for computing Poisson probabilities and cumulative probabilities is called POISSON.DIST. It works in much the same way as the Excel function for computing binomial probabilities. Here we show how to use it to compute Poisson probabilities and cumulative probabilities. To illustrate, we use the example introduced earlier in this section; cars arrive at a bank drive-up teller window at the mean rate of 10 per 15-minute time interval. Refer to Figure 5.8 as we describe the tasks involved.

Enter/Access Data: In order to compute a Poisson probability, we must know the mean number of occurrences (μ) per time period and the number of occurrences for which we want to compute the probability (x). For the drive-up teller window example, the occurrences of interest are the arrivals of cars. The mean arrival rate is 10, which has been entered into cell D1. Earlier in this section, we computed the probability of 5 arrivals. But suppose we now want to compute the probability of 0 up through 20 arrivals. To do so, we enter the values 0, 1, 2, . . . , 20 into cells A4:A24.

Enter Functions and Formulas: The POISSON.DIST function has three inputs: The first is the value of x, the second is the value of μ, and the third is FALSE or TRUE. We choose FALSE for the third input if a probability is desired and TRUE if a cumulative probability

FIGURE 5.8 EXCEL WORKSHEET FOR COMPUTING POISSON PROBABILITIES

	A	B	C	D	E
1			Mean No. of Occurrences	10	
2					
3	No. of Arrivals (x)	Probability $f(x)$			
4	0	=POISSON.DIST(A4,$D$1,FALSE)			
5	1	=POISSON.DIST(A5,$D$1,FALSE)			
6	2	=POISSON.DIST(A6,$D$1,FALSE)			
7	3	=POISSON.DIST(A7,$D$1,FALSE)			
8	4	=POISSON.DIST(A8,$D$1,FALSE)			
9	5	=POISSON.DIST(A9,$D$1,FALSE)			
10	6	=POISSON.DIST(A10,$D$1,FALSE)			
11	7	=POISSON.DIST(A11,$D$1,FALSE)			
12	8	=POISSON.DIST(A12,$D$1,FALSE)			
13	9	=POISSON.DIST(A13,$D$1,FALSE)			
14	10	=POISSON.DIST(A14,$D$1,FALSE)			
15	11	=POISSON.DIST(A15,$D$1,FALSE)			
16	12	=POISSON.DIST(A16,$D$1,FALSE)			
17	13	=POISSON.DIST(A17,$D$1,FALSE)			
18	14	=POISSON.DIST(A18,$D$1,FALSE)			
19	15	=POISSON.DIST(A19,$D$1,FALSE)			
20	16	=POISSON.DIST(A20,$D$1,FALSE)			
21	17	=POISSON.DIST(A21,$D$1,FALSE)			
22	18	=POISSON.DIST(A22,$D$1,FALSE)			
23	19	=POISSON.DIST(A23,$D$1,FALSE)			
24	20	=POISSON.DIST(A24,$D$1,FALSE)			
25					

	A	B	C	D
1		Mean No. of Occurrences		10
2				
3	No. of Arrivals (x)	Probability $f(x)$		
4	0	0.0000		
5	1	0.0005		
6	2	0.0023		
7	3	0.0076		
8	4	0.0189		
9	5	0.0378		
10	6	0.0631		
11	7	0.0901		
12	8	0.1126		
13	9	0.1251		
14	10	0.1251		
15	11	0.1137		
16	12	0.0948		
17	13	0.0729		
18	14	0.0521		
19	15	0.0347		
20	16	0.0217		
21	17	0.0128		
22	18	0.0071		
23	19	0.0037		
24	20	0.0019		
25				

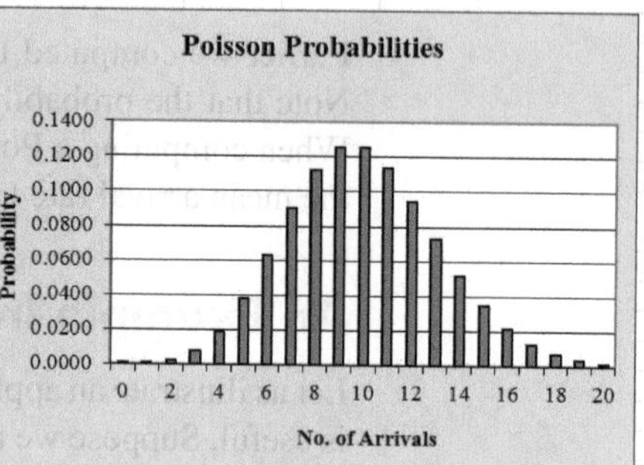

Poisson Probabilities
Probability
0.1400
0.1200
0.1000
0.0800
0.0600
0.0400
0.0200
0.0000
0 2 4 6 8 10 12 14 16 18 20
No. of Arrivals

is desired. The formula =POISSON.DIST(A4,$D$1,FALSE) has been entered into cell B4 to compute the probability of 0 arrivals in a 15-minute period. The value worksheet in the foreground shows that the probability of 0 arrivals is 0.0000. The formula in cell B4 is copied to cells B5:B24 to compute the probabilities for 1 through 20 arrivals. Note, in cell B9 of the value worksheet, that the probability of 5 arrivals is .0378. This result is the same as we calculated earlier in the text.

Notice how easy it was to compute all the probabilities for 0 through 20 arrivals using the POISSON.DIST function. These calculations would take quite a bit of work using a calculator. We have also used Excel's chart tools to develop a graph of the Poisson probability distribution of arrivals. See the value worksheet in Figure 5.8. This chart gives a nice graphical presentation of the probabilities for the various number of arrival possibilities in a 15-minute interval. We can quickly see that the most likely number of arrivals is 9 or 10 and that the probabilities fall off rather smoothly for smaller and larger values.

Let us now see how cumulative probabilities are generated using Excel's POISSON.DIST function. It is really a simple extension of what we have already done. We again use the example of arrivals at a drive-up teller window. Refer to Figure 5.9 as we describe the tasks involved.

Enter/Access Data: To compute cumulative Poisson probabilities we must provide the mean number of occurrences (μ) per time period and the values of x that we are interested in. The mean arrival rate (10) has been entered into cell D1. Suppose we want to compute the cumulative probabilities for a number of arrivals ranging from zero up through 20. To do so, we enter the values 0, 1, 2, . . . , 20 into cells A4:A24.

FIGURE 5.9 EXCEL WORKSHEET FOR COMPUTING CUMULATIVE POISSON PROBABILITIES

	A	B	C	D	E
1			Mean No. of Occurrences	10	
2					
3	No. of Arrivals (x)	Probability $f(x)$			
4	0	=POISSON.DIST(A4,$D$1,TRUE)			
5	1	=POISSON.DIST(A5,$D$1,TRUE)			
6	2	=POISSON.DIST(A6,$D$1,TRUE)			
7	3	=POISSON.DIST(A7,$D$1,TRUE)			
8	4	=POISSON.DIST(A8,$D$1,TRUE)			
9	5	=POISSON.DIST(A9,$D$1,TRUE)			
10	6	=POISSON.DIST(A10,$D$1,TRUE)			
11	7	=POISSON.DIST(A11,$D$1,TRUE)			
12	8	=POISSON.DIST(A12,$D$1,TRUE)			
13	9	=POISSON.DIST(A13,$D$1,TRUE)			
14	10	=POISSON.DIST(A14,$D$1,TRUE)			
15	11	=POISSON.DIST(A15,$D$1,TRUE)			
16	12	=POISSON.DIST(A16,$D$1,TRUE)			
17	13	=POISSON.DIST(A17,$D$1,TRUE)			
18	14	=POISSON.DIST(A18,$D$1,TRUE)			
19	15	=POISSON.DIST(A19,$D$1,TRUE)			
20	16	=POISSON.DIST(A20,$D$1,TRUE)			
21	17	=POISSON.DIST(A21,$D$1,TRUE)			
22	18	=POISSON.DIST(A22,$D$1,TRUE)			
23	19	=POISSON.DIST(A23,$D$1,TRUE)			
24	20	=POISSON.DIST(A24,$D$1,TRUE)			
25					

	A	B	C	D	E
1		Mean No. of Occurrences		10	
2					
3	No. of Arrivals (x)	Probability $f(x)$			
4	0	0.0000			
5	1	0.0005			
6	2	0.0028			
7	3	0.0103			
8	4	0.0293			
9	5	0.0671			
10	6	0.1301			
11	7	0.2202			
12	8	0.3328			
13	9	0.4579			
14	10	0.5830			
15	11	0.6968			
16	12	0.7916			
17	13	0.8645			
18	14	0.9165			
19	15	0.9513			
20	16	0.9730			
21	17	0.9857			
22	18	0.9928			
23	19	0.9965			
24	20	0.9984			
25					

Enter Functions and Formulas: Refer to the formula worksheet in the background of Figure 5.8. The formulas we enter into cells B4:B24 of Figure 5.9 are the same as in Figure 5.8 with one exception. Instead of FALSE for the third input, we enter the word TRUE to obtain cumulative probabilities. After entering these formulas into cells B4:B24 of the worksheet in Figure 5.9, the cumulative probabilities shown were obtained.

Note, in Figure 5.9, that the probability of 5 or fewer arrivals is .0671 and that the probability of 4 or fewer arrivals is .0293. Thus, the probability of exactly 5 arrivals is the difference in these two numbers: $f(5) = .0671 - .0293 = .0378$. We computed this probability earlier in this section and in Figure 5.8. Using these cumulative probabilities, it is easy to compute the probability that a random variable lies within a certain interval. For instance, suppose we wanted to know the probability of more than 5 and fewer than 16 arrivals. We would just find the cumulative probability of 15 arrivals and subtract from that the cumulative probability for 5 arrivals. Referring to Figure 5.9 to obtain the appropriate probabilities, we obtain $.9513 - .0671 = .8842$. With such a high probability, we could conclude that 6 to 15 cars will arrive in most 15-minute intervals. Using the cumulative probability for 20 arrivals, we can also conclude that the probability of more than 20 arrivals in a 15-minute period is $1 - .9984 = .0016$; thus, there is almost no chance of more than 20 cars arriving.

Exercises

Methods

38. Consider a Poisson distribution with $\mu = 3$.
    a. Write the appropriate Poisson probability function.
    b. Compute $f(2)$.
    c. Compute $f(1)$.
    d. Compute $P(x \geq 2)$.

39. Consider a Poisson distribution with a mean of two occurrences per time period.
    a. Write the appropriate Poisson probability function.
    b. What is the expected number of occurrences in three time periods?
    c. Write the appropriate Poisson probability function to determine the probability of x occurrences in three time periods.
    d. Compute the probability of two occurrences in one time period.
    e. Compute the probability of six occurrences in three time periods.
    f. Compute the probability of five occurrences in two time periods.

Applications

40. Phone calls arrive at the rate of 48 per hour at the reservation desk for Regional Airways.
    a. Compute the probability of receiving three calls in a 5-minute interval of time.
    b. Compute the probability of receiving exactly 10 calls in 15 minutes.
    c. Suppose no calls are currently on hold. If the agent takes 5 minutes to complete the current call, how many callers do you expect to be waiting by that time? What is the probability that none will be waiting?
    d. If no calls are currently being processed, what is the probability that the agent can take 3 minutes for personal time without being interrupted by a call?
41. During the period of time that a local university takes phone-in registrations, calls come in at the rate of one every two minutes.
    a. What is the expected number of calls in one hour?
    b. What is the probability of three calls in five minutes?
    c. What is the probability of no calls in a five-minute period?
42. In 2011, New York City had a total of 11,232 motor vehicle accidents that occurred on Monday through Friday between the hours of 3 P.M. and 6 P.M. (New York State Department of Motor Vehicles website, October 24, 2012). This corresponds to mean of 14.4 accidents per hour.
    a. Compute the probability of no accidents in a 15-minute period.
    b. Compute the probability of at least one accident in a 15-minute period.
    c. Compute the probability of four or more accidents in a 15-minute period.
43. Airline passengers arrive randomly and independently at the passenger-screening facility at a major international airport. The mean arrival rate is 10 passengers per minute.
    a. Compute the probability of no arrivals in a one-minute period.
    b. Compute the probability that three or fewer passengers arrive in a one-minute period.
    c. Compute the probability of no arrivals in a 15-second period.
    d. Compute the probability of at least one arrival in a 15-second period.
44. According to the National Oceanic and Atmospheric Administration (NOAA), the state of Colorado averages 18 tornadoes every June (NOAA website, November 8, 2012). (*Note:* There are 30 days in June.)
    a. Compute the mean number of tornadoes per day.
    b. Compute the probability of no tornadoes during a day.
    c. Compute the probability of exactly one tornado during a day.
    d. Compute the probability of more than one tornado during a day.

45. The National Safety Council (NSC) estimates that off-the-job accidents cost U.S. businesses almost \$200 billion annually in lost productivity (National Safety Council, March 2006). Based on NSC estimates, companies with 50 employees are expected to average three employee off-the-job accidents per year. Answer the following questions for companies with 50 employees.
    a. What is the probability of no off-the-job accidents during a one-year period?
    b. What is the probability of at least two off-the-job accidents during a one-year period?
    c. What is the expected number of off-the-job accidents during six months?
    d. What is the probability of no off-the-job accidents during the next six months?

5.6 Hypergeometric Probability Distribution

The **hypergeometric probability distribution** is closely related to the binomial distribution. The two probability distributions differ in two key ways. With the hypergeometric distribution, the trials are not independent, and the probability of success changes from trial to trial.

In the usual notation for the hypergeometric distribution, r denotes the number of elements in the population of size N labeled success, and $N - r$ denotes the number of elements in the population labeled failure. The **hypergeometric probability function** is used to compute the probability that in a random selection of n elements, selected without replacement, we obtain x elements labeled success and $n - x$ elements labeled failure. For this outcome to occur, we must obtain x successes from the r successes in the population and $n - x$ failures from the $N - r$ failures. The following hypergeometric probability function provides $f(x)$, the probability of obtaining x successes in n trials.

HYPERGEOMETRIC PROBABILITY FUNCTION

$$f(x) = \frac{\binom{r}{x}\binom{N-r}{n-x}}{\binom{N}{n}} \tag{5.12}$$

where

x = the number of successes
n = the number of trials
$f(x)$ = the probability of x successes in n trials
N = the number of elements in the population
r = the number of elements in the population labeled success

Note that $\binom{N}{n}$ represents the number of ways n elements can be selected from a population of size N; $\binom{r}{x}$ represents the number of ways that x successes can be selected from a total of r successes in the population; and $\binom{N-r}{n-x}$ represents the number of ways that $n - x$ failures can be selected from a total of $N - r$ failures in the population.

For the hypergeometric probability distribution, x is a discrete random variable and the probability function $f(x)$ given by equation (5.12) is usually applicable for values of $x = 0, 1, 2, \ldots, n$. However, only values of x where the number of observed successes is *less than or equal* to the number of successes in the population ($x \leq r$) and where the number of observed failures is *less than or equal to* the number of failures in the population ($n - x \leq N - r$) are valid. If these two conditions do not hold for one or more values of x, the corresponding $f(x) = 0$, indicating that the probability of this value of x is zero.

To illustrate the computations involved in using equation (5.12), let us consider the following quality control application. Electric fuses produced by Ontario Electric are packaged in boxes of 12 units each. Suppose an inspector randomly selects 3 of the 12 fuses in a box for testing. If the box contains exactly 5 defective fuses, what is the probability that the inspector will find exactly one of the 3 fuses defective? In this application, $n = 3$ and $N = 12$. With $r = 5$ defective fuses in the box the probability of finding $x = 1$ defective fuse is

$$f(1) = \frac{\binom{5}{1}\binom{7}{2}}{\binom{12}{3}} = \frac{\left(\frac{5!}{1!4!}\right)\left(\frac{7!}{2!5!}\right)}{\left(\frac{12!}{3!9!}\right)} = \frac{(5)(21)}{220} = .4773$$

Now suppose that we wanted to know the probability of finding *at least* 1 defective fuse. The easiest way to answer this question is to first compute the probability that the inspector does not find any defective fuses. The probability of $x = 0$ is

$$f(0) = \frac{\binom{5}{0}\binom{7}{3}}{\binom{12}{3}} = \frac{\left(\frac{5!}{0!5!}\right)\left(\frac{7!}{3!4!}\right)}{\left(\frac{12!}{3!9!}\right)} = \frac{(1)(35)}{220} = .1591$$

With a probability of zero defective fuses $f(0) = .1591$, we conclude that the probability of finding at least 1 defective fuse must be $1 - .1591 = .8409$. Thus, there is a reasonably high probability that the inspector will find at least 1 defective fuse.

The mean and variance of a hypergeometric distribution are as follows.

$$E(x) = \mu = n\left(\frac{r}{N}\right) \tag{5.13}$$

$$Var(x) = \sigma^2 = n\left(\frac{r}{N}\right)\left(1 - \frac{r}{N}\right)\left(\frac{N - n}{N - 1}\right) \tag{5.14}$$

In the preceding example $n = 3$, $r = 5$, and $N = 12$. Thus, the mean and variance for the number of defective fuses are

$$\mu = n\left(\frac{r}{N}\right) = 3\left(\frac{5}{12}\right) = 1.25$$

$$\sigma^2 = n\left(\frac{r}{N}\right)\left(1 - \frac{r}{N}\right)\left(\frac{N - n}{N - 1}\right) = 3\left(\frac{5}{12}\right)\left(1 - \frac{5}{12}\right)\left(\frac{12 - 3}{12 - 1}\right) = .60$$

The standard deviation is $\sigma = \sqrt{.60} = .77$.

Using Excel to Compute Hypergeometric Probabilities

The Excel function for computing hypergeometric probabilities is HYPGEOM.DIST. It has five inputs: the first is the value of x, the second is the value of n, the third is the value of r, the fourth is the value of N, and the fifth is FALSE or TRUE. We choose FALSE if a probability is desired and TRUE if a cumulative probability is desired. This function's usage is similar to that of BINOM.DIST for the binomial distribution and POISSON.DIST for the Poisson distribution, so we dispense with showing a worksheet figure and just explain how to use the function.

Let us reconsider the example of selecting 3 fuses for inspection from a fuse box containing 12 fuses, 5 of which are defective. We want to find the probability that 1 of the 3 fuses selected is defective. In this case, the five inputs are $x = 1$, $n = 3$, $r = 5$, $N = 12$, and FALSE. So, the appropriate formula to place in a cell of an Excel worksheet is =HYPGEOM.DIST(1,3,5,12,FALSE). Placing this formula in a cell of an Excel worksheet provides a hypergeometric probability of .4773.

If we want to know the probability that none of the 3 fuses selected is defective, the five function inputs are $x = 0$, $n = 3$, $r = 5$, $N = 12$, and FALSE. So, using the HYPGEOM.DIST function to compute the probability of randomly selecting 3 fuses without any being defective, we would enter the following formula into an Excel worksheet: =HYPGEOM.DIST(0,3,5,12,FALSE). The probability is .1591.

Cumulative probabilities can be obtained in a similar fashion by using TRUE for the fifth input. For instance, to compute the probability of finding at most 1 defective fuse, the appropriate formula is =HYPGEOM.DIST(1,3,5,12,TRUE). Placing this formula in a cell of an Excel worksheet provides a hypergeometric cumulative probability of .6364.

NOTE AND COMMENT

Consider a hypergeometric distribution with n trials. Let $p = (r/N)$ denote the probability of a success on the first trial. If the population size is large, the term $(N - n)/(N - 1)$ in equation (5.14) approaches 1. As a result, the expected value and variance can be written $E(x) = np$ and $Var(x) = np(1 - p)$. Note that these expressions are the same as the expressions used to compute the expected value and variance of a binomial distribution, as in equations (5.9) and (5.10). When the population size is large, a hypergeometric distribution can be approximated by a binomial distribution with n trials and a probability of success $p = (r/N)$.

Exercises

Methods

46. Suppose $N = 10$ and $r = 3$. Compute the hypergeometric probabilities for the following values of n and x.
    a. $n = 4, x = 1$.
    b. $n = 2, x = 2$.
    c. $n = 2, x = 0$.
    d. $n = 4, x = 2$.
    e. $n = 4, x = 4$.
47. Suppose $N = 15$ and $r = 4$. What is the probability of $x = 3$ for $n = 10$?

Applications

48. A recent survey showed that a majority of Americans plan on doing their holiday shopping online because they don't want to spend money on gas driving from store to store (SOASTA

website, October 24, 2012). Suppose we have a group of 10 shoppers; 7 prefer to do their holiday shopping online and 3 prefer to do their holiday shopping in stores. A random sample of 3 of these 10 shoppers is selected for a more in-depth study of how the economy has impacted their shopping behavior.

a. What is the probability that exactly 2 prefer shopping online?
b. What is the probability that the majority (either 2 or 3) prefer shopping online?

49. Blackjack, or twenty-one as it is frequently called, is a popular gambling game played in Las Vegas casinos. A player is dealt two cards. Face cards (jacks, queens, and kings) and tens have a point value of 10. Aces have a point value of 1 or 11. A 52-card deck contains 16 cards with a point value of 10 (jacks, queens, kings, and tens) and four aces.

a. What is the probability that both cards dealt are aces or 10-point cards?
b. What is the probability that both of the cards are aces?
c. What is the probability that both of the cards have a point value of 10?
d. A blackjack is a 10-point card and an ace for a value of 21. Use your answers to parts (a), (b), and (c) to determine the probability that a player is dealt blackjack. (*Hint:* Part (d) is not a hypergeometric problem. Develop your own logical relationship as to how the hypergeometric probabilities from parts (a), (b), and (c) can be combined to answer this question.)

50. Axline Computers manufactures personal computers at two plants, one in Texas and the other in Hawaii. The Texas plant has 40 employees; the Hawaii plant has 20. A random sample of 10 employees is to be asked to fill out a benefits questionnaire.

a. What is the probability that none of the employees in the sample work at the plant in Hawaii?
b. What is the probability that 1 of the employees in the sample works at the plant in Hawaii?
c. What is the probability that 2 or more of the employees in the sample work at the plant in Hawaii?
d. What is the probability that 9 of the employees in the sample work at the plant in Texas?

51. The Zagat Restaurant Survey provides food, decor, and service ratings for some of the top restaurants across the United States. For 15 restaurants located in Boston, the average price of a dinner, including one drink and tip, was $48.60. You are leaving on a business trip to Boston and will eat dinner at three of these restaurants. Your company will reimburse you for a maximum of $50 per dinner. Business associates familiar with these restaurants have told you that the meal cost at one-third of these restaurants will exceed $50. Suppose that you randomly select three of these restaurants for dinner.

a. What is the probability that none of the meals will exceed the cost covered by your company?
b. What is the probability that one of the meals will exceed the cost covered by your company?
c. What is the probability that two of the meals will exceed the cost covered by your company?
d. What is the probability that all three of the meals will exceed the cost covered by your company?

52. The Troubled Asset Relief Program (TARP), passed by the U.S. Congress in October 2008, provided $700 billion in assistance for the struggling U.S. economy. Over $200 billion was given to troubled financial institutions with the hope that there would be an increase in lending to help jump-start the economy. But three months later, a Federal Reserve survey found that two-thirds of the banks that had received TARP funds had tightened terms for business loans (*The Wall Street Journal*, February 3, 2009). Of the 10 banks that were the biggest recipients of TARP funds, only 3 had actually increased lending during this period.

Increased Lending	Decreased Lending
BB&T	Bank of America
Sun Trust Banks	Capital One
U.S. Bancorp	Citigroup
	Fifth Third Bancorp
	J.P. Morgan Chase
	Regions Financial
	Wells Fargo

For the purposes of this exercise, assume that you will randomly select 3 of these 10 banks for a study that will continue to monitor bank lending practices. Let x be a random variable indicating the number of banks in the study that had increased lending.

a. What is $f(0)$? What is your interpretation of this value?
b. What is $f(3)$? What is your interpretation of this value?
c. Compute $f(1)$ and $f(2)$. Show the probability distribution for the number of banks in the study that had increased lending. What value of x has the highest probability?
d. What is the probability that the study will have at least one bank that had increased lending?
e. Compute the expected value, variance, and standard deviation for the random variable.

Summary

A random variable provides a numerical description of the outcome of an experiment. The probability distribution for a random variable describes how the probabilities are distributed over the values the random variable can assume. For any discrete random variable x, the probability distribution is defined by a probability function, denoted by $f(x)$, which provides the probability associated with each value of the random variable.

We introduced two types of discrete probability distributions. The first type involved providing a list of the values of the random variable and the associated probabilities in a table. We showed how the relative frequency method of assigning probabilities could be used to develop empirical discrete probability distributions of this type.

The second type of discrete probability distribution we discussed involved the use of a mathematical function to provide the probabilities for the random variable. The binomial, Poisson, and hypergeometric distributions discussed were all of this type. The binomial distribution can be used to determine the probability of x successes in n trials whenever the random experiment has the following properties:

1. The experiment consists of a sequence of n identical trials.
2. Two outcomes are possible on each trial, one called success and the other failure.
3. The probability of a success p does not change from trial to trial. Consequently, the probability of failure, $1 - p$, does not change from trial to trial.
4. The trials are independent.

When the four properties hold, the binomial probability function can be used to determine the probability of obtaining x successes in n trials. Formulas were also presented for the mean and variance of the binomial distribution.

The Poisson distribution is used when it is desirable to determine the probability of obtaining x occurrences over an interval of time or space. The following assumptions are necessary for the Poisson distribution to be applicable:

1. The probability of an occurrence of the event is the same for any two intervals of equal length.

2. The occurrence or nonoccurrence of the event in any interval is independent of the occurrence or nonoccurrence of the event in any other interval.

A third discrete probability distribution, the hypergeometric, was introduced in Section 5.6. Like the binomial, it is used to compute the probability of x successes in n trials. But, in contrast to the binomial, the probability of success changes from trial to trial.

Glossary

Random variable A numerical description of the outcome of an experiment.
Discrete random variable A random variable that may assume either a finite number of values or an infinite sequence of values.
Continuous random variable A random variable that may assume any numerical value in an interval or collection of intervals.
Probability distribution A description of how the probabilities are distributed over the values of the random variable.
Probability function A function, denoted by $f(x)$, that provides the probability that x assumes a particular value for a discrete random variable.
Empirical discrete distribution A discrete probability distribution for which the relative frequency method is used to assign the probabilities.
Discrete uniform probability distribution A probability distribution for which each possible value of the random variable has the same probability.
Expected value A measure of the central location, or mean, of a random variable.
Variance A measure of the variability, or dispersion, of a random variable.
Standard deviation The positive square root of the variance.
Binomial experiment A random experiment having the four properties stated at the beginning of Section 5.5.
Binomial probability distribution A probability distribution showing the probability of x successes in n trials of a binomial experiment.
Binomial probability function The function used to compute binomial probabilities.
Poisson probability distribution A probability distribution showing the probability of x occurrences of an event over a specified interval of time or space.
Poisson probability function The function used to compute Poisson probabilities.
Hypergeometric probability distribution A probability distribution showing the probability of x successes in n trials from a population with r successes and $N - r$ failures.
Hypergeometric probability function The function used to compute hypergeometric probabilities.

Key Formulas

Discrete Uniform Probability Function

$$f(x) = 1/n \tag{5.3}$$

Expected Value of a Discrete Random Variable

$$E(x) = \mu = \Sigma x f(x) \tag{5.4}$$

Variance of a Discrete Random Variable

$$Var(x) = \sigma^2 = \Sigma(x - \mu)^2 f(x) \tag{5.5}$$

Number of Experimental Outcomes Providing Exactly x Successes in n Trials

$$\binom{n}{x} = \frac{n!}{x!(n - x)!} \tag{5.6}$$

Binomial Probability Function

$$f(x) = \binom{n}{x} p^x (1 - p)^{(n-x)} \tag{5.8}$$

Expected Value for the Binomial Distribution

$$E(x) = \mu = np \tag{5.9}$$

Variance for the Binomial Distribution

$$Var(x) = \sigma^2 = np(1 - p) \tag{5.10}$$

Poisson Probability Function

$$f(x) = \frac{\mu^x e^{-\mu}}{x!} \tag{5.11}$$

Hypergeometric Probability Function

$$f(x) = \frac{\binom{r}{x}\binom{N - r}{n - x}}{\binom{N}{n}} \tag{5.12}$$

Expected Value for the Hypergeometric Distribution

$$E(x) = \mu = n\left(\frac{r}{N}\right) \tag{5.13}$$

Variance for the Hypergeometric Distribution

$$Var(x) = \sigma^2 = n\left(\frac{r}{N}\right)\left(1 - \frac{r}{N}\right)\left(\frac{N - n}{N - 1}\right) \tag{5.14}$$

Supplementary Exercises

53. The U.S. Coast Guard (USCG) provides a wide variety of information on boating accidents including the wind condition at the time of the accident. The following table shows the results obtained for 4401 accidents (USCG website, November 8, 2012).

Wind Condition	Percentage of Accidents
None	9.6
Light	57.0
Moderate	23.8
Strong	7.7
Storm	1.9

Let x be a random variable reflecting the known wind condition at the time of each accident. Set $x = 0$ for none, $x = 1$ for light, $x = 2$ for moderate, $x = 3$ for strong, and $x = 4$ for storm.

a. Develop a probability distribution for x.
b. Compute the expected value of x.
c. Compute the variance and standard deviation for x.
d. Comment on what your results imply about the wind conditions during boating accidents.

54. The Car Repair Ratings website provides consumer reviews and ratings for garages in the United States and Canada. The time customers wait for service to be completed is one of the categories rated. The following table provides a summary of the wait-time ratings (1 = Slow/Delays; 10 = Quick/On Time) for 40 randomly selected garages located in the province of Ontario, Canada (Car Repair Ratings website, November 14, 2012).

Wait-Time Rating	Number of Garages
1	6
2	2
3	3
4	2
5	5
6	2
7	4
8	5
9	5
10	6

a. Develop a probability distribution for x = wait-time rating.
b. Any garage that receives a wait-time rating of at least 9 is considered to provide outstanding service. If a consumer randomly selects one of the 40 garages for their next car service, what is the probability the garage selected will provide outstanding wait-time service?
c. What is the expected value and variance for x?
d. Suppose that 7 of the 40 garages reviewed were new car dealerships. Of the 7 new car dealerships, two were rated as providing outstanding wait-time service. Compare the likelihood of a new car dealership achieving an outstanding wait-time service rating as compared to other types of service providers.

55. The budgeting process for a midwestern college resulted in expense forecasts for the coming year (in $ millions) of $9, $10, $11, $12, and $13. Because the actual expenses are unknown, the following respective probabilities are assigned: .3, .2, .25, .05, and .2.
a. Show the probability distribution for the expense forecast.

b. What is the expected value of the expense forecast for the coming year?
c. What is the variance of the expense forecast for the coming year?
d. If income projections for the year are estimated at $12 million, comment on the financial position of the college.

56. The Pew Research Center surveyed adults who own/use the following technologies: Internet, smartphone, email, and land-line phone (*USA Today*, March 26, 2014) and asked which of these technologies would be "very hard" to give up. The following responses were obtained: Internet 53%, smartphone 49%, email 36%, and land-line phone 28%.
   a. If 20 adult Internet users are surveyed, what is the probability that 3 users will report that it would be very hard to give it up?
   b. If 20 adults who own a land-line phone are surveyed, what is the probability that 5 or fewer will report that it would be very hard to give it up?
   c. If 2000 owners of smartphones were surveyed, what is the expected number that will report that it would be very hard to give it up?
   d. If 2000 users of email were surveyed, what is expected number that will report that it would be very hard to give it up? What is the variance and standard deviation?

57. The following table shows the percentage of individuals in each age group who use an online tax program to prepare their federal income tax return (CompleteTax website, November 9, 2012).

Age	Online Tax Program (%)
18–34	16
35–44	12
45–54	10
55–64	8
65+	2

Suppose a follow-up study consisting of personal interviews is to be conducted to determine the most important factors in selecting a method for filing taxes.
   a. How many 18–34-year-olds must be sampled to find an expected number of at least 25 who use an online tax program to prepare their federal income tax return?
   b. How many 35–44-year-olds must be sampled to find an expected number of at least 25 who use an online tax program to prepare their federal income tax return?
   c. How many 65+-year-olds must be sampled to find an expected number of at least 25 who use an online tax program to prepare their federal income tax return?
   d. If the number of 18–34-year-olds sampled is equal to the value identified in part (a), what is the standard deviation of the percentage who use an online tax program?
   e. If the number of 35–44-year-olds sampled is equal to the value identified in part (b), what is the standard deviation of the percentage who use an online tax program?

58. Many companies use a quality control technique called acceptance sampling to monitor incoming shipments of parts, raw materials, and so on. In the electronics industry, component parts are commonly shipped from suppliers in large lots. Inspection of a sample of n components can be viewed as the n trials of a binomial experiment. The outcome for each component tested (trial) will be that the component is classified as good or defective. Reynolds Electronics accepts a lot from a particular supplier if the defective components in the lot do not exceed 1%. Suppose a random sample of five items from a recent shipment is tested.
   a. Assume that 1% of the shipment is defective. Compute the probability that no items in the sample are defective.
   b. Assume that 1% of the shipment is defective. Compute the probability that exactly one item in the sample is defective.

c. What is the probability of observing one or more defective items in the sample if 1% of the shipment is defective?
d. Would you feel comfortable accepting the shipment if one item was found to be defective? Why or why not?

59. The unemployment rate in the state of Arizona is 4.1% (CNN Money website, May 2, 2007). Assume that 100 employable people in Arizona are selected randomly.
a. What is the expected number of people who are unemployed?
b. What are the variance and standard deviation of the number of people who are unemployed?

60. Mahoney Custom Home Builders, Inc. of Canyon Lake, Texas, asked visitors to their website what is most important when choosing a home builder. Possible responses were quality, price, customer referral, years in business, and special features. Results showed that 23.5% of the respondents chose price as the most important factor (Mahoney Custom Homes website, November 13, 2012). Suppose a sample of 200 potential home buyers in the Canyon Lake area was selected.
a. How many people would you expect to choose price as the most important factor when choosing a home builder?
b. What is the standard deviation of the number of respondents who would choose price as the most important factor in selecting a home builder?
c. What is the standard deviation of the number of respondents who do not list price as the most important factor in selecting a home builder?

61. Cars arrive at a car wash randomly and independently; the probability of an arrival is the same for any two time intervals of equal length. The mean arrival rate is 15 cars per hour. What is the probability that 20 or more cars will arrive during any given hour of operation?

62. A new automated production process averages 1.5 breakdowns per day. Because of the cost associated with a breakdown, management is concerned about the possibility of having 3 or more breakdowns during a day. Assume that breakdowns occur randomly, that the probability of a breakdown is the same for any two time intervals of equal length, and that breakdowns in one period are independent of breakdowns in other periods. What is the probability of having 3 or more breakdowns during a day?

63. A regional director responsible for business development in the state of Pennsylvania is concerned about the number of small business failures. If the mean number of small business failures per month is 10, what is the probability that exactly 4 small businesses will fail during a given month? Assume that the probability of a failure is the same for any two months and that the occurrence or nonoccurrence of a failure in any month is independent of failures in any other month.

64. Customer arrivals at a bank are random and independent; the probability of an arrival in any one-minute period is the same as the probability of an arrival in any other one-minute period. Answer the following questions, assuming a mean arrival rate of three customers per minute.
a. What is the probability of exactly three arrivals in a one-minute period?
b. What is the probability of at least three arrivals in a one-minute period?

65. A deck of playing cards contains 52 cards, four of which are aces. What is the probability that the deal of a five-card hand provides
a. A pair of aces?
b. Exactly one ace?
c. No aces?
d. At least one ace?

66. *U.S. News & World Report*'s ranking of America's best graduate schools of business showed Harvard University and Stanford University in a tie for first place. In addition, 7 of the top 10 graduate schools of business showed students with an average undergraduate

grade point average (GPA) of 3.50 or higher (*America's Best Graduate Schools, 2009 Edition, U.S. News & World Report*). Suppose that we randomly select 2 of the top 10 graduate schools of business.

a. What is the probability that exactly one school has students with an average undergraduate GPA of 3.50 or higher?
b. What is the probability that both schools have students with an average undergraduate GPA of 3.50 or higher?
c. What is the probability that neither school has students with an average undergraduate GPA of 3.50 or higher?

CHAPTER 6

Continuous Probability Distributions

CONTENTS

STATISTICS IN PRACTICE: PROCTER & GAMBLE

6.1 UNIFORM PROBABILITY DISTRIBUTION
- Area as a Measure of Probability

6.2 NORMAL PROBABILITY DISTRIBUTION
- Normal Curve
- Standard Normal Probability Distribution
- Computing Probabilities for Any Normal Probability Distribution
- Grear Tire Company Problem
- Using Excel to Compute Normal Probabilities

6.3 EXPONENTIAL PROBABILITY DISTRIBUTION
- Computing Probabilities for the Exponential Distribution
- Relationship Between the Poisson and Exponential Distributions
- Using Excel to Compute Exponential Probabilities

STATISTICS *in* PRACTICE

PROCTER & GAMBLE*
CINCINNATI, OHIO

Procter & Gamble (P&G) produces and markets such products as detergents, disposable diapers, over-the-counter pharmaceuticals, dentifrices, bar soaps, mouthwashes, and paper towels. Worldwide, it has the leading brand in more categories than any other consumer products company. Since its merger with Gillette, P&G also produces and markets razors, blades, and many other personal care products.

As a leader in the application of statistical methods in decision making, P&G employs people with diverse academic backgrounds: engineering, statistics, operations research, and business. The major quantitative technologies for which these people provide support are probabilistic decision and risk analysis, advanced simulation, quality improvement, and quantitative methods (e.g., linear programming, regression analysis, probability analysis).

The Industrial Chemicals Division of P&G is a major supplier of fatty alcohols derived from natural substances such as coconut oil and from petroleum-based derivatives. The division wanted to know the economic risks and opportunities of expanding its fatty-alcohol production facilities, so it called in P&G's experts in probabilistic decision and risk analysis to help. After structuring and modeling the problem, they determined that the key to profitability was the cost difference between the petroleum- and coconut-based raw materials. Future costs were unknown, but the analysts were able to approximate them with the following continuous random variables.

x = the coconut oil price per pound of fatty alcohol

and

y = the petroleum raw material price per pound of fatty alcohol

Because the key to profitability was the difference between these two random variables, a third random variable, $d = x - y$, was used in the analysis. Experts were interviewed to determine the probability distributions for x and y. In turn, this information was used to develop a probability distribution for the difference in prices d. This continuous probability distribution showed a .90 probability that the price difference would be \$.0655 or less and a .50 probability that the price difference would be \$.035 or less. In addition, there was only a .10 probability that the price difference would be \$.0045 or less.†

Procter & Gamble is a leader in the application of statistical methods in decision making.

The Industrial Chemicals Division thought that being able to quantify the impact of raw material price differences was key to reaching a consensus. The probabilities obtained were used in a sensitivity analysis of the raw material price difference. The analysis yielded sufficient insight to form the basis for a recommendation to management.

The use of continuous random variables and their probability distributions was helpful to P&G in analyzing the economic risks associated with its fatty-alcohol production. In this chapter, you will gain an understanding of continuous random variables and their probability distributions, including one of the most important probability distributions in statistics, the normal distribution.

*The authors are indebted to Joel Kahn of Procter & Gamble for providing this Statistics in Practice.

†The price differences stated here have been modified to protect proprietary data.

In the preceding chapter we discussed discrete random variables and their probability distributions. In this chapter we turn to the study of continuous random variables. Specifically, we discuss three continuous probability distributions: the uniform, the normal, and the exponential.

A fundamental difference separates discrete and continuous random variables in terms of how probabilities are computed. For a discrete random variable, the probability function $f(x)$ provides the probability that the random variable assumes a particular value. With continuous random variables, the counterpart of the probability function is the **probability density function**, also denoted by $f(x)$. The difference is that the probability density function does not directly provide probabilities. However, the area under the graph of $f(x)$ corresponding to a given interval does provide the probability that the continuous random variable x assumes a value in that interval. So when we compute probabilities for continuous random variables we are computing the probability that the random variable assumes any value in an interval.

Because the area under the graph of $f(x)$ at any particular point is zero, one of the implications of the definition of probability for continuous random variables is that the probability of any particular value of the random variable is zero. In Section 6.1 we demonstrate these concepts for a continuous random variable that has a uniform distribution.

Much of the chapter is devoted to describing and showing applications of the normal distribution. The normal distribution is of major importance because of its wide applicability and its extensive use in statistical inference. The chapter closes with a discussion of the exponential distribution. The exponential distribution is useful in applications involving such factors as waiting times and service times.

6.1 Uniform Probability Distribution

Whenever the probability is proportional to the length of the interval, the random variable is uniformly distributed.

Consider the random variable x representing the flight time of an airplane traveling from Chicago to New York. Suppose the flight time can be any value in the interval from 120 minutes to 140 minutes. Because the random variable x can assume any value in that interval, x is a continuous rather than a discrete random variable. Let us assume that sufficient actual flight data are available to conclude that the probability of a flight time within any 1-minute interval is the same as the probability of a flight time within any other 1-minute interval contained in the larger interval from 120 to 140 minutes. With every 1-minute interval being equally likely, the random variable x is said to have a **uniform probability distribution**. The probability density function, which defines the uniform distribution for the flight-time random variable, is

$$f(x) = \begin{cases} 1/20 & \text{for } 120 \leq x \leq 140 \\ 0 & \text{elsewhere} \end{cases}$$

Figure 6.1 is a graph of this probability density function. In general, the uniform probability density function for a random variable x is defined by the following formula.

UNIFORM PROBABILITY DENSITY FUNCTION

$$f(x) = \begin{cases} \dfrac{1}{b-a} & \text{for } a \leq x \leq b \\ 0 & \text{elsewhere} \end{cases} \tag{6.1}$$

For the flight-time random variable, $a = 120$ and $b = 140$.

FIGURE 6.1 UNIFORM PROBABILITY DISTRIBUTION FOR FLIGHT TIME

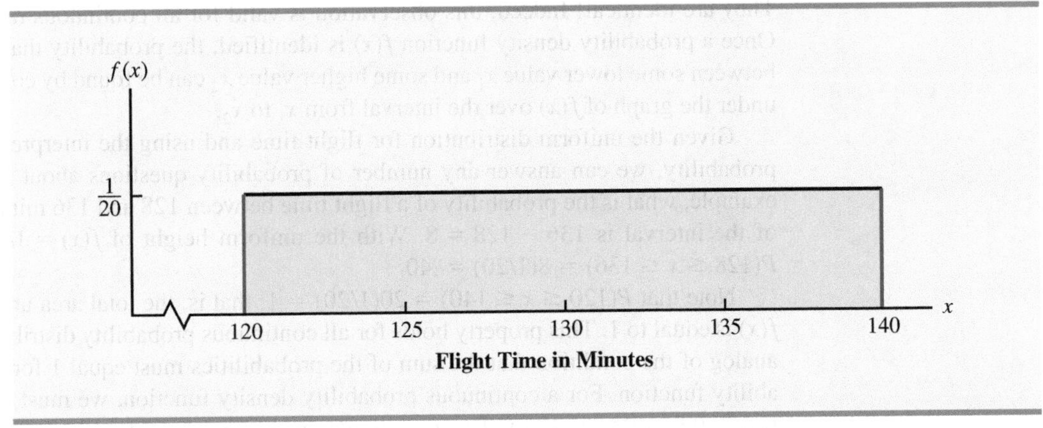

As noted in the introduction, for a continuous random variable, we consider probability only in terms of the likelihood that a random variable assumes a value within a specified interval. In the flight time example, an acceptable probability question is: What is the probability that the flight time is between 120 and 130 minutes? That is, what is $P(120 \leq x \leq 130)$? Because the flight time must be between 120 and 140 minutes and because the probability is described as being uniform over this interval, we feel comfortable saying that $P(120 \leq x \leq 130) = .50$. In the following subsection we show that this probability can be computed as the area under the graph of $f(x)$ from 120 to 130 (see Figure 6.2).

Area as a Measure of Probability

Let us make an observation about the graph in Figure 6.2. Consider the area under the graph of $f(x)$ in the interval from 120 to 130. The area is rectangular, and the area of a rectangle is simply the width multiplied by the height. With the width of the interval equal to $130 - 120 = 10$ and the height equal to the value of the probability density function $f(x) = 1/20$, we have area = width $\times$ height $= 10(1/20) = 10/20 = .50$.

FIGURE 6.2 AREA PROVIDES PROBABILITY OF A FLIGHT TIME BETWEEN 120 AND 130 MINUTES

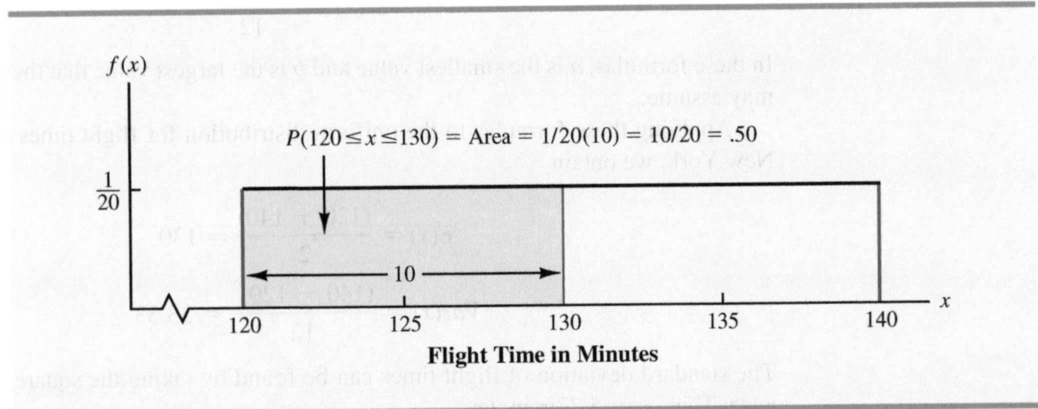

What observation can you make about the area under the graph of $f(x)$ and probability? They are identical! Indeed, this observation is valid for all continuous random variables. Once a probability density function $f(x)$ is identified, the probability that x takes a value between some lower value x_1 and some higher value x_2 can be found by computing the area under the graph of $f(x)$ over the interval from x_1 to x_2.

Given the uniform distribution for flight time and using the interpretation of area as probability, we can answer any number of probability questions about flight times. For example, what is the probability of a flight time between 128 and 136 minutes? The width of the interval is $136 - 128 = 8$. With the uniform height of $f(x) = 1/20$, we see that $P(128 \le x \le 136) = 8(1/20) = .40$.

Note that $P(120 \le x \le 140) = 20(1/20) = 1$; that is, the total area under the graph of $f(x)$ is equal to 1. This property holds for all continuous probability distributions and is the analog of the condition that the sum of the probabilities must equal 1 for a discrete probability function. For a continuous probability density function, we must also require that $f(x) \ge 0$ for all values of x. This requirement is the analog of the requirement that $f(x) \ge 0$ for discrete probability functions.

Two major differences stand out between the treatment of continuous random variables and the treatment of their discrete counterparts.

1. We no longer talk about the probability of the random variable assuming a particular value. Instead, we talk about the probability of the random variable assuming a value within some given interval.
2. The probability of a continuous random variable assuming a value within some given interval from x_1 to x_2 is defined to be the area under the graph of the probability density function between x_1 and x_2. Because a single point is an interval of zero width, this implies that the probability of a continuous random variable assuming any particular value exactly is zero. It also means that the probability of a continuous random variable assuming a value in any interval is the same whether or not the endpoints are included.

To see that the probability of any single point is 0, refer to Figure 6.2 and compute the probability of a single point, say, $x = 125$. $P(x = 125) = P(125 \le x \le 125) = 0(1/20) = 0$.

The calculation of the expected value and variance for a continuous random variable is analogous to that for a discrete random variable. However, because the computational procedure involves integral calculus, we leave the derivation of the appropriate formulas to more advanced texts.

For the uniform continuous probability distribution introduced in this section, the formulas for the expected value and variance are

$$E(x) = \frac{a + b}{2}$$

$$Var(x) = \frac{(b - a)^2}{12}$$

In these formulas, a is the smallest value and b is the largest value that the random variable may assume.

Applying these formulas to the uniform distribution for flight times from Chicago to New York, we obtain

$$E(x) = \frac{(120 + 140)}{2} = 130$$

$$Var(x) = \frac{(140 - 120)^2}{12} = 33.33$$

The standard deviation of flight times can be found by taking the square root of the variance. Thus, $\sigma = 5.77$ minutes.

NOTE AND COMMENT

To see more clearly why the height of a probability density function is not a probability, think about a random variable with the following uniform probability distribution.

$$f(x) = \begin{cases} 2 & \text{for } 0 \le x \le .5 \\ 0 & \text{elsewhere} \end{cases}$$

The height of the probability density function, $f(x)$, is 2 for values of x between 0 and .5. However, we know probabilities can never be greater than 1. Thus, we see that $f(x)$ cannot be interpreted as the probability of x.

Exercises

Methods

1. The random variable x is known to be uniformly distributed between 1.0 and 1.5.
   a. Show the graph of the probability density function.
   b. Compute $P(x = 1.25)$.
   c. Compute $P(1.0 \le x \le 1.25)$.
   d. Compute $P(1.20 < x < 1.5)$.
2. The random variable x is known to be uniformly distributed between 10 and 20.
   a. Show the graph of the probability density function.
   b. Compute $P(x < 15)$.
   c. Compute $P(12 \le x \le 18)$.
   d. Compute $E(x)$.
   e. Compute $Var(x)$.

Applications

3. Delta Airlines quotes a flight time of 2 hours, 5 minutes for its flights from Cincinnati to Tampa. Suppose we believe that actual flight times are uniformly distributed between 2 hours and 2 hours, 20 minutes.
   a. Show the graph of the probability density function for flight time.
   b. What is the probability that the flight will be no more than 5 minutes late?
   c. What is the probability that the flight will be more than 10 minutes late?
   d. What is the expected flight time?

SELF test

4. Most computer languages include a function that can be used to generate random numbers. In Excel, the RAND function can be used to generate random numbers between 0 and 1. If we let x denote a random number generated using RAND, then x is a continuous random variable with the following probability density function.

$$f(x) = \begin{cases} 1 & \text{for } 0 \le x \le 1 \\ 0 & \text{elsewhere} \end{cases}$$

   a. Graph the probability density function.
   b. What is the probability of generating a random number between .25 and .75?
   c. What is the probability of generating a random number with a value less than or equal to .30?
   d. What is the probability of generating a random number with a value greater than .60?
   e. Generate 50 random numbers by entering =RAND() into 50 cells of an Excel worksheet.
   f. Compute the mean and standard deviation for the random numbers in part (e).

5. In October 2012, Apple introduced a much smaller variant of the Apple iPad, known as the iPad Mini. Weighing less than 11 ounces, it was about 50% lighter than the standard iPad. Battery tests for the iPad Mini showed a mean life of 10.25 hours (*The Wall Street Journal*, October 31, 2012). Assume that battery life of the iPad Mini is uniformly distributed between 8.5 and 12 hours.
   a. Give a mathematical expression for the probability density function of battery life.
   b. What is the probability that the battery life for an iPad Mini will be 10 hours or less?
   c. What is the probability that the battery life for an iPad Mini will be at least 11 hours?
   d. What is the probability that the battery life for an iPad Mini will be between 9.5 and 11.5 hours?
   e. In a shipment of 100 iPad Minis, how many should have a battery life of at least 9 hours?

6. A Gallup Daily Tracking Survey found that the mean daily discretionary spending by Americans earning over $90,000 per year was $136 per day (*USA Today*, July 30, 2012). The discretionary spending excluded home purchases, vehicle purchases, and regular monthly bills. Let x = the discretionary spending per day and assume that a uniform probability density function applies with $f(x) = .00625$ for $a \le x \le b$.
   a. Find the values of a and b for the probability density function.
   b. What is the probability that consumers in this group have daily discretionary spending between $100 and $200?
   c. What is the probability that consumers in this group have daily discretionary spending of $150 or more?
   d. What is the probability that consumers in this group have daily discretionary spending of $80 or less?

7. Suppose we are interested in bidding on a piece of land and we know one other bidder is interested.[1] The seller announced that the highest bid in excess of $10,000 will be accepted. Assume that the competitor's bid x is a random variable that is uniformly distributed between $10,000 and $15,000.
   a. Suppose you bid $12,000. What is the probability that your bid will be accepted?
   b. Suppose you bid $14,000. What is the probability that your bid will be accepted?
   c. What amount should you bid to maximize the probability that you get the property?
   d. Suppose you know someone who is willing to pay you $16,000 for the property. Would you consider bidding less than the amount in part (c)? Why or why not?

6.2 Normal Probability Distribution

Abraham de Moivre, a French mathematician, published The Doctrine of Chances *in 1733. He derived the normal distribution.*

The most important probability distribution for describing a continuous random variable is the **normal probability distribution**. The normal distribution has been used in a wide variety of practical applications in which the random variables are heights and weights of people, test scores, scientific measurements, amounts of rainfall, and other similar values. It is also widely used in statistical inference, which is the major topic of the remainder of this book. In such applications, the normal distribution provides a description of the likely results obtained through sampling.

Normal Curve

The form, or shape, of the normal distribution is illustrated by the bell-shaped normal curve in Figure 6.3. The probability density function that defines the bell-shaped curve of the normal distribution follows.

[1]This exercise is based on a problem suggested to us by Professor Roger Myerson of Northwestern University.

FIGURE 6.3 BELL-SHAPED CURVE FOR THE NORMAL DISTRIBUTION

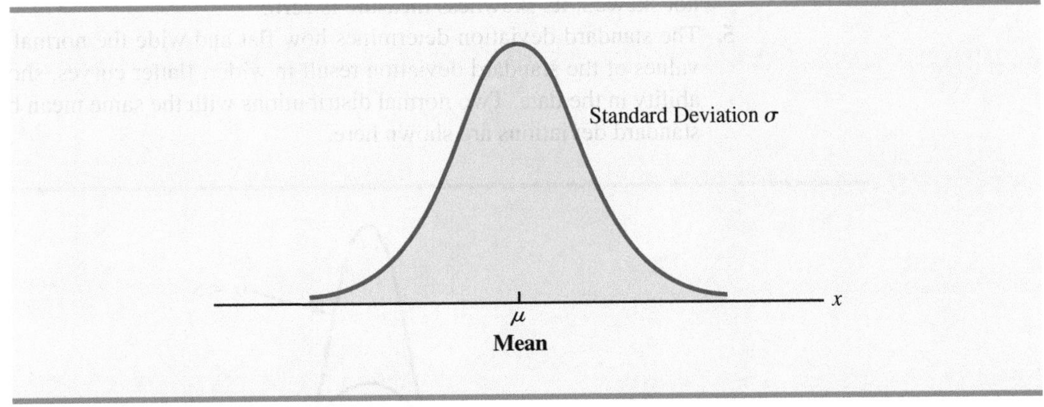

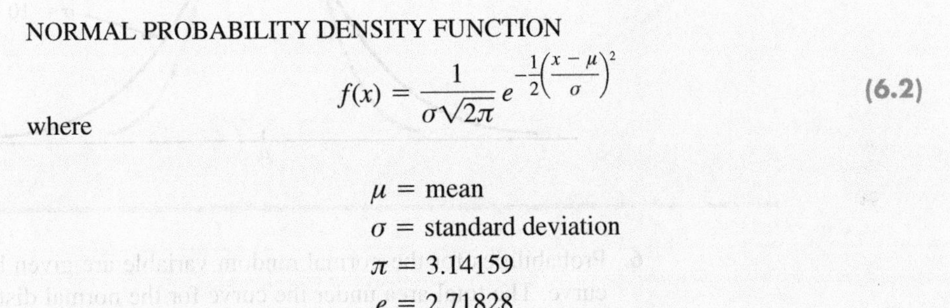

NORMAL PROBABILITY DENSITY FUNCTION

$$f(x) = \frac{1}{\sigma\sqrt{2\pi}} e^{-\frac{1}{2}\left(\frac{x-\mu}{\sigma}\right)^2} \tag{6.2}$$

where

μ = mean
σ = standard deviation
π = 3.14159
e = 2.71828

We make several observations about the characteristics of the normal distribution.

The normal curve has two parameters, μ and σ. They determine the location and shape of the normal distribution.

1. The entire family of normal distributions is differentiated by two parameters: the mean μ and the standard deviation σ.
2. The highest point on the normal curve is at the mean, which is also the median and mode of the distribution.
3. The mean of the distribution can be any numerical value: negative, zero, or positive. Three normal distributions with the same standard deviation but three different means (−10, 0, and 20) are shown here.

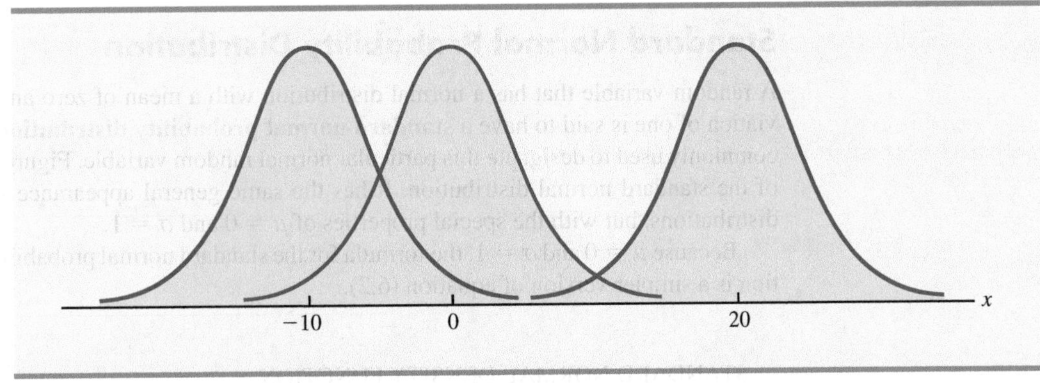

4. The normal distribution is symmetric, with the shape of the normal curve to the left of the mean a mirror image of the shape of the normal curve to the right of the mean. The tails of the normal curve extend to infinity in both directions and theoretically

never touch the horizontal axis. Because it is symmetric, the normal distribution is not skewed; its skewness measure is zero.

5. The standard deviation determines how flat and wide the normal curve is. Larger values of the standard deviation result in wider, flatter curves, showing more variability in the data. Two normal distributions with the same mean but with different standard deviations are shown here.

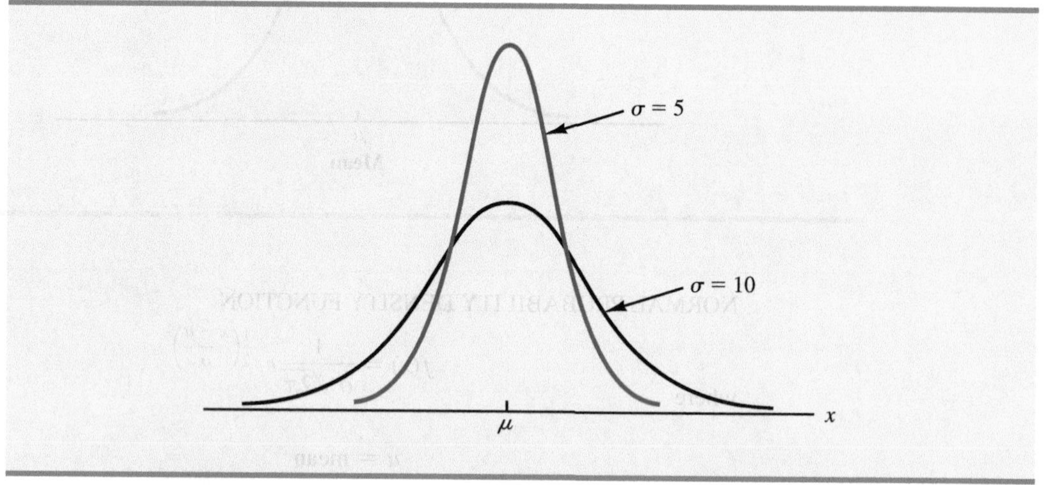

6. Probabilities for the normal random variable are given by areas under the normal curve. The total area under the curve for the normal distribution is 1. Because the distribution is symmetric, the area under the curve to the left of the mean is .50 and the area under the curve to the right of the mean is .50.
7. The percentages of values in some commonly used intervals are
   a. 68.3% of the values of a normal random variable are within plus or minus one standard deviation of its mean.
   b. 95.4% of the values of a normal random variable are within plus or minus two standard deviations of its mean.
   c. 99.7% of the values of a normal random variable are within plus or minus three standard deviations of its mean.

These percentages are the basis for the empirical rule introduced in Section 3.3.

Figure 6.4 shows properties (a), (b), and (c) graphically.

Standard Normal Probability Distribution

A random variable that has a normal distribution with a mean of zero and a standard deviation of one is said to have a **standard normal probability distribution**. The letter z is commonly used to designate this particular normal random variable. Figure 6.5 is the graph of the standard normal distribution. It has the same general appearance as other normal distributions, but with the special properties of $\mu = 0$ and $\sigma = 1$.

Because $\mu = 0$ and $\sigma = 1$, the formula for the standard normal probability density function is a simpler version of equation (6.2).

STANDARD NORMAL DENSITY FUNCTION

$$f(z) = \frac{1}{\sqrt{2\pi}} e^{-z^2/2}$$

FIGURE 6.4 AREAS UNDER THE CURVE FOR ANY NORMAL DISTRIBUTION

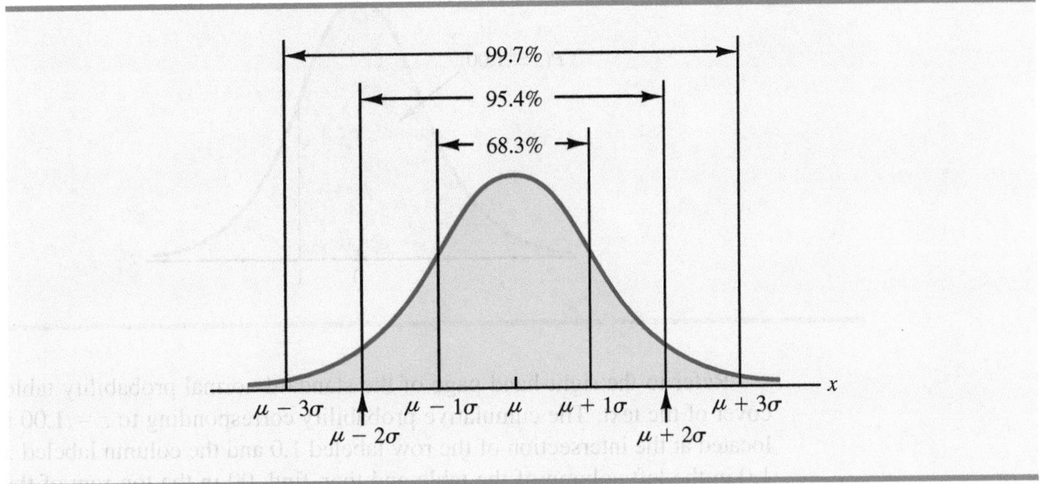

FIGURE 6.5 THE STANDARD NORMAL DISTRIBUTION

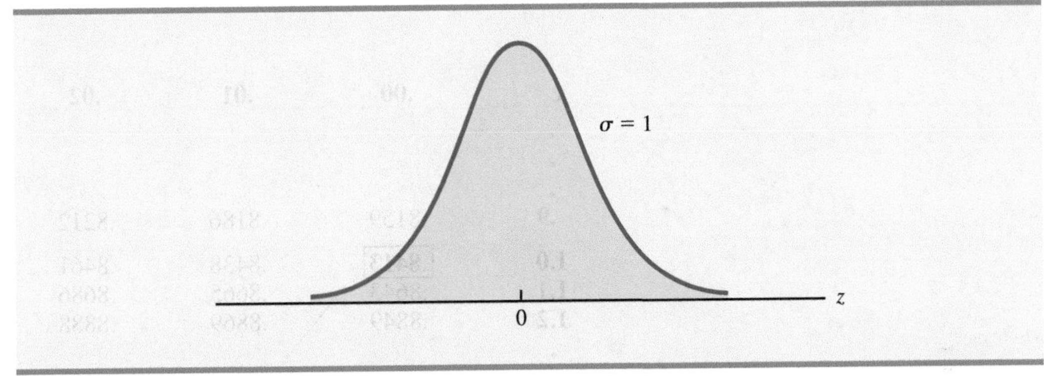

As with other continuous random variables, probability calculations with any normal distribution are made by computing areas under the graph of the probability density function. Thus, to find the probability that a normal random variable is within any specific interval, we must compute the area under the normal curve over that interval.

For the normal probability density function, the height of the normal curve varies and more advanced mathematics is required to compute the areas that represent probability.

For the standard normal distribution, areas under the normal curve have been computed and are available in tables that can be used to compute probabilities. Such a table appears on the two pages inside the front cover of the text. The table on the left-hand page contains areas, or cumulative probabilities, for z values less than or equal to the mean of zero. The table on the right-hand page contains areas, or cumulative probabilities, for z values greater than or equal to the mean of zero.

The three types of probabilities we need to compute include (1) the probability that the standard normal random variable z will be less than or equal to a given value; (2) the probability that z will be between two given values; and (3) the probability that z will be greater than or equal to a given value. To see how the cumulative probability table for the standard normal distribution can be used to compute these three types of probabilities, let us consider some examples.

Because the standard normal random variable is continuous, $P(z \leq 1.00) = P(z < 1.00)$.

We start by showing how to compute the probability that z is less than or equal to 1.00; that is, $P(z \leq 1.00)$. This cumulative probability is the area under the normal curve to the left of $z = 1.00$ in the following graph.

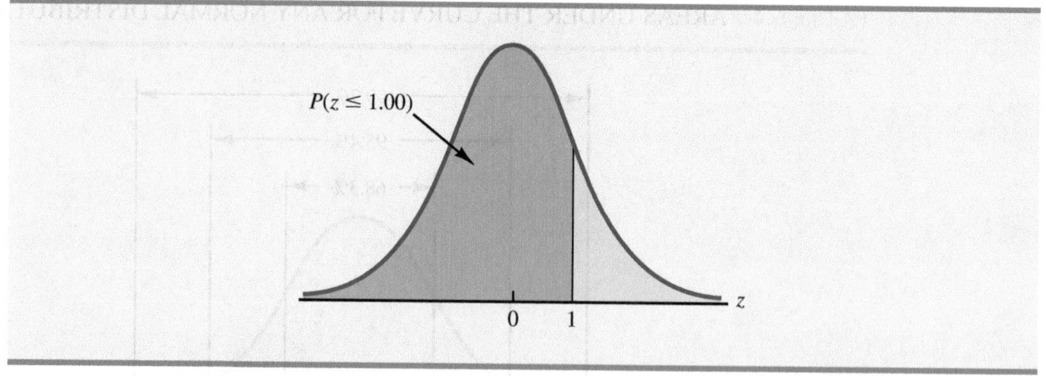

Refer to the right-hand page of the standard normal probability table inside the front cover of the text. The cumulative probability corresponding to $z = 1.00$ is the table value located at the intersection of the row labeled 1.0 and the column labeled .00. First we find 1.0 in the left column of the table and then find .00 in the top row of the table. By looking in the body of the table, we find that the 1.0 row and the .00 column intersect at the value of .8413; thus, $P(z \leq 1.00) = .8413$. The following excerpt from the probability table shows these steps.

z	**.00**	**.01**	**.02**
•			
•			
•			
.9	.8159	.8186	.8212
1.0	**.8413**	.8438	.8461
1.1	.8643	.8665	.8686
1.2	.8849	.8869	.8888
•			
•			
•			

$P(z \leq 1.00)$

To illustrate the second type of probability calculation, we show how to compute the probability that z is in the interval between $-.50$ and 1.25; that is, $P(-.50 \leq z \leq 1.25)$. The following graph shows this area, or probability.

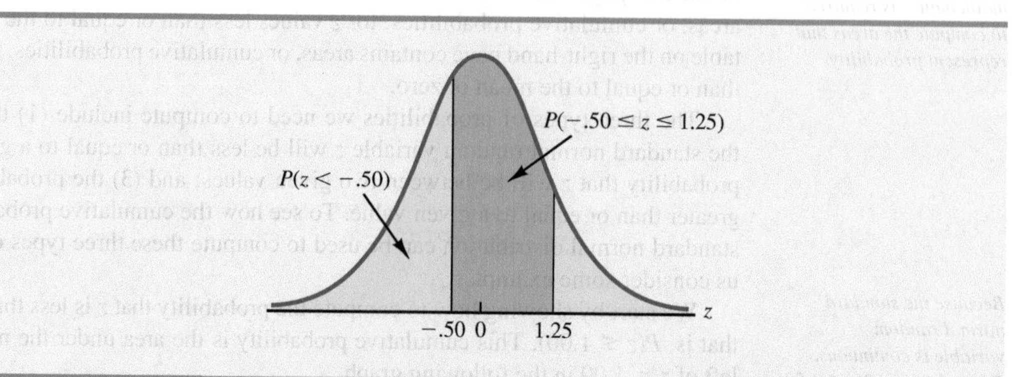

Three steps are required to compute this probability. First, we find the area under the normal curve to the left of $z = 1.25$. Second, we find the area under the normal curve to the left of $z = -.50$. Finally, we subtract the area to the left of $z = -.50$ from the area to the left of $z = 1.25$ to find $P(-.50 \le z \le 1.25)$.

To find the area under the normal curve to the left of $z = 1.25$, we first locate the 1.2 row in the standard normal probability table and then move across to the .05 column. Because the table value in the 1.2 row and the .05 column is .8944, $P(z \le 1.25) = .8944$. Similarly, to find the area under the curve to the left of $z = -.50$, we use the left-hand page of the table to locate the table value in the $-.5$ row and the .00 column; with a table value of .3085, $P(z \le -.50) = .3085$. Thus, $P(-.50 \le z \le 1.25) = P(z \le 1.25) - P(z \le -.50) = .8944 - .3085 = .5859$.

Let us consider another example of computing the probability that z is in the interval between two given values. Often it is of interest to compute the probability that a normal random variable assumes a value within a certain number of standard deviations of the mean. Suppose we want to compute the probability that the standard normal random variable is within one standard deviation of the mean; that is, $P(-1.00 \le z \le 1.00)$. To compute this probability we must find the area under the curve between -1.00 and 1.00. Earlier we found that $P(z \le 1.00) = .8413$. Referring again to the table inside the front cover of the book, we find that the area under the curve to the left of $z = -1.00$ is .1587, so $P(z \le -1.00) = .1587$. Therefore, $P(-1.00 \le z \le 1.00) = P(z \le 1.00) - P(z \le -1.00) = .8413 - .1587 = .6826$. This probability is shown graphically in the following figure.

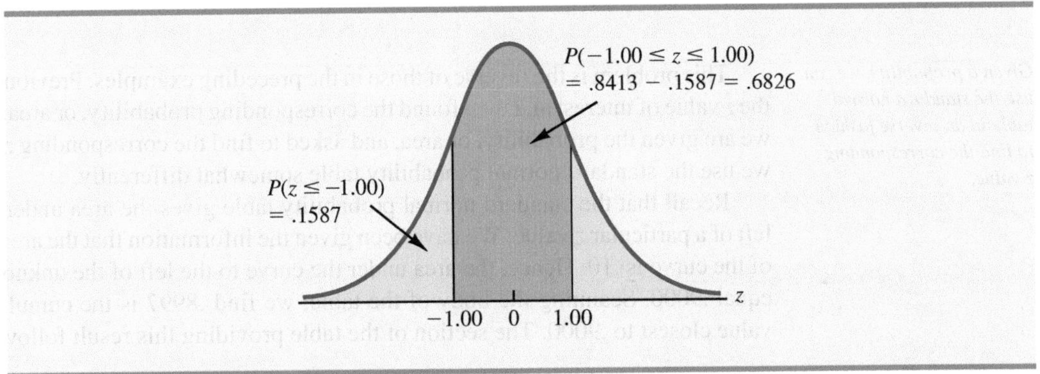

To illustrate how to make the third type of probability computation, suppose we want to compute the probability of obtaining a z value of at least 1.58; that is, $P(z \ge 1.58)$. The value in the $z = 1.5$ row and the .08 column of the cumulative normal table is .9429; thus, $P(z < 1.58) = .9429$. However, because the total area under the normal curve is 1, $P(z \ge 1.58) = 1 - .9429 = .0571$. This probability is shown in the following figure.

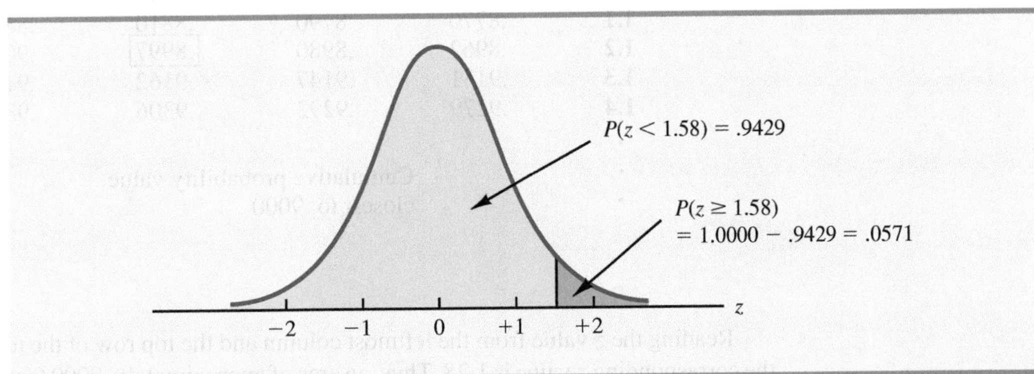

In the preceding illustrations, we showed how to compute probabilities given specified z values. In some situations, we are given a probability and are interested in working backward to find the corresponding z value. Suppose we want to find a z value such that the probability of obtaining a larger z value is .10. The following figure shows this situation graphically.

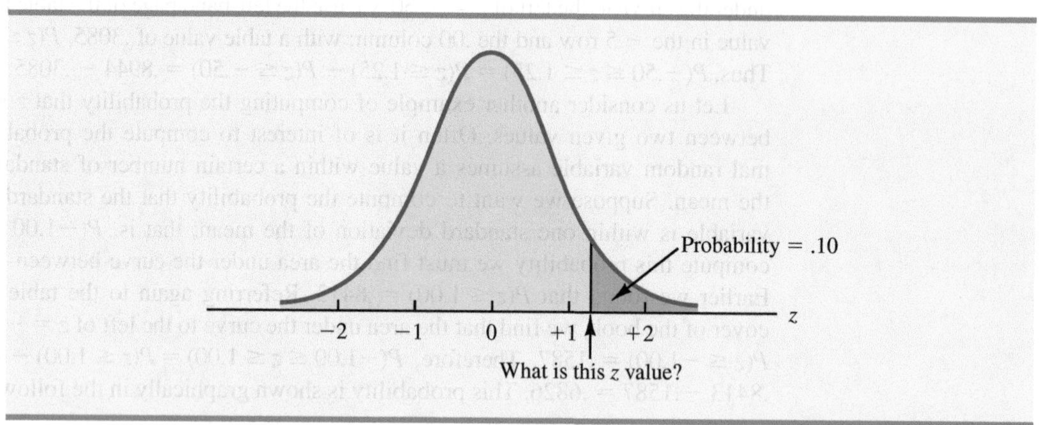

Given a probability, we can use the standard normal table in an inverse fashion to find the corresponding z value.

This problem is the inverse of those in the preceding examples. Previously, we specified the z value of interest and then found the corresponding probability, or area. In this example, we are given the probability, or area, and asked to find the corresponding z value. To do so, we use the standard normal probability table somewhat differently.

Recall that the standard normal probability table gives the area under the curve to the left of a particular z value. We have been given the information that the area in the upper tail of the curve is .10. Hence, the area under the curve to the left of the unknown z value must equal .9000. Scanning the body of the table, we find .8997 is the cumulative probability value closest to .9000. The section of the table providing this result follows.

z	.06	.07	.08	.09
•				
•				
•				
1.0	.8554	.8577	.8599	.8621
1.1	.8770	.8790	.8810	.8830
1.2	.8962	.8980	[.8997]	.9015
1.3	.9131	.9147	.9162	.9177
1.4	.9279	.9292	.9306	.9319
•				
•				
•				

Cumulative probability value closest to .9000

Reading the z value from the leftmost column and the top row of the table, we find that the corresponding z value is 1.28. Thus, an area of approximately .9000 (actually .8997) will be to the left of $z = 1.28$.[2] In terms of the question originally asked, there is an approximately .10 probability of a z value larger than 1.28.

The examples illustrate that the table of cumulative probabilities for the standard normal probability distribution can be used to find probabilities associated with values of the standard normal random variable z. Two types of questions can be asked. The first type of question specifies a value, or values, for z and asks us to use the table to determine the corresponding areas or probabilities. The second type of question provides an area, or probability, and asks us to use the table to determine the corresponding z value. Thus, we need to be flexible in using the standard normal probability table to answer the desired probability question. In most cases, sketching a graph of the standard normal probability distribution and shading the appropriate area will help to visualize the situation and aid in determining the correct answer.

Computing Probabilities for Any Normal Probability Distribution

The reason for discussing the standard normal distribution so extensively is that probabilities for all normal distributions are computed by using the standard normal distribution. That is, when we have a normal distribution with any mean μ and any standard deviation σ, we answer probability questions about the distribution by first converting to the standard normal distribution. Then we can use the standard normal probability table and the appropriate z values to find the desired probabilities. The formula used to convert any normal random variable x with mean μ and standard deviation σ to the standard normal random variable z follows.

The formula for the standard normal random variable is similar to the formula we introduced in Chapter 3 for computing z-scores for a data set.

CONVERTING TO THE STANDARD NORMAL RANDOM VARIABLE

$$z = \frac{x - \mu}{\sigma} \tag{6.3}$$

A value of x equal to its mean μ results in $z = (\mu - \mu)/\sigma = 0$. Thus, we see that a value of x equal to its mean μ corresponds to $z = 0$. Now suppose that x is one standard deviation above its mean; that is, $x = \mu + \sigma$. Applying equation (6.3), we see that the corresponding z value is $z = [(\mu + \sigma) - \mu]/\sigma = \sigma/\sigma = 1$. Thus, an x value that is one standard deviation above its mean corresponds to $z = 1$. In other words, *we can interpret z as the number of standard deviations that the normal random variable x is from its mean μ.*

To see how this conversion enables us to compute probabilities for any normal distribution, suppose we have a normal distribution with $\mu = 10$ and $\sigma = 2$. What is the probability that the random variable x is between 10 and 14? Using equation (6.3), we see that at $x = 10$, $z = (x - \mu)/\sigma = (10 - 10)/2 = 0$ and that at $x = 14$, $z = (14 - 10)/2 = 4/2 = 2$. Thus, the answer to our question about the probability of x being between 10 and 14 is given by the equivalent probability that z is between 0 and 2 for the standard normal distribution. In other words, the probability that we are seeking is the probability that the random variable x is between its mean and two standard deviations above the mean. Using $z = 2.00$ and the standard normal probability table inside the front cover of the text, we see that $P(z \le 2) = .9772$.

[2]We could use interpolation in the body of the table to get a better approximation of the z value that corresponds to an area of .9000. Doing so to provide one more decimal place of accuracy would yield a z value of 1.282. However, in most practical situations, sufficient accuracy is obtained by simply using the table value closest to the desired probability.

Because $P(z \leq 0) = .5000$, we can compute $P(.00 \leq z \leq 2.00) = P(z \leq 2) - P(z \leq 0) = .9772 - .5000 = .4772$. Hence the probability that x is between 10 and 14 is .4772.

Grear Tire Company Problem

We turn now to an application of the normal probability distribution. Suppose the Grear Tire Company developed a new steel-belted radial tire to be sold through a national chain of discount stores. Because the tire is a new product, Grear's managers believe that the mileage guarantee offered with the tire will be an important factor in the acceptance of the product. Before finalizing the tire mileage guarantee policy, Grear's managers want probability information about x = number of miles the tires will last.

From actual road tests with the tires, Grear's engineering group estimated that the mean tire mileage is $\mu = 36{,}500$ miles and that the standard deviation is $\sigma = 5000$. In addition, the data collected indicate that a normal distribution is a reasonable assumption. What percentage of the tires can be expected to last more than 40,000 miles? In other words, what is the probability that the tire mileage, x, will exceed 40,000? This question can be answered by finding the area of the darkly shaded region in Figure 6.6.

At $x = 40{,}000$, we have

$$z = \frac{x - \mu}{\sigma} = \frac{40{,}000 - 36{,}500}{5000} = \frac{3500}{5000} = .70$$

Refer now to the bottom of Figure 6.6. We see that a value of $x = 40{,}000$ on the Grear Tire normal distribution corresponds to a value of $z = .70$ on the standard normal distribution. Using the standard normal probability table, we see that the area under the standard normal curve to the left of $z = .70$ is .7580. Thus, $1.000 - .7580 = .2420$ is the probability that z will exceed .70 and hence x will exceed 40,000. We can conclude that about 24.2% of the tires will exceed 40,000 in mileage.

Let us now assume that Grear is considering a guarantee that will provide a discount on replacement tires if the original tires do not provide the guaranteed mileage. What should

FIGURE 6.6 GREAR TIRE COMPANY MILEAGE DISTRIBUTION

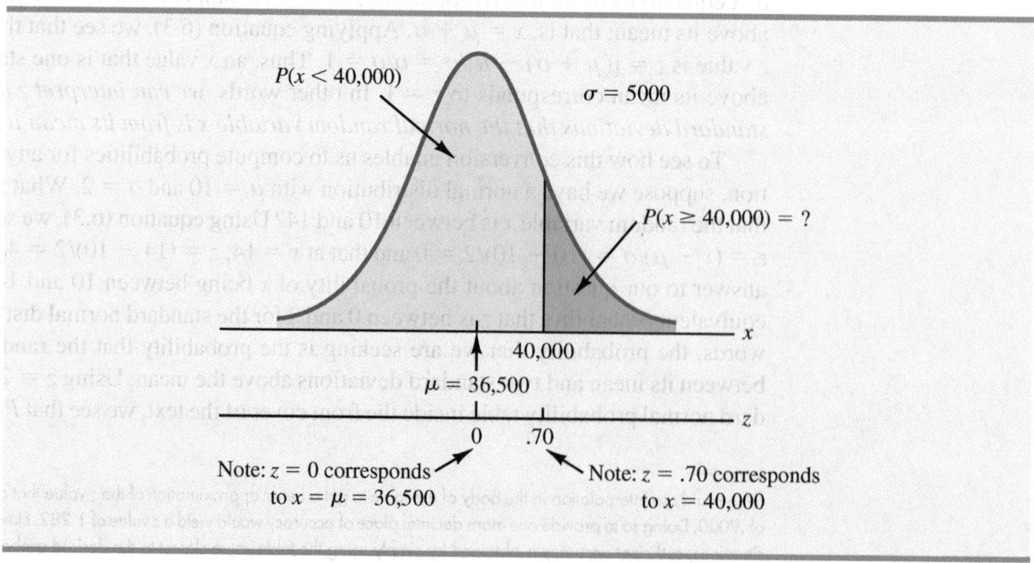

FIGURE 6.7 GREAR'S DISCOUNT GUARANTEE

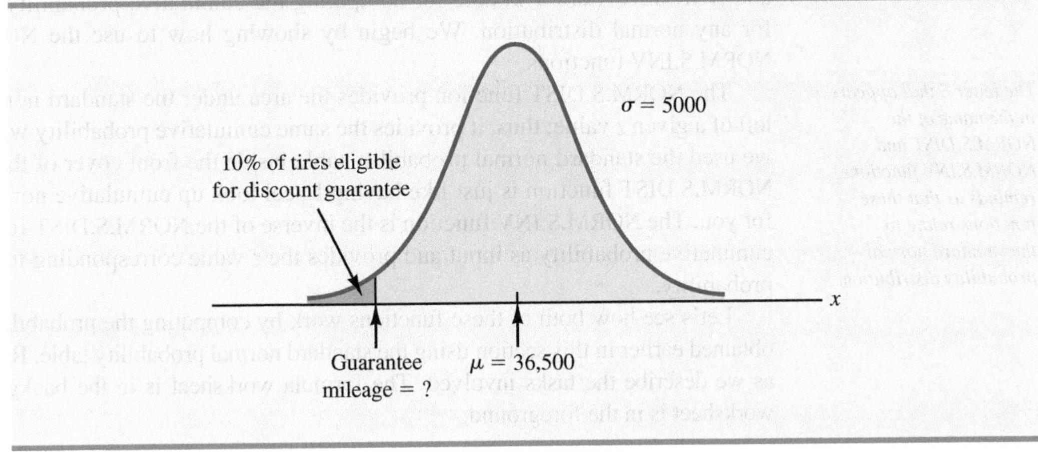

the guarantee mileage be if Grear wants no more than 10% of the tires to be eligible for the discount guarantee? This question is interpreted graphically in Figure 6.7.

According to Figure 6.7, the area under the curve to the left of the unknown guarantee mileage must be .10. So, we must first find the z value that cuts off an area of .10 in the left tail of a standard normal distribution. Using the standard normal probability table, we see that $z = -1.28$ cuts off an area of .10 in the lower tail. Hence, $z = -1.28$ is the value of the standard normal random variable corresponding to the desired mileage guarantee on the Grear Tire normal distribution. To find the value of x corresponding to $z = -1.28$, we have

The guarantee mileage we need to find is 1.28 standard deviations below the mean. Thus, $x = \mu - 1.28\sigma$.

$$z = \frac{x - \mu}{\sigma} = -1.28$$

$$x - \mu = -1.28\sigma$$

$$x = \mu - 1.28\sigma$$

With $\mu = 36{,}500$ and $\sigma = 5000$,

$$x = 36{,}500 - 1.28(5000) = 30{,}100$$

With the guarantee set at 30,000 miles, the actual percentage eligible for the guarantee will be 9.68%.

Thus, a guarantee of 30,100 miles will meet the requirement that approximately 10% of the tires will be eligible for the guarantee. Perhaps, with this information, the firm will set its tire mileage guarantee at 30,000 miles.

Again, we see the important role that probability distributions play in providing decision-making information. Namely, once a probability distribution is established for a particular application, it can be used to obtain probability information about the problem. Probability does not make a decision recommendation directly, but it provides information that helps the decision maker better understand the risks and uncertainties associated with the problem. Ultimately, this information may assist the decision maker in reaching a good decision.

Using Excel to Compute Normal Probabilities

Excel provides two functions for computing probabilities and z values for a standard normal probability distribution: NORM.S.DIST and NORM.S.INV. The NORM.S.DIST function computes the cumulative probability given a z value, and the NORM.S.INV function computes the z value given a cumulative probability. Two similar functions, NORM.DIST and NORM.INV, are available for computing the cumulative probability and the x value for any normal distribution. We begin by showing how to use the NORM.S.DIST and NORM.S.INV functions.

The letter S that appears in the name of the NORM.S.DIST and NORM.S.INV functions reminds us that these functions relate to the standard normal probability distribution.

The NORM.S.DIST function provides the area under the standard normal curve to the left of a given z value; thus, it provides the same cumulative probability we would obtain if we used the standard normal probability table inside the front cover of the text. Using the NORM.S.DIST function is just like having Excel look up cumulative normal probabilities for you. The NORM.S.INV function is the inverse of the NORM.S.DIST function; it takes a cumulative probability as input and provides the z value corresponding to that cumulative probability.

Let's see how both of these functions work by computing the probabilities and z values obtained earlier in this section using the standard normal probability table. Refer to Figure 6.8 as we describe the tasks involved. The formula worksheet is in the background; the value worksheet is in the foreground.

Enter/Access Data: Open a blank worksheet. No data are entered in the worksheet. We will simply enter the appropriate z values and probabilities directly into the formulas as needed.

Enter Functions and Formulas: The NORM.S.DIST function has two inputs: the z value and a value of TRUE or FALSE. For the second input we enter TRUE if a cumulative probability is desired, and we enter FALSE if the height of the standard normal curve is desired. Because we will always be using NORM.S.DIST to compute cumulative probabilities, we always choose TRUE for the second input. To illustrate the use of the NORM.S.DIST function, we compute the four probabilities shown in cells D3:D6 of Figure 6.8.

The probabilities in cells D4, 0.5858, and D5, 0.6827, differ from what we computed earlier due to rounding.

To compute the cumulative probability to the left of a given z value (area in lower tail), we simply evaluate NORM.S.DIST at the z value. For instance, to compute $P(z \leq 1)$ we entered the formula =NORM.S.DIST(1,TRUE) into cell D3. The result, .8413, is the same as obtained using the standard normal probability table.

To compute the probability of z being in an interval we compute the value of NORM.S.DIST at the upper endpoint of the interval and subtract the value of NORM.S.DIST

FIGURE 6.8 EXCEL WORKSHEET FOR COMPUTING PROBABILITIES AND z VALUES FOR THE STANDARD NORMAL DISTRIBUTION

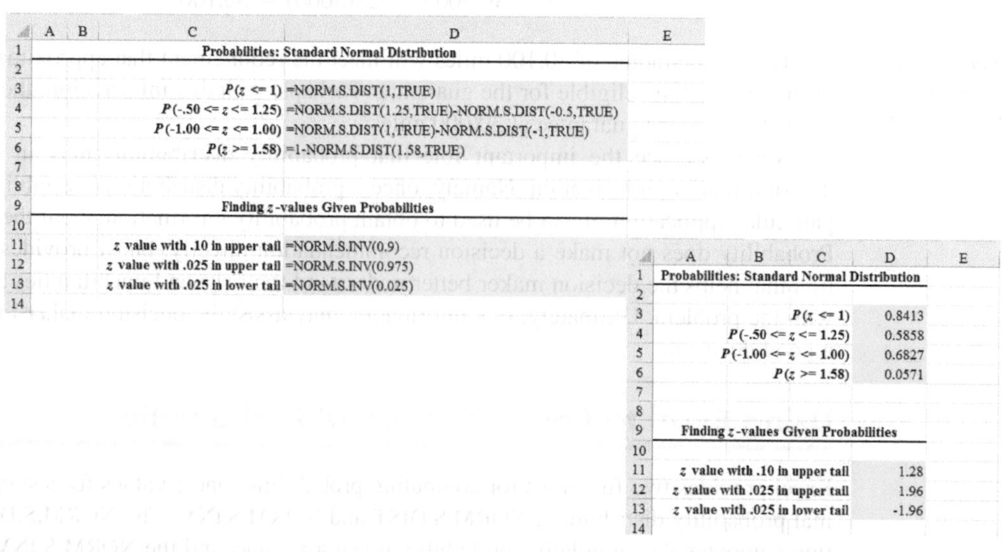

at the lower endpoint of the interval. For instance, to find $P(-.50 \le z \le 1.25)$, we entered the formula =NORM.S.DIST(1.25,TRUE)-NORM.S.DIST(-.50,TRUE) into cell D4. The interval probability in cell D5 is computed in a similar fashion.

To compute the probability to the right of a given z value (upper tail area), we must subtract the cumulative probability represented by the area under the curve below the z value (lower tail area) from 1. For example, to compute $P(z \ge 1.58)$ we entered the formula =1-NORM.S.DIST(1.58,TRUE) into cell D6.

To compute the z value for a given cumulative probability (lower tail area), we use the NORM.S.INV function. To find the z value corresponding to an upper tail probability of .10, we note that the corresponding lower tail area is .90 and enter the formula =NORM.S.INV(0.9) into cell D11. Actually, NORM.S.INV(0.9) gives us the z value providing a cumulative probability (lower tail area) of .9. But it is also the z value associated with an upper tail area of .10.

Two other z values are computed in Figure 6.8. These z values will be used extensively in succeeding chapters. To compute the z value corresponding to an upper tail probability of .025, we entered the formula =NORM.S.INV(0.975) into cell D12. To compute the z value corresponding to a lower tail probability of .025, we entered the formula =NORM.S.INV(0.025) into cell D13. We see that $z = 1.96$ corresponds to an upper tail probability of .025, and $z = -1.96$ corresponds to a lower tail probability of .025.

Let us now turn to the Excel functions for computing cumulative probabilities and x values for any normal distribution. The NORM.DIST function provides the area under the normal curve to the left of a given value of the random variable x; thus it provides cumulative probabilities. The NORM.INV function is the inverse of the NORM.DIST function; it takes a cumulative probability as input and provides the value of x corresponding to that cumulative probability. The NORM.DIST and NORM.INV functions do the same thing for any normal distribution that the NORM.S.DIST and NORM.S.INV functions do for the standard normal distribution.

Let's see how both of these functions work by computing probabilities and x values for the Grear Tire Company example introduced earlier in this section. Recall that the lifetime of a Grear tire has a mean of 36,500 miles and a standard deviation of 5000 miles. Refer to Figure 6.9 as we describe the tasks involved. The formula worksheet is in the background; the value worksheet is in the foreground.

FIGURE 6.9 EXCEL WORKSHEET FOR COMPUTING PROBABILITIES AND x VALUES FOR THE NORMAL DISTRIBUTION

	A	B	C	D	E
1				**Probabilities: Normal Distribution**	
2					
3			**P(x <= 20000)**	=NORM.DIST(20000,36500,5000,TRUE)	
4			**P(20000 <= x <= 40000)**	=NORMDIST(40000,36500,5000,TRUE)-NORM.DIST(20000,36500,5000,TRUE)	
5			**P(x >= 40000)**	=1-NORM.DIST(40000,36500,5000,TRUE)	
6					
7				**Finding x values Given Probabilities**	
8					
9			**x value with .10 in lower tail**	=NORM.INV(0.1,36500,5000)	
10			**x value with .025 in upper tail**	=NORM.INV(0.975,36500,5000)	
11					

	A	B	C	D	E
1		**Probabilities: Normal Distribution**			
2					
3			**P(x <= 20000)**	0.0005	
4			**P(20000 <= x <= 40000)**	0.7576	
5			**P(x >= 40000)**	0.2420	
6					
7		**Finding x values Given Probabilities**			
8					
9			**x value with .10 in lower tail**	30092.24	
10			**x value with .025 in upper tail**	46299.82	
11					

Enter/Access Data: Open a blank worksheet. No data are entered in the worksheet. We simply enter the appropriate x values and probabilities directly into the formulas as needed.

Enter Functions and Formulas: The NORM.DIST function has four inputs: (1) the x value we want to compute the cumulative probability for, (2) the mean, (3) the standard deviation, and (4) a value of TRUE or FALSE. For the fourth input, we enter TRUE if a cumulative probability is desired, and we enter FALSE if the height of the curve is desired. Because we will always be using NORM.DIST to compute cumulative probabilities, we will always choose TRUE for the fourth input.

To compute the cumulative probability to the left of a given x value (lower tail area), we simply evaluate NORM.DIST at the x value. For instance, to compute the probability that a Grear tire will last 20,000 miles or less, we entered the formula =NORM.DIST(20000,36500,5000,TRUE) into cell D3. The value worksheet shows that this cumulative probability is .0005. So, we can conclude that almost all Grear tires will last at least 20,000 miles.

To compute the probability of x being in an interval, we compute the value of NORM.DIST at the upper endpoint of the interval and subtract the value of NORM.DIST at the lower endpoint of the interval. The formula in cell D4 provides the probability that a tire's lifetime is between 20,000 and 40,000 miles, $P(20{,}000 \leq x \leq 40{,}000)$. In the value worksheet, we see that this probability is .7576.

To compute the probability to the right of a given x value (upper tail area), we must subtract the cumulative probability represented by the area under the curve below the x value (lower tail area) from 1. The formula in cell D5 computes the probability that a Grear tire will last for at least 40,000 miles. We see that this probability is .2420.

To compute the x value for a given cumulative probability, we use the NORM.INV function. The NORM.INV function has only three inputs. The first input is the cumulative probability; the second and third inputs are the mean and standard deviation. For instance, to compute the tire mileage corresponding to a lower tail area of .1 for Grear Tire, we enter the formula =NORM.INV(0.1,36500,5000) into cell D9. From the value worksheet, we see that 10% of the Grear tires will last for 30,092.24 miles or less.

To compute the minimum tire mileage for the top 2.5% of Grear tires, we want to find the value of x corresponding to an area of .025 in the upper tail. This calculation is the same as finding the x value that provides a cumulative probability of .975. Thus we entered the formula =NORM.INV(0.975,36500,5000) into cell D10 to compute this tire mileage. From the value worksheet, we see that 2.5% of the Grear tires will last at least 46,299.82 miles.

Exercises

Methods

8. Using Figure 6.4 as a guide, sketch a normal curve for a random variable x that has a mean of $\mu = 100$ and a standard deviation of $\sigma = 10$. Label the horizontal axis with values of 70, 80, 90, 100, 110, 120, and 130.

9. A random variable is normally distributed with a mean of $\mu = 50$ and a standard deviation of $\sigma = 5$.
   a. Sketch a normal curve for the probability density function. Label the horizontal axis with values of 35, 40, 45, 50, 55, 60, and 65. Figure 6.4 shows that the normal curve almost touches the horizontal axis at three standard deviations below and at three standard deviations above the mean (in this case at 35 and 65).
   b. What is the probability that the random variable will assume a value between 45 and 55?

c. What is the probability that the random variable will assume a value between 40 and 60?

10. Draw a graph for the standard normal distribution. Label the horizontal axis at values of $-3, -2, -1, 0, 1, 2$, and 3. Then compute the following probabilities.
   a. $P(z \leq 1.5)$
   b. $P(z \leq 1)$
   c. $P(1 \leq z \leq 1.5)$
   d. $P(0 < z < 2.5)$

11. Given that z is a standard normal random variable, compute the following probabilities.
   a. $P(z \leq -1.0)$
   b. $P(z \geq -1)$
   c. $P(z \geq -1.5)$
   d. $P(-2.5 \leq z)$
   e. $P(-3 < z \leq 0)$

12. Given that z is a standard normal random variable, compute the following probabilities.
   a. $P(0 \leq z \leq .83)$
   b. $P(-1.57 \leq z \leq 0)$
   c. $P(z > .44)$
   d. $P(z \geq -.23)$
   e. $P(z < 1.20)$
   f. $P(z \leq -.71)$

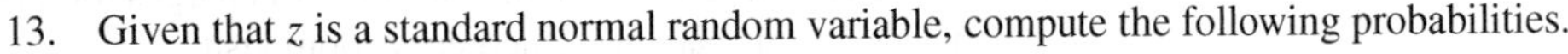

13. Given that z is a standard normal random variable, compute the following probabilities.
   a. $P(-1.98 \leq z \leq .49)$
   b. $P(.52 \leq z \leq 1.22)$
   c. $P(-1.75 \leq z \leq -1.04)$

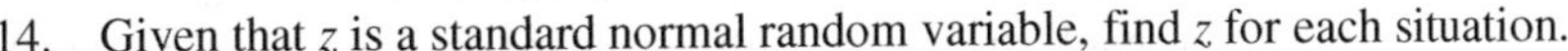

14. Given that z is a standard normal random variable, find z for each situation.
   a. The area to the left of z is .9750.
   b. The area between 0 and z is .4750.
   c. The area to the left of z is .7291.
   d. The area to the right of z is .1314.
   e. The area to the left of z is .6700.
   f. The area to the right of z is .3300.

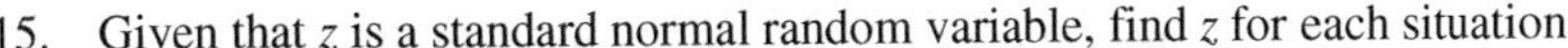

15. Given that z is a standard normal random variable, find z for each situation.
   a. The area to the left of z is .2119.
   b. The area between $-z$ and z is .9030.
   c. The area between $-z$ and z is .2052.
   d. The area to the left of z is .9948.
   e. The area to the right of z is .6915.

16. Given that z is a standard normal random variable, find z for each situation.
   a. The area to the right of z is .01.
   b. The area to the right of z is .025.
   c. The area to the right of z is .05.
   d. The area to the right of z is .10.

Applications

17. The mean cost of domestic airfares in the United States rose to an all-time high of \$385 per ticket (Bureau of Transportation Statistics website, November 2, 2012). Airfares were based on the total ticket value, which consisted of the price charged by the airlines plus any additional taxes and fees. Assume domestic airfares are normally distributed with a standard deviation of \$110.

a. What is the probability that a domestic airfare is $550 or more?
b. What is the probability that a domestic airfare is $250 or less?
c. What if the probability that a domestic airfare is between $300 and $500?
d. What is the cost for the 3% highest domestic airfares?

18. The average return for large-cap domestic stock funds over the three years 2009–2011 was 14.4% (*AAII Journal*, February, 2012). Assume the three-year returns were normally distributed across funds with a standard deviation of 4.4%.
    a. What is the probability an individual large-cap domestic stock fund had a three-year return of at least 20%?
    b. What is the probability an individual large-cap domestic stock fund had a three-year return of 10% or less?
    c. How big does the return have to be to put a domestic stock fund in the top 10% for the three-year period?
19. In an article about the cost of health care, *Money* magazine reported that a visit to a hospital emergency room for something as simple as a sore throat has a mean cost of $328 (*Money*, January 2009). Assume that the cost for this type of hospital emergency room visit is normally distributed with a standard deviation of $92. Answer the following questions about the cost of a hospital emergency room visit for this medical service.
    a. What is the probability that the cost will be more than $500?
    b. What is the probability that the cost will be less than $250?
    c. What is the probability that the cost will be between $300 and $400?
    d. If the cost to a patient is in the lower 8% of charges for this medical service, what was the cost of this patient's emergency room visit?
20. The average price for a gallon of gasoline in the United States is $3.73 and in Russia it is $3.40 (*Bloomberg Businessweek*, March 5–March 11, 2012). Assume these averages are the population means in the two countries and that the probability distributions are normally distributed with a standard deviation of $.25 in the United States and a standard deviation of $.20 in Russia.
    a. What is the probability that a randomly selected gas station in the United States charges less than $3.50 per gallon?
    b. What percentage of the gas stations in Russia charge less than $3.50 per gallon?
    c. What is the probability that a randomly selected gas station in Russia charged more than the mean price in the United States?
21. A person must score in the upper 2% of the population on an IQ test to qualify for membership in Mensa, the international high-IQ society. There are 110,000 Mensa members in 100 countries throughout the world (Mensa International website, January 8, 2013). If IQ scores are normally distributed with a mean of 100 and a standard deviation of 15, what score must a person have to qualify for Mensa?
22. Television viewing reached a new high when the Nielsen Company reported a mean daily viewing time of 8.35 hours per household (*USA Today*, November 11, 2009). Use a normal probability distribution with a standard deviation of 2.5 hours to answer the following questions about daily television viewing per household.
    a. What is the probability that a household views television between 5 and 10 hours a day?
    b. How many hours of television viewing must a household have in order to be in the top 3% of all television viewing households?
    c. What is the probability that a household views television more than 3 hours a day?
23. The time needed to complete a final examination in a particular college course is normally distributed with a mean of 80 minutes and a standard deviation of 10 minutes. Answer the following questions.
    a. What is the probability of completing the exam in one hour or less?
    b. What is the probability that a student will complete the exam in more than 60 minutes but less than 75 minutes?

c. Assume that the class has 60 students and that the examination period is 90 minutes in length. How many students do you expect will be unable to complete the exam in the allotted time?

24. The American Automobile Association (AAA) reported that families planning to travel over the Labor Day weekend would spend an average of \$749 (The Associated Press, August 12, 2012). Assume that the amount spent is normally distributed with a standard deviation of \$225.
    a. What the probability of family expenses for the weekend being less that \$400?
    b. What is the probability of family expenses for the weekend being \$800 or more?
    c. What is the probability that family expenses for the weekend will be between \$500 and \$1000?
    d. What would the Labor Day weekend expenses have to be for the 5% of the families with the most expensive travel plans?

25. New York City is the most expensive city in the United States for lodging. The mean hotel room rate is \$204 per night (*USA Today*, April 30, 2012). Assume that room rates are normally distributed with a standard deviation of \$55.
    a. What is the probability that a hotel room costs \$225 or more per night?
    b. What is the probability that a hotel room costs less than \$140 per night?
    c. What is the probability that a hotel room costs between \$200 and \$300 per night?
    d. What is the cost of the 20% most expensive hotel rooms in New York City?

Exponential Probability Distribution

The **exponential probability distribution** may be used for random variables such as the time between arrivals at a car wash, the time required to load a truck, the distance between major defects in a highway, and so on. The exponential probability density function follows.

EXPONENTIAL PROBABILITY DENSITY FUNCTION

$$f(x) = \frac{1}{\mu} e^{-x/\mu} \quad \text{for } x \geq 0 \tag{6.4}$$

where

μ = expected value or mean
e = 2.71828

As an example of the exponential distribution, suppose that x represents the loading time for a truck at the Schips loading dock and follows such a distribution. If the mean, or average, loading time is 15 minutes ($\mu = 15$), the appropriate probability density function for x is

$$f(x) = \frac{1}{15} e^{-x/15}$$

Figure 6.10 is the graph of this probability density function.

FIGURE 6.10 EXPONENTIAL DISTRIBUTION FOR THE SCHIPS LOADING DOCK EXAMPLE

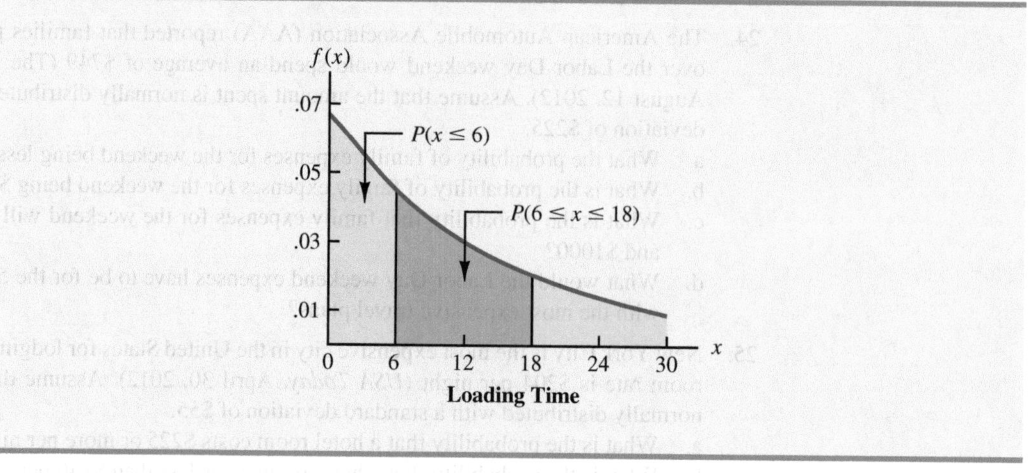

Computing Probabilities for the Exponential Distribution

In waiting line applications, the exponential distribution is often used for service time.

As with any continuous probability distribution, the area under the curve corresponding to an interval provides the probability that the random variable assumes a value in that interval. In the Schips loading dock example, the probability that loading a truck will take 6 minutes or less $P(x \leq 6)$ is defined to be the area under the curve in Figure 6.10 from $x = 0$ to $x = 6$. Similarly, the probability that the loading time will be 18 minutes or less $P(x \leq 18)$ is the area under the curve from $x = 0$ to $x = 18$. Note also that the probability that the loading time will be between 6 minutes and 18 minutes $P(6 \leq x \leq 18)$ is given by the area under the curve from $x = 6$ to $x = 18$.

To compute exponential probabilities such as those just described, we use the following formula. It provides the cumulative probability of obtaining a value for the exponential random variable of less than or equal to some specific value denoted by x_0.

EXPONENTIAL DISTRIBUTION: CUMULATIVE PROBABILITIES

$$P(x \leq x_0) = 1 - e^{-x_0/\mu} \tag{6.5}$$

For the Schips loading dock example, x = loading time in minutes and $\mu = 15$ minutes. Using equation (6.5),

$$P(x \leq x_0) = 1 - e^{-x_0/15}$$

Hence, the probability that loading a truck will take 6 minutes or less is

$$P(x \leq 6) = 1 - e^{-6/15} = .3297$$

Using equation (6.5), we calculate the probability of loading a truck in 18 minutes or less.

$$P(x \leq 18) = 1 - e^{-18/15} = .6988$$

Thus, the probability that loading a truck will take between 6 minutes and 18 minutes is equal to .6988 − .3297 = .3691. Probabilities for any other interval can be computed similarly.

A property of the exponential distribution is that the mean and standard deviation are equal.

In the preceding example, the mean time it takes to load a truck is $\mu = 15$ minutes. A property of the exponential distribution is that the mean of the distribution and the standard deviation of the distribution are *equal.* Thus, the standard deviation for the time it takes to load a truck is $\sigma = 15$ minutes. The variance is $\sigma^2 = (15)^2 = 225$.

Relationship Between the Poisson and Exponential Distributions

In Section 5.5 we introduced the Poisson distribution as a discrete probability distribution that is often useful in examining the number of occurrences of an event over a specified interval of time or space. Recall that the Poisson probability function is

$$f(x) = \frac{\mu^x e^{-\mu}}{x!}$$

where

μ = expected value or mean number of occurrences over a specified interval

If arrivals follow a Poisson distribution, the time between arrivals must follow an exponential distribution.

The continuous exponential probability distribution is related to the discrete Poisson distribution. If the Poisson distribution provides an appropriate description of the number of occurrences per interval, the exponential distribution provides a description of the length of the interval between occurrences.

To illustrate this relationship, suppose the number of cars that arrive at a car wash during one hour is described by a Poisson probability distribution with a mean of 10 cars per hour. The Poisson probability function that gives the probability of x arrivals per hour is

$$f(x) = \frac{10^x e^{-10}}{x!}$$

Because the average number of arrivals is 10 cars per hour, the average time between cars arriving is

$$\frac{1 \text{ hour}}{10 \text{ cars}} = .1 \text{ hour/car}$$

Thus, the corresponding exponential distribution that describes the time between the arrivals has a mean of $\mu = .1$ hour per car; as a result, the appropriate exponential probability density function is

$$f(x) = \frac{1}{.1}e^{-x/.1} = 10e^{-10x}$$

Using Excel to Compute Exponential Probabilities

Excel's EXPON.DIST function can be used to compute exponential probabilities. We will illustrate by computing probabilities associated with the time it takes to load a truck at the Schips loading dock. This example was introduced at the beginning of the section. Refer to

FIGURE 6.11 EXCEL WORKSHEET FOR COMPUTING PROBABILITIES FOR THE EXPONENTIAL PROBABILITY DISTRIBUTION

	A	B	C	D	E
1			Probabilities: Exponential Distribution		
2					
3			P(x <= 18)	=EXPON.DIST(18,1/15,TRUE)	
4			P(6 <= x <= 18)	=EXPON.DIST(18,1/15,TRUE)-EXPON.DIST(6,1/15,TRUE)	
5			P(x >= 8)	=1-EXPON.DIST(8,1/15,TRUE)	
6					

	A	B	C	D	E
1	Probabilities: Exponential Distribution				
2					
3			P(x <= 18)	0.6988	
4			P(6 <= x <= 18)	0.3691	
5			P(x >= 8)	0.5866	
6					

Figure 6.11 as we describe the tasks involved. The formula worksheet is in the background; the value worksheet is in the foreground.

Enter/Access Data: Open a blank worksheet. No data are entered in the worksheet. We simply enter the appropriate values for the exponential random variable into the formulas as needed. The random variable is $x =$ loading time.

Enter Functions and Formulas: The EXPON.DIST function has three inputs: The first is the value of x, the second is $1/\mu$, and the third is TRUE or FALSE. We choose TRUE for the third input if a cumulative probability is desired and FALSE if the height of the probability density function is desired. We will always use TRUE because we will be computing cumulative probabilities.

The first probability we compute is the probability that the loading time is 18 minutes or less. For the Schips problem, $1/\mu = 1/15$, so we enter the formula =EXPON.DIST(18,1/15,TRUE) into cell D3 to compute the desired cumulative probability. From the value worksheet, we see that the probability of loading a truck in 18 minutes or less is .6988.

The second probability we compute is the probability that the loading time is between 6 and 18 minutes. To find this probability we first compute the cumulative probability for the upper endpoint of the time interval and subtract the cumulative probability for the lower endpoint of the interval. The formula we have entered into cell D4 calculates this probability. The value worksheet shows that this probability is .3691.

The last probability we calculate is the probability that the loading time is at least 8 minutes. Because the EXPON.DIST function computes only cumulative (lower tail) probabilities, we compute this probability by entering the formula =1-EXPON.DIST(8,1/15,TRUE) into cell D5. The value worksheet shows that the probability of a loading time of 8 minutes or more is .5866.

NOTE AND COMMENT

As we can see in Figure 6.10, the exponential distribution is skewed to the right. Indeed, the skewness measure for the exponential distributions is 2. The exponential distribution gives us a good idea what a skewed distribution looks like.

Exercises

Methods

26. Consider the following exponential probability density function.

$$f(x) = \frac{1}{8} e^{-x/8} \qquad \text{for } x \geq 0$$

   a. Find $P(x \leq 6)$.
   b. Find $P(x \leq 4)$.
   c. Find $P(x \geq 6)$.
   d. Find $P(4 \leq x \leq 6)$.

27. Consider the following exponential probability density function.

$$f(x) = \frac{1}{3} e^{-x/3} \qquad \text{for } x \geq 0$$

   a. Write the formula for $P(x \leq x_0)$.
   b. Find $P(x \leq 2)$.
   c. Find $P(x \geq 3)$.
   d. Find $P(x \leq 5)$.
   e. Find $P(2 \leq x \leq 5)$.

Applications

28. Battery life between charges for the Motorola Droid Razr Maxx is 20 hours when the primary use is talk time (*The Wall Street Journal*, March 7, 2012). The battery life drops to 7 hours when the phone is primarily used for Internet applications over cellular. Assume that the battery life in both cases follows an exponential distribution.
   a. Show the probability density function for battery life for the Droid Razr Maxx phone when its primary use is talk time.
   b. What is the probability that the battery charge for a randomly selected Droid Razr Maxx phone will last no more than 15 hours when its primary use is talk time?
   c. What is the probability that the battery charge for a randomly selected Droid Razr Maxx phone will last more than 20 hours when its primary use is talk time?
   d. What is the probability that the battery charge for a randomly selected Droid Razr Maxx phone will last no more than 5 hours when its primary use is Internet applications?

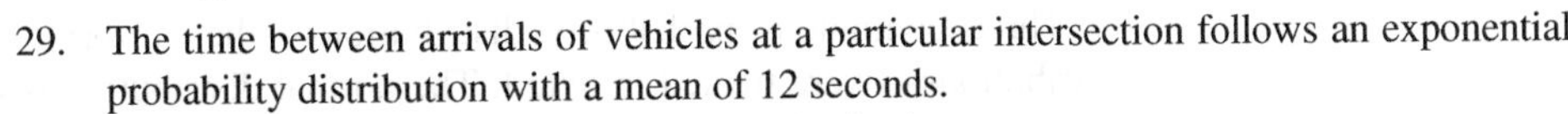

29. The time between arrivals of vehicles at a particular intersection follows an exponential probability distribution with a mean of 12 seconds.
   a. Sketch this exponential probability distribution.
   b. What is the probability that the arrival time between vehicles is 12 seconds or less?
   c. What is the probability that the arrival time between vehicles is 6 seconds or less?
   d. What is the probability of 30 or more seconds between vehicle arrivals?

30. Comcast Corporation is the largest cable television company, the second largest Internet service provider, and the fourth largest telephone service provider in the United States. Generally known for quality and reliable service, the company periodically experiences unexpected service interruptions. On January 14, 2014, such an interruption occurred for the Comcast customers living in southwest Florida. When customers called the Comcast office, a recorded message told them that the company was aware of the service outage and that it was anticipated that service would be restored in two hours. Assume that two hours is the mean time to do the repair and that the repair time has an exponential probability distribution.

a. What is the probability that the cable service will be repaired in one hour or less?
b. What is the probability that the repair will take between one hour and two hours?
c. For a customer who calls the Comcast office at 1:00 P.M., what is the probability that the cable service will not be repaired by 5:00 P.M.?

31. Collina's Italian Café in Houston, Texas, advertises that carryout orders take about 25 minutes (Collina's website, February 27, 2008). Assume that the time required for a carryout order to be ready for customer pickup has an exponential distribution with a mean of 25 minutes.
    a. What is the probability that a carryout order will be ready within 20 minutes?
    b. If a customer arrives 30 minutes after placing an order, what is the probability that the order will not be ready?
    c. A particular customer lives 15 minutes from Collina's Italian Café. If the customer places a telephone order at 5:20 P.M., what is the probability that the customer can drive to the café, pick up the order, and return home by 6:00 P.M.?

32. The Boston Fire Department receives 911 calls at a mean rate of 1.6 calls per hour (Mass.gov website, November 2012). Suppose the number of calls per hour follows a Poisson probability distribution.
    a. What is the mean time between 911 calls to the Boston Fire Department in minutes?
    b. Using the mean in part (a), show the probability density function for the time between 911 calls in minutes.
    c. What is the probability that there will be less than one hour between 911 calls?
    d. What is the probability that there will be 30 minutes or more between 911 calls?
    e. What is the probability that there will be more than 5 minutes, but less than 20 minutes between 911 calls?

Summary

This chapter extended the discussion of probability distributions to the case of continuous random variables. The major conceptual difference between discrete and continuous probability distributions involves the method of computing probabilities. With discrete distributions, the probability function $f(x)$ provides the probability that the random variable x assumes various values. With continuous distributions, the probability density function $f(x)$ does not provide probability values directly. Instead, probabilities are given by areas under the curve or graph of the probability density function $f(x)$. Because the area under the curve above a single point is zero, we observe that the probability of any particular value is zero for a continuous random variable.

Three continuous probability distributions—the uniform, normal, and exponential distributions—were treated in detail. The normal distribution is used widely in statistical inference and will be used extensively throughout the remainder of the text.

Glossary

Probability density function A function used to compute probabilities for a continuous random variable. The area under the graph of a probability density function over an interval represents probability.

Uniform probability distribution A continuous probability distribution for which the probability that the random variable will assume a value in any interval is the same for each interval of equal length.

Normal probability distribution A continuous probability distribution. Its probability density function is bell shaped and determined by its mean μ and standard deviation σ.

Standard normal probability distribution A normal distribution with a mean of zero and a standard deviation of one.

Exponential probability distribution A continuous probability distribution that is useful in computing probabilities for the time it takes to complete a task.

Key Formulas

Uniform Probability Density Function

$$f(x) = \begin{cases} \dfrac{1}{b-a} & \text{for } a \leq x \leq b \\ 0 & \text{elsewhere} \end{cases} \tag{6.1}$$

Normal Probability Density Function

$$f(x) = \frac{1}{\sigma\sqrt{2\pi}} e^{-(x-\mu)^2/2\sigma^2} \tag{6.2}$$

Converting to the Standard Normal Random Variable

$$z = \frac{x-\mu}{\sigma} \tag{6.3}$$

Exponential Probability Density Function

$$f(x) = \frac{1}{\mu} e^{-x/\mu} \quad \text{for } x \geq 0 \tag{6.4}$$

Exponential Distribution: Cumulative Probabilities

$$P(x \leq x_0) = 1 - e^{-x_0/\mu} \tag{6.5}$$

Supplementary Exercises

33. A business executive, transferred from Chicago to Atlanta, needs to sell her house in Chicago quickly. The executive's employer has offered to buy the house for $210,000, but the offer expires at the end of the week. The executive does not currently have a better offer but can afford to leave the house on the market for another month. From conversations with her realtor, the executive believes the price she will get by leaving the house on the market for another month is uniformly distributed between $200,000 and $225,000.
    a. If she leaves the house on the market for another month, what is the mathematical expression for the probability density function of the sales price?
    b. If she leaves it on the market for another month, what is the probability that she will get at least $215,000 for the house?
    c. If she leaves it on the market for another month, what is the probability that she will get less than $210,000?
    d. Should the executive leave the house on the market for another month? Why or why not?
34. The NCAA estimates that the yearly value of a full athletic scholarship at in-state public universities is $19,000 (*The Wall Street Journal*, March 12, 2012). Assume the scholarship value is normally distributed with a standard deviation of $2100.

a. For the 10% of athletic scholarships of least value, how much are they worth?
b. What percentage of athletic scholarships are valued at $22,000 or more?
c. For the 3% of athletic scholarships that are most valuable, how much are they worth?

35. Motorola used the normal distribution to determine the probability of defects and the number of defects expected in a production process. Assume a production process produces items with a mean weight of 10 ounces. Calculate the probability of a defect and the expected number of defects for a 1000-unit production run in the following situations.
    a. The process standard deviation is .15, and the process control is set at plus or minus one standard deviation. Units with weights less than 9.85 or greater than 10.15 ounces will be classified as defects.
    b. Through process design improvements, the process standard deviation can be reduced to .05. Assume the process control remains the same, with weights less than 9.85 or greater than 10.15 ounces being classified as defects.
    c. What is the advantage of reducing process variation, thereby causing process control limits to be at a greater number of standard deviations from the mean?

36. During early 2012, economic hardship was stretching the limits of France's welfare system. One indicator of the level of hardship was the increase in the number of people bringing items to a Paris pawnbroker; the number of people bringing items to the pawnbroker had increased to 658 per day (*Bloomberg Businessweek*, March 5–March 11, 2012). Assume the number of people bringing items to the pawnshop per day in 2012 is normally distributed with a mean of 658.
    a. Suppose you learn that on 3% of the days, 610 or fewer people brought items to the pawnshop. What is the standard deviation of the number of people bringing items to the pawnshop per day?
    b. On any given day, what is the probability that between 600 and 700 people bring items to the pawnshop?
    c. How many people bring items to the pawnshop on the busiest 3% of days?

37. The port of South Louisiana, located along 54 miles of the Mississippi River between New Orleans and Baton Rouge, is the largest bulk cargo port in the world. The U.S. Army Corps of Engineers reports that the port handles a mean of 4.5 million tons of cargo per week (*USA Today*, September 25, 2012). Assume that the number of tons of cargo handled per week is normally distributed with a standard deviation of .82 million tons.
    a. What is the probability that the port handles less than 5 million tons of cargo per week?
    b. What is the probability that the port handles 3 or more million tons of cargo per week?
    c. What is the probability that the port handles between 3 million and 4 million tons of cargo per week?
    d. Assume that 85% of the time the port can handle the weekly cargo volume without extending operating hours. What is the number of tons of cargo per week that will require the port to extend its operating hours?

38. Ward Doering Auto Sales is considering offering a special service contract that will cover the total cost of any service work required on leased vehicles. From experience, the company manager estimates that yearly service costs are approximately normally distributed, with a mean of $150 and a standard deviation of $25.
    a. If the company offers the service contract to customers for a yearly charge of $200, what is the probability that any one customer's service costs will exceed the contract price of $200?
    b. What is Ward's expected profit per service contract?

39. A minibar in a hotel room generally provides an impression that the hotel experience is more upscale. PKF Hospitality research reported that minibars provide a mean annual revenue of $368 per hotel room (*USA Today*, February 9, 2012). Consider an upscale hotel in San Antonio, Texas, that has a total of 330 rooms, all with minibars. Assume that the monthly revenues from the minibar service are normally distributed, with a standard deviation of $2200, to answer the following questions.

a. Using the mean annual minibar revenue of \$368 per hotel room, what is the mean monthly revenue for the minibar service at this hotel?
b. What is the probability that the minibar service provides over \$12,000 in monthly revenues for this hotel?
c. What is the probability that the minibar service provides less than \$7500 in monthly revenues for this hotel?
d. The hotel is considering upgrading its minibar selections to make the minibar service more interesting for its midnight-snacking guests. New minibar offerings are expected to raise the mean annual revenue to \$420 per room. Assume a normal distribution with a standard deviation in monthly minibar revenues of \$2500 to answer parts (b) and (c) for the minibar service with the upgraded minibar selections. What is the increase in annual revenues for the upgraded minibar service? Do you agree with the strategy of upgrading the hotel's minibar selections?

40. Assume that the test scores from a college admissions test are normally distributed, with a mean of 450 and a standard deviation of 100.
    a. What percentage of the people taking the test score between 400 and 500?
    b. Suppose someone receives a score of 630. What percentage of the people taking the test score better? What percentage score worse?
    c. If a particular university will not admit anyone scoring below 480, what percentage of the persons taking the test would be acceptable to the university?

41. According to Salary Wizard, the average base salary for a brand manager in Houston, Texas, is \$88,592 and the average base salary for a brand manager in Los Angeles, California, is \$97,417 (Salary Wizard website, February 27, 2008). Assume that salaries are normally distributed, the standard deviation for brand managers in Houston is \$19,900, and the standard deviation for brand managers in Los Angeles is \$21,800.
    a. What is the probability that a brand manager in Houston has a base salary in excess of \$100,000?
    b. What is the probability that a brand manager in Los Angeles has a base salary in excess of \$100,000?
    c. What is the probability that a brand manager in Los Angeles has a base salary of less than \$75,000?
    d. How much would a brand manager in Los Angeles have to make in order to have a higher salary than 99% of the brand managers in Houston?

42. A machine fills containers with a particular product. The standard deviation of filling weights is known from past data to be .6 ounce. If only 2% of the containers hold less than 18 ounces, what is the mean filling weight for the machine? That is, what must μ equal? Assume the filling weights have a normal distribution.

43. The Information Systems Audit and Control Association surveyed office workers to learn about the anticipated usage of office computers for personal holiday shopping (*USA Today,* November 11, 2009). Assume that the number of hours a worker spends doing holiday shopping on an office computer follows an exponential distribution.
    a. The study reported that there is a .53 probability that a worker uses the office computer for holiday shopping 5 hours or less. Is the mean time spent using an office computer for holiday shopping closest to 5.8, 6.2, 6.6, or 7 hours?
    b. Using the mean time from part (a), what is the probability that a worker uses the office computer for holiday shopping more than 10 hours?
    c. What is the probability that a worker uses the office computer for holiday shopping between 4 and 8 hours?

44. A website for bed and breakfast inns gets approximately seven visitors per minute. Suppose the number of website visitors per minute follows a Poisson probability distribution.
    a. What is the mean time between visits to the website?
    b. Show the exponential probability density function for the time between website visits.

c. What is the probability that no one will access the website in a 1-minute period?
d. What is the probability that no one will access the website in a 12-second period?

45. The American Community Survey showed that residents of New York City have the longest travel times to get to work compared to residents of other cities in the United States (U.S. Census Bureau website, August 2008). According to the latest statistics available, the average travel time to work for residents of New York City is 38.3 minutes.
   a. Assume the exponential probability distribution is applicable and show the probability density function for the travel time to work for a resident of this city.
   b. What is the probability that it will take a resident of this city between 20 and 40 minutes to travel to work?
   c. What is the probability that it will take a resident of this city more than one hour to travel to work?

46. The time (in minutes) between telephone calls at an insurance claims office has the following exponential probability distribution.

$$f(x) = .50e^{-.50x} \quad \text{for } x \geq 0$$

   a. What is the mean time between telephone calls?
   b. What is the probability of having 30 seconds or less between telephone calls?
   c. What is the probability of having 1 minute or less between telephone calls?
   d. What is the probability of having 5 or more minutes without a telephone call?

Case Problem Specialty Toys

Specialty Toys, Inc., sells a variety of new and innovative children's toys. Management learned that the preholiday season is the best time to introduce a new toy, because many families use this time to look for new ideas for December holiday gifts. When Specialty discovers a new toy with good market potential, it chooses an October market entry date.

In order to get toys in its stores by October, Specialty places one-time orders with its manufacturers in June or July of each year. Demand for children's toys can be highly volatile. If a new toy catches on, a sense of shortage in the marketplace often increases the demand to high levels and large profits can be realized. However, new toys can also flop, leaving Specialty stuck with high levels of inventory that must be sold at reduced prices. The most important question the company faces is deciding how many units of a new toy should be purchased to meet anticipated sales demand. If too few are purchased, sales will be lost; if too many are purchased, profits will be reduced because of low prices realized in clearance sales.

For the coming season, Specialty plans to introduce a new product called Weather Teddy. This variation of a talking teddy bear is made by a company in Taiwan. When a child presses Teddy's hand, the bear begins to talk. A built-in barometer selects one of five responses that predict the weather conditions. The responses range from "It looks to be a very nice day! Have fun" to "I think it may rain today. Don't forget your umbrella." Tests with the product show that, even though it is not a perfect weather predictor, its predictions are surprisingly good. Several of Specialty's managers claimed Teddy gave predictions of the weather that were as good as many local television weather forecasters.

As with other products, Specialty faces the decision of how many Weather Teddy units to order for the coming holiday season. Members of the management team suggested order quantities of 15,000, 18,000, 24,000, or 28,000 units. The wide range of order quantities suggested indicates considerable disagreement concerning the market potential. The product management team asks you for an analysis of the stock-out probabilities for various order quantities, for an estimate of the profit potential, and for help with making an order quantity recommendation. Specialty expects to sell Weather Teddy for $24 based on a cost of $16 per unit. If inventory remains after the holiday season, Specialty will sell all surplus inventory for $5 per unit. After reviewing the sales history of similar products, Specialty's senior sales forecaster predicted an expected demand of 20,000 units with a .95 probability that demand would be between 10,000 units and 30,000 units.

Managerial Report

Prepare a managerial report that addresses the following issues and recommends an order quantity for the Weather Teddy product.

1. Use the sales forecaster's prediction to describe a normal probability distribution that can be used to approximate the demand distribution. Sketch the distribution and show its mean and standard deviation.
2. Compute the probability of a stock-out for the order quantities suggested by members of the management team.
3. Compute the projected profit for the order quantities suggested by the management team under three scenarios: worst case in which sales = 10,000 units, most likely case in which sales = 20,000 units, and best case in which sales = 30,000 units.
4. One of Specialty's managers felt that the profit potential was so great that the order quantity should have a 70% chance of meeting demand and only a 30% chance of any stock-outs. What quantity would be ordered under this policy, and what is the projected profit under the three sales scenarios?
5. Provide your own recommendation for an order quantity and note the associated profit projections. Provide a rationale for your recommendation.

CHAPTER 7

Sampling and Sampling Distributions

CONTENTS

STATISTICS IN PRACTICE: MEADWESTVACO CORPORATION

7.1 THE ELECTRONICS ASSOCIATES SAMPLING PROBLEM

7.2 SELECTING A SAMPLE
Sampling from a Finite Population
Sampling from an Infinite Population

7.3 POINT ESTIMATION
Practical Advice

7.4 INTRODUCTION TO SAMPLING DISTRIBUTIONS

7.5 SAMPLING DISTRIBUTION OF $\bar{x}$
Expected Value of $\bar{x}$
Standard Deviation of $\bar{x}$
Form of the Sampling Distribution of $\bar{x}$
Sampling Distribution of $\bar{x}$ for the EAI Problem
Practical Value of the Sampling Distribution of $\bar{x}$
Relationship Between the Sample Size and the Sampling Distribution of $\bar{x}$

7.6 SAMPLING DISTRIBUTION OF $\bar{p}$
Expected Value of $\bar{p}$
Standard Deviation of $\bar{p}$
Form of the Sampling Distribution of $\bar{p}$
Practical Value of the Sampling Distribution of $\bar{p}$

7.7 OTHER SAMPLING METHODS
Stratified Random Sampling
Cluster Sampling
Systematic Sampling
Convenience Sampling
Judgment Sampling

STATISTICS *in* PRACTICE

MEADWESTVACO CORPORATION*
STAMFORD, CONNECTICUT

MeadWestvaco Corporation, a leading producer of packaging, coated and specialty papers, and specialty chemicals, employs more than 17,000 people. It operates worldwide in 30 countries and serves customers located in approximately 100 countries. MeadWestvaco's internal consulting group uses sampling to provide a variety of information that enables the company to obtain significant productivity benefits and remain competitive.

For example, MeadWestvaco maintains large woodland holdings, which supply the trees, or raw material, for many of the company's products. Managers need reliable and accurate information about the timberlands and forests to evaluate the company's ability to meet its future raw material needs. What is the present volume in the forests? What is the past growth of the forests? What is the projected future growth of the forests? With answers to these important questions MeadWestvaco's managers can develop plans for the future, including long-term planting and harvesting schedules for the trees.

How does MeadWestvaco obtain the information it needs about its vast forest holdings? Data collected from sample plots throughout the forests are the basis for learning about the population of trees owned by the company. To identify the sample plots, the timberland holdings are first divided into three sections based on location and types of trees. Using maps and random numbers, MeadWestvaco analysts identify random samples of 1/5- to 1/7-acre plots in each section of the forest. MeadWestvaco foresters collect data from these sample plots to learn about the forest population.

*The authors are indebted to Dr. Edward P. Winkofsky for providing this Statistics in Practice.

Random sampling of its forest holdings enables MeadWestvaco Corporation to meet future raw material needs. © Robert Crum/Shutterstock.com.

Foresters throughout the organization participate in the field data collection process. Periodically, two-person teams gather information on each tree in every sample plot. The sample data are entered into the company's continuous forest inventory (CFI) computer system. Reports from the CFI system include a number of frequency distribution summaries containing statistics on types of trees, present forest volume, past forest growth rates, and projected future forest growth and volume. Sampling and the associated statistical summaries of the sample data provide the reports essential for the effective management of MeadWestvaco's forests and timberlands.

In this chapter you will learn about simple random sampling and the sample selection process. In addition, you will learn how statistics such as the sample mean and sample proportion are used to estimate the population mean and population proportion. The important concept of a sampling distribution is also introduced.

In Chapter 1 we presented the following definitions of an element, a population, and a sample.

- An *element* is the entity on which data are collected.
- A *population* is the collection of all the elements of interest.
- A *sample* is a subset of the population.

The reason we select a sample is to collect data to make inferences and answer research questions about a population.

Let us begin by citing two examples in which sampling was used to answer a research question about a population.

1. Members of a political party in Texas were considering supporting a particular candidate for election to the U.S. Senate, and party leaders wanted to estimate the proportion of registered voters in the state favoring the candidate. A sample of 400 registered voters in Texas was selected and 160 of the 400 voters indicated a preference for the candidate. Thus, an estimate of the proportion of the population of registered voters favoring the candidate is 160/400 = .40.
2. A tire manufacturer is considering producing a new tire designed to provide an increase in mileage over the firm's current line of tires. To estimate the mean useful life of the new tires, the manufacturer produced a sample of 120 tires for testing. The test results provided a sample mean of 36,500 miles. Hence, an estimate of the mean useful life for the population of new tires was 36,500 miles.

A sample mean provides an estimate of a population mean, and a sample proportion provides an estimate of a population proportion. With estimates such as these, some estimation error can be expected. This chapter provides the basis for determining how large that error might be.

It is important to realize that sample results provide only *estimates* of the values of the corresponding population characteristics. We do not expect exactly .40, or 40%, of the population of registered voters to favor the candidate, nor do we expect the sample mean of 36,500 miles to exactly equal the mean mileage for the population of all new tires produced. The reason is simply that the sample contains only a portion of the population. Some sampling error is to be expected. With proper sampling methods, the sample results will provide "good" estimates of the population parameters. But how good can we expect the sample results to be? Fortunately, statistical procedures are available for answering this question.

Let us define some of the terms used in sampling. The **sampled population** is the population from which the sample is drawn, and a **frame** is a list of the elements that the sample will be selected from. In the first example, the sampled population is all registered voters in Texas, and the frame is a list of all the registered voters. Because the number of registered voters in Texas is a finite number, the first example is an illustration of sampling from a finite population. In Section 7.2, we discuss how a simple random sample can be selected when sampling from a finite population.

The sampled population for the tire mileage example is more difficult to define because the sample of 120 tires was obtained from a production process at a particular point in time. We can think of the sampled population as the conceptual population of all the tires that could have been made by the production process at that particular point in time. In this sense the sampled population is considered infinite, making it impossible to construct a frame to draw the sample from. In Section 7.2, we discuss how to select a random sample in such a situation.

In this chapter, we show how simple random sampling can be used to select a sample from a finite population and describe how a random sample can be taken from an infinite population that is generated by an ongoing process. We then show how data obtained from a sample can be used to compute estimates of a population mean, a population standard deviation, and a population proportion. In addition, we introduce the important concept of a sampling distribution. As we will show, knowledge of the appropriate sampling distribution enables us to make statements about how close the sample estimates are to the corresponding population parameters. The last section discusses some alternatives to simple random sampling that are often employed in practice.

7.1 The Electronics Associates Sampling Problem

The director of personnel for Electronics Associates, Inc. (EAI), has been assigned the task of developing a profile of the company's 2500 employees. The characteristics to be identified include the mean annual salary for the employees and the proportion of employees having completed the company's management training program.

EAI

Using the 2500 employees as the population for this study, we can find the annual salary and the training program status for each individual by referring to the firm's personnel records. The data set containing this information for all 2500 employees in the population is in the WEBfile named EAI.

Using the EAI data and the formulas presented in Chapter 3, we compute the population mean and the population standard deviation for the annual salary data.

$$\text{Population mean:} \quad \mu = \$51{,}800$$
$$\text{Population standard deviation:} \quad \sigma = \$4000$$

The data for the training program status show that 1500 of the 2500 employees completed the training program.

Numerical characteristics of a population are called **parameters**. Letting p denote the proportion of the population that completed the training program, we see that $p = 1500/2500 = .60$. The population mean annual salary ($\mu = \$51{,}800$), the population standard deviation of annual salary ($\sigma = \$4000$), and the population proportion that completed the training program ($p = .60$) are parameters of the population of EAI employees.

Often the cost of collecting information from a sample is substantially less than from a population, especially when personal interviews must be conducted to collect the information.

Now, suppose that the necessary information on all the EAI employees was not readily available in the company's database. The question we now consider is how the firm's director of personnel can obtain estimates of the population parameters by using a sample of employees rather than all 2500 employees in the population. Suppose that a sample of 30 employees will be used. Clearly, the time and the cost of developing a profile would be substantially less for 30 employees than for the entire population. If the personnel director could be assured that a sample of 30 employees would provide adequate information about the population of 2500 employees, working with a sample would be preferable to working with the entire population. Let us explore the possibility of using a sample for the EAI study by first considering how we can identify a sample of 30 employees.

7.2 Selecting a Sample

In this section we describe how to select a sample. We first describe how to sample from a finite population and then describe how to select a sample from an infinite population.

Sampling from a Finite Population

Other methods of probability sampling are described in Section 7.7.

Statisticians recommend selecting a probability sample when sampling from a finite population because a probability sample allows them to make valid statistical inferences about the population. The simplest type of probability sample is one in which each sample of size n has the same probability of being selected. It is called a simple random sample. A simple random sample of size n from a finite population of size N is defined as follows.

SIMPLE RANDOM SAMPLE (FINITE POPULATION)

A **simple random sample** of size n from a finite population of size N is a sample selected such that each possible sample of size n has the same probability of being selected.

The random numbers generated using Excel's RAND function follow a uniform probability distribution between 0 and 1.

The procedures used to select a simple random sample from a finite population are based upon the use of random numbers. We can use Excel's RAND function to generate a random number between 0 and 1 by entering the formula =RAND() into any cell in a worksheet. The number generated is called a random number because the mathematical

TABLE 7.1 NATIONAL BASEBALL LEAGUE TEAMS

Arizona	New York
Atlanta	Philadelphia
Chicago	Pittsburgh
Cincinnati	San Diego
Colorado	San Francisco
Los Angeles	St. Louis
Miami	Washington
Milwaukee	

procedure used by the RAND function guarantees that every number between 0 and 1 has the same probability of being selected. Let us see how these random numbers can be used to select a simple random sample.

Our procedure for selecting a simple random sample of size n from a population of size N involves two steps.

Step 1. Assign a random number to each element of the population.
Step 2. Select the n elements corresponding to the n smallest random numbers.

Because each set of n elements in the population has the same probability of being assigned the n smallest random numbers, each set of n elements has the same probability of being selected for the sample. If we select the sample using this two-step procedure, every sample of size n has the same probability of being selected; thus, the sample selected satisfies the definition of a simple random sample.

Let us consider an example involving selecting a simple random sample of size $n = 5$ from a population of size $N = 15$. Table 7.1 contains a list of the 15 teams in the National Baseball League. Suppose we want to select a simple random sample of 5 teams to conduct in-depth interviews about how they manage their minor league franchises.

Step 1 of our simple random sampling procedure requires that we assign a random number to each of the 15 teams in the population. Figure 7.1 shows a worksheet used to generate a random number corresponding to each of the 15 teams in the population. The names of the baseball teams are in column A, and the random numbers generated are in column B. From the formula worksheet in the background we see that the formula =RAND() has been entered into cells B2:B16 to generate the random numbers between 0 and 1. From the value worksheet in the foreground we see that Arizona is assigned the random number .850862, Atlanta has been assigned the random number .706245, and so on.

The second step is to select the five teams corresponding to the five smallest random numbers as our sample. Looking through the random numbers in Figure 7.1, we see that the team corresponding to the smallest random number (.066942) is St. Louis, and that the four teams corresponding to the next four smallest random numbers are Washington, Miami, San Diego, and San Francisco. Thus, these five teams make up the simple random sample.

Searching through the list of random numbers in Figure 7.1 to find the five smallest random numbers is tedious, and it is easy to make mistakes. Excel's Sort procedure simplifies this step. We illustrate by sorting the list of baseball teams in Figure 7.1 to find the five teams corresponding to the five smallest random numbers. Refer to the foreground worksheet in Figure 7.1 as we describe the steps involved.

Step 1. Select any cell in the range B2:B16
Step 2. Click the **Home** tab on the Ribbon
Step 3. In the **Editing** group, click **Sort & Filter**
Step 4. Choose **Sort Smallest to Largest**

FIGURE 7.1 WORKSHEET USED TO GENERATE A RANDOM NUMBER CORRESPONDING TO EACH TEAM

National League

	A	B	C
1	Team	Random Numbers	
2	Arizona	=RAND()	
3	Atlanta	=RAND()	
4	Chicago	=RAND()	
5	Cincinnati	=RAND()	
6	Colorado	=RAND()	
7	Los Angeles	=RAND()	
8	Miami	=RAND()	
9	Milwaukee	=RAND()	
10	New York	=RAND()	
11	Philadelphia	=RAND()	
12	Pittsburgh	=RAND()	
13	San Diego	=RAND()	
14	San Francisco	=RAND()	
15	St. Louis	=RAND()	
16	Washington	=RAND()	
17			

	A	B	C
1	Team	Random Numbers	
2	Arizona	0.850862	
3	Atlanta	0.706245	
4	Chicago	0.724789	
5	Cincinnati	0.614784	
6	Colorado	0.553815	
7	Los Angeles	0.525636	
8	Miami	0.179123	
9	Milwaukee	0.471490	
10	New York	0.523103	
11	Philadelphia	0.851552	
12	Pittsburgh	0.806185	
13	San Diego	0.327713	
14	San Francisco	0.374168	
15	St. Louis	0.066942	
16	Washington	0.158452	
17			

After completing these steps we obtain the worksheet shown in Figure 7.2.[1] The teams listed in rows 2–6 are the ones corresponding to the smallest five random numbers; they are our simple random sample. Note that the random numbers shown in Figure 7.2 are in ascending order, and that the teams are not in their original order. For instance, St. Louis is the next to last team listed in Figure 7.1, but it is the first team selected in the simple random sample. Washington, the second team in our sample, is the sixteenth team in the original list, and so on.

The Excel Sort procedure for identifying the employees associated with the 30 smallest random numbers is especially valuable with such a large population.

We now use this simple random sampling procedure to select a simple random sample of 30 EAI employees from the population of 2500 EAI employees. We begin by generating 2500 random numbers, one for each employee in the population. Then we the select 30 employees corresponding to the 30 smallest random numbers as our sample. Refer to Figure 7.3 as we describe the steps involved.

Enter/Access Data: Open the WEBfile named EAI. The first three columns of the worksheet in the background show the annual salary data and training program status for the first 30 employees in the population of 2500 EAI employees. (The complete worksheet contains all 2500 employees.)

[1]In order to show the random numbers from Figure 7.1 in ascending order in this worksheet, we turned off the automatic recalculation option prior to sorting for illustrative purposes. If the recalculation option were not turned off, a new set of random numbers would have been generated when the sort was completed. But the same five teams would be selected.

FIGURE 7.2 USING EXCEL'S SORT PROCEDURE TO SELECT THE SIMPLE RANDOM SAMPLE OF FIVE TEAMS

	A	B	C
1	**Team**	**Random Numbers**	
2	St. Louis	0.066942	
3	Washington	0.158452	
4	Miami	0.179123	
5	San Diego	0.327713	
6	San Francisco	0.374168	
7	Milwaukee	0.471490	
8	New York	0.523103	
9	Los Angeles	0.525636	
10	Colorado	0.553815	
11	Cincinnati	0.614784	
12	Atlanta	0.706245	
13	Chicago	0.724789	
14	Pittsburgh	0.806185	
15	Arizona	0.850862	
16	Philadelphia	0.851552	
17			

Enter Functions and Formulas: In the background worksheet, the label **Random Numbers** has been entered into cell D1 and the formula =RAND() has been entered into cells D2:D2501 to generate a random number between 0 and 1 for each of the 2500 EAI employees. The random number generated for the first employee is 0.613872, the random number generated for the second employee is 0.473204, and so on.

Apply Tools: All that remains is to find the employees associated with the 30 smallest random numbers. To do so, we sort the data in columns A through D into ascending order by the random numbers in column D.

Step 1. Select any cell in the range D2:D2501
Step 2. Click the **Home** tab on the Ribbon
Step 3. In the **Editing** group, click **Sort & Filter**
Step 4. Choose **Sort Smallest to Largest**

After completing these steps we obtain the worksheet shown in the foreground of Figure 7.3. The employees listed in rows 2–31 are the ones corresponding to the smallest 30 random numbers that were generated. Hence, this group of 30 employees is a simple random sample. Note that the random numbers shown in the foreground of Figure 7.3 are in ascending order, and that the employees are not in their original order. For instance, employee 812 in the population is associated with the smallest random number and is the first element in the sample, and employee 13 in the population (see row 14 of the background worksheet) has been included as the 22nd observation in the sample (row 23 of the foreground worksheet).

Sampling from an Infinite Population

Sometimes we want to select a sample from a population, but the population is infinitely large or the elements of the population are being generated by an ongoing process for which

FIGURE 7.3 USING EXCEL TO SELECT A SIMPLE RANDOM SAMPLE

	A	B	C	D
1	Employee	Annual Salary	Training Program	Random Numbers
2	1	55769.50	No	0.613872
3	2	50823.00	Yes	0.473204
4	3	48408.20	No	0.549011
5	4	49787.50	No	0.047482
6	5	52801.60	Yes	0.531085
7	6	51767.70	No	0.994296
8	7	58346.60	Yes	0.189065
9	8	46670.20	No	0.020714
10	9	50246.80	Yes	0.647318
11	10	51255.00	No	0.524341
12	11	52546.60	No	0.764998
13	12	49512.50	Yes	0.255244
14	13	51753.00	Yes	0.010923
15	14	53547.10	No	0.238003
16	15	48052.20	No	0.635675
17	16	44652.50	Yes	0.177294
18	17	51764.90	Yes	0.415097
19	18	45187.80	Yes	0.883440
20	19	49867.50	Yes	0.476824
21	20	53706.30	Yes	0.101065
22	21	52039.50	Yes	0.775323
23	22	52973.60	No	0.011729
24	23	53372.50	No	0.762026
25	24	54592.00	Yes	0.066344
26	25	55738.10	Yes	0.776766
27	26	52975.10	Yes	0.828493
28	27	52386.20	Yes	0.841532
29	28	51051.60	Yes	0.899427
30	29	52095.60	Yes	0.486284
31	30	44956.50	No	0.264628
32				

The formula in cells D2:D2501 is =RAND().

Note: Rows 32–2501 are not shown.

	A	B	C	D
1	Employee	Annual Salary	Training Program	Random Numbers
2	812	49094.30	Yes	0.000193
3	1411	53263.90	Yes	0.000484
4	1795	49643.50	Yes	0.002641
5	2095	49894.90	Yes	0.002763
6	1235	47621.60	No	0.002940
7	744	55924.00	Yes	0.002977
8	470	49092.30	Yes	0.003182
9	1606	51404.40	Yes	0.003448
10	1744	50957.70	Yes	0.004203
11	179	55109.70	Yes	0.005293
12	1387	45922.60	Yes	0.005709
13	1782	57268.40	No	0.005729
14	1006	55688.80	Yes	0.005796
15	278	51564.70	No	0.005966
16	1850	56188.20	No	0.006250
17	844	51766.00	Yes	0.006708
18	2028	52541.30	No	0.007767
19	1654	44980.00	Yes	0.008095
20	444	51932.60	Yes	0.009686
21	556	52973.00	Yes	0.009711
22	2449	45120.90	Yes	0.010595
23	13	51753.00	Yes	0.010923
24	2187	54391.80	No	0.011364
25	1633	50164.20	No	0.011603
26	22	52973.60	No	0.011729
27	1530	50241.30	No	0.013570
28	820	52793.90	No	0.013669
29	1258	50979.40	Yes	0.014042
30	2349	55860.90	Yes	0.014532
31	1698	57309.10	No	0.014539
32				

there is no limit on the number of elements that can be generated. Thus, it is not possible to develop a list of all the elements in the population. This is considered the infinite population case. With an infinite population, we cannot select a simple random sample because we cannot construct a frame consisting of all the elements. In the infinite population case, statisticians recommend selecting what is called a random sample.

RANDOM SAMPLE (INFINITE POPULATION)

A **random sample** of size n from an infinite population is a sample selected such that the following conditions are satisfied.

1. Each element selected comes from the same population.
2. Each element is selected independently.

Care and judgment must be exercised in implementing the selection process for obtaining a random sample from an infinite population. Each case may require a different selection procedure. Let us consider two examples to see what we mean by the conditions: (1) Each element selected comes from the same population and (2) each element is selected independently.

A common quality control application involves a production process where there is no limit on the number of elements that can be produced. The conceptual population we are sampling from is all the elements that could be produced (not just the ones that are produced) by the ongoing production process. Because we cannot develop a list of all the elements that could be produced, the population is considered infinite. To be more specific, let us consider a production line designed to fill boxes of a breakfast cereal with a mean weight of 24 ounces of breakfast cereal per box. Samples of 12 boxes filled by this process are periodically selected by a quality control inspector to determine if the process is operating properly or if, perhaps, a machine malfunction has caused the process to begin underfilling or overfilling the boxes.

With a production operation such as this, the biggest concern in selecting a random sample is to make sure that condition 1, the sampled elements are selected from the same population, is satisfied. To ensure that this condition is satisfied, the boxes must be selected at approximately the same point in time. This way the inspector avoids the possibility of selecting some boxes when the process is operating properly and other boxes when the process is not operating properly and is underfilling or overfilling the boxes. With a production process such as this, the second condition, each element is selected independently, is satisfied by designing the production process so that each box of cereal is filled independently. With this assumption, the quality control inspector only needs to worry about satisfying the same population condition.

As another example of selecting a random sample from an infinite population, consider the population of customers arriving at a fast-food restaurant. Suppose an employee is asked to select and interview a sample of customers in order to develop a profile of customers who visit the restaurant. The customer arrival process is ongoing and there is no way to obtain a list of all customers in the population. So, for practical purposes, the population for this ongoing process is considered infinite. As long as a sampling procedure is designed so that all the elements in the sample are customers of the restaurant and they are selected independently, a random sample will be obtained. In this case, the employee collecting the sample needs to select the sample from people who come into the restaurant and make a purchase to ensure that the same population condition is satisfied. If, for instance, the employee selected someone for the sample who came into the restaurant just to use the restroom, that person would not be a customer and the same population condition would be violated. So, as long as the interviewer selects the sample from people making a purchase at the restaurant, condition 1 is satisfied. Ensuring that the customers are selected independently can be more difficult.

The purpose of the second condition of the random sample selection procedure (each element is selected independently) is to prevent selection bias. In this case, selection bias would occur if the interviewer were free to select customers for the sample arbitrarily. The interviewer might feel more comfortable selecting customers in a particular age group and might avoid customers in other age groups. Selection bias would also occur if the interviewer selected a group of five customers who entered the restaurant together and asked all of them to participate in the sample. Such a group of customers would be likely to exhibit similar characteristics, which might provide misleading information about the population of customers. Selection bias such as this can be avoided by ensuring that the selection of a particular customer does not influence the selection of any other customer. In other words, the elements (customers) are selected independently.

McDonald's, the fast-food restaurant leader, implemented a random sampling procedure for this situation. The sampling procedure was based on the fact that some customers presented discount coupons. Whenever a customer presented a discount coupon, the next customer served was asked to complete a customer profile questionnaire. Because arriving customers presented discount coupons randomly and independently of other customers, this sampling procedure ensured that customers were selected independently. As a result, the sample satisfied the requirements of a random sample from an infinite population.

Situations involving sampling from an infinite population are usually associated with a process that operates over time. Examples include parts being manufactured on a production line, repeated experimental trials in a laboratory, transactions occurring at a bank, telephone calls arriving at a technical support center, and customers entering a retail store. In each case, the situation may be viewed as a process that generates elements from an infinite population. As long as the sampled elements are selected from the same population and are selected independently, the sample is considered a random sample from an infinite population.

NOTES AND COMMENTS

1. In this section we have been careful to define two types of samples: a simple random sample from a finite population and a random sample from an infinite population. In the remainder of the text, we will generally refer to both of these as either a *random sample* or simply a *sample*. We will not make a distinction of the sample being a "simple" random sample unless it is necessary for the exercise or discussion.
2. Statisticians who specialize in sample surveys from finite populations use sampling methods that provide probability samples. With a probability sample, each possible sample has a known probability of selection and a random process is used to select the elements for the sample. Simple random sampling is one of these methods. In Section 7.7, we describe some other probability sampling methods: stratified random sampling, cluster sampling, and systematic sampling. We use the term *simple* in simple random sampling to clarify that this is the probability sampling method that assures each sample of size n has the same probability of being selected.
3. The number of different simple random samples of size n that can be selected from a finite population of size N is

$$\frac{N!}{n!(N-n)!}$$

In this formula, $N!$ and $n!$ are the factorial formulas discussed in Chapter 4. For the EAI problem with $N = 2500$ and $n = 30$, this expression can be used to show that approximately 2.75×10^{69} different simple random samples of 30 EAI employees can be obtained.

Exercises

Methods

1. Consider a finite population with five elements labeled A, B, C, D, and E. Ten possible simple random samples of size 2 can be selected.
   a. List the 10 samples beginning with AB, AC, and so on.
   b. Using simple random sampling, what is the probability that each sample of size 2 is selected?

c. Suppose we use Excel's RAND function to assign random numbers to the five elements: A (.7266), B (.0476), C (.2459), D (.0957), E (.9408). List the simple random sample of size 2 that will be selected by using these random numbers.

2. Assume a finite population has 10 elements. Number the elements from 1 to 10 and use the following 10 random numbers to select a sample of size 4.

.7545 .0936 .0341 .3242 .1449 .9060 .2420 .9773 .5428 .0729

3. The American League consists of 15 baseball teams. Suppose a sample of 5 teams is to be selected to conduct player interviews. The following table lists the 15 teams and the random numbers assigned by Excel's RAND function. Use these random numbers to select a sample of size 5.

American League

Team	Random Number	Team	Random Number
New York	0.178624	Boston	0.290197
Baltimore	0.578370	Tampa Bay	0.867778
Toronto	0.965807	Minnesota	0.811810
Chicago	0.562178	Cleveland	0.960271
Detroit	0.253574	Kansas City	0.326836
Oakland	0.288287	Los Angeles	0.895267
Texas	0.500879	Seattle	0.839071
Houston	0.713682		

4. The U.S. Golf Association is considering a ban on long and belly putters. This has caused a great deal of controversy among both amateur golfers and members of the Professional Golf Association (PGA) (*Golfweek*, October 26, 2012). Shown below are the names of the top 10 finishers in the recent PGA Tour McGladrey Classic golf tournament.

1. Tommy Gainey	6. Davis Love III
2. David Toms	7. Chad Campbell
3. Jim Furyk	8. Greg Owens
4. Brendon de Jonge	9. Charles Howell III
5. D. J. Trahan	10. Arjun Atwal

Select a simple random sample of 3 of these players to assess their opinions on the use of long and belly putters.

EAI

5. In this section we used a two-step procedure to select a simple random sample of 30 EAI employees. Use this procedure to select a simple random sample of 50 EAI employees.

6. Indicate which of the following situations involve sampling from a finite population and which involve sampling from an infinite population. In cases where the sampled population is finite, describe how you would construct a frame.
   a. Select a sample of licensed drivers in the state of New York.
   b. Select a sample of boxes of cereal off the production line for the Breakfast Choice Company.
   c. Select a sample of cars crossing the Golden Gate Bridge on a typical weekday.
   d. Select a sample of students in a statistics course at Indiana University.
   e. Select a sample of the orders being processed by a mail-order firm.

7.3 Point Estimation

Now that we have described how to select a simple random sample, let us return to the EAI problem. A simple random sample of 30 employees and the corresponding data on annual salary and management training program participation are as shown in Table 7.2.

TABLE 7.2 ANNUAL SALARY AND TRAINING PROGRAM STATUS FOR A SIMPLE RANDOM SAMPLE OF 30 EAI EMPLOYEES

Annual Salary ($)	Management Training Program	Annual Salary ($)	Management Training Program
x_1 = 49,094.30	Yes	x_{16} = 51,766.00	Yes
x_2 = 53,263.90	Yes	x_{17} = 52,541.30	No
x_3 = 49,643.50	Yes	x_{18} = 44,980.00	Yes
x_4 = 49,894.90	Yes	x_{19} = 51,932.60	Yes
x_5 = 47,621.60	No	x_{20} = 52,973.00	Yes
x_6 = 55,924.00	Yes	x_{21} = 45,120.90	Yes
x_7 = 49,092.30	Yes	x_{22} = 51,753.00	Yes
x_8 = 51,404.40	Yes	x_{23} = 54,391.80	No
x_9 = 50,957.70	Yes	x_{24} = 50,164.20	No
x_{10} = 55,109.70	Yes	x_{25} = 52,973.60	No
x_{11} = 45,922.60	Yes	x_{26} = 50,241.30	No
x_{12} = 57,268.40	No	x_{27} = 52,793.90	No
x_{13} = 55,688.80	Yes	x_{28} = 50,979.40	Yes
x_{14} = 51,564.70	No	x_{29} = 55,860.90	Yes
x_{15} = 56,188.20	No	x_{30} = 57,309.10	No

The notation x_1, x_2, and so on is used to denote the annual salary of the first employee in the sample, the annual salary of the second employee in the sample, and so on. Participation in the management training program is indicated by Yes in the management training program column.

To estimate the value of a population parameter, we compute a corresponding characteristic of the sample, referred to as a **sample statistic**. For example, to estimate the population mean μ and the population standard deviation σ for the annual salary of EAI employees, we use the data in Table 7.2 to calculate the corresponding sample statistics: the sample mean and the sample standard deviation s. Using the formulas for a sample mean and a sample standard deviation presented in Chapter 3, the sample mean is

$$\bar{x} = \frac{\Sigma x_i}{n} = \frac{1,554,420}{30} = \$51,814$$

and the sample standard deviation is

$$s = \sqrt{\frac{\Sigma(x_i - \bar{x})^2}{n - 1}} = \sqrt{\frac{325,009,260}{29}} = \$3348$$

To estimate p, the proportion of employees in the population who completed the management training program, we use the corresponding sample proportion $\bar{p}$. Let x denote the number of employees in the sample who completed the management training program. The data in Table 7.2 show that $x = 19$. Thus, with a sample size of $n = 30$, the sample proportion is

$$\bar{p} = \frac{x}{n} = \frac{19}{30} = .63$$

By making the preceding computations, we perform the statistical procedure called *point estimation*. We refer to the sample mean $\bar{x}$ as the **point estimator** of the population mean μ, the sample standard deviation s as the point estimator of the population standard deviation σ, and the sample proportion $\bar{p}$ as the point estimator of the population proportion p. The numerical value obtained for $\bar{x}$, s, or $\bar{p}$ is called the **point estimate**. Thus, for

TABLE 7.3 SUMMARY OF POINT ESTIMATES OBTAINED FROM A SIMPLE RANDOM SAMPLE OF 30 EAI EMPLOYEES

Population Parameter	Parameter Value	Point Estimator	Point Estimate
μ = Population mean annual salary	\$51,800	$\bar{x}$ = Sample mean annual salary	\$51,814
σ = Population standard deviation for annual salary	\$4000	s = Sample standard deviation for annual salary	\$3348
p = Population proportion having completed the management training program	.60	$\bar{p}$ = Sample proportion having completed the management training program	.63

the simple random sample of 30 EAI employees shown in Table 7.2, \$51,814 is the point estimate of μ, \$3348 is the point estimate of σ, and .63 is the point estimate of p. Table 7.3 summarizes the sample results and compares the point estimates to the actual values of the population parameters.

As is evident from Table 7.3, the point estimates differ somewhat from the corresponding population parameters. This difference is to be expected because a sample, and not a census of the entire population, is being used to develop the point estimates. In the next chapter, we will show how to construct an interval estimate in order to provide information about how close the point estimate is to the population parameter.

Practical Advice

The subject matter of most of the rest of the book is concerned with statistical inference. Point estimation is a form of statistical inference. We use a sample statistic to make an inference about a population parameter. When making inferences about a population based on a sample, it is important to have a close correspondence between the sampled population and the target population. The **target population** is the population we want to make inferences about, while the sampled population is the population from which the sample is actually taken. In this section, we have described the process of drawing a simple random sample from the population of EAI employees and making point estimates of characteristics of that same population. So the sampled population and the target population are identical, which is the desired situation. But in other cases, it is not as easy to obtain a close correspondence between the sampled and target populations.

Consider the case of an amusement park selecting a sample of its customers to learn about characteristics such as age and time spent at the park. Suppose all the sample elements were selected on a day when park attendance was restricted to employees of a large company. Then the sampled population would be composed of employees of that company and members of their families. If the target population we wanted to make inferences about were typical park customers over a typical summer, then we might encounter a significant difference between the sampled population and the target population. In such a case, we would question the validity of the point estimates being made. Park management would be in the best position to know whether a sample taken on a particular day was likely to be representative of the target population.

In summary, whenever a sample is used to make inferences about a population, we should make sure that the study is designed so that the sampled population and the target population are in close agreement. Good judgment is a necessary ingredient of sound statistical practice.

Exercises

Methods

7. The following data are from a simple random sample.

5 8 10 7 10 14

a. What is the point estimate of the population mean?
b. What is the point estimate of the population standard deviation?

8. A survey question for a sample of 150 individuals yielded 75 Yes responses, 55 No responses, and 20 No Opinions.
a. What is the point estimate of the proportion in the population who respond Yes?
b. What is the point estimate of the proportion in the population who respond No?

Applications

9. A simple random sample of 5 months of sales data provided the following information:

Month:	1	2	3	4	5
Units Sold:	94	100	85	94	92

a. Develop a point estimate of the population mean number of units sold per month.
b. Develop a point estimate of the population standard deviation.

WEB file

Morningstar

10. Morningstar publishes ratings data on 1208 company stocks (Morningstar website, October 24, 2012). A sample of 40 of these stocks is contained in the WEBfile named Morningstar. Use the Morningstar data set to answer the following questions.
a. Develop a point estimate of the proportion of the stocks that receive Morningstar's highest rating of 5 Stars.
b. Develop a point estimate of the proportion of the Morningstar stocks that are rated Above Average with respect to business risk.
c. Develop a point estimate of the proportion of the Morningstar stocks that are rated 2 Stars or less.

11. The National Football League (NFL) polls fans to develop a rating for each football game (NFL website, October 24, 2012). Each game is rated on a scale from 0 (forgettable) to 100 (memorable). The fan ratings for a random sample of 12 games follow.

57	61	86	74	72	73
20	57	80	79	83	74

a. Develop a point estimate of mean fan rating for the population of NFL games.
b. Develop a point estimate of the standard deviation for the population of NFL games.

12. A sample of 426 U.S. adults age 50 and older were asked how important a variety of issues were in choosing whom to vote for in the 2012 presidential election (*AARP Bulletin*, March, 2012).
a. What is the sampled population for this study?
b. Social Security and Medicare were cited as "very important" by 350 respondents. Estimate the proportion of the population of U.S. adults age 50 and over who believe this issue is very important.
c. Education was cited as "very important" by 74% of the respondents. Estimate the number of respondents who believe this issue is very important.
d. Job Growth was cited as "very important" by 354 respondents. Estimate the proportion of U.S. adults age 50 and over who believe job growth is very important.
e. What is the target population for the inferences being made in parts (b) and (d)? Is it the same as the sampled population you identified in part (a)? Suppose you later learn

that the sample was restricted to members of the AARP. Would you still feel the inferences being made in parts (b) and (d) are valid? Why or why not?

13. One of the questions in the Pew Internet & American Life Project asked adults if they used the Internet at least occasionally (Pew website, October 23, 2012). The results showed that 454 out of 478 adults aged 18–29 answered Yes; 741 out of 833 adults aged 30–49 answered Yes; 1058 out of 1644 adults aged 50 and over answered Yes.
    a. Develop a point estimate of the proportion of adults aged 18–29 who use the Internet.
    b. Develop a point estimate of the proportion of adults aged 30–49 who use the Internet.
    c. Develop a point estimate of the proportion of adults aged 50 and over who use the Internet.
    d. Comment on any relationship between age and Internet use that seems apparent.
    e. Suppose your target population of interest is that of all adults (18 years of age and over). Develop an estimate of the proportion of that population who use the Internet.

EAI

14. In this section we showed how a simple random sample of 30 EAI employees can be used to develop point estimates of the population mean annual salary, the population standard deviation for annual salary, and the population proportion having completed the management training program.
    a. Use Excel to select a simple random sample of 50 EAI employees.
    b. Develop a point estimate of the mean annual salary.
    c. Develop a point estimate of the population standard deviation for annual salary.
    d. Develop a point estimate of the population proportion having completed the management training program.

7.4 Introduction to Sampling Distributions

In the preceding section we said that the sample mean $\bar{x}$ is the point estimator of the population mean μ, and the sample proportion $\bar{p}$ is the point estimator of the population proportion p. For the simple random sample of 30 EAI employees shown in Table 7.2, the point estimate of μ is $\bar{x} = \$51,814$ and the point estimate of p is $\bar{p} = .63$. Suppose we select another simple random sample of 30 EAI employees and obtain the following point estimates:

$$\text{Sample mean: } \bar{x} = \$52,670$$
$$\text{Sample proportion: } \bar{p} = .70$$

Note that different values of $\bar{x}$ and $\bar{p}$ were obtained. Indeed, a second simple random sample of 30 EAI employees cannot be expected to provide the same point estimates as the first sample.

Now, suppose we repeat the process of selecting a simple random sample of 30 EAI employees over and over again, each time computing the values of $\bar{x}$ and $\bar{p}$. Table 7.4 contains

TABLE 7.4 VALUES OF $\bar{x}$ AND $\bar{p}$ FROM 500 SIMPLE RANDOM SAMPLES OF 30 EAI EMPLOYEES

Sample Number	Sample Mean ($\bar{x}$)	Sample Proportion ($\bar{p}$)
1	51,814	.63
2	52,670	.70
3	51,780	.67
4	51,588	.53
•	•	•
•	•	•
•	•	•
500	51,752	.50

TABLE 7.5 FREQUENCY AND RELATIVE FREQUENCY DISTRIBUTIONS OF $\bar{x}$ FROM 500 SIMPLE RANDOM SAMPLES OF 30 EAI EMPLOYEES

Mean Annual Salary ($)	Frequency	Relative Frequency
49,500.00–49,999.99	2	.004
50,000.00–50,499.99	16	.032
50,500.00–50,999.99	52	.104
51,000.00–51,499.99	101	.202
51,500.00–51,999.99	133	.266
52,000.00–52,499.99	110	.220
52,500.00–52,999.99	54	.108
53,000.00–53,499.99	26	.052
53,500.00–53,999.99	6	.012
Totals	500	1.000

a portion of the results obtained for 500 simple random samples, and Table 7.5 shows the frequency and relative frequency distributions for the 500 $\bar{x}$ values. Figure 7.4 shows the relative frequency histogram for the $\bar{x}$ values.

In Chapter 5 we defined a random variable as a numerical description of the outcome of an experiment. If we consider the process of selecting a simple random sample as an experiment, the sample mean $\bar{x}$ is the numerical description of the outcome of the experiment. Thus, the sample mean $\bar{x}$ is a random variable. As a result, just like other random variables, $\bar{x}$ has a mean or expected value, a standard deviation, and a probability distribution.

FIGURE 7.4 RELATIVE FREQUENCY HISTOGRAM OF $\bar{x}$ VALUES FROM 500 SIMPLE RANDOM SAMPLES OF SIZE 30 EACH

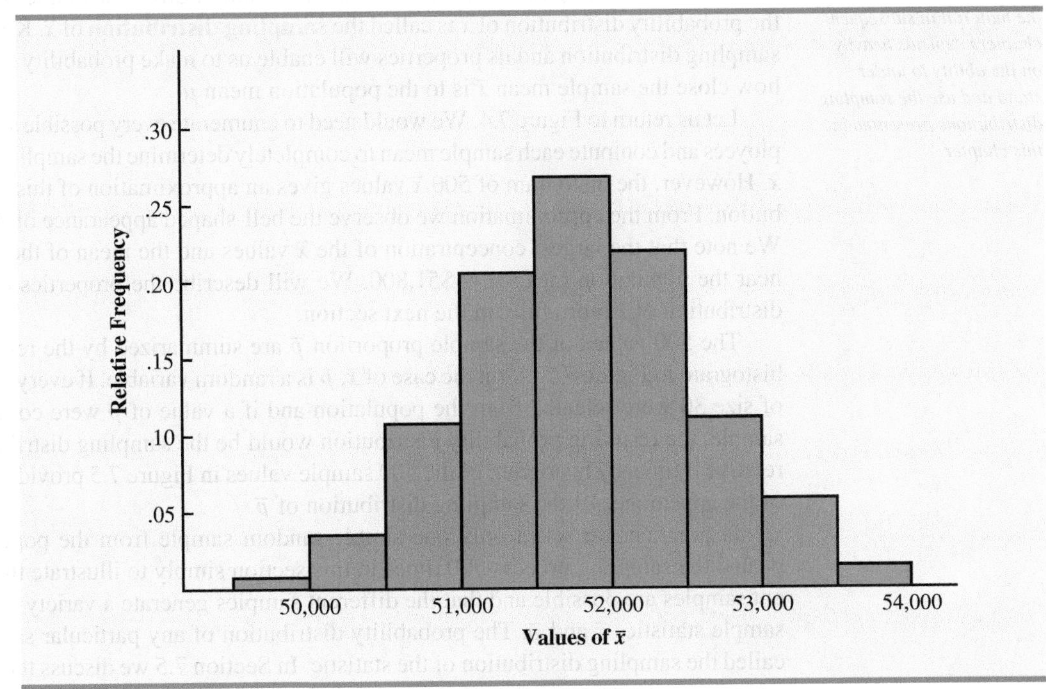

FIGURE 7.5 RELATIVE FREQUENCY HISTOGRAM OF $\bar{p}$ VALUES FROM 500 SIMPLE RANDOM SAMPLES OF SIZE 30 EACH

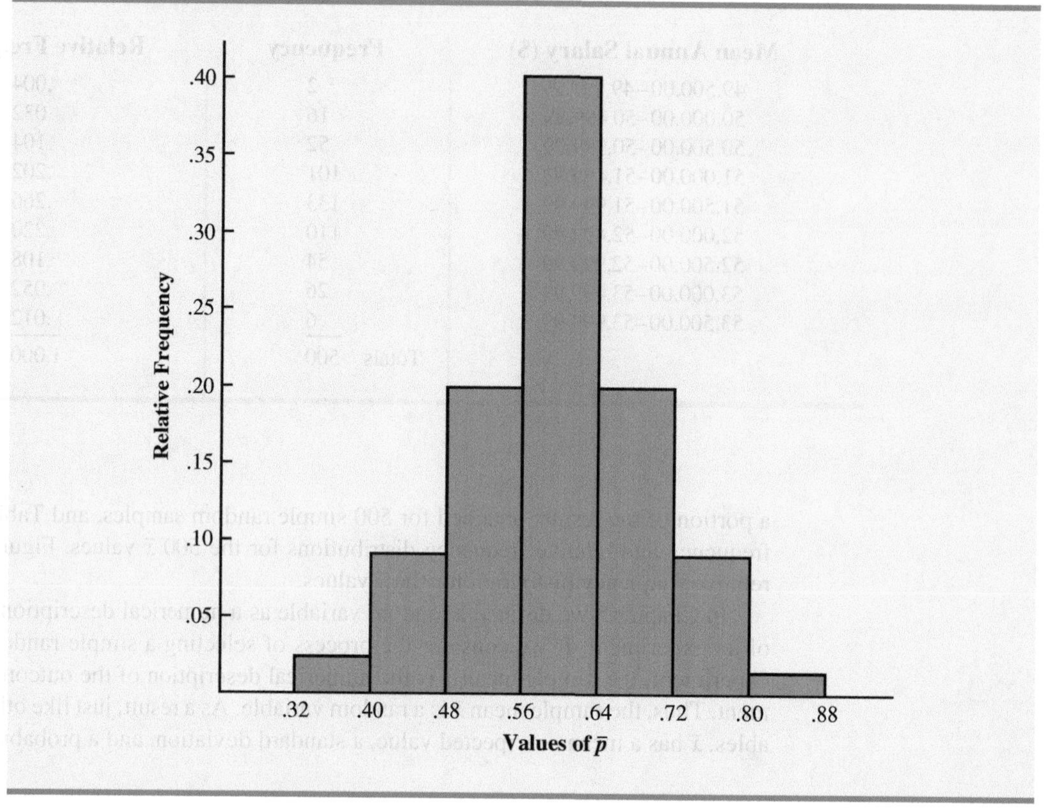

The ability to understand the material in subsequent chapters depends heavily on the ability to understand and use the sampling distributions presented in this chapter.

Because the various possible values of $\bar{x}$ are the result of different simple random samples, the probability distribution of $\bar{x}$ is called the **sampling distribution** of $\bar{x}$. Knowledge of this sampling distribution and its properties will enable us to make probability statements about how close the sample mean $\bar{x}$ is to the population mean μ.

Let us return to Figure 7.4. We would need to enumerate every possible sample of 30 employees and compute each sample mean to completely determine the sampling distribution of $\bar{x}$. However, the histogram of 500 $\bar{x}$ values gives an approximation of this sampling distribution. From the approximation we observe the bell-shaped appearance of the distribution. We note that the largest concentration of the $\bar{x}$ values and the mean of the 500 $\bar{x}$ values is near the population mean $\mu = \$51,800$. We will describe the properties of the sampling distribution of $\bar{x}$ more fully in the next section.

The 500 values of the sample proportion $\bar{p}$ are summarized by the relative frequency histogram in Figure 7.5. As in the case of $\bar{x}$, $\bar{p}$ is a random variable. If every possible sample of size 30 were selected from the population and if a value of $\bar{p}$ were computed for each sample, the resulting probability distribution would be the sampling distribution of $\bar{p}$. The relative frequency histogram of the 500 sample values in Figure 7.5 provides a general idea of the appearance of the sampling distribution of $\bar{p}$.

In practice, we select only one simple random sample from the population. We repeated the sampling process 500 times in this section simply to illustrate that many different samples are possible and that the different samples generate a variety of values for the sample statistics $\bar{x}$ and $\bar{p}$. The probability distribution of any particular sample statistic is called the sampling distribution of the statistic. In Section 7.5 we discuss the characteristics of the sampling distribution of $\bar{x}$. In Section 7.6 we discuss the characteristics of the sampling distribution of $\bar{p}$.

Sampling Distribution of $\bar{x}$

In the previous section we said that the sample mean $\bar{x}$ is a random variable and its probability distribution is called the sampling distribution of $\bar{x}$.

SAMPLING DISTRIBUTION OF $\bar{x}$

The sampling distribution of $\bar{x}$ is the probability distribution of all possible values of the sample mean $\bar{x}$.

This section describes the properties of the sampling distribution of $\bar{x}$. Just as with other probability distributions we studied, the sampling distribution of $\bar{x}$ has an expected value or mean, a standard deviation, and a characteristic shape or form. Let us begin by considering the mean of all possible $\bar{x}$ values, which is referred to as the expected value of $\bar{x}$.

Expected Value of $\bar{x}$

In the EAI sampling problem we saw that different simple random samples result in a variety of values for the sample mean $\bar{x}$. Because many different values of the random variable $\bar{x}$ are possible, we are often interested in the mean of all possible values of $\bar{x}$ that can be generated by the various simple random samples. The mean of the $\bar{x}$ random variable is the expected value of $\bar{x}$. Let $E(\bar{x})$ represent the expected value of $\bar{x}$ and μ represent the mean of the population from which we are selecting a simple random sample. It can be shown that with simple random sampling, $E(\bar{x})$ and μ are equal.

The expected value of $\bar{x}$ equals the mean of the population from which the sample is selected.

EXPECTED VALUE OF $\bar{x}$

$$E(\bar{x}) = \mu \tag{7.1}$$

where

$$E(\bar{x}) = \text{the expected value of } \bar{x}$$
$$\mu = \text{the population mean}$$

This result shows that with simple random sampling, the expected value or mean of the sampling distribution of $\bar{x}$ is equal to the mean of the population. In Section 7.1 we saw that the mean annual salary for the population of EAI employees is μ = \$51,800. Thus, according to equation (7.1), the mean of all possible sample means for the EAI study is also \$51,800.

When the expected value of a point estimator equals the population parameter, we say the point estimator is **unbiased**. Thus, equation (7.1) shows that $\bar{x}$ is an unbiased estimator of the population mean μ.

Standard Deviation of $\bar{x}$

Let us define the standard deviation of the sampling distribution of $\bar{x}$. We will use the following notation.

$\sigma_{\bar{x}}$ = the standard deviation of $\bar{x}$
σ = the standard deviation of the population
n = the sample size
N = the population size

It can be shown that the formula for the standard deviation of $\bar{x}$ depends on whether the population is finite or infinite. The two formulas for the standard deviation of $\bar{x}$ follow.

STANDARD DEVIATION OF $\bar{x}$

Finite Population	*Infinite Population*	
$\sigma_{\bar{x}} = \sqrt{\frac{N-n}{N-1}}\left(\frac{\sigma}{\sqrt{n}}\right)$	$\sigma_{\bar{x}} = \frac{\sigma}{\sqrt{n}}$	**(7.2)**

In comparing the two formulas in equation (7.2), we see that the factor $\sqrt{(N-n)/(N-1)}$ is required for the finite population case but not for the infinite population case. This factor is commonly referred to as the **finite population correction factor**. In many practical sampling situations, we find that the population involved, although finite, is "large," whereas the sample size is relatively "small." In such cases the finite population correction factor $\sqrt{(N-n)/(N-1)}$ is close to 1. As a result, the difference between the values of the standard deviation of $\bar{x}$ for the finite and infinite population cases becomes negligible. Then, $\sigma_{\bar{x}} = \sigma/\sqrt{n}$ becomes a good approximation to the standard deviation of $\bar{x}$ even though the population is finite. This observation leads to the following general guideline, or rule of thumb, for computing the standard deviation of $\bar{x}$.

USE THE FOLLOWING EXPRESSION TO COMPUTE THE STANDARD DEVIATION OF $\bar{x}$

$$\sigma_{\bar{x}} = \frac{\sigma}{\sqrt{n}} \tag{7.3}$$

whenever

1. The population is infinite; or
2. The population is finite *and* the sample size is less than or equal to 5% of the population size; that is, $n/N \leq .05$.

Exercise 17 shows that when $n/N \leq .05$, the finite population correction factor has little effect on the value of $\sigma_{\bar{x}}$.

In cases where $n/N > .05$, the finite population version of formula (7.2) should be used in the computation of $\sigma_{\bar{x}}$. Unless otherwise noted, throughout the text we will assume that the population size is "large," $n/N \leq .05$, and expression (7.3) can be used to compute $\sigma_{\bar{x}}$.

The term standard error *is used throughout statistical inference to refer to the standard deviation of a point estimator.*

To compute $\sigma_{\bar{x}}$, we need to know σ, the standard deviation of the population. To further emphasize the difference between $\sigma_{\bar{x}}$ and σ, we refer to the standard deviation of $\bar{x}$, $\sigma_{\bar{x}}$, as the **standard error** of the mean. In general, the term *standard error* refers to the standard deviation of a point estimator. Later we will see that the value of the standard error of the mean is helpful in determining how far the sample mean may be from the population mean. Let us now return to the EAI example and compute the standard error of the mean associated with simple random samples of 30 EAI employees.

In Section 7.1 we saw that the standard deviation of annual salary for the population of 2500 EAI employees is $\sigma = 4000$. In this case, the population is finite, with $N = 2500$. However, with a sample size of 30, we have $n/N = 30/2500 = .012$. Because the sample size is less than 5% of the population size, we can ignore the finite population correction factor and use equation (7.3) to compute the standard error.

$$\sigma_{\bar{x}} = \frac{\sigma}{\sqrt{n}} = \frac{4000}{\sqrt{30}} = 730.3$$

Form of the Sampling Distribution of $\bar{x}$

The preceding results concerning the expected value and standard deviation for the sampling distribution of $\bar{x}$ are applicable for any population. The final step in identifying the characteristics of the sampling distribution of $\bar{x}$ is to determine the form or shape of the sampling distribution. We will consider two cases: (1) The population has a normal distribution; and (2) the population does not have a normal distribution.

Population has a normal distribution In many situations it is reasonable to assume that the population from which we are selecting a random sample has a normal, or nearly normal, distribution. When the population has a normal distribution, the sampling distribution of $\bar{x}$ is normally distributed for any sample size.

Population does not have a normal distribution When the population from which we are selecting a random sample does not have a normal distribution, the **central limit theorem** is helpful in identifying the shape of the sampling distribution of $\bar{x}$. A statement of the central limit theorem as it applies to the sampling distribution of $\bar{x}$ follows.

CENTRAL LIMIT THEOREM

In selecting random samples of size n from a population, the sampling distribution of the sample mean $\bar{x}$ can be approximated by a *normal distribution* as the sample size becomes large.

Figure 7.6 shows how the central limit theorem works for three different populations; each column refers to one of the populations. The top panel of the figure shows that none of the populations are normally distributed. Population I follows a uniform distribution. Population II is often called the rabbit-eared distribution. It is symmetric, but the more likely values fall in the tails of the distribution. Population III is shaped like the exponential distribution; it is skewed to the right.

The bottom three panels of Figure 7.6 show the shape of the sampling distribution for samples of size $n = 2$, $n = 5$, and $n = 30$. When the sample size is 2, we see that the shape of each sampling distribution is different from the shape of the corresponding population distribution. For samples of size 5, we see that the shapes of the sampling distributions

FIGURE 7.6 ILLUSTRATION OF THE CENTRAL LIMIT THEOREM FOR THREE POPULATIONS

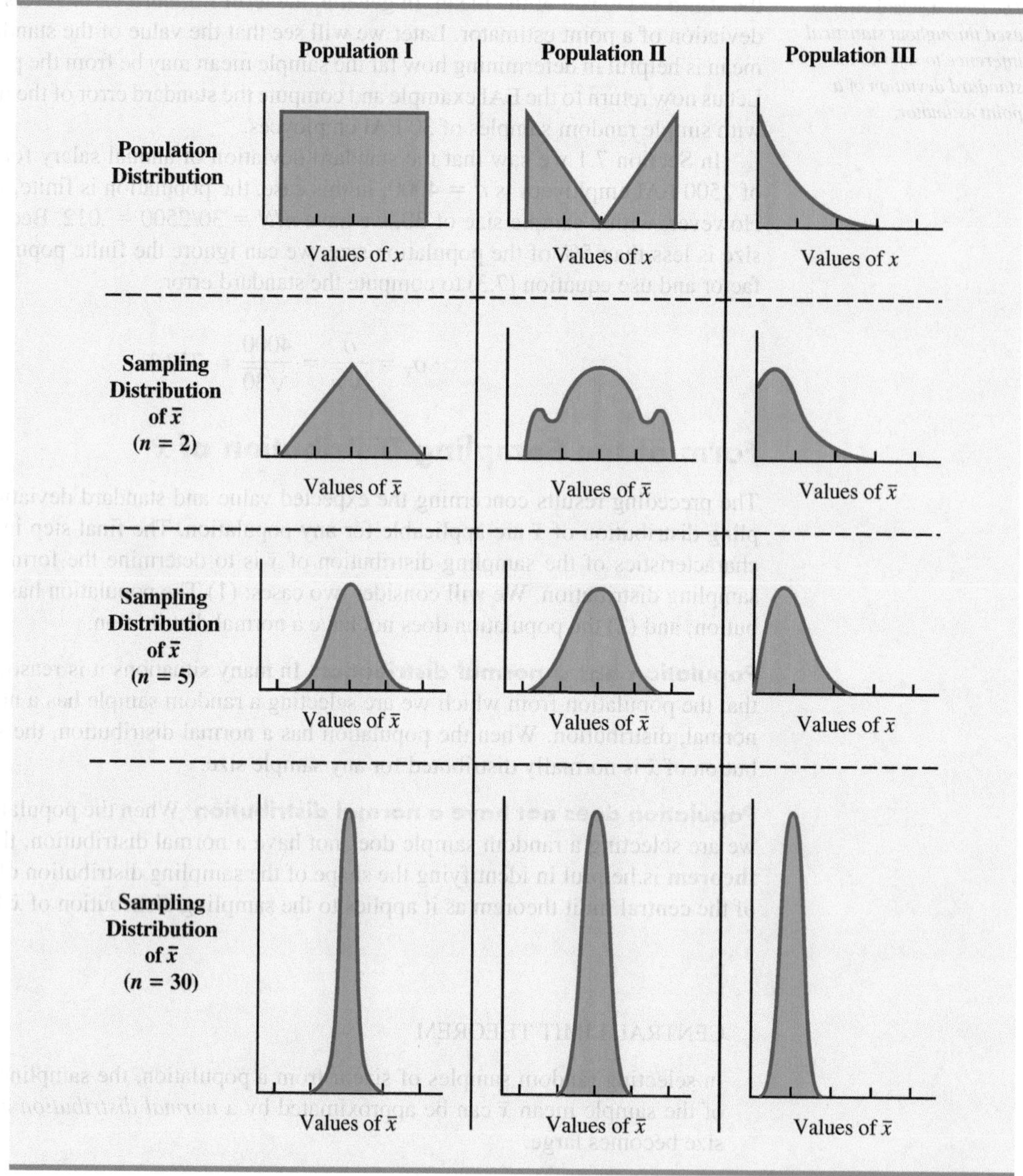

for populations I and II begin to look similar to the shape of a normal distribution. Even though the shape of the sampling distribution for population III begins to look similar to the shape of a normal distribution, some skewness to the right is still present. Finally, for samples of size 30, the shapes of each of the three sampling distributions are approximately normal.

From a practitioner standpoint, we often want to know how large the sample size needs to be before the central limit theorem applies and we can assume that the shape of the sampling distribution is approximately normal. Statistical researchers have investigated this question by studying the sampling distribution of $\bar{x}$ for a variety of populations and a variety of sample sizes. General statistical practice is to assume that, for most applications, the sampling distribution of $\bar{x}$ can be approximated by a normal distribution whenever the sample is size 30 or more. In cases where the population is highly skewed or outliers are present, samples of size 50 may be needed. Finally, if the population is discrete, the sample size needed for a normal approximation often depends on the population proportion. We say more about this issue when we discuss the sampling distribution of $\bar{p}$ in Section 7.6.

Sampling Distribution of $\bar{x}$ for the EAI Problem

Let us return to the EAI problem where we previously showed that $E(\bar{x}) = \$51,800$ and $\sigma_{\bar{x}} = 730.3$. At this point, we do not have any information about the population distribution; it may or may not be normally distributed. If the population has a normal distribution, the sampling distribution of $\bar{x}$ is normally distributed. If the population does not have a normal distribution, the simple random sample of 30 employees and the central limit theorem enable us to conclude that the sampling distribution of $\bar{x}$ can be approximated by a normal distribution. In either case, we are comfortable proceeding with the conclusion that the sampling distribution of $\bar{x}$ can be described by the normal distribution shown in Figure 7.7.

Practical Value of the Sampling Distribution of $\bar{x}$

Whenever a simple random sample is selected and the value of the sample mean is used to estimate the value of the population mean μ, we cannot expect the sample mean to exactly equal the population mean. The practical reason we are interested in the sampling distribution of $\bar{x}$ is that it can be used to provide probability information about the difference between the sample mean and the population mean. To demonstrate this use, let us return to the EAI problem.

Suppose the personnel director believes the sample mean will be an acceptable estimate of the population mean if the sample mean is within \$500 of the population mean. However, it is not possible to guarantee that the sample mean will be within \$500 of the population mean. Indeed, Table 7.5 and Figure 7.4 show that some of the 500 sample means differed

FIGURE 7.7 SAMPLING DISTRIBUTION OF $\bar{x}$ FOR THE MEAN ANNUAL SALARY OF A SIMPLE RANDOM SAMPLE OF 30 EAI EMPLOYEES

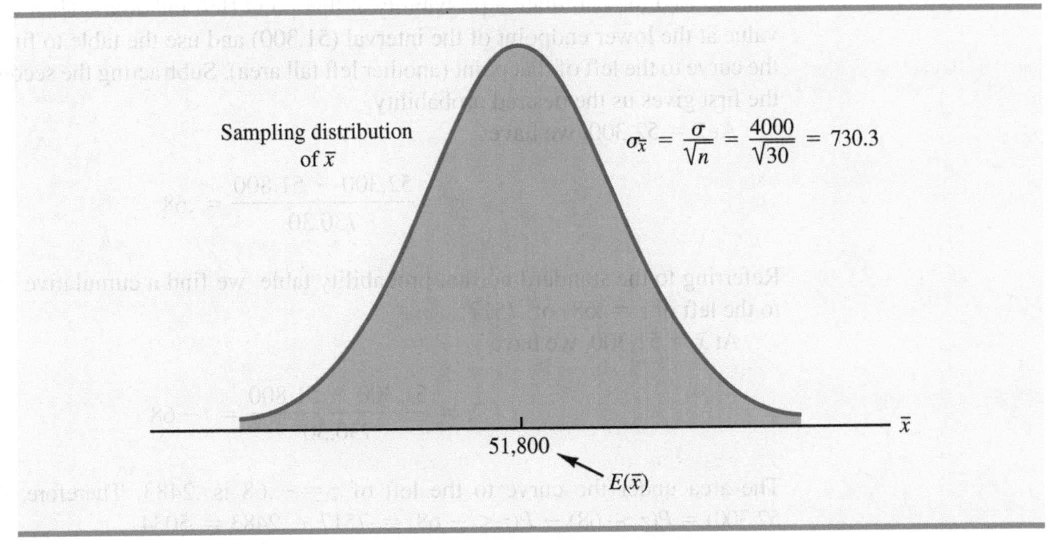

FIGURE 7.8 PROBABILITY OF A SAMPLE MEAN BEING WITHIN $500 OF THE POPULATION MEAN FOR A SIMPLE RANDOM SAMPLE OF 30 EAI EMPLOYEES

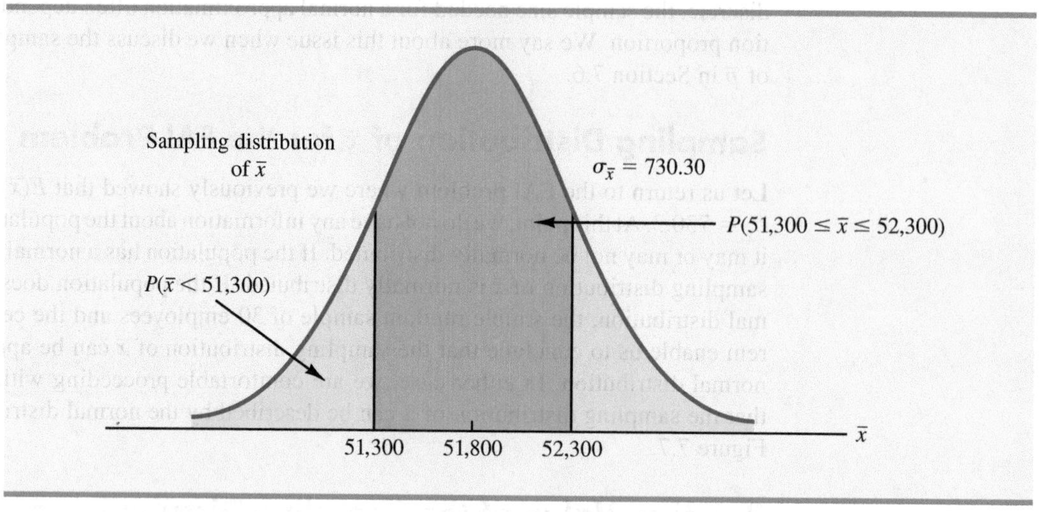

by more than $2000 from the population mean. So we must think of the personnel director's request in probability terms. That is, the personnel director is concerned with the following question: What is the probability that the sample mean computed using a simple random sample of 30 EAI employees will be within $500 of the population mean?

Because we have identified the properties of the sampling distribution of $\bar{x}$ (see Figure 7.7), we will use this distribution to answer the probability question. Refer to the sampling distribution of $\bar{x}$ shown again in Figure 7.8. With a population mean of $51,800, the personnel director wants to know the probability that $\bar{x}$ is between $51,300 and $52,300. This probability is given by the darkly shaded area of the sampling distribution shown in Figure 7.8. Because the sampling distribution is normally distributed, with mean 51,800 and standard error of the mean 730.3, we can use the standard normal probability table to find the area or probability.

We first calculate the z value at the upper endpoint of the interval (52,300) and use the table to find the cumulative probability at that point (left tail area). Then we compute the z value at the lower endpoint of the interval (51,300) and use the table to find the area under the curve to the left of that point (another left tail area). Subtracting the second tail area from the first gives us the desired probability.

At $\bar{x} = 52{,}300$, we have

$$z = \frac{52{,}300 - 51{,}800}{730.30} = .68$$

Referring to the standard normal probability table, we find a cumulative probability (area to the left of $z = .68$) of .7517.

At $\bar{x} = 51{,}300$, we have

$$z = \frac{51{,}300 - 51{,}800}{730.30} = -.68$$

The area under the curve to the left of $z = -.68$ is .2483. Therefore, $P(51{,}300 \le \bar{x} \le 52{,}300) = P(z \le .68) - P(z < -.68) = .7517 - .2483 = .5034$.

Using Excel's NORM.DIST function is easier and provides more accurate results than using the tables with rounded values for z.

The desired probability can also be computed using Excel's NORM.DIST function. The advantage of using the NORM.DIST function is that we do not have to make a separate computation of the z value. Evaluating the NORM.DIST function at the upper endpoint of the interval provides the cumulative probability at 52,300. Entering the formula =NORM.DIST(52300,51800,730.30,TRUE) into a cell of an Excel worksheet provides .7532 for this cumulative probability. Evaluating the NORM.DIST function at the lower endpoint of the interval provides the area under the curve to the left of 51,300. Entering the formula =NORM.DIST(51300,51800,730.30,TRUE) into a cell of an Excel worksheet provides .2468 for this cumulative probability. The probability of $\bar{x}$ being in the interval from 51,300 to 52,300 is then given by $.7532 - .2468 = .5064$. We note that this result is slightly different from the probability obtained using the table, because in using the normal table we rounded to two decimal places of accuracy when computing the z value. The result obtained using NORM.DIST is thus more accurate.

The sampling distribution of $\bar{x}$ can be used to provide probability information about how close the sample mean $\bar{x}$ is to the population mean μ.

The preceding computations show that a simple random sample of 30 EAI employees has a .5064 probability of providing a sample mean $\bar{x}$ that is within \$500 of the population mean. Thus, there is a $1 - .5064 = .4936$ probability that the sampling error will be more than \$500. In other words, a simple random sample of 30 EAI employees has roughly a 50–50 chance of providing a sample mean within the allowable \$500. Perhaps a larger sample size should be considered. Let us explore this possibility by considering the relationship between the sample size and the sampling distribution of $\bar{x}$.

Relationship Between the Sample Size and the Sampling Distribution of $\bar{x}$

Suppose that in the EAI sampling problem we select a simple random sample of 100 EAI employees instead of the 30 originally considered. Intuitively, it would seem that with more data provided by the larger sample size, the sample mean based on $n = 100$ should provide a better estimate of the population mean than the sample mean based on $n = 30$. To see how much better, let us consider the relationship between the sample size and the sampling distribution of $\bar{x}$.

First note that $E(\bar{x}) = \mu$ regardless of the sample size. Thus, the mean of all possible values of $\bar{x}$ is equal to the population mean μ regardless of the sample size n. However, note that the standard error of the mean, $\sigma_{\bar{x}} = \sigma/\sqrt{n}$, is related to the square root of the sample size. Whenever the sample size is increased, the standard error of the mean $\sigma_{\bar{x}}$ decreases. With $n = 30$, the standard error of the mean for the EAI problem is 730.3. However, with the increase in the sample size to $n = 100$, the standard error of the mean is decreased to

$$\sigma_{\bar{x}} = \frac{\sigma}{\sqrt{n}} = \frac{4000}{\sqrt{100}} = 400$$

The sampling distributions of $\bar{x}$ with $n = 30$ and $n = 100$ are shown in Figure 7.9. Because the sampling distribution with $n = 100$ has a smaller standard error, the values of $\bar{x}$ have less variation and tend to be closer to the population mean than the values of $\bar{x}$ with $n = 30$.

We can use the sampling distribution of $\bar{x}$ for the case with $n = 100$ to compute the probability that a simple random sample of 100 EAI employees will provide a sample mean that is within \$500 of the population mean. In this case the sampling distribution is normal with a mean of 51,800 and a standard deviation of 400 (see Figure 7.10). Again, we could compute the appropriate z values and use the standard normal probability distribution table to make this probability calculation. However, Excel's NORM.DIST function is easier to use and provides more accurate results. Entering the formula =NORM.DIST(52300,51800,400,TRUE) into a cell of an Excel worksheet provides the cumulative probability corresponding to $\bar{x} = 52{,}300$. The value provided by Excel is .8944. Entering the formula =NORM.DIST

FIGURE 7.9 A COMPARISON OF THE SAMPLING DISTRIBUTIONS OF $\bar{x}$ FOR SIMPLE RANDOM SAMPLES OF $n = 30$ AND $n = 100$ EAI EMPLOYEES

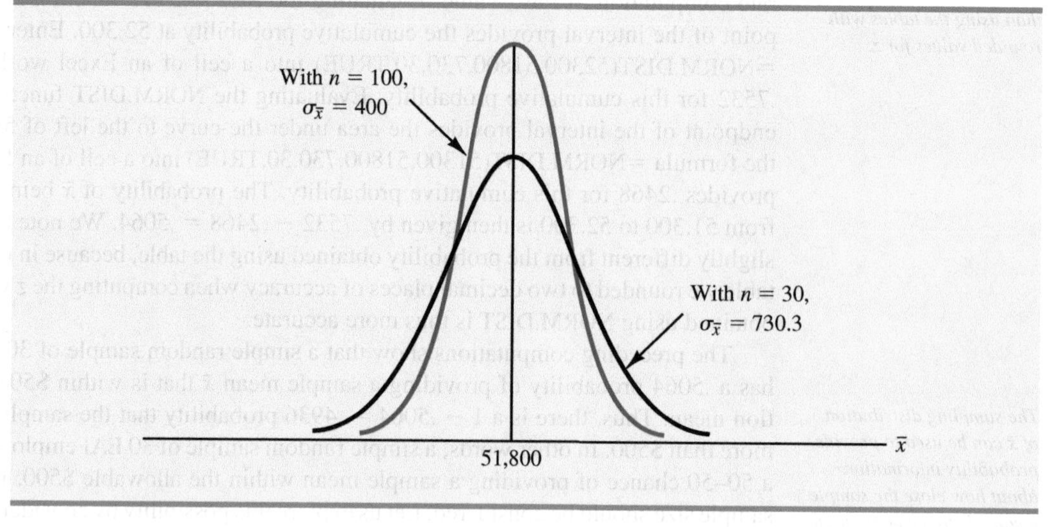

FIGURE 7.10 PROBABILITY OF A SAMPLE MEAN BEING WITHIN $500 OF THE POPULATION MEAN FOR A SIMPLE RANDOM SAMPLE OF 100 EAI EMPLOYEES

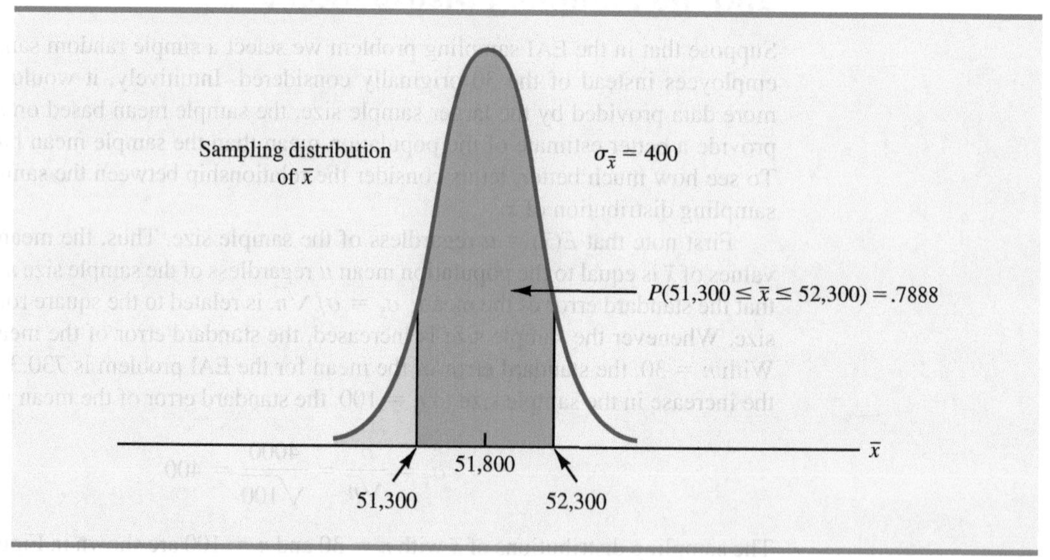

(51300,51800,400,TRUE) into a cell of an Excel worksheet provides the cumulative probability corresponding to $\bar{x} = 51{,}300$. The value provided by Excel is .1056. Thus, the probability of $\bar{x}$ being in the interval from 51,300 to 52,300 is given by $.8944 - .1056 = .7888$. By increasing the sample size from 30 to 100 EAI employees, we increase the probability that the sampling error will be $500 or less; that is, the probability of obtaining a sample mean within $500 of the population mean increases from .5064 to .7888.

The important point in this discussion is that as the sample size increases, the standard error of the mean decreases. As a result, a larger sample size will provide a higher probability that the sample mean falls within a specified distance of the population mean.

NOTE AND COMMENT

In presenting the sampling distribution of $\bar{x}$ for the EAI problem, we took advantage of the fact that the population mean $\mu = 51{,}800$ and the population standard deviation $\sigma = 4000$ were known. However, usually the values of the population mean μ and the population standard deviation σ that are needed to determine the sampling distribution of $\bar{x}$ will be unknown. In Chapter 8 we show how the sample mean $\bar{x}$ and the sample standard deviation s are used when μ and σ are unknown.

Exercises

Methods

15. A population has a mean of 200 and a standard deviation of 50. Suppose a simple random sample of size 100 is selected and $\bar{x}$ is used to estimate μ.
    a. What is the probability that the sample mean will be within ± 5 of the population mean?
    b. What is the probability that the sample mean will be within ± 10 of the population mean?
16. Assume the population standard deviation is $\sigma = 25$. Compute the standard error of the mean, $\sigma_{\bar{x}}$, for sample sizes of 50, 100, 150, and 200. What can you say about the size of the standard error of the mean as the sample size is increased?
17. Suppose a random sample of size 50 is selected from a population with $\sigma = 10$. Find the value of the standard error of the mean in each of the following cases (use the finite population correction factor if appropriate).
    a. The population size is infinite.
    b. The population size is $N = 50{,}000$.
    c. The population size is $N = 5000$.
    d. The population size is $N = 500$.

Applications

18. Refer to the EAI sampling problem. Suppose a simple random sample of 60 employees is used.
    a. Sketch the sampling distribution of $\bar{x}$ when simple random samples of size 60 are used.
    b. What happens to the sampling distribution of $\bar{x}$ if simple random samples of size 120 are used?
    c. What general statement can you make about what happens to the sampling distribution of $\bar{x}$ as the sample size is increased? Does this generalization seem logical? Explain.

19. In the EAI sampling problem (see Figure 7.8), we showed that for $n = 30$, there was .5064 probability of obtaining a sample mean within $\pm\$500$ of the population mean.
    a. What is the probability that $\bar{x}$ is within \$500 of the population mean if a sample of size 60 is used?
    b. Answer part (a) for a sample of size 120.
20. *Barron's* reported that the average number of weeks an individual is unemployed is 17.5 weeks (*Barron's*, February 18, 2008). Assume that for the population of all unemployed individuals the population mean length of unemployment is 17.5 weeks and that the population standard deviation is 4 weeks. Suppose you would like to select a random sample of 50 unemployed individuals for a follow-up study.
    a. Show the sampling distribution of $\bar{x}$, the sample mean average for a sample of 50 unemployed individuals.
    b. What is the probability that a simple random sample of 50 unemployed individuals will provide a sample mean within 1 week of the population mean?

c. What is the probability that a simple random sample of 50 unemployed individuals will provide a sample mean within 1/2 week of the population mean?

21. The College Board reported the following mean scores for the three parts of the SAT (*The World Almanac*, 2009):

Critical Reading	502
Mathematics	515
Writing	494

Assume that the population standard deviation on each part of the test is $\sigma = 100$.

a. What is the probability that a random sample of 90 test takers will provide a sample mean test score within 10 points of the population mean of 502 on the Critical Reading part of the test?

b. What is the probability that a random sample of 90 test takers will provide a sample mean test score within 10 points of the population mean of 515 on the Mathematics part of the test? Compare this probability to the value computed in part (a).

c. What is the probability that a random sample of 100 test takers will provide a sample mean test score within 10 of the population mean of 494 on the Writing part of the test? Comment on the differences between this probability and the values computed in parts (a) and (b).

22. For the year 2010, 33% of taxpayers with adjusted gross incomes between $30,000 and $60,000 itemized deductions on their federal income tax return (*The Wall Street Journal*, October 25, 2012). The mean amount of deductions for this population of taxpayers was $16,642. Assume the standard deviation is $\sigma = \$2400$.

a. What is the probability that a sample of taxpayers from this income group who have itemized deductions will show a sample mean within $200 of the population mean for each of the following sample sizes: 30, 50, 100, and 400?

b. What is the advantage of a larger sample size when attempting to estimate the population mean?

23. The Economic Policy Institute periodically issues reports on wages of entry-level workers. The institute reported that entry-level wages for male college graduates were $21.68 per hour and for female college graduates were $18.80 per hour in 2011 (Economic Policy Institute website, March 30, 2012). Assume the standard deviation for male graduates is $2.30, and for female graduates it is $2.05.

a. What is the probability that a sample of 50 male graduates will provide a sample mean within $.50 of the population mean, $21.68?

b. What is the probability that a sample of 50 female graduates will provide a sample mean within $.50 of the population mean, $18.80?

c. In which of the preceding two cases, part (a) or part (b), do we have a higher probability of obtaining a sample estimate within $.50 of the population mean? Why?

d. What is the probability that a sample of 120 female graduates will provide a sample mean more than $.30 below the population mean?

24. The state of California has a mean annual rainfall of 22 inches, whereas the state of New York has a mean annual rainfall of 42 inches (Current Results website, October 27, 2012). Assume that the standard deviation for both states is 4 inches. A sample of 30 years of rainfall for California and a sample of 45 years of rainfall for New York has been taken.

a. Show the probability distribution of the sample mean annual rainfall for California.

b. What is the probability that the sample mean is within 1 inch of the population mean for California?

c. What is the probability that the sample mean is within 1 inch of the population mean for New York?

d. In which case, part (b) or part (c), is the probability of obtaining a sample mean within 1 inch of the population mean greater? Why?

25. The mean preparation fee H&R Block charged retail customers in 2012 was $183 (*The Wall Street Journal*, March 7, 2012). Use this price as the population mean and assume the population standard deviation of preparation fees is $50.
    a. What is the probability that the mean price for a sample of 30 H&R Block retail customers is within $8 of the population mean?
    b. What is the probability that the mean price for a sample of 50 H&R Block retail customers is within $8 of the population mean?
    c. What is the probability that the mean price for a sample of 100 H&R Block retail customers is within $8 of the population mean?
    d. Which, if any, of the sample sizes in parts (a), (b), and (c) would you recommend to have at least a .95 probability that the sample mean is within $8 of the population mean?

26. To estimate the mean age for a population of 4000 employees, a simple random sample of 40 employees is selected.
    a. Would you use the finite population correction factor in calculating the standard error of the mean? Explain.
    b. If the population standard deviation is $\sigma = 8.2$ years, compute the standard error both with and without the finite population correction factor. What is the rationale for ignoring the finite population correction factor whenever $n/N \leq .05$?
    c. What is the probability that the sample mean age of the employees will be within ± 2 years of the population mean age?

7.6 Sampling Distribution of $\bar{p}$

The sample proportion $\bar{p}$ is the point estimator of the population proportion p. The formula for computing the sample proportion is

$$\bar{p} = \frac{x}{n}$$

where

x = the number of elements in the sample that possess the characteristic of interest

n = sample size

As noted in Section 7.4, the sample proportion $\bar{p}$ is a random variable and its probability distribution is called the sampling distribution of $\bar{p}$.

SAMPLING DISTRIBUTION OF $\bar{p}$

The sampling distribution of $\bar{p}$ is the probability distribution of all possible values of the sample proportion $\bar{p}$.

To determine how close the sample proportion $\bar{p}$ is to the population proportion p, we need to understand the properties of the sampling distribution of $\bar{p}$: the expected value of $\bar{p}$, the standard deviation of $\bar{p}$, and the shape or form of the sampling distribution of $\bar{p}$.

Expected Value of $\bar{p}$

The expected value of $\bar{p}$, the mean of all possible values of $\bar{p}$, is equal to the population proportion p.

EXPECTED VALUE OF $\bar{p}$

$$E(\bar{p}) = p \tag{7.4}$$

where

$$E(\bar{p}) = \text{the expected value of } \bar{p}$$
$$p = \text{the population proportion}$$

Because $E(\bar{p}) = p$, $\bar{p}$ is an unbiased estimator of p. Recall from Section 7.1 we noted that $p = .60$ for the EAI population, where p is the proportion of the population of employees who participated in the company's management training program. Thus, the expected value of $\bar{p}$ for the EAI sampling problem is .60.

Standard Deviation of $\bar{p}$

Just as we found for the standard deviation of $\bar{x}$, the standard deviation of $\bar{p}$ depends on whether the population is finite or infinite. The two formulas for computing the standard deviation of $\bar{p}$ follow.

STANDARD DEVIATION OF $\bar{p}$

Finite Population *Infinite Population*

$$\sigma_{\bar{p}} = \sqrt{\frac{N-n}{N-1}}\sqrt{\frac{p(1-p)}{n}} \qquad \sigma_{\bar{p}} = \sqrt{\frac{p(1-p)}{n}} \tag{7.5}$$

Comparing the two formulas in equation (7.5), we see that the only difference is the use of the finite population correction factor $\sqrt{(N-n)/(N-1)}$.

As was the case with the sample mean $\bar{x}$, the difference between the expressions for the finite population and the infinite population becomes negligible if the size of the finite population is large in comparison to the sample size. We follow the same rule of thumb that we recommended for the sample mean. That is, if the population is finite with $n/N \leq .05$, we will use $\sigma_{\bar{p}} = \sqrt{p(1-p)/n}$. However, if the population is finite with $n/N > .05$, the finite population correction factor should be used. Again, unless specifically noted, throughout the text we will assume that the population size is large in relation to the sample size and thus the finite population correction factor is unnecessary.

In Section 7.5 we used the term *standard error of the mean* to refer to the standard deviation of $\bar{x}$. We stated that in general the term *standard error* refers to the standard deviation of a point estimator. Thus, for proportions we use *standard error of the proportion* to refer to the standard deviation of $\bar{p}$. Let us now return to the EAI example and compute the standard error of the proportion associated with simple random samples of 30 EAI employees.

For the EAI study we know that the population proportion of employees who participated in the management training program is $p = .60$. With $n/N = 30/2500 = .012$, we can ignore the finite population correction factor when we compute the standard error of the proportion. For the simple random sample of 30 employees, $\sigma_{\bar{p}}$ is

$$\sigma_{\bar{p}} = \sqrt{\frac{p(1-p)}{n}} = \sqrt{\frac{.60(1-.60)}{30}} = .0894$$

Form of the Sampling Distribution of $\bar{p}$

Now that we know the mean and standard deviation of the sampling distribution of $\bar{p}$, the final step is to determine the form or shape of the sampling distribution. The sample proportion is $\bar{p} = x/n$. For a simple random sample from a large population, the value of x is a binomial random variable indicating the number of elements in the sample with the characteristic of interest. Because n is a constant, the probability of x/n is the same as the binomial probability of x, which means that the sampling distribution of $\bar{p}$ is also a discrete probability distribution and that the probability for each value of x/n is the same as the probability of x.

Statisticians have shown that a binomial distribution can be approximated by a normal distribution whenever the sample size is large enough to satisfy the following two conditions:

$$np \geq 5 \quad \text{and} \quad n(1 - p) \geq 5$$

Assuming these two conditions are satisfied, the probability distribution of x in the sample proportion, $\bar{p} = x/n$, can be approximated by a normal distribution. And because n is a constant, the sampling distribution of $\bar{p}$ can also be approximated by a normal distribution. This approximation is stated as follows:

> The sampling distribution of $\bar{p}$ can be approximated by a normal distribution whenever $np \geq 5$ and $n(1 - p) \geq 5$.

In practical applications, when an estimate of a population proportion is desired, we find that sample sizes are almost always large enough to permit the use of a normal approximation for the sampling distribution of $\bar{p}$.

Recall that for the EAI sampling problem we know that the population proportion of employees who participated in the training program is $p = .60$. With a simple random sample of size 30, we have $np = 30(.60) = 18$ and $n(1 - p) = 30(.40) = 12$. Thus, the sampling distribution of $\bar{p}$ can be approximated by a normal distribution shown in Figure 7.11.

FIGURE 7.11 SAMPLING DISTRIBUTION OF $\bar{p}$ FOR THE PROPORTION OF EAI EMPLOYEES WHO PARTICIPATED IN THE MANAGEMENT TRAINING PROGRAM

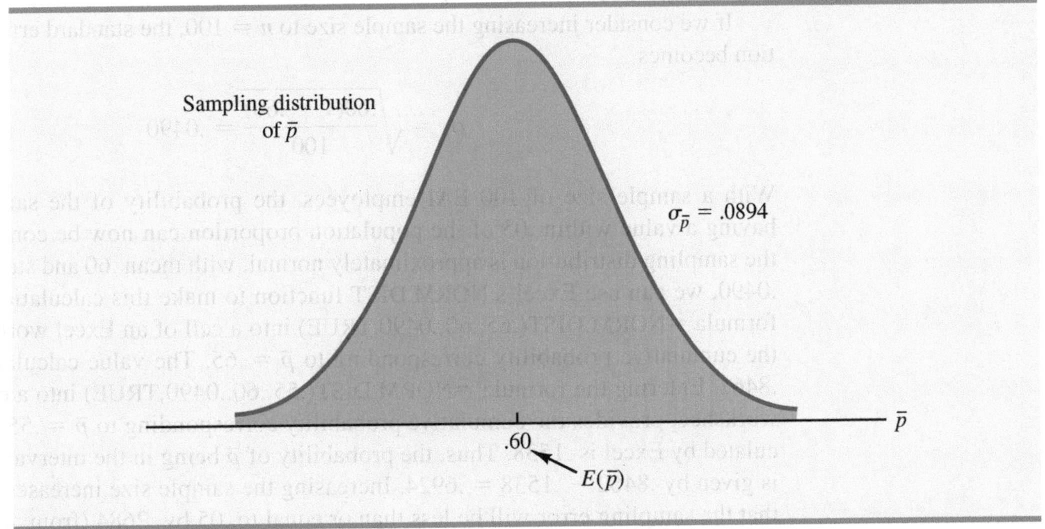

FIGURE 7.12 PROBABILITY OF OBTAINING $\bar{p}$ BETWEEN .55 AND .65

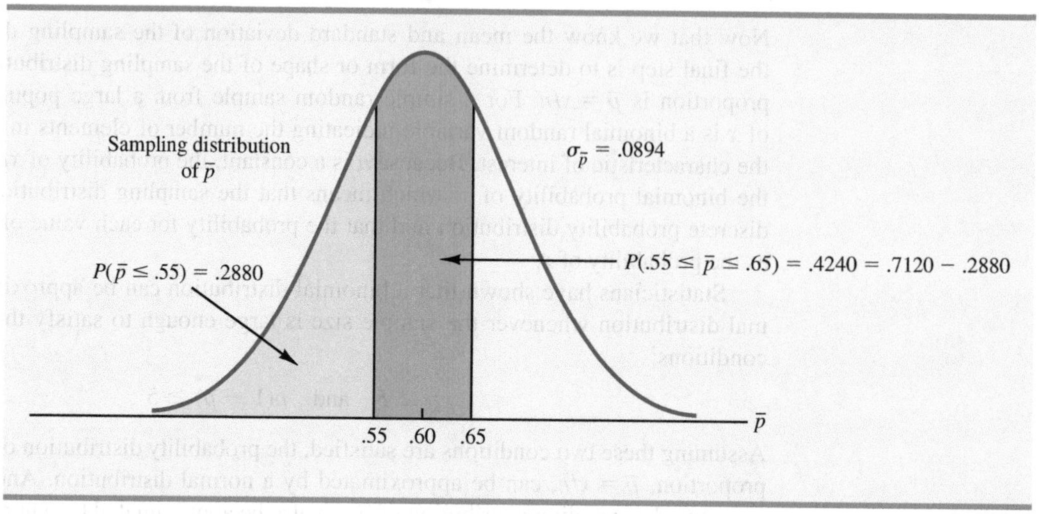

Practical Value of the Sampling Distribution of $\bar{p}$

The practical value of the sampling distribution of $\bar{p}$ is that it can be used to provide probability information about the difference between the sample proportion and the population proportion. For instance, suppose that in the EAI problem the personnel director wants to know the probability of obtaining a value of $\bar{p}$ that is within .05 of the population proportion of EAI employees who participated in the training program. That is, what is the probability of obtaining a sample with a sample proportion $\bar{p}$ between .55 and .65? The darkly shaded area in Figure 7.12 shows this probability. Using the fact that the sampling distribution of $\bar{p}$ can be approximated by a normal probability distribution with a mean of .60 and a standard error of $\sigma_{\bar{p}} = .0894$, we can use Excel's NORM.DIST function to make this calculation. Entering the formula =NORM.DIST(.65,.60,.0894,TRUE) into a cell of an Excel worksheet provides the cumulative probability corresponding to $\bar{p} = .65$. The value calculated by Excel is .7120. Entering the formula =NORM.DIST(.55,.60,.0894,TRUE) into a cell of an Excel worksheet provides the cumulative probability corresponding to $\bar{p} = .55$. The value calculated by Excel is .2880. Thus, the probability of $\bar{p}$ being in the interval from .55 to .65 is given by $.7120 - .2880 = .4240$.

If we consider increasing the sample size to $n = 100$, the standard error of the proportion becomes

$$\sigma_{\bar{p}} = \sqrt{\frac{.60(1 - .60)}{100}} = .0490$$

With a sample size of 100 EAI employees, the probability of the sample proportion having a value within .05 of the population proportion can now be computed. Because the sampling distribution is approximately normal, with mean .60 and standard deviation .0490, we can use Excel's NORM.DIST function to make this calculation. Entering the formula =NORM.DIST(.65,.60,.0490,TRUE) into a cell of an Excel worksheet provides the cumulative probability corresponding to $\bar{p} = .65$. The value calculated by Excel is .8462. Entering the formula =NORM.DIST(.55,.60,.0490,TRUE) into a cell of an Excel worksheet provides the cumulative probability corresponding to $\bar{p} = .55$. The value calculated by Excel is .1538. Thus, the probability of $\bar{p}$ being in the interval from .55 to .65 is given by $.8462 - .1538 = .6924$. Increasing the sample size increases the probability that the sampling error will be less than or equal to .05 by .2684 (from .4240 to .6924).

Exercises

Methods

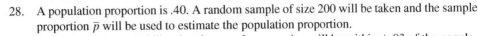

27. A random sample of size 100 is selected from a population with $p = .40$.
    a. What is the expected value of $\overline{p}$?
    b. What is the standard error of $\overline{p}$?
    c. Show the sampling distribution of $\overline{p}$.
    d. What does the sampling distribution of $\overline{p}$ show?

SELF test

28. A population proportion is .40. A random sample of size 200 will be taken and the sample proportion $\overline{p}$ will be used to estimate the population proportion.
    a. What is the probability that the sample proportion will be within $\pm.03$ of the population proportion?
    b. What is the probability that the sample proportion will be within $\pm.05$ of the population proportion?

29. Assume that the population proportion is .55. Compute the standard error of the proportion, $\sigma_{\overline{p}}$, for sample sizes of 100, 200, 500, and 1000. What can you say about the size of the standard error of the proportion as the sample size is increased?

30. The population proportion is .30. What is the probability that a sample proportion will be within $\pm.04$ of the population proportion for each of the following sample sizes?
    a. $n = 100$
    b. $n = 200$
    c. $n = 500$
    d. $n = 1000$
    e. What is the advantage of a larger sample size?

Applications

31. The president of Doerman Distributors, Inc., believes that 30% of the firm's orders come from first-time customers. A random sample of 100 orders will be used to estimate the proportion of first-time customers.
    a. Assume that the president is correct and $p = .30$. What is the sampling distribution of $\overline{p}$ for this study?
    b. What is the probability that the sample proportion $\overline{p}$ will be between .20 and .40?
    c. What is the probability that the sample proportion will be between .25 and .35?

32. *The Wall Street Journal* reported that the age at first startup for 55% of entrepreneurs was 29 years of age or less and the age at first startup for 45% of entrepreneurs was 30 years of age or more (*The Wall Street Journal*, March 19, 2012).
    a. Suppose a sample of 200 entrepreneurs will be taken to learn about the most important qualities of entrepreneurs. Show the sampling distribution of $\overline{p}$ where $\overline{p}$ is the sample proportion of entrepreneurs whose first startup was at 29 years of age or less.
    b. What is the probability that the sample proportion in part (a) will be within $\pm.05$ of its population proportion?
    c. Suppose a sample of 200 entrepreneurs will be taken to learn about the most important qualities of entrepreneurs. Show the sampling distribution of $\overline{p}$ where $\overline{p}$ is now the sample proportion of entrepreneurs whose first startup was at 30 years of age or more.
    d. What is the probability that the sample proportion in part (c) will be within $\pm.05$ of its population proportion?
    e. Is the probability different in parts (b) and (d)? Why?
    f. Answer part (b) for a sample of size 400. Is the probability smaller? Why?

33. People end up tossing 12% of what they buy at the grocery store (*Reader's Digest*, March, 2009). Assume this is the true population proportion and that you plan to take a sample survey of 540 grocery shoppers to further investigate their behavior.

a. Show the sampling distribution of $\bar{p}$, the proportion of groceries thrown out by your sample respondents.
b. What is the probability that your survey will provide a sample proportion within $\pm.03$ of the population proportion?
c. What is the probability that your survey will provide a sample proportion within $\pm.015$ of the population proportion?

34. Forty-two percent of primary care doctors think their patients receive unnecessary medical care (*Reader's Digest*, December 2011/January 2012).
a. Suppose a sample of 300 primary care doctors was taken. Show the sampling distribution of the proportion of the doctors who think their patients receive unnecessary medical care.
b. What is the probability that the sample proportion will be within $\pm.03$ of the population proportion?
c. What is the probability that the sample proportion will be within $\pm.05$ of the population proportion?
d. What would be the effect of taking a larger sample on the probabilities in parts (b) and (c)? Why?

35. In 2008 the Better Business Bureau settled 75% of complaints it received (*USA Today*, March 2, 2009). Suppose you have been hired by the Better Business Bureau to investigate the complaints it received this year involving new car dealers. You plan to select a sample of new car dealer complaints to estimate the proportion of complaints the Better Business Bureau is able to settle. Assume the population proportion of complaints settled for new car dealers is .75, the same as the overall proportion of complaints settled in 2008.
a. Suppose you select a sample of 450 complaints involving new car dealers. Show the sampling distribution of $\bar{p}$.
b. Based upon a sample of 450 complaints, what is the probability that the sample proportion will be within .04 of the population proportion?
c. Suppose you select a sample of 200 complaints involving new car dealers. Show the sampling distribution of $\bar{p}$.
d. Based upon the smaller sample of only 200 complaints, what is the probability that the sample proportion will be within .04 of the population proportion?
e. As measured by the increase in probability, how much do you gain in precision by taking the larger sample in part (b)?

36. The Grocery Manufacturers of America reported that 76% of consumers read the ingredients listed on a product's label. Assume the population proportion is $p = .76$ and a sample of 400 consumers is selected from the population.
a. Show the sampling distribution of the sample proportion $\bar{p}$, where $\bar{p}$ is the proportion of the sampled consumers who read the ingredients listed on a product's label.
b. What is the probability that the sample proportion will be within $\pm.03$ of the population proportion?
c. Answer part (b) for a sample of 750 consumers.

37. The Food Marketing Institute shows that 17% of households spend more than \$100 per week on groceries. Assume the population proportion is $p = .17$ and a simple random sample of 800 households will be selected from the population.
a. Show the sampling distribution of $\bar{p}$, the sample proportion of households spending more than \$100 per week on groceries.
b. What is the probability that the sample proportion will be within $\pm.02$ of the population proportion?
c. Answer part (b) for a sample of 1600 households.

Other Sampling Methods

This section provides a brief introduction to survey sampling methods other than simple random sampling.

We described simple random sampling as a procedure for sampling from a finite population and discussed the properties of the sampling distributions of $\bar{x}$ and $\bar{p}$ when simple random sampling is used. Other methods such as stratified random sampling, cluster sampling, and systematic sampling provide advantages over simple random sampling in some of these situations. In this section we briefly introduce these alternative sampling methods.

Stratified Random Sampling

Stratified random sampling works best when the variance among elements in each stratum is relatively small.

In **stratified random sampling,** the elements in the population are first divided into groups called *strata,* such that each element in the population belongs to one and only one stratum. The basis for forming the strata, such as department, location, age, industry type, and so on, is at the discretion of the designer of the sample. However, the best results are obtained when the elements within each stratum are as much alike as possible. Figure 7.13 is a diagram of a population divided into H strata.

After the strata are formed, a simple random sample is taken from each stratum. Formulas are available for combining the results for the individual stratum samples into one estimate of the population parameter of interest. The value of stratified random sampling depends on how homogeneous the elements are within the strata. If elements within strata are alike, the strata will have low variances. Thus relatively small sample sizes can be used to obtain good estimates of the strata characteristics. If strata are homogeneous, the stratified random sampling procedure provides results just as precise as those of simple random sampling by using a smaller total sample size.

Cluster Sampling

Cluster sampling works best when each cluster provides a small-scale representation of the population.

In **cluster sampling,** the elements in the population are first divided into separate groups called *clusters.* Each element of the population belongs to one and only one cluster (see Figure 7.14). A simple random sample of the clusters is then taken. All elements within each sampled cluster form the sample. Cluster sampling tends to provide the best results when the elements within the clusters are not alike. In the ideal case, each cluster is a representative small-scale version of the entire population. The value of cluster sampling depends on how representative each cluster is of the entire population. If all clusters are alike in this regard, sampling a small number of clusters will provide good estimates of the population parameters.

FIGURE 7.13 DIAGRAM FOR STRATIFIED RANDOM SAMPLING

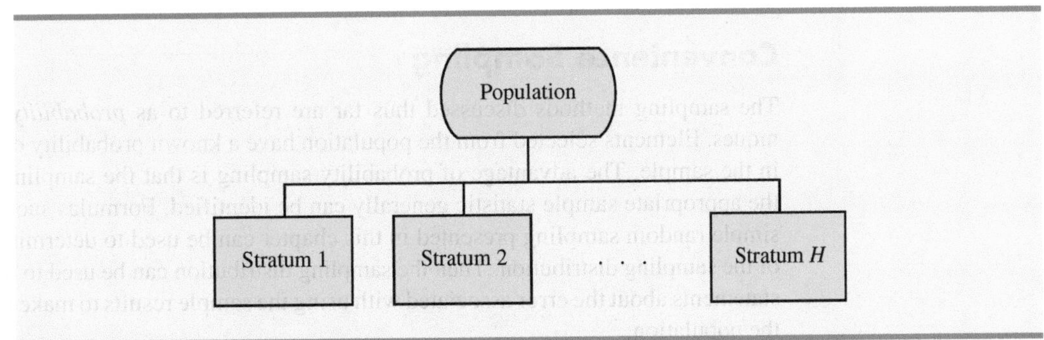

FIGURE 7.14 DIAGRAM FOR CLUSTER SAMPLING

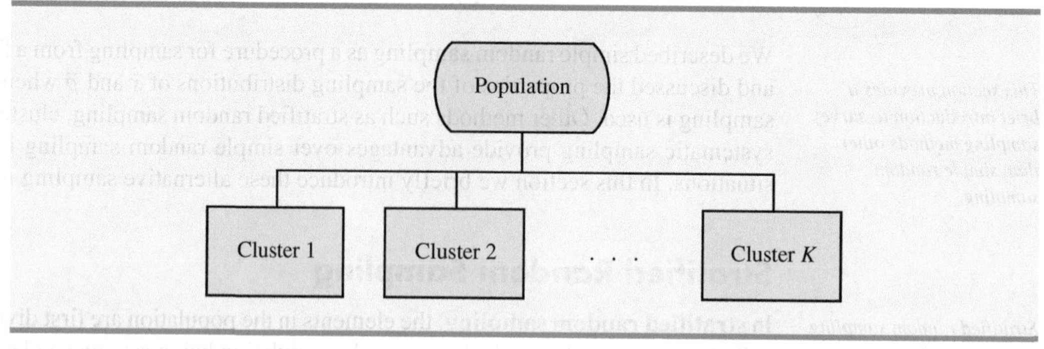

One of the primary applications of cluster sampling is area sampling, where clusters are city blocks or other well-defined areas. Cluster sampling generally requires a larger total sample size than either simple random sampling or stratified random sampling. However, it can result in cost savings because of the fact that when an interviewer is sent to a sampled cluster (e.g., a city-block location), many sample observations can be obtained in a relatively short time. Hence, a larger sample size may be obtainable with a significantly lower total cost.

Systematic Sampling

In some sampling situations, especially those with large populations, it is time-consuming to select a simple random sample by first finding a random number and then counting or searching through the list of the population until the corresponding element is found. An alternative to simple random sampling is **systematic sampling**. For example, if a sample size of 50 is desired from a population containing 5000 elements, we will sample one element for every 5000/50 = 100 elements in the population. A systematic sample for this case involves selecting randomly one of the first 100 elements from the population list. Other sample elements are identified by starting with the first sampled element and then selecting every 100th element that follows in the population list. In effect, the sample of 50 is identified by moving systematically through the population and identifying every 100th element after the first randomly selected element. The sample of 50 usually will be easier to identify in this way than it would be if simple random sampling were used. Because the first element selected is a random choice, a systematic sample is usually assumed to have the properties of a simple random sample. This assumption is especially applicable when the list of elements in the population is a random ordering of the elements.

Convenience Sampling

The sampling methods discussed thus far are referred to as *probability sampling* techniques. Elements selected from the population have a known probability of being included in the sample. The advantage of probability sampling is that the sampling distribution of the appropriate sample statistic generally can be identified. Formulas such as the ones for simple random sampling presented in this chapter can be used to determine the properties of the sampling distribution. Then the sampling distribution can be used to make probability statements about the error associated with using the sample results to make inferences about the population.

Convenience sampling is a *nonprobability sampling* technique. As the name implies, the sample is identified primarily by convenience. Elements are included in the sample without prespecified or known probabilities of being selected. For example, a professor conducting research at a university may use student volunteers to constitute a sample simply because they are readily available and will participate as subjects for little or no cost. Similarly, an inspector may sample a shipment of oranges by selecting oranges haphazardly from among several crates. Labeling each orange and using a probability method of sampling would be impractical. Samples such as wildlife captures and volunteer panels for consumer research are also convenience samples.

Convenience samples have the advantage of relatively easy sample selection and data collection; however, it is impossible to evaluate the "goodness" of the sample in terms of its representativeness of the population. A convenience sample may provide good results or it may not; no statistically justified procedure allows a probability analysis and inference about the quality of the sample results. Sometimes researchers apply statistical methods designed for probability samples to a convenience sample, arguing that the convenience sample can be treated as though it were a probability sample. However, this argument cannot be supported, and we should be cautious in interpreting the results of convenience samples that are used to make inferences about populations.

Judgment Sampling

One additional nonprobability sampling technique is **judgment sampling**. In this approach, the person most knowledgeable on the subject of the study selects elements of the population that he or she feels are most representative of the population. Often this method is a relatively easy way of selecting a sample. For example, a reporter may sample two or three senators, judging that those senators reflect the general opinion of all senators. However, the quality of the sample results depends on the judgment of the person selecting the sample. Again, great caution is warranted in drawing conclusions based on judgment samples used to make inferences about populations.

NOTE AND COMMENT

We recommend using probability sampling methods when sampling from finite populations: simple random sampling, stratified random sampling, cluster sampling, or systematic sampling. For these methods, formulas are available for evaluating the "goodness" of the sample results in terms of the closeness of the results to the population parameters being estimated. An evaluation of the goodness cannot be made with convenience or judgment sampling. Thus, great care should be used in interpreting the results based on nonprobability sampling methods.

Summary

In this chapter we presented the concepts of sampling and sampling distributions. We demonstrated how a simple random sample can be selected from a finite population and how a random sample can be selected from an infinite population. The data collected from such samples can be used to develop point estimates of population parameters. Because different samples provide different values for the point estimators, point estimators such as $\bar{x}$ and $\bar{p}$ are random variables. The probability distribution of such a random variable is called a sampling distribution. In particular, we described in detail the sampling distributions of the sample mean $\bar{x}$ and the sample proportion $\bar{p}$.

In considering the characteristics of the sampling distributions of $\bar{x}$ and $\bar{p}$, we stated that $E(\bar{x}) = \mu$ and $E(\bar{p}) = p$. After developing the standard deviation or standard error formulas for these estimators, we described the conditions necessary for the sampling distributions of $\bar{x}$ and $\bar{p}$ to follow a normal distribution. Other sampling methods including stratified random sampling, cluster sampling, systematic sampling, convenience sampling, and judgment sampling were discussed.

Glossary

Sampled population The population from which the sample is taken.
Frame A listing of the elements the sample will be selected from.
Parameter A numerical characteristic of a population, such as a population mean μ, a population standard deviation σ, a population proportion p, and so on.
Simple random sample A simple random sample of size n from a finite population of size N is a sample selected such that each possible sample of size n has the same probability of being selected.
Random sample A random sample from an infinite population is a sample selected such that the following conditions are satisfied: (1) Each element selected comes from the same population; (2) each element is selected independently.
Sample statistic A sample characteristic, such as a sample mean $\bar{x}$, a sample standard deviation s, a sample proportion $\bar{p}$, and so on. The value of the sample statistic is used to estimate the value of the corresponding population parameter.
Point estimator The sample statistic, such as $\bar{x}$, s, or $\bar{p}$, that provides the point estimate of the population parameter.
Point estimate The value of a point estimator used in a particular instance as an estimate of a population parameter.
Target population The population for which statistical inferences such as point estimates are made. It is important for the target population to correspond as closely as possible to the sampled population.
Sampling distribution A probability distribution consisting of all possible values of a sample statistic.
Unbiased A property of a point estimator that is present when the expected value of the point estimator is equal to the population parameter it estimates.
Finite population correction factor The term $\sqrt{(N - n)/(N - 1)}$ that is used in the formulas for $\sigma_{\bar{x}}$ and $\sigma_{\bar{p}}$ whenever a finite population, rather than an infinite population, is being sampled. The generally accepted rule of thumb is to ignore the finite population correction factor whenever $n/N \leq .05$.
Standard error The standard deviation of a point estimator.
Central limit theorem A theorem that enables one to use the normal probability distribution to approximate the sampling distribution of $\bar{x}$ whenever the sample size is large.
Stratified random sampling A probability sampling method in which the population is first divided into strata and a simple random sample is then taken from each stratum.
Cluster sampling A probability sampling method in which the population is first divided into clusters and then a simple random sample of the clusters is taken.
Systematic sampling A probability sampling method in which we randomly select one of the first k elements and then select every kth element thereafter.
Convenience sampling A nonprobability method of sampling whereby elements are selected for the sample on the basis of convenience.
Judgment sampling A nonprobability method of sampling whereby elements are selected for the sample based on the judgment of the person doing the study.

Key Formulas

Expected Value of $\bar{x}$

$$E(\bar{x}) = \mu \tag{7.1}$$

Standard Deviation of $\bar{x}$ (Standard Error)

Finite Population	*Infinite Population*	
$\sigma_{\bar{x}} = \sqrt{\frac{N-n}{N-1}}\left(\frac{\sigma}{\sqrt{n}}\right)$	$\sigma_{\bar{x}} = \frac{\sigma}{\sqrt{n}}$	(7.2)

Expected Value of $\bar{p}$

$$E(\bar{p}) = p \tag{7.4}$$

Standard Deviation of $\bar{p}$ (Standard Error)

Finite Population	*Infinite Population*	
$\sigma_{\bar{p}} = \sqrt{\frac{N-n}{N-1}}\sqrt{\frac{p(1-p)}{n}}$	$\sigma_{\bar{p}} = \sqrt{\frac{p(1-p)}{n}}$	(7.5)

Supplementary Exercises

ShadowStocks

38. Jack Lawler, a financial analyst, wants to prepare an article on the Shadow Stock portfolio developed by the American Association of Individual Investors (AAII). A list of the 30 companies in the Shadow Stock portfolio as of March 2014 is contained in the WEBfile named ShadowStocks (AAII website March 27, 2014). Jack would like to select a simple random sample of 5 of these companies for an interview concerning management practices.
    a. In the WEBfile the Shadow Stock companies are listed in column A of an Excel worksheet. In column B we have generated a random number for each of the companies. Use these random numbers to select a simple random sample of 5 of these companies for Jack.
    b. Generate a new set of random numbers and use them to select a new simple random sample. Did you select the same companies?
39. The latest available data showed health expenditures were $8086 per person in the United States or 17.6% of gross domestic product (Centers for Medicare & Medicaid Services website, April 1, 2012). Use $8086 as the population mean and suppose a survey research firm will take a sample of 100 people to investigate the nature of their health expenditures. Assume the population standard deviation is $2500.
    a. Show the sampling distribution of the mean amount of health care expenditures for a sample of 100 people.
    b. What is the probability the sample mean will be within ±$200 of the population mean?
    c. What is the probability the sample mean will be greater than $9000? If the survey research firm reports a sample mean greater than $9000, would you question whether the firm followed correct sampling procedures? Why or why not?

40. Foot Locker uses sales per square foot as a measure of store productivity. Sales are currently running at an annual rate of $406 per square foot (*The Wall Street Journal*, March 7, 2012). You have been asked by management to conduct a study of a sample of 64 Foot Locker stores. Assume the standard deviation in annual sales per square foot for the population of all 3400 Foot Locker stores is $80.
    a. Show the sampling distribution of $\bar{x}$, the sample mean annual sales per square foot for a sample of 64 Foot Locker stores.
    b. What is the probability that the sample mean will be within $15 of the population mean?
    c. Suppose you find a sample mean of $380. What is the probability of finding a sample mean of $380 or less? Would you consider such a sample to be an unusually low performing group of stores?
41. Allegiant Airlines charges a mean base fare of $89. In addition, the airline charges for making a reservation on its website, checking bags, and inflight beverages. These additional charges average $39 per passenger (*Bloomberg Businessweek*, October 8–14, 2012). Suppose a random sample of 60 passengers is taken to determine the total cost of their flight on Allegiant Airlines. The population standard deviation of total flight cost is known to be $40.
    a. What is the population mean cost per flight?
    b. What is the probability the sample mean will be within $10 of the population mean cost per flight?
    c. What is the probability the sample mean will be within $5 of the population mean cost per flight?
42. After deducting grants based on need, the average cost to attend the University of Southern California (USC) is $27,175 (*U.S. News & World Report, America's Best Colleges*, 2009 ed.). Assume the population standard deviation is $7400. Suppose that a random sample of 60 USC students will be taken from this population.
    a. What is the value of the standard error of the mean?
    b. What is the probability that the sample mean will be more than $27,175?
    c. What is the probability that the sample mean will be within $1000 of the population mean?
    d. How would the probability in part (c) change if the sample size were increased to 100?
43. Three firms carry inventories that differ in size. Firm A's inventory contains 2000 items, firm B's inventory contains 5000 items, and firm C's inventory contains 10,000 items. The population standard deviation for the cost of the items in each firm's inventory is $\sigma = 144$. A statistical consultant recommends that each firm take a sample of 50 items from its inventory to provide statistically valid estimates of the average cost per item. Employees of the small firm state that because it has the smallest population, it should be able to make the estimate from a much smaller sample than that required by the larger firms. However, the consultant states that to obtain the same standard error and thus the same precision in the sample results, all firms should use the same sample size regardless of population size.
    a. Using the finite population correction factor, compute the standard error for each of the three firms given a sample of size 50.
    b. What is the probability that for each firm the sample mean $\bar{x}$ will be within ± 25 of the population mean μ?
44. A researcher reports survey results by stating that the standard error of the mean is 20. The population standard deviation is 500.
    a. How large was the sample used in this survey?
    b. What is the probability that the point estimate was within ± 25 of the population mean?
45. A production process is checked periodically by a quality control inspector. The inspector selects simple random samples of 30 finished products and computes the sample mean product weights $\bar{x}$. If test results over a long period of time show that 5% of the $\bar{x}$ values

are over 2.1 pounds and 5% are under 1.9 pounds, what are the mean and the standard deviation for the population of products produced with this process?

46. Fifteen percent of Australians smoke. By introducing tough laws banning brand labels on cigarette packages, Australia hopes to reduce the percentage of people smoking to 10% by 2018 (Reuters website, October 23, 2012). Answer the following questions based on a sample of 240 Australians.
    a. Show the sampling distribution of $\bar{p}$, the proportion of Australians who are smokers.
    b. What is the probability the sample proportion will be within $\pm.04$ of the population proportion?
    c. What is the probability the sample proportion will be within $\pm.02$ of the population proportion?

47. A market research firm conducts telephone surveys with a 40% historical response rate. What is the probability that in a new sample of 400 telephone numbers, at least 150 individuals will cooperate and respond to the questions? In other words, what is the probability that the sample proportion will be at least 150/400 = .375?

48. Advertisers contract with Internet service providers and search engines to place ads on websites. They pay a fee based on the number of potential customers who click on their ad. Unfortunately, click fraud—the practice of someone clicking on an ad solely for the purpose of driving up advertising revenue—has become a problem. Forty percent of advertisers claim they have been a victim of click fraud (*BusinessWeek,* March 13, 2006). Suppose a simple random sample of 380 advertisers will be taken to learn more about how they are affected by this practice.
    a. What is the probability that the sample proportion will be within $\pm.04$ of the population proportion experiencing click fraud?
    b. What is the probability that the sample proportion will be greater than .45?

49. The proportion of individuals insured by the All-Driver Automobile Insurance Company who received at least one traffic ticket during a five-year period is .15.
    a. Show the sampling distribution of $\bar{p}$ if a random sample of 150 insured individuals is used to estimate the proportion having received at least one ticket.
    b. What is the probability that the sample proportion will be within $\pm.03$ of the population proportion?

50. Lori Jeffrey is a successful sales representative for a major publisher of college textbooks. Historically, Lori obtains a book adoption on 25% of her sales calls. Viewing her sales calls for one month as a sample of all possible sales calls, assume that a statistical analysis of the data yields a standard error of the proportion of .0625.
    a. How large was the sample used in this analysis? That is, how many sales calls did Lori make during the month?
    b. Let $\bar{p}$ indicate the sample proportion of book adoptions obtained during the month. Show the sampling distribution of $\bar{p}$.
    c. Using the sampling distribution of $\bar{p}$, compute the probability that Lori will obtain book adoptions on 30% or more of her sales calls during a one-month period.

CHAPTER 8

Interval Estimation

CONTENTS

STATISTICS IN PRACTICE: FOOD LION

8.1 POPULATION MEAN: σ KNOWN
Margin of Error and the Interval Estimate
Using Excel
Practical Advice

8.2 POPULATION MEAN: σ UNKNOWN
Margin of Error and the Interval Estimate
Using Excel
Practical Advice
Using a Small Sample
Summary of Interval Estimation Procedures

8.3 DETERMINING THE SAMPLE SIZE

8.4 POPULATION PROPORTION
Using Excel
Determining the Sample Size

STATISTICS *in* PRACTICE

FOOD LION*
SALISBURY, NORTH CAROLINA

© Davis Turner/Bloomberg/Getty Images.

Founded in 1957 as Food Town, Food Lion is one of the largest supermarket chains in the United States, with 1300 stores in 11 Southeastern and Mid-Atlantic states. The company sells more than 24,000 different products and offers nationally and regionally advertised brand-name merchandise, as well as a growing number of high-quality private label products manufactured especially for Food Lion. The company maintains its low price leadership and quality assurance through operating efficiencies such as standard store formats, innovative warehouse design, energy-efficient facilities, and data synchronization with suppliers. Food Lion looks to a future of continued innovation, growth, price leadership, and service to its customers.

Being in an inventory-intense business, Food Lion made the decision to adopt the LIFO (last-in, first-out) method of inventory valuation. This method matches current costs against current revenues, which minimizes the effect of radical price changes on profit and loss results. In addition, the LIFO method reduces net income, thereby reducing income taxes during periods of inflation.

Food Lion establishes a LIFO index for each of seven inventory pools: Grocery, Paper/Household, Pet Supplies, Health & Beauty Aids, Dairy, Cigarette/Tobacco, and Beer/Wine. For example, a LIFO index of 1.008 for the Grocery pool would indicate that the company's grocery inventory value at current costs reflects a 0.8% increase due to inflation over the most recent one-year period.

A LIFO index for each inventory pool requires that the year-end inventory count for each product be valued at the current year-end cost and at the preceding year-end cost. To avoid excessive time and expense associated with counting the inventory in all 1200 store locations, Food Lion selects a random sample of 50 stores. Year-end physical inventories are taken in each of the sample stores. The current-year and preceding-year costs for each item are then used to construct the required LIFO indexes for each inventory pool.

For a recent year, the sample estimate of the LIFO index for the Health & Beauty Aids inventory pool was 1.015. Using a 95% confidence level, Food Lion computed a margin of error of .006 for the sample estimate. Thus, the interval from 1.009 to 1.021 provided a 95% confidence interval estimate of the population LIFO index. This level of precision was judged to be very good.

In this chapter you will learn how to compute the margin of error associated with sample estimates. You will also learn how to use this information to construct and interpret interval estimates of a population mean and a population proportion.

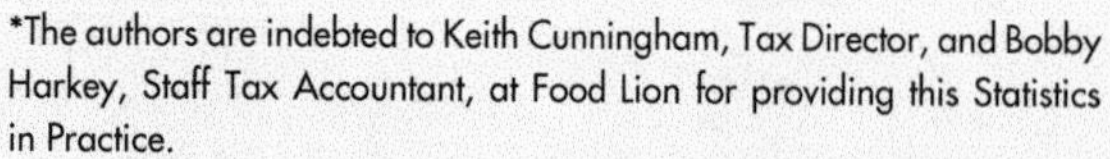

*The authors are indebted to Keith Cunningham, Tax Director, and Bobby Harkey, Staff Tax Accountant, at Food Lion for providing this Statistics in Practice.

In Chapter 7, we stated that a point estimator is a sample statistic used to estimate a population parameter. For instance, the sample mean $\bar{x}$ is a point estimator of the population mean μ and the sample proportion $\bar{p}$ is a point estimator of the population proportion p. Because a point estimator cannot be expected to provide the exact value of the population parameter, an **interval estimate** is often computed by adding and subtracting a value, called the **margin of error**, to the point estimate. The general form of an interval estimate is as follows:

$$\text{Point estimate} \pm \text{Margin of error}$$

The purpose of an interval estimate is to provide information about how close the point estimate, provided by the sample, is to the value of the population parameter.

In this chapter we show how to compute interval estimates of a population mean μ and a population proportion p. The general form of an interval estimate of a population mean is

$$\bar{x} \pm \text{Margin of error}$$

Similarly, the general form of an interval estimate of a population proportion is

$$\bar{p} \pm \text{Margin of error}$$

The sampling distributions of $\bar{x}$ and $\bar{p}$ play key roles in computing these interval estimates.

8.1 Population Mean: σ Known

In order to develop an interval estimate of a population mean, either the population standard deviation σ or the sample standard deviation s must be used to compute the margin of error. In most applications σ is not known, and s is used to compute the margin of error. In some applications, however, large amounts of relevant historical data are available and can be used to estimate the population standard deviation prior to sampling. Also, in quality control applications where a process is assumed to be operating correctly, or "in control," it is appropriate to treat the population standard deviation as known. We refer to such cases as **σ known** cases. In this section we introduce an example in which it is reasonable to treat σ as known and show how to construct an interval estimate for this case.

Each week Lloyd's Department Store selects a simple random sample of 100 customers in order to learn about the amount spent per shopping trip. With x representing the amount spent per shopping trip, the sample mean $\bar{x}$ provides a point estimate of μ, the mean amount spent per shopping trip for the population of all Lloyd's customers. Lloyd's has been using the weekly survey for several years. Based on the historical data, Lloyd's now assumes a known value of σ = \$20 for the population standard deviation. The historical data also indicate that the population follows a normal distribution.

Lloyd's

During the most recent week, Lloyd's surveyed 100 customers (n = 100) and obtained a sample mean of $\bar{x}$ = \$82. The sample mean amount spent provides a point estimate of the population mean amount spent per shopping trip, μ. In the discussion that follows, we show how to compute the margin of error for this estimate and develop an interval estimate of the population mean.

Margin of Error and the Interval Estimate

In Chapter 7 we showed that the sampling distribution of $\bar{x}$ can be used to compute the probability that $\bar{x}$ will be within a given distance of μ. In the Lloyd's example, the historical data show that the population of amounts spent is normally distributed with a standard deviation of $\sigma = 20$. So, using what we learned in Chapter 7, we can conclude that the sampling distribution of $\bar{x}$ follows a normal distribution with a standard error of $\sigma_{\bar{x}} = \sigma/\sqrt{n} = 20/\sqrt{100} = 2$. This sampling distribution is shown in Figure 8.1.[1] Because the sampling distribution shows how values of $\bar{x}$ are distributed around the population mean μ, the sampling distribution of $\bar{x}$ provides information about the possible differences between $\bar{x}$ and μ.

[1] We use the fact that the population of amounts spent has a normal distribution to conclude that the sampling distribution of $\bar{x}$ has a normal distribution. If the population did not have a normal distribution, we could rely on the central limit theorem and the sample size of n = 100 to conclude that the sampling distribution of $\bar{x}$ is approximately normal. In either case, the sampling distribution of $\bar{x}$ would appear as shown in Figure 8.1.

FIGURE 8.1 SAMPLING DISTRIBUTION OF THE SAMPLE MEAN AMOUNT SPENT FROM SIMPLE RANDOM SAMPLES OF 100 CUSTOMERS

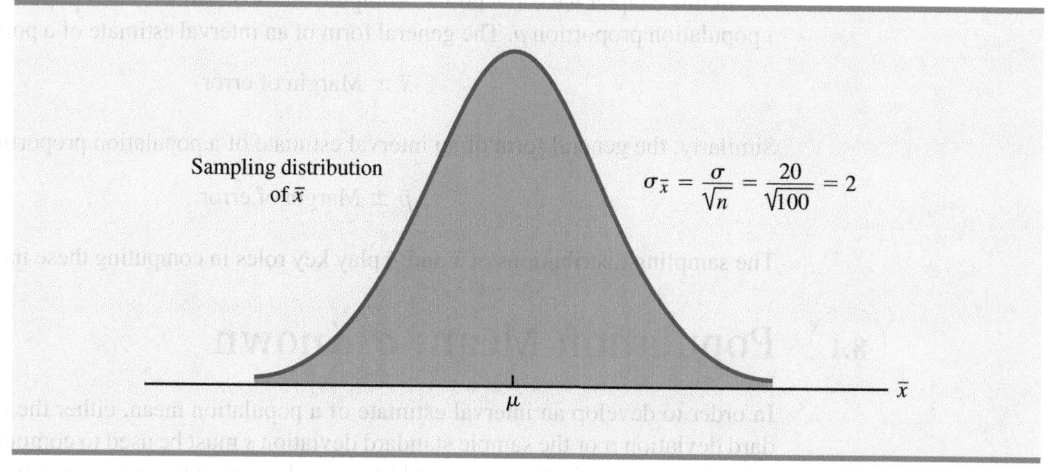

Using the standard normal probability table, we find that 95% of the values of any normally distributed random variable are within ± 1.96 standard deviations of the mean. Thus, when the sampling distribution of $\bar{x}$ is normally distributed, 95% of the $\bar{x}$ values must be within $\pm 1.96\sigma_{\bar{x}}$ of the mean μ. In the Lloyd's example we know that the sampling distribution of $\bar{x}$ is normally distributed with a standard error of $\sigma_{\bar{x}} = 2$. Because $\pm 1.96\sigma_{\bar{x}} = 1.96(2) = 3.92$, we can conclude that 95% of all $\bar{x}$ values obtained using a sample size of $n = 100$ will be within ± 3.92 of the population mean μ. See Figure 8.2.

In the introduction to this chapter we said that the general form of an interval estimate of the population mean μ is $\bar{x} \pm$ margin of error. For the Lloyd's example, suppose we set

FIGURE 8.2 SAMPLING DISTRIBUTION OF $\bar{x}$ SHOWING THE LOCATION OF SAMPLE MEANS THAT ARE WITHIN 3.92 OF μ

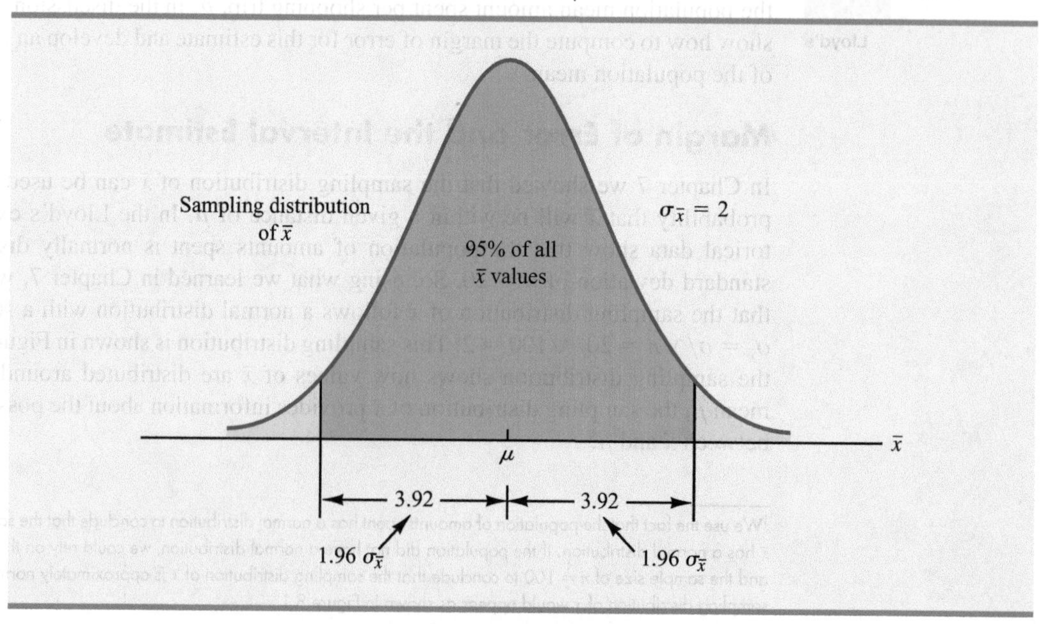

FIGURE 8.3 INTERVALS FORMED FROM SELECTED SAMPLE MEANS AT LOCATIONS $\bar{x}_1$, $\bar{x}_2$, AND $\bar{x}_3$

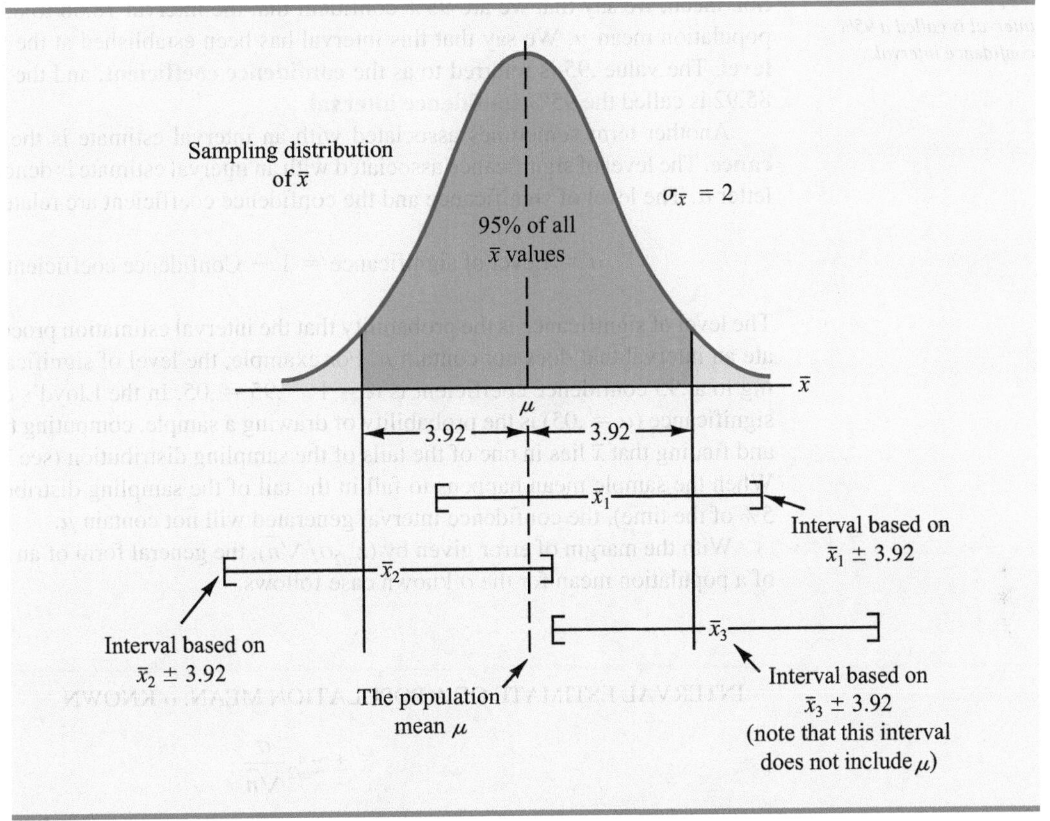

the margin of error equal to 3.92 and compute the interval estimate of μ using $\bar{x} \pm 3.92$. To provide an interpretation for this interval estimate, let us consider the values of $\bar{x}$ that could be obtained if we took three *different* simple random samples, each consisting of 100 Lloyd's customers. The first sample mean might turn out to have the value shown as $\bar{x}_1$ in Figure 8.3. In this case, Figure 8.3 shows that the interval formed by subtracting 3.92 from $\bar{x}_1$ and adding 3.92 to $\bar{x}_1$ includes the population mean μ. Now consider what happens if the second sample mean turns out to have the value shown as $\bar{x}_2$ in Figure 8.3. Although this sample mean differs from the first sample mean, we see that the interval formed by subtracting 3.92 from $\bar{x}_2$ and adding 3.92 to $\bar{x}_2$ also includes the population mean μ. However, consider what happens if the third sample mean turns out to have the value shown as $\bar{x}_3$ in Figure 8.3. In this case, the interval formed by subtracting 3.92 from $\bar{x}_3$ and adding 3.92 to $\bar{x}_3$ does not include the population mean μ. Because $\bar{x}_3$ falls in the upper tail of the sampling distribution and is farther than 3.92 from μ, subtracting and adding 3.92 to $\bar{x}_3$ forms an interval that does not include μ.

Any sample mean $\bar{x}$ that is within the darkly shaded region of Figure 8.3 will provide an interval that contains the population mean μ. Because 95% of all possible sample means are in the darkly shaded region, 95% of all intervals formed by subtracting 3.92 from $\bar{x}$ and adding 3.92 to $\bar{x}$ will include the population mean μ.

Recall that during the most recent week, the quality assurance team at Lloyd's surveyed 100 customers and obtained a sample mean amount spent of $\bar{x} = 82$. Using $\bar{x} \pm 3.92$ to construct the interval estimate, we obtain 82 ± 3.92. Thus, the specific interval estimate

This discussion provides insight as to why the interval is called a 95% confidence interval.

of μ based on the data from the most recent week is $82 - 3.92 = 78.08$ to $82 + 3.92 = 85.92$. Because 95% of all the intervals constructed using $\bar{x} \pm 3.92$ will contain the population mean, we say that we are 95% confident that the interval 78.08 to 85.92 includes the population mean μ. We say that this interval has been established at the 95% **confidence level**. The value .95 is referred to as the **confidence coefficient**, and the interval 78.08 to 85.92 is called the 95% **confidence interval**.

Another term sometimes associated with an interval estimate is the **level of significance**. The level of significance associated with an interval estimate is denoted by the Greek letter α. The level of significance and the confidence coefficient are related as follows:

$$\alpha = \text{Level of significance} = 1 - \text{Confidence coefficient}$$

The level of significance is the probability that the interval estimation procedure will generate an interval that does not contain μ. For example, the level of significance corresponding to a .95 confidence coefficient is $\alpha = 1 - .95 = .05$. In the Lloyd's case, the level of significance ($\alpha = .05$) is the probability of drawing a sample, computing the sample mean, and finding that $\bar{x}$ lies in one of the tails of the sampling distribution (see $\bar{x}_3$ in Figure 8.3). When the sample mean happens to fall in the tail of the sampling distribution (and it will 5% of the time), the confidence interval generated will not contain μ.

With the margin of error given by $(z_{\alpha/2}\sigma/\sqrt{n})$, the general form of an interval estimate of a population mean for the σ known case follows.

INTERVAL ESTIMATE OF A POPULATION MEAN: σ KNOWN

$$\bar{x} \pm z_{\alpha/2}\frac{\sigma}{\sqrt{n}} \tag{8.1}$$

where $(1 - \alpha)$ is the confidence coefficient and $z_{\alpha/2}$ is the z value providing an area of $\alpha/2$ in the upper tail of the standard normal probability distribution.

Let us use expression (8.1) to construct a 95% confidence interval for the Lloyd's example. For a 95% confidence interval, the confidence coefficient is $(1 - \alpha) = .95$ and thus, $\alpha = .05$. Using the standard normal probability table, an area of $\alpha/2 = .05/2 = .025$ in the upper tail provides $z_{.025} = 1.96$. With the Lloyd's sample mean $\bar{x} = 82$, $\sigma = 20$, and a sample size $n = 100$, we obtain

$$82 \pm 1.96\frac{20}{\sqrt{100}}$$

$$82 \pm 3.92$$

Thus, using expression (8.1), the margin of error is 3.92 and the 95% confidence interval is $82 - 3.92 = 78.08$ to $82 + 3.92 = 85.92$.

Although a 95% confidence level is frequently used, other confidence levels such as 90% and 99% may be considered. Values of $z_{\alpha/2}$ for the most commonly used confidence levels are shown in Table 8.1. Using these values and expression (8.1), the 90% confidence interval for the Lloyd's example is

$$82 \pm 1.645\frac{20}{\sqrt{100}}$$

$$82 \pm 3.29$$

TABLE 8.1 VALUES OF $z_{\alpha/2}$ FOR THE MOST COMMONLY USED CONFIDENCE LEVELS

Confidence Level	α	$\alpha/2$	$z_{\alpha/2}$
90%	.10	.05	1.645
95%	.05	.025	1.960
99%	.01	.005	2.576

Thus, at 90% confidence, the margin of error is 3.29 and the confidence interval is $82 - 3.29 = 78.71$ to $82 + 3.29 = 85.29$. Similarly, the 99% confidence interval is

$$82 \pm 2.576 \frac{20}{\sqrt{100}}$$

$$82 \pm 5.15$$

Thus, at 99% confidence, the margin of error is 5.15 and the confidence interval is $82 - 5.15 = 76.85$ to $82 + 5.15 = 87.15$.

Comparing the results for the 90%, 95%, and 99% confidence levels, we see that in order to have a higher level of confidence, the margin of error and thus the width of the confidence interval must be larger.

Using Excel

We will use the Lloyd's Department Store data to illustrate how Excel can be used to construct an interval estimate of the population mean for the σ known case. Refer to Figure 8.4 as we describe the tasks involved. The formula worksheet is in the background; the value worksheet appears in the foreground.

Enter/Access Data: Open the WEBFile named Lloyd's. A label and the sales data are entered into cells A1:A101.

FIGURE 8.4 EXCEL WORKSHEET: CONSTRUCTING A 95% CONFIDENCE INTERVAL FOR LLOYD'S DEPARTMENT STORE

	A	B	C	D	E
1	Amount		Interval Estimate of a Population Mean:		
2	72		σ Known Case		
3	91				
4	74		Sample Size	=COUNT(A1:A101)	
5	115		Sample Mean	=AVERAGE(A1:A101)	
6	71				
7	120		Population Standard Deviation	20	
8	37		Confidence Coefficient	0.95	
9	96		Level of Significance	=1-D8	
10	91				
11	105		Margin of Error	=CONFIDENCE.NORM(D9,D7,D4)	
12	104				
13	89		Point Estimate	=D5	
14	70		Lower Limit	=D13-D11	
15	125		Upper Limit	=D13+D11	
16	43				
17	61				
100	71				
101	84				
102					

	A	B	C	D	E
1	Amount		Interval Estimate of a Population Mean:		
2	72		σ Known Case		
3	91				
4	74		Sample Size	100	
5	115		Sample Mean	82	
6	71				
7	120		Population Standard Deviation	20	
8	37		Confidence Coefficient	0.95	
9	96		Level of Significance	0.05	
10	91				
11	105		Margin of Error	3.92	
12	104				
13	89		Point Estimate	82	
14	70		Lower Limit	78.08	
15	125		Upper Limit	85.92	
16	43				
17	61				
100	71				
101	84				
102					

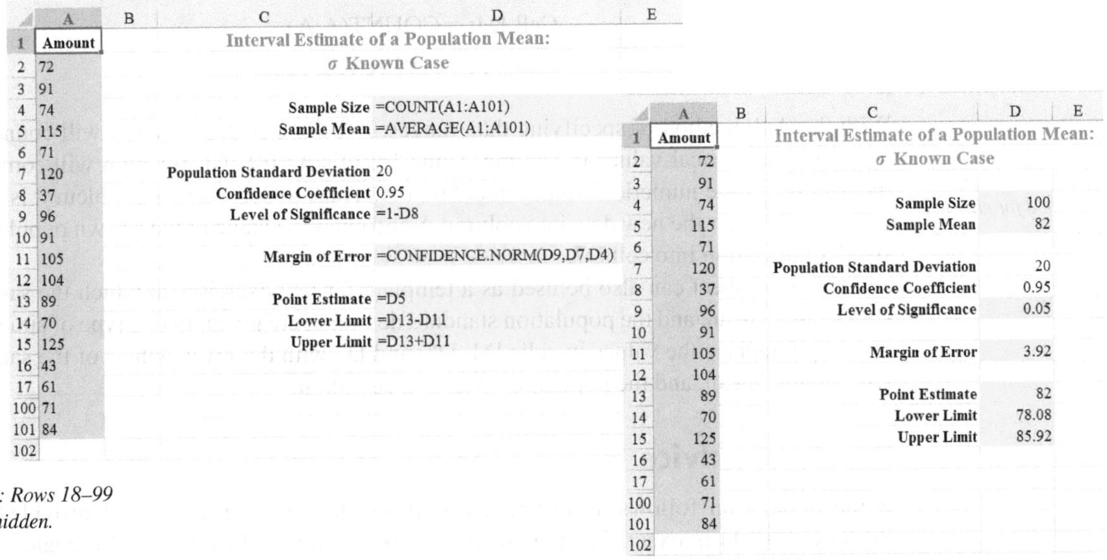

Note: Rows 18–99 are hidden.

Enter Functions and Formulas: The sample size and sample mean are computed in cells D4:D5 using Excel's COUNT and AVERAGE functions, respectively. The value worksheet shows that the sample size is 100 and the sample mean is 82. The value of the known population standard deviation (20) is entered into cell D7 and the desired confidence coefficient (.95) is entered into cell D8. The level of significance is computed in cell D9 by entering the formula =1-D8; the value worksheet shows that the level of significance associated with a confidence coefficient of .95 is .05. The margin of error is computed in cell D11 using Excel's CONFIDENCE.NORM function. The CONFIDENCE.NORM function has three inputs: the level of significance (cell D9); the population standard deviation (cell D7); and the sample size (cell D4). Thus, to compute the margin of error associated with a 95% confidence interval, the following formula is entered into cell D11:

=CONFIDENCE.NORM(D9,D7,D4)

The resulting value of 3.92 is the margin of error associated with the interval estimate of the population mean amount spent per week.

Cells D13:D15 provide the point estimate and the lower and upper limits for the confidence interval. Because the point estimate is just the sample mean, the formula =D5 is entered into cell D13. To compute the lower limit of the 95% confidence interval, $\bar{x}$ − (margin of error), we enter the formula =D13-D11 into cell D14. To compute the upper limit of the 95% confidence interval, $\bar{x}$ + (margin of error), we enter the formula =D13+D11 into cell D15. The value worksheet shows a lower limit of 78.08 and an upper limit of 85.92. In other words, the 95% confidence interval for the population mean is from 78.08 to 85.92.

A template for other problems To use this worksheet as a template for another problem of this type, we must first enter the new problem data in column A. Then, the cell formulas in cells D4 and D5 must be updated with the new data range and the known population standard deviation must be entered into cell D7. After doing so, the point estimate and a 95% confidence interval will be displayed in cells D13:D15. If a confidence interval with a different confidence coefficient is desired, we simply change the value in cell D8.

We can further simplify the use of Figure 8.4 as a template for other problems by eliminating the need to enter new data ranges in cells D4 and D5. To do so we rewrite the cell formulas as follows:

Cell D4: =COUNT(A:A)
Cell D5: =AVERAGE(A:A)

The Lloyd's data set includes a worksheet entitled Template that uses the A:A method for entering the data ranges.

With the A:A method of specifying data ranges, Excel's COUNT function will count the number of numerical values in column A and Excel's AVERAGE function will compute the average of the numerical values in column A. Thus, to solve a new problem it is only necessary to enter the new data into column A and enter the value of the known population standard deviation into cell D7.

This worksheet can also be used as a template for text exercises in which the sample size, sample mean, and the population standard deviation are given. In this type of situation we simply replace the values in cells D4, D5, and D7 with the given values of the sample size, sample mean, and the population standard deviation.

Practical Advice

If the population follows a normal distribution, the confidence interval provided by expression (8.1) is exact. In other words, if expression (8.1) were used repeatedly to generate 95% confidence intervals, exactly 95% of the intervals generated would contain the population mean. If the population does not follow a normal distribution, the confidence interval provided by expression (8.1) will be approximate. In this case, the quality of the approximation depends on both the distribution of the population and the sample size.

In most applications, a sample size of $n \geq 30$ is adequate when using expression (8.1) to develop an interval estimate of a population mean. If the population is not normally distributed, but is roughly symmetric, sample sizes as small as 15 can be expected to provide good approximate confidence intervals. With smaller sample sizes, expression (8.1) should only be used if the analyst believes, or is willing to assume, that the population distribution is at least approximately normal.

NOTES AND COMMENTS

1. The interval estimation procedure discussed in this section is based on the assumption that the population standard deviation σ is known. By σ known we mean that historical data or other information are available that permit us to obtain a good estimate of the population standard deviation prior to taking the sample that will be used to develop an estimate of the population mean. So technically we don't mean that σ is actually known with certainty. We just mean that we obtained a good estimate of the standard deviation prior to sampling and thus we won't be using the same sample to estimate both the population mean and the population standard deviation.
2. The sample size n appears in the denominator of the interval estimation expression (8.1). Thus, if a particular sample size provides too wide an interval to be of any practical use, we may want to consider increasing the sample size. With n in the denominator, a larger sample size will provide a smaller margin of error, a narrower interval, and greater precision. The procedure for determining the size of a simple random sample necessary to obtain a desired precision is discussed in Section 8.3.

Exercises

Methods

1. A simple random sample of 40 items resulted in a sample mean of 25. The population standard deviation is $\sigma = 5$.
   a. What is the standard error of the mean, $\sigma_{\bar{x}}$?
   b. At 95% confidence, what is the margin of error?

2. A simple random sample of 50 items from a population with $\sigma = 6$ resulted in a sample mean of 32.
   a. Provide a 90% confidence interval for the population mean.
   b. Provide a 95% confidence interval for the population mean.
   c. Provide a 99% confidence interval for the population mean.
3. A simple random sample of 60 items resulted in a sample mean of 80. The population standard deviation is $\sigma = 15$.
   a. Compute the 95% confidence interval for the population mean.
   b. Assume that the same sample mean was obtained from a sample of 120 items. Provide a 95% confidence interval for the population mean.
   c. What is the effect of a larger sample size on the interval estimate?
4. A 95% confidence interval for a population mean was reported to be 152 to 160. If $\sigma = 15$, what sample size was used in this study?

Applications

5. Data were collected on the amount spent by 64 customers for lunch at a major Houston restaurant. These data are contained in the WEBfile named Houston. Based upon past studies the population standard deviation is known with $\sigma = \$6$.
   a. At 99% confidence, what is the margin of error?
   b. Develop a 99% confidence interval estimate of the mean amount spent for lunch.

Houston

6. In an attempt to assess total daily travel taxes in various cities, the Global Business Travel Association conducted a study of daily travel taxes on lodging, rental car, and meals (GBTA Foundation website, October 30, 2012). The data contained in the WEBfile named TravelTax are consistent with the findings of that study for business travel to Chicago. Assume the population standard deviation is known to be \$8.50 and develop a 95% confidence interval of the population mean total daily travel taxes for Chicago.

TravelTax

7. *The Wall Street Journal* reported that automobile crashes cost the United States \$162 billion annually (*The Wall Street Journal,* March 5, 2008). The average cost per person for crashes in the Tampa, Florida, area was reported to be \$1599. Suppose this average cost was based on a sample of 50 persons who had been involved in car crashes and that the population standard deviation is $\sigma = \$600$. What is the margin of error for a 95% confidence interval? What would you recommend if the study required a margin of error of \$150 or less?

8. Studies show that massage therapy has a variety of health benefits and it is not too expensive (*The Wall Street Journal,* March 13, 2012). A sample of 10 typical one-hour massage therapy sessions showed an average charge of \$59. The population standard deviation for a one-hour session is $\sigma = \$5.50$.
   a. What assumptions about the population should we be willing to make if a margin of error is desired?
   b. Using 95% confidence, what is the margin of error?
   c. Using 99% confidence, what is the margin of error?

TaxReturn

9. AARP reported on a study conducted to learn how long it takes individuals to prepare their federal income tax return (*AARP Bulletin*, April 2008). The data contained in the WEBfile named TaxReturn are consistent with the study results. These data provide the time in hours required for 40 individuals to complete their federal income tax returns. Using past years' data, the population standard deviation can be assumed known with $\sigma = 9$ hours. What is the 95% confidence interval estimate of the mean time it takes an individual to complete a federal income tax return?

10. Costs are rising for all kinds of medical care. The mean monthly rent at assisted-living facilities was reported to have increased 17% over the last five years to \$3486 (*The Wall Street Journal*, October 27, 2012). Assume this cost estimate is based on a sample of 120 facilities and, from past studies, it can be assumed that the population standard deviation is $\sigma = \$650$.
    a. Develop a 90% confidence interval estimate of the population mean monthly rent.
    b. Develop a 95% confidence interval estimate of the population mean monthly rent.
    c. Develop a 99% confidence interval estimate of the population mean monthly rent.
    d. What happens to the width of the confidence interval as the confidence level is increased? Does this seem reasonable? Explain.

8.2 Population Mean: σ Unknown

When developing an interval estimate of a population mean, we usually do not have a good estimate of the population standard deviation either. In these cases, we must use the same sample to estimate both μ and σ. This situation represents the **σ unknown** case. When s is used to estimate σ, the margin of error and the interval estimate for the population mean are

FIGURE 8.5 COMPARISON OF THE STANDARD NORMAL DISTRIBUTION WITH t DISTRIBUTIONS HAVING 10 AND 20 DEGREES OF FREEDOM

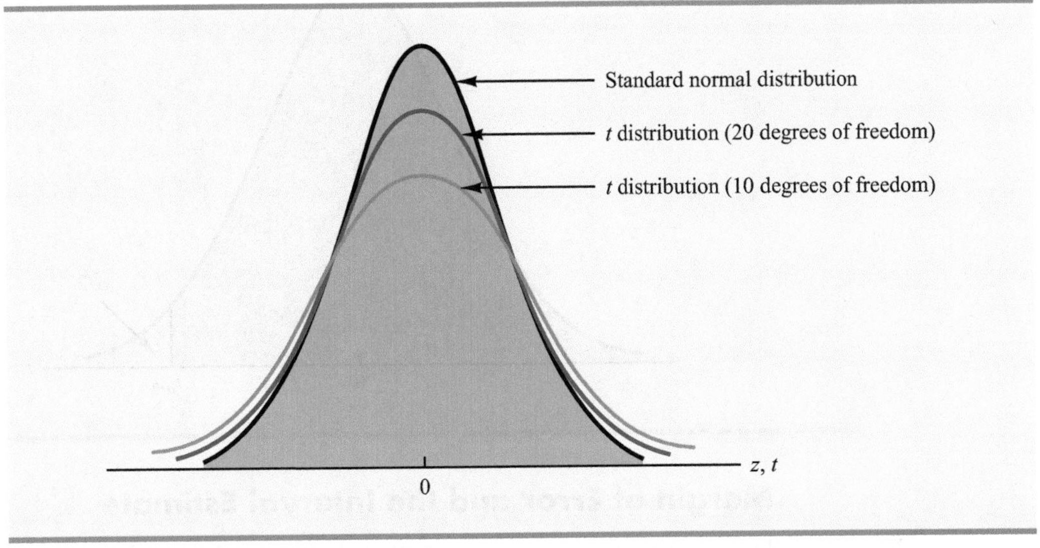

based on a probability distribution known as the t **distribution**. Although the mathematical development of the t distribution is based on the assumption of a normal distribution for the population we are sampling from, research shows that the t distribution can be successfully applied in many situations where the population deviates significantly from normal. Later in this section we provide guidelines for using the t distribution if the population is not normally distributed.

William Sealy Gosset, writing under the name "Student," is the founder of the t distribution. Gosset, an Oxford graduate in mathematics, worked for the Guinness Brewery in Dublin, Ireland. He developed the t distribution while working on small-scale materials and temperature experiments.

The t distribution is a family of similar probability distributions, with a specific t distribution depending on a parameter known as the **degrees of freedom**. The t distribution with 1 degree of freedom is unique, as is the t distribution with 2 degrees of freedom, with 3 degrees of freedom, and so on. As the number of degrees of freedom increases, the difference between the t distribution and the standard normal distribution becomes smaller and smaller. Figure 8.5 shows t distributions with 10 and 20 degrees of freedom and their relationship to the standard normal probability distribution. Note that a t distribution with more degrees of freedom exhibits less variability and more closely resembles the standard normal distribution. Note also that the mean of the t distribution is zero.

We place a subscript on t to indicate the area in the upper tail of the t distribution. For example, just as we used $z_{.025}$ to indicate the z value providing a .025 area in the upper tail of a standard normal distribution, we will use $t_{.025}$ to indicate a .025 area in the upper tail of a t distribution. In general, we will use the notation $t_{\alpha/2}$ to represent a t value with an area of $\alpha/2$ in the upper tail of the t distribution. See Figure 8.6.

Table 2 in Appendix B contains a table for the t distribution. A portion of this table is shown in Table 8.2. Each row in the table corresponds to a separate t distribution with the degrees of freedom shown. For example, for a t distribution with 9 degrees of freedom, $t_{.025} = 2.262$. Similarly, for a t distribution with 60 degrees of freedom, $t_{.025} = 2.000$. As the degrees of freedom continue to increase, $t_{.025}$ approaches $z_{.025} = 1.96$. In fact, the standard normal distribution z values can be found in the infinite degrees of freedom row (labeled ∞) of the t distribution table. If the degrees of freedom exceed 100, the infinite degrees of freedom row can be used to approximate the actual t value; in other words, for more than 100 degrees of freedom, the standard normal z value provides a good approximation to the t value.

As the degrees of freedom increase, the t distribution approaches the standard normal distribution.

FIGURE 8.6 t DISTRIBUTION WITH $\alpha/2$ AREA OR PROBABILITY IN THE UPPER TAIL

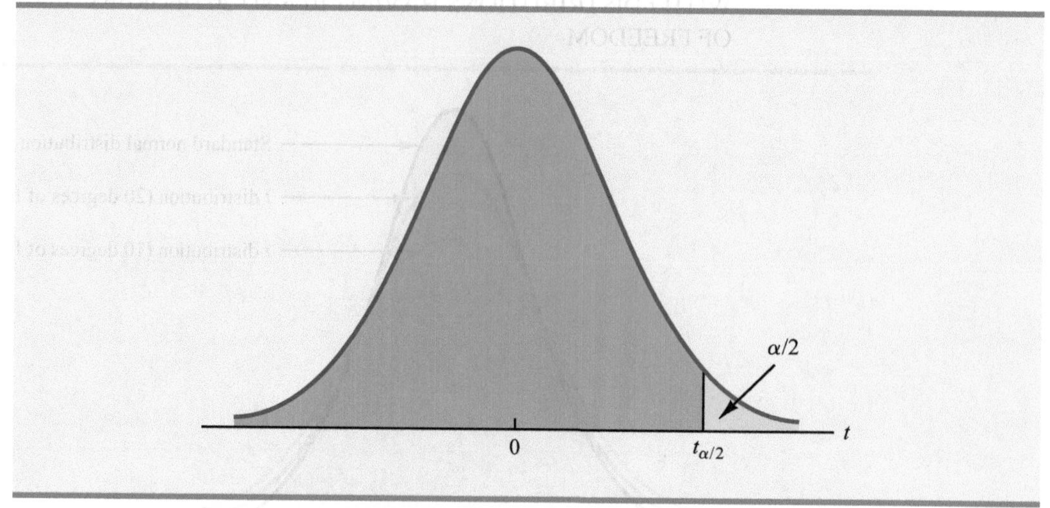

Margin of Error and the Interval Estimate

In Section 8.1 we showed that an interval estimate of a population mean for the σ known case is

$$\bar{x} \pm z_{\alpha/2}\frac{\sigma}{\sqrt{n}}$$

To compute an interval estimate of μ for the σ unknown case, the sample standard deviation s is used to estimate σ, and $z_{\alpha/2}$ is replaced by the t distribution value $t_{\alpha/2}$. The margin of error is then given by $t_{\alpha/2}s/\sqrt{n}$. With this margin of error, the general expression for an interval estimate of a population mean when σ is unknown follows.

INTERVAL ESTIMATE OF A POPULATION MEAN: σ UNKNOWN

$$\bar{x} \pm t_{\alpha/2}\frac{s}{\sqrt{n}} \tag{8.2}$$

where s is the sample standard deviation, $(1 - \alpha)$ is the confidence coefficient, and $t_{\alpha/2}$ is the t value providing an area of $\alpha/2$ in the upper tail of the t distribution with $n - 1$ degrees of freedom.

The reason the number of degrees of freedom associated with the t value in expression (8.2) is $n - 1$ concerns the use of s as an estimate of the population standard deviation σ. The expression for the sample standard deviation is

$$s = \sqrt{\frac{\Sigma(x_i - \bar{x})^2}{n - 1}}$$

Degrees of freedom refer to the number of independent pieces of information that go into the computation of $\Sigma(x_i - \bar{x})^2$. The n pieces of information involved in computing $\Sigma(x_i - \bar{x})^2$ are as follows: $x_1 - \bar{x}, x_2 - \bar{x}, \ldots, x_n - \bar{x}$. In Section 3.2 we indicated that $\Sigma(x_i - \bar{x}) = 0$ for any data set. Thus, only $n - 1$ of the $x_i - \bar{x}$ values are independent; that is, if we know $n - 1$ of the values, the remaining value can be determined exactly by

TABLE 8.2 SELECTED VALUES FROM THE t DISTRIBUTION TABLE*

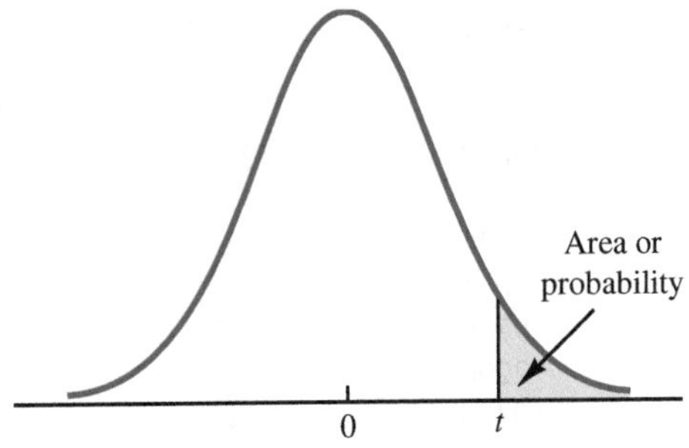

Degrees of Freedom	Area in Upper Tail					
	.20	**.10**	**.05**	**.025**	**.01**	**.005**
1	1.376	3.078	6.314	12.706	31.821	63.656
2	1.061	1.886	2.920	4.303	6.965	9.925
3	.978	1.638	2.353	3.182	4.541	5.841
4	.941	1.533	2.132	2.776	3.747	4.604
5	.920	1.476	2.015	2.571	3.365	4.032
6	.906	1.440	1.943	2.447	3.143	3.707
7	.896	1.415	1.895	2.365	2.998	3.499
8	.889	1.397	1.860	2.306	2.896	3.355
9	.883	1.383	1.833	2.262	2.821	3.250
⋮	⋮	⋮	⋮	⋮	⋮	⋮
60	.848	1.296	1.671	2.000	2.390	2.660
61	.848	1.296	1.670	2.000	2.389	2.659
62	.847	1.295	1.670	1.999	2.388	2.657
63	.847	1.295	1.669	1.998	2.387	2.656
64	.847	1.295	1.669	1.998	2.386	2.655
65	.847	1.295	1.669	1.997	2.385	2.654
66	.847	1.295	1.668	1.997	2.384	2.652
67	.847	1.294	1.668	1.996	2.383	2.651
68	.847	1.294	1.668	1.995	2.382	2.650
69	.847	1.294	1.667	1.995	2.382	2.649
⋮	⋮	⋮	⋮	⋮	⋮	⋮
90	.846	1.291	1.662	1.987	2.368	2.632
91	.846	1.291	1.662	1.986	2.368	2.631
92	.846	1.291	1.662	1.986	2.368	2.630
93	.846	1.291	1.661	1.986	2.367	2.630
94	.845	1.291	1.661	1.986	2.367	2.629
95	.845	1.291	1.661	1.985	2.366	2.629
96	.845	1.290	1.661	1.985	2.366	2.628
97	.845	1.290	1.661	1.985	2.365	2.627
98	.845	1.290	1.661	1.984	2.365	2.627
99	.845	1.290	1.660	1.984	2.364	2.626
100	.845	1.290	1.660	1.984	2.364	2.626
∞	.842	1.282	1.645	1.960	2.326	2.576

**Note:* A more extensive table is provided as Table 2 of Appendix B.

TABLE 8.3 CREDIT CARD BALANCES FOR A SAMPLE OF 70 HOUSEHOLDS

NewBalance

9430	14661	7159	9071	9691	11032
7535	12195	8137	3603	11448	6525
4078	10544	9467	16804	8279	5239
5604	13659	12595	13479	5649	6195
5179	7061	7917	14044	11298	12584
4416	6245	11346	6817	4353	15415
10676	13021	12806	6845	3467	15917
1627	9719	4972	10493	6191	12591
10112	2200	11356	615	12851	9743
6567	10746	7117	13627	5337	10324
13627	12744	9465	12557	8372	
18719	5742	19263	6232	7445	

using the condition that the sum of the $x_i - \bar{x}$ values must be 0. Thus, $n - 1$ is the number of degrees of freedom associated with $\Sigma(x_i - \bar{x})^2$ and hence the number of degrees of freedom for the t distribution in expression (8.2).

To illustrate the interval estimation procedure for the σ unknown case, we will consider a study designed to estimate the mean credit card debt for the population of U.S. households. A sample of $n = 70$ households provided the credit card balances shown in Table 8.3. For this situation, no previous estimate of the population standard deviation σ is available. Thus, the sample data must be used to estimate both the population mean and the population standard deviation. Using the data in Table 8.3, we compute the sample mean $\bar{x} = \$9312$ and the sample standard deviation $s = \$4007$. With 95% confidence and $n - 1 = 69$ degrees of freedom, Table 8.2 can be used to obtain the appropriate value for $t_{.025}$. We want the t value in the row with 69 degrees of freedom, and the column corresponding to .025 in the upper tail. The value shown is $t_{.025} = 1.995$.

We use expression (8.2) to compute an interval estimate of the population mean credit card balance.

$$9312 \pm 1.995 \frac{4007}{\sqrt{70}}$$

$$9312 \pm 955$$

The point estimate of the population mean is \$9312, the margin of error is \$955, and the 95% confidence interval is $9312 - 955 = \$8357$ to $9312 + 955 = \$10,267$. Thus, we are 95% confident that the mean credit card balance for the population of all households is between \$8357 and \$10,267.

Using Excel

We will use the credit card balances in Table 8.3 to illustrate how Excel can be used to construct an interval estimate of the population mean for the σ unknown case. We start by summarizing the data using Excel's Descriptive Statistics tool described in Chapter 3. Refer to Figure 8.7 as we describe the tasks involved. The formula worksheet is in the background; the value worksheet is in the foreground.

Enter/Access Data: Open the WEBfile named NewBalance. A label and the credit card balances are entered into cells A1:A71.

Apply Analysis Tools: The following steps describe how to use Excel's Descriptive Statistics tool for these data:

FIGURE 8.7 EXCEL WORKSHEET: 95% CONFIDENCE INTERVAL FOR CREDIT CARD BALANCES

	A	B	C	D	E
1	NewBalance		*NewBalance*		
2	9430				
3	7535		Mean	9312	
4	4078		Standard Error	478.9281	
5	5604		Median	9466	
6	5179		Mode	13627	
7	4416		Standard Deviation	4007	
8	10676		Sample Variance	16056048	
9	1627		Kurtosis	-0.2960	
10	10112		Skewness	0.1879	
11	6567		Range	18648	
12	13627		Minimum	615	
13	18719		Maximum	19263	
14	14661		Sum	651840	
15	12195		Count	70	
16	10544		Confidence Level(95.0%)	955	
17	13659				
18	7061		Point Estimate	=D3	
19	6245		Lower Limit	=D18-D16	
20	13021		Upper Limit	=D3+D16	
70	9743				
71	10324				
72					

Note: Rows 21–69 are hidden.

	A	B	C	D	E	F
1	NewBalance		*NewBalance*			
2	9430				Point Estimate	
3	7535		Mean	9312		
4	4078		Standard Error	478.9281		
5	5604		Median	9466		
6	5179		Mode	13627		
7	4416		Standard Deviation	4007		
8	10676		Sample Variance	16056048		
9	1627		Kurtosis	-0.2960		
10	10112		Skewness	0.1879		
11	6567		Range	18648		
12	13627		Minimum	615		
13	18719		Maximum	19263		
14	14661		Sum	651840		
15	12195		Count	70	Margin of Error	
16	10544		Confidence Level(95.0%)	955		
17	13659					
18	7061		Point Estimate	9312		
19	6245		Lower Limit	8357		
20	13021		Upper Limit	10267		
70	9743					
71	10324					
72						

Step 1. Click the **Data** tab on the Ribbon
Step 2. In the **Analysis** group, click **Data Analysis**
Step 3. Choose **Descriptive Statistics** from the list of Analysis Tools
Step 4. When the Descriptive Statistics dialog box appears:
Enter A1:A71 in the **Input Range** box
Select **Grouped By Columns**
Select **Labels in First Row**
Select **Output Range:**
Enter C1 in the **Output Range** box
Select **Summary Statistics**
Select **Confidence Level for Mean**
Enter 95 in the **Confidence Level for Mean** box
Click **OK**

The sample mean ($\bar{x}$) is in cell D3. The margin of error, labeled "Confidence Level(95%)," appears in cell D16. The value worksheet shows $\bar{x} = 9312$ and a margin of error equal to 955.

Enter Functions and Formulas: Cells D18:D20 provide the point estimate and the lower and upper limits for the confidence interval. Because the point estimate is just the sample mean, the formula =D3 is entered into cell D18. To compute the lower limit of the 95%

confidence interval, $\bar{x}$ − (margin of error), we enter the formula =D18-D16 into cell D19. To compute the upper limit of the 95% confidence interval, $\bar{x}$ + (margin of error), we enter the formula =D18+D16 into cell D20. The value worksheet shows a lower limit of 8357 and an upper limit of 10,267. In other words, the 95% confidence interval for the population mean is from 8357 to 10,267.

Practical Advice

If the population follows a normal distribution, the confidence interval provided by expression (8.2) is exact and can be used for any sample size. If the population does not follow a normal distribution, the confidence interval provided by expression (8.2) will be approximate. In this case, the quality of the approximation depends on both the distribution of the population and the sample size.

Larger sample sizes are needed if the distribution of the population is highly skewed or includes outliers.

In most applications, a sample size of $n \geq 30$ is adequate when using expression (8.2) to develop an interval estimate of a population mean. However, if the population distribution is highly skewed or contains outliers, most statisticians would recommend increasing the sample size to 50 or more. If the population is not normally distributed but is roughly symmetric, sample sizes as small as 15 can be expected to provide good approximate confidence intervals. With smaller sample sizes, expression (8.2) should only be used if the analyst believes, or is willing to assume, that the population distribution is at least approximately normal.

Using a Small Sample

In the following example we develop an interval estimate for a population mean when the sample size is small. As we already noted, an understanding of the distribution of the population becomes a factor in deciding whether the interval estimation procedure provides acceptable results.

Scheer Industries is considering a new computer-assisted program to train maintenance employees to do machine repairs. In order to fully evaluate the program, the director of manufacturing requested an estimate of the population mean time required for maintenance employees to complete the computer-assisted training.

A sample of 20 employees is selected, with each employee in the sample completing the training program. Data on the training time in days for the 20 employees are shown in Table 8.4. A histogram of the sample data appears in Figure 8.8. What can we say about the distribution of the population based on this histogram? First, the sample data do not support the conclusion that the distribution of the population is normal, yet we do not see any evidence of skewness or outliers. Therefore, using the guidelines in the previous subsection, we conclude that an interval estimate based on the t distribution appears acceptable for the sample of 20 employees.

We continue by computing the sample mean and sample standard deviation as follows.

$$\bar{x} = \frac{\Sigma x_i}{n} = \frac{1030}{20} = 51.5 \text{ days}$$

$$s = \sqrt{\frac{\Sigma(x_i - \bar{x})^2}{n - 1}} = \sqrt{\frac{889}{20 - 1}} = 6.84 \text{ days}$$

TABLE 8.4 TRAINING TIME IN DAYS FOR A SAMPLE OF 20 SCHEER INDUSTRIES EMPLOYEES

52	59	54	42
44	50	42	48
55	54	60	55
44	62	62	57
45	46	43	56

FIGURE 8.8 HISTOGRAM OF TRAINING TIMES FOR THE SCHEER INDUSTRIES SAMPLE

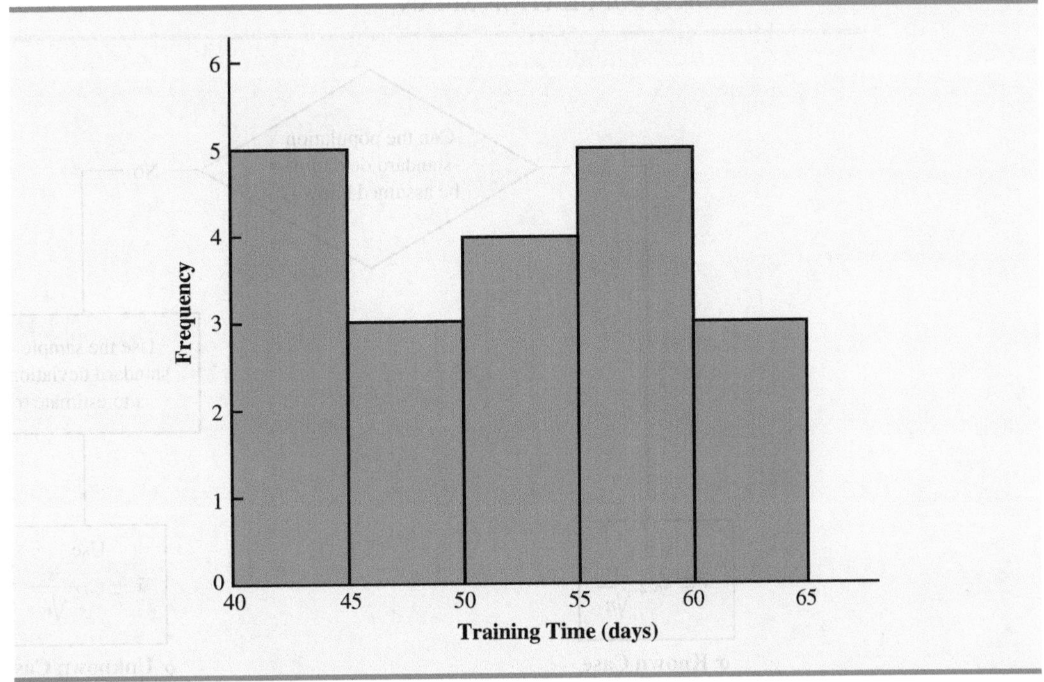

For a 95% confidence interval, we use Table 2 of Appendix B and $n - 1 = 19$ degrees of freedom to obtain $t_{.025} = 2.093$. Expression (8.2) provides the interval estimate of the population mean.

$$51.5 \pm 2.093\left(\frac{6.84}{\sqrt{20}}\right)$$

$$51.5 \pm 3.2$$

The point estimate of the population mean is 51.5 days. The margin of error is 3.2 days and the 95% confidence interval is $51.5 - 3.2 = 48.3$ days to $51.5 + 3.2 = 54.7$ days.

Using a histogram of the sample data to learn about the distribution of a population is not always conclusive, but in many cases it provides the only information available. The histogram, along with judgment on the part of the analyst, can often be used to decide whether expression (8.2) can be used to develop the interval estimate.

Summary of Interval Estimation Procedures

We provided two approaches to developing an interval estimate of a population mean. For the σ known case, σ and the standard normal distribution are used in expression (8.1) to compute the margin of error and to develop the interval estimate. For the σ unknown case, the sample standard deviation s and the t distribution are used in expression (8.2) to compute the margin of error and to develop the interval estimate.

A summary of the interval estimation procedures for the two cases is shown in Figure 8.9. In most applications, a sample size of $n \geq 30$ is adequate. If the population has a normal or approximately normal distribution, however, smaller sample sizes may be used. For the σ unknown case a sample size of $n \geq 50$ is recommended if the population distribution is believed to be highly skewed or has outliers.

FIGURE 8.9 SUMMARY OF INTERVAL ESTIMATION PROCEDURES FOR A POPULATION MEAN

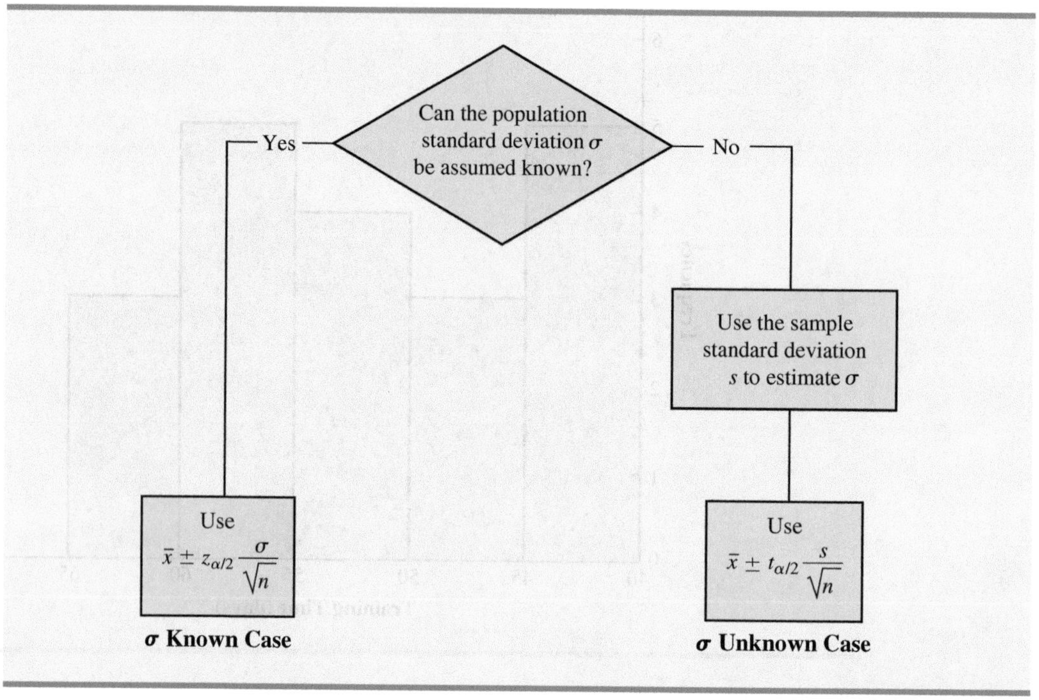

Can the population standard deviation σ be assumed known?

Yes: Use $\bar{x} \pm z_{\alpha/2} \dfrac{\sigma}{\sqrt{n}}$ — **σ Known Case**

No: Use the sample standard deviation s to estimate σ. Use $\bar{x} \pm t_{\alpha/2} \dfrac{s}{\sqrt{n}}$ — **σ Unknown Case**

NOTES AND COMMENTS

1. When σ is known, the margin of error, $z_{\alpha/2}(\sigma/\sqrt{n})$, is fixed and is the same for all samples of size n. When σ is unknown, the margin of error, $t_{\alpha/2}(s/\sqrt{n})$, varies from sample to sample. This variation occurs because the sample standard deviation s varies depending upon the sample selected. A large value for s provides a larger margin of error, while a small value for s provides a smaller margin of error.
2. What happens to confidence interval estimates when the population is skewed? Consider a population that is skewed to the right with large data values stretching the distribution to the right. When such skewness exists, the sample mean $\bar{x}$ and the sample standard deviation s are positively correlated. Larger values of s tend to be associated with larger values of $\bar{x}$. Thus, when $\bar{x}$ is larger than the population mean, s tends to be larger than σ. This skewness causes the margin of error, $t_{\alpha/2}(s/\sqrt{n})$, to be larger than it would be with σ known. The confidence interval with the larger margin of error tends to include the population mean μ more often than it would if the true value of σ were used. But when $\bar{x}$ is smaller than the population mean, the correlation between $\bar{x}$ and s causes the margin of error to be small. In this case, the confidence interval with the smaller margin of error tends to miss the population mean more than it would if we knew σ and used it. For this reason, we recommend using larger sample sizes with highly skewed population distributions.

Exercises

Methods

11. For a t distribution with 16 degrees of freedom, find the area, or probability, in each region.
    a. To the right of 2.120
    b. To the left of 1.337
    c. To the left of -1.746

d. To the right of 2.583
e. Between −2.120 and 2.120
f. Between −1.746 and 1.746

12. Find the t value(s) for each of the following cases.
  a. Upper tail area of .025 with 12 degrees of freedom
  b. Lower tail area of .05 with 50 degrees of freedom
  c. Upper tail area of .01 with 30 degrees of freedom
  d. Where 90% of the area falls between these two t values with 25 degrees of freedom
  e. Where 95% of the area falls between these two t values with 45 degrees of freedom

SELF test

13. The following sample data are from a normal population: 10, 8, 12, 15, 13, 11, 6, 5.
  a. What is the point estimate of the population mean?
  b. What is the point estimate of the population standard deviation?
  c. With 95% confidence, what is the margin of error for the estimation of the population mean?
  d. What is the 95% confidence interval for the population mean?

14. A simple random sample with $n = 54$ provided a sample mean of 22.5 and a sample standard deviation of 4.4.
  a. Develop a 90% confidence interval for the population mean.
  b. Develop a 95% confidence interval for the population mean.
  c. Develop a 99% confidence interval for the population mean.
  d. What happens to the margin of error and the confidence interval as the confidence level is increased?

Applications

15. Sales personnel for Skillings Distributors submit weekly reports listing the customer contacts made during the week. A sample of 65 weekly reports showed a sample mean of 19.5 customer contacts per week. The sample standard deviation was 5.2. Provide 90% and 95% confidence intervals for the population mean number of weekly customer contacts for the sales personnel.

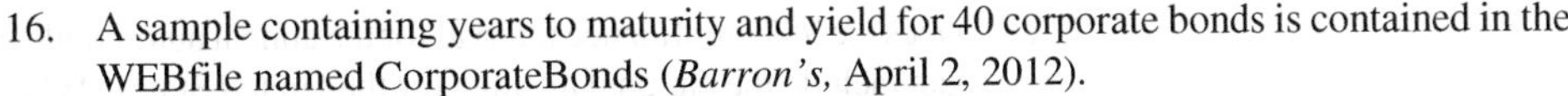

WEB file

CorporateBonds

16. A sample containing years to maturity and yield for 40 corporate bonds is contained in the WEBfile named CorporateBonds (*Barron's*, April 2, 2012).
  a. What is the sample mean years to maturity for corporate bonds and what is the sample standard deviation?
  b. Develop a 95% confidence interval for the population mean years to maturity.
  c. What is the sample mean yield on corporate bonds and what is the sample standard deviation?
  d. Develop a 95% confidence interval for the population mean yield on corporate bonds.

Miami

17. The International Air Transport Association surveys business travelers to develop quality ratings for transatlantic gateway airports. The maximum possible rating is 10. Suppose a simple random sample of 50 business travelers is selected and each traveler is asked to provide a rating for the Miami International Airport. The ratings obtained from the sample of 50 business travelers follow.

6	4	6	8	7	7	6	3	3	8	10	4	8
7	8	7	5	9	5	8	4	3	8	5	5	4
4	4	8	4	5	6	2	5	9	9	8	4	8
9	9	5	9	7	8	3	10	8	9	6		

Develop a 95% confidence interval estimate of the population mean rating for Miami.

18. Older people often have a hard time finding work. AARP reported on the number of weeks it takes a worker aged 55 plus to find a job. The data on number of weeks spent searching for a job contained in the WEBfile named JobSearch are consistent with the AARP findings (*AARP Bulletin*, April 2008).
    a. Provide a point estimate of the population mean number of weeks it takes a worker aged 55 plus to find a job.
    b. At 95% confidence, what is the margin of error?
    c. What is the 95% confidence interval estimate of the mean?
    d. Discuss the degree of skewness found in the sample data. What suggestion would you make for a repeat of this study?

19. The average cost per night of a hotel room in New York City is $273 (*SmartMoney*, March 2009). Assume this estimate is based on a sample of 45 hotels and that the sample standard deviation is $65.
    a. With 95% confidence, what is the margin of error?
    b. What is the 95% confidence interval estimate of the population mean?
    c. Two years ago the average cost of a hotel room in New York City was $229. Discuss the change in cost over the two-year period.

WEB file
AutoInsurance

20. The average annual premium for automobile insurance in the United States is $1503 (Insure.com website, March 6, 2014). The following annual premiums ($) are representative of the website's findings for the state of Michigan.

1905	3112	2312
2725	2545	2981
2677	2525	2627
2600	2370	2857
2962	2545	2675
2184	2529	2115
2332	2442	

Assume the population is approximately normal.
    a. Provide a point estimate of the mean annual automobile insurance premium in Michigan.
    b. Develop a 95% confidence interval for the mean annual automobile insurance premium in Michigan.
    c Does the 95% confidence interval for the annual automobile insurance premium in Michigan include the national average for the United States? What is your interpretation of the relationship between auto insurance premiums in Michigan and the national average?

21. Health insurers are beginning to offer telemedicine services online that replace the common office visit. Wellpoint provides a video service that allows subscribers to connect with a physician online and receive prescribed treatments (*Bloomberg Businessweek*, March 4–9, 2014). Wellpoint claims that users of its LiveHealth Online service saved a significant amount of money on a typical visit. The data shown below ($), for a sample of 20 online doctor visits, are consistent with the savings per visit reported by Wellpoint.

92	34	40
105	83	55
56	49	40
76	48	96
93	74	73
78	93	100
53	82	

Assuming the population is roughly symmetric, construct a 95% confidence interval for the mean savings for a televisit to the doctor as opposed to an office visit.

22. Disney's *Hannah Montana: The Movie* opened on Easter weekend in April 2009. Over the three-day weekend, the movie became the number-one box office attraction (*The*

TicketSales

Wall Street Journal, April 13, 2009). The ticket sales revenue in dollars for a sample of 25 theaters is as follows.

20,200	10,150	13,000	11,320	9700
8350	7300	14,000	9940	11,200
10,750	6240	12,700	7430	13,500
13,900	4200	6750	6700	9330
13,185	9200	21,400	11,380	10,800

a. What is the 95% confidence interval estimate for the mean ticket sales revenue per theater? Interpret this result.
b. Using the movie ticket price of \$7.16 per ticket, what is the estimate of the mean number of customers per theater?
c. The movie was shown in 3118 theaters. Estimate the total number of customers who saw *Hannah Montana: The Movie* and the total box office ticket sales for the three-day weekend.

8.3 Determining the Sample Size

If a desired margin of error is selected prior to sampling, the procedures in this section can be used to determine the sample size necessary to satisfy the margin of error requirement.

In providing practical advice in the two preceding sections, we commented on the role of the sample size in providing good approximate confidence intervals when the population is not normally distributed. In this section, we focus on another aspect of the sample size issue. We describe how to choose a sample size large enough to provide a desired margin of error. To understand how this process works, we return to the σ known case presented in Section 8.1. Using expression (8.1), the interval estimate is

$$\bar{x} \pm z_{\alpha/2}\frac{\sigma}{\sqrt{n}}$$

The quantity $z_{\alpha/2}(\sigma/\sqrt{n})$ is the margin of error. Thus, we see that $z_{\alpha/2}$, the population standard deviation σ, and the sample size n combine to determine the margin of error. Once we select a confidence coefficient $1 - \alpha$, $z_{\alpha/2}$ can be determined. Then, if we have a value for σ, we can determine the sample size n needed to provide any desired margin of error. Development of the formula used to compute the required sample size n follows.

Let E = the desired margin of error:

$$E = z_{\alpha/2}\frac{\sigma}{\sqrt{n}}$$

Solving for $\sqrt{n}$, we have

$$\sqrt{n} = \frac{z_{\alpha/2}\sigma}{E}$$

Squaring both sides of this equation, we obtain the following expression for the sample size.

Equation (8.3) can be used to provide a good sample size recommendation. However, judgment on the part of the analyst should be used to determine whether the final sample size should be adjusted upward.

SAMPLE SIZE FOR AN INTERVAL ESTIMATE OF A POPULATION MEAN

$$n = \frac{(z_{\alpha/2})^2\sigma^2}{E^2} \tag{8.3}$$

This sample size provides the desired margin of error at the chosen confidence level.

In equation (8.3), E is the margin of error that the user is willing to accept, and the value of $z_{\alpha/2}$ follows directly from the confidence level to be used in developing the interval estimate. Although user preference must be considered, 95% confidence is the most frequently chosen value ($z_{.025} = 1.96$).

Finally, use of equation (8.3) requires a value for the population standard deviation σ. However, even if σ is unknown, we can use equation (8.3) provided we have a preliminary or *planning value* for σ. In practice, one of the following procedures can be chosen.

A planning value for the population standard deviation σ must be specified before the sample size can be determined. Three methods of obtaining a planning value for σ are discussed here.

1. Use the estimate of the population standard deviation computed from data of previous studies as the planning value for σ.
2. Use a pilot study to select a preliminary sample. The sample standard deviation from the preliminary sample can be used as the planning value for σ.
3. Use judgment or a "best guess" for the value of σ. For example, we might begin by estimating the largest and smallest data values in the population. The difference between the largest and smallest values provides an estimate of the range for the data. Finally, the range divided by 4 is often suggested as a rough approximation of the standard deviation and thus an acceptable planning value for σ.

Let us demonstrate the use of equation (8.3) to determine the sample size by considering the following example. A previous study that investigated the cost of renting automobiles in the United States found a mean cost of approximately \$55 per day for renting a midsize automobile. Suppose that the organization that conducted this study would like to conduct a new study in order to estimate the population mean daily rental cost for a midsize automobile in the United States. In designing the new study, the project director specifies that the population mean daily rental cost be estimated with a margin of error of \$2 and a 95% level of confidence.

The project director specified a desired margin of error of $E = 2$, and the 95% level of confidence indicates $z_{.025} = 1.96$. Thus, we only need a planning value for the population standard deviation σ in order to compute the required sample size. At this point, an analyst reviewed the sample data from the previous study and found that the sample standard deviation for the daily rental cost was \$9.65. Using 9.65 as the planning value for σ, we obtain

Equation (8.3) provides the minimum sample size needed to satisfy the desired margin of error requirement. If the computed sample size is not an integer, rounding up to the next integer value will provide a margin of error slightly smaller than required.

$$n = \frac{(z_{\alpha/2})^2\sigma^2}{E^2} = \frac{(1.96)^2(9.65)^2}{2^2} = 89.43$$

Thus, the sample size for the new study needs to be at least 89.43 midsize automobile rentals in order to satisfy the project director's \$2 margin-of-error requirement. In cases where the computed n is not an integer, we round up to the next integer value; hence, the recommended sample size is 90 midsize automobile rentals.

NOTE AND COMMENT

Equation (8.3) provides the recommended sample size n for an infinite population as well as for a large finite population of size N provided $n/N \leq .05$. This is fine for most statistical studies. However, if we have a finite population such that $n/N > .05$, a smaller sample size can be used to obtain the desired margin of error. The smaller sample size, denoted by n', can be computed using the following equation.

$$n' = \frac{n}{(1 + n/N)}$$

For example, suppose that the example presented in this section showing $n = 89.43$ was computed for a population of size $N = 500$. With $n/N = 89.43/500 = .18 > .05$, a smaller sample size can be computed by

$$n' = \frac{n}{1 + n/N} = \frac{89.43}{1 + 89.43/500} = 75.86$$

Thus, for the finite population of $N = 500$, the sample size required to obtain the desired margin of error $E = 2$ would be reduced from 90 to 76.

Exercises

Methods

23. How large a sample should be selected to provide a 95% confidence interval with a margin of error of 10? Assume that the population standard deviation is 40.

SELF test

24. The range for a set of data is estimated to be 36.
    a. What is the planning value for the population standard deviation?
    b. At 95% confidence, how large a sample would provide a margin of error of 3?
    c. At 95% confidence, how large a sample would provide a margin of error of 2?

Applications

25. Refer to the Scheer Industries example in Section 8.2. Use 6.84 days as a planning value for the population standard deviation.
    a. Assuming 95% confidence, what sample size would be required to obtain a margin of error of 1.5 days?
    b. If the precision statement was made with 90% confidence, what sample size would be required to obtain a margin of error of 2 days?

26. The U.S. Energy Information Administration (US EIA) reported that the average price for a gallon of regular gasoline is $3.94 (US EIA website, April 6, 2012). The US EIA updates its estimates of average gas prices on a weekly basis. Assume the standard deviation is $.25 for the price of a gallon of regular gasoline and recommend the appropriate sample size for the US EIA to use if it wishes to report each of the following margins of error at 95% confidence.
    a. The desired margin of error is $.10.
    b. The desired margin of error is $.07.
    c. The desired margin of error is $.05.

27. Annual starting salaries for college graduates with degrees in business administration are generally expected to be between $30,000 and $45,000. Assume that a 95% confidence interval estimate of the population mean annual starting salary is desired. What is the planning value for the population standard deviation? How large a sample should be taken if the desired margin of error is
    a. $500?
    b. $200?
    c. $100?
    d. Would you recommend trying to obtain the $100 margin of error? Explain.

28. Many medical professionals believe that eating too much red meat increases the risk of heart disease and cancer (WebMD website, March 12, 2014). Suppose you would like to conduct a survey to determine the yearly consumption of beef by a typical American and want to use 3 pounds as the desired margin of error for a confidence interval estimate of the population mean amount of beef consumed annually. Use 25 pounds as a planning value for the population standard deviation and recommend a sample size for each of the following situations.
    a. A 90% confidence interval is desired for the mean amount of beef consumed.
    b. A 95% confidence interval is desired for the mean amount of beef consumed.
    c. A 99% confidence interval is desired for the mean amount of beef consumed.
    d. When the desired margin of error is set, what happens to the sample size as the confidence level is increased? Would you recommend using a 99% confidence interval in this case? Discuss.

29. Customers arrive at a movie theater at the advertised movie time only to find that they have to sit through several previews and prepreview ads before the movie starts. Many complain that the time devoted to previews is too long (*The Wall Street Journal*, October 12, 2012). A preliminary sample conducted by *The Wall Street Journal* showed that the

standard deviation of the amount of time devoted to previews was 4 minutes. Use that as a planning value for the standard deviation in answering the following questions.

a. If we want to estimate the population mean time for previews at movie theaters with a margin of error of 75 seconds, what sample size should be used? Assume 95% confidence.

b. If we want to estimate the population mean time for previews at movie theaters with a margin of error of 1 minute, what sample size should be used? Assume 95% confidence.

30. There has been a trend toward less driving in the recent past, especially by young people. From 2001 to 2009 the annual vehicle miles traveled by people from 16 to 34 years of age decreased from 10,300 to 7900 miles per person (U.S. PIRG and Education Fund website, April 6, 2012). Assume the standard deviation was 2000 miles in 2009. Suppose you would like to conduct a survey to develop a 95% confidence interval estimate of the annual vehicle-miles per person for people 16 to 34 years of age at the current time. A margin of error of 100 miles is desired. How large a sample should be used for the current survey?

8.4 Population Proportion

In the introduction to this chapter we said that the general form of an interval estimate of a population proportion p is

$$\bar{p} \pm \text{Margin of error}$$

The sampling distribution of $\bar{p}$ plays a key role in computing the margin of error for this interval estimate.

In Chapter 7 we said that the sampling distribution of $\bar{p}$ can be approximated by a normal distribution whenever $np \geq 5$ and $n(1 - p) \geq 5$. Figure 8.10 shows the normal approximation of the sampling distribution of $\bar{p}$. The mean of the sampling distribution of $\bar{p}$ is the population proportion p, and the standard error of $\bar{p}$ is

$$\sigma_{\bar{p}} = \sqrt{\frac{p(1-p)}{n}} \tag{8.4}$$

FIGURE 8.10 NORMAL APPROXIMATION OF THE SAMPLING DISTRIBUTION OF $\bar{p}$

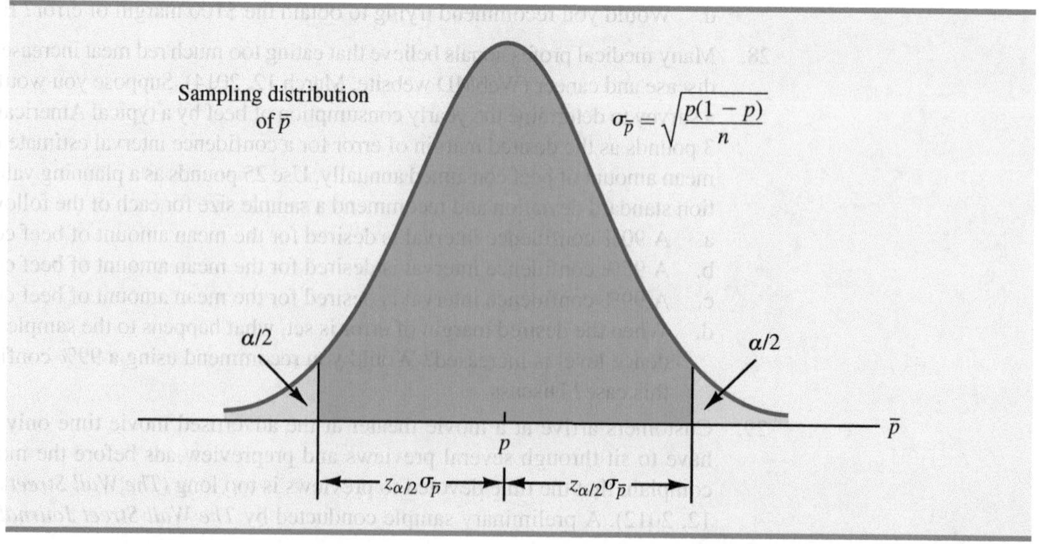

Because the sampling distribution of $\bar{p}$ is normally distributed, if we choose $z_{\alpha/2}\sigma_{\bar{p}}$ as the margin of error in an interval estimate of a population proportion, we know that $100(1 - \alpha)\%$ of the intervals generated will contain the true population proportion. But $\sigma_{\bar{p}}$ cannot be used directly in the computation of the margin of error because p will not be known; p is what we are trying to estimate. So $\bar{p}$ is substituted for p and the margin of error for an interval estimate of a population proportion is given by

$$\text{Margin of error} = z_{\alpha/2}\sqrt{\frac{\bar{p}(1 - \bar{p})}{n}} \tag{8.5}$$

With this margin of error, the general expression for an interval estimate of a population proportion is as follows.

When developing confidence intervals for proportions, the quantity $z_{\alpha/2}\sqrt{\bar{p}(1 - \bar{p})/n}$ provides the margin of error.

INTERVAL ESTIMATE OF A POPULATION PROPORTION

$$\bar{p} \pm z_{\alpha/2}\sqrt{\frac{\bar{p}(1 - \bar{p})}{n}} \tag{8.6}$$

where $1 - \alpha$ is the confidence coefficient and $z_{\alpha/2}$ is the z value providing an area of $\alpha/2$ in the upper tail of the standard normal distribution.

TeeTimes

The following example illustrates the computation of the margin of error and interval estimate for a population proportion. A national survey of 900 women golfers was conducted to learn how women golfers view their treatment at golf courses in the United States. The survey found that 396 of the women golfers were satisfied with the availability of tee times. Thus, the point estimate of the proportion of the population of women golfers who are satisfied with the availability of tee times is 396/900 = .44. Using expression (8.6) and a 95% confidence level,

$$\bar{p} \pm z_{\alpha/2}\sqrt{\frac{\bar{p}(1 - \bar{p})}{n}}$$

$$.44 \pm 1.96\sqrt{\frac{.44(1 - .44)}{900}}$$

$$.44 \pm .0324$$

Thus, the margin of error is .0324 and the 95% confidence interval estimate of the population proportion is .4076 to .4724. Using percentages, the survey results enable us to state with 95% confidence that between 40.76% and 47.24% of all women golfers are satisfied with the availability of tee times.

Using Excel

Excel can be used to construct an interval estimate of the population proportion of women golfers who are satisfied with the availability of tee times. The responses in the survey were recorded as a Yes or No for each woman surveyed. Refer to Figure 8.11 as we describe the tasks involved in constructing a 95% confidence interval. The formula worksheet is in the background; the value worksheet appears in the foreground.

Enter/Access Data: Open the WEBfile named TeeTimes. A label and the Yes/No data for the 900 women golfers are entered into cells A1:A901.

FIGURE 8.11 EXCEL WORKSHEET: 95% CONFIDENCE INTERVAL FOR SURVEY OF WOMEN GOLFERS

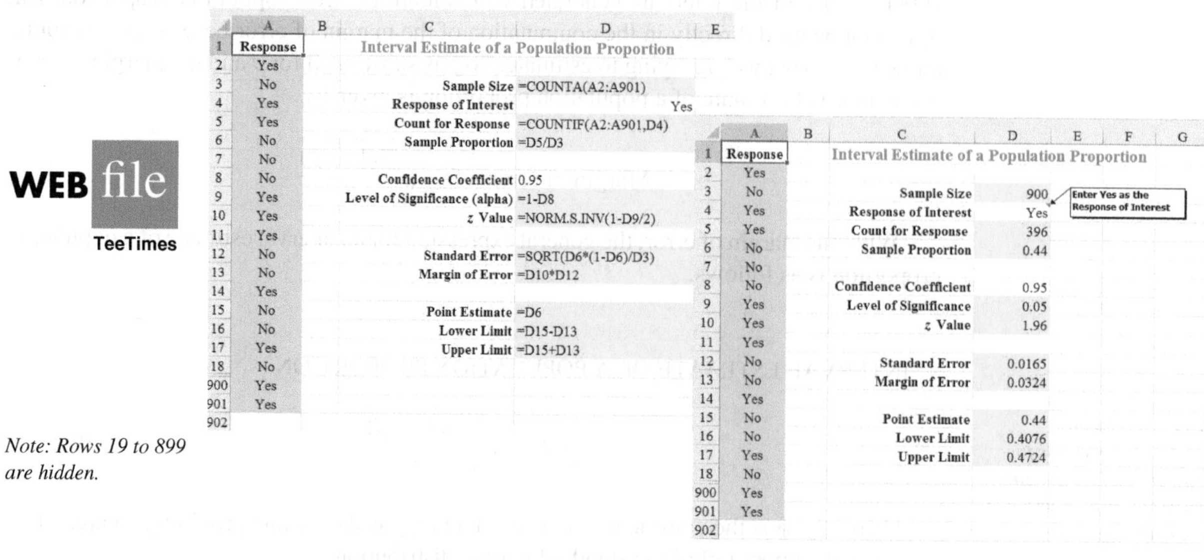

Enter Functions and Formulas: The descriptive statistics we need and the response of interest are provided in cells D3:D6. Because Excel's COUNT function works only with numerical data, we used the COUNTA function in cell D3 to compute the sample size. The response for which we want to develop an interval estimate, Yes or No, is entered into cell D4. Figure 8.11 shows that Yes has been entered into cell D4, indicating that we want to develop an interval estimate of the population proportion of women golfers who are satisfied with the availability of tee times. If we had wanted to develop an interval estimate of the population proportion of women golfers who are not satisfied with the availability of tee times, we would have entered No in cell D4. With Yes entered in cell D4, the COUNTIF function in cell D5 counts the number of Yes responses in the sample. The sample proportion is then computed in cell D6 by dividing the number of Yes responses in cell D5 by the sample size in cell D3.

Cells D8:D10 are used to compute the appropriate z value. The confidence coefficient (0.95) is entered into cell D8 and the level of significance (α) is computed in cell D9 by entering the formula =1-D8. The z value corresponding to an upper tail area of $\alpha/2$ is computed by entering the formula =NORM.S.INV(1-D9/2) into cell D10. The value worksheet shows that $z_{.025} = 1.96$.

Cells D12:D13 provide the estimate of the standard error and the margin of error. In cell D12, we entered the formula =SQRT(D6*(1-D6)/D3) to compute the standard error using the sample proportion and the sample size as inputs. The formula =D10*D12 is entered into cell D13 to compute the margin of error.

Cells D15:D17 provide the point estimate and the lower and upper limits for a confidence interval. The point estimate in cell D15 is the sample proportion. The lower and upper limits in cells D16 and D17 are obtained by subtracting and adding the margin of error to the point estimate. We note that the 95% confidence interval for the proportion of women golfers who are satisfied with the availability of tee times is .4076 to .4724.

A template for other problems The worksheet in Figure 8.11 can be used as a template for developing confidence intervals about a population proportion p. To use this worksheet for another problem of this type, we must first enter the new problem data in column A. The response of interest would then be typed in cell D4, and the ranges for the formulas in cells

D3 and D5 would be revised to correspond to the new data. After doing so, the point estimate and a 95% confidence interval will be displayed in cells D15:D17. If a confidence interval with a different confidence coefficient is desired, we simply change the value in cell D8.

Determining the Sample Size

Let us consider the question of how large the sample size should be to obtain an estimate of a population proportion at a specified level of precision. The rationale for the sample size determination in developing interval estimates of p is similar to the rationale used in Section 8.3 to determine the sample size for estimating a population mean.

Previously in this section we said that the margin of error associated with an interval estimate of a population proportion is $z_{\alpha/2}\sqrt{\bar{p}(1 - \bar{p})/n}$. The margin of error is based on the value of $z_{\alpha/2}$, the sample proportion $\bar{p}$, and the sample size n. Larger sample sizes provide a smaller margin of error and better precision.

Let E denote the desired margin of error.

$$E = z_{\alpha/2}\sqrt{\frac{\bar{p}(1 - \bar{p})}{n}}$$

Solving this equation for n provides a formula for the sample size that will provide a margin of error of size E.

$$n = \frac{(z_{\alpha/2})^2\bar{p}(1 - \bar{p})}{E^2}$$

Note, however, that we cannot use this formula to compute the sample size that will provide the desired margin of error because $\bar{p}$ will not be known until after we select the sample. What we need, then, is a planning value for $\bar{p}$ that can be used to make the computation. Using p^* to denote the planning value for $\bar{p}$, the following formula can be used to compute the sample size that will provide a margin of error of size E.

SAMPLE SIZE FOR AN INTERVAL ESTIMATE OF A POPULATION PROPORTION

$$n = \frac{(z_{\alpha/2})^2 p^*(1 - p^*)}{E^2} \tag{8.7}$$

In practice, the planning value p^* can be chosen by one of the following procedures.

1. Use the sample proportion from a previous sample of the same or similar units.
2. Use a pilot study to select a preliminary sample. The sample proportion from this sample can be used as the planning value, p^*.
3. Use judgment or a “best guess” for the value of p^*.
4. If none of the preceding alternatives apply, use a planning value of $p^* = .50$.

Let us return to the survey of women golfers and assume that the company is interested in conducting a new survey to estimate the current proportion of the population of women golfers who are satisfied with the availability of tee times. How large should the sample be if the survey director wants to estimate the population proportion with a margin of error of .025 at 95% confidence? With $E = .025$ and $z_{\alpha/2} = 1.96$, we need a planning value p^* to answer the sample size question. Using the previous survey result of $\bar{p} = .44$ as the planning value p^*, equation (8.7) shows that

$$n = \frac{(z_{\alpha/2})^2 p^*(1 - p^*)}{E^2} = \frac{(1.96)^2(.44)(1 - .44)}{(.025)^2} = 1514.5$$

TABLE 8.5 SOME POSSIBLE VALUES FOR $p^*(1 - p^*)$

p^*	$p^*(1 - p^*)$	
.10	(.10)(.90) = .09	
.30	(.30)(.70) = .21	
.40	(.40)(.60) = .24	
.50	(.50)(.50) = .25	← Largest value for $p^*(1 - p^*)$
.60	(.60)(.40) = .24	
.70	(.70)(.30) = .21	
.90	(.90)(.10) = .09	

Thus, the sample size must be at least 1514.5 women golfers to satisfy the margin of error requirement. Rounding up to the next integer value indicates that a sample of 1515 women golfers is recommended to satisfy the margin of error requirement.

The fourth alternative suggested for selecting a planning value p^* is to use $p^* = .50$. This value of p^* is frequently used when no other information is available. To understand why, note that the numerator of equation (8.7) shows that the sample size is proportional to the quantity $p^*(1 - p^*)$. A larger value for the quantity $p^*(1 - p^*)$ will result in a larger sample size. Table 8.5 gives some possible values of $p^*(1 - p^*)$. Note that the largest value of $p^*(1 - p^*)$ occurs when $p^* = .50$. Thus, in case of any uncertainty about an appropriate planning value, we know that $p^* = .50$ will provide the largest sample size recommendation. In effect, we play it safe by recommending the largest necessary sample size. If the sample proportion turns out to be different from the .50 planning value, the margin of error will be smaller than anticipated. Thus, in using $p^* = .50$, we guarantee that the sample size will be sufficient to obtain the desired margin of error.

In the survey of women golfers example, a planning value of $p^* = .50$ would have provided the sample size

$$n = \frac{(z_{\alpha/2})^2 p^*(1 - p^*)}{E^2} = \frac{(1.96)^2(.50)(1 - .50)}{(.025)^2} = 1536.6$$

Thus, a slightly larger sample size of 1537 women golfers would be recommended.

NOTES AND COMMENTS

1. The desired margin of error for estimating a population proportion is almost always .10 or less. In national public opinion polls conducted by organizations such as Gallup and Harris, a .03 or .04 margin of error is common. With such margins of error, equation (8.7) will almost always provide a sample size that is large enough to satisfy the requirements of $np \geq 5$ and $n(1 - p) \geq 5$ for using a normal distribution as an approximation for the sampling distribution of $\bar{x}$.
2. Equation (8.7) provides the recommended sample size n for an infinite population as well as for a large finite population of size N provided $n/N < .05$. This is fine for most statistical studies. However, if we have a finite population such that $n/N > .05$, a smaller sample size can be used to obtain the desired margin of error. The smaller sample size denoted by n' can be computed using the following equation.

$$n' = \frac{n}{(1 + n/N)}$$

For example, suppose that the example presented in this section showing $n = 1536.6$ was computed for a population of size $N = 2500$. With $n/N = 1536.6/2500 = .61 > .05$, a smaller sample size can be computed by

$$n' = \frac{n}{(1 + n/N)} = \frac{1536.6}{(1 + 1536.6/2500)} = 951.67$$

Thus, for the finite population of $N = 2500$, the sample size required to obtain the desired margin of error $E = .025$ would be reduced from 1537 to 952.

Exercises

Methods

31. A simple random sample of 400 individuals provides 100 Yes responses.
    a. What is the point estimate of the proportion of the population that would provide Yes responses?
    b. What is your estimate of the standard error of the proportion, $\sigma_{\bar{p}}$?
    c. Compute the 95% confidence interval for the population proportion.
32. A simple random sample of 800 elements generates a sample proportion $\bar{p} = .70$.
    a. Provide a 90% confidence interval for the population proportion.
    b. Provide a 95% confidence interval for the population proportion.
33. In a survey, the planning value for the population proportion is $p^* = .35$. How large a sample should be taken to provide a 95% confidence interval with a margin of error of .05?
34. At 95% confidence, how large a sample should be taken to obtain a margin of error of .03 for the estimation of a population proportion? Assume that past data are not available for developing a planning value for p^*.

Applications

35. The Consumer Reports National Research Center conducted a telephone survey of 2000 adults to learn about the major economic concerns for the future (*Consumer Reports*, January 2009). The survey results showed that 1760 of the respondents think the future health of Social Security is a major economic concern.
    a. What is the point estimate of the population proportion of adults who think the future health of Social Security is a major economic concern?
    b. At 90% confidence, what is the margin of error?
    c. Develop a 90% confidence interval for the population proportion of adults who think the future health of Social Security is a major economic concern.
    d. Develop a 95% confidence interval for this population proportion.

36. According to statistics reported on CNBC, a surprising number of motor vehicles are not covered by insurance (CNBC, February 23, 2006). Sample results, consistent with the CNBC report, showed 46 of 200 vehicles were not covered by insurance.
    a. What is the point estimate of the proportion of vehicles not covered by insurance?
    b. Develop a 95% confidence interval for the population proportion.

ChildOutlook

37. One of the questions on a survey of 1000 adults asked if today's children will be better off than their parents (Rasmussen Reports website, October 26, 2012). Representative data are shown in the WEBfile named ChildOutlook. A response of Yes indicates that the adult surveyed did think today's children will be better off than their parents. A response of No indicates that the adult surveyed did not think today's children will be better off than their parents. A response of Not Sure was given by 23% of the adults surveyed.
    a. What is the point estimate of the proportion of the population of adults who do think that today's children will be better off than their parents?
    b. At 95% confidence, what is the margin of error?
    c. What is the 95% confidence interval for the proportion of adults who do think that today's children will be better off than their parents?
    d. What is the 95% confidence interval for the proportion of adults who do not think that today's children will be better off than their parents?
    e. Which of the confidence intervals in parts (c) and (d) has the smaller margin of error? Why?
38. According to Thomson Financial, through January 25, 2006, the majority of companies reporting profits had beaten estimates (*BusinessWeek*, February 6, 2006). A sample of 162 companies showed that 104 beat estimates, 29 matched estimates, and 29 fell short.

a. What is the point estimate of the proportion that fell short of estimates?
b. Determine the margin of error and provide a 95% confidence interval for the proportion that beat estimates.
c. How large a sample is needed if the desired margin of error is .05?

39. The percentage of people not covered by health care insurance in 2003 was 15.6% (*Statistical Abstract of the United States*, 2006). A congressional committee has been charged with conducting a sample survey to obtain more current information.
a. What sample size would you recommend if the committee's goal is to estimate the current proportion of individuals without health care insurance with a margin of error of .03? Use a 95% confidence level.
b. Repeat part (a) using a 99% confidence level.

40. For many years businesses have struggled with the rising cost of health care. But recently, the increases have slowed due to less inflation in health care prices and employees paying for a larger portion of health care benefits. A recent Mercer survey showed that 52% of U.S. employers were likely to require higher employee contributions for health care coverage in 2009 (*BusinessWeek*, February 16, 2009). Suppose the survey was based on a sample of 800 companies. Compute the margin of error and a 95% confidence interval for the proportion of companies likely to require higher employee contributions for health care coverage in 2009.

41. Fewer young people are driving. In 1983, 87% of 19-year-olds had a driver's license. Twenty-five years later that percentage had dropped to 75% (University of Michigan Transportation Research Institute website, April 7, 2012). Suppose these results are based on a random sample of 1200 19-year-olds in 1983 and again in 2008.
a. At 95% confidence, what is the margin of error and the interval estimate of the number of 19-year-old drivers in 1983?
b. At 95% confidence, what is the margin of error and the interval estimate of the number of 19-year-old drivers in 2008?
c. Is the margin of error the same in parts (a) and (b)? Why or why not?

42. A poll for the presidential campaign sampled 491 potential voters in June. A primary purpose of the poll was to obtain an estimate of the proportion of potential voters who favored each candidate. Assume a planning value of $p^* = .50$ and a 95% confidence level.
a. For $p^* = .50$, what was the planned margin of error for the June poll?
b. Closer to the November election, better precision and smaller margins of error are desired. Assume the following margins of error are requested for surveys to be conducted during the presidential campaign. Compute the recommended sample size for each survey.

Survey	Margin of Error
September	.04
October	.03
Early November	.02
Pre-Election Day	.01

43. The Pew Research Center Internet Project, conducted on the 25th anniversary of the Internet, involved a survey of 857 Internet users (Pew Research Center website, April 1, 2014). It provided a variety of statistics on Internet users. For instance, in 2014, 87% of American adults were Internet users. In 1995 only 14% of American adults used the Internet.
a The sample survey showed that 90% of respondents said the Internet has been a good thing for them personally. Develop a 95% confidence interval for the proportion of respondents who say the Internet has been a good thing for them personally.
b. The sample survey showed that 67% of Internet users said the Internet has generally strengthened their relationship with family and friends. Develop a 95% confidence interval for the proportion of respondents who say the Internet has strengthened their relationship with family and friends.

c. Fifty-six percent of Internet users have seen an online group come together to help a person or community solve a problem, whereas only 25% have left an online group because of unpleasant interaction. Develop a 95% confidence interval for the proportion of Internet users who say online groups have helped solve a problem.

d. Compare the margin of error for the interval estimates in parts (a), (b), and (c). How is the margin of error related to the sample proportion?

Summary

In this chapter we presented methods for developing interval estimates of a population mean and a population proportion. A point estimator may or may not provide a good estimate of a population parameter. The use of an interval estimate provides a measure of the precision of an estimate. Both the interval estimate of the population mean and the population proportion are of the form: point estimate ± margin of error.

We presented interval estimates for a population mean for two cases. In the σ known case, historical data or other information is used to develop an estimate of σ prior to taking a sample. Analysis of new sample data then proceeds based on the assumption that σ is known. In the σ unknown case, the sample data are used to estimate both the population mean and the population standard deviation. The final choice of which interval estimation procedure to use depends upon the analyst's understanding of which method provides the best estimate of σ.

In the σ known case, the interval estimation procedure is based on the assumed value of σ and the use of the standard normal distribution. In the σ unknown case, the interval estimation procedure uses the sample standard deviation s and the t distribution. In both cases the quality of the interval estimates obtained depends on the distribution of the population and the sample size. If the population is normally distributed, the interval estimates will be exact in both cases, even for small sample sizes. If the population is not normally distributed, the interval estimates obtained will be approximate. Larger sample sizes will provide better approximations, but the more highly skewed the population is, the larger the sample size needs to be to obtain a good approximation. Practical advice about the sample size necessary to obtain good approximations was included in Sections 8.1 and 8.2. In most cases a sample of size 30 or more will provide good approximate confidence intervals.

The general form of the interval estimate for a population proportion is $\bar{p}$ ± margin of error. In practice the sample sizes used for interval estimates of a population proportion are generally large. Thus, the interval estimation procedure is based on the standard normal distribution.

Often a desired margin of error is specified prior to developing a sampling plan. We showed how to choose a sample size large enough to provide the desired precision.

Glossary

Interval estimate An estimate of a population parameter that provides an interval believed to contain the value of the parameter. For the interval estimates in this chapter, it has the form: point estimate ± margin of error.

Margin of error The ± value added to and subtracted from a point estimate in order to develop an interval estimate of a population parameter.

σ known The case when historical data or other information provide a good value for the population standard deviation prior to taking a sample. The interval estimation procedure uses this known value of σ in computing the margin of error.

Confidence level The confidence associated with an interval estimate. For example, if an interval estimation procedure provides intervals such that 95% of the intervals formed using the procedure will include the population parameter, the interval estimate is said to be constructed at the 95% confidence level.

Confidence coefficient The confidence level expressed as a decimal value. For example, .95 is the confidence coefficient for a 95% confidence level.

Confidence interval Another name for an interval estimate.

Level of significance The probability that the interval estimation procedure will generate an interval that does not contain μ.

σ unknown The more common case when no good basis exists for estimating the population standard deviation prior to taking the sample. The interval estimation procedure uses the sample standard deviation s in computing the margin of error.

***t* distribution** A family of probability distributions that can be used to develop an interval estimate of a population mean whenever the population standard deviation σ is unknown and is estimated by the sample standard deviation s.

Degrees of freedom A parameter of the t distribution. When the t distribution is used in the computation of an interval estimate of a population mean, the appropriate t distribution has $n - 1$ degrees of freedom, where n is the size of the sample.

Key Formulas

Interval Estimate of a Population Mean: σ Known

$$\bar{x} \pm z_{\alpha/2} \frac{\sigma}{\sqrt{n}} \tag{8.1}$$

Interval Estimate of a Population Mean: σ Unknown

$$\bar{x} \pm t_{\alpha/2} \frac{s}{\sqrt{n}} \tag{8.2}$$

Sample Size for an Interval Estimate of a Population Mean

$$n = \frac{(z_{\alpha/2})^2 \sigma^2}{E^2} \tag{8.3}$$

Interval Estimate of a Population Proportion

$$\bar{p} \pm z_{\alpha/2} \sqrt{\frac{\bar{p}(1 - \bar{p})}{n}} \tag{8.6}$$

Sample Size for an Interval Estimate of a Population Proportion

$$n = \frac{(z_{\alpha/2})^2 p^*(1 - p^*)}{E^2} \tag{8.7}$$

Supplementary Exercises

44. A sample survey of 54 discount brokers showed that the mean price charged for a trade of 100 shares at $50 per share was $33.77 (*AAII Journal*, February 2006). The survey is conducted annually. With the historical data available, assume a known population standard deviation of $15.
    a. Using the sample data, what is the margin of error associated with a 95% confidence interval?
    b. Develop a 95% confidence interval for the mean price charged by discount brokers for a trade of 100 shares at $50 per share.

45. A survey conducted by the American Automobile Association (AAA) showed that a family of four spends an average of \$215.60 per day while on vacation. Suppose a sample of 64 families of four vacationing at Niagara Falls resulted in a sample mean of \$252.45 per day and a sample standard deviation of \$74.50.
    a. Develop a 95% confidence interval estimate of the mean amount spent per day by a family of four visiting Niagara Falls.
    b. Based on the confidence interval from part (a), does it appear that the population mean amount spent per day by families visiting Niagara Falls differs from the mean reported by the American Automobile Association? Explain.

46. The 92 million Americans of age 50 and over control 50% of all discretionary income (*AARP Bulletin*, March 2008). AARP estimated that the average annual expenditure on restaurants and carryout food was \$1873 for individuals in this age group. Suppose this estimate is based on a sample of 80 persons and that the sample standard deviation is \$550.
    a. At 95% confidence, what is the margin of error?
    b. What is the 95% confidence interval for the population mean amount spent on restaurants and carryout food?
    c. What is your estimate of the total amount spent by Americans of age 50 and over on restaurants and carryout food?
    d. If the amount spent on restaurants and carryout food is skewed to the right, would you expect the median amount spent to be greater or less than \$1873?

47. Russia has recently started a push for stronger smoking regulations much like those in Western countries concerning cigarette advertising, smoking in public places, and so on. The WEBfile named Russia contains sample data on smoking habits of Russians that are consistent with those reported by *The Wall Street Journal* (*The Wall Street Journal*, October 16, 2012). Analyze the data using Excel and answer the following questions.
    a. Develop a point estimate and a 95% confidence interval for the proportion of Russians who smoke.
    b. Develop a point estimate and a 95% confidence interval for the mean annual per capita consumption (number of cigarettes) of a Russian.
    c. For those Russians who do smoke, estimate the number of cigarettes smoked per day.

48. The Health Care Cost Institute tracks health care expenditures for beneficiaries under the age of 65 who are covered by employer-sponsored private health insurance (Health Care Cost Institute website, November 4, 2012). The data contained in the WEBfile named DrugCost are consistent with the institute's findings concerning annual prescription costs per employee. Analyze the data using Excel and answer the following questions.
    a. Develop a 90% confidence interval for the annual cost of prescription drugs.
    b. Develop a 90% confidence interval for the amount of out-of-pocket expense per employee.
    c. What is your point estimate of the proportion of employees who incurred no prescription drug costs?
    d. Which, if either, of the confidence intervals in parts (a) and (b) has a larger margin of error. Why?

49. An article reported that there are approximately 11 minutes of actual playing time in a typical National Football League (NFL) game (*The Wall Street Journal*, January 15, 2010). The article included information about the amount of time devoted to replays, the amount of time devoted to commercials, and the amount of time the players spend standing around between plays. Data consistent with the findings published in *The Wall Street Journal* are in the WEBfile named Standing. These data provide the amount of time players spend standing around between plays for a sample of 60 NFL games.
    a. Use the Standing data set to develop a point estimate of the number of minutes during an NFL game that players are standing around between plays. Compare this to the actual playing time reported in the article. Are you surprised?
    b. What is the sample standard deviation?
    c. Develop a 95% confidence interval for the number of minutes players spend standing around between plays.

50. Mileage tests are conducted for a particular model of automobile. If a 98% confidence interval with a margin of error of 1 mile per gallon is desired, how many automobiles should be used in the test? Assume that preliminary mileage tests indicate the standard deviation is 2.6 miles per gallon.

51. In developing patient appointment schedules, a medical center wants to estimate the mean time that a staff member spends with each patient. How large a sample should be taken if the desired margin of error is two minutes at a 95% level of confidence? How large a sample should be taken for a 99% level of confidence? Use a planning value for the population standard deviation of eight minutes.

52. Annual salary plus bonus data for chief executive officers are presented in an annual pay survey. A preliminary sample showed that the standard deviation is $675 with data provided in thousands of dollars. How many chief executive officers should be in a sample if we want to estimate the population mean annual salary plus bonus with a margin of error of $100,000? (*Note:* The desired margin of error would be $E = 100$ if the data are in thousands of dollars.) Use 95% confidence.

53. The National Center for Education Statistics reported that 47% of college students work to pay for tuition and living expenses. Assume that a sample of 450 college students was used in the study.
   a. Provide a 95% confidence interval for the population proportion of college students who work to pay for tuition and living expenses.
   b. Provide a 99% confidence interval for the population proportion of college students who work to pay for tuition and living expenses.
   c. What happens to the margin of error as the confidence is increased from 95% to 99%?

54. A *USA Today*/CNN/Gallup survey of 369 working parents found 200 who said they spend too little time with their children because of work commitments.
   a. What is the point estimate of the proportion of the population of working parents who feel they spend too little time with their children because of work commitments?
   b. At 95% confidence, what is the margin of error?
   c. What is the 95% confidence interval estimate of the population proportion of working parents who feel they spend too little time with their children because of work commitments?

55. The Pew Research Center has conducted extensive research on the young adult population (Pew Research website, November 6, 2012). One finding was that 93% of adults aged 18 to 29 use the Internet. Another finding was that 21% of those aged 18 to 28 are married. Assume the sample size associated with both findings is 500.
   a. Develop a 95% confidence interval for the proportion of adults aged 18 to 29 who use the Internet.
   b. Develop a 99% confidence interval for the proportion of adults aged 18 to 28 who are married.
   c. In which case, part (a) or part (b), is the margin of error larger? Explain why.

56. A survey of 750 likely voters in Ohio was conducted by the Rasmussen Poll just prior to the general election (Rasmussen Reports website, November 4, 2012). The state of the economy was thought to be an important determinant of how people would vote. Among other things, the survey found that 165 of the respondents rated the economy as good or excellent and 315 rated the economy as poor.
   a. Develop a point estimate of the proportion of likely voters in Ohio who rated the economy as good or excellent.
   b. Construct a 95% confidence interval for the proportion of likely voters in Ohio who rated the economy as good or excellent.
   c. Construct a 95% confidence interval for the proportion of likely voters in Ohio who rated the economy as poor.
   d. Which of the confidence intervals in parts (b) and (c) is wider? Why?

57. The *2003 Statistical Abstract of the United States* reported the percentage of people 18 years of age and older who smoke. Suppose that a study designed to collect new data on smokers and nonsmokers uses a preliminary estimate of the proportion who smoke of .30.
    a. How large a sample should be taken to estimate the proportion of smokers in the population with a margin of error of .02? Use 95% confidence.
    b. Assume that the study uses your sample size recommendation in part (a) and finds 520 smokers. What is the point estimate of the proportion of smokers in the population?
    c. What is the 95% confidence interval for the proportion of smokers in the population?

58. A well-known bank credit card firm wishes to estimate the proportion of credit card holders who carry a nonzero balance at the end of the month and incur an interest charge. Assume that the desired margin of error is .03 at 98% confidence.
    a. How large a sample should be selected if it is anticipated that roughly 70% of the firm's card holders carry a nonzero balance at the end of the month?
    b. How large a sample should be selected if no planning value for the proportion could be specified?

59. Workers in several industries were surveyed to determine the proportion of workers who feel their industry is understaffed. In the government sector 37% of the respondents said they were understaffed, in the health care sector 33% said they were understaffed, and in the education sector 28% said they were understaffed (*USA Today,* January 11, 2010). Suppose that 200 workers were surveyed in each industry.
    a. Construct a 95% confidence interval for the proportion of workers in each of these industries who feel their industry is understaffed.
    b. Assuming the same sample size will be used in each industry, how large would the sample need to be to ensure that the margin of error is .05 or less for each of the three confidence intervals?

60. Although airline schedules and cost are important factors for business travelers when choosing an airline carrier, a *USA Today* survey found that business travelers list an airline's frequent flyer program as the most important factor. From a sample of $n = 1993$ business travelers who responded to the survey, 618 listed a frequent flyer program as the most important factor.
    a. What is the point estimate of the proportion of the population of business travelers who believe a frequent flyer program is the most important factor when choosing an airline carrier?
    b. Develop a 95% confidence interval estimate of the population proportion.
    c. How large a sample would be required to report the margin of error of .01 at 95% confidence? Would you recommend that *USA Today* attempt to provide this degree of precision? Why or why not?

Case Problem 1 *Young Professional* Magazine

Young Professional magazine was developed for a target audience of recent college graduates who are in their first 10 years in a business/professional career. In its two years of publication, the magazine has been fairly successful. Now the publisher is interested in expanding the magazine's advertising base. Potential advertisers continually ask about the demographics and interests of subscribers to *Young Professional.* To collect this information, the magazine commissioned a survey to develop a profile of its subscribers. The survey results will be used to help the magazine choose articles of interest and provide advertisers with a profile of subscribers. As a new employee of the magazine, you have been asked to help analyze the survey results.

TABLE 8.6 PARTIAL SURVEY RESULTS FOR *YOUNG PROFESSIONAL* MAGAZINE

Age	Gender	Real Estate Purchases	Value of Investments($)	Number of Transactions	Broadband Access	Household Income($)	Children
38	Female	No	12200	4	Yes	75200	Yes
30	Male	No	12400	4	Yes	70300	Yes
41	Female	No	26800	5	Yes	48200	No
28	Female	Yes	19600	6	No	95300	No
31	Female	Yes	15100	5	No	73300	Yes
⋮	⋮	⋮	⋮	⋮	⋮	⋮	⋮

Professional

Some of the survey questions follow:

1. What is your age?
2. Are you: Male________ Female________
3. Do you plan to make any real estate purchases in the next two years? Yes______ No______
4. What is the approximate total value of financial investments, exclusive of your home, owned by you or members of your household?
5. How many stock/bond/mutual fund transactions have you made in the past year?
6. Do you have broadband access to the Internet at home? Yes______ No______
7. Please indicate your total household income last year.
8. Do you have children? Yes______ No______

The WEBfile named Professional contains the responses to these questions. Table 8.6 shows the portion of the file pertaining to the first five survey respondents.

Managerial Report

Prepare a managerial report summarizing the results of the survey. In addition to statistical summaries, discuss how the magazine might use these results to attract advertisers. You might also comment on how the survey results could be used by the magazine's editors to identify topics that would be of interest to readers. Your report should address the following issues, but do not limit your analysis to just these areas.

1. Develop appropriate descriptive statistics to summarize the data.
2. Develop 95% confidence intervals for the mean age and household income of subscribers.
3. Develop 95% confidence intervals for the proportion of subscribers who have broadband access at home and the proportion of subscribers who have children.
4. Would *Young Professional* be a good advertising outlet for online brokers? Justify your conclusion with statistical data.
5. Would this magazine be a good place to advertise for companies selling educational software and computer games for young children?
6. Comment on the types of articles you believe would be of interest to readers of *Young Professional.*

Case Problem 2 Gulf Real Estate Properties

Gulf Real Estate Properties, Inc., is a real estate firm located in southwest Florida. The company, which advertises itself as "expert in the real estate market," monitors condominium sales by collecting data on location, list price, sale price, and number of days

TABLE 8.7 SALES DATA FOR GULF REAL ESTATE PROPERTIES

Gulf View Condominiums			No Gulf View Condominiums		
List Price	**Sale Price**	**Days to Sell**	**List Price**	**Sale Price**	**Days to Sell**
495.0	475.0	130	217.0	217.0	182
379.0	350.0	71	148.0	135.5	338
529.0	519.0	85	186.5	179.0	122
552.5	534.5	95	239.0	230.0	150
334.9	334.9	119	279.0	267.5	169
550.0	505.0	92	215.0	214.0	58
169.9	165.0	197	279.0	259.0	110
210.0	210.0	56	179.9	176.5	130
975.0	945.0	73	149.9	144.9	149
314.0	314.0	126	235.0	230.0	114
315.0	305.0	88	199.8	192.0	120
885.0	800.0	282	210.0	195.0	61
975.0	975.0	100	226.0	212.0	146
469.0	445.0	56	149.9	146.5	137
329.0	305.0	49	160.0	160.0	281
365.0	330.0	48	322.0	292.5	63
332.0	312.0	88	187.5	179.0	48
520.0	495.0	161	247.0	227.0	52
425.0	405.0	149			
675.0	669.0	142			
409.0	400.0	28			
649.0	649.0	29			
319.0	305.0	140			
425.0	410.0	85			
359.0	340.0	107			
469.0	449.0	72			
895.0	875.0	129			
439.0	430.0	160			
435.0	400.0	206			
235.0	227.0	91			
638.0	618.0	100			
629.0	600.0	97			
329.0	309.0	114			
595.0	555.0	45			
339.0	315.0	150			
215.0	200.0	48			
395.0	375.0	135			
449.0	425.0	53			
499.0	465.0	86			
439.0	428.5	158			

GulfProp

it takes to sell each unit. Each condominium is classified as *Gulf View* if it is located directly on the Gulf of Mexico or *No Gulf View* if it is located on the bay or a golf course, near but not on the Gulf. Sample data from the Multiple Listing Service in Naples, Florida, provided recent sales data for 40 Gulf View condominiums and 18 No Gulf View condominiums.* Prices are in thousands of dollars. The data are shown in Table 8.7.

*Data based on condominium sales reported in the Naples MLS (Coldwell Banker, June 2000).

Managerial Report

1. Use appropriate descriptive statistics to summarize each of the three variables for the 40 Gulf View condominiums.
2. Use appropriate descriptive statistics to summarize each of the three variables for the 18 No Gulf View condominiums.
3. Compare your summary results. Discuss any specific statistical results that would help a real estate agent understand the condominium market.
4. Develop a 95% confidence interval estimate of the population mean sales price and population mean number of days to sell for Gulf View condominiums. Interpret your results.
5. Develop a 95% confidence interval estimate of the population mean sales price and population mean number of days to sell for No Gulf View condominiums. Interpret your results.
6. Assume the branch manager requested estimates of the mean selling price of Gulf View condominiums with a margin of error of $40,000 and the mean selling price of No Gulf View condominiums with a margin of error of $15,000. Using 95% confidence, how large should the sample sizes be?
7. Gulf Real Estate Properties just signed contracts for two new listings: a Gulf View condominium with a list price of $589,000 and a No Gulf View condominium with a list price of $285,000. What is your estimate of the final selling price and number of days required to sell each of these units?

Case Problem 3 Metropolitan Research, Inc.

Metropolitan Research, Inc., a consumer research organization, conducts surveys designed to evaluate a wide variety of products and services available to consumers. In one particular study, Metropolitan looked at consumer satisfaction with the performance of automobiles produced by a major Detroit manufacturer. A questionnaire sent to owners of one of the manufacturer's full-sized cars revealed several complaints about early transmission problems. To learn more about the transmission failures, Metropolitan used a sample of actual transmission repairs provided by a transmission repair firm in the Detroit area. The following data show the actual number of miles driven for 50 vehicles at the time of transmission failure.

Auto

85,092	32,609	59,465	77,437	32,534	64,090	32,464	59,902
39,323	89,641	94,219	116,803	92,857	63,436	65,605	85,861
64,342	61,978	67,998	59,817	101,769	95,774	121,352	69,568
74,276	66,998	40,001	72,069	25,066	77,098	69,922	35,662
74,425	67,202	118,444	53,500	79,294	64,544	86,813	116,269
37,831	89,341	73,341	85,288	138,114	53,402	85,586	82,256
77,539	88,798						

Managerial Report

1. Use appropriate descriptive statistics to summarize the transmission failure data.
2. Develop a 95% confidence interval for the mean number of miles driven until transmission failure for the population of automobiles with transmission failure. Provide a managerial interpretation of the interval estimate.

3. Discuss the implication of your statistical findings in terms of the belief that some owners of the automobiles experienced early transmission failures.
4. How many repair records should be sampled if the research firm wants the population mean number of miles driven until transmission failure to be estimated with a margin of error of 5000 miles? Use 95% confidence.
5. What other information would you like to gather to evaluate the transmission failure problem more fully?

CHAPTER 9

Hypothesis Tests

CONTENTS

STATISTICS IN PRACTICE:
JOHN MORRELL & COMPANY

9.1 DEVELOPING NULL AND ALTERNATIVE HYPOTHESES
The Alternative Hypothesis as a Research Hypothesis
The Null Hypothesis as an Assumption to Be Challenged
Summary of Forms for Null and Alternative Hypotheses

9.2 TYPE I AND TYPE II ERRORS

9.3 POPULATION MEAN: σ KNOWN
One-Tailed Test
Two-Tailed Test
Using Excel
Summary and Practical Advice
Relationship Between Interval Estimation and Hypothesis Testing

9.4 POPULATION MEAN: σ UNKNOWN
One-Tailed Test
Two-Tailed Test
Using Excel
Summary and Practical Advice

9.5 POPULATION PROPORTION
Using Excel
Summary

STATISTICS *in* PRACTICE

JOHN MORRELL & COMPANY*
CINCINNATI, OHIO

John Morrell & Company, which began in England in 1827, is considered the oldest continuously operating meat manufacturer in the United States. It is a wholly owned and independently managed subsidiary of Smithfield Foods, Smithfield, Virginia. John Morrell & Company offers an extensive product line of processed meats and fresh pork to consumers under 13 regional brands, including John Morrell, E-Z-Cut, Tobin's First Prize, Dinner Bell, Hunter, Kretschmar, Rath, Rodeo, Shenson, Farmers Hickory Brand, Iowa Quality, and Peyton's. Each regional brand enjoys high brand recognition and loyalty among consumers.

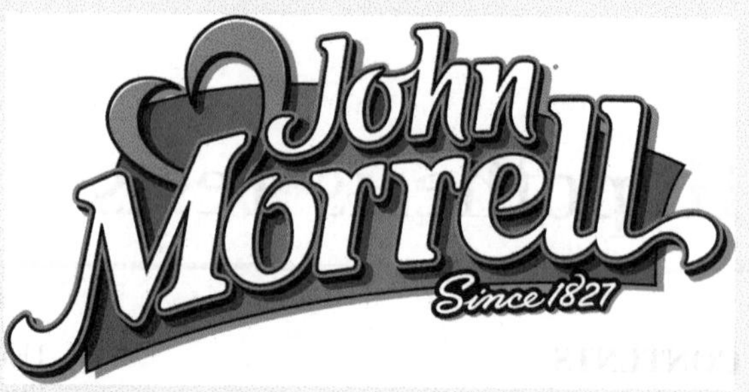

Hypothesis testing helps John Morrell & Company analyze market research about its products.
© AP Images/PRNewsFoto/John Morrell & Co.

Market research at Morrell provides management with up-to-date information on the company's various products and how the products compare with competing brands of similar products. A recent study compared a Beef Pot Roast made by Morrell to similar beef products from two major competitors. In the three-product comparison test, a sample of consumers was used to indicate how the products rated in terms of taste, appearance, aroma, and overall preference.

One research question concerned whether the Beef Pot Roast made by Morrell was the preferred choice of more than 50% of the consumer population. Letting p indicate the population proportion preferring Morrell's product, the hypothesis test for the research question is as follows:

$$H_0: p \leq .50$$
$$H_a: p > .50$$

The null hypothesis H_0 indicates the preference for Morrell's product is less than or equal to 50%. If the sample data support rejecting H_0 in favor of the alternative hypothesis H_a, Morrell will draw the research conclusion that in a three-product comparison, its Beef Pot Roast is preferred by more than 50% of the consumer population.

In an independent taste test study using a sample of 224 consumers in Cincinnati, Milwaukee, and Los Angeles, 150 consumers selected the Beef Pot Roast made by Morrell as the preferred product. Using statistical hypothesis testing procedures, the null hypothesis H_0 was rejected. The study provided statistical evidence supporting H_a and the conclusion that the Morrell product is preferred by more than 50% of the consumer population.

The point estimate of the population proportion was $\bar{p} = 150/224 = .67$. Thus, the sample data provided support for a food magazine advertisement showing that in a three-product taste comparison, Beef Pot Roast made by Morrell was "preferred 2 to 1 over the competition."

In this chapter we will discuss how to formulate hypotheses and how to conduct tests like the one used by Morrell. Through the analysis of sample data, we will be able to determine whether a hypothesis should or should not be rejected.

*The authors are indebted to Marty Butler, Vice President of Marketing, John Morrell, for providing this Statistics in Practice.

In Chapters 7 and 8 we showed how a sample could be used to develop point and interval estimates of population parameters. In this chapter we continue the discussion of statistical inference by showing how hypothesis testing can be used to determine whether a statement about the value of a population parameter should or should not be rejected.

In hypothesis testing we begin by making a tentative assumption about a population parameter. This tentative assumption is called the **null hypothesis** and is denoted by H_0.

We then define another hypothesis, called the **alternative hypothesis**, which is the opposite of what is stated in the null hypothesis. The alternative hypothesis is denoted by H_a. The hypothesis testing procedure uses data from a sample to test the validity of the two competing statements indicated by H_0 and H_a.

This chapter shows how hypothesis tests can be conducted about a population mean and a population proportion. We begin by providing examples that illustrate approaches to developing null and alternative hypotheses.

9.1 Developing Null and Alternative Hypotheses

It is not always obvious how the null and alternative hypotheses should be formulated. Care must be taken to structure the hypotheses appropriately so that the hypothesis testing conclusion provides the information the researcher or decision maker wants. The context of the situation is very important in determining how the hypotheses should be stated. All hypothesis testing applications involve collecting a sample and using the sample results to provide evidence for drawing a conclusion. Good questions to consider when formulating the null and alternative hypotheses are, What is the purpose of collecting the sample? What conclusions are we hoping to make?

Learning to formulate hypotheses correctly will take some practice. Expect some initial confusion over the proper choice of the null and alternative hypotheses. The examples in this section are intended to provide guidelines.

In the chapter introduction, we stated that the null hypothesis H_0 is a tentative assumption about a population parameter such as a population mean or a population proportion. The alternative hypothesis H_a is a statement that is the opposite of what is stated in the null hypothesis. In some situations it is easier to identify the alternative hypothesis first and then develop the null hypothesis. In other situations it is easier to identify the null hypothesis first and then develop the alternative hypothesis. We will illustrate these situations in the following examples.

The Alternative Hypothesis as a Research Hypothesis

Many applications of hypothesis testing involve an attempt to gather evidence in support of a research hypothesis. In these situations, it is often best to begin with the alternative hypothesis and make it the conclusion that the researcher hopes to support. Consider a particular automobile that currently attains a fuel efficiency of 24 miles per gallon in city driving. A product research group has developed a new fuel injection system designed to increase the miles-per-gallon rating. The group will run controlled tests with the new fuel injection system looking for statistical support for the conclusion that the new fuel injection system provides more miles per gallon than the current system.

Several new fuel injection units will be manufactured, installed in test automobiles, and subjected to research-controlled driving conditions. The sample mean miles per gallon for these automobiles will be computed and used in a hypothesis test to determine if it can be concluded that the new system provides more than 24 miles per gallon. In terms of the population mean miles per gallon μ, the research hypothesis $\mu > 24$ becomes the alternative hypothesis. Since the current system provides an average or mean of 24 miles per gallon, we will make the tentative assumption that the new system is not any better than the current system and choose $\mu \leq 24$ as the null hypothesis. The null and alternative hypotheses are:

$$H_0: \mu \leq 24$$
$$H_a: \mu > 24$$

If the sample results lead to the conclusion to reject H_0, the inference can be made that H_a: $\mu > 24$ is true. The researchers have the statistical support to state that the new

The conclusion that the research hypothesis is true is made if the sample data provide sufficient evidence to show that the null hypothesis can be rejected.

fuel injection system increases the mean number of miles per gallon. The production of automobiles with the new fuel injection system should be considered. However, if the sample results lead to the conclusion that H_0 cannot be rejected, the researchers cannot conclude that the new fuel injection system is better than the current system. Production of automobiles with the new fuel injection system on the basis of better gas mileage cannot be justified. Perhaps more research and further testing can be conducted.

Successful companies stay competitive by developing new products, new methods, new systems, and the like that are better than what is currently available. Before adopting something new, it is desirable to conduct research to determine if there is statistical support for the conclusion that the new approach is indeed better. In such cases, the research hypothesis is stated as the alternative hypothesis. For example, a new teaching method is developed that is believed to be better than the current method. The alternative hypothesis is that the new method is better. The null hypothesis is that the new method is no better than the old method. A new sales force bonus plan is developed in an attempt to increase sales. The alternative hypothesis is that the new bonus plan increases sales. The null hypothesis is that the new bonus plan does not increase sales. A new drug is developed with the goal of lowering blood pressure more than an existing drug. The alternative hypothesis is that the new drug lowers blood pressure more than the existing drug. The null hypothesis is that the new drug does not provide lower blood pressure than the existing drug. In each case, rejection of the null hypothesis H_0 provides statistical support for the research hypothesis. We will see many examples of hypothesis tests in research situations such as these throughout this chapter and in the remainder of the text.

The Null Hypothesis as an Assumption to Be Challenged

Of course, not all hypothesis tests involve research hypotheses. In the following discussion we consider applications of hypothesis testing where we begin with a belief or an assumption that a statement about the value of a population parameter is true. We will then use a hypothesis test to challenge the assumption and determine if there is statistical evidence to conclude that the assumption is incorrect. In these situations, it is helpful to develop the null hypothesis first. The null hypothesis H_0 expresses the belief or assumption about the value of the population parameter. The alternative hypothesis H_a is that the belief or assumption is incorrect.

As an example, consider the situation of a manufacturer of soft drink products. The label on a soft drink bottle states that it contains 67.6 fluid ounces. We consider the label correct provided the population mean filling weight for the bottles is *at least* 67.6 fluid ounces. Without any reason to believe otherwise, we would give the manufacturer the benefit of the doubt and assume that the statement provided on the label is correct. Thus, in a hypothesis test about the population mean fluid weight per bottle, we would begin with the assumption that the label is correct and state the null hypothesis as $\mu \geq 67.6$. The challenge to this assumption would imply that the label is incorrect and the bottles are being underfilled. This challenge would be stated as the alternative hypothesis $\mu < 67.6$. Thus, the null and alternative hypotheses are:

$$H_0: \mu \geq 67.6$$
$$H_a: \mu < 67.6$$

A manufacturer's product information is usually assumed to be true and stated as the null hypothesis. The conclusion that the information is incorrect can be made if the null hypothesis is rejected.

A government agency with the responsibility for validating manufacturing labels could select a sample of soft drink bottles, compute the sample mean filling weight, and use the sample results to test the preceding hypotheses. If the sample results lead to the conclusion to reject H_0, the inference that H_a: $\mu < 67.6$ is true can be made. With this statistical support, the agency is justified in concluding that the label is incorrect and underfilling of the bottles is occurring. Appropriate action to force the manufacturer to comply with labeling standards would be considered. However, if the sample results indicate H_0 cannot be rejected, the assumption that the manufacturer's labeling is correct cannot be rejected. With this conclusion, no action would be taken.

Let us now consider a variation of the soft drink bottle-filling example by viewing the same situation from the manufacturer's point of view. The bottle-filling operation has been designed to fill soft drink bottles with 67.6 fluid ounces as stated on the label. The company does not want to underfill the containers because that could result in an underfilling complaint from customers or, perhaps, a government agency. However, the company does not want to overfill containers either because putting more soft drink than necessary into the containers would be an unnecessary cost. The company's goal would be to adjust the bottle-filling operation so that the population mean filling weight per bottle is 67.6 fluid ounces as specified on the label.

Although this is the company's goal, from time to time any production process can get out of adjustment. If this occurs in our example, underfilling or overfilling of the soft drink bottles will occur. In either case, the company would like to know about it in order to correct the situation by readjusting the bottle-filling operation to the designed 67.6 fluid ounces. In this hypothesis testing application, we would begin with the assumption that the production process is operating correctly and state the null hypothesis as $\mu = 67.6$ fluid ounces. The alternative hypothesis that challenges this assumption is that $\mu \neq 67.6$, which indicates either overfilling or underfilling is occurring. The null and alternative hypotheses for the manufacturer's hypothesis test are:

$$H_0\colon \mu = 67.6$$
$$H_a\colon \mu \neq 67.6$$

Suppose that the soft drink manufacturer uses a quality control procedure to periodically select a sample of bottles from the filling operation and computes the sample mean filling weight per bottle. If the sample results lead to the conclusion to reject H_0, the inference is made that $H_a\colon \mu \neq 67.6$, is true. We conclude that the bottles are not being filled properly and the production process should be adjusted to restore the population mean to 67.6 fluid ounces per bottle. However, if the sample results indicate H_0 cannot be rejected, the assumption that the manufacturer's bottle-filling operation is functioning properly cannot be rejected. In this case, no further action would be taken and the production operation would continue to run.

The two preceding forms of the soft drink manufacturing hypothesis test show that the null and alternative hypotheses may vary depending upon the point of view of the researcher or decision maker. To formulate hypotheses correctly it is important to understand the context of the situation and structure the hypotheses to provide the information the researcher or decision maker wants.

Summary of Forms for Null and Alternative Hypotheses

The hypothesis tests in this chapter involve two population parameters: the population mean and the population proportion. Depending on the situation, hypothesis tests about a population parameter may take one of three forms: Two use inequalities in the null hypothesis; the third uses an equality in the null hypothesis. For hypothesis tests involving a population mean, we let μ_0 denote the hypothesized value and we must choose one of the following three forms for the hypothesis test.

The three possible forms of hypotheses H_0 and H_a are shown here. Note that the equality always *appears in the null hypothesis H_0.*

$$H_0\colon \mu \geq \mu_0 \qquad H_0\colon \mu \leq \mu_0 \qquad H_0\colon \mu = \mu_0$$
$$H_a\colon \mu < \mu_0 \qquad H_a\colon \mu > \mu_0 \qquad H_a\colon \mu \neq \mu_0$$

For reasons that will be clear later, the first two forms are called one-tailed tests. The third form is called a two-tailed test.

In many situations, the choice of H_0 and H_a is not obvious and judgment is necessary to select the proper form. However, as the preceding forms show, the equality part of the expression (either $\geq$, $\leq$, or $=$) *always* appears in the null hypothesis. In selecting the proper form of H_0 and H_a, keep in mind that the alternative hypothesis is often what the test is attempting to establish. Hence, asking whether the user is looking for evidence to support $\mu < \mu_0$, $\mu > \mu_0$, or $\mu \neq \mu_0$ will help determine H_a. The following exercises are designed to provide practice in choosing the proper form for a hypothesis test involving a population mean.

Exercises

1. The manager of the Danvers-Hilton Resort Hotel stated that the mean guest bill for a weekend is $600 or less. A member of the hotel's accounting staff noticed that the total charges for guest bills have been increasing in recent months. The accountant will use a sample of future weekend guest bills to test the manager's claim.
   a. Which form of the hypotheses should be used to test the manager's claim? Explain.

$$H_0\colon \mu \geq 600 \qquad H_0\colon \mu \leq 600 \qquad H_0\colon \mu = 600$$
$$H_a\colon \mu < 600 \qquad H_a\colon \mu > 600 \qquad H_a\colon \mu \neq 600$$

   b. What conclusion is appropriate when H_0 cannot be rejected?
   c. What conclusion is appropriate when H_0 can be rejected?

2. The manager of an automobile dealership is considering a new bonus plan designed to increase sales volume. Currently, the mean sales volume is 14 automobiles per month. The manager wants to conduct a research study to see whether the new bonus plan increases sales volume. To collect data on the plan, a sample of sales personnel will be allowed to sell under the new bonus plan for a one-month period.
   a. Develop the null and alternative hypotheses most appropriate for this situation.
   b. Comment on the conclusion when H_0 cannot be rejected.
   c. Comment on the conclusion when H_0 can be rejected.
3. A production line operation is designed to fill cartons with laundry detergent to a mean weight of 32 ounces. A sample of cartons is periodically selected and weighed to determine whether underfilling or overfilling is occurring. If the sample data lead to a conclusion of underfilling or overfilling, the production line will be shut down and adjusted to obtain proper filling.
   a. Formulate the null and alternative hypotheses that will help in deciding whether to shut down and adjust the production line.
   b. Comment on the conclusion and the decision when H_0 cannot be rejected.
   c. Comment on the conclusion and the decision when H_0 can be rejected.
4. Because of high production-changeover time and costs, a director of manufacturing must convince management that a proposed manufacturing method reduces costs before the new method can be implemented. The current production method operates with a mean cost of $220 per hour. A research study will measure the cost of the new method over a sample production period.
   a. Develop the null and alternative hypotheses most appropriate for this study.
   b. Comment on the conclusion when H_0 cannot be rejected.
   c. Comment on the conclusion when H_0 can be rejected.

9.2 Type I and Type II Errors

The null and alternative hypotheses are competing statements about the population. Either the null hypothesis H_0 is true or the alternative hypothesis H_a is true, but not both. Ideally the hypothesis testing procedure should lead to the acceptance of H_0 when H_0 is true and the rejection of H_0 when H_a is true. Unfortunately, the correct conclusions are not always possible. Because hypothesis tests are based on sample information, we must allow for the possibility of errors. Table 9.1 illustrates the two kinds of errors that can be made in hypothesis testing.

The first row of Table 9.1 shows what can happen if the conclusion is to accept H_0. If H_0 is true, this conclusion is correct. However, if H_a is true, we make a **Type II error**; that is, we accept H_0 when it is false. The second row of Table 9.1 shows what can happen if the conclusion is to reject H_0. If H_0 is true, we make a **Type I error**; that is, we reject H_0 when it is true. However, if H_a is true, rejecting H_0 is correct.

Recall the hypothesis testing illustration discussed in Section 9.1, in which an automobile product research group developed a new fuel injection system designed to increase the miles-per-gallon rating of a particular automobile. With the current model obtaining an average of 24 miles per gallon, the hypothesis test was formulated as follows.

$$H_0\colon \mu \leq 24$$
$$H_a\colon \mu > 24$$

The alternative hypothesis, $H_a\colon \mu > 24$, indicates that the researchers are looking for sample evidence to support the conclusion that the population mean miles per gallon with the new fuel injection system is greater than 24.

In this application, the Type I error of rejecting H_0 when it is true corresponds to the researchers claiming that the new system improves the miles-per-gallon rating ($\mu > 24$) when in fact the new system is not any better than the current system. In contrast, the Type II error of accepting H_0 when it is false corresponds to the researchers concluding that the new system is not any better than the current system ($\mu \leq 24$) when in fact the new system improves miles-per-gallon performance.

For the miles-per-gallon rating hypothesis test, the null hypothesis is $H_0\colon \mu \leq 24$. Suppose the null hypothesis is true as an equality; that is, $\mu = 24$. The probability of making a Type I error when the null hypothesis is true as an equality is called the **level of significance**. Thus, for the miles-per-gallon rating hypothesis test, the level of significance is the probability of rejecting $H_0\colon \mu \leq 24$ when $\mu = 24$. Because of the importance of this concept, we now restate the definition of level of significance.

TABLE 9.1 ERRORS AND CORRECT CONCLUSIONS IN HYPOTHESIS TESTING

		Population Condition	
		H_0 True	**H_a True**
Conclusion	**Accept H_0**	Correct conclusion	Type II error
	Reject H_0	Type I error	Correct conclusion

LEVEL OF SIGNIFICANCE

The level of significance is the probability of making a Type I error when the null hypothesis is true as an equality.

The Greek symbol α (alpha) is used to denote the level of significance, and common choices for α are .05 and .01.

In practice, the person responsible for the hypothesis test specifies the level of significance. By selecting α, that person is controlling the probability of making a Type I error. If the cost of making a Type I error is high, small values of α are preferred. If the cost of making a Type I error is not too high, larger values of α are typically used. Applications of hypothesis testing that only control for the Type I error are called *significance tests.* Many applications of hypothesis testing are of this type.

If the sample data are consistent with the null hypothesis H_0, we will follow the practice of concluding "do not reject H_0." This conclusion is preferred over "accept H_0," because the conclusion to accept H_0 puts us at risk of making a Type II error.

Although most applications of hypothesis testing control for the probability of making a Type I error, they do not always control for the probability of making a Type II error. Hence, if we decide to accept H_0, we cannot determine how confident we can be with that decision. Because of the uncertainty associated with making a Type II error when conducting significance tests, statisticians usually recommend that we use the statement "do not reject H_0" instead of "accept H_0." Using the statement "do not reject H_0" carries the recommendation to withhold both judgment and action. In effect, by not directly accepting H_0, the statistician avoids the risk of making a Type II error. Whenever the probability of making a Type II error has not been determined and controlled, we will not make the statement "accept H_0." In such cases, only two conclusions are possible: *do not reject* H_0 or *reject* H_0.

Although controlling for a Type II error in hypothesis testing is not common, it can be done. More advanced texts describe procedures for determining and controlling the probability of making a Type II error.[1] If proper controls have been established for this error, action based on the "accept H_0" conclusion can be appropriate.

NOTE AND COMMENT

Walter Williams, syndicated columnist and professor of economics at George Mason University, points out that the possibility of making a Type I or a Type II error is always present in decision making (*The Cincinnati Enquirer,* August 14, 2005). He notes that the Food and Drug Administration runs the risk of making these errors in its drug approval process. The FDA must either approve a new drug or not approve it. Thus, the FDA runs the risk of making a Type I error by approving a new drug that is not safe and effective, or making a Type II error by failing to approve a new drug that is safe and effective. Regardless of the decision made, the possibility of making a costly error cannot be eliminated.

Exercises

5. Duke Energy reported that the cost of electricity for an efficient home in a particular neighborhood of Cincinnati, Ohio, was \$104 per month (*Home Energy Report,* Duke Energy, March 2012). A researcher believes that the cost of electricity for a comparable neighborhood in Chicago, Illinois, is higher. A sample of homes in this Chicago neighborhood will

[1]See, for example, D. R. Anderson, D. J. Sweeney, and T. A. Williams, *Statistics for Business and Economics,* 12th edition (Mason, OH: Cengage Learning, 2014).

be taken and the sample mean monthly cost of electricity will be used to test the following null and alternative hypotheses.

$$H_0: \mu \leq 104$$
$$H_a: \mu > 104$$

a. Assume the sample data lead to rejection of the null hypothesis. What would be your conclusion about the cost of electricity in the Chicago neighborhood?
b. What is the Type I error in this situation? What are the consequences of making this error?
c. What is the Type II error in this situation? What are the consequences of making this error?

6. The label on a 3-quart container of orange juice states that the orange juice contains an average of 1 gram of fat or less. Answer the following questions for a hypothesis test that could be used to test the claim on the label.
   a. Develop the appropriate null and alternative hypotheses.
   b. What is the Type I error in this situation? What are the consequences of making this error?
   c. What is the Type II error in this situation? What are the consequences of making this error?
7. Carpetland salespersons average \$8000 per week in sales. Steve Contois, the firm's vice president, proposes a compensation plan with new selling incentives. Steve hopes that the results of a trial selling period will enable him to conclude that the compensation plan increases the average sales per salesperson.
   a. Develop the appropriate null and alternative hypotheses.
   b. What is the Type I error in this situation? What are the consequences of making this error?
   c. What is the Type II error in this situation? What are the consequences of making this error?
8. Suppose a new production method will be implemented if a hypothesis test supports the conclusion that the new method reduces the mean operating cost per hour.
   a. State the appropriate null and alternative hypotheses if the mean cost for the current production method is \$220 per hour.
   b. What is the Type I error in this situation? What are the consequences of making this error?
   c. What is the Type II error in this situation? What are the consequences of making this error?

9.3 Population Mean: σ Known

In Chapter 8 we said that the σ known case corresponds to applications in which historical data and/or other information are available that enable us to obtain a good estimate of the population standard deviation prior to sampling. In such cases the population standard deviation can, for all practical purposes, be considered known. In this section we show how to conduct a hypothesis test about a population mean for the σ known case.

The methods presented in this section are exact if the sample is selected from a population that is normally distributed. In cases where it is not reasonable to assume the population is normally distributed, these methods are still applicable if the sample size is large enough. We provide some practical advice concerning the population distribution and the sample size at the end of this section.

One-Tailed Test

One-tailed tests about a population mean take one of the following two forms.

Lower Tail Test	Upper Tail Test
$H_0: \mu \geq \mu_0$	$H_0: \mu \leq \mu_0$
$H_a: \mu < \mu_0$	$H_a: \mu > \mu_0$

Let us consider an example involving a lower tail test.

The Federal Trade Commission (FTC) periodically conducts statistical studies designed to test the claims that manufacturers make about their products. For example, the label on a large can of Hilltop Coffee states that the can contains 3 pounds of coffee. The FTC knows that Hilltop's production process cannot place exactly 3 pounds of coffee in each can, even if the mean filling weight for the population of all cans filled is 3 pounds per can. However, as long as the population mean filling weight is at least 3 pounds per can, the rights of consumers will be protected. Thus, the FTC interprets the label information on a large can of coffee as a claim by Hilltop that the population mean filling weight is at least 3 pounds per can. We will show how the FTC can check Hilltop's claim by conducting a lower tail hypothesis test.

The first step is to develop the null and alternative hypotheses for the test. If the population mean filling weight is at least 3 pounds per can, Hilltop's claim is correct. This establishes the null hypothesis for the test. However, if the population mean weight is less than 3 pounds per can, Hilltop's claim is incorrect. This establishes the alternative hypothesis. With μ denoting the population mean filling weight, the null and alternative hypotheses are as follows:

$$H_0\colon \mu \geq 3$$
$$H_a\colon \mu < 3$$

Note that the hypothesized value of the population mean is $\mu_0 = 3$.

If the sample data indicate that H_0 cannot be rejected, the statistical evidence does not support the conclusion that a label violation has occurred. Hence, no action should be taken against Hilltop. However, if the sample data indicate that H_0 can be rejected, we will conclude that the alternative hypothesis, $H_a\colon \mu < 3$, is true. In this case a conclusion of underfilling and a charge of a label violation against Hilltop would be justified.

Suppose a sample of 36 cans of coffee is selected and the sample mean $\bar{x}$ is computed as an estimate of the population mean μ. If the value of the sample mean $\bar{x}$ is less than 3 pounds, the sample results will cast doubt on the null hypothesis. What we want to know is how much less than 3 pounds must $\bar{x}$ be before we would be willing to declare the difference significant and risk making a Type I error by falsely accusing Hilltop of a label violation. A key factor in addressing this issue is the value the decision maker selects for the level of significance.

As noted in the preceding section, the level of significance, denoted by α, is the probability of making a Type I error by rejecting H_0 when the null hypothesis is true as an equality. The decision maker must specify the level of significance. If the cost of making a Type I error is high, a small value should be chosen for the level of significance. If the cost is not high, a larger value is more appropriate. In the Hilltop Coffee study, the director of the FTC's testing program made the following statement: "If the company is meeting its weight specifications at $\mu = 3$, I do not want to take action against them. But, I am willing to risk a 1% chance of making such an error." From the director's statement, we set the level of significance for the hypothesis test at $\alpha = .01$. Thus, we must design the hypothesis test so that the probability of making a Type I error when $\mu = 3$ is .01.

For the Hilltop Coffee study, by developing the null and alternative hypotheses and specifying the level of significance for the test, we carry out the first two steps required in conducting every hypothesis test. We are now ready to perform the third step of hypothesis testing: collect the sample data and compute the value of what is called a test statistic.

Test statistic For the Hilltop Coffee study, previous FTC tests show that the population standard deviation can be assumed known with a value of $\sigma = .18$. In addition, these tests also show that the population of filling weights can be assumed to have a normal distribution. From the study of sampling distributions in Chapter 7 we know that if the

FIGURE 9.1 SAMPLING DISTRIBUTION OF $\bar{x}$ FOR THE HILLTOP COFFEE STUDY WHEN THE NULL HYPOTHESIS IS TRUE AS AN EQUALITY ($\mu = 3$)

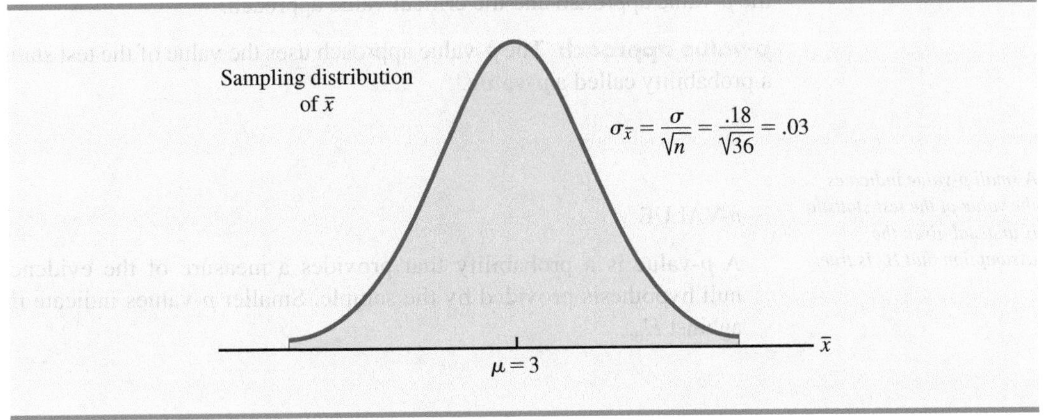

The standard error of $\bar{x}$ is the standard deviation of the sampling distribution of $\bar{x}$.

population from which we are sampling is normally distributed, the sampling distribution of $\bar{x}$ will also be normally distributed. Thus, for the Hilltop Coffee study, the sampling distribution of $\bar{x}$ is normally distributed. With a known value of $\sigma = .18$ and a sample size of $n = 36$, Figure 9.1 shows the sampling distribution of $\bar{x}$ when the null hypothesis is true as an equality, that is, when $\mu = \mu_0 = 3$.[2] Note that the standard error of $\bar{x}$ is given by $\sigma_{\bar{x}} = \sigma/\sqrt{n} = .18/\sqrt{36} = .03$.

Because the sampling distribution of $\bar{x}$ is normally distributed, the sampling distribution of

$$z = \frac{\bar{x} - \mu_0}{\sigma_{\bar{x}}} = \frac{\bar{x} - 3}{.03}$$

is a standard normal distribution. A value of $z = -1$ means that the value of $\bar{x}$ is one standard error below the hypothesized value of the mean, a value of $z = -2$ means that the value of $\bar{x}$ is two standard errors below the hypothesized value of the mean, and so on. We can use the standard normal probability table to find the lower tail probability corresponding to any z value. For instance, the lower tail area at $z = -3.00$ is .0013. Hence, the probability of obtaining a value of z that is three or more standard errors below the mean is .0013. As a result, the probability of obtaining a value of $\bar{x}$ that is 3 or more standard errors below the hypothesized population mean $\mu_0 = 3$ is also .0013. Such a result is unlikely if the null hypothesis is true.

For hypothesis tests about a population mean in the σ known case, we use the standard normal random variable z as a **test statistic** to determine whether $\bar{x}$ deviates from the hypothesized value of μ enough to justify rejecting the null hypothesis. With $\sigma_{\bar{x}} = \sigma/\sqrt{n}$, the test statistic is as follows.

TEST STATISTIC FOR HYPOTHESIS TESTS ABOUT A POPULATION MEAN: σ KNOWN

$$z = \frac{\bar{x} - \mu_0}{\sigma/\sqrt{n}} \tag{9.1}$$

[2]In constructing sampling distributions for hypothesis tests, it is assumed that H_0 is satisfied as an equality.

The key question for a lower tail test is, How small must the test statistic z be before we choose to reject the null hypothesis? Two approaches can be used to answer this question: the p-value approach and the critical value approach.

p-value approach The p-value approach uses the value of the test statistic z to compute a probability called a ***p*-value**.

A small p-value indicates the value of the test statistic is unusual given the assumption that H_0 is true.

p-VALUE

A p-value is a probability that provides a measure of the evidence against the null hypothesis provided by the sample. Smaller p-values indicate more evidence against H_0.

The p-value is used to determine whether the null hypothesis should be rejected.

Let us see how the p-value is computed and used. The value of the test statistic is used to compute the p-value. The method used depends on whether the test is a lower tail, an upper tail, or a two-tailed test. For a lower tail test, the p-value is the probability of obtaining a value for the test statistic as small as or smaller than that provided by the sample. Thus, to compute the p-value for the lower tail test in the σ known case, we must find, using the standard normal distribution, the probability that z is less than or equal to the value of the test statistic. After computing the p-value, we must then decide whether it is small enough to reject the null hypothesis; as we will show, this decision involves comparing the p-value to the level of significance.

Coffee

Let us now compute the p-value for the Hilltop Coffee lower tail test. Suppose the sample of 36 Hilltop coffee cans provides a sample mean of $\bar{x} = 2.92$ pounds. Is $\bar{x} = 2.92$ small enough to cause us to reject H_0? Because this is a lower tail test, the p-value is the area under the standard normal curve for values of $z \leq$ the value of the test statistic. Using $\bar{x} = 2.92$, $\sigma = .18$, and $n = 36$, we compute the value of the test statistic z.

$$z = \frac{\bar{x} - \mu_0}{\sigma/\sqrt{n}} = \frac{2.92 - 3}{.18/\sqrt{36}} = -2.67$$

Thus, the p-value is the probability that z is less than or equal to -2.67 (the lower tail area corresponding to the value of the test statistic).

Using the standard normal probability table, we find that the lower tail area at $z = -2.67$ is .0038. Figure 9.2 shows that $\bar{x} = 2.92$ corresponds to $z = -2.67$ and a p-value $= .0038$. This p-value indicates a small probability of obtaining a sample mean of $\bar{x} = 2.92$ (and a test statistic of -2.67) or smaller when sampling from a population with $\mu = 3$. This p-value does not provide much support for the null hypothesis, but is it small enough to cause us to reject H_0? The answer depends upon the level of significance for the test.

As noted previously, the director of the FTC's testing program selected a value of .01 for the level of significance. The selection of $\alpha = .01$ means that the director is willing to tolerate a probability of .01 of rejecting the null hypothesis when it is true as an equality ($\mu_0 = 3$). The sample of 36 coffee cans in the Hilltop Coffee study resulted in a p-value $=$ .0038, which means that the probability of obtaining a value of $\bar{x} = 2.92$ or less when the null hypothesis is true as an equality is .0038. Because .0038 is less than or equal to $\alpha = .01$, we reject H_0. Therefore, we find sufficient statistical evidence to reject the null hypothesis at the .01 level of significance.

FIGURE 9.2 p-VALUE FOR THE HILLTOP COFFEE STUDY WHEN $\bar{x} = 2.92$ AND $z = -2.67$

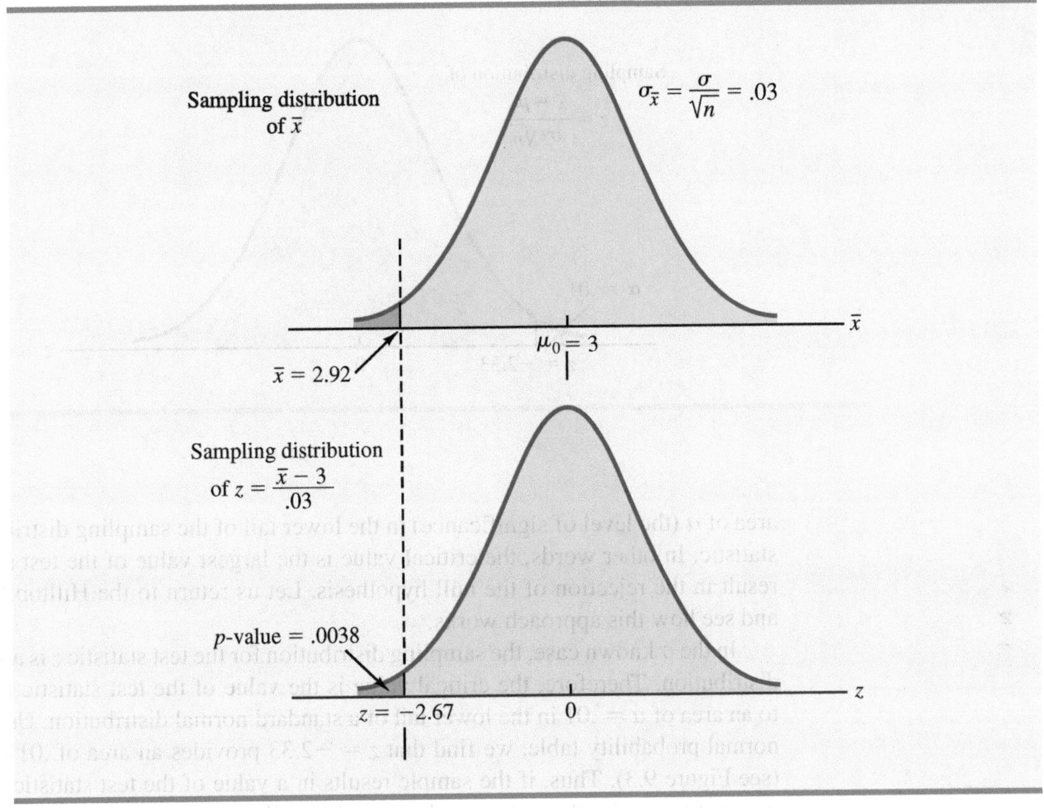

We can now state the general rule for determining whether the null hypothesis can be rejected when using the p-value approach. For a level of significance α, the rejection rule using the p-value approach is as follows.

REJECTION RULE USING p-VALUE

Reject H_0 if p-value $\leq \alpha$

In the Hilltop Coffee test, the p-value of .0038 resulted in the rejection of the null hypothesis. Although the basis for making the rejection decision involves a comparison of the p-value to the level of significance specified by the FTC director, the observed p-value of .0038 means that we would reject H_0 for any value of $\alpha \geq .0038$. For this reason, the p-value is also called the *observed level of significance*.

Different decision makers may express different opinions concerning the cost of making a Type I error and may choose a different level of significance. By providing the p-value as part of the hypothesis testing results, another decision maker can compare the reported p-value to his or her own level of significance and possibly make a different decision with respect to rejecting H_0.

Critical value approach The critical value approach requires that we first determine a value for the test statistic called the **critical value**. For a lower tail test, the critical value serves as a benchmark for determining whether the value of the test statistic is small enough to reject the null hypothesis. It is the value of the test statistic that corresponds to an

FIGURE 9.3 CRITICAL VALUE = −2.33 FOR THE HILLTOP COFFEE HYPOTHESIS TEST

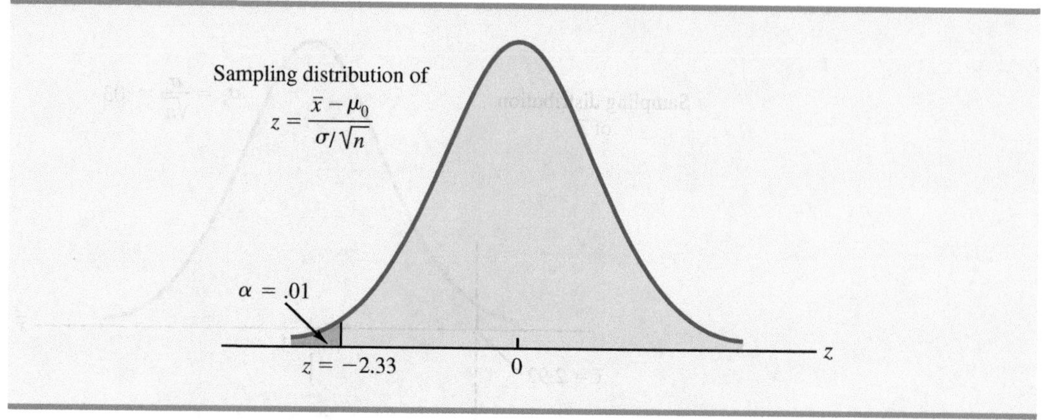

area of α (the level of significance) in the lower tail of the sampling distribution of the test statistic. In other words, the critical value is the largest value of the test statistic that will result in the rejection of the null hypothesis. Let us return to the Hilltop Coffee example and see how this approach works.

In the σ known case, the sampling distribution for the test statistic z is a standard normal distribution. Therefore, the critical value is the value of the test statistic that corresponds to an area of $\alpha = .01$ in the lower tail of a standard normal distribution. Using the standard normal probability table, we find that $z = -2.33$ provides an area of .01 in the lower tail (see Figure 9.3). Thus, if the sample results in a value of the test statistic that is less than or equal to −2.33, the corresponding p-value will be less than or equal to .01; in this case, we should reject the null hypothesis. Hence, for the Hilltop Coffee study the critical value rejection rule for a level of significance of .01 is

$$\text{Reject } H_0 \text{ if } z \leq -2.33$$

In the Hilltop Coffee example, $\bar{x} = 2.92$ and the test statistic is $z = -2.67$. Because $z = -2.67 < -2.33$, we can reject H_0 and conclude that Hilltop Coffee is underfilling cans.

We can generalize the rejection rule for the critical value approach to handle any level of significance. The rejection rule for a lower tail test follows.

REJECTION RULE FOR A LOWER TAIL TEST: CRITICAL VALUE APPROACH

$$\text{Reject } H_0 \text{ if } z \leq -z_\alpha$$

where $-z_\alpha$ is the critical value; that is, the z value that provides an area of α in the lower tail of the standard normal distribution.

Summary The p-value approach to hypothesis testing and the critical value approach will always lead to the same rejection decision; that is, whenever the p-value is less than or equal to α, the value of the test statistic will be less than or equal to the critical value. The advantage of the p-value approach is that the p-value tells us *how* significant the results are (the observed level of significance). If we use the critical value approach, we only know that the results are significant at the stated level of significance.

At the beginning of this section, we said that one-tailed tests about a population mean take one of the following two forms:

Lower Tail Test	Upper Tail Test
$H_0\colon \mu \geq \mu_0$	$H_0\colon \mu \leq \mu_0$
$H_a\colon \mu < \mu_0$	$H_a\colon \mu > \mu_0$

We used the Hilltop Coffee study to illustrate how to conduct a lower tail test. We can use the same general approach to conduct an upper tail test. The test statistic z is still computed using equation (9.1). But, for an upper tail test, the p-value is the probability of obtaining a value for the test statistic as large as or larger than that provided by the sample. Thus, to compute the p-value for the upper tail test in the σ known case, we must use the standard normal distribution to compute the probability that z is greater than or equal to the value of the test statistic. Using the critical value approach causes us to reject the null hypothesis if the value of the test statistic is greater than or equal to the critical value z_α; in other words, we reject H_0 if $z \geq z_\alpha$.

Let us summarize the steps involved in computing p-values for one-tailed hypothesis tests.

COMPUTATION OF p-VALUES FOR ONE-TAILED TESTS

1. Compute the value of the test statistic using equation (9.1).
2. **Lower tail test:** Using the standard normal distribution, compute the probability that z is less than or equal to the value of the test statistic (area in the lower tail).
3. **Upper tail test:** Using the standard normal distribution, compute the probability that z is greater than or equal to the value of the test statistic (area in the upper tail).

Two-Tailed Test

In hypothesis testing, the general form for a **two-tailed test** about a population mean is as follows:

$$H_0\colon \mu = \mu_0$$
$$H_a\colon \mu \neq \mu_0$$

In this subsection we show how to conduct a two-tailed test about a population mean for the σ known case. As an illustration, we consider the hypothesis testing situation facing MaxFlight, Inc.

The U.S. Golf Association (USGA) establishes rules that manufacturers of golf equipment must meet if their products are to be acceptable for use in USGA events. MaxFlight uses a high-technology manufacturing process to produce golf balls with a mean driving distance of 295 yards. Sometimes, however, the process gets out of adjustment and produces golf balls with a mean driving distance different from 295 yards. When the mean distance falls below 295 yards, the company worries about losing sales because the golf balls do not provide as much distance as advertised. When the mean distance passes 295 yards, MaxFlight's golf balls may be rejected by the USGA for exceeding the overall distance standard concerning carry and roll.

MaxFlight's quality control program involves taking periodic samples of 50 golf balls to monitor the manufacturing process. For each sample, a hypothesis test is conducted to determine whether the process has fallen out of adjustment. Let us develop the null and alternative hypotheses. We begin by assuming that the process is functioning correctly; that is, the golf balls being produced have a mean distance of 295 yards. This assumption establishes the null hypothesis. The alternative hypothesis is that the mean distance is not equal to 295 yards. With a hypothesized value of $\mu_0 = 295$, the null and alternative hypotheses for the MaxFlight hypothesis test are as follows:

$$H_0: \mu = 295$$
$$H_a: \mu \neq 295$$

If the sample mean $\bar{x}$ is significantly less than 295 yards or significantly greater than 295 yards, we will reject H_0. In this case, corrective action will be taken to adjust the manufacturing process. On the other hand, if $\bar{x}$ does not deviate from the hypothesized mean $\mu_0 = 295$ by a significant amount, H_0 will not be rejected and no action will be taken to adjust the manufacturing process.

The quality control team selected $\alpha = .05$ as the level of significance for the test. Data from previous tests conducted when the process was known to be in adjustment show that the population standard deviation can be assumed known with a value of $\sigma = 12$. Thus, with a sample size of $n = 50$, the standard error of $\bar{x}$ is

$$\sigma_{\bar{x}} = \frac{\sigma}{\sqrt{n}} = \frac{12}{\sqrt{50}} = 1.7$$

Because the sample size is large, the central limit theorem (see Chapter 7) allows us to conclude that the sampling distribution of $\bar{x}$ can be approximated by a normal distribution. Figure 9.4 shows the sampling distribution of $\bar{x}$ for the MaxFlight hypothesis test with a hypothesized population mean of $\mu_0 = 295$.

GolfTest

Suppose that a sample of 50 golf balls is selected and that the sample mean is $\bar{x} = 297.6$ yards. This sample mean provides support for the conclusion that the population mean is larger than 295 yards. Is this value of $\bar{x}$ enough larger than 295 to cause us to reject H_0 at the .05 level of significance? In the previous section we described two approaches that can be used to answer this question: the *p*-value approach and the critical value approach.

p-value approach Recall that the *p*-value is a probability used to determine whether the null hypothesis should be rejected. For a two-tailed test, values of the test statistic in *either* tail provide evidence against the null hypothesis. For a two-tailed test, the *p*-value is the probability of obtaining a value for the test statistic *as unlikely as or more unlikely than* that provided by the sample. Let us see how the *p*-value is computed for the MaxFlight hypothesis test.

FIGURE 9.4 SAMPLING DISTRIBUTION OF $\bar{x}$ FOR THE MAXFLIGHT HYPOTHESIS TEST

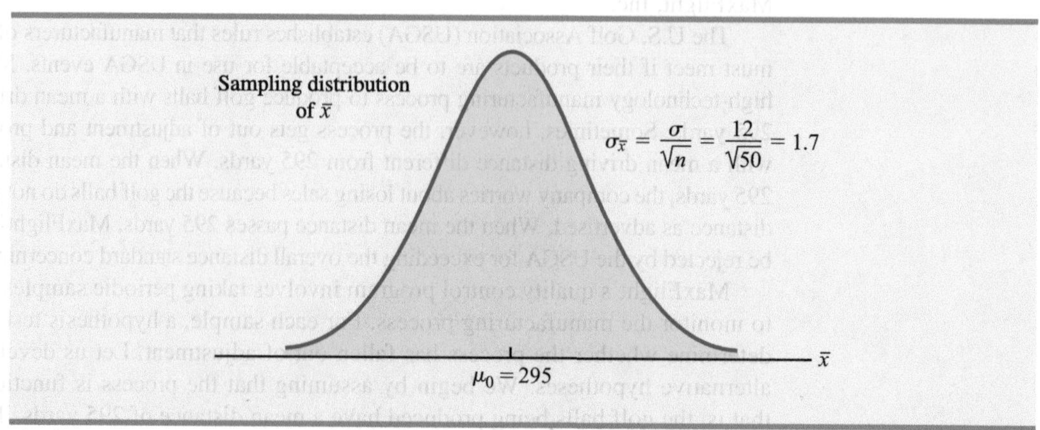

FIGURE 9.5 p-VALUE FOR THE MAXFLIGHT HYPOTHESIS TEST

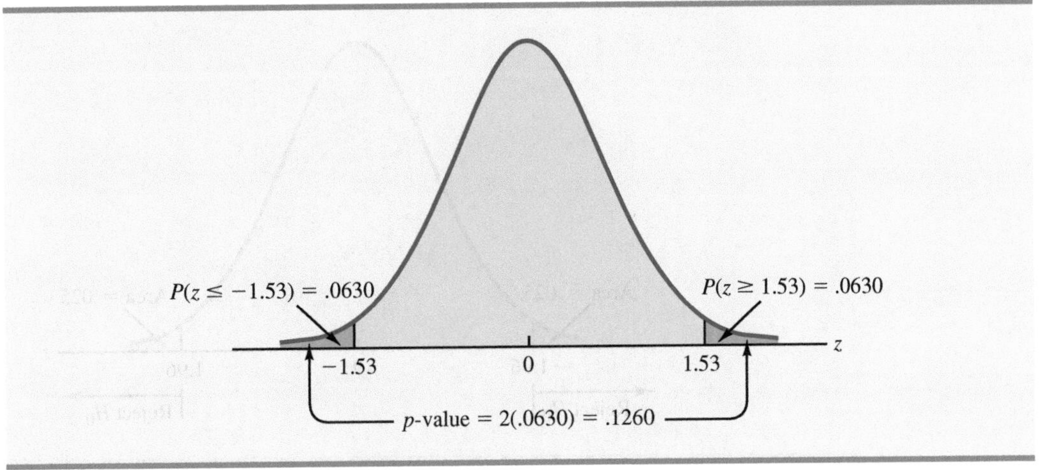

First we compute the value of the test statistic. For the σ known case, the test statistic z is a standard normal random variable. Using equation (9.1) with $\bar{x} = 297.6$, the value of the test statistic is

$$z = \frac{\bar{x} - \mu_0}{\sigma/\sqrt{n}} = \frac{297.6 - 295}{12/\sqrt{50}} = 1.53$$

Now to compute the p-value we must find the probability of obtaining a value for the test statistic *at least as unlikely as* $z = 1.53$. Clearly values of $z \ge 1.53$ are *at least as unlikely*. But, because this is a two-tailed test, values of $z \le -1.53$ are also *at least as unlikely as* the value of the test statistic provided by the sample. In Figure 9.5, we see that the two-tailed p-value in this case is given by $P(z \le -1.53) + P(z \ge 1.53)$. Because the normal curve is symmetric, we can compute this probability by finding $P(z \ge 1.53)$ and doubling it. The table for the standard normal distribution shows that $P(z < 1.53) = .9370$. Thus, the upper tail area is $P(z \ge 1.53) = 1.0000 - .9370 = .0630$. Doubling this, we find that the p-value for the MaxFlight two-tailed hypothesis test is p-value $= 2(.0630) = .1260$.

Next we compare the p-value to the level of significance to see whether the null hypothesis should be rejected. With a level of significance of $\alpha = .05$, we do not reject H_0 because the p-value $= .1260 > .05$. Because the null hypothesis is not rejected, no action will be taken to adjust the MaxFlight manufacturing process.

Let us summarize the steps involved in computing p-values for two-tailed hypothesis tests.

COMPUTATION OF p-VALUES FOR TWO-TAILED TESTS

1. **Compute the value of the test statistic using equation (9.1).**
2. **If the value of the test statistic is in the upper tail, compute the probability that z is greater than or equal to the value of the test statistic (the upper tail area). If the value of the test statistic is in the lower tail, compute the probability that z is less than or equal to the value of the test statistic (the lower tail area).**
3. **Double the probability (or tail area) from step 2 to obtain the p-value.**

Critical value approach Before leaving this section, let us see how the test statistic z can be compared to a critical value to make the hypothesis testing decision for a two-tailed test.

FIGURE 9.6 CRITICAL VALUES FOR THE MAXFLIGHT HYPOTHESIS TEST

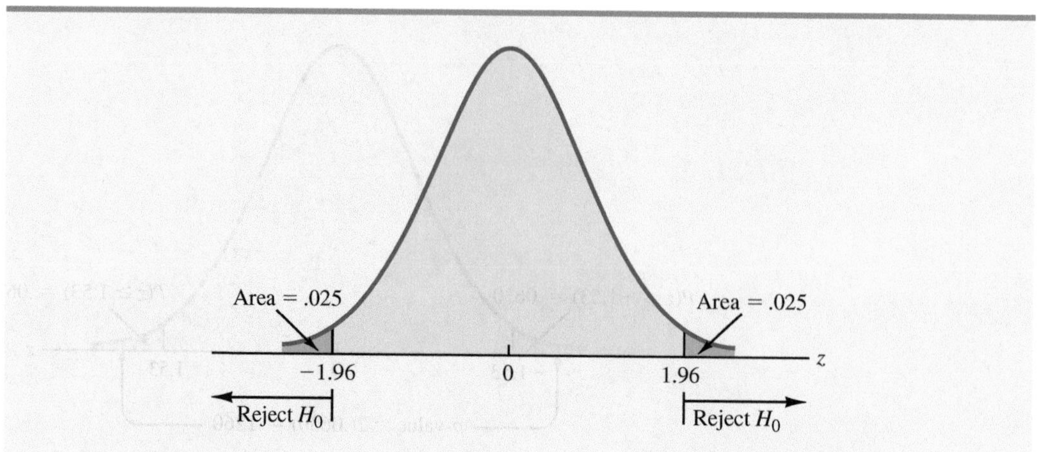

Figure 9.6 shows that the critical values for the test will occur in both the lower and upper tails of the standard normal distribution. With a level of significance of $\alpha = .05$, the area in each tail corresponding to the critical values is $\alpha/2 = .05/2 = .025$. Using the standard normal probability table, we find the critical values for the test statistic are $-z_{.025} = -1.96$ and $z_{.025} = 1.96$. Thus, using the critical value approach, the two-tailed rejection rule is

$$\text{Reject } H_0 \text{ if } z \leq -1.96 \text{ or if } z \geq 1.96$$

Because the value of the test statistic for the MaxFlight study is $z = 1.53$, the statistical evidence will not permit us to reject the null hypothesis at the .05 level of significance.

Using Excel

Excel can be used to conduct one-tailed and two-tailed hypothesis tests about a population mean for the σ known case using the p-value approach. Recall that the method used to compute a p-value depends upon whether the test is lower tail, upper tail, or two-tailed. Therefore, in the Excel procedure we describe we will use the sample results to compute three p-values: p-value (Lower Tail), p-value (Upper Tail), and p-value (Two Tail). The user can then choose α and draw a conclusion using whichever p-value is appropriate for the type of hypothesis test being conducted. We will illustrate using the MaxFlight two-tailed hypothesis test. Refer to Figure 9.7 as we describe the tasks involved. The formula worksheet is in the background; the value worksheet is in the foreground.

Enter/Access Data: Open the WEBfile named GolfTest. A label and the distance data for the sample of 50 golf balls are entered into cells A1:A51.

Enter Functions and Formulas: The descriptive statistics needed are provided in cells D4 and D5. Excel's COUNT and AVERAGE functions compute the sample size and the sample mean, respectively. The value of the known population standard deviation (12) is entered into cell D7, and the hypothesized value of the population mean (295) is entered into cell D8.

The standard error is obtained in cell D10 by entering the formula =D7/SQRT(D4). The formula =(D5-D8)/D10 entered into cell D11 computes the test statistic z(1.5321). To compute the p-value for a lower tail test, we enter the formula =NORM.S.DIST(D11,TRUE) into cell D13. The p-value for an upper tail test is then computed in cell D14 as 1 minus the p-value for the lower tail test. Finally, the p-value for a two-tailed test is computed in cell D15 as

FIGURE 9.7 EXCEL WORKSHEET: HYPOTHESIS TEST FOR THE σ KNOWN CASE

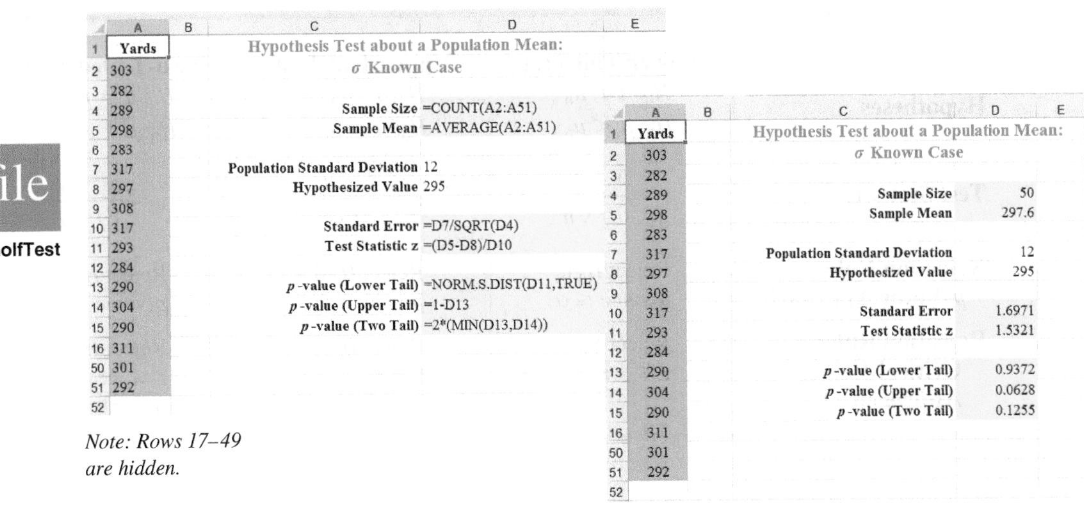

WEB file GolfTest

two times the minimum of the two one-tailed p-values. The value worksheet shows that p-value (Lower Tail) = 0.9372, p-value (Upper Tail) = 0.0628, and p-value (Two Tail) = 0.1255.

The development of the worksheet is now complete. For the two-tailed Max-Flight problem we cannot reject H_0: $\mu = 295$ using $\alpha = .05$ because the p-value (Two Tail) = 0.1255 is greater than α. Thus, the quality control manager has no reason to doubt that the manufacturing process is producing golf balls with a population mean distance of 295 yards.

A template for other problems The worksheet in Figure 9.7 can be used as a template for conducting any one-tailed and two-tailed hypothesis tests for the σ known case. Just enter the appropriate data in column A, adjust the ranges for the formulas in cells D4 and D5, enter the population standard deviation in cell D7, and enter the hypothesized value in cell D8. The standard error, the test statistic, and the three p-values will then appear. Depending on the form of the hypothesis test (lower tail, upper tail, or two-tailed), we can then choose the appropriate p-value to make the rejection decision.

We can further simplify the use of Figure 9.7 as a template for other problems by eliminating the need to enter new data ranges in cells D4 and D5. To do so we rewrite the cell formulas as follows:

Cell D4: =COUNT(A:A)
Cell D5: =AVERAGE(A:A)

The WEBfile named GolfTest includes a worksheet entitled Template that uses the A:A method for entering the data ranges.

With the A:A method of specifying data ranges, Excel's COUNT function will count the number of numerical values in column A and Excel's AVERAGE function will compute the average of the numerical values in column A. Thus, to solve a new problem it is only necessary to enter the new data in column A, enter the value of the known population standard deviation in cell D7, and enter the hypothesized value of the population mean in cell D8.

The worksheet can also be used as a template for text exercises in which n, $\bar{x}$, and σ are given. Just ignore the data in column A and enter the values for n, $\bar{x}$, and σ into cells D4, D5, and D7, respectively. Then enter the appropriate hypothesized value for the population mean into cell D8. The p-values corresponding to lower tail, upper tail, and two-tailed hypothesis tests will then appear in cells D13:D15.

TABLE 9.2 SUMMARY OF HYPOTHESIS TESTS ABOUT A POPULATION MEAN: σ KNOWN CASE

	Lower Tail Test	**Upper Tail Test**	**Two-Tailed Test**
Hypotheses	$H_0: \mu \geq \mu_0$ $H_a: \mu < \mu_0$	$H_0: \mu \leq \mu_0$ $H_a: \mu > \mu_0$	$H_0: \mu = \mu_0$ $H_a: \mu \neq \mu_0$
Test Statistic	$z = \dfrac{\bar{x} - \mu_0}{\sigma/\sqrt{n}}$	$z = \dfrac{\bar{x} - \mu_0}{\sigma/\sqrt{n}}$	$z = \dfrac{\bar{x} - \mu_0}{\sigma/\sqrt{n}}$
Rejection Rule: *p*-Value Approach	Reject H_0 if p-value $\leq \alpha$	Reject H_0 if p-value $\leq \alpha$	Reject H_0 if p-value $\leq \alpha$
Rejection Rule: Critical Value Approach	Reject H_0 if $z \leq -z_\alpha$	Reject H_0 if $z \geq z_\alpha$	Reject H_0 if $z \leq -z_{\alpha/2}$ or if $z \geq z_{\alpha/2}$

Summary and Practical Advice

We presented examples of a lower tail test and a two-tailed test about a population mean. Based upon these examples, we can now summarize the hypothesis testing procedures about a population mean for the σ known case as shown in Table 9.2. Note that μ_0 is the hypothesized value of the population mean.

The hypothesis testing steps followed in the two examples presented in this section are common to every hypothesis test.

STEPS OF HYPOTHESIS TESTING

Step 1. Develop the null and alternative hypotheses.
Step 2. Specify the level of significance.
Step 3. Collect the sample data and compute the value of the test statistic.

p-Value Approach

Step 4. Use the value of the test statistic to compute the *p*-value.
Step 5. Reject H_0 if the p-value $\leq \alpha$.
Step 6. Interpret the statistical conclusion in the context of the application.

Critical Value Approach

Step 4. Use the level of significance to determine the critical value and the rejection rule.
Step 5. Use the value of the test statistic and the rejection rule to determine whether to reject H_0.
Step 6. Interpret the statistical conclusion in the context of the application.

Practical advice about the sample size for hypothesis tests is similar to the advice we provided about the sample size for interval estimation in Chapter 8. In most applications, a sample size of $n \geq 30$ is adequate when using the hypothesis testing procedure described in this section. In cases where the sample size is less than 30, the distribution of the population from which we are sampling becomes an important consideration. If the population is normally distributed, the hypothesis testing procedure that we described is exact and can be used for any sample size. If the population is not normally distributed but is at least roughly symmetric, sample sizes as small as 15 can be expected to provide acceptable results.

Relationship Between Interval Estimation and Hypothesis Testing

In Chapter 8 we showed how to develop a confidence interval estimate of a population mean. For the σ known case, the $(1 - \alpha)\%$ confidence interval estimate of a population mean is given by

$$\bar{x} \pm z_{\alpha/2} \frac{\sigma}{\sqrt{n}}$$

In this chapter we showed that a two-tailed hypothesis test about a population mean takes the following form:

$$H_0: \mu = \mu_0$$
$$H_a: \mu \neq \mu_0$$

where μ_0 is the hypothesized value for the population mean.

Suppose that we follow the procedure described in Chapter 8 for constructing a $100(1 - \alpha)\%$ confidence interval for the population mean. We know that $100(1 - \alpha)\%$ of the confidence intervals generated will contain the population mean and $100\alpha\%$ of the confidence intervals generated will not contain the population mean. Thus, if we reject H_0 whenever the confidence interval does not contain μ_0, we will be rejecting the null hypothesis when it is true ($\mu = \mu_0$) with probability α. Recall that the level of significance is the probability of rejecting the null hypothesis when it is true. So constructing a $100(1 - \alpha)\%$ confidence interval and rejecting H_0 whenever the interval does not contain μ_0 is equivalent to conducting a two-tailed hypothesis test with α as the level of significance. The procedure for using a confidence interval to conduct a two-tailed hypothesis test can now be summarized.

A CONFIDENCE INTERVAL APPROACH TO TESTING A HYPOTHESIS OF THE FORM

$$H_0: \mu = \mu_0$$
$$H_a: \mu \neq \mu_0$$

1. **Select a simple random sample from the population and use the value of the sample mean $\bar{x}$ to develop the confidence interval for the population mean μ.**

$$\bar{x} \pm z_{\alpha/2} \frac{\sigma}{\sqrt{n}}$$

2. **If the confidence interval contains the hypothesized value μ_0, do not reject H_0. Otherwise, reject[3] H_0.**

For a two-tailed hypothesis test, the null hypothesis can be rejected if the confidence interval does not include μ_0.

Let us illustrate by conducting the MaxFlight hypothesis test using the confidence interval approach. The MaxFlight hypothesis test takes the following form:

$$H_0: \mu = 295$$
$$H_a: \mu \neq 295$$

[3]To be consistent with the rule for rejecting H_0 when the p-value $\leq \alpha$, we would also reject H_0 using the confidence interval approach if μ_0 happens to be equal to one of the endpoints of the $100(1 - \alpha)\%$ confidence interval.

To test these hypotheses with a level of significance of $\alpha = .05$, we sampled 50 golf balls and found a sample mean distance of $\bar{x} = 297.6$ yards. Recall that the population standard deviation is $\sigma = 12$. Using these results with $z_{.025} = 1.96$, we find that the 95% confidence interval estimate of the population mean is

$$\bar{x} \pm z_{.025}\frac{\sigma}{\sqrt{n}}$$

$$297.6 \pm 1.96\frac{12}{\sqrt{50}}$$

$$297.6 \pm 3.3$$

or

$$294.3 \text{ to } 300.9$$

This finding enables the quality control manager to conclude with 95% confidence that the mean distance for the population of golf balls is between 294.3 and 300.9 yards. Because the hypothesized value for the population mean, $\mu_0 = 295$, is in this interval, the hypothesis testing conclusion is that the null hypothesis, H_0: $\mu = 295$, cannot be rejected.

Note that this discussion and example pertain to two-tailed hypothesis tests about a population mean. However, the same confidence interval and two-tailed hypothesis testing relationship exists for other population parameters. The relationship can also be extended to one-tailed tests about population parameters. Doing so, however, requires the development of one-sided confidence intervals, which are rarely used in practice.

NOTE AND COMMENT

We have shown how to use *p*-values. The smaller the *p*-value the greater the evidence against H_0 and the more the evidence in favor of H_a. Here are some guidelines statisticians suggest for interpreting small *p*-values.

- Less than .01—Overwhelming evidence to conclude that H_a is true
- Between .01 and .05—Strong evidence to conclude that H_a is true
- Between .05 and .10—Weak evidence to conclude that H_a is true
- Greater than .10—Insufficient evidence to conclude that H_a is true

Exercises

Note to Student: Some of the exercises that follow ask you to use the *p*-value approach and others ask you to use the critical value approach. Both methods will provide the same hypothesis testing conclusion. We provide exercises with both methods to give you practice using both. In later sections and in following chapters, we will generally emphasize the *p*-value approach as the preferred method, but you may select either based on personal preference.

Methods

9. Consider the following hypothesis test:

$$H_0: \mu \geq 20$$
$$H_a: \mu < 20$$

A sample of 50 provided a sample mean of 19.4. The population standard deviation is 2.

a. Compute the value of the test statistic.
b. What is the p-value?
c. Using $\alpha = .05$, what is your conclusion?
d. What is the rejection rule using the critical value? What is your conclusion?

10. Consider the following hypothesis test:

SELF test

$$H_0: \mu \leq 25$$
$$H_a: \mu > 25$$

A sample of 40 provided a sample mean of 26.4. The population standard deviation is 6.

a. Compute the value of the test statistic.
b. What is the p-value?
c. At $\alpha = .01$, what is your conclusion?
d. What is the rejection rule using the critical value? What is your conclusion?

11. Consider the following hypothesis test:

$$H_0: \mu = 15$$
$$H_a: \mu \neq 15$$

A sample of 50 provided a sample mean of 14.15. The population standard deviation is 3.

a. Compute the value of the test statistic.
b. What is the p-value?
c. At $\alpha = .05$, what is your conclusion?
d. What is the rejection rule using the critical value? What is your conclusion?

12. Consider the following hypothesis test:

$$H_0: \mu \geq 80$$
$$H_a: \mu < 80$$

A sample of 100 is used and the population standard deviation is 12. Compute the p-value and state your conclusion for each of the following sample results. Use $\alpha = .01$.

a. $\bar{x} = 78.5$
b. $\bar{x} = 77$
c. $\bar{x} = 75.5$
d. $\bar{x} = 81$

13. Consider the following hypothesis test:

$$H_0: \mu \leq 50$$
$$H_a: \mu > 50$$

A sample of 60 is used and the population standard deviation is 8. Use the critical value approach to state your conclusion for each of the following sample results. Use $\alpha = .05$.

a. $\bar{x} = 52.5$
b. $\bar{x} = 51$
c. $\bar{x} = 51.8$

14. Consider the following hypothesis test:

$$H_0: \mu = 22$$
$$H_a: \mu \neq 22$$

A sample of 75 is used and the population standard deviation is 10. Compute the p-value and state your conclusion for each of the following sample results. Use $\alpha = .01$.

a. $\bar{x} = 23$
b. $\bar{x} = 25.1$
c. $\bar{x} = 20$

Applications

15. Individuals filing federal income tax returns prior to March 31 received an average refund of $1056. Consider the population of "last-minute" filers who mail their tax return during the last five days of the income tax period (typically April 10 to April 15).
    a. A researcher suggests that a reason individuals wait until the last five days is that on average these individuals receive lower refunds than do early filers. Develop appropriate hypotheses such that rejection of H_0 will support the researcher's contention.
    b. For a sample of 400 individuals who filed a tax return between April 10 and 15, the sample mean refund was $910. Based on prior experience, a population standard deviation of $\sigma = \$1600$ may be assumed. What is the p-value?
    c. At $\alpha = .05$, what is your conclusion?
    d. Repeat the preceding hypothesis test using the critical value approach.
16. In a study entitled How Undergraduate Students Use Credit Cards, it was reported that undergraduate students have a mean credit card balance of $3173 (Sallie Mae, April 2009). This figure was an all-time high and had increased 44% over the previous five years. Assume that a current study is being conducted to determine if it can be concluded that the mean credit card balance for undergraduate students has continued to increase compared to the April 2009 report. Based on previous studies, use a population standard deviation $\sigma = \$1000$.
    a. State the null and alternative hypotheses.
    b. What is the p-value for a sample of 180 undergraduate students with a sample mean credit card balance of $3325?
    c. Using a .05 level of significance, what is your conclusion?
17. The mean hourly wage for employees in goods-producing industries is currently $24.57 (Bureau of Labor Statistics website, April, 12, 2012). Suppose we take a sample of employees from the manufacturing industry to see if the mean hourly wage differs from the reported mean of $24.57 for the goods-producing industries.
    a. State the null and alternative hypotheses we should use to test whether the population mean hourly wage in the manufacturing industry differs from the population mean hourly wage in the goods-producing industries.
    b. Suppose a sample of 30 employees from the manufacturing industry showed a sample mean of $23.89 per hour. Assume a population standard deviation of $2.40 per hour and compute the p-value.
    c. With $\alpha = .05$ as the level of significance, what is your conclusion?
    d. Repeat the preceding hypothesis test using the critical value approach.
18. Young millennials, adults aged 18 to 34, are viewed as the future of the restaurant industry. During 2011, this group consumed a mean of 192 restaurant meals per person (NPD Group website, November 7, 2012). Conduct a hypothesis test to determine if the poor economy caused a change in the frequency of consuming restaurant meals by young millennials in 2012.
    a. Formulate hypotheses that can be used to determine whether the annual mean number of restaurant meals per person has changed for young millennials in 2012.
    b. Based on a sample, the NPD Group stated that the mean number of restaurant meals consumed by young millennials in 2012 was 182. Assume the sample size was 150 and that, based on past studies, the population standard deviation can be assumed to be $\sigma = 55$. Use the sample results to compute the test statistic and p-value for your hypothesis test.
    c. At $\alpha = .05$, what is your conclusion?

19. The Internal Revenue Service (IRS) provides a toll-free help line for taxpayers to call in and get answers to questions as they prepare their tax returns. In recent years, the IRS has been inundated with taxpayer calls and has redesigned its phone service as well as posting answers to frequently asked questions on its website (*The Cincinnati Enquirer*, January 7, 2010). According to a report by a taxpayer advocate, callers using the new system can expect to wait on hold for an unreasonably long time of 12 minutes before being able to talk to an IRS employee. Suppose you select a sample of 50 callers after the new phone service has been implemented; the sample results show a mean waiting time of 10 minutes before an IRS employee comes on line. Based upon data from past years, you decide it is reasonable to assume that the standard deviation of waiting times is 8 minutes. Using your sample results, can you conclude that the actual mean waiting time turned out to be significantly less than the 12-minute claim made by the taxpayer advocate? Use $\alpha = .05$.

20. Annual expenditure for prescription drugs was $838 per person in the Northeast of the country (Hospital Care Cost Institute website, November 7, 2012). A sample of 60 individuals in the Midwest showed a per person annual expenditure for prescription drugs of $745. Use a population standard deviation of $300 to answer the following questions.
    a. Formulate hypotheses for a test to determine whether the sample data support the conclusion that the population annual expenditure for prescription drugs per person is lower in the Midwest than in the Northeast.
    b. What is the value of the test statistic?
    c. What is the p-value?
    d. At $\alpha = .01$, what is your conclusion?

Fowle

21. Fowle Marketing Research, Inc., bases charges to a client on the assumption that telephone surveys can be completed in a mean time of 15 minutes or less. If a longer mean survey time is necessary, a premium rate is charged. A sample of 35 surveys provided the survey times shown in the WEBfile named Fowle. Based upon past studies, the population standard deviation is assumed known with $\sigma = 4$ minutes. Is the premium rate justified?
    a. Formulate the null and alternative hypotheses for this application.
    b. Compute the value of the test statistic.
    c. What is the p-value?
    d. At $\alpha = .01$, what is your conclusion?

22. CCN and ActMedia provided a television channel targeted to individuals waiting in supermarket checkout lines. The channel showed news, short features, and advertisements. The length of the program was based on the assumption that the population mean time a shopper stands in a supermarket checkout line is 8 minutes. A sample of actual waiting times will be used to test this assumption and determine whether actual mean waiting time differs from this standard.
    a. Formulate the hypotheses for this application.
    b. A sample of 120 shoppers showed a sample mean waiting time of 8.4 minutes. Assume a population standard deviation of $\sigma = 3.2$ minutes. What is the p-value?
    c. At $\alpha = .05$, what is your conclusion?
    d. Compute a 95% confidence interval for the population mean. Does it support your conclusion?

9.4 Population Mean: σ Unknown

In this section we describe how to conduct hypothesis tests about a population mean for the σ unknown case. Because the σ unknown case corresponds to situations in which an estimate of the population standard deviation cannot be developed prior to sampling, the sample must be used to develop an estimate of both μ and σ. Thus, to conduct a hypothesis test about a population mean for the σ unknown case, the sample mean $\bar{x}$ is used as an estimate of μ and the sample standard deviation s is used as an estimate of σ.

The steps of the hypothesis testing procedure for the σ unknown case are the same as those for the σ known case described in Section 9.3. But, with σ unknown, the computation of the test statistic and p-value is a bit different. Recall that for the σ known case, the sampling distribution of the test statistic has a standard normal distribution. For the σ unknown case, however, the sampling distribution of the test statistic follows the t distribution; it has slightly more variability because the sample is used to develop estimates of both μ and σ.

In Section 8.2 we showed that an interval estimate of a population mean for the σ unknown case is based on a probability distribution known as the t distribution. Hypothesis tests about a population mean for the σ unknown case are also based on the t distribution. For the σ unknown case, the test statistic has a t distribution with $n - 1$ degrees of freedom.

TEST STATISTIC FOR HYPOTHESIS TESTS ABOUT A POPULATION MEAN: σ UNKNOWN

$$t = \frac{\bar{x} - \mu_0}{s/\sqrt{n}} \tag{9.2}$$

In Chapter 8 we said that the t distribution is based on an assumption that the population from which we are sampling has a normal distribution. However, research shows that this assumption can be relaxed considerably when the sample size is large enough. We provide some practical advice concerning the population distribution and sample size at the end of the section.

One-Tailed Test

Let us consider an example of a one-tailed test about a population mean for the σ unknown case. A business travel magazine wants to classify transatlantic gateway airports according to the mean rating for the population of business travelers. A rating scale with a low score of 0 and a high score of 10 will be used, and airports with a population mean rating greater than 7 will be designated as superior service airports. The magazine staff surveyed a sample of 60 business travelers at each airport to obtain the ratings data. The sample for London's Heathrow Airport provided a sample mean rating of $\bar{x} = 7.25$ and a sample standard deviation of $s = 1.052$. Do the data indicate that Heathrow should be designated as a superior service airport?

AirRating

We want to develop a hypothesis test for which the decision to reject H_0 will lead to the conclusion that the population mean rating for the Heathrow Airport is *greater* than 7. Thus, an upper tail test with H_a: $\mu > 7$ is required. The null and alternative hypotheses for this upper tail test are as follows:

$$H_0: \mu \le 7$$
$$H_a: \mu > 7$$

We will use $\alpha = .05$ as the level of significance for the test.

Using equation (9.2) with $\bar{x} = 7.25$, $\mu_0 = 7$, $s = 1.052$, and $n = 60$, the value of the test statistic is

$$t = \frac{\bar{x} - \mu_0}{s/\sqrt{n}} = \frac{7.25 - 7}{1.052/\sqrt{60}} = 1.84$$

The sampling distribution of t has $n - 1 = 60 - 1 = 59$ degrees of freedom. Because the test is an upper tail test, the p-value is $P(t \geq 1.84)$, that is, the upper tail area corresponding to the value of the test statistic.

The t distribution table provided in most textbooks will not contain sufficient detail to determine the exact p-value, such as the p-value corresponding to $t = 1.84$. For instance, using Table 2 in Appendix B, the t distribution with 59 degrees of freedom (df) provides the following information.

Area in Upper Tail	**.20**	**.10**	**.05**	**.025**	**.01**	**.005**
***t* Value (59 *df*)**	.848	1.296	1.671	2.001	2.391	2.662

$t = 1.84$

We see that $t = 1.84$ is between 1.671 and 2.001. Although the table does not provide the exact p-value, the values in the "Area in Upper Tail" row show that the p-value must be less than .05 and greater than .025. With a level of significance of $\alpha = .05$, this placement is all we need to know to make the decision to reject the null hypothesis and conclude that Heathrow should be classified as a superior service airport.

It is cumbersome to use a t table to compute p-values, and only approximate values are obtained. We describe how to compute exact p-values using Excel's T.DIST function in the Using Excel subsection which follows. The exact upper tail p-value for the Heathrow Airport hypothesis test is .0354. With $.0354 < .05$, we reject the null hypothesis and conclude that Heathrow should be classified as a superior service airport.

The decision whether to reject the null hypothesis in the σ unknown case can also be made using the critical value approach. The critical value corresponding to an area of $\alpha = .05$ in the upper tail of a t distribution with 59 degrees of freedom is $t_{.05} = 1.671$. Thus the rejection rule using the critical value approach is to reject H_0 if $t \geq 1.671$. Because $t = 1.84 > 1.671$, H_0 is rejected. Heathrow should be classified as a superior service airport.

Two-Tailed Test

To illustrate how to conduct a two-tailed test about a population mean for the σ unknown case, let us consider the hypothesis testing situation facing Holiday Toys. The company manufactures and distributes its products through more than 1000 retail outlets. In planning production levels for the coming winter season, Holiday must decide how many units of each product to produce prior to knowing the actual demand at the retail level. For this year's most important new toy, Holiday's marketing director is expecting demand to average 40 units per retail outlet. Prior to making the final production decision based upon this estimate, Holiday decided to survey a sample of 25 retailers in order to develop more information about the demand for the new product. Each retailer was provided with information about the features of the new toy along with the cost and the suggested selling price. Then each retailer was asked to specify an anticipated order quantity.

With μ denoting the population mean order quantity per retail outlet, the sample data will be used to conduct the following two-tailed hypothesis test:

$$H_0: \mu = 40$$
$$H_a: \mu \neq 40$$

If H_0 cannot be rejected, Holiday will continue its production planning based on the marketing director's estimate that the population mean order quantity per retail outlet will be $\mu = 40$ units. However, if H_0 is rejected, Holiday will immediately reevaluate its production plan for the product. A two-tailed hypothesis test is used because Holiday wants to reevaluate the production plan if the population mean quantity per retail outlet is less than anticipated or greater than anticipated. Because no historical data are available (it's a new product), the population mean μ and the population standard deviation must both be estimated using $\bar{x}$ and s from the sample data.

Orders

The sample of 25 retailers provided a mean of $\bar{x} = 37.4$ and a standard deviation of $s = 11.79$ units. Before going ahead with the use of the t distribution, the analyst constructed a histogram of the sample data in order to check on the form of the population distribution. The histogram of the sample data showed no evidence of skewness or any extreme outliers, so the analyst concluded that the use of the t distribution with $n - 1 = 24$ degrees of freedom was appropriate. Using equation (9.2) with $\bar{x} = 37.4$, $\mu_0 = 40$, $s = 11.79$, and $n = 25$, the value of the test statistic is

$$t = \frac{\bar{x} - \mu_0}{s/\sqrt{n}} = \frac{37.4 - 40}{11.79/\sqrt{25}} = -1.10$$

Because we have a two-tailed test, the p-value is two times the area under the curve of the t distribution for $t \leq -1.10$. Using Table 2 in Appendix B, the t distribution table for 24 degrees of freedom provides the following information.

Area in Upper Tail	.20	.10	.05	.025	.01	.005
***t*-Value (24 *df*)**	.857	1.318	1.711	2.064	2.492	2.797

$t = 1.10$

The t distribution table contains only positive t values (corresponding to areas in the upper tail). Because the t distribution is symmetric, however, the upper tail area for $t = 1.10$ is the same as the lower tail area for $t = -1.10$. We see that $t = 1.10$ is between 0.857 and 1.318. From the "Area in Upper Tail" row, we see that the area in the tail to the right of $t = 1.10$ is between .20 and .10. When we double these amounts, we see that the p-value must be between .40 and .20. With a level of significance of $\alpha = .05$, we now know that the p-value is greater than α. Therefore, H_0 cannot be rejected. Sufficient evidence is not available to conclude that Holiday should change its production plan for the coming season.

In the Using Excel subsection which follows, we show how to compute the exact p-value for this hypothesis test using Excel. The p-value obtained is .2811. With a level of significance of $\alpha = .05$, we cannot reject H_0 because $.2811 > .05$.

The test statistic can also be compared to the critical value to make the two-tailed hypothesis testing decision. With $\alpha = .05$ and the t distribution with 24 degrees of freedom, $-t_{.025} = -2.064$ and $t_{.025} = 2.064$ are the critical values for the two-tailed test. The rejection rule using the test statistic is

$$\text{Reject } H_0 \text{ if } t \leq -2.064 \text{ or if } t \geq 2.064$$

Based on the test statistic $t = -1.10$, H_0 cannot be rejected. This result indicates that Holiday should continue its production planning for the coming season based on the expectation that $\mu = 40$.

Using Excel

Excel can be used to conduct one-tailed and two-tailed hypothesis tests about a population mean for the σ unknown case. The approach is similar to the procedure used in the σ known case. The sample data and the test statistic (t) are used to compute three p-values: p-value (Lower Tail), p-value (Upper Tail), and p-value (Two Tail). The user can then choose α

FIGURE 9.8 EXCEL WORKSHEET: HYPOTHESIS TEST FOR THE σ UNKNOWN CASE

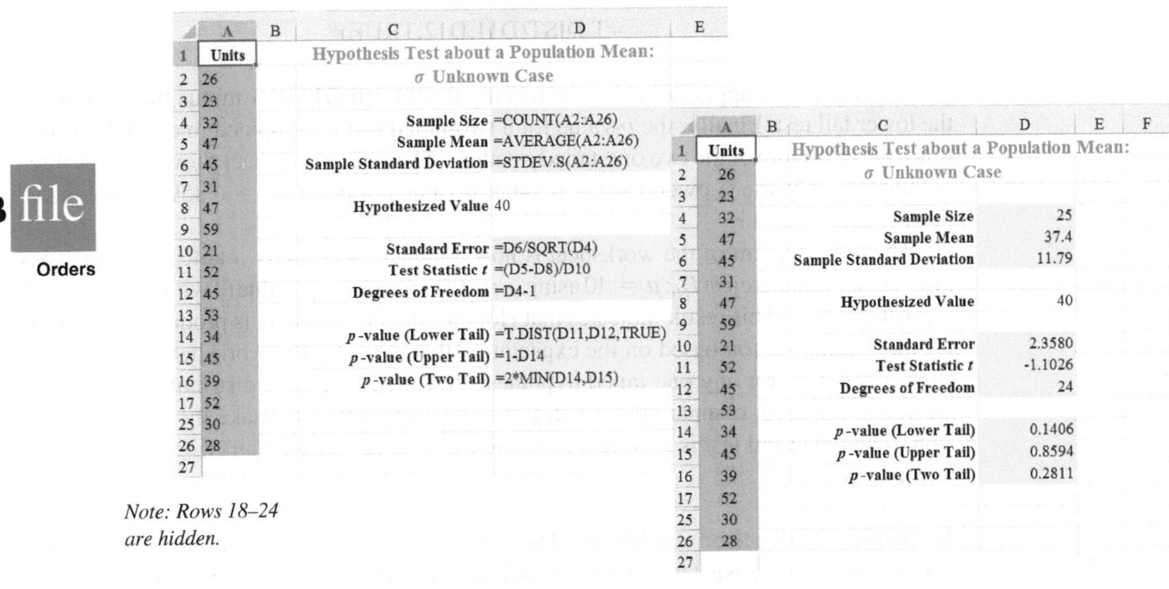

	A	B	C	D	E
1	Units		Hypothesis Test about a Population Mean:		
			σ Unknown Case		
2	26				
3	23				
4	32		Sample Size	=COUNT(A2:A26)	
5	47		Sample Mean	=AVERAGE(A2:A26)	
6	45		Sample Standard Deviation	=STDEV.S(A2:A26)	
7	31				
8	47		Hypothesized Value	40	
9	59				
10	21		Standard Error	=D6/SQRT(D4)	
11	52		Test Statistic *t*	=(D5-D8)/D10	
12	45		Degrees of Freedom	=D4-1	
13	53				
14	34		*p*-value (Lower Tail)	=T.DIST(D11,D12,TRUE)	
15	45		*p*-value (Upper Tail)	=1-D14	
16	39		*p*-value (Two Tail)	=2*MIN(D14,D15)	
17	52				
25	30				
26	28				
27					

	A	B	C	D	E	F
1	Units		Hypothesis Test about a Population Mean:			
			σ Unknown Case			
2	26					
3	23					
4	32		Sample Size	25		
5	47		Sample Mean	37.4		
6	45		Sample Standard Deviation	11.79		
7	31					
8	47		Hypothesized Value	40		
9	59					
10	21		Standard Error	2.3580		
11	52		Test Statistic *t*	-1.1026		
12	45		Degrees of Freedom	24		
13	53					
14	34		*p*-value (Lower Tail)	0.1406		
15	45		*p*-value (Upper Tail)	0.8594		
16	39		*p*-value (Two Tail)	0.2811		
17	52					
25	30					
26	28					
27						

Note: Rows 18–24 are hidden.

WEB file Orders

and draw a conclusion using whichever *p*-value is appropriate for the type of hypothesis test being conducted.

Let's start by showing how to use Excel's T.DIST function to compute a lower tail *p*-value. The T.DIST function has three inputs; its general form is as follows:

T.DIST(test statistic, degrees of freedom, cumulative)

For the first input, we enter the value of the test statistic, for the second input we enter the number of degrees of freedom. For the third input, we enter TRUE if we want a cumulative probability and FALSE if we want the height of the curve. When we want to compute a lower tail *p*-value, we enter TRUE.

Once the lower tail *p*-value has been computed, it is easy to compute the upper tail and the two-tailed *p*-values. The upper tail *p*-value is just 1 minus the lower tail *p*-value. And the two-tailed *p*-value is given by two times the smaller of the lower and upper tail *p*-values.

Let us now construct an Excel worksheet to conduct the two-tailed hypothesis test for the Holiday Toys study. Refer to Figure 9.8 as we describe the tasks involved. The formula worksheet is in the background; the value worksheet is in the foreground.

Enter/Access Data: Open the WEBfile named Orders. A label and the order quantity data for the sample of 25 retailers are entered into cells A1:A26.

Enter Functions and Formulas: The descriptive statistics needed are provided in cells D4:D6. Excel's COUNT, AVERAGE, and STDEV.S functions compute the sample size, the sample mean, and the sample standard deviation, respectively. The hypothesized value of the population mean (40) is entered into cell D8.

Using the sample standard deviation as an estimate of the population standard deviation, an estimate of the standard error is obtained in cell D10 by dividing the sample standard deviation in cell D6 by the square root of the sample size in cell D4. The formula =(D5-D8)/D10 entered into cell D11 computes the test statistic $t(-1.1026)$. The degrees of freedom are computed in cell D12 as the sample size in cell D4 minus 1.

To compute the p-value for a lower tail test, we enter the following formula into cell D14:

=T.DIST(D11,D12,TRUE)

The p-value for an upper tail test is then computed in cell D15 as 1 minus the p-value for the lower tail test. Finally, the p-value for a two-tailed test is computed in cell D16 as two times the minimum of the two one-tailed p-values. The value worksheet shows that the three p-values are p-value (Lower Tail) = 0.1406, p-value (Upper Tail) = 0.8594, and p-value (Two Tail) = 0.2811.

The development of the worksheet is now complete. For the two-tailed Holiday Toys problem we cannot reject $H_0: \mu = 40$ using $\alpha = .05$ because the p-value (Two Tail) = 0.2811 is greater than α. This result indicates that Holiday should continue its production planning for the coming season based on the expectation that $\mu = 40$. The worksheet in Figure 9.8 can also be used for any one-tailed hypothesis test involving the t distribution. If a lower tail test is required, compare the p-value (Lower Tail) with α to make the rejection decision. If an upper tail test is required, compare the p-value (Upper Tail) with α to make the rejection decision.

A template for other problems The worksheet in Figure 9.8 can be used as a template for any hypothesis tests about a population mean for the σ unknown case. Just enter the appropriate data in column A, adjust the ranges for the formulas in cells D4:D6, and enter the hypothesized value in cell D8. The standard error, the test statistic, and the three p-values will then appear. Depending on the form of the hypothesis test (lower tail, upper tail, or two-tailed), we can then choose the appropriate p-value to make the rejection decision.

We can further simplify the use of Figure 9.8 as a template for other problems by eliminating the need to enter new data ranges in cells D4:D6. To do so we rewrite the cell formulas as follows:

Cell D4: =COUNT(A:A)
Cell D5: =AVERAGE(A:A)
Cell D6: =STDEV(A:A)

The WEBfile named Orders includes a worksheet entitled Template that uses the A:A method for entering the data ranges.

With the A:A method of specifying data ranges, Excel's COUNT function will count the number of numeric values in column A, Excel's AVERAGE function will compute the average of the numeric values in column A, and Excel's STDEV function will compute the standard deviation of the numeric values in Column A. Thus, to solve a new problem it is only necessary to enter the new data in column A and enter the hypothesized value of the population mean in cell D8.

Summary and Practical Advice

Table 9.3 provides a summary of the hypothesis testing procedures about a population mean for the σ unknown case. The key difference between these procedures and the ones for the σ known case is that s is used, instead of σ, in the computation of the test statistic. For this reason, the test statistic follows the t distribution.

The applicability of the hypothesis testing procedures of this section is dependent on the distribution of the population being sampled from and the sample size. When the population is normally distributed, the hypothesis tests described in this section provide exact results for any sample size. When the population is not normally distributed, the procedures are approximations. Nonetheless, we find that sample sizes of 30 or greater will provide

TABLE 9.3 SUMMARY OF HYPOTHESIS TESTS ABOUT A POPULATION MEAN: σ UNKNOWN CASE

	Lower Tail Test	Upper Tail Test	Two-Tailed Test
Hypotheses	$H_0: \mu \geq \mu_0$ $H_a: \mu < \mu_0$	$H_0: \mu \leq \mu_0$ $H_a: \mu > \mu_0$	$H_0: \mu = \mu_0$ $H_a: \mu \neq \mu_0$
Test Statistic	$t = \dfrac{\bar{x} - \mu_0}{s/\sqrt{n}}$	$t = \dfrac{\bar{x} - \mu_0}{s/\sqrt{n}}$	$t = \dfrac{\bar{x} - \mu_0}{s/\sqrt{n}}$
Rejection Rule: *p*-Value Approach	Reject H_0 if p-value $\leq \alpha$	Reject H_0 if p-value $\leq \alpha$	Reject H_0 if p-value $\leq \alpha$
Rejection Rule: Critical Value Approach	Reject H_0 if $t \leq -t_\alpha$	Reject H_0 if $t \geq t_\alpha$	Reject H_0 if $t \leq -t_{\alpha/2}$ or if $t \geq t_{\alpha/2}$

good results in most cases. If the population is approximately normal, small sample sizes (e.g., $n < 15$) can provide acceptable results. If the population is highly skewed or contains outliers, sample sizes approaching 50 are recommended.

Exercises

Methods

23. Consider the following hypothesis test:

$$H_0: \mu \leq 12$$
$$H_a: \mu > 12$$

A sample of 25 provided a sample mean $\bar{x} = 14$ and a sample standard deviation $s = 4.32$.

a. Compute the value of the test statistic.
b. Use the t distribution table (Table 2 in Appendix B) to compute a range for the p-value.
c. At $\alpha = .05$, what is your conclusion?
d. What is the rejection rule using the critical value? What is your conclusion?

24. Consider the following hypothesis test:

$$H_0: \mu = 18$$
$$H_a: \mu \neq 18$$

A sample of 48 provided a sample mean $\bar{x} = 17$ and a sample standard deviation $s = 4.5$.

a. Compute the value of the test statistic.
b. Use the t distribution table (Table 2 in Appendix B) to compute a range for the p-value.
c. At $\alpha = .05$, what is your conclusion?
d. What is the rejection rule using the critical value? What is your conclusion?

25. Consider the following hypothesis test:

$$H_0: \mu \geq 45$$
$$H_a: \mu < 45$$

A sample of 36 is used. Identify the p-value and state your conclusion for each of the following sample results. Use $\alpha = .01$.

a. $\bar{x} = 44$ and $s = 5.2$
b. $\bar{x} = 43$ and $s = 4.6$
c. $\bar{x} = 46$ and $s = 5.0$

26. Consider the following hypothesis test:

$$H_0: \mu = 100$$
$$H_a: \mu \neq 100$$

A sample of 65 is used. Identify the p-value and state your conclusion for each of the following sample results. Use $\alpha = .05$.

a. $\bar{x} = 103$ and $s = 11.5$
b. $\bar{x} = 96.5$ and $s = 11.0$
c. $\bar{x} = 102$ and $s = 10.5$

Applications

27. Which is cheaper: eating out or dining in? The mean cost of a flank steak, broccoli, and rice bought at the grocery store is $13.04 (Money.msn website, November 7, 2012). A sample of 100 neighborhood restaurants showed a mean price of $12.75 and a standard deviation of $2 for a comparable restaurant meal.
    a. Develop appropriate hypotheses for a test to determine whether the sample data support the conclusion that the mean cost of a restaurant meal is less than fixing a comparable meal at home.
    b. Using the sample from the 100 restaurants, what is the p-value?
    c. At $\alpha = .05$, what is your conclusion?
    d. Repeat the preceding hypothesis test using the critical value approach.

28. A shareholders' group, in lodging a protest, claimed that the mean tenure for a chief executive officer (CEO) was at least nine years. A survey of companies reported in *The Wall Street Journal* found a sample mean tenure of $\bar{x} = 7.27$ years for CEOs with a standard deviation of $s = 6.38$ years (*The Wall Street Journal*, January 2, 2007).
    a. Formulate hypotheses that can be used to challenge the validity of the claim made by the shareholders' group.
    b. Assume 85 companies were included in the sample. What is the p-value for your hypothesis test?
    c. At $\alpha = .01$, what is your conclusion?

29. The national mean annual salary for a school administrator is $90,000 a year (*The Cincinnati Enquirer,* April 7, 2012). A school official took a sample of 25 school administrators in the state of Ohio to learn about salaries in that state to see if they differed from the national average.
    a. Formulate hypotheses that can be used to determine whether the population mean annual administrator salary in Ohio differs from the national mean of $90,000.
    b. The sample data for 25 Ohio administrators is contained in the WEBfile named Administrator. What is the p-value for your hypothesis test in part (a)?
    c. At $\alpha = .05$, can your null hypothesis be rejected? What is your conclusion?
    d. Repeat the preceding hypothesis test using the critical value approach.

30. The time married men with children spend on child care averages 6.4 hours per week (*Time,* March 12, 2012). You belong to a professional group on family practices that would like to do its own study to determine if the time married men in your area spend on child care per week differs from the reported mean of 6.4 hours per week. A sample of 40 married couples will be used with the data collected showing the hours per week the husband spends on child care. The sample data are contained in the WEBfile named ChildCare.

a. What are the hypotheses if your group would like to determine if the population mean number of hours married men are spending in child care differs from the mean reported by *Time* in your area?
b. What is the sample mean and the p-value?
c. Select your own level of significance. What is your conclusion?

31. The Coca-Cola Company reported that the mean per capita annual sales of its beverages in the United States was 423 eight-ounce servings (Coca-Cola Company website, February 3, 2009). Suppose you are curious whether the consumption of Coca-Cola beverages is higher in Atlanta, Georgia, the location of Coca-Cola's corporate headquarters. A sample of 36 individuals from the Atlanta area showed a sample mean annual consumption of 460.4 eight-ounce servings with a standard deviation of $s = 101.9$ ounces. Using $\alpha = .05$, do the sample results support the conclusion that mean annual consumption of Coca-Cola beverage products is higher in Atlanta?

UsedCars

32. According to the National Automobile Dealers Association, the mean price for used cars is $10,192. A manager of a Kansas City used car dealership reviewed a sample of 50 recent used car sales at the dealership in an attempt to determine whether the population mean price for used cars at this particular dealership differed from the national mean. The prices for the sample of 50 cars are shown in the WEBfile named UsedCars.
a. Formulate the hypotheses that can be used to determine whether a difference exists in the mean price for used cars at the dealership.
b. What is the p-value?
c. At $\alpha = .05$, what is your conclusion?

33. The mean annual premium for automobile insurance in the United States is $1503 (Insure.com website, March 6, 2014). Being from Pennsylvania, you believe automobile insurance is cheaper there and wish to develop statistical support for your opinion. A sample of 25 automobile insurance policies from the state of Pennsylvania showed a mean annual premium of $1440 with a standard deviation of $s = \$165$.
a. Develop a hypothesis test that can be used to determine whether the mean annual premium in Pennsylvania is lower than the national mean annual premium.
b. What is a point estimate of the difference between the mean annual premium in Pennsylvania and the national mean?
c. At $\alpha = .05$, test for a significant difference. What is your conclusion?

34. Joan's Nursery specializes in custom-designed landscaping for residential areas. The estimated labor cost associated with a particular landscaping proposal is based on the number of plantings of trees, shrubs, and so on to be used for the project. For cost-estimating purposes, managers use two hours of labor time for the planting of a medium-sized tree. Actual times from a sample of 10 plantings during the past month follow (times in hours).

1.7	1.5	2.6	2.2	2.4	2.3	2.6	3.0	1.4	2.3

With a .05 level of significance, test to see whether the mean tree-planting time differs from two hours.
a. State the null and alternative hypotheses.
b. Compute the sample mean.
c. Compute the sample standard deviation.
d. What is the p-value?
e. What is your conclusion?

9.5 Population Proportion

In this section we show how to conduct a hypothesis test about a population proportion p. Using p_0 to denote the hypothesized value for the population proportion, the three forms for a hypothesis test about a population proportion are as follows.

$$H_0: p \geq p_0 \qquad H_0: p \leq p_0 \qquad H_0: p = p_0$$
$$H_a: p < p_0 \qquad H_a: p > p_0 \qquad H_a: p \neq p_0$$

The first form is called a lower tail test, the second form is called an upper tail test, and the third form is called a two-tailed test.

Hypothesis tests about a population proportion are based on the difference between the sample proportion $\bar{p}$ and the hypothesized population proportion p_0. The methods used to conduct the hypothesis test are similar to those used for hypothesis tests about a population mean. The only difference is that we use the sample proportion and its standard error to compute the test statistic. The p-value approach or the critical value approach is then used to determine whether the null hypothesis should be rejected.

Let us consider an example involving a situation faced by Pine Creek golf course. Over the past year, 20% of the players at Pine Creek were women. In an effort to increase the proportion of women players, Pine Creek implemented a special promotion designed to attract women golfers. One month after the promotion was implemented, the course manager requested a statistical study to determine whether the proportion of women players at Pine Creek had increased. Because the objective of the study is to determine whether the proportion of women golfers increased, an upper tail test with H_a: $p > .20$ is appropriate. The null and alternative hypotheses for the Pine Creek hypothesis test are as follows:

$$H_0: p \leq .20$$
$$H_a: p > .20$$

If H_0 can be rejected, the test results will give statistical support for the conclusion that the proportion of women golfers increased and the promotion was beneficial. The course manager specified that a level of significance of $\alpha = .05$ be used in carrying out this hypothesis test.

The next step of the hypothesis testing procedure is to select a sample and compute the value of an appropriate test statistic. To show how this step is done for the Pine Creek upper tail test, we begin with a general discussion of how to compute the value of the test statistic for any form of a hypothesis test about a population proportion. The sampling distribution of $\bar{p}$, the point estimator of the population parameter p, is the basis for developing the test statistic.

When the null hypothesis is true as an equality, the expected value of $\bar{p}$ equals the hypothesized value p_0; that is, $E(\bar{p}) = p_0$. The standard error of $\bar{p}$ is given by

$$\sigma_{\bar{p}} = \sqrt{\frac{p_0(1 - p_0)}{n}}$$

In Chapter 7 we said that if $np \geq 5$ and $n(1 - p) \geq 5$, the sampling distribution of $\bar{p}$ can be approximated by a normal distribution.[4] Under these conditions, which usually apply in practice, the quantity

$$z = \frac{\bar{p} - p_0}{\sigma_{\bar{p}}} \tag{9.3}$$

has a standard normal probability distribution. With $\sigma_{\bar{p}} = \sqrt{p_0(1 - p_0)/n}$, the standard normal random variable z is the test statistic used to conduct hypothesis tests about a population proportion.

[4]In most applications involving hypothesis tests of a population proportion, sample sizes are large enough to use the normal approximation. The exact sampling distribution of $\bar{p}$ is discrete, with the probability for each value of $\bar{p}$ given by the binomial distribution. So hypothesis testing is a bit more complicated for small samples when the normal approximation cannot be used.

TEST STATISTIC FOR HYPOTHESIS TESTS ABOUT A POPULATION PROPORTION

$$z = \frac{\bar{p} - p_0}{\sqrt{\frac{p_0(1 - p_0)}{n}}} \tag{9.4}$$

We can now compute the test statistic for the Pine Creek hypothesis test. Suppose a random sample of 400 players was selected, and that 100 of the players were women. The proportion of women golfers in the sample is

$$\bar{p} = \frac{100}{400} = .25$$

Using equation (9.4), the value of the test statistic is

$$z = \frac{\bar{p} - p_0}{\sqrt{\frac{p_0(1 - p_0)}{n}}} = \frac{.25 - .20}{\sqrt{\frac{.20(1 - .20)}{400}}} = \frac{.05}{.02} = 2.50$$

Because the Pine Creek hypothesis test is an upper tail test, the p-value is the probability that z is greater than or equal to $z = 2.50$; that is, it is the upper tail area corresponding to $z \geq 2.50$. Using the standard normal probability table, we find that the lower tail area for $z = 2.50$ is .9938. Thus, the p-value for the Pine Creek test is $1.0000 - .9938 = .0062$. Figure 9.9 shows this p-value calculation.

Recall that the course manager specified a level of significance of $\alpha = .05$. A p-value $= .0062 < .05$ gives sufficient statistical evidence to reject H_0 at the .05 level of significance. Thus, the test provides statistical support for the conclusion that the special promotion increased the proportion of women players at the Pine Creek golf course.

The decision whether to reject the null hypothesis can also be made using the critical value approach. The critical value corresponding to an area of .05 in the upper tail of a normal probability distribution is $z_{.05} = 1.645$. Thus, the rejection rule using the critical value approach is to reject H_0 if $z \geq 1.645$. Because $z = 2.50 > 1.645$, H_0 is rejected.

Again, we see that the p-value approach and the critical value approach lead to the same hypothesis testing conclusion, but the p-value approach provides more information. With a p-value $= .0062$, the null hypothesis would be rejected for any level of significance greater than or equal to .0062.

FIGURE 9.9 CALCULATION OF THE p-VALUE FOR THE PINE CREEK HYPOTHESIS TEST

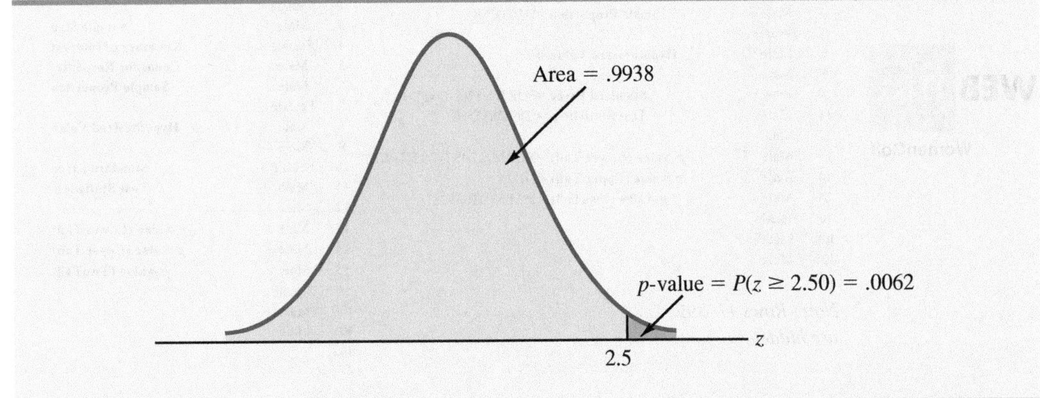

Using Excel

Excel can be used to conduct one-tailed and two-tailed hypothesis tests about a population proportion using the *p*-value approach. The procedure is similar to the approach used with Excel in conducting hypothesis tests about a population mean. The primary difference is that the test statistic is based on the sampling distribution of $\bar{x}$ for hypothesis tests about a population mean and on the sampling distribution of $\bar{p}$ for hypothesis tests about a population proportion. Thus, although different formulas are used to compute the test statistic needed to make the hypothesis testing decision, the computations of the critical value and the *p*-value for the tests are identical.

We will illustrate the procedure by showing how Excel can be used to conduct the upper tail hypothesis test for the Pine Creek golf course study. Refer to Figure 9.10 as we describe the tasks involved. The formula worksheet is in the background; the value worksheet is in the foreground.

Enter/Access Data: Open the WEBfile named WomenGolf. A label and the gender of each golfer in the study are entered into cells A1:A401.

Enter Functions and Formulas: The descriptive statistics needed are provided in cells D3, D5, and D6. Because the data are not numeric, Excel's COUNTA function, not the COUNT function, is used in cell D3 to determine the sample size. We entered Female in cell D4 to identify the response for which we wish to compute a proportion. The COUNTIF function is then used in cell D5 to determine the number of responses of the type identified in cell D4. The sample proportion is then computed in cell D6 by dividing the response count by the sample size.

The hypothesized value of the population proportion (.20) is entered into cell D8. The standard error is obtained in cell D10 by entering the formula =SQRT(D8*(1-D8)/D3). The formula =(D6-D8)/D10 entered into cell D11 computes the test statistic z(2.50). To compute the *p*-value for a lower tail test, we enter the formula =NORM.S.DIST(D11,TRUE) into cell D13. The *p*-value for an upper tail test is then computed in cell D14 as 1 minus the *p*-value for the lower tail test. Finally, the *p*-value for a two-tailed test is computed in cell D15 as two times the minimum of the two one-tailed *p*-values. The value worksheet shows that the three *p*-values are as follows: *p*-value (Lower Tail) = 0.9938; *p*-value (Upper Tail) = 0.0062; and *p*-value (Two Tail) = 0.0124.

The development of the worksheet is now complete. For the Pine Creek upper tail hypothesis test, we reject the null hypothesis that the population proportion is .20 or less

FIGURE 9.10 EXCEL WORKSHEET: HYPOTHESIS TEST FOR PINE CREEK GOLF COURSE

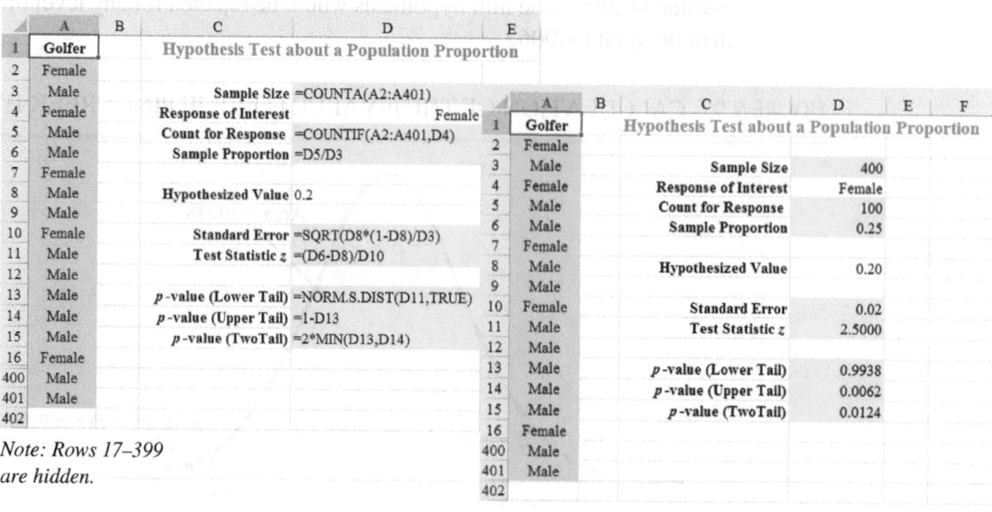

WomenGolf

TABLE 9.4 SUMMARY OF HYPOTHESIS TESTS ABOUT A POPULATION PROPORTION

	Lower Tail Test	Upper Tail Test	Two-Tailed Test
Hypotheses	$H_0: p \geq p_0$ $H_a: p < p_0$	$H_0: p \leq p_0$ $H_a: p > p_0$	$H_0: p = p_0$ $H_a: p \neq p_0$
Test Statistic	$z = \dfrac{\bar{p} - p_0}{\sqrt{\dfrac{p_0(1 - p_0)}{n}}}$	$z = \dfrac{\bar{p} - p_0}{\sqrt{\dfrac{p_0(1 - p_0)}{n}}}$	$z = \dfrac{\bar{p} - p_0}{\sqrt{\dfrac{p_0(1 - p_0)}{n}}}$
Rejection Rule: *p*-Value Approach	Reject H_0 if p-value $\leq \alpha$	Reject H_0 if p-value $\leq \alpha$	Reject H_0 if p-value $\leq \alpha$
Rejection Rule: Critical Value Approach	Reject H_0 if $z \leq -z_\alpha$	Reject H_0 if $z \geq z_\alpha$	Reject H_0 if $z \leq -z_{\alpha/2}$ or if $z \geq z_{\alpha/2}$

because the p-value (Upper Tail) $= 0.0062$ is less than $\alpha = .05$. Indeed, with this p-value we would reject the null hypothesis for any level of significance of .0062 or greater.

A template for other problems The worksheet in Figure 9.10 can be used as a template for hypothesis tests about a population proportion whenever $np \geq 5$ and $n(1 - p) \geq 5$. Just enter the appropriate data in column A, adjust the ranges for the formulas in cells D3 and D5, enter the appropriate response in cell D4, and enter the hypothesized value in cell D8. The standard error, the test statistic, and the three p-values will then appear. Depending on the form of the hypothesis test (lower tail, upper tail, or two-tailed), we can then choose the appropriate p-value to make the rejection decision.

Summary

The procedure used to conduct a hypothesis test about a population proportion is similar to the procedure used to conduct a hypothesis test about a population mean. Although we only illustrated how to conduct a hypothesis test about a population proportion for an upper tail test, similar procedures can be used for lower tail and two-tailed tests. Table 9.4 provides a summary of the hypothesis tests about a population proportion. We assume that $np \geq 5$ and $n(1 - p) \geq 5$; thus the normal probability distribution can be used to approximate the sampling distribution of $\bar{p}$.

Exercises

Methods

35. Consider the following hypothesis test:

$$H_0: p = .20$$
$$H_a: p \neq .20$$

A sample of 400 provided a sample proportion $\bar{p} = .175$.

a. Compute the value of the test statistic.
b. What is the p-value?
c. At $\alpha = .05$, what is your conclusion?
d. What is the rejection rule using the critical value? What is your conclusion?

36. Consider the following hypothesis test:

$$H_0: p \geq .75$$
$$H_a: p < .75$$

A sample of 300 items was selected. Compute the p-value and state your conclusion for each of the following sample results. Use $\alpha = .05$.

a. $\bar{p} = .68$
b. $\bar{p} = .72$
c. $\bar{p} = .70$
d. $\bar{p} = .77$

Applications

37. A study found that, in 2005, 12.5% of U.S. workers belonged to unions (*The Wall Street Journal*, January 21, 2006). Suppose a sample of 400 U.S. workers is collected in 2006 to determine whether union efforts to organize have increased union membership.
    a. Formulate the hypotheses that can be used to determine whether union membership increased in 2006.
    b. If the sample results show that 52 of the workers belonged to unions, what is the p-value for your hypothesis test?
    c. At $\alpha = .05$, what is your conclusion?

38. A study by *Consumer Reports* showed that 64% of supermarket shoppers believe supermarket brands to be as good as national name brands. To investigate whether this result applies to its own product, the manufacturer of a national name-brand ketchup asked a sample of shoppers whether they believed that supermarket ketchup was as good as the national brand ketchup.
    a. Formulate the hypotheses that could be used to determine whether the percentage of supermarket shoppers who believe that the supermarket ketchup was as good as the national brand ketchup differed from 64%.
    b. If a sample of 100 shoppers showed 52 stating that the supermarket brand was as good as the national brand, what is the p-value?
    c. At $\alpha = .05$, what is your conclusion?
    d. Should the national brand ketchup manufacturer be pleased with this conclusion? Explain.

HomeState

39. What percentage of the population live in their state of birth? According to the U.S. Census Bureau's American Community Survey, the figure ranges from 25% in Nevada to 78.7% in Louisiana (*AARP Bulletin*, March 2014). The average percentage across all states and the District of Columbia is 57.7%. The data in the WEBfile Homestate are consistent with the findings in the American Community Survey. The data are for a random sample of 120 Arkansas residents and for a random sample of 180 Virginia residents.
    a. Formulate hypotheses that can be used to determine whether the percentage of stay-at-home residents in the two states differs from the overall average of 57.7%.
    b. Estimate the proportion of stay-at-home residents in Arkansas. Does this proportion differ significantly from the mean proportion for all states? Use $\alpha = .05$.
    c. Estimate the proportion of stay-at-home residents in Virginia. Does this proportion differ significantly from the mean proportion for all states? Use $\alpha = .05$.
    d. Would you expect the proportion of stay-at-home residents to be higher in Virginia than in Arkansas? Support your conclusion with the results obtained in parts (b) and (c).

40. In 2008, 46% of business owners gave a holiday gift to their employees. A 2009 survey of business owners indicated that 35% plan to provide a holiday gift to their employees (Radio WEZV, Myrtle Beach, South Carolina, November 11, 2009). Suppose the survey results are based on a sample of 60 business owners.
    a. How many business owners in the survey plan to provide a holiday gift to their employees?

b. Suppose the business owners in the sample do as they plan. Compute the p-value for a hypothesis test that can be used to determine if the proportion of business owners providing holiday gifts has decreased from the 2008 level.
c. Using a .05 level of significance, would you conclude that the proportion of business owners providing gifts has decreased? What is the smallest level of significance for which you could draw such a conclusion?

41. Ten years ago 53% of American families owned stocks or stock funds. Sample data collected by the Investment Company Institute indicate that the percentage is now 46% (*The Wall Street Journal*, October 5, 2012).
    a. Develop appropriate hypotheses such that rejection of H_0 will support the conclusion that a smaller proportion of American families own stocks or stock funds in 2012 than 10 years ago.
    b. Assume the Investment Company Institute sampled 300 American families to estimate that the percent owning stocks or stock funds was 46% in 2012. What is the p-value for your hypothesis test?
    c. At $\alpha = .01$, what is your conclusion?

42. According to the University of Nevada Center for Logistics Management, 6% of all merchandise sold in the United States gets returned (*BusinessWeek*, January 15, 2007). A Houston department store sampled 80 items sold in January and found that 12 of the items were returned.
    a. Construct a point estimate of the proportion of items returned for the population of sales transactions at the Houston store.
    b. Construct a 95% confidence interval for the porportion of returns at the Houston store.
    c. Is the proportion of returns at the Houston store significantly different from the returns for the nation as a whole? Provide statistical support for your answer.

Eagle

43. Eagle Outfitters is a chain of stores specializing in outdoor apparel and camping gear. It is considering a promotion that involves mailing discount coupons to all its credit card customers. This promotion will be considered a success if more than 10% of those receiving the coupons use them. Before going national with the promotion, coupons were sent to a sample of 100 credit card customers.
    a. Develop hypotheses that can be used to test whether the population proportion of those who will use the coupons is sufficient to go national.
    b. The WEBfile named Eagle contains the sample data. Develop a point estimate of the population proportion.
    c. Use $\alpha = .05$ to conduct your hypothesis test. Should Eagle go national with the promotion?

LawSuit

44. One of the reasons health care costs have been rising rapidly in recent years is the increasing cost of malpractice insurance for physicians. Also, fear of being sued causes doctors to run more precautionary tests (possibly unnecessary) just to make sure they are not guilty of missing something (*Reader's Digest*, October 2012). These precautionary tests also add to health care costs. Data in the WEBfile named LawSuit are consistent with findings in the *Reader's Digest* article and can be used to estimate the proportion of physicians over the age of 55 who have been sued at least once.
    a. Formulate hypotheses that can be used to see if these data can support a finding that more than half of physicians over the age of 55 have been sued at least once.
    b. Use Excel and the WEBfile named LawSuit to compute the sample proportion of physicians over the age of 55 who have been sued at least once. What is the p-value for your hypothesis test?
    c. At $\alpha = .01$, what is your conclusion?

45. The American Association of Individual Investors conducts a weekly survey of its members to measure the percent who are bullish, bearish, and neutral on the stock market for the next six months. For the week ending November 7, 2012, the survey results showed 38.5% bullish, 21.6% neutral, and 39.9% bearish (AAII website, November 12, 2012). Assume these results are based on a sample of 300 AAII members.

a. Over the long term, the proportion of bullish AAII members is .39. Conduct a hypothesis test at the 5% level of significance to see if the current sample results show that bullish sentiment differs from its long term average of .39. What are your findings?
b. Over the long term, the proportion of bearish AAII members is .30. Conduct a hypothesis test at the 1% level of significance to see if the current sample results show that bearish sentiment is above its long term average of .30. What are your findings?
c. Would you feel comfortable extending these results to all investors? Why or why not?

Summary

Hypothesis testing is a statistical procedure that uses sample data to determine whether a statement about the value of a population parameter should or should not be rejected. The hypotheses are two competing statements about a population parameter. One statement is called the null hypothesis (H_0), and the other statement is called the alternative hypothesis (H_a). In Section 9.1 we provided guidelines for developing hypotheses for situations frequently encountered in practice.

Whenever historical data or other information provide a basis for assuming that the population standard deviation is known, the hypothesis testing procedure for the population mean is based on the standard normal distribution. Whenever σ is unknown, the sample standard deviation s is used to estimate σ and the hypothesis testing procedure is based on the t distribution. In both cases, the quality of results depends on both the form of the population distribution and the sample size. If the population has a normal distribution, both hypothesis testing procedures are applicable, even with small sample sizes. If the population is not normally distributed, larger sample sizes are needed. General guidelines about the sample size were provided in Sections 9.3 and 9.4. In the case of hypothesis tests about a population proportion, the hypothesis testing procedure uses a test statistic based on the standard normal distribution.

In all cases, the value of the test statistic can be used to compute a p-value for the test. A p-value is a probability used to determine whether the null hypothesis should be rejected. If the p-value is less than or equal to the level of significance α, the null hypothesis can be rejected.

Hypothesis testing conclusions can also be made by comparing the value of the test statistic to a critical value. For lower tail tests, the null hypothesis is rejected if the value of the test statistic is less than or equal to the critical value. For upper tail tests, the null hypothesis is rejected if the value of the test statistic is greater than or equal to the critical value. Two-tailed tests consist of two critical values: one in the lower tail of the sampling distribution and one in the upper tail. In this case, the null hypothesis is rejected if the value of the test statistic is less than or equal to the critical value in the lower tail or greater than or equal to the critical value in the upper tail.

Glossary

Null hypothesis The hypothesis tentatively assumed true in the hypothesis testing procedure.
Alternative hypothesis The hypothesis concluded to be true if the null hypothesis is rejected.
Type II error The error of accepting H_0 when it is false.
Type I error The error of rejecting H_0 when it is true.
Level of significance The probability of making a Type I error when the null hypothesis is true as an equality.
One-tailed test A hypothesis test in which rejection of the null hypothesis occurs for values of the test statistic in one tail of its sampling distribution.

Test statistic A statistic whose value helps determine whether a null hypothesis should be rejected.

***p*-value** A probability that provides a measure of the evidence against the null hypothesis provided by the sample. Smaller *p*-values indicate more evidence against H_0. For a lower tail test, the *p*-value is the probability of obtaining a value for the test statistic as small as or smaller than that provided by the sample. For an upper tail test, the *p*-value is the probability of obtaining a value for the test statistic as large as or larger than that provided by the sample. For a two-tailed test, the *p*-value is the probability of obtaining a value for the test statistic at least as unlikely as or more unlikely than that provided by the sample.

Critical value A value that is compared with the test statistic to determine whether H_0 should be rejected.

Two-tailed test A hypothesis test in which rejection of the null hypothesis occurs for values of the test statistic in either tail of its sampling distribution.

Key Formulas

Test Statistic for Hypothesis Tests About a Population Mean: σ Known

$$z = \frac{\bar{x} - \mu_0}{\sigma/\sqrt{n}} \tag{9.1}$$

Test Statistic for Hypothesis Tests About a Population Mean: σ Unknown

$$t = \frac{\bar{x} - \mu_0}{s/\sqrt{n}} \tag{9.2}$$

Test Statistic for Hypothesis Tests About a Population Proportion

$$z = \frac{\bar{p} - p_0}{\sqrt{\dfrac{p_0(1 - p_0)}{n}}} \tag{9.4}$$

Supplementary Exercises

46. A production line operates with a mean filling weight of 16 ounces per container. Overfilling or underfilling presents a serious problem and when detected requires the operator to shut down the production line to readjust the filling mechanism. From past data, a population standard deviation $\sigma = .8$ ounces is assumed. A quality control inspector selects a sample of 30 items every hour and at that time makes the decision of whether to shut down the line for readjustment. The level of significance is $\alpha = .05$.
    a. State the hypothesis test for this quality control application.
    b. If a sample mean of $\bar{x} = 16.32$ ounces were found, what is the *p*-value? What action would you recommend?
    c. If a sample mean of $\bar{x} = 15.82$ ounces were found, what is the *p*-value? What action would you recommend?
    d. Use the critical value approach. What is the rejection rule for the preceding hypothesis testing procedure? Repeat parts (b) and (c). Do you reach the same conclusion?
47. At Western University the historical mean of scholarship examination scores for freshman applications is 900. A historical population standard deviation $\sigma = 180$ is assumed

known. Each year, the assistant dean uses a sample of applications to determine whether the mean examination score for the new freshman applications has changed.

a. State the hypotheses.
b. What is the 95% confidence interval estimate of the population mean examination score if a sample of 200 applications provided a sample mean of $\bar{x} = 935$?
c. Use the confidence interval to conduct a hypothesis test. Using $\alpha = .05$, what is your conclusion?
d. What is the p-value?

48. Young children in the United States are exposed to an average of 4 hours of background television per day (CNN website, November 13, 2012). Having the television on in the background while children are doing other activities may have adverse consequences on a child's well-being. You have a research hypothesis that children from low-income families are exposed to more than 4 hours of daily background television. In order to test this hypothesis, you have collected a random sample of 60 children from low-income families and found that these children were exposed to a sample mean of 4.5 hours of daily background television.
    a. Develop hypotheses that can be used to test your research hypothesis.
    b. Based on a previous study, you are willing to assume that the population standard deviation is $\sigma = 0.5$ hours. What is the p-value based on your sample of 60 children from low-income families?
    c. Use $\alpha = .01$ as the level of significance. What is your conclusion?

49. The *Wall Street Journal* reported that bachelor's degree recipients with majors in business received average starting salaries of \$53,900 in 2012 (*The Wall Street Journal*, March 17, 2014). The results for a sample of 100 business majors receiving a bachelor's degree in 2013 showed a mean starting salary of \$55,144 with a sample standard deviation of \$5200. Conduct a hypothesis test to determine whether the mean starting salary for business majors in 2013 is greater than the mean starting salary in 2012. Use $\alpha = .01$ as the level of significance.

FirstBirth

50. Data released by the National Center for Health Statistics showed that the mean age at which women had their first child was 25.0 in 2006 (*The Wall Street Journal*, February 4, 2009). The reporter, Sue Shellenbarger, noted that this was the first decrease in the average age at which women had their first child in several years. A recent sample of 42 women provided the data in the WEBfile named FirstBirth concerning the age at which these women had their first child. Do the data indicate a change from 2006 in the mean age at which women had their first child? Use $\alpha = .05$.

WeeklyPay

51. A recent issue of the *AARP Bulletin* reported that the average weekly pay for a woman with a high school diploma was \$520 (*AARP Bulletin*, January–February 2010). Suppose you would like to determine if the average weekly pay for all working women is significantly greater than that for women with a high school diploma. Data providing the weekly pay for a sample of 50 working women are available in the WEBfile named WeeklyPay. These data are consistent with the findings reported in the article mentioned above.
    a. State the hypotheses that should be used to test whether the mean weekly pay for all women is significantly greater than the mean weekly pay for women with a high school diploma.
    b. Use the data in the WEBfile named WeeklyPay to compute the sample mean, the test statistic, and the p-value.
    c. Use $\alpha = .05$. What is your conclusion?
    d. Repeat the hypothesis test using the critical value approach.

52. The chamber of commerce of a Florida Gulf Coast community advertises that area residential property is available at a mean cost of \$125,000 or less per lot. Suppose a sample of 32 properties provided a sample mean of \$130,000 per lot and a sample standard deviation of \$12,500. Use a .05 level of significance to test the validity of the advertising claim.

53. In Hamilton County, Ohio, the mean number of days needed to sell a house is 86 days (Cincinnati Multiple Listing Service, April, 2012). Data for the sale of 40 houses in a nearby county showed a sample mean of 80 days with a sample standard deviation of 20 days. Conduct a hypothesis test to determine whether the mean number of days until a house is sold is different than the Hamilton County mean of 86 days in the nearby county. Use $\alpha = .05$ for the level of significance, and state your conclusion.

54. On December 25, 2009, an airline passenger was subdued while attempting to blow up a Northwest Airlines flight headed for Detroit, Michigan. The passenger had smuggled explosives hidden in his underwear past a metal detector at an airport screening facility. As a result, the Transportation Security Administration (TSA) proposed installing full-body scanners to replace the metal detectors at the nation's largest airports. This proposal resulted in strong objections from privacy advocates, who considered the scanners an invasion of privacy. On January 5–6, 2010, *USA Today* conducted a poll of 542 adults to learn what proportion of airline travelers approved of using full-body scanners (*USA Today,* January 11, 2010). The poll results showed that 455 of the respondents felt that full-body scanners would improve airline security and 423 indicated that they approved of using the devices.
   a. Conduct a hypothesis test to determine if the results of the poll justify concluding that over 80% of airline travelers feel that the use of full-body scanners will improve airline security. Use $\alpha = .05$.
   b. Suppose the TSA will go forward with the installation and mandatory use of full-body scanners if over 75% of airline travelers approve of using the devices. You have been told to conduct a statistical analysis using the poll results to determine if the TSA should go forward with mandatory use of the full-body scanners. Because this is viewed as a very sensitive decision, use $\alpha = .01$. What is your recommendation? (Author's note: The TSA has begun to use full-body scanners.)

55. A recent article concerning bullish and bearish sentiment about the stock market reported that 41% of investors responding to an American Institute of Individual Investors (AAII) poll were bullish on the market and 26% were bearish (*USA Today,* January 11, 2010). The article also reported that the long-term average measure of bullishness is .39 or 39%. Suppose the AAII poll used a sample size of 450. Using .39 (the long-term average) as the population proportion of investors who are bullish, conduct a hypothesis test to determine if the current proportion of investors who are bullish is significantly greater than the long-term average proportion.
   a. State the appropriate hypotheses for your significance test.
   b. Use the sample results to compute the test statistic and the p-value.
   c. Using $\alpha = .10$, what is your conclusion?

56. Members of the millennial generation are continuing to be dependent on their parents (either living with or otherwise receiving support from parents) into early adulthood (*The Enquirer*, March 16, 2014). A family research organization has claimed that, in past generations, no more than 30% of individuals aged 18 to 32 continued to be dependent on their parents. Suppose that a sample of 400 individuals aged 18 to 32 showed that 136 of them continue to be dependent on their parents.
   a. Develop hypotheses for a test to determine whether the proportion of millennials continuing to be dependent on their parents is higher than for past generations.
   b. What is your point estimate of the proportion of millennials that are continuing to be dependent on their parents?
   c. What is the p-value provided by the sample data?
   d. What is your hypothesis testing conclusion? Use $\alpha = .05$ as the level of significance.

57. The unemployment rate for 18- to 34-year-olds was reported to be 10.8% (*The Cincinnati Enquirer*, November 6, 2012). Assume that this report was based on a random sample of four hundred 18- to 34-year-olds.
   a. A political campaign manager wants to know if the sample results can be used to conclude that the unemployment rate for 18- to 34-years-olds is significantly higher than the unemployment rate for all adults. According to the Bureau of Labor

Statistics, the unemployment rate for all adults was 7.9%. Develop a hypothesis test that can be used to see if the conclusion that the unemployment rate is higher for 18- to 34-year-olds can be supported.

b. Use the sample data collected for the 18- to 34-year-olds to compute the p-value for the hypothesis test in part (a). Using $\alpha = .05$, what is your conclusion?

c. Explain to the campaign manager what can be said about the observed level of significance for the hypothesis testing results using the p-value.

58. A radio station in Myrtle Beach announced that at least 90% of the hotels and motels would be full for the Memorial Day weekend. The station advised listeners to make reservations in advance if they planned to be in the resort over the weekend. On Saturday night a sample of 58 hotels and motels showed 49 with a no-vacancy sign and 9 with vacancies. What is your reaction to the radio station's claim after seeing the sample evidence? Use $\alpha = .05$ in making the statistical test. What is the p-value?

59. In recent years more people have been working past the age of 65. In 2005, 27% of people aged 65–69 worked. A recent report from the Organization for Economic Co-operation and Development (OECD) claimed that the percentage working had increased (*USA Today*, November 16, 2012). The findings reported by the OECD were consistent with taking a sample of 600 people aged 65–69 and finding that 180 of them were working.

a. Develop a point estimate of the proportion of people aged 65–69 who are working.

b. Set up a hypothesis test so that the rejection of H_0 will allow you to conclude that the proportion of people aged 65–69 working has increased from 2005.

c. Conduct your hypothesis test using $\alpha = .05$. What is your conclusion?

Case Problem 1 Quality Associates, Inc.

Quality Associates, Inc., a consulting firm, advises its clients about sampling and statistical procedures that can be used to control their manufacturing processes. In one particular application, a client gave Quality Associates a sample of 800 observations taken during a time in which that client's process was operating satisfactorily. The sample standard deviation for these data was .21; hence, with so much data, the population standard deviation was assumed to be .21. Quality Associates then suggested that random samples of size 30 be taken periodically to monitor the process on an ongoing basis. By analyzing the new samples, the client could quickly learn whether the process was operating satisfactorily. When the process was not operating satisfactorily, corrective action could be taken to eliminate the problem. The design specification indicated the mean for the process should be 12. The hypothesis test suggested by Quality Associates follows.

$$H_0: \mu = 12$$
$$H_a: \mu \neq 12$$

Corrective action will be taken any time H_0 is rejected.

The samples listed in the following table were collected at hourly intervals during the first day of operation of the new statistical process control procedure. These data are available in the WEBfile named Quality.

Managerial Report

1. Conduct a hypothesis test for each sample at the .01 level of significance and determine what action, if any, should be taken. Provide the test statistic and p-value for each test.

Quality

Sample 1	Sample 2	Sample 3	Sample 4
11.55	11.62	11.91	12.02
11.62	11.69	11.36	12.02
11.52	11.59	11.75	12.05
11.75	11.82	11.95	12.18
11.90	11.97	12.14	12.11
11.64	11.71	11.72	12.07
11.64	11.71	11.72	12.07
11.80	11.87	11.61	12.05
12.03	12.10	11.85	11.64
11.94	12.01	12.16	12.39
11.92	11.99	11.91	11.65
12.13	12.20	12.12	12.11
12.09	12.16	11.61	11.90
11.93	12.00	12.21	12.22
12.21	12.28	11.56	11.88
12.32	12.39	11.95	12.03
11.93	12.00	12.01	12.35
11.85	11.92	12.06	12.09
11.76	11.83	11.76	11.77
12.16	12.23	11.82	12.20
11.77	11.84	12.12	11.79
12.00	12.07	11.60	12.30
12.04	12.11	11.95	12.27
11.98	12.05	11.96	12.29
12.30	12.37	12.22	12.47
12.18	12.25	11.75	12.03
11.97	12.04	11.96	12.17
12.17	12.24	11.95	11.94
11.85	11.92	11.89	11.97
12.30	12.37	11.88	12.23
12.15	12.22	11.93	12.25

2. Compute the standard deviation for each of the four samples. Does the assumption of .21 for the population standard deviation appear reasonable?
3. Compute limits for the sample mean $\bar{x}$ around $\mu = 12$ such that, as long as a new sample mean is within those limits, the process will be considered to be operating satisfactorily. If $\bar{x}$ exceeds the upper limit or if $\bar{x}$ is below the lower limit, corrective action will be taken. These limits are referred to as upper and lower control limits for quality control purposes.
4. Discuss the implications of changing the level of significance to a larger value. What mistake or error could increase if the level of significance is increased?

Case Problem 2 Ethical Behavior of Business Students at Bayview University

During the global recession of 2008 and 2009, there were many accusations of unethical behavior by Wall Street executives, financial managers, and other corporate officers. At that time, an article appeared that suggested that part of the reason for such unethical business behavior may stem from the fact that cheating has become more prevalent among business students (*Chronicle of Higher Education*, February 10, 2009). The article reported that 56% of business students admitted to cheating at some time during their academic career as compared to 47% of nonbusiness students.

Cheating has been a concern of the dean of the College of Business at Bayview University for several years. Some faculty members in the college believe that cheating is more widespread at Bayview than at other universities, whereas other faculty members think that cheating is not a major problem in the college. To resolve some of these issues, the dean commissioned a study to assess the current ethical behavior of business students at Bayview. As part of this study, an anonymous exit survey was administered to a sample of 90 business students from this year's graduating class. Responses to the following questions were used to obtain data regarding three types of cheating.

During your time at Bayview, did you ever present work copied off the Internet as your own?

Yes ________ No ________

During your time at Bayview, did you ever copy answers off another student's exam?

Yes ________ No ________

During your time at Bayview, did you ever collaborate with other students on projects that were supposed to be completed individually?

Yes ________ No ________

Any student who answered Yes to one or more of these questions was considered to have been involved in some type of cheating. A portion of the data collected follows. The complete data set is in the WEBfile named Bayview.

Student	Copied from Internet	Copied on Exam	Collaborated on Individual Project	Gender
1	No	No	No	Female
2	No	No	No	Male
3	Yes	No	Yes	Male
4	Yes	Yes	No	Male
5	No	No	Yes	Male
6	Yes	No	No	Female
⋮	⋮	⋮	⋮	⋮
88	No	No	No	Male
89	No	Yes	Yes	Male
90	No	No	No	Female

Managerial Report

Prepare a report for the dean of the college that summarizes your assessment of the nature of cheating by business students at Bayview University. Be sure to include the following items in your report.

1. Use descriptive statistics to summarize the data and comment on your findings.
2. Develop 95% confidence intervals for the proportion of all students, the proportion of male students, and the proportion of female students who were involved in some type of cheating.
3. Conduct a hypothesis test to determine if the proportion of business students at Bayview University who were involved in some type of cheating is less than that of business students at other institutions as reported by the *Chronicle of Higher Education.*

4. Conduct a hypothesis test to determine if the proportion of business students at Bayview University who were involved in some form of cheating is less than that of nonbusiness students at other institutions as reported by the *Chronicle of Higher Education.*
5. What advice would you give to the dean based upon your analysis of the data?

CHAPTER 10

Comparisons Involving Means, Experimental Design, and Analysis of Variance

CONTENTS

STATISTICS IN PRACTICE: U.S. FOOD AND DRUG ADMINISTRATION

10.1 INFERENCES ABOUT THE DIFFERENCE BETWEEN TWO POPULATION MEANS: σ_1 AND σ_2 KNOWN
Interval Estimation of $\mu_1 - \mu_2$
Using Excel to Construct a Confidence Interval
Hypothesis Tests About $\mu_1 - \mu_2$
Using Excel to Conduct a Hypothesis Test
Practical Advice

10.2 INFERENCES ABOUT THE DIFFERENCE BETWEEN TWO POPULATION MEANS: σ_1 AND σ_2 UNKNOWN
Interval Estimation of $\mu_1 - \mu_2$
Using Excel to Construct a Confidence Interval
Hypothesis Tests About $\mu_1 - \mu_2$
Using Excel to Conduct a Hypothesis Test
Practical Advice

10.3 INFERENCES ABOUT THE DIFFERENCE BETWEEN TWO POPULATION MEANS: MATCHED SAMPLES
Using Excel to Conduct a Hypothesis Test

10.4 AN INTRODUCTION TO EXPERIMENTAL DESIGN AND ANALYSIS OF VARIANCE
Data Collection
Assumptions for Analysis of Variance
Analysis of Variance: A Conceptual Overview

10.5 ANALYSIS OF VARIANCE AND THE COMPLETELY RANDOMIZED DESIGN
Between-Treatments Estimate of Population Variance
Within-Treatments Estimate of Population Variance
Comparing the Variance Estimates: The *F* Test
ANOVA Table
Computer Results for Analysis of Variance
Testing for the Equality of *k* Population Means: An Observational Study

STATISTICS *in* PRACTICE

U.S. FOOD AND DRUG ADMINISTRATION
WASHINGTON, D.C.

It is the responsibility of the U.S. Food and Drug Administration (FDA), through its Center for Drug Evaluation and Research (CDER), to ensure that drugs are safe and effective. But CDER does not do the actual testing of new drugs itself. It is the responsibility of the company seeking to market a new drug to test it and submit evidence that it is safe and effective. CDER statisticians and scientists then review the evidence submitted.

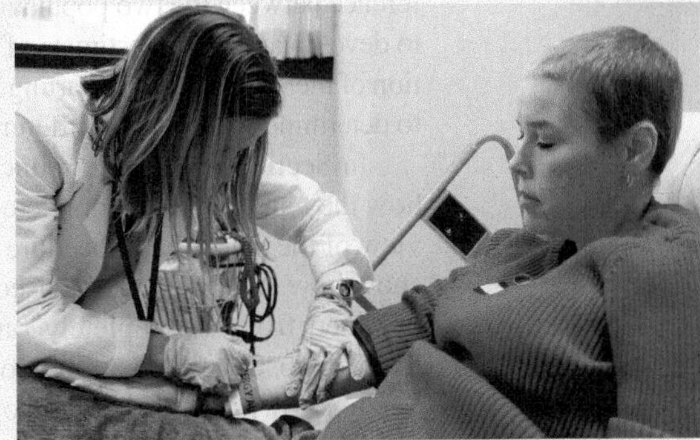

Statistical methods are used to test and develop new drugs. © John Kuntz/The Plain Dealer/Landov.

Companies seeking approval of a new drug conduct extensive statistical studies to support their application. The testing process in the pharmaceutical industry usually consists of three stages: (1) preclinical testing, (2) testing for long-term usage and safety, and (3) clinical efficacy testing. At each successive stage, the chance that a drug will pass the rigorous tests decreases; however, the cost of further testing increases dramatically. Industry surveys indicate that on average the research and development for one new drug costs $250 million and takes 12 years. Hence, it is important to eliminate unsuccessful new drugs in the early stages of the testing process, as well as to identify promising ones for further testing.

Statistics plays a major role in pharmaceutical research, where government regulations are stringent and rigorously enforced. In preclinical testing, a two- or three-population statistical study typically is used to determine whether a new drug should continue to be studied in the long-term usage and safety program. The populations may consist of the new drug, a control, and a standard drug. The preclinical testing process begins when a new drug is sent to the pharmacology group for evaluation of efficacy—the capacity of the drug to produce the desired effects. As part of the process, a statistician is asked to design an experiment that can be used to test the new drug. The design must specify the sample size and the statistical methods of analysis. In a two-population study, one sample is used to obtain data on the efficacy of the new drug (population 1) and a second sample is used to obtain data on the efficacy of a standard drug (population 2). Depending on the intended use, the new and standard drugs are tested in such disciplines as neurology, cardiology, and immunology. In most studies, the statistical method involves hypothesis testing for the difference between the means of the new drug population and the standard drug population. If a new drug lacks efficacy or produces undesirable effects in comparison with the standard drug, the new drug is rejected and withdrawn from further testing. Only new drugs that show promising comparisons with the standard drugs are forwarded to the long-term usage and safety testing program.

Further data collection and multipopulation studies are conducted in the long-term usage and safety testing program and in the clinical testing programs. The FDA requires that statistical methods be defined prior to such testing to avoid data-related biases. In addition, to avoid human biases, some of the clinical trials are double or triple blind. That is, neither the subject nor the investigator knows what drug is administered to whom. If the new drug meets all requirements in relation to the standard drug, a new drug application (NDA) is filed with the FDA. The application is rigorously scrutinized by statisticians and scientists at the agency.

In this chapter you will learn how to construct interval estimates and make hypothesis tests about means with two or more populations. Techniques will be presented for analyzing independent random samples as well as matched samples.

In Chapters 8 and 9 we showed how to develop interval estimates and conduct hypothesis tests for situations involving a single population mean and a single population proportion. In Sections 10.1–10.3 we continue our discussion of statistical inference by showing how interval estimates and hypothesis tests can be developed for situations involving two populations, when the difference between the two population means is of prime importance. For example, we may want to develop an interval estimate of the difference between the mean starting salary for a population of men and the mean starting salary for a population of women or conduct a hypothesis test to determine whether any difference is present between the two population means.

In Section 10.4 we introduce the basic principles of an experimental study and show how they are used in a completely randomized design. We also provide a conceptual overview of the statistical procedure called analysis of variance (ANOVA). In Section 10.5 we show how ANOVA can be used to test for the equality of k population means using data obtained from a completely randomized experimental design as well as data obtained from an observational study. So, in this sense, ANOVA extends the statistical material in Sections 10.1–10.3 from two population means to three or more population means.

We begin our discussion of statistical inference about two populations by showing how to develop interval estimates and conduct hypothesis tests about the difference between the means of two populations when the standard deviations of the two populations are assumed known.

10.1 Inferences About the Difference Between Two Population Means: σ_1 and σ_2 Known

Letting μ_1 denote the mean of population 1 and μ_2 denote the mean of population 2, we will focus on inferences about the difference between the means: $\mu_1 - \mu_2$. To make an inference about this difference, we select a random sample of n_1 units from population 1 and a second random sample of n_2 units from population 2. The two samples, taken separately and independently, are referred to as **independent random samples**. In this section, we assume that information is available such that the two population standard deviations, σ_1 and σ_2, can be assumed known prior to collecting the samples. We refer to this situation as the σ_1 and σ_2 known case. In the following example we show how to compute a margin of error and develop an interval estimate of the difference between the two population means when σ_1 and σ_2 are known.

Interval Estimation of $\mu_1 - \mu_2$

HomeStyle sells furniture at two stores in Buffalo, New York: One is in the inner city and the other is in a suburban shopping center. The regional manager noticed that products that sell well in one store do not always sell well in the other. The manager believes this situation may be attributable to differences in customer demographics at the two locations. Customers may differ in age, education, income, and so on. Suppose the manager asks us to investigate the difference between the mean ages of the customers who shop at the two stores.

Let us define population 1 as all customers who shop at the inner-city store and population 2 as all customers who shop at the suburban store.

μ_1 = mean of population 1 (i.e., the mean age of all customers who shop at the inner-city store)

μ_2 = mean of population 2 (i.e., the mean age of all customers who shop at the suburban store)

The difference between the two population means is $\mu_1 - \mu_2$.

To estimate $\mu_1 - \mu_2$, we will select a random sample of n_1 customers from population 1 and a random sample of n_2 customers from population 2. We then compute the two sample means.

$\bar{x}_1$ = sample mean age for the random sample of n_1 inner-city customers
$\bar{x}_2$ = sample mean age for the random sample of n_2 suburban customers

The point estimator of the difference between the two population means is the difference between the two sample means.

POINT ESTIMATOR OF THE DIFFERENCE BETWEEN TWO POPULATION MEANS

$$\bar{x}_1 - \bar{x}_2 \qquad (10.1)$$

Figure 10.1 provides an overview of the process used to estimate the difference between two population means based on two independent random samples.

The standard error of $\bar{x}_1 - \bar{x}_2$ is the standard deviation of the sampling distribution of $\bar{x}_1 - \bar{x}_2$.

As with other point estimators, the point estimator $\bar{x}_1 - \bar{x}_2$ has a standard error that describes the variation in the sampling distribution of the estimator. With two independent random samples, the standard error of $\bar{x}_1 - \bar{x}_2$ is as follows.

STANDARD ERROR OF $\bar{x}_1 - \bar{x}_2$

$$\sigma_{\bar{x}_1 - \bar{x}_2} = \sqrt{\frac{\sigma_1^2}{n_1} + \frac{\sigma_2^2}{n_2}} \qquad (10.2)$$

If both populations have a normal distribution, or if the sample sizes are large enough that the central limit theorem enables us to conclude that the sampling distributions of $\bar{x}_1$ and $\bar{x}_2$ can be approximated by a normal distribution, the sampling distribution of $\bar{x}_1 - \bar{x}_2$ will have a normal distribution with mean given by $\mu_1 - \mu_2$.

FIGURE 10.1 ESTIMATING THE DIFFERENCE BETWEEN TWO POPULATION MEANS

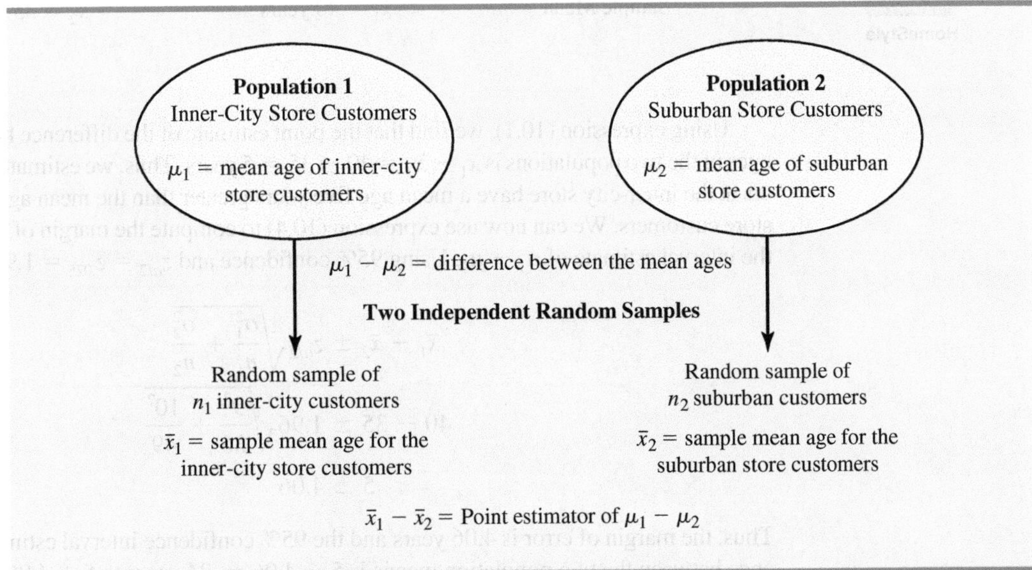

As we showed in Chapter 8, an interval estimate is given by a point estimate ± a margin of error. In the case of estimation of the difference between two population means, an interval estimate will take the following form:

$$\bar{x}_1 - \bar{x}_2 \pm \text{Margin of error}$$

With the sampling distribution of $\bar{x}_1 - \bar{x}_2$ having a normal distribution, we can write the margin of error as follows:

The margin of error is given by multiplying the standard error by $z_{\alpha/2}$.

$$\text{Margin of error} = z_{\alpha/2}\sigma_{\bar{x}_1-\bar{x}_2} = z_{\alpha/2}\sqrt{\frac{\sigma_1^2}{n_1}+\frac{\sigma_2^2}{n_2}} \quad (10.3)$$

Thus the interval estimate of the difference between two population means is as follows.

INTERVAL ESTIMATE OF THE DIFFERENCE BETWEEN TWO POPULATION MEANS: σ_1 AND σ_2 KNOWN

$$\bar{x}_1 - \bar{x}_2 \pm z_{\alpha/2}\sqrt{\frac{\sigma_1^2}{n_1}+\frac{\sigma_2^2}{n_2}} \quad (10.4)$$

where $1 - \alpha$ is the confidence coefficient.

Let us return to the HomeStyle example. Based on data from previous customer demographic studies, the two population standard deviations are known with $\sigma_1 = 9$ years and $\sigma_2 = 10$ years. The data collected from the two independent random samples of HomeStyle customers provided the following results.

HomeStyle

	Inner-City Store	Suburban Store
Sample Size	$n_1 = 36$	$n_2 = 49$
Sample Mean	$\bar{x}_1 = 40$ years	$\bar{x}_2 = 35$ years

Using expression (10.1), we find that the point estimate of the difference between the mean ages of the two populations is $\bar{x}_1 - \bar{x}_2 = 40 - 35 = 5$ years. Thus, we estimate that the customers at the inner-city store have a mean age five years greater than the mean age of the suburban store customers. We can now use expression (10.4) to compute the margin of error and provide the interval estimate of $\mu_1 - \mu_2$. Using 95% confidence and $z_{\alpha/2} = z_{.025} = 1.96$, we have

$$\bar{x}_1 - \bar{x}_2 \pm z_{\alpha/2}\sqrt{\frac{\sigma_1^2}{n_1}+\frac{\sigma_2^2}{n_2}}$$

$$40 - 35 \pm 1.96\sqrt{\frac{9^2}{36}+\frac{10^2}{49}}$$

$$5 \pm 4.06$$

Thus, the margin of error is 4.06 years and the 95% confidence interval estimate of the difference between the two population means is $5 - 4.06 = .94$ years to $5 + 4.06 = 9.06$ years.

Using Excel to Construct a Confidence Interval

Excel's data analysis tools do not provide a procedure for developing interval estimates involving two population means. However, we can develop an Excel worksheet that can be used as a template to construct interval estimates. We will illustrate by constructing an interval estimate of the difference between the population means in the HomeStyle Furniture Stores study. Refer to Figure 10.2 as we describe the tasks involved. The formula worksheet is in the background; the value worksheet is in the foreground.

Enter/Access Data: Open the WEBfile named HomeStyle. Column A contains the age data and a label for the random sample of 36 inner-city customers, and column B contains the age data and a label for the random sample of 49 suburban customers.

Enter Functions and Formulas: The descriptive statistics needed are provided in cells E5:F6. The known population standard deviations are entered into cells E8 and F8. Using the two population standard deviations and the sample sizes, the standard error of the point estimator $\bar{x}_1 - \bar{x}_2$, is computed using equation (10.2) by entering the following formula into cell E9:

$$=\text{SQRT(E8\^{}2/E5+F8\^{}2/F5)}$$

Cells E11:E14 are used to compute the appropriate z value and the margin of error. The confidence coefficient is entered into cell E11 (.95) and the corresponding level of significance ($\alpha = 1 -$ confidence coefficient) is computed in cell E12. In cell E13, we used the NORM.S.INV function to compute the z value needed for the interval estimate. The margin of error is computed in cell E14 by multiplying the z value by the standard error.

In cell E16 the difference in the sample means is used to compute the point estimate of the difference in the two population means. The lower limit of the confidence interval is computed in cell E17 (.94) and the upper limit is computed in cell E18 (9.06); thus, the 95% confidence interval estimate of the difference in the two population means is .94 to 9.06.

FIGURE 10.2 EXCEL WORKSHEET: CONSTRUCTING A 95% CONFIDENCE INTERVAL FOR HOMESTYLE FURNITURE STORES

	A	B	C	D	E	F	G	H
1	Inner City	Suburban		Interval Estimate of Difference in Population Means:				
2	38	29		σ_1 and σ_2 Known Case				
3	46	35						
4	32	39			Inner City	Suburban		
5	23	10		Sample Size	=COUNT(A2:A37)	=COUNT(B2:B50)		
6	39	37		Sample Mean	=AVERAGE(A2:A37)	=AVERAGE(B2:B50)		
7	40	52						
8	35	40		Population Standard Deviation	9	10		
9	35	37		Standard Error	=SQRT(E8^2/E5+F8^2/F5			
10	36	43						
11	41	38		Confidence Coefficient	0.95			
12	32	28		Level of Significance	=1-E11			
13	38	37		z Value	=NORM.S.INV(1-E12/2)			
14	44	51		Margin of Error	=E13*E9			
15	50	23						
16	47	25		Point Estimate of Difference	=E6-F6			
17	59	37		Lower Limit	=E16-E14			
18	38	38		Upper Limit	=E16+E14			
36	44	19						
37	62	40						
49		22						
50		47						
51								

	A	B	C	D	E	F	G	H
1	Inner City	Suburban		Interval Estimate of Difference in Population Means:				
2	38	29		σ_1 and σ_2 Known Case				
3	46	35						
4	32	39			Inner City	Suburban		
5	23	10		Sample Size	36	49		
6	39	37		Sample Mean	40	35		
7	40	52						
8	35	40		Population Standard Deviation	9	10		
9	35	37		Standard Error	2.07			
10	36	43						
11	41	38		Confidence Coefficient	0.95			
12	32	28		Level of Significance	0.05			
13	38	37		z Value	1.960			
14	44	51		Margin of Error	4.06			
15	50	23						
16	47	25		Point Estimate of Difference	5			
17	59	37		Lower Limit	0.94			
18	38	38		Upper Limit	9.06			
36	44	19						
37	62	40						
49		22						
50		47						
51								

Note: Rows 19–35 and 38–48 are hidden.

A template for other problems This worksheet can be used as a template for developing interval estimates of the difference in population means when the population standard deviations are assumed known. For another problem of this type, we must first enter the new problem data in columns A and B. The data ranges in cells E5:F6 must be modified in order to compute the sample means and sample sizes for the new data. Also, the assumed known population standard deviations must be entered into cells E8 and F8. After doing so, the point estimate and a 95% confidence interval will be displayed in cells E16:E18. If a confidence interval with a different confidence coefficient is desired, we simply change the value in cell E11.

We can further simplify the use of Figure 10.2 as a template for other problems by eliminating the need to enter new data ranges in cells E5:F6. We rewrite the cell formulas as follows:

Cell E5: =COUNT(A:A)
Cell F5: =COUNT(B:B)
Cell E6: =AVERAGE(A:A)
Cell F6: =AVERAGE(B:B)

The WEBfile named HomeStyle includes a worksheet entitled Template that uses the A:A and B:B methods for entering the data ranges.

Using the A:A method of specifying data ranges in cells E5 and E6, Excel's COUNT function will count the number of numerical values in column A and Excel's AVERAGE function will compute the average of the numerical values in column A. Similarly, using the B:B method of specifying data ranges in cells F5 and F6, Excel's COUNT function will count the number of numerical values in column B and Excel's AVERAGE function will compute the average of the numerical values in column B. Thus, to solve a new problem it is only necessary to enter the new data into columns A and B and enter the known population standard deviations in cells E8 and F8.

This worksheet can also be used as a template for text exercises in which the sample sizes, sample means, and population standard deviations are given. In this type of situation, no change in the data is necessary. We simply replace the values in cells E5:F6 and E8:F8 with the given values of the sample sizes, sample means, and population standard deviations. If something other than a 95% confidence interval is desired, the confidence coefficient in cell E11 must also be changed.

Hypothesis Tests About $\mu_1 - \mu_2$

Let us consider hypothesis tests about the difference between two population means. Using D_0 to denote the hypothesized difference between μ_1 and μ_2, the three forms for a hypothesis test are as follows:

$$H_0: \mu_1 - \mu_2 \geq D_0 \qquad H_0: \mu_1 - \mu_2 \leq D_0 \qquad H_0: \mu_1 - \mu_2 = D_0$$
$$H_a: \mu_1 - \mu_2 < D_0 \qquad H_a: \mu_1 - \mu_2 > D_0 \qquad H_a: \mu_1 - \mu_2 \neq D_0$$

In many applications, $D_0 = 0$. Using the two-tailed test as an example, when $D_0 = 0$ the null hypothesis is H_0: $\mu_1 - \mu_2 = 0$. In this case, the null hypothesis is that μ_1 and μ_2 are equal. Rejection of H_0 leads to the conclusion that H_a: $\mu_1 - \mu_2 \neq 0$ is true; that is, μ_1 and μ_2 are not equal.

The steps for conducting hypothesis tests presented in Chapter 9 are applicable here. We must choose a level of significance, compute the value of the test statistic, and find the p-value to determine whether the null hypothesis should be rejected. With two independent random samples, we showed that the point estimator $\bar{x}_1 - \bar{x}_2$ has a standard error $\sigma_{\bar{x}_1 - \bar{x}_2}$ given by expression (10.2) and, when the sample sizes are large enough, the distribution of $\bar{x}_1 - \bar{x}_2$ can be described by a normal distribution. In this case, the test statistic for the difference between two population means when σ_1 and σ_2 are known is as follows.

TEST STATISTIC FOR HYPOTHESIS TESTS ABOUT $\mu_1 - \mu_2$: σ_1 AND σ_2 KNOWN

$$z = \frac{(\bar{x}_1 - \bar{x}_2) - D_0}{\sqrt{\frac{\sigma_1^2}{n_1} + \frac{\sigma_2^2}{n_2}}} \tag{10.5}$$

Let us demonstrate the use of this test statistic in the following hypothesis testing example.

As part of a study to evaluate differences in education quality between two training centers, a standardized examination is given to individuals who are trained at the centers. The difference between the mean examination scores is used to assess quality differences between the centers. The population means for the two centers are as follows.

μ_1 = the mean examination score for the population of individuals trained at center A

μ_2 = the mean examination score for the population of individuals trained at center B

We begin with the tentative assumption that no difference exists between the training quality provided at the two centers. Hence, in terms of the mean examination scores, the null hypothesis is that $\mu_1 - \mu_2 = 0$. If sample evidence leads to the rejection of this hypothesis, we will conclude that the mean examination scores differ for the two populations. This conclusion indicates a quality differential between the two centers and suggests that a follow-up study investigating the reason for the differential may be warranted. The null and alternative hypotheses for this two-tailed test are written as follows.

$$H_0: \mu_1 - \mu_2 = 0$$
$$H_a: \mu_1 - \mu_2 \neq 0$$

The standardized examination given previously in a variety of settings always resulted in an examination score standard deviation near 10 points. Thus, we will use this information to assume that the population standard deviations are known with $\sigma_1 = 10$ and $\sigma_2 = 10$. An $\alpha = .05$ level of significance is specified for the study.

ExamScores

Independent random samples of $n_1 = 30$ individuals from training center A and $n_2 = 40$ individuals from training center B are taken. The respective sample means are $\bar{x}_1 = 82$ and $\bar{x}_2 = 78$. Do these data suggest a significant difference between the population means at the two training centers? To help answer this question, we compute the test statistic using equation (10.5).

$$z = \frac{(\bar{x}_1 - \bar{x}_2) - D_0}{\sqrt{\frac{\sigma_1^2}{n_1} + \frac{\sigma_2^2}{n_2}}} = \frac{(82 - 78) - 0}{\sqrt{\frac{10^2}{30} + \frac{10^2}{40}}} = 1.66$$

Next let us compute the p-value for this two-tailed test. Because the test statistic z is in the upper tail, we first compute the upper tail area corresponding to $z = 1.66$. Using the standard normal distribution table, the area to the left of $z = 1.66$ is .9515. Thus, the area in the upper tail of the distribution is $1.0000 - .9515 = .0485$. Because this test is a two-tailed test, we must double the tail area: p-value $= 2(.0485) = .0970$. Following the usual rule to reject H_0 if p-value $\leq \alpha$, we see that the p-value of .0970 does not allow us to reject H_0 at the .05 level of significance. The sample results do not provide sufficient evidence to conclude that the training centers differ in quality.

In this chapter we will use the p-value approach to hypothesis testing as described in Chapter 9. However, if you prefer, the test statistic and the critical value rejection rule may be used. With $\alpha = .05$ and $z_{\alpha/2} = z_{.025} = 1.96$, the rejection rule employing the critical value approach would be reject H_0 if $z \leq -1.96$ or if $z \geq 1.96$. With $z = 1.66$, we reach the same do not reject H_0 conclusion.

In the preceding example, we demonstrated a two-tailed hypothesis test about the difference between two population means. Lower tail and upper tail tests can also be considered. These tests use the same test statistic as given in equation (10.5). The procedure for computing the p-value and the rejection rules for these one-tailed tests are the same as those presented in Chapter 9.

Using Excel to Conduct a Hypothesis Test

The Excel tool used to conduct the hypothesis test to determine whether there is a significant difference in population means when σ_1 and σ_2 are assumed known is called *z-Test: Two Sample for Means.* We illustrate using the sample data for exam scores at center A and at center B. With an assumed known standard deviation of 10 points at each center, the known variance of exam scores for each of the two populations is equal to $10^2 = 100$. Refer to the Excel worksheets shown in Figure 10.3 and Figure 10.4 as we describe the tasks involved.

Enter/Access Data: Open the WEBfile named ExamScores. Column A in Figure 10.3 contains the examination score data and a label for the random sample of 30 individuals trained at center A, and column B contains the examination score data and a label for the random sample of 40 individuals trained at center B.

Apply Tools: The following steps will provide the information needed to conduct the hypothesis test to see whether there is a significant difference in test scores at the two centers.

FIGURE 10.3 DIALOG BOX FOR EXCEL'S z-TEST: TWO SAMPLE FOR MEANS TOOL

Note: Rows 18–28 and 33–39 are hidden.

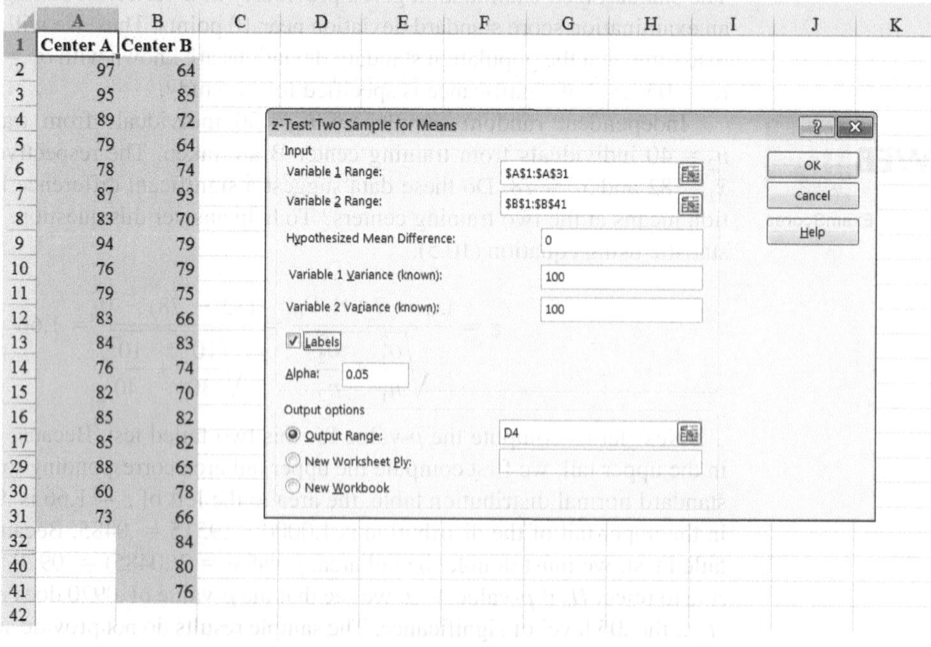

FIGURE 10.4 EXCEL RESULTS FOR THE HYPOTHESIS TEST ABOUT EQUALITY OF EXAM SCORES AT TWO TRAINING CENTERS

	A	B	C	D	E	F	G
1	Center A	Center B					
2	97	64					
3	95	85					
4	89	72		z-Test: Two Sample for Means			
5	79	64					
6	78	74			*Center A*	*Center B*	
7	87	93		Mean	82	78	
8	83	70		Known Variance	100	100	
9	94	79		Observations	30	40	
10	76	79		Hypothesized Mean Difference	0		
11	79	75		z	1.6562		
12	83	66		P(Z<=z) one-tail	0.0488		
13	84	83		z Critical one-tail	1.6449		
14	76	74		P(Z<=z) two-tail	0.0977		
15	82	70		z Critical two-tail	1.9600		
16	85	82					
17	85	82					
29	88	65					
30	60	78					
31	73	66					
32		84					
40		80					
41		76					
42							

Note: Rows 18–28 and 33–39 are hidden.

Step 1. Click the **Data** tab on the Ribbon
Step 2. In the **Analysis** group, click **Data Analysis**
Step 3. Choose **z-Test: Two Sample for Means** from the list of Analysis Tools
Step 4. When the z-Test: Two Sample for Means dialog box appears (Figure 10.3):
Enter A1:A31 in the **Variable 1 Range** box
Enter B1:B41 in the **Variable 2 Range** box
Enter 0 in the **Hypothesized Mean Difference** box
Enter 100 in the **Variable 1 Variance (known)** box
Enter 100 in the **Variable 2 Variance (known)** box
Select **Labels**
Enter .05 in the **Alpha** box
Select **Output Range** and enter D4 in the box
Click **OK**

The value of the test statistic shown here (1.6562) and the p-value (.0977) differ slightly from those shown previously, because we rounded the test statistic to two places (1.66) in the text.

The results are shown in Figure 10.4. Descriptive statistics for the two samples are shown in cells E7:F9. The value of the test statistic, 1.6562, is shown in cell E11. The *p*-value for the test, labeled P(Z<=z) two-tail, is shown in cell E14. Because the *p*-value, .0977, is greater than the level of significance, $\alpha = .05$, we cannot conclude that the means for the two populations are different.

The z-Test: Two Sample for Means tool can also be used to conduct one-tailed hypothesis tests. The only change required to make the hypothesis testing decision is that we need to use the *p*-value for a one-tailed test, labeled P(Z<=z) one-tail (see cell E12).

Practical Advice

In most applications of the interval estimation and hypothesis testing procedures presented in this section, random samples with $n_1 \geq 30$ and $n_2 \geq 30$ are adequate. In cases where either or both sample sizes are less than 30, the distributions of the populations become important considerations. In general, with smaller sample sizes, it is more important for the analyst to be satisfied that it is reasonable to assume that the distributions of the two populations are at least approximately normal.

Exercises

Methods

1. The following results come from two independent random samples taken of two populations.

Sample 1	Sample 2
$n_1 = 50$	$n_2 = 35$
$\bar{x}_1 = 13.6$	$\bar{x}_2 = 11.6$
$\sigma_1 = 2.2$	$\sigma_2 = 3.0$

   a. What is the point estimate of the difference between the two population means?
   b. Provide a 90% confidence interval for the difference between the two population means.
   c. Provide a 95% confidence interval for the difference between the two population means.

SELF test

2. Consider the following hypothesis test.

$$H_0: \mu_1 - \mu_2 \leq 0$$
$$H_a: \mu_1 - \mu_2 > 0$$

The following results are for two independent samples taken from the two populations.

Sample 1	Sample 2
$n_1 = 40$	$n_2 = 50$
$\bar{x}_1 = 25.2$	$\bar{x}_2 = 22.8$
$\sigma_1 = 5.2$	$\sigma_2 = 6.0$

   a. What is the value of the test statistic?
   b. What is the p-value?
   c. With $\alpha = .05$, what is your hypothesis testing conclusion?

3. Consider the following hypothesis test.

$$H_0: \mu_1 - \mu_2 = 0$$
$$H_a: \mu_1 - \mu_2 \neq 0$$

The following results are for two independent samples taken from the two populations.

Sample 1	Sample 2
$n_1 = 80$	$n_2 = 70$
$\bar{x}_1 = 104$	$\bar{x}_2 = 106$
$\sigma_1 = 8.4$	$\sigma_2 = 7.6$

a. What is the value of the test statistic?
b. What is the p-value?
c. With $\alpha = .05$, what is your hypothesis testing conclusion?

Applications

4. *Condé Nast Traveler* conducts an annual survey in which readers rate their favorite cruise ship. All ships are rated on a 100-point scale, with higher values indicating better service. A sample of 37 ships that carry fewer than 500 passengers resulted in an average rating of 85.36, and a sample of 44 ships that carry 500 or more passengers provided an average rating of 81.40 (*Condé Nast Traveler,* February 2008). Assume that the population standard deviation is 4.55 for ships that carry fewer than 500 passengers and 3.97 for ships that carry 500 or more passengers.
   a. What is the point estimate of the difference between the population mean rating for ships that carry fewer than 500 passengers and the population mean rating for ships that carry 500 or more passengers?
   b. At 95% confidence, what is the margin of error?
   c. What is a 95% confidence interval estimate of the difference between the population mean ratings for the two sizes of ships?
5. The average expenditure on Valentine's Day was expected to be \$100.89 (*USA Today,* February 13, 2006). Do male and female consumers differ in the amounts they spend? The average expenditure in a sample survey of 40 male consumers was \$135.67, and the average expenditure in a sample survey of 30 female consumers was \$68.64. Based on past surveys, the standard deviation for male consumers is assumed to be \$35, and the standard deviation for female consumers is assumed to be \$20.
   a. What is the point estimate of the difference between the population mean expenditure for males and the population mean expenditure for females?
   b. At 99% confidence, what is the margin of error?
   c. Develop a 99% confidence interval for the difference between the two population means.

Hotel

6. Suppose that you are responsible for making arrangements for a business convention. Because of budget cuts due to the recent recession, you have been charged with choosing a city for the convention that has the least expensive hotel rooms. You have narrowed your choices to Atlanta and Houston. The WEBfile named Hotel contains samples of prices for rooms in Atlanta and Houston that are consistent with the results reported by Smith Travel Research (*SmartMoney,* March 2009). Because considerable historical data on the prices of rooms in both cities are available, the population standard deviations for the prices can be assumed to be \$20 in Atlanta and \$25 in Houston. Based on the sample data, can you conclude that the mean price of a hotel room in Atlanta is lower than one in Houston?
7. *Consumer Reports* uses a survey of readers to obtain customer satisfaction ratings for the nation's largest retailers (*Consumer Reports,* March 2012). Each survey respondent is asked to rate a specified retailer in terms of six factors: quality of products, selection, value, checkout efficiency, service, and store layout. An overall satisfaction score summarizes the rating for each respondent with 100 meaning the respondent is completely satisfied in terms of all six factors. Sample data representative of independent samples of Target and Walmart customers are shown below.

Target	Walmart
$n_1 = 25$	$n_2 = 30$
$\bar{x}_1 = 79$	$\bar{x}_2 = 71$

   a. Formulate the null and alternative hypotheses to test whether there is a difference between the population mean customer satisfaction scores for the two retailers.

b. Assume that experience with the *Consumer Reports* satisfaction rating scale indicates that a population standard deviation of 12 is a reasonable assumption for both retailers. Conduct the hypothesis test and report the p-value. At a .05 level of significance what is your conclusion?

c. Which retailer, if either, appears to have the greater customer satisfaction? Provide a 95% confidence interval for the difference between the population mean customer satisfaction scores for the two retailers.

8. Will improving customer service result in higher stock prices for the companies providing the better service? "When a company's satisfaction score has improved over the prior year's results and is above the national average (currently 75.7), studies show its shares have a good chance of outperforming the broad stock market in the long run" (*BusinessWeek,* March 2, 2009). The following satisfaction scores of three companies for the 4th quarters of 2007 and 2008 were obtained from the American Customer Satisfaction Index. Assume that the scores are based on a poll of 60 customers from each company. Because the polling has been done for several years, the standard deviation can be assumed to equal 6 points in each case.

Company	2007 Score	2008 Score
Rite Aid	73	76
Expedia	75	77
JCPenney	77	78

a. For Rite Aid, is the increase in the satisfaction score from 2007 to 2008 statistically significant? Use $\alpha = .05$. What can you conclude?

b. Can you conclude that the 2008 score for Rite Aid is above the national average of 75.7? Use $\alpha = .05$.

c. For Expedia, is the increase from 2007 to 2008 statistically significant? Use $\alpha = .05$.

d. When conducting a hypothesis test with the values given for the standard deviation, sample size, and α, how large must the increase from 2007 to 2008 be for it to be statistically significant?

e. Use the result of part (d) to state whether the increase for JCPenney from 2007 to 2008 is statistically significant.

Inferences About the Difference Between Two Population Means: σ_1 and σ_2 Unknown

In this section we extend the discussion of inferences about the difference between two population means to the case when the two population standard deviations, σ_1 and σ_2, are unknown. In this case, we will use the sample standard deviations, s_1 and s_2, to estimate the unknown population standard deviations. When we use the sample standard deviations, the interval estimation and hypothesis testing procedures will be based on the t distribution rather than the standard normal distribution.

Interval Estimation of $\mu_1 - \mu_2$

In the following example we show how to compute a margin of error and develop an interval estimate of the difference between two population means when σ_1 and σ_2 are unknown. Clearwater National Bank is conducting a study designed to identify differences between checking account practices by customers at two of its branch banks. A random sample of 28 checking accounts is selected from the Cherry Grove Branch and an independent random sample of 22 checking accounts is selected from the Beechmont Branch. The current checking account balance is recorded for each of the checking accounts. A summary of the account balances follows:

CheckAcct

	Cherry Grove	Beechmont
Sample Size	$n_1 = 28$	$n_2 = 22$
Sample Mean	$\bar{x}_1 = \$1025$	$\bar{x}_2 = \$910$
Sample Standard Deviation	$s_1 = \$150$	$s_2 = \$125$

Clearwater National Bank would like to estimate the difference between the mean checking account balance maintained by the population of Cherry Grove customers and the population of Beechmont customers. Let us develop the margin of error and an interval estimate of the difference between these two population means.

In Section 10.1, we provided the following interval estimate for the case when the population standard deviations, σ_1 and σ_2, are known.

$$\bar{x}_1 - \bar{x}_2 \pm z_{\alpha/2}\sqrt{\frac{\sigma_1^2}{n_1} + \frac{\sigma_2^2}{n_2}}$$

When σ_1 and σ_2 are estimated by s_1 and s_2, the t distribution is used to make inferences about the difference between two population means.

With σ_1 and σ_2 unknown, we will use the sample standard deviations s_1 and s_2 to estimate σ_1 and σ_2 and replace $z_{\alpha/2}$ with $t_{\alpha/2}$. As a result, the interval estimate of the difference between two population means is given by the following expression.

INTERVAL ESTIMATE OF THE DIFFERENCE BETWEEN TWO POPULATION MEANS: σ_1 AND σ_2 UNKNOWN

$$\bar{x}_1 - \bar{x}_2 \pm t_{\alpha/2}\sqrt{\frac{s_1^2}{n_1} + \frac{s_2^2}{n_2}} \tag{10.6}$$

where $1 - \alpha$ is the confidence coefficient.

In this expression, the use of the t distribution is an approximation, but it provides excellent results and is relatively easy to use. The only difficulty that we encounter in using expression (10.6) is determining the appropriate degrees of freedom for $t_{\alpha/2}$. Statistical software packages compute the appropriate degrees of freedom automatically. The formula used is as follows.

DEGREES OF FREEDOM: t DISTRIBUTION WITH TWO INDEPENDENT RANDOM SAMPLES

$$df = \frac{\left(\frac{s_1^2}{n_1} + \frac{s_2^2}{n_2}\right)^2}{\frac{1}{n_1 - 1}\left(\frac{s_1^2}{n_1}\right)^2 + \frac{1}{n_2 - 1}\left(\frac{s_2^2}{n_2}\right)^2} \tag{10.7}$$

Let us return to the Clearwater National Bank example and show how to use expression (10.6) to provide a 95% confidence interval estimate of the difference between the population mean checking account balances at the two branch banks. The sample data show $n_1 =$ 28, $\bar{x}_1 = \$1025$, and $s_1 = \$150$ for the Cherry Grove branch, and $n_2 = 22$, $\bar{x}_2 = \$910$, and

$s_2 = \$125$ for the Beechmont branch. The calculation for degrees of freedom for $t_{\alpha/2}$ is as follows:

$$df = \frac{\left(\frac{s_1^2}{n_1} + \frac{s_2^2}{n_2}\right)^2}{\frac{1}{n_1 - 1}\left(\frac{s_1^2}{n_1}\right)^2 + \frac{1}{n_2 - 1}\left(\frac{s_2^2}{n_2}\right)^2} = \frac{\left(\frac{150^2}{28} + \frac{125^2}{22}\right)^2}{\frac{1}{28 - 1}\left(\frac{150^2}{28}\right)^2 + \frac{1}{22 - 1}\left(\frac{125^2}{22}\right)^2} = 47.8$$

We round the noninteger degrees of freedom *down* to 47 to provide a larger t value and a more conservative interval estimate. Using the t distribution table with 47 degrees of freedom, we find $t_{.025} = 2.012$. Using expression (10.6), we develop the 95% confidence interval estimate of the difference between the two population means as follows.

$$\bar{x}_1 - \bar{x}_2 \pm t_{.025}\sqrt{\frac{s_1^2}{n_1} + \frac{s_2^2}{n_2}}$$

$$1025 - 910 \pm 2.012\sqrt{\frac{150^2}{28} + \frac{125^2}{22}}$$

$$115 \pm 78$$

The point estimate of the difference between the population mean checking account balances at the two branches is \$115. The margin of error is \$78, and the 95% confidence interval estimate of the difference between the two population means is 115 − 78 = \$37 to 115 + 78 = \$193.

This suggestion should help if you are using equation (10.7) to calculate the degrees of freedom by hand.

The computation of the degrees of freedom (equation (10.7)) is cumbersome if you are doing the calculation by hand, but it is easily implemented with a computer software package. However, note that the expressions s_1^2/n_1 and s_2^2/n_2 appear in both expression (10.6) and equation (10.7). These values only need to be computed once in order to evaluate both (10.6) and (10.7).

Using Excel to Construct a Confidence Interval

Excel's data analysis tools do not provide a procedure for developing interval estimates involving two population means. However, we can develop an Excel worksheet that can be used as a template to construct interval estimates. We will illustrate by constructing an interval estimate of the difference between the population means in the Clearwater National Bank study. Refer to Figure 10.5 as we describe the tasks involved. The formula worksheet is in the background; the value worksheet is in the foreground.

Enter/Access Data: Open the WEBfile named CheckAcct. Column A contains the account balances and a label for the random sample of 28 customers at the Cherry Grove Branch, and column B contains the account balances and a label for the random sample of 22 customers at the Beechmont Branch.

Enter Functions and Formulas: The descriptive statistics needed are provided in cells E5:F7. Using the two sample standard deviations and the sample sizes, an estimate of the variance of the point estimator $\bar{x}_1 - \bar{x}_2$ is computed by entering the following formula into cell E9:

=E7^2/E5+F7^2/F5

An estimate of the standard error is then computed in cell E10 by taking the square root of the variance.

FIGURE 10.5 EXCEL WORKSHEET: CONSTRUCTING A 95% CONFIDENCE INTERVAL FOR CLEARWATER NATIONAL BANK

	A	B	C	D	E	F	G
1	Cherry Grove	Beechmont		Interval Estimate of Difference in Population Means:			
2	1263	996.7		σ_1 and σ_2 Unknown Case			
3	897	897					
4	849	912			Cherry Grove	Beechmont	
5	891	894.9		Sample Size	=COUNT(A2:A29)	=COUNT(B2:B23)	
6	964	785		Sample Mean	=AVERAGE(A2:A29)	=AVERAGE(B2:B23)	
7	810	750.7		Sample Standard Deviation	=STDEV.S(A2:A29)	=STDEV.S(B2:B23)	
8	877	882.2					
9	899	1110		Estimate of Variance	=E7^2/E5+F7^2/F5		
10	847	907.2		Standard Error	=SQRT(E9)		
11	1070	1226.1					
12	1252	762.1		Confidence Coefficient	0.95		
13	920	835.5		Level of Significance	=1-E12		
14	1256	1048		Degrees of Freedom	=E9^2/((1/(E5-1))*(E7^2/E5)^2+(1/(F5-1)*(F7^2/F5)^2))		
15	1196	773.8		*t* Value	=T.INV.2T(E13,E14)		
16	1150	807		Margin of Error	=E15*E10		
17	1024	972					
18	1016	980		Point Estimate of Difference	=E6-F6		
19	1126	876.6		Lower Limit	=E18-E16		
20	1289	943		Upper Limit	=E18+E16		
21	1220	992.7					
22	912	704.3					
23	1026	962.9					
24	786						
25	989						
26	1133						
27	990						
28	999						
29	1049						
30							

	A	B	C	D	E	F	G
1	Cherry Grove	Beechmont		Interval Estimate of Difference in Population Means:			
2	1263	997		σ_1 and σ_2 Unknown Case			
3	897	897					
4	849	912			Cherry Grove	Beechmont	
5	891	895		Sample Size	28	22	
6	964	785		Sample Mean	1025	910	
7	810	751		Sample Standard Deviation	150	125	
8	877	882					
9	899	1110		Estimate of Variance	1513.8550		
10	847	907		Standard Error	38.9083		
11	1070	1226					
12	1252	762		Confidence Coefficient	0.95		
13	920	836		Level of Significance	0.05		
14	1256	1048		Degrees of Freedom	47.8		
15	1196	774		*t* Value	2.012		
16	1150	807		Margin of Error	78		
17	1024	972					
18	1016	980		Point Estimate of Difference	115		
19	1126	877		Lower Limit	37		
20	1289	943		Upper Limit	193		
21	1220	993					
22	912	704					
23	1026	963					
24	786						
25	989						
26	1133						
27	990						
28	999						
29	1049						
30							

Cells E12:E16 are used to compute the appropriate *t* value and the margin of error. The confidence coefficient is entered into cell E12 (.95) and the corresponding level of significance is computed in cell E13 ($\alpha = .05$). In cell E14, we used formula (10.7) to compute the degrees of freedom (47.8). In cell E15, we used the T.INV.2T function to compute the *t* value needed for the interval estimate. The margin of error is computed in cell E16 by multiplying the *t* value by the standard error.

In cell E18 the difference in the sample means is used to compute the point estimate of the difference in the two population means (115). The lower limit of the confidence interval is computed in cell E19 (37) and the upper limit is computed in cell E20 (193); thus, the 95% confidence interval estimate of the difference in the two population means is 37 to 193.

A template for other problems This worksheet can be used as a template for developing interval estimates of the difference in population means when the population standard deviations are unknown. For another problem of this type, we must first enter the new problem data in columns A and B. The data ranges in cells E5:F7 must be modified in order to compute the sample means, sample sizes, and sample standard deviations for the new data. After doing so, the point estimate and a 95% confidence interval will be displayed in cells E18:E20. If a confidence interval with a different confidence coefficient is desired, we simply change the value in cell E12.

We can further simplify the use of Figure 10.5 as a template for other problems by eliminating the need to enter new data ranges in cells E5:F7. We rewrite the cell formulas as follows:

Cell E5: =COUNT(A:A)
Cell F5: =COUNT(B:B)
Cell E6: =AVERAGE(A:A)
Cell F6: =AVERAGE(B:B)
Cell E7: =STDEV.S(A:A)
Cell F7: =STDEV.S(B:B)

The WEBfile named CheckAcct includes a worksheet entitled Template that uses the A:A and B:B methods for entering the data ranges.

Using the A:A method of specifying data ranges in cells E5:E7, Excel's COUNT function will count the number of numeric values in column A, Excel's AVERAGE function will compute the average of the numeric values in column A, and Excel's STDEV function will compute the standard deviation of the numeric values in column A. Similarly, using the B:B method of specifying data ranges in cells F5:F7, Excel's COUNT function will count the number of numeric values in column B, Excel's AVERAGE function will compute the average of the numeric values in column B, and Excel's STDEV.S function will compute the standard deviation of the numeric values in column B. Thus, to solve a new problem it is only necessary to enter the new data into columns A and B.

This worksheet can also be used as a template for text exercises in which the sample sizes, sample means, and sample standard deviations are given. In this type of situation, no change in the data is necessary. We simply replace the values in cells E5:F7 with the given values of the sample sizes, sample means, and sample standard deviations. If something other than a 95% confidence interval is desired, the confidence coefficient in cell E12 must also be changed.

Hypothesis Tests About $\mu_1 - \mu_2$

Let us now consider hypothesis tests about the difference between the means of two populations when the population standard deviations σ_1 and σ_2 are unknown. Letting D_0 denote the hypothesized difference between μ_1 and μ_2, Section 10.1 showed that the test statistic used for the case where σ_1 and σ_2 are known is as follows.

$$z = \frac{(\bar{x}_1 - \bar{x}_2) - D_0}{\sqrt{\dfrac{\sigma_1^2}{n_1} + \dfrac{\sigma_2^2}{n_2}}}$$

The test statistic, z, follows the standard normal distribution.

When σ_1 and σ_2 are unknown, we use s_1 as an estimator of σ_1 and s_2 as an estimator of σ_2. Substituting these sample standard deviations for σ_1 and σ_2 provides the following test statistic when σ_1 and σ_2 are unknown.

TEST STATISTIC FOR HYPOTHESIS TESTS ABOUT $\mu_1 - \mu_2$: σ_1 AND σ_2 UNKNOWN

$$t = \frac{(\bar{x}_1 - \bar{x}_2) - D_0}{\sqrt{\dfrac{s_1^2}{n_1} + \dfrac{s_2^2}{n_2}}} \tag{10.8}$$

The degrees of freedom for t are given by equation (10.7).

Let us demonstrate the use of this test statistic in the following hypothesis testing example.

Consider a new computer software package developed to help systems analysts reduce the time required to design, develop, and implement an information system. To evaluate the benefits of the new software package, a random sample of 24 systems analysts is selected. Each analyst is given specifications for a hypothetical information system. Then 12 of the analysts are instructed to produce the information system by using current technology. The other 12 analysts are trained in the use of the new software package and then instructed to use it to produce the information system.

This study involves two populations: a population of systems analysts using the current technology and a population of systems analysts using the new software package. In terms of the time required to complete the information system design project, the population means are as follows.

μ_1 = the mean project completion time for systems analysts using the current technology

μ_2 = the mean project completion time for systems analysts using the new software package

The researcher in charge of the new software evaluation project hopes to show that the new software package will provide a shorter mean project completion time. Thus, the researcher is looking for evidence to conclude that μ_2 is less than μ_1; in this case, the difference between the two population means, $\mu_1 - \mu_2$, will be greater than zero. The research hypothesis $\mu_1 - \mu_2 > 0$ is stated as the alternative hypothesis. Thus, the hypothesis test becomes

$$H_0\colon \mu_1 - \mu_2 \leq 0$$
$$H_a\colon \mu_1 - \mu_2 > 0$$

We will use $\alpha = .05$ as the level of significance.

Suppose that the 24 analysts complete the study with the results shown in Table 10.1. Using the test statistic in equation (10.8), we have

$$t = \frac{(\bar{x}_1 - \bar{x}_2) - D_0}{\sqrt{\dfrac{s_1^2}{n_1} + \dfrac{s_2^2}{n_2}}} = \frac{(325 - 286) - 0}{\sqrt{\dfrac{40^2}{12} + \dfrac{44^2}{12}}} = 2.27$$

TABLE 10.1 COMPLETION TIME DATA AND SUMMARY STATISTICS FOR THE SOFTWARE TESTING STUDY

SoftwareTest

	Current Technology	New Software
	300	274
	280	220
	344	308
	385	336
	372	198
	360	300
	288	315
	321	258
	376	318
	290	310
	301	332
	283	263
Summary Statistics		
Sample size	$n_1 = 12$	$n_2 = 12$
Sample mean	$\bar{x}_1 = 325$ hours	$\bar{x}_2 = 286$ hours
Sample standard deviation	$s_1 = 40$	$s_2 = 44$

Computing the degrees of freedom using equation (10.7), we have

$$df = \frac{\left(\frac{s_1^2}{n_1} + \frac{s_2^2}{n_2}\right)^2}{\frac{1}{n_1 - 1}\left(\frac{s_1^2}{n_1}\right)^2 + \frac{1}{n_2 - 1}\left(\frac{s_2^2}{n_2}\right)^2} = \frac{\left(\frac{40^2}{12} + \frac{44^2}{12}\right)^2}{\frac{1}{12 - 1}\left(\frac{40^2}{12}\right)^2 + \frac{1}{12 - 1}\left(\frac{44^2}{12}\right)^2} = 21.8$$

Rounding down, we will use a *t* distribution with 21 degrees of freedom. This row of the *t* distribution table is as follows:

Area in Upper Tail	**.20**	**.10**	**.05**	**.025**	**.01**	**.005**
***t*-Value (21 *df*)**	0.859	1.323	1.721	2.080	2.518	2.831

$t = 2.27$

Using the t distribution table, we can only determine a range for the p-value. Use of Excel (see Figure 10.7) shows the exact p-value = .017.

With an upper tail test, the *p*-value is the area in the upper tail to the right of $t = 2.27$. From the above results, we see that the *p*-value is between .025 and .01. Thus, the *p*-value is less than $\alpha = .05$ and H_0 is rejected. The sample results enable the researcher to conclude that $\mu_1 - \mu_2 > 0$, or $\mu_1 > \mu_2$. Thus, the research study supports the conclusion that the new software package provides a smaller population mean completion time.

Using Excel to Conduct a Hypothesis Test

The Excel tool used to conduct a hypothesis test to determine whether there is a significant difference in population means when the population standard deviations are unknown is called *t-Test: Two-Sample Assuming Unequal Variances.* We illustrate using the sample data for the software evaluation study. Twelve systems analysts developed an information system using current technology, and 12 systems analysts developed an information system using a new software package. A one-tailed hypothesis test is to be conducted to see whether the mean completion time is shorter using the new software package. Refer to the Excel worksheets shown in Figure 10.6 and Figure 10.7 as we describe the tasks involved.

Enter/Access Data: Open the WEBfile named SoftwareTest. Column A in Figure 10.6 contains the completion time data and a label for the random sample of 12 individuals using the current technology, and column B contains the completion time data and a label for the random sample of 12 individuals using the new software.

Apply Tools: The following steps will provide the information needed to conduct the hypothesis test to see whether there is a significant difference in favor of the new software.

Step 1. Click the **Data** tab on the Ribbon
Step 2. In the **Analysis** group, click **Data Analysis**
Step 3. Choose **t-Test: Two-Sample Assuming Unequal Variances** from the list of Analysis Tools
Step 4. When the t-Test: Two-Sample Assuming Unequal Variances dialog box appears (Figure 10.6):
Enter A1:A13 in the **Variable 1 Range** box
Enter B1:B13 in the **Variable 2 Range** box
Enter 0 in the **Hypothesized Mean Difference** box
Select **Labels**
Enter .05 in the **Alpha** box
Select **Output Range** and enter D1 in the box
Click **OK**

FIGURE 10.6 DIALOG BOX FOR EXCEL'S t-TEST: TWO-SAMPLE ASSUMING UNEQUAL VARIANCES TOOL

	A	B
1	Current	New
2	300	274
3	280	220
4	344	308
5	385	336
6	372	198
7	360	300
8	288	315
9	321	258
10	376	318
11	290	310
12	301	332
13	283	263
14		
15		
16		
17		

t-Test: Two-Sample Assuming Unequal Variances

Input
Variable 1 Range: $A$1:$A$13
Variable 2 Range: $B$1:$B$13
Hypothesized Mean Difference: 0
☑ Labels
Alpha: 0.05

Output options
◉ Output Range: D1
○ New Worksheet Ply:
○ New Workbook

OK
Cancel
Help

The results are shown in Figure 10.7. Descriptive statistics for the two samples are shown in cells E4:F6. The value of the test statistic, 2.2721, is shown in cell E9. The p-value for the test, labeled P(T<=t) one-tail, is shown in cell E10. Because the p-value, .0166, is less than the level of significance $\alpha = .05$, we can conclude that the mean completion time for the population using the new software package is smaller.

The t-Test: Two-Sample Assuming Unequal Variances tool can also be used to conduct two-tailed hypothesis tests. The only change required to make the hypothesis testing decision is that we need to use the p-value for a two-tailed test, labeled P(T<=t) two-tail (see cell E12).

FIGURE 10.7 EXCEL RESULTS FOR THE HYPOTHESIS TEST ABOUT EQUALITY OF MEAN PROJECT COMPLETION TIMES

	A	B	C	D	E	F
1	Current	New		t-Test: Two-Sample Assuming Unequal Variances		
2	300	274				
3	280	220			*Current*	*New*
4	344	308		Mean	325	286
5	385	336		Variance	1599.6364	1935.8182
6	372	198		Observations	12	12
7	360	300		Hypothesized Mean Difference	0	
8	288	315		df	22	
9	321	258		t Stat	2.2721	
10	376	318		P(T<=t) one-tail	0.0166	
11	290	310		t Critical one-tail	1.7171	
12	301	332		P(T<=t) two-tail	0.0332	
13	283	263		t Critical two-tail	2.0739	
14						

Practical Advice

Whenever possible, equal sample sizes, $n_1 = n_2$, are recommended.

The interval estimation and hypothesis testing procedures presented in this section are robust and can be used with relatively small sample sizes. In most applications, equal or nearly equal sample sizes such that the total sample size $n_1 + n_2$ is at least 20 can be expected to provide very good results even if the populations are not normal. Larger sample sizes are recommended if the distributions of the populations are highly skewed or contain outliers. Smaller sample sizes should only be used if the analyst is satisfied that the distributions of the populations are at least approximately normal.

NOTE AND COMMENT

Another approach used to make inferences about the difference between two population means when σ_1 and σ_2 are unknown is based on the assumption that the two population standard deviations are *equal* ($\sigma_1 = \sigma_2 = \sigma$). Under this assumption, the two sample standard deviations are combined to provide the following *pooled sample variance:*

$$s_p^2 = \frac{(n_1 - 1)s_1^2 + (n_2 - 1)s_2^2}{n_1 + n_2 - 2}$$

The t test statistic becomes

$$t = \frac{(\bar{x}_1 - \bar{x}_2) - D_0}{s_p\sqrt{\frac{1}{n_1} + \frac{1}{n_2}}}$$

and has $n_1 + n_2 - 2$ degrees of freedom. At this point, the computation of the p-value and the interpretation of the sample results are identical to the procedures discussed earlier in this section.

A difficulty with this procedure is that the assumption that the two population standard deviations are equal is usually difficult to verify. Unequal population standard deviations are frequently encountered. Using the pooled procedure may not provide satisfactory results, especially if the sample sizes n_1 and n_2 are quite different.

The t procedure that we presented in this section does not require the assumption of equal population standard deviations and can be applied whether the population standard deviations are equal or not. It is a more general procedure and is recommended for most applications.

Exercises

Methods

9. The following results are for independent random samples taken from two populations.

Sample 1	Sample 2
$n_1 = 20$	$n_2 = 30$
$\bar{x}_1 = 22.5$	$\bar{x}_2 = 20.1$
$s_1 = 2.5$	$s_2 = 4.8$

a. What is the point estimate of the difference between the two population means?
b. What is the degrees of freedom for the t distribution?
c. At 95% confidence, what is the margin of error?
d. What is the 95% confidence interval for the difference between the two population means?

10. Consider the following hypothesis test.

$$H_0: \mu_1 - \mu_2 = 0$$
$$H_a: \mu_1 - \mu_2 \neq 0$$

The following results are from independent samples taken from two populations.

Sample 1	Sample 2
$n_1 = 35$	$n_2 = 40$
$\bar{x}_1 = 13.6$	$\bar{x}_2 = 10.1$
$s_1 = 5.2$	$s_2 = 8.5$

a. What is the value of the test statistic?
b. What is the degrees of freedom for the t distribution?
c. What is the p-value?
d. At $\alpha = .05$, what is your conclusion?

11. Consider the following data for two independent random samples taken from two normal populations.

Sample 1	10	7	13	7	9	8
Sample 2	8	7	8	4	6	9

a. Compute the two sample means.
b. Compute the two sample standard deviations.
c. What is the point estimate of the difference between the two population means?
d. What is the 90% confidence interval estimate of the difference between the two population means?

Applications

12. The U.S. Department of Transportation provides the number of miles that residents of the 75 largest metropolitan areas travel per day in a car. Suppose that for a random sample of 50 Buffalo residents the mean is 22.5 miles a day and the standard deviation is 8.4 miles a day, and for an independent random sample of 40 Boston residents the mean is 18.6 miles a day and the standard deviation is 7.4 miles a day.
   a. What is the point estimate of the difference between the mean number of miles that Buffalo residents travel per day and the mean number of miles that Boston residents travel per day?
   b. What is the 95% confidence interval for the difference between the two population means?

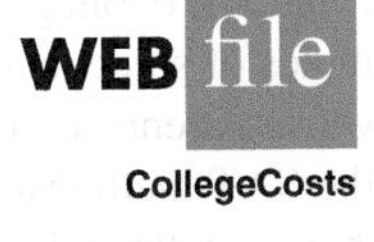

CollegeCosts

13. The average annual cost (including tuition, room, board, books, and fees) to attend a public college takes nearly a third of the annual income of a typical family with college-age children (*Money*, April 2012). At private colleges, the average annual cost is equal to about 60% of the typical family's income. The following random samples show the annual cost of attending private and public colleges. Data are in thousands of dollars.

Private Colleges

52.8	43.2	45.0	33.3	44.0	
30.6	45.8	37.8	50.5	42.0	

Public Colleges

20.3	22.0	28.2	15.6	24.1	28.5
22.8	25.8	18.5	25.6	14.4	21.8

a. Compute the sample mean and sample standard deviation for private and public colleges.

b. What is the point estimate of the difference between the two population means? Interpret this value in terms of the annual cost of attending private and public colleges.
c. Develop a 95% confidence interval of the difference between the mean annual cost of attending private and pubic colleges.

14. Are nursing salaries in Tampa, Florida, lower than those in Dallas, Texas? Salary data show staff nurses in Tampa earn less than staff nurses in Dallas (*The Tampa Tribune*, January 15, 2007). Suppose that in a follow-up study of 40 staff nurses in Tampa and 50 staff nurses in Dallas you obtain the following results.

Tampa	Dallas
$n_1 = 40$	$n_2 = 50$
$\bar{x}_1 = \$56{,}100$	$\bar{x}_2 = \$59{,}400$
$s_1 = \$6000$	$s_2 = \$7000$

a. Formulate a hypothesis so that, if the null hypothesis is rejected, we can conclude that salaries for staff nurses in Tampa are significantly lower than for those in Dallas. Use $\alpha = .05$.
b. What is the value of the test statistic?
c. What is the *p*-value?
d. What is your conclusion?

15. Commercial real estate prices and rental rates suffered substantial declines in 2008 and 2009 (*Newsweek*, July 27, 2009). These declines were particularly severe in Asia; annual lease rates in Tokyo, Hong Kong, and Singapore declined by 40% or more. Even with such large declines, annual lease rates in Asia were still higher than those in many cities in Europe. Annual lease rates for a sample of 30 commercial properties in Hong Kong showed a mean of $1114 per square meter with a standard deviation of $230. Annual lease rates for a sample of 40 commercial properties in Paris showed a mean lease rate of $989 per square meter with a standard deviation of $195.
a. On the basis of the sample results, can we conclude that the mean annual lease rate is higher in Hong Kong than in Paris? Develop appropriate null and alternative hypotheses.
b. Use $\alpha = .01$. What is your conclusion?

SATMath

16. The College Board provided comparisons of Scholastic Aptitude Test (SAT) scores based on the highest level of education attained by the test taker's parents. A research hypothesis was that students whose parents had attained a higher level of education would on average score higher on the SAT. The overall mean SAT math score was 514 (College Board website, January 8, 2012). SAT math scores for independent samples of students follow. The first sample shows the SAT math test scores for students whose parents are college graduates with a bachelor's degree. The second sample shows the SAT math test scores for students whose parents are high school graduates but do not have a college degree.

Students' Parents

College Grads		High School Grads	
485	487	442	492
534	533	580	478
650	526	479	425
554	410	486	485
550	515	528	390
572	578	524	535
497	448		
592	469		

a. Formulate the hypotheses that can be used to determine whether the sample data support the hypothesis that students show a higher population mean math score on the SAT if their parents attained a higher level of education.
b. What is the point estimate of the difference between the means for the two populations?
c. Compute the p-value for the hypothesis test.
d. At $\alpha = .05$, what is your conclusion?

17. Periodically, Merrill Lynch customers are asked to evaluate Merrill Lynch financial consultants and services. Higher ratings on the client satisfaction survey indicate better service, with 7 the maximum service rating. Independent samples of service ratings for two financial consultants are summarized here. Consultant A has 10 years of experience, whereas consultant B has 1 year of experience. Use $\alpha = .05$ and test to see whether the consultant with more experience has the higher population mean service rating.

Consultant A	Consultant B
$n_1 = 16$	$n_2 = 10$
$\bar{x}_1 = 6.82$	$\bar{x}_2 = 6.25$
$s_1 = .64$	$s_2 = .75$

a. State the null and alternative hypotheses.
b. Compute the value of the test statistic.
c. What is the p-value?
d. What is your conclusion?

18. Researchers at Purdue University and Wichita State University found that airlines are doing a better job of getting passengers to their destinations on time (Associated Press, April 2, 2012). AirTran Airways and Southwest Airlines were among the leaders in on-time arrivals, with both having 88% of their flights arriving on time. But for the 12% of flights that were delayed, how many minutes were these flights late? Sample data showing the number of minutes that delayed flights were late are provided in the WEBfile named AirDelay. Data are shown for both airlines.
a. Formulate the hypotheses that can be used to test for a difference between the population mean minutes late for delayed flights by these two airlines.
b. What is the sample mean number of minutes late for delayed flights for each of these two airlines?
c. Using a .05 level of significance, what is the p-value and what is your conclusion?

10.3 Inferences About the Difference Between Two Population Means: Matched Samples

Suppose employees at a manufacturing company can use two different methods to perform a production task. To maximize production output, the company wants to identify the method with the smaller population mean completion time. Let μ_1 denote the population mean completion time for production method 1 and μ_2 denote the population mean completion time for production method 2. With no preliminary indication of the preferred production method, we begin by tentatively assuming that the two production methods have the same population mean completion time. Thus, the null hypothesis is H_0: $\mu_1 - \mu_2 = 0$. If this hypothesis is rejected, we can conclude that the population mean completion times differ. In this case, the method providing the smaller mean completion time would be recommended. The null and alternative hypotheses are written as follows.

$$H_0: \mu_1 - \mu_2 = 0$$
$$H_a: \mu_1 - \mu_2 \neq 0$$

In choosing the sampling procedure that will be used to collect production time data and test the hypotheses, we consider two alternative designs. One is based on independent samples and the other is based on **matched samples**.

1. *Independent sample design:* A random sample of workers is selected and each worker in the sample uses method 1. A second independent random sample of workers is selected and each worker in this sample uses method 2. The test of the difference between population means is based on the procedures in Section 10.2.
2. *Matched sample design:* One random sample of workers is selected. Each worker first uses one method and then uses the other method. The order of the two methods is assigned randomly to the workers, with some workers performing method 1 first and others performing method 2 first. Each worker provides a pair of data values, one value for method 1 and another value for method 2.

In the matched sample design the two production methods are tested under similar conditions (i.e., with the same workers); hence this design often leads to a smaller sampling error than the independent sample design. The primary reason is that in a matched sample design, variation between workers is eliminated because the same workers are used for both production methods.

Let us demonstrate the analysis of a matched sample design by assuming it is the method used to test the difference between population means for the two production methods. A random sample of six workers is used. The data on completion times for the six workers are given in Table 10.2. Note that each worker provides a pair of data values, one for each production method. Also note that the last column contains the difference in completion times d_i for each worker in the sample.

The key to the analysis of the matched sample design is to realize that we consider only the column of differences. Therefore, we have six data values (.6, −.2, .5, .3, .0, and .6) that will be used to analyze the difference between population means of the two production methods.

TABLE 10.2 TASK COMPLETION TIMES FOR A MATCHED SAMPLE DESIGN

Worker	Completion Time for Method 1 (minutes)	Completion Time for Method 2 (minutes)	Difference in Completion Times (d_i)
1	6.0	5.4	.6
2	5.0	5.2	−.2
3	7.0	6.5	.5
4	6.2	5.9	.3
5	6.0	6.0	.0
6	6.4	5.8	.6

Let μ_d = the mean of the *difference* in values for the population of workers. With this notation, the null and alternative hypotheses are rewritten as follows.

$$H_0: \mu_d = 0$$
$$H_a: \mu_d \neq 0$$

If H_0 is rejected, we can conclude that the population mean completion times differ.

Other than the use of the d notation, the formulas for the sample mean and sample standard deviation are the same ones used previously in the text.

The d notation is a reminder that the matched sample provides *difference* data. The sample mean and sample standard deviation for the six difference values in Table 10.2 follow.

$$\bar{d} = \frac{\Sigma d_i}{n} = \frac{1.8}{6} = .30$$

$$s_d = \sqrt{\frac{s\Sigma(d_i - \bar{d})^2}{n - 1}} = \sqrt{\frac{.56}{5}} = .335$$

It is not necessary to make the assumption that the population has a normal distribution if the sample size is large. Sample size guidelines for using the t distribution were presented in Chapters 8 and 9.

With the small sample of $n = 6$ workers, we need to make the assumption that the population of differences has a normal distribution. This assumption is necessary so that we may use the t distribution for hypothesis testing and interval estimation procedures. Based on this assumption, the following test statistic has a t distribution with $n - 1$ degrees of freedom.

TEST STATISTIC FOR HYPOTHESIS TESTS INVOLVING MATCHED SAMPLES

$$t = \frac{\bar{d} - \mu_d}{s_d/\sqrt{n}} \tag{10.9}$$

Once the difference data are computed, the t distribution procedure for matched samples is the same as the one-population estimation and hypothesis testing procedures described in Chapters 8 and 9.

Let us use equation (10.9) to test the hypotheses $H_0: \mu_d = 0$ and $H_a: \mu_d \neq 0$, using $\alpha = .05$. Substituting the sample results $\bar{d} = .30$, $s_d = .335$, and $n = 6$ into equation (10.9), we compute the value of the test statistic.

$$t = \frac{\bar{d} - \mu_d}{s_d/\sqrt{n}} = \frac{.30 - 0}{.335/\sqrt{6}} = 2.20$$

Now let us compute the p-value for this two-tailed test. Because $t = 2.20 > 0$, the test statistic is in the upper tail of the t distribution. With $t = 2.20$, the area in the upper tail to the right of the test statistic can be found by using the t distribution table with degrees of freedom $= n - 1 = 6 - 1 = 5$. Information from the 5 degrees of freedom row of the t distribution table is as follows:

Area in Upper Tail	**.20**	**.10**	**.05**	**.025**	**.01**	**.005**
***t*-Value (5 *df*)**	0.920	1.476	2.015	2.571	3.365	4.032

$t = 2.20$

Thus, we see that the area in the upper tail is between .05 and .025. Because this test is a two-tailed test, we double these values to conclude that the p-value is between .10 and .05.

This p-value is greater than $\alpha = .05$. Thus, the null hypothesis H_0: $\mu_d = 0$ is not rejected. Using Excel and the data in Table 10.2, we find the exact p-value $= .0795$.

In addition we can obtain an interval estimate of the difference between the two population means by using the single population methodology of Chapter 8. At 95% confidence, the calculation follows.

$$\bar{d} \pm t_{.025}\frac{s_d}{\sqrt{n}}$$

$$.3 \pm 2.571\left(\frac{.335}{\sqrt{6}}\right)$$

$$.3 \pm .35$$

Thus, the margin of error is .35 and the 95% confidence interval for the difference between the population means of the two production methods is $-.05$ minutes to .65 minutes.

Using Excel to Conduct a Hypothesis Test

Excel's t-Test: Paired Two Sample for Means tool can be used to conduct a hypothesis test about the difference between the population means when a matched sample design is used. We illustrate by conducting the hypothesis test involving the two production methods. Refer to the Excel worksheets shown in Figure 10.8 and Figure 10.9 as we describe the tasks involved.

Enter/Access Data: Open the WEBfile named Matched. Column A in Figure 10.8 is used to identify each of the six workers who participated in the study. Column B contains the completion time data for each worker using method 1, and column C contains the completion time data for each worker using method 2.

Apply Tools: The following steps describe how to use Excel's t-Test: Paired Two Sample for Means tool to conduct the hypothesis test about the difference between the means of the two production methods.

FIGURE 10.8 DIALOG BOX FOR EXCEL'S t-TEST: PAIRED TWO SAMPLE FOR MEANS TOOL

	A	B	C
1	Worker	Method 1	Method 2
2	1	6	5.4
3	2	5	5.2
4	3	7	6.5
5	4	6.2	5.9
6	5	6	6
7	6	6.4	5.8
8			
9			
10			
11			
12			
13			
14			
15			
16			

t-Test: Paired Two Sample for Means

Input

Variable 1 Range: $B$1:$B$7

Variable 2 Range: $C$1:$C$7

Hypothesized Mean Difference: 0

☑ Labels

Alpha: 0.05

Output options

◉ Output Range: E1

○ New Worksheet Ply:

○ New Workbook

OK

Cancel

Help

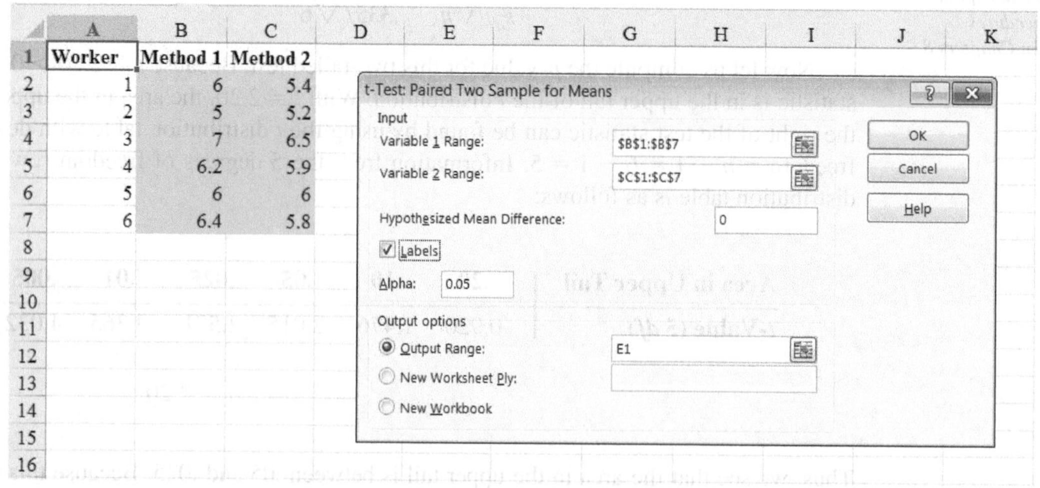

FIGURE 10.9 EXCEL RESULTS FOR THE HYPOTHESIS TEST IN THE MATCHED SAMPLES STUDY

	A	B	C	D	E	F	G	H
1	Worker	Method 1	Method 2		t-Test: Paired Two Sample for Means			
2	1	6	5.4					
3	2	5	5.2			*Method 1*	*Method 2*	
4	3	7	6.5		Mean	6.1	5.8	
5	4	6.2	5.9		Variance	0.428	0.212	
6	5	6	6		Observations	6	6	
7	6	6.4	5.8		Pearson Correlation	0.8764		
8					Hypothesized Mean Difference	0		
9					df	5		
10					t Stat	2.196		
11					P(T<=t) one-tail	0.0398		
12					t Critical one-tail	2.015		
13					P(T<=t) two-tail	0.0795		
14					t Critical two-tail	2.571		
15								

Step 1. Click the **Data** tab on the Ribbon
Step 2. In the **Analysis** group, click **Data Analysis**
Step 3. Choose **t-Test: Paired Two Sample for Means** from the list of Analysis Tools
Step 4. When the t-Test: Paired Two Sample for Means dialog box appears (Figure 10.8):
Enter B1:B7 in the **Variable 1 Range** box
Enter C1:C7 in the **Variable 2 Range** box
Enter 0 in the **Hypothesized Mean Difference** box
Select **Labels**
Enter .05 in the **Alpha** box
Select **Output Range**
Enter E1 in the **Output Range** box (to identify the upper left corner of the section of the worksheet where the output will appear)
Click **OK**

The results are shown in cells E1:G14 of the worksheet shown in Figure 10.9. The p-value for the test, labeled P(T<=t) two-tail, is shown in cell F13. Because the p-value, .0795, is greater than the level of significance $\alpha = .05$, we cannot reject the null hypothesis that the mean completion times are equal.

The same procedure can also be used to conduct one-tailed hypothesis tests. The only change required to make the hypothesis testing decision is that we need to use the p-value for a one-tailed test, labeled P(T<=t) one-tail (see cell F11).

NOTES AND COMMENTS

1. In the example presented in this section, workers performed the production task with first one method and then the other method. This example illustrates a matched sample design in which each sampled element (worker) provides a pair of data values. It is also possible to use different but "similar" elements to provide the pair of data values. For example, a worker at one location could be matched with a similar worker at another location (similarity based on age, education, gender, experience, etc.). The pairs of workers would provide the difference data that could be used in the matched sample analysis.
2. A matched sample procedure for inferences about two population means generally provides better precision than the independent sample approach; therefore it is the recommended design. However, in some applications the matching cannot be achieved, or perhaps the time and cost associated with matching are excessive. In such cases, the independent sample design should be used.

Exercises

Methods

19. Consider the following hypothesis test.

$$H_0: \mu_d \leq 0$$
$$H_a: \mu_d > 0$$

The following data are from matched samples taken from two populations.

	Population	
Element	**1**	**2**
1	21	20
2	28	26
3	18	18
4	20	20
5	26	24

a. Compute the difference value for each element.
b. Compute $\bar{d}$.
c. Compute the standard deviation s_d.
d. Conduct a hypothesis test using $\alpha = .05$. What is your conclusion?

20. The following data are from matched samples taken from two populations.

	Population	
Element	**1**	**2**
1	11	8
2	7	8
3	9	6
4	12	7
5	13	10
6	15	15
7	15	14

a. Compute the difference value for each element.
b. Compute $\bar{d}$.
c. Compute the standard deviation s_d.
d. What is the point estimate of the difference between the two population means?
e. Provide a 95% confidence interval for the difference between the two population means.

Applications

21. A market research firm used a sample of individuals to rate the purchase potential of a particular product before and after the individuals saw a new television commercial about the product. The purchase potential ratings were based on a 0 to 10 scale, with higher values indicating a higher purchase potential. The null hypothesis stated that the mean rating "after" would be less than or equal to the mean rating "before." Rejection of this hypothesis would show that the commercial improved the mean purchase potential rating. Use $\alpha = .05$ and the following data to test the hypothesis and comment on the value of the commercial.

	Purchase Rating			Purchase Rating	
Individual	After	Before	Individual	After	Before
1	6	5	5	3	5
2	6	4	6	9	8
3	7	7	7	7	5
4	4	3	8	6	6

StockPrices

22. The price per share of stock for a sample of 25 companies was recorded at the beginning of 2012 and then again at the end of the 1st quarter of 2012 (*The Wall Street Journal*, April 2, 2012). How stocks perform during the 1st quarter is an indicator of what is ahead for the stock market and the economy. Use the sample data in the WEBfile named StockPrices to answer the following.
   a. Let d_i denote the change in price per share for company i where d_i = 1st quarter of 2012 price per share minus the beginning of 2012 price per share. Use the sample mean of these values to estimate the dollar amount a share of stock has changed during the 1st quarter.
   b. What is the 95% confidence interval estimate of the population mean change in the price per share of stock during the first quarter? Interpret this result.

23. Bank of America's Consumer Spending Survey collected data on annual credit card charges in seven different categories of expenditures: transportation, groceries, dining out, household expenses, home furnishings, apparel, and entertainment. Using data from a sample of 42 credit card accounts, assume that each account was used to identify the annual credit card charges for groceries (population 1) and the annual credit card charges for dining out (population 2). Using the difference data, the sample mean difference was $\bar{d} = \$850$, and the sample standard deviation was $s_d = \$1123$.
   a. Formulate the null and alternative hypotheses to test for no difference between the population mean credit card charges for groceries and the population mean credit card charges for dining out.
   b. Use a .05 level of significance. Can you conclude that the population means differ? What is the p-value?
   c. Which category, groceries or dining out, has a higher population mean annual credit card charge? What is the point estimate of the difference between the population means? What is the 95% confidence interval estimate of the difference between the population means?

BusinessTravel

24. The Global Business Travel Association reported the domestic airfare for business travel for the current year and the previous year (*Inc.* magazine, February 2012). Below is a sample of 12 flights with their domestic airfares shown for both years.

Current Year	Previous Year	Current Year	Previous Year
345	315	635	585
526	463	710	650
420	462	605	545
216	206	517	547
285	275	570	508
405	432	610	580

   a. Formulate the hypotheses and test for a significant increase in the mean domestic airfare for business travel for the one-year period. What is the p-value? Using a .05 level of significance, what is your conclusion?
   b. What is the sample mean domestic airfare for business travel for each year?
   c. What is the percentage change in the airfare for the one-year period?

25. The College Board SAT college entrance exam consists of three parts: math, writing, and critical reading (*The World Almanac*, 2012). Sample data showing the math and writing scores for a sample of 12 students who took the SAT follow.

TestScores

Student	Math	Writing	Student	Math	Writing
1	540	474	7	480	430
2	432	380	8	499	459
3	528	463	9	610	615
4	574	612	10	572	541
5	448	420	11	390	335
6	502	526	12	593	613

a. Use a .05 level of significance and test for a difference between the population mean for the math scores and the population mean for the writing scores. What is the p-value and what is your conclusion?
b. What is the point estimate of the difference between the mean scores for the two tests? What are the estimates of the population mean scores for the two tests? Which test reports the higher mean score?

26. Scores in the first and fourth (final) rounds for a sample of 20 golfers who competed in PGA tournaments are shown in the following table (*Golfweek*, February 14, 2009, and February 28, 2009). Suppose you would like to determine if the mean score for the first round of a PGA Tour event is significantly different than the mean score for the fourth and final round. Does the pressure of playing in the final round cause scores to go up? Or does the increased player concentration cause scores to come down?

GolfScores

Player	First Round	Final Round	Player	First Round	Final Round
Michael Letzig	70	72	Aron Price	72	72
Scott Verplank	71	72	Charles Howell	72	70
D. A. Points	70	75	Jason Dufner	70	73
Jerry Kelly	72	71	Mike Weir	70	77
Soren Hansen	70	69	Carl Pettersson	68	70
D. J. Trahan	67	67	Bo Van Pelt	68	65
Bubba Watson	71	67	Ernie Els	71	70
Reteif Goosen	68	75	Cameron Beckman	70	68
Jeff Klauk	67	73	Nick Watney	69	68
Kenny Perry	70	69	Tommy Armour III	67	71

a. Use $\alpha = .10$ to test for a statistically significantly difference between the population means for first- and fourth-round scores. What is the p-value? What is your conclusion?
b. What is the point estimate of the difference between the two population means? For which round is the population mean score lower?
c. What is the margin of error for a 90% confidence interval estimate for the difference between the population means? Could this confidence interval have been used to test the hypothesis in part (a)? Explain.

27. A manufacturer produces both a deluxe and a standard model of an automatic sander designed for home use. Selling prices obtained from a sample of retail outlets follow.

Retail Outlet	Model Price ($) Deluxe	Standard	Retail Outlet	Model Price ($) Deluxe	Standard
1	39	27	5	40	30
2	39	28	6	39	34
3	45	35	7	35	29
4	38	30			

a. The manufacturer's suggested retail prices for the two models show a $10 price differential. Use a .05 level of significance and test that the mean difference between the prices of the two models is $10.
b. What is the 95% confidence interval for the difference between the mean prices of the two models?

10.4 An Introduction to Experimental Design and Analysis of Variance

In Chapter 1 we stated that statistical studies can be classified as either experimental or observational. In an experimental statistical study, an experiment is conducted to generate the data. An experiment begins with identifying a variable of interest. Then one or more other variables, thought to be related, are identified and controlled. Then data are collected to learn if and how those variables influence the variable of interest.

In an observational study, data are usually obtained through sample surveys and not a controlled experiment. Good design principles are still employed, but the rigorous controls associated with an experimental statistical study are often not possible. For instance, in a study of the relationship between smoking and lung cancer the researcher cannot assign a smoking habit to subjects. The researcher is restricted to simply observing the effects of smoking on people who already smoke and the effects of not smoking on people who do not already smoke.

Sir Ronald Aylmer Fisher (1890–1962) invented the branch of statistics known as experimental design. In addition to being accomplished in statistics, he was a noted scientist in the field of genetics.

In this section we introduce the basic principles of an experimental study and show how they are used in a completely randomized design. We also provide a conceptual overview of the statistical procedure called analysis of variance (ANOVA). In the following section we show how ANOVA can be used to test for the equality of k population means using data obtained from a completely randomized design as well as data obtained from an observational study. So, in this sense, ANOVA extends the statistical material in the preceding sections from two population means to three or more population means. In later chapters, we will see that ANOVA plays a key role in analyzing the results of regression studies involving both experimental and observational data.

Cause-and-effect relationships can be difficult to establish in observational studies; such relationships are easier to establish in experimental studies.

As an example of an experimental statistical study, let us consider the problem facing Chemitech, Inc. Chemitech developed a new filtration system for municipal water supplies. The components for the new filtration system will be purchased from several suppliers, and Chemitech will assemble the components at its plant in Columbia, South Carolina. The industrial engineering group is responsible for determining the best assembly method for the new filtration system. After considering a variety of possible approaches, the group narrows the alternatives to three: method A, method B, and method C. These methods differ in the sequence of steps used to assemble the system. Managers at Chemitech want to determine which assembly method can produce the greatest number of filtration systems per week.

In the Chemitech experiment, assembly method is the independent variable or **factor**. Because three assembly methods correspond to this factor, we say that three treatments are associated with this experiment; each **treatment** corresponds to one of the three assembly methods. The Chemitech problem is an example of a **single-factor experiment**; it involves one categorical factor (method of assembly). More complex experiments may consist of multiple factors; some factors may be categorical and others may be quantitative.

The three assembly methods or treatments define the three populations of interest for the Chemitech experiment. One population is all Chemitech employees who use assembly method A, another is those who use method B, and the third is those who use method C. Note that for each population the dependent or **response variable** is the number of filtration systems assembled per week, and the primary statistical objective of the experiment is to determine whether the mean number of units produced per week is the same for all three populations (methods).

Randomization is the process of assigning the treatments to the experimental units at random. Prior to the work of Sir R. A. Fisher, treatments were assigned on a systematic or subjective basis.

Suppose a random sample of three employees is selected from all assembly workers at the Chemitech production facility. In experimental design terminology, the three randomly selected workers are the **experimental units**. The experimental design that we will use for the Chemitech problem is called a **completely randomized design**. This type of design requires that each of the three assembly methods or treatments be assigned randomly to one of the experimental units or workers. For example, method A might be randomly assigned to the second worker, method B to the first worker, and method C to the third worker. The concept of *randomization,* as illustrated in this example, is an important principle of all experimental designs.

Note that this experiment would result in only one measurement or number of units assembled for each treatment. To obtain additional data for each assembly method, we must repeat or replicate the basic experimental process. Suppose, for example, that instead of selecting just three workers at random we selected 15 workers and then randomly assigned each of the three treatments to 5 of the workers. Because each method of assembly is assigned to 5 workers, we say that five replicates have been obtained. The process of *replication* is another important principle of experimental design. Figure 10.10 shows the completely randomized design for the Chemitech experiment.

FIGURE 10.10 COMPLETELY RANDOMIZED DESIGN FOR EVALUATING THE CHEMITECH ASSEMBLY METHOD EXPERIMENT

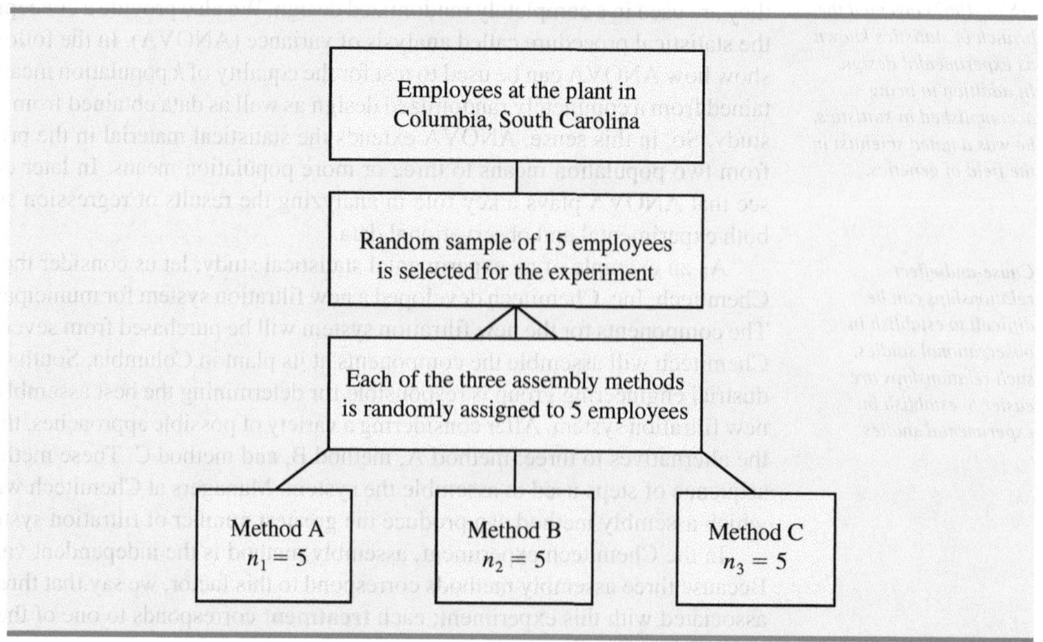

TABLE 10.3 NUMBER OF UNITS PRODUCED BY 15 WORKERS

Chemitech

	Method		
	A	**B**	**C**
	58	58	48
	64	69	57
	55	71	59
	66	64	47
	67	68	49
Sample mean	62	66	52
Sample variance	27.5	26.5	31.0
Sample standard deviation	5.244	5.148	5.568

Data Collection

Once we are satisfied with the experimental design, we proceed by collecting and analyzing the data. In the Chemitech case, the employees would be instructed in how to perform the assembly method assigned to them and then would begin assembling the new filtration systems using that method. After this assignment and training, the number of units assembled by each employee during one week is as shown in Table 10.3. The sample means, sample variances, and sample standard deviations for each assembly method are also provided. Thus, the sample mean number of units produced using method A is 62; the sample mean using method B is 66; and the sample mean using method C is 52. From these data, method B appears to result in higher production rates than either of the other methods.

The real issue is whether the three sample means observed are different enough for us to conclude that the means of the populations corresponding to the three methods of assembly are different. To write this question in statistical terms, we introduce the following notation.

If H_0 is rejected, we cannot conclude that all population means are different. Rejecting H_0 means that at least two population means have different values.

μ_1 = mean number of units produced per week using method A
μ_2 = mean number of units produced per week using method B
μ_3 = mean number of units produced per week using method C

Although we will never know the actual values of μ_1, μ_2, and μ_3, we want to use the sample means to test the following hypotheses.

$$H_0: \mu_1 = \mu_2 = \mu_3$$
$$H_a: \text{Not all population means are equal}$$

As we will demonstrate shortly, analysis of variance (ANOVA) is the statistical procedure used to determine whether the observed differences in the three sample means are large enough to reject H_0.

Assumptions for Analysis of Variance

If the sample sizes are equal, analysis of variance is not sensitive to departures from the assumption of normally distributed populations.

Three assumptions are required to use analysis of variance.

1. **For each population, the response variable is normally distributed.** Implication: In the Chemitech experiment the number of units produced per week (response variable) must be normally distributed for each assembly method.

2. **The variance of the response variable, denoted σ^2, is the same for all of the populations.** Implication: In the Chemitech experiment, the variance of the number of units produced per week must be the same for each assembly method.
3. **The observations must be independent.** Implication: In the Chemitech experiment, the number of units produced per week for each employee must be independent of the number of units produced per week for any other employee.

Analysis of Variance: A Conceptual Overview

If the means for the three populations are equal, we would expect the three sample means to be close together. In fact, the closer the three sample means are to one another, the weaker the evidence we have for the conclusion that the population means differ. Alternatively, the more the sample means differ, the stronger the evidence we have for the conclusion that the population means differ. In other words, if the variability among the sample means is "small," it supports H_0; if the variability among the sample means is "large," it supports H_a.

If the null hypothesis, H_0: $\mu_1 = \mu_2 = \mu_3$, is true, we can use the variability among the sample means to develop an estimate of σ^2. First, note that if the assumptions for analysis of variance are satisfied and the null hypothesis is true, each sample will have come from the same normal distribution with mean μ and variance σ^2. Recall from Chapter 7 that the sampling distribution of the sample mean $\bar{x}$ for a simple random sample of size n from a normal population will be normally distributed with mean μ and variance σ^2/n. Figure 10.11 illustrates such a sampling distribution.

Thus, if the null hypothesis is true, we can think of each of the three sample means, $\bar{x}_1 = 62$, $\bar{x}_2 = 66$, and $\bar{x}_3 = 52$ from Table 10.3, as values drawn at random from the sampling distribution shown in Figure 10.11. In this case, the mean and variance of the three $\bar{x}$ values can be used to estimate the mean and variance of the sampling distribution. When the sample sizes are equal, as in the Chemitech experiment, the best estimate of the mean of the sampling distribution of $\bar{x}$ is the mean or average of the sample means. In the Chemitech experiment, an estimate of the mean of the sampling distribution of $\bar{x}$ is $(62 + 66 + 52)/3 = 60$. We refer to this estimate as the *overall sample mean.* An estimate

FIGURE 10.11 SAMPLING DISTRIBUTION OF $\bar{x}$ GIVEN H_0 IS TRUE

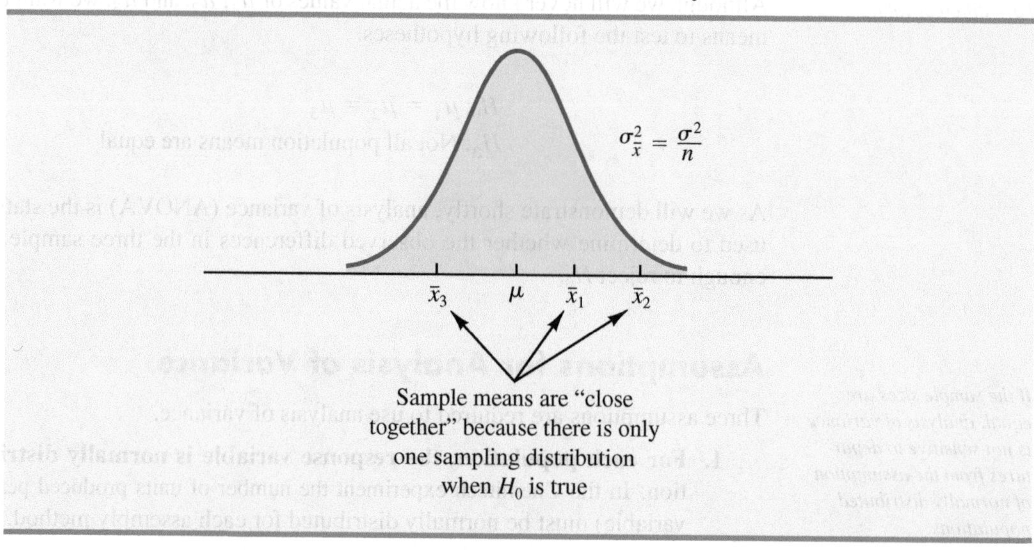

of the variance of the sampling distribution of $\bar{x}$, $\sigma^2_{\bar{x}}$, is provided by the variance of the three sample means.

$$s^2_{\bar{x}} = \frac{(62 - 60)^2 + (66 - 60)^2 + (52 - 60)^2}{3 - 1} = \frac{104}{2} = 52$$

Because $\sigma^2_{\bar{x}} = \sigma^2/n$, solving for σ^2 gives

$$\sigma^2 = n\sigma^2_{\bar{x}}$$

Hence,

$$\text{Estimate of } \sigma^2 = n\,(\text{Estimate of } \sigma^2_{\bar{x}}) = ns^2_{\bar{x}} = 5(52) = 260$$

The result, $ns^2_{\bar{x}} = 260$, is referred to as the *between-treatments* estimate of σ^2.

The between-treatments estimate of σ^2 is based on the assumption that the null hypothesis is true. In this case, each sample comes from the same population, and there is only one sampling distribution of $\bar{x}$. To illustrate what happens when H_0 is false, suppose the population means all differ. Note that because the three samples are from normal populations with different means, they will result in three different sampling distributions. Figure 10.12 shows that in this case, the sample means are not as close together as they were when H_0 was true. Thus, $s^2_{\bar{x}}$ will be larger, causing the between-treatments estimate of σ^2 to be larger. In general, when the population means are not equal, the between-treatments estimate will overestimate the population variance σ^2.

The variation within each of the samples also has an effect on the conclusion we reach in analysis of variance. When a random sample is selected from each population, each of the sample variances provides an unbiased estimate of σ^2. Hence, we can combine or pool the individual estimates of σ^2 into one overall estimate. The estimate of σ^2 obtained in this way is called the *pooled* or *within-treatments* estimate of σ^2. Because each sample variance provides an estimate of σ^2 based only on the variation within each sample, the within-treatments estimate of σ^2 is not affected by whether the population means are equal. When the sample sizes are equal, the within-treatments estimate of σ^2 can be obtained by

FIGURE 10.12 SAMPLING DISTRIBUTIONS OF $\bar{x}$ GIVEN H_0 IS FALSE

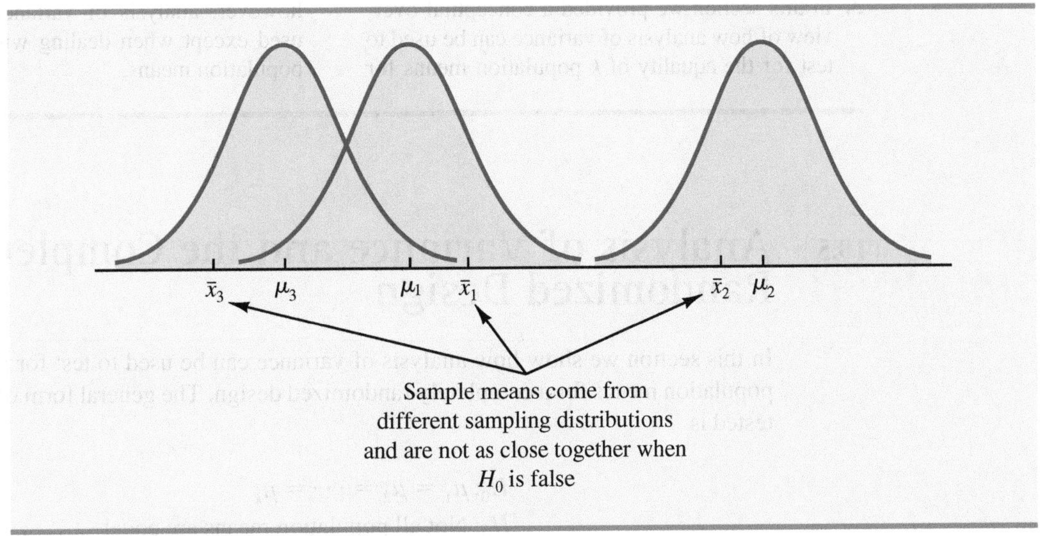
$\bar{x}_3$
μ_3
μ_1
$\bar{x}_1$
$\bar{x}_2$
μ_2
Sample means come from
different sampling distributions
and are not as close together when
H_0 is false

computing the average of the individual sample variances. For the Chemitech experiment we obtain

$$\text{Within-treatments estimate of } \sigma^2 = \frac{27.5 + 26.5 + 31.0}{3} = \frac{85}{3} = 28.33$$

In the Chemitech experiment, the between-treatments estimate of σ^2 (260) is much larger than the within-treatments estimate of σ^2 (28.33). In fact, the ratio of these two estimates is 260/28.33 = 9.18. Recall, however, that the between-treatments approach provides a good estimate of σ^2 only if the null hypothesis is true; if the null hypothesis is false, the between-treatments approach overestimates σ^2. The within-treatments approach provides a good estimate of σ^2 in either case. Thus, if the null hypothesis is true, the two estimates will be similar and their ratio will be close to 1. If the null hypothesis is false, the between-treatments estimate will be larger than the within-treatments estimate, and their ratio will be large. In the next section we will show how large this ratio must be to reject H_0.

In summary, the logic behind ANOVA is based on the development of two independent estimates of the common population variance σ^2. One estimate of σ^2 is based on the variability among the sample means themselves, and the other estimate of σ^2 is based on the variability of the data within each sample. By comparing these two estimates of σ^2, we will be able to determine whether the population means are equal.

NOTES AND COMMENTS

1. Randomization in experimental design is the analog of probability sampling in an observational study.
2. In many medical experiments, potential bias is eliminated by using a double-blind experimental design. With this design, neither the physician applying the treatment nor the subject knows which treatment is being applied. Many other types of experiments could benefit from this type of design.
3. In this section we provided a conceptual overview of how analysis of variance can be used to test for the equality of k population means for a completely randomized experimental design. We will see that the same procedure can also be used to test for the equality of k population means for an observational or nonexperimental study.
4. In Sections 10.1 and 10.2 we presented statistical methods for testing the hypothesis that the means of two populations are equal. ANOVA can also be used to test the hypothesis that the means of two populations are equal. In practice, however, analysis of variance is usually not used except when dealing with three or more population means.

10.5 Analysis of Variance and the Completely Randomized Design

In this section we show how analysis of variance can be used to test for the equality of k population means for a completely randomized design. The general form of the hypotheses tested is

$$H_0\colon \mu_1 = \mu_2 = \cdots = \mu_k$$
$$H_a\colon \text{Not all population means are equal}$$

where

$$\mu_j = \text{mean of the } j\text{th population}$$

We assume that a random sample of size n_j has been selected from each of the k populations or treatments. For the resulting sample data, let

$$\begin{aligned}
x_{ij} &= \text{value of observation } i \text{ for treatment } j \\
n_j &= \text{number of observations for treatment } j \\
\bar{x}_j &= \text{sample mean for treatment } j \\
s_j^2 &= \text{sample variance for treatment } j \\
s_j &= \text{sample standard deviation for treatment } j
\end{aligned}$$

The formulas for the sample mean and sample variance for treatment j are as follows.

$$\bar{x}_j = \frac{\sum_{i=1}^{n_j} x_{ij}}{n_j} \tag{10.10}$$

$$s_j^2 = \frac{\sum_{i=1}^{n_j} (x_{ij} - \bar{x}_j)^2}{n_j - 1} \tag{10.11}$$

The overall sample mean, denoted $\bar{\bar{x}}$, is the sum of all the observations divided by the total number of observations. That is,

$$\bar{\bar{x}} = \frac{\sum_{j=1}^{k} \sum_{i=1}^{n_j} x_{ij}}{n_T} \tag{10.12}$$

where

$$n_T = n_1 + n_2 + \cdots + n_k \tag{10.13}$$

If the size of each sample is n, $n_T = kn$; in this case equation (10.12) reduces to

$$\bar{\bar{x}} = \frac{\sum_{j=1}^{k} \sum_{i=1}^{n_j} x_{ij}}{kn} = \frac{\sum_{j=1}^{k} \sum_{i=1}^{n_j} x_{ij}/n}{k} = \frac{\sum_{j=1}^{k} \bar{x}_j}{k} \tag{10.14}$$

In other words, whenever the sample sizes are the same, the overall sample mean is just the average of the k sample means.

Because each sample in the Chemitech experiment consists of $n = 5$ observations, the overall sample mean can be computed by using equation (10.14). For the data in Table 10.3 we obtained the following result.

$$\bar{\bar{x}} = \frac{62 + 66 + 52}{3} = 60$$

If the null hypothesis is true ($\mu_1 = \mu_2 = \mu_3 = \mu$), the overall sample mean of 60 is the best estimate of the population mean μ.

Between-Treatments Estimate of Population Variance

In the preceding section, we introduced the concept of a between-treatments estimate of σ^2 and showed how to compute it when the sample sizes were equal. This estimate of σ^2 is called the *mean square due to treatments* and is denoted MSTR. The general formula for computing MSTR is

$$\text{MSTR} = \frac{\sum_{j=1}^{k} n_j(\bar{x}_j - \bar{\bar{x}})^2}{k - 1} \tag{10.15}$$

The numerator in equation (10.15) is called the *sum of squares due to treatments* and is denoted SSTR. The denominator, $k - 1$, represents the degrees of freedom associated with SSTR. Hence, the mean square due to treatments can be computed using the following formula.

MEAN SQUARE DUE TO TREATMENTS

$$\text{MSTR} = \frac{\text{SSTR}}{k - 1} \tag{10.16}$$

where

$$\text{SSTR} = \sum_{j=1}^{k} n_j(\bar{x}_j - \bar{\bar{x}})^2 \tag{10.17}$$

If H_0 is true, MSTR provides an unbiased estimate of σ^2. However, if the means of the k populations are not equal, MSTR is not an unbiased estimate of σ^2; in fact, in that case, MSTR should overestimate σ^2.

For the Chemitech data in Table 10.3, we obtain the following results.

$$\text{SSTR} = \sum_{j=1}^{k} n_j(\bar{x}_j - \bar{\bar{x}})^2 = 5(62 - 60)^2 + 5(66 - 60)^2 + 5(52 - 60)^2 = 520$$

$$\text{MSTR} = \frac{\text{SSTR}}{k - 1} = \frac{520}{2} = 260$$

Within-Treatments Estimate of Population Variance

Earlier, we introduced the concept of a within-treatments estimate of σ^2 and showed how to compute it when the sample sizes were equal. This estimate of σ^2 is called the *mean square due to error* and is denoted MSE. The general formula for computing MSE is

$$\text{MSE} = \frac{\sum_{j=1}^{k} (n_j - 1)s_j^2}{n_T - k} \tag{10.18}$$

The numerator in equation (10.18) is called the *sum of squares due to error* and is denoted SSE. The denominator of MSE is referred to as the degrees of freedom associated with SSE. Hence, the formula for MSE can also be stated as follows.

MEAN SQUARE DUE TO ERROR

$$\text{MSE} = \frac{\text{SSE}}{n_T - k} \tag{10.19}$$

where

$$\text{SSE} = \sum_{j=1}^{k} n_j(n_j - 1)s_j^2 \tag{10.20}$$

Note that MSE is based on the variation within each of the treatments; it is not influenced by whether the null hypothesis is true. Thus, MSE always provides an unbiased estimate of σ^2.

For the Chemitech data in Table 10.3 we obtain the following results.

$$\text{SSE} = \sum_{j=1}^{k} (n_j - 1)s_j^2 = (5 - 1)27.5 + (5 - 1)26.5 + (5 - 1)31 = 340$$

$$\text{MSE} = \frac{\text{SSE}}{n_T - k} = \frac{340}{15 - 3} = \frac{340}{12} = 28.33$$

Comparing the Variance Estimates: The F Test

If the null hypothesis is true, MSTR and MSE provide two independent, unbiased estimates of σ^2. If the ANOVA assumptions are also valid, the sampling distribution of MSTR/MSE is an **F distribution** with numerator degrees of freedom equal to $k - 1$ and denominator degrees of freedom equal to $n_T - k$. The general shape of the F distribution is shown in Figure 10.13. If the null hypothesis is true, the value of MSTR/MSE should appear to have been selected from this F distribution.

However, if the null hypothesis is false, the value of MSTR/MSE will be inflated because MSTR overestimates σ^2. Hence, we will reject H_0 if the resulting value of MSTR/MSE appears to be too large to have been selected from an F distribution with $k - 1$ numerator degrees of freedom and $n_T - k$ denominator degrees of freedom. Because the decision to reject H_0 is based on the value of MSTR/MSE, the test statistic used to test for the equality of k population means is as follows.

TEST STATISTIC FOR THE EQUALITY OF k POPULATION MEANS

$$F = \frac{\text{MSTR}}{\text{MSE}} \tag{10.21}$$

The test statistic follows an F distribution with $k - 1$ degrees of freedom in the numerator and $n_T - k$ degrees of freedom in the denominator.

Let us return to the Chemitech experiment and use a level of significance $\alpha = .05$ to conduct the hypothesis test. The value of the test statistic is

$$F = \frac{\text{MSTR}}{\text{MSE}} = \frac{260}{28.33} = 9.18$$

FIGURE 10.13 COMPUTATION OF *p*-VALUE USING THE SAMPLING DISTRIBUTION OF MSTR/MSE

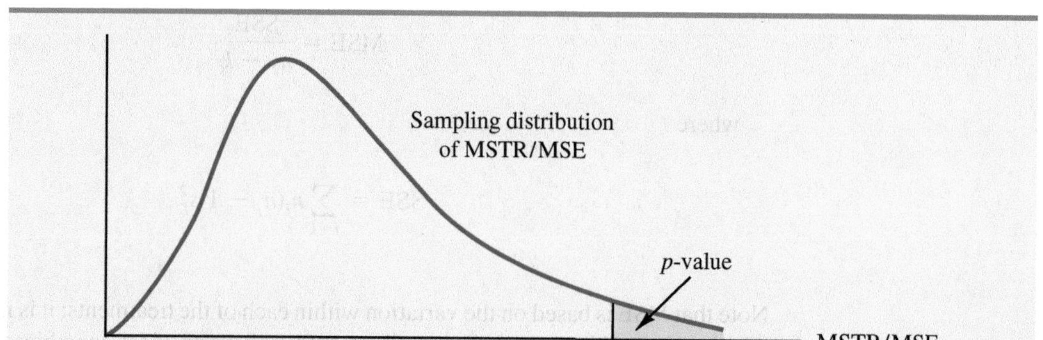

The numerator degrees of freedom is $k - 1 = 3 - 1 = 2$ and the denominator degrees of freedom is $n_T - k = 15 - 3 = 12$. Because we will only reject the null hypothesis for large values of the test statistic, the *p*-value is the upper tail area of the *F* distribution to the right of the test statistic $F = 9.18$. Figure 10.13 shows the sampling distribution of $F =$ MSTR/ MSE, the value of the test statistic, and the upper tail area that is the *p*-value for the hypothesis test.

From Table 4 of Appendix B we find the following areas in the upper tail of an *F* distribution with 2 numerator degrees of freedom and 12 denominator degrees of freedom.

Area in Upper Tail	**.10**	**.05**	**.025**	**.01**
***F* Value ($df_1 = 2, df_2 = 12$)**	2.81	3.89	5.10	6.93

$F = 9.18$

Because $F = 9.18$ is greater than 6.93, the area in the upper tail at $F = 9.18$ is less than .01. Thus, the *p*-value is less than .01. Excel can be used to show that the *p*-value is .004. With *p*-value $\leq \alpha = .05$, H_0 is rejected. The test provides sufficient evidence to conclude that the means of the three populations are not equal. In other words, analysis of variance supports the conclusion that the population mean number of units produced per week for the three assembly methods are not equal.

As with other hypothesis testing procedures, the critical value approach may also be used. With $\alpha = .05$, the critical *F* value occurs with an area of .05 in the upper tail of an *F* distribution with 2 and 12 degrees of freedom. From the *F* distribution table, we find $F_{.05} = 3.89$. Hence, the appropriate upper tail rejection rule for the Chemitech experiment is

$$\text{Reject } H_0 \text{ if } F \geq 3.89$$

With $F = 9.18$, we reject H_0 and conclude that the means of the three populations are not equal. A summary of the overall procedure for testing for the equality of *k* population means follows.

TEST FOR THE EQUALITY OF k POPULATION MEANS

$$H_0: \mu_1 = \mu_2 = \cdots = \mu_k$$
$$H_a: \text{Not all population means are equal}$$

TEST STATISTIC

$$F = \frac{\text{MSTR}}{\text{MSE}}$$

REJECTION RULE

p-value approach: Reject H_0 if p-value $\leq \alpha$

Critical value approach: Reject H_0 if $F \geq F_\alpha$

where the value of F is based on an F distribution with $k - 1$ numerator degrees of freedom and $n_T - k$ denominator degrees of freedom.

ANOVA Table

The results of the preceding calculations can be displayed conveniently in a table referred to as the analysis of variance or **ANOVA table**. The general form of the ANOVA table for a completely randomized design is shown in Table 10.4; Table 10.5 is the corresponding ANOVA table for the Chemitech experiment. The sum of squares associated with the source of variation referred to as "Total" is called the total sum of squares (SST). Note that the results for the Chemitech experiment suggest that SST = SSTR + SSE, and that the degrees of freedom associated with this total sum of squares is the sum of the degrees of freedom associated with the sum of squares due to treatments and the sum of squares due to error.

We point out that SST divided by its degrees of freedom $n_T - 1$ is nothing more than the overall sample variance that would be obtained if we treated the entire set of 15 observations as one data set. With the entire data set as one sample, the formula for computing the total sum of squares, SST, is

$$\text{SST} = \sum_{j=1}^{k} \sum_{i=1}^{n_j} (x_{ij} - \bar{\bar{x}})^2 \qquad \textbf{(10.22)}$$

It can be shown that the results we observed for the analysis of variance table for the Chemitech experiment also apply to other problems. That is,

$$\text{SST} = \text{SSTR} + \text{SSE} \qquad \textbf{(10.23)}$$

TABLE 10.4 ANOVA TABLE FOR A COMPLETELY RANDOMIZED DESIGN

Source of Variation	Sum of Squares	Degrees of Freedom	Mean Square	F	p-Value
Treatments	SSTR	$k - 1$	$\text{MSTR} = \dfrac{\text{SSTR}}{k-1}$	$\dfrac{\text{MSTR}}{\text{MSE}}$	
Error	SSE	$n_T - k$	$\text{MSE} = \dfrac{\text{SSE}}{n_T - k}$		
Total	SST	$n_T - 1$			

TABLE 10.5 ANOVA TABLE FOR THE CHEMITECH EXPERIMENT

Source of Variation	Sum of Squares	Degrees of Freedom	Mean Square	F	p-Value
Treatments	520	2	260.00	9.18	.004
Error	340	12	28.33		
Total	860	14			

Analysis of variance can be thought of as a statistical procedure for partitioning the total sum of squares into separate components.

In other words, SST can be partitioned into two sums of squares: the sum of squares due to treatments and the sum of squares due to error. Note also that the degrees of freedom corresponding to SST, $n_T - 1$, can be partitioned into the degrees of freedom corresponding to SSTR, $k - 1$, and the degrees of freedom corresponding to SSE, $n_T - k$. The analysis of variance can be viewed as the process of **partitioning** the total sum of squares and the degrees of freedom into their corresponding sources: treatments and error. Dividing the sum of squares by the appropriate degrees of freedom provides the variance estimates, the F value, and the p-value used to test the hypothesis of equal population means.

Using Excel

Excel's Anova: Single Factor tool can be used to conduct a hypothesis test about the difference between the population means for the Chemitech experiment.

Enter/Access Data: Open the WEBfile named Chemitech. The data are in cells A2:C6 and labels are in cells A1:C1.

Apply Tools: The following steps describe how to use Excel's Anova: Single Factor tool to test the hypothesis that the mean number of units produced per week is the same for all three methods of assembly.

Step 1. Click the **Data** tab on the Ribbon
Step 2. In the **Analysis** group, click **Data Analysis**
Step 3. Choose **Anova: Single Factor** from the list of Analysis Tools
Step 4. When the Anova: Single Factor dialog box appears (see Figure 10.14):
Enter A1:C6 in the **Input Range** box
Select **Grouped By: Columns**
Select **Labels in First Row**
Enter .05 in the **Alpha** box
Select **Output Range**
Enter A8 in the **Output Range** box (to identify the upper left corner of the section of the worksheet where the output will appear)
Click **OK**

The output, titled *Anova: Single Factor,* appears in cells A8:G22 of the worksheet shown in Figure 10.15. Cells A10:E14 provide a summary of the data. Note that the sample mean and sample variance for each method of assembly are the same as shown in Table 10.3. The ANOVA table, shown in cells A17:G22, is basically the same as the ANOVA table shown in Table 10.5. Excel identifies the treatments source of variation using the label *Between Groups* and the error source of variation using the label *Within Groups.* In addition, the Excel output provides the p-value associated with the test as well as the critical F value.

We can use the p-value shown in cell F19, 0.0038, to make the hypothesis testing decision. Thus, at the $\alpha = .05$ level of significance, we reject H_0 because the p-value =

FIGURE 10.14 EXCEL'S ANOVA: SINGLE FACTOR TOOL DIALOG BOX FOR THE CHEMITECH EXPERIMENT

	A	B	C
1	Method A	Method B	Method C
2	58	58	48
3	64	69	57
4	55	71	59
5	66	64	47
6	67	68	49

Anova: Single Factor

Input
Input Range: $A$1:$C$6
Grouped By: Columns / Rows
Labels in first row
Alpha: 0.05

Output options
Output Range: $A$8
New Worksheet Ply:
New Workbook

OK | Cancel | Help

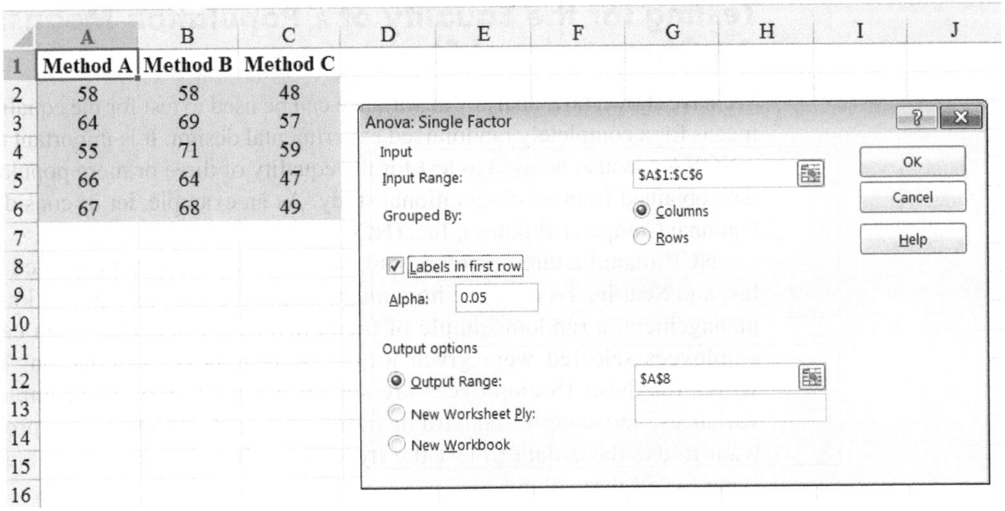

FIGURE 10.15 EXCEL'S ANOVA: SINGLE FACTOR TOOL OUTPUT FOR THE CHEMITECH EXPERIMENT

	A	B	C	D	E	F	G
1	Method A	Method B	Method C				
2	58	58	48				
3	64	69	57				
4	55	71	59				
5	66	64	47				
6	67	68	49				
7							
8	Anova: Single Factor						
9							
10	SUMMARY						
11	*Groups*	*Count*	*Sum*	*Average*	*Variance*		
12	Method A	5	310	62	27.5		
13	Method B	5	330	66	26.5		
14	Method C	5	260	52	31		
15							
16							
17	ANOVA						
18	*Source of Variation*	*SS*	*df*	*MS*	*F*	*P-value*	*F crit*
19	Between Groups	520	2	260	9.1765	0.0038	3.8853
20	Within Groups	340	12	28.3333			
21							
22	Total	860	14				
23							

$0.0038 < \alpha = .05$. Hence, using the *p*-value approach we still conclude that the mean number of units produced per week are not the same for the three assembly methods.

Testing for the Equality of *k* Population Means: An Observational Study

We have shown how analysis of variance can be used to test for the equality of *k* population means for a completely randomized experimental design. It is important to understand that ANOVA can also be used to test for the equality of three or more population means using data obtained from an observational study. As an example, let us consider the situation at National Computer Products, Inc. (NCP).

NCP manufactures printers and fax machines at plants located in Atlanta, Dallas, and Seattle. To measure how much employees at these plants know about quality management, a random sample of 6 employees was selected from each plant and the employees selected were given a quality awareness examination. The examination scores for these 18 employees are shown in Table 10.6. The sample means, sample variances, and sample standard deviations for each group are also provided. Managers want to use these data to test the hypothesis that the mean examination score is the same for all three plants.

We define population 1 as all employees at the Atlanta plant, population 2 as all employees at the Dallas plant, and population 3 as all employees at the Seattle plant. Let

$$\mu_1 = \text{mean examination score for population 1}$$
$$\mu_2 = \text{mean examination score for population 2}$$
$$\mu_3 = \text{mean examination score for population 3}$$

Although we will never know the actual values of μ_1, μ_2, and μ_3, we want to use the sample results to test the following hypotheses.

$$H_0: \mu_1 = \mu_2 = \mu_3$$
$$H_a: \text{Not all population means are equal}$$

Note that the hypothesis test for the NCP observational study is exactly the same as the hypothesis test for the Chemitech experiment. Indeed, the same analysis of variance

TABLE 10.6 EXAMINATION SCORES FOR 18 EMPLOYEES

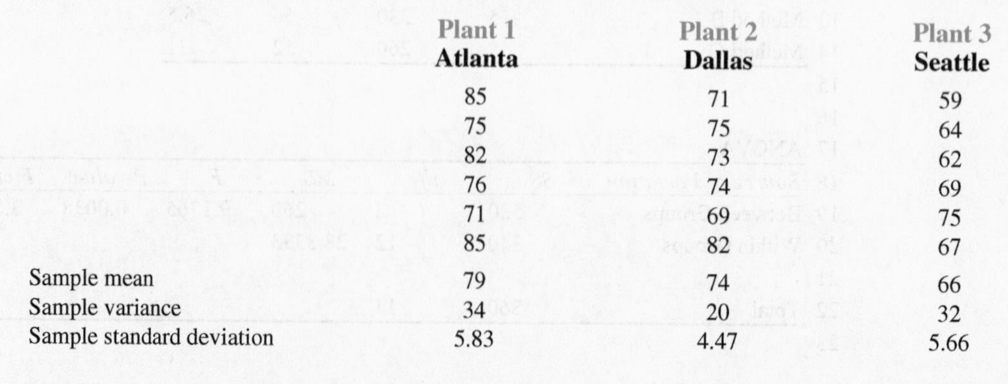

	Plant 1 Atlanta	Plant 2 Dallas	Plant 3 Seattle
	85	71	59
	75	75	64
	82	73	62
	76	74	69
	71	69	75
	85	82	67
Sample mean	79	74	66
Sample variance	34	20	32
Sample standard deviation	5.83	4.47	5.66

NCP

Exercise 35 will ask you to analyze the NCP data using the analysis of variance procedure.

methodology we used to analyze the Chemitech experiment can also be used to analyze the data from the NCP observational study.

Even though the same ANOVA methodology is used for the analysis, it is worth noting how the NCP observational statistical study differs from the Chemitech experimental statistical study. The individuals who conducted the NCP study had no control over how the plants were assigned to individual employees. That is, the plants were already in operation and a particular employee worked at one of the three plants. All that NCP could do was to select a random sample of 6 employees from each plant and administer the quality awareness examination. To be classified as an experimental study, NCP would have had to be able to randomly select 18 employees and then assign the plants to each employee in a random fashion.

NOTES AND COMMENTS

1. The overall sample mean can also be computed as a weighted average of the k sample means.

$$\bar{\bar{x}} = \frac{n_1\bar{x}_1 + n_2\bar{x}_2 + \cdots + n_k\bar{x}_k}{n_T}$$

In problems where the sample means are provided, this formula is simpler than equation (10.12) for computing the overall mean.

2. If each sample consists of n observations, equation (10.15) can be written as

$$\text{MSTR} = \frac{n\sum_{j=1}^{k}(\bar{x}_j - \bar{\bar{x}})^2}{k-1} = n\left[\frac{\sum_{j=1}^{k}(\bar{x}_j - \bar{\bar{x}})^2}{k-1}\right] = ns_{\bar{x}}^2$$

Note that this result is the same as presented in Section 10.4 when we introduced the concept of the between-treatments estimate of σ^2. Equation (10.15) is simply a generalization of this result to the unequal sample-size case.

3. If each sample has n observations, $n_T = kn$; thus, $n_T - k = k(n-1)$, and equation (10.18) can be rewritten as

$$\text{MSE} = \frac{\sum_{j=1}^{k}(n-1)s_j^2}{k(n-1)} = \frac{(n-1)\sum_{j=1}^{k}s_j^2}{k(n-1)} = \frac{\sum_{j=1}^{k}s_j^2}{k}$$

In other words, if the sample sizes are the same, MSE is the average of the k sample variances. Note that it is the same result we used in Section 10.4 when we introduced the concept of the within-treatments estimate of σ^2.

Exercises

Methods

28. The following data are from a completely randomized design.

	Treatment		
	A	**B**	**C**
	162	142	126
	142	156	122
	165	124	138
	145	142	140
	148	136	150
	174	152	128
Sample mean	156	142	134
Sample variance	164.4	131.2	110.4

a. Compute the sum of squares between treatments.
b. Compute the mean square between treatments.
c. Compute the sum of squares due to error.
d. Compute the mean square due to error.
e. Set up the ANOVA table for this problem.
f. At the $\alpha = .05$ level of significance, test whether the means for the three treatments are equal.

29. In a completely randomized design, seven experimental units were used for each of the five levels of the factor. Complete the following ANOVA table.

Source of Variation	Sum of Squares	Degrees of Freedom	Mean Square	F	p-Value
Treatments	300				
Error					
Total	460				

30. Refer to exercise 29.
a. What hypotheses are implied in this problem?
b. At the $\alpha = .05$ level of significance, can we reject the null hypothesis in part (a)? Explain.

31. In an experiment designed to test the output levels of three different treatments, the following results were obtained: SST = 400, SSTR = 150, $n_T = 19$. Set up the ANOVA table and test for any significant difference between the mean output levels of the three treatments. Use $\alpha = .05$.

32. In a completely randomized design, 12 experimental units were used for the first treatment, 15 for the second treatment, and 20 for the third treatment. Complete the following analysis of variance. At a .05 level of significance, is there a significant difference between the treatments?

Source of Variation	Sum of Squares	Degrees of Freedom	Mean Square	F	p-Value
Treatments	1200				
Error					
Total	1800				

33. Develop the analysis of variance computations for the following completely randomized design. At $\alpha = .05$, is there a significant difference between the treatment means?

Exer33

	Treatment		
	A	B	C
	136	107	92
	120	114	82
	113	125	85
	107	104	101
	131	107	89
	114	109	117
	129	97	110
	102	114	120
		104	98
		89	106
$\bar{x}_j$	119	107	100
s_j^2	146.86	96.44	173.78

Applications

34. Three different methods for assembling a product were proposed by an industrial engineer. To investigate the number of units assembled correctly with each method, 30 employees were randomly selected and randomly assigned to the three proposed methods in such a way that each method was used by 10 workers. The number of units assembled correctly was recorded, and the analysis of variance procedure was applied to the resulting data set. The following results were obtained: SST = 10,800; SSTR = 4560.
    a. Set up the ANOVA table for this problem.
    b. Use $\alpha = .05$ to test for any significant difference in the means for the three assembly methods.
35. Refer to the NCP data in Table 10.6. Set up the ANOVA table and test for any significant difference in the mean examination score for the three plants. Use $\alpha = .05$.
36. To study the effect of temperature on yield in a chemical process, five batches were produced at each of three temperature levels. The results follow. Use a .05 level of significance to test whether the temperature level has an effect on the mean yield of the process.

Temperature		
50° C	**60° C**	**70° C**
34	30	23
24	31	28
36	34	28
39	23	30
32	27	31

37. Auditors must make judgments about various aspects of an audit on the basis of their own direct experience, indirect experience, or a combination of the two. In a study, auditors were asked to make judgments about the frequency of errors to be found in an audit. The judgments by the auditors were then compared to the actual results. Suppose the following data were obtained from a similar study; lower scores indicate better judgments.

AudJudg

Direct	Indirect	Combination
17.0	16.6	25.2
18.5	22.2	24.0
15.8	20.5	21.5
18.2	18.3	26.8
20.2	24.2	27.5
16.0	19.8	25.8
13.3	21.2	24.2

Use $\alpha = .05$ to test to see whether the basis for the judgment affects the quality of the judgment. What is your conclusion?

38. Four different paints are advertised as having the same drying time. To check the manufacturer's claims, five samples were tested for each of the paints. The time in minutes until the paint was dry enough for a second coat to be applied was recorded. The following data were obtained.

Paint 1	Paint 2	Paint 3	Paint 4
128	144	133	150
137	133	143	142
135	142	137	135
124	146	136	140
141	130	131	153

At the $\alpha = .05$ level of significance, test to see whether the mean drying time is the same for each type of paint.

39. The *Consumer Reports* Restaurant Customer Satisfaction Survey is based upon 148,599 visits to full-service restaurant chains (*Consumer Reports* website). One of the variables in the study is meal price, the average amount paid per person for dinner and drinks, minus the tip. Suppose a reporter for the *Sun Coast Times* thought that it would be of interest to her readers to conduct a similar study for restaurants located on the Grand Strand section in Myrtle Beach, South Carolina. The reporter selected a sample of 8 seafood restaurants, 8 Italian restaurants, and 8 steakhouses. The following data show the meal prices ($) obtained for the 24 restaurants sampled. Use $\alpha = .05$ to test whether there is a significant difference among the mean meal price for the three types of restaurants.

Italian	Seafood	Steakhouse
$12	$16	$24
13	18	19
15	17	23
17	26	25
18	23	21
20	15	22
17	19	27
24	18	31

Summary

In this chapter we discussed procedures for developing interval estimates and conducting hypothesis tests involving two populations. First, we showed how to make inferences about the difference between two population means when independent simple random samples are selected. We first considered the case where the population standard deviations σ_1 and σ_2 could be assumed known. The standard normal distribution z was used to develop the interval estimate and served as the test statistic for hypothesis tests. We then considered the case where the population standard deviations were unknown and estimated by the sample standard deviations s_1 and s_2. In this case, the t distribution was used to develop the interval estimate and the t value served as the test statistic for hypothesis tests.

Inferences about the difference between two population means were then discussed for the matched sample design. In the matched sample design each element provides a pair of data values, one from each population. The difference between the paired data values is then used in the statistical analysis. The matched sample design is generally preferred to the independent sample design because the matched-sample procedure often improves the precision of the estimate.

In the final two sections we provided an introduction to experimental design and analysis of variance (ANOVA). Experimental studies differ from observational studies in the sense that an experiment is conducted to generate the data. The completely randomized design was described and the analysis of variance was used to test for a treatment effect.

The same analysis of variance procedure can be used to test for the difference among k population means in an observational study.

Glossary

Independent random samples Samples selected from two populations in such a way that the elements making up one sample are chosen independently of the elements making up the other sample.
Matched samples One simple random sample of elements is selected and two data values are obtained for each element. For example, to compare two production methods, one simple random sample of n workers is selected. Each worker first uses one method and then the other method. The order of the two methods is assigned randomly.
Factor Another word for the independent variable of interest.
Treatments Different levels of a factor.
Single-factor experiment An experiment involving only one factor with k populations or treatments.
Response variable Another word for the dependent variable of interest.
Experimental units The objects of interest in the experiment.
Completely randomized design An experimental design in which the treatments are randomly assigned to the experimental units.
***F* distribution** A probability distribution based on the ratio of two independent estimates of the variance of a normal population. The F distribution is used in hypothesis tests about the equality of k population means.
ANOVA table A table used to summarize the analysis of variance computations and results. It contains columns showing the source of variation, the sum of squares, the degrees of freedom, the mean square, the F value(s), and the p-value(s).
Partitioning The process of allocating the total sum of squares and degrees of freedom to the various components.

Key Formulas

Point Estimator of the Difference Between Two Population Means

$$\bar{x}_1 - \bar{x}_2 \tag{10.1}$$

Standard Error of $\bar{x}_1 - \bar{x}_2$

$$\sigma_{\bar{x}_1 - \bar{x}_2} = \sqrt{\frac{\sigma_1^2}{n_1} + \frac{\sigma_2^2}{n_2}} \tag{10.2}$$

Interval Estimate of the Difference Between Two Population Means: σ_1 and σ_2 Known

$$\bar{x}_1 - \bar{x}_2 \pm z_{\alpha/2}\sqrt{\frac{\sigma_1^2}{n_1} + \frac{\sigma_2^2}{n_2}} \tag{10.4}$$

Test Statistic for Hypothesis Tests About $\mu_1 - \mu_2$: σ_1 and σ_1 Known

$$z = \frac{(\bar{x}_1 - \bar{x}_2) - D_0}{\sqrt{\frac{\sigma_1^2}{n_1} + \frac{\sigma_2^2}{n_2}}} \tag{10.5}$$

Interval Estimate of the Difference Between Two Population Means: σ_1 and σ_2 Unknown

$$\bar{x}_1 - \bar{x}_2 \pm t_{\alpha/2}\sqrt{\frac{s_1^2}{n_1} + \frac{s_2^2}{n_2}} \tag{10.6}$$

Degrees of Freedom: *t* Distribution with Two Independent Random Samples

$$df = \frac{\left(\frac{s_1^2}{n_1} + \frac{s_2^2}{n_2}\right)^2}{\frac{1}{n_1 - 1}\left(\frac{s_1^2}{n_1}\right)^2 + \frac{1}{n_2 - 1}\left(\frac{s_2^2}{n_2}\right)^2} \tag{10.7}$$

Test Statistic for Hypothesis Tests About $\mu_1 - \mu_2$: σ_1 and σ_2 Unknown

$$t = \frac{(\bar{x}_1 - \bar{x}_2) - D_0}{\sqrt{\frac{s_1^2}{n_1} + \frac{s_2^2}{n_2}}} \tag{10.8}$$

Test Statistic for Hypothesis Tests Involving Matched Samples

$$t = \frac{\bar{d} - \mu_d}{s_d/\sqrt{n}} \tag{10.9}$$

Sample Mean for Treatment *j*

$$\bar{x}_j = \frac{\sum_{i=1}^{n_j} x_{ij}}{n_j} \tag{10.10}$$

Sample Variance for Treatment *j*

$$s_j^2 = \frac{\sum_{i=1}^{n_j} (x_{ij} - \bar{x}_j)^2}{n_j - 1} \tag{10.11}$$

Overall Sample Mean

$$\bar{\bar{x}} = \frac{\sum_{j=1}^{k}\sum_{i=1}^{n_j} x_{ij}}{n_T} \tag{10.12}$$

$$n_T = n_1 + n_2 + \cdots + n_k \tag{10.13}$$

Mean Square Due to Treatments

$$\text{MSTR} = \frac{\text{SSTR}}{k - 1} \tag{10.16}$$

Sum of Squares Due to Treatments

$$\text{SSTR} = \sum_{j=1}^{k} n_j(\bar{x}_j - \bar{\bar{x}})^2 \tag{10.17}$$

Mean Square Due to Error

$$\text{MSE} = \frac{\text{SSE}}{n_T - k} \tag{10.19}$$

Sum of Squares Due to Error

$$\text{SSE} = \sum_{j=1}^{k} n_j(n_j - 1)s_j^2 \tag{10.20}$$

Test Statistic for the Equality of k Population Means

$$F = \frac{\text{MSTR}}{\text{MSE}} \tag{10.21}$$

Total Sum of Squares

$$\text{SST} = \sum_{j=1}^{k}\sum_{i=1}^{n_j}(x_{ij} - \bar{\bar{x}})^2 \tag{10.22}$$

Partitioning of Sum of Squares

$$\text{SST} = \text{SSTR} + \text{SSE} \tag{10.23}$$

Supplementary Exercises

40. Safegate Foods, Inc., is redesigning the checkout lanes in its supermarkets throughout the country and is considering two designs. Tests on customer checkout times conducted at two stores where the two new systems have been installed result in the following summary of the data.

System A	System B
$n_1 = 120$	$n_2 = 100$
$\bar{x}_1 = 4.1$ minutes	$\bar{x}_2 = 3.4$ minutes
$\sigma_1 = 2.2$ minutes	$\sigma_2 = 1.5$ minutes

Test at the .05 level of significance to determine whether the population mean checkout times of the two systems differ. Which system is preferred?

HomePrices

41. Home values tend to increase over time under normal conditions, but the recession of 2008 and 2009 has reportedly caused the resale price of existing homes to fall nationwide (*BusinessWeek*, March 9, 2009). You would like to see if the data support this conclusion. The file HomePrices contains data on 30 existing home sales in 2006 and 40 existing home sales in 2009.
    a. Provide a point estimate of the difference between the population mean prices for the two years.
    b. Develop a 99% confidence interval estimate of the difference between the resale prices of houses in 2006 and 2009.
    c. Would you feel justified in concluding that resale prices of existing homes have declined from 2006 to 2009? Why or why not?

42. Mutual funds are classified as *load* or *no-load* funds. Load funds require an investor to pay an initial fee based on a percentage of the amount invested in the fund. The no-load funds do not require this initial fee. Some financial advisors argue that the load mutual funds

may be worth the extra fee because these funds provide a higher mean rate of return than the no-load mutual funds. A sample of 30 load mutual funds and a sample of 30 no-load mutual funds were selected. Data were collected on the annual return for the funds over a five-year period. The data are contained in the data set Mutual. The data for the first five load and first five no-load mutual funds are as follows.

Mutual

Mutual Funds—Load	Return	Mutual Funds—No Load	Return
American National Growth	15.51	Amana Income Fund	13.24
Arch Small Cap Equity	14.57	Berger One Hundred	12.13
Bartlett Cap Basic	17.73	Columbia International Stock	12.17
Calvert World International	10.31	Dodge & Cox Balanced	16.06
Colonial Fund A	16.23	Evergreen Fund	17.61

a. Formulate H_0 and H_a such that rejection of H_0 leads to the conclusion that the load mutual funds have a higher mean annual return over the five-year period.
b. Use the 60 mutual funds in the data set Mutual to conduct the hypothesis test. What is the p-value? At · = .05, what is your conclusion?

43. The National Association of Home Builders provided data on the cost of the most popular home remodeling projects. Sample data on cost in thousands of dollars for two types of remodeling projects are as follows.

Kitchen	Master Bedroom	Kitchen	Master Bedroom
25.2	18.0	23.0	17.8
17.4	22.9	19.7	24.6
22.8	26.4	16.9	21.0
21.9	24.8	21.8	
19.7	26.9	23.6	

a. Develop a point estimate of the difference between the population mean remodeling costs for the two types of projects.
b. Develop a 90% confidence interval for the difference between the two population means.

44. In early 2009, the economy was experiencing a recession. But how was the recession affecting the stock market? Shown are data from a sample of 15 companies. Shown for each company is the price per share of stock on January 1 and April 30 (*The Wall Street Journal*, May 1, 2009).

PriceChange

Company	January 1 ($)	April 30 ($)
Applied Materials	10.13	12.21
Bank of New York	28.33	25.48
Chevron	73.97	66.10
Cisco Systems	16.30	19.32
Coca-Cola	45.27	43.05
Comcast	16.88	15.46
Ford Motors	2.29	5.98
General Electric	16.20	12.65
Johnson & Johnson	59.83	52.36
JP Morgan Chase	31.53	33.00
Microsoft	19.44	20.26
Oracle	17.73	19.34
Pfizer	17.71	13.36
Philip Morris	43.51	36.18
Procter & Gamble	61.82	49.44

a. What is the change in the mean price per share of stock over the four-month period?
b. Provide a 90% confident interval estimate of the change in the mean price per share of stock. Interpret the results.
c. What was the percentage change in the mean price per share of stock over the four-month period?
d. If this same percentage change were to occur for the next four months and again for the four months after that, what would be the mean price per share of stock at the end of the year 2009?

45. In a completely randomized experimental design, three brands of paper towels were tested for their ability to absorb water. Equal-size towels were used, with four sections of towels tested per brand. The absorbency rating data follow. At a .05 level of significance, does there appear to be a difference in the ability of the brands to absorb water?

	Brand	
x	y	z
91	99	83
100	96	88
88	94	89
89	99	76

46. A study reported in the *Journal of Small Business Management* concluded that self-employed individuals do not experience higher job satisfaction than individuals who are not self-employed. In this study, job satisfaction is measured using 18 items, each of which is rated using a Likert-type scale with 1–5 response options ranging from strong agreement to strong disagreement. A higher score on this scale indicates a higher degree of job satisfaction. The sum of the ratings for the 18 items, ranging from 18 to 90, is used as the measure of job satisfaction. Suppose that this approach was used to measure the job satisfaction for lawyers, physical therapists, cabinetmakers, and systems analysts. The results obtained for a sample of 10 individuals from each profession follow.

WEB file

SatisJob

Lawyer	Physical Therapist	Cabinetmaker	Systems Analyst
44	55	54	44
42	78	65	73
74	80	79	71
42	86	69	60
53	60	79	64
50	59	64	66
45	62	59	41
48	52	78	55
64	55	84	76
38	50	60	62

At the $\alpha = .05$ level of significance, test for any difference in the job satisfaction among the four professions.

47. The U.S. Environmental Protection Agency (EPA) monitors levels of pollutants in the air for cities across the country. Ozone pollution levels are measured using a 500-point scale; lower scores indicate little health risk, and higher scores indicate greater health risk. The following data show the peak levels of ozone pollution in four cities (Birmingham, Alabama; Memphis, Tennessee; Little Rock, Arkansas; and Jackson, Mississippi) for 10 dates in 2012 (U.S. EPA website, March 20, 2012).

OzoneLevels

	City			
Date	**Birmingham AL**	**Memphis TN**	**Little Rock AR**	**Jackson MS**
Jan 9	18	20	18	14
Jan17	23	31	22	30
Jan 18	19	25	22	21
Jan 31	29	36	28	35
Feb 1	27	31	28	24
Feb 6	26	31	31	25
Feb 14	31	24	19	25
Feb 17	31	31	28	28
Feb 20	33	35	35	34
Feb 29	20	42	42	21

Use $\alpha = .05$ to test for any significant difference in the mean peak ozone levels among the four cities.

48. The U.S. Census Bureau computes quarterly vacancy and homeownership rates by state and metropolitan statistical area. Each metropolitan statistical area (MSA) has at least one urbanized area of 50,000 or more inhabitants. The following data are the rental vacancy rates (%) for MSAs in four geographic regions of the United States for the first quarter of 2008 (U.S. Census Bureau website, January 2009).

WEB file RentalVacancy

Midwest	Northeast	South	West
16.2	2.7	16.6	7.9
10.1	11.5	8.5	6.6
8.6	6.6	12.1	6.9
12.3	7.9	9.8	5.6
10.0	5.3	9.3	4.3
16.9	10.7	9.1	15.2
16.9	8.6	5.6	5.7
5.4	5.5	9.4	4.0
18.1	12.7	11.6	12.3
11.9	8.3	15.6	3.6
11.0	6.7	18.3	11.0
9.6	14.2	13.4	12.1
7.6	1.7	6.5	8.7
12.9	3.6	11.4	5.0
12.2	11.5	13.1	4.7
13.6	16.3	4.4	3.3
		8.2	3.4
		24.0	5.5
		12.2	
		22.6	
		12.0	
		14.5	
		12.6	
		9.5	
		10.1	

Use $\alpha = .05$ to test whether the mean vacancy rate is the same for each geographic region.

49. Three different assembly methods have been proposed for a new product. A completely randomized experimental design was chosen to determine which assembly method results in the greatest number of parts produced per hour, and 30 workers were randomly selected

and assigned to use one of the proposed methods. The number of units produced by each worker follows.

WEB file
Assembly

	Method	
A	**B**	**C**
97	93	99
73	100	94
93	93	87
100	55	66
73	77	59
91	91	75
100	85	84
86	73	72
92	90	88
95	83	86

Use these data and test to see whether the mean number of parts produced is the same with each method. Use $\alpha = .05$.

50. In a study conducted to investigate browsing activity by shoppers, each shopper was initially classified as a nonbrowser, light browser, or heavy browser. For each shopper, the study obtained a measure to determine how comfortable the shopper was in a store. Higher scores indicated greater comfort. Suppose the following data were collected.

Browsing

Nonbrowser	Light Browser	Heavy Browser
4	5	5
5	6	7
6	5	5
3	4	7
3	7	4
4	4	6
5	6	5
4	5	7

Use $\alpha = .05$ to test for differences among comfort levels for the three types of browsers.

Case Problem 1 Par, Inc.

Par, Inc., is a major manufacturer of golf equipment. Management believes that Par's market share could be increased with the introduction of a cut-resistant, longer-lasting golf ball. Therefore, the research group at Par has been investigating a new golf ball coating designed to resist cuts and provide a more durable ball. The tests with the coating have been promising.

One of the researchers voiced concern about the effect of the new coating on driving distances. Par would like the new cut-resistant ball to offer driving distances comparable to those of the current-model golf ball. To compare the driving distances for the two balls,

40 balls of both the new and current models were subjected to distance tests. The testing was performed with a mechanical hitting machine so that any difference between the mean distances for the two models could be attributed to a difference in the two models. The results of the tests, with distances measured to the nearest yard, follow. These data are available on the website that accompanies this text in the file named Golf.

Model		Model		Model		Model	
Current	New	Current	New	Current	New	Current	New
264	277	270	272	263	274	281	283
261	269	287	259	264	266	274	250
267	263	289	264	284	262	273	253
272	266	280	280	263	271	263	260
258	262	272	274	260	260	275	270
283	251	275	281	283	281	267	263
258	262	265	276	255	250	279	261
266	289	260	269	272	263	274	255
259	286	278	268	266	278	276	263
270	264	275	262	268	264	262	279

Managerial Report

1. Formulate and present the rationale for a hypothesis test that Par could use to compare the driving distances of the current and new golf balls.
2. Analyze the data to provide the hypothesis testing conclusion. What is the p-value for your test? What is your recommendation for Par, Inc.?
3. Provide descriptive statistical summaries of the data for each model.
4. What is the 95% confidence interval for the population mean of each model, and what is the 95% confidence interval for the difference between the means of the two populations?
5. Do you see a need for larger sample sizes and more testing with the golf balls? Discuss.

Case Problem 2 Wentworth Medical Center

As part of a long-term study of individuals 65 years of age or older, sociologists and physicians at the Wentworth Medical Center in upstate New York investigated the relationship between geographic location and depression. A sample of 60 individuals, all in reasonably good health, was selected; 20 individuals were residents of Florida, 20 were residents of New York, and 20 were residents of North Carolina. Each of the individuals sampled was given a standardized test to measure depression. The data collected follow; higher test scores indicate higher levels of depression. These data are available on the website that accompanies this text in the file named Medical1.

A second part of the study considered the relationship between geographic location and depression for individuals 65 years of age or older who had a chronic health condition such as arthritis, hypertension, and/or heart ailment. A sample of 60 individuals with such conditions was identified. Again, 20 were residents of Florida, 20 were residents of New York, and 20 were residents of North Carolina. The levels of depression recorded for this study follow. These data are available on the website that accompanies this text in the file named Medical2.

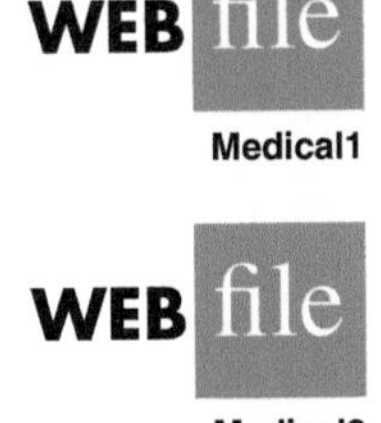

Data from Medical1			Data from Medical2		
Florida	New York	North Carolina	Florida	New York	North Carolina
3	8	10	13	14	10
7	11	7	12	9	12
7	9	3	17	15	15
3	7	5	17	12	18
8	8	11	20	16	12
8	7	8	21	24	14
8	8	4	16	18	17
5	4	3	14	14	8
5	13	7	13	15	14
2	10	8	17	17	16
6	6	8	12	20	18
2	8	7	9	11	17
6	12	3	12	23	19
6	8	9	15	19	15
9	6	8	16	17	13
7	8	12	15	14	14
5	5	6	13	9	11
4	7	3	10	14	12
7	7	8	11	13	13
3	8	11	17	11	11

Managerial Report

1. Use descriptive statistics to summarize the data from the two studies. What are your preliminary observations about the depression scores?
2. Use analysis of variance on both data sets. State the hypotheses being tested in each case. What are your conclusions?
3. Use inferences about individual treatment means where appropriate. What are your conclusions?

CHAPTER 11

Comparisons Involving Proportions and a Test of Independence

CONTENTS

STATISTICS IN PRACTICE: UNITED WAY

11.1 INFERENCES ABOUT THE DIFFERENCE BETWEEN TWO POPULATION PROPORTIONS
Interval Estimation of $p_1 - p_2$
Using Excel to Construct a Confidence Interval
Hypothesis Tests About $p_1 - p_2$
Using Excel to Conduct a Hypothesis Test

11.2 TESTING THE EQUALITY OF POPULATION PROPORTIONS FOR THREE OR MORE POPULATIONS
Using Excel to Conduct a Test of Multiple Proportions

11.3 TEST OF INDEPENDENCE
Using Excel to Conduct a Test of Independence

STATISTICS *in* PRACTICE

UNITED WAY*
ROCHESTER, NEW YORK

United Way of Greater Rochester is a nonprofit organization dedicated to improving the quality of life for all people in the seven counties it serves by meeting the community's most important human care needs.

The annual United Way/Red Cross fund-raising campaign, conducted each spring, funds hundreds of programs offered by more than 200 service providers. These providers meet a wide variety of human needs—physical, mental, and social—and serve people of all ages, backgrounds, and economic means.

Because of enormous volunteer involvement, United Way of Greater Rochester is able to hold its operating costs at just eight cents of every dollar raised.

The United Way of Greater Rochester decided to conduct a survey to learn more about community perceptions of charities. Focus-group interviews were held with professional, service, and general worker groups to get preliminary information on perceptions. The information obtained was then used to help develop the questionnaire for the survey. The questionnaire was pretested, modified, and distributed to 440 individuals; 323 completed questionnaires were obtained.

A variety of descriptive statistics, including frequency distributions and crosstabulations, were provided from the data collected. An important part of the analysis involved the use of contingency tables and chi-square tests of independence. One use of such statistical tests was to determine whether perceptions of administrative expenses were independent of occupation.

The hypotheses for the test of independence were

H_0: Perception of United Way administrative expenses is independent of the occupation of the respondent.

H_a: Perception of United Way administrative expenses is not independent of the occupation of the respondent.

*The authors are indebted to Dr. Philip R. Tyler, Marketing Consultant to the United Way, for providing this Statistics in Practice.

The after-school program at Wesley House Community Center. © Jim West/Alamy.

Two questions in the survey provided the data for the statistical test. One question obtained data on perceptions of the percentage of funds going to administrative expenses (up to 10%, 11–20%, and 21% or more). The other question asked for the occupation of the respondent.

The chi-square test at a .05 level of significance led to rejection of the null hypothesis of independence and to the conclusion that perceptions of United Way's administrative expenses did vary by occupation. Actual administrative expenses were less than 9%, but 35% of the respondents perceived that administrative expenses were 21% or more. Hence, many had inaccurate perceptions of administrative costs. In this group, production-line, clerical, sales, and professional-technical employees had more inaccurate perceptions than other groups.

The community perceptions study helped United Way of Rochester to develop adjustments to its programs and fund-raising activities. In this chapter, you will learn how a statistical test of independence, such as that described here, is conducted.

Many statistical applications call for a comparison of population proportions. In Section 11.1, we describe statistical inferences concerning differences in the proportions for two populations. Two samples are required, one from each population, and the statistical inference is based on the two sample proportions. Section 11.2 extends the procedure for testing the difference between two population proportions to testing for the equality of population proportions for three or more populations. The test is based on independent random samples from each of the populations. In Section 11.3, we show how contingency tables can be used to test for the independence of two variables from a single population. One sample is used for the test of independence, but measures on two variables are required for each sampled element. Both Sections 11.2 and 11.3 rely on the use of a chi-square statistical test.

11.1 Inferences About the Difference Between Two Population Proportions

Letting p_1 denote the proportion for population 1 and p_2 denote the proportion for population 2, we next consider inferences about the difference between the two population proportions: $p_1 - p_2$. To make an inference about this difference, we will select independent random samples consisting of n_1 units from population 1 and n_2 units from population 2.

Interval Estimation of $p_1 - p_2$

In the following example, we show how to compute a margin of error and develop an interval estimate of the difference between two population proportions.

A tax preparation firm is interested in comparing the quality of work at two of its regional offices. By randomly selecting samples of tax returns prepared at each office and verifying the sample returns' accuracy, the firm will be able to estimate the proportion of erroneous returns prepared at each office. Of particular interest is the difference between these proportions.

p_1 = proportion of erroneous returns for population 1 (office 1)

p_2 = proportion of erroneous returns for population 2 (office 2)

$\bar{p}_1$ = sample proportion for a simple random sample from population 1

$\bar{p}_2$ = sample proportion for a simple random sample from population 2

The difference between the two population proportions is given by $p_1 - p_2$. The point estimator of $p_1 - p_2$ is as follows.

POINT ESTIMATOR OF THE DIFFERENCE BETWEEN TWO POPULATION PROPORTIONS

$$\bar{p}_1 - \bar{p}_2 \tag{11.1}$$

Thus, the point estimator of the difference between two population proportions is the difference between the sample proportions of two independent simple random samples.

As with other point estimators, the point estimator $\bar{p}_1 - \bar{p}_2$ has a sampling distribution that reflects the possible values of $\bar{p}_1 - \bar{p}_2$ if we repeatedly took two independent random samples. The mean of this sampling distribution is $p_1 - p_2$ and the standard error of $\bar{p}_1 - \bar{p}_2$ is as follows:

STANDARD ERROR OF $\bar{p}_1 - \bar{p}_2$

$$\sigma_{\bar{p}_1 - \bar{p}_2} = \sqrt{\frac{p_1(1 - p_1)}{n_1} + \frac{p_2(1 - p_2)}{n_2}} \tag{11.2}$$

Sample sizes involving proportions are usually large enough to use this approximation.

If the sample sizes are large enough that n_1p_1, $n_1(1 - p_1)$, n_2p_2, and $n_2(1 - p_2)$ are all greater than or equal to 5, the sampling distribution of $\bar{p}_1 - \bar{p}_2$ can be approximated by a normal distribution.

As we showed previously, an interval estimate is given by a point estimate $\pm$ a margin of error. In the estimation of the difference between two population proportions, an interval estimate will take the following form:

$$\bar{p}_1 - \bar{p}_2 \pm \text{Margin of error}$$

With the sampling distribution of $\bar{p}_1 - \bar{p}_2$ approximated by a normal distribution, we would like to use $z_{\alpha/2}\sigma_{\bar{p}_1 - \bar{p}_2}$ as the margin of error. However, $\sigma_{\bar{p}_1 - \bar{p}_2}$ given by equation (11.2) cannot be used directly because the two population proportions, p_1 and p_2, are unknown. Using the sample proportion $\bar{p}_1$ to estimate p_1 and the sample proportion $\bar{p}_2$ to estimate p_2, the margin of error is as follows.

$$\text{Margin of error} = z_{\alpha/2}\sqrt{\frac{\bar{p}_1(1 - \bar{p}_1)}{n_1} + \frac{\bar{p}_2(1 - \bar{p}_2)}{n_2}} \tag{11.3}$$

The general form of an interval estimate of the difference between two population proportions is as follows.

INTERVAL ESTIMATE OF THE DIFFERENCE BETWEEN TWO POPULATION PROPORTIONS

$$\bar{p}_1 - \bar{p}_2 \pm z_{\alpha/2}\sqrt{\frac{\bar{p}_1(1 - \bar{p}_1)}{n_1} + \frac{\bar{p}_2(1 - \bar{p}_2)}{n_2}} \tag{11.4}$$

where $1 - \alpha$ is the confidence coefficient.

Returning to the tax preparation example, we find that independent random samples from the two offices provide the following information.

Office 1	**Office 2**
$n_1 = 250$	$n_2 = 300$
Number of returns with errors = 35	Number of returns with errors = 27

TaxPrep

The sample proportions for the two offices follow.

$$\bar{p}_1 = \frac{35}{250} = .14$$

$$\bar{p}_2 = \frac{27}{300} = .09$$

The point estimate of the difference between the proportions of erroneous tax returns for the two populations is $\bar{p}_1 - \bar{p}_2 = .14 - .09 = .05$. Thus, we estimate that office 1 has a .05, or 5%, greater error rate than office 2.

Expression (11.4) can now be used to provide a margin of error and interval estimate of the difference between the two population proportions. Using a 90% confidence interval with $z_{\alpha/2} = z_{.05} = 1.645$, we have

$$\bar{p}_1 - \bar{p}_2 \pm z_{\alpha/2}\sqrt{\frac{\bar{p}_1(1-\bar{p}_1)}{n_1} + \frac{\bar{p}_2(1-\bar{p}_2)}{n_2}}$$

$$.14 - .09 \pm 1.645\sqrt{\frac{.14(1-.14)}{250} + \frac{.09(1-.09)}{300}}$$

$$.05 \pm .045$$

Thus, the margin of error is .045, and the 90% confidence interval is .005 to .095.

Using Excel to Construct a Confidence Interval

We can create a worksheet for developing an interval estimate of the difference between population proportions. Let us illustrate by developing an interval estimate of the difference between the proportions of erroneous tax returns at the two offices of the tax preparation firm. Refer to Figure 11.1 as we describe the tasks involved. The formula worksheet is in the background; the value worksheet appears in the foreground.

Enter/Access Data: Open the WEBfile named TaxPrep. Columns A and B contain headings and Yes or No data that indicate which of the tax returns from each office contain an error.

FIGURE 11.1 CONSTRUCTING A 90% CONFIDENCE INTERVAL FOR THE DIFFERENCE IN THE PROPORTION OF ERRONEOUS TAX RETURNS PREPARED BY TWO OFFICES

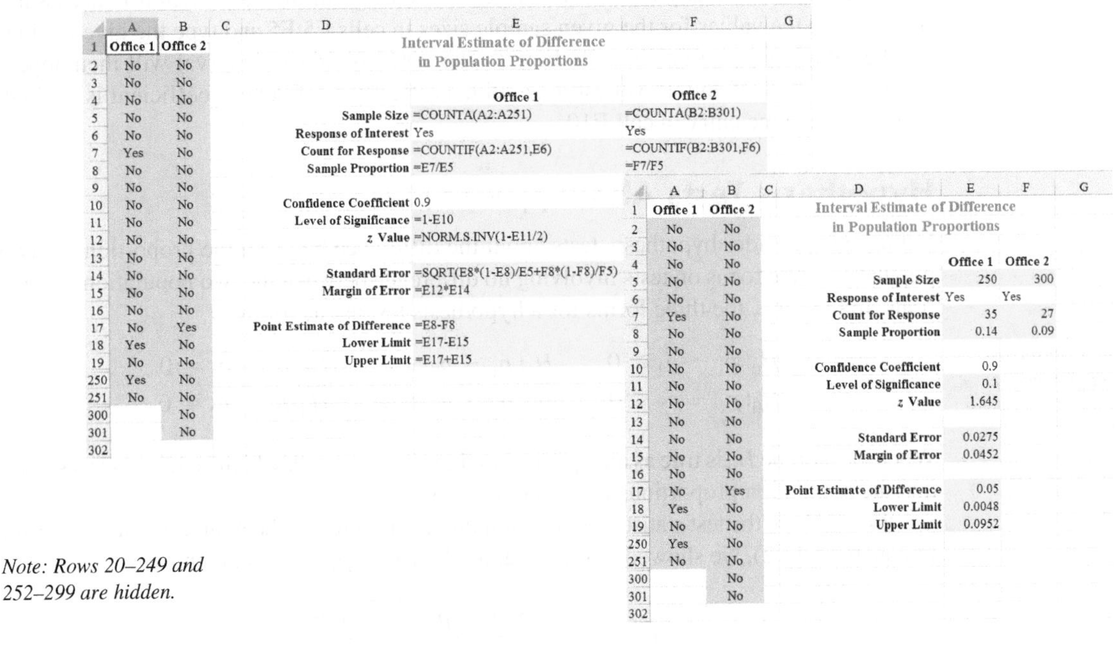

Formula worksheet:

	A	B	C	D	E	F
1	Office 1	Office 2			Interval Estimate of Difference in Population Proportions	
2	No	No				
3	No	No				
4	No	No			Office 1	Office 2
5	No	No		Sample Size	=COUNTA(A2:A251)	=COUNTA(B2:B301)
6	No	No		Response of Interest	Yes	Yes
7	Yes	No		Count for Response	=COUNTIF(A2:A251,E6)	=COUNTIF(B2:B301,F6)
8	No	No		Sample Proportion	=E7/E5	=F7/F5
9	No	No				
10	No	No		Confidence Coefficient	0.9	
11	No	No		Level of Significance	=1-E10	
12	No	No		z Value	=NORM.S.INV(1-E11/2)	
13	No	No				
14	No	No		Standard Error	=SQRT(E8*(1-E8)/E5+F8*(1-F8)/F5)	
15	No	No		Margin of Error	=E12*E14	
16	No	No				
17	No	Yes		Point Estimate of Difference	=E8-F8	
18	Yes	No		Lower Limit	=E17-E15	
19	No	No		Upper Limit	=E17+E15	
250	Yes	No				
251	No	No				
300		No				
301		No				
302						

Value worksheet:

	A	B	C	D	E	F
1	Office 1	Office 2		Interval Estimate of Difference in Population Proportions		
2	No	No				
3	No	No				
4	No	No			Office 1	Office 2
5	No	No		Sample Size	250	300
6	No	No		Response of Interest	Yes	Yes
7	Yes	No		Count for Response	35	27
8	No	No		Sample Proportion	0.14	0.09
9	No	No				
10	No	No		Confidence Coefficient	0.9	
11	No	No		Level of Significance	0.1	
12	No	No		z Value	1.645	
13	No	No				
14	No	No		Standard Error	0.0275	
15	No	No		Margin of Error	0.0452	
16	No	No				
17	No	Yes		Point Estimate of Difference	0.05	
18	Yes	No		Lower Limit	0.0048	
19	No	No		Upper Limit	0.0952	
250	Yes	No				
251	No	No				
300		No				
301		No				
302						

Note: Rows 20–249 and 252–299 are hidden.

Enter Functions and Formulas: The descriptive statistics needed are provided in cells E5:F5 and E7:F8. Note that Excel's COUNTA function is used in cells E5 and F5 to count the number of observations for each of the samples. The value worksheet indicates 250 returns in the sample from office 1 and 300 returns in the sample from office 2. In cells E6 and F6, we type Yes to indicate the response of interest (an erroneous return). Excel's COUNTIF function is used in cells E7 and F7 to count the number of Yes responses from each office. Formulas entered into cells E8 and F8 compute the sample proportions. The confidence coefficient entered into cell E10 (.9) is used to compute the corresponding level of significance ($\alpha = .10$) in cell E11. In cell E12 we use the NORM.S.INV function to compute the z value needed to compute the margin of error for the interval estimate.

In cell E14, a point estimate of $\sigma_{\bar{p}_1 - \bar{p}_2}$, the standard error of the point estimator $\bar{p}_1 - \bar{p}_2$, is computed based on the two sample proportions (E8 and F8) and sample sizes (E5 and F5). The margin of error is then computed in cell E15 by multiplying the z value by the estimate of the standard error.

The point estimate of the difference in the two population proportions is computed in cell E17 as the difference in the sample proportions; the result, shown in the value worksheet, is .05. The lower limit of the confidence interval is computed in cell E18 by subtracting the margin of error from the point estimate. The upper limit is computed in cell E19 by adding the margin of error to the point estimate. The value worksheet shows that the 90% confidence interval estimate of the difference in the two population proportions is .0048 to .0952.

A template for other problems This worksheet can be used as a template for other problems requiring an interval estimate of the difference in population proportions. The new data must be entered in columns A and B. The data ranges in the cells used to compute the sample size (E5:F5) and the cells used to compute a count of the response of interest (E7:F7) must be changed to correctly indicate the location of the new data. The response of interest must be typed into cells E6:F6. The 90% confidence interval for the new data will then appear in cells E17:E19. If an interval estimate with a different confidence coefficient is desired, simply change the entry in cell E10.

This worksheet can also be used as a template for solving text exercises in which the sample data have already been summarized. No change in the data section is necessary. Simply type the values for the given sample sizes in cells E5:F5 and type the given values for the sample proportions in cells E8:F8. The 90% confidence interval will then appear in cells E17:E19. If an interval estimate with a different confidence coefficient is desired, simply change the entry in cell E10.

Hypothesis Tests About $p_1 - p_2$

Let us now consider hypothesis tests about the difference between the proportions of two populations. We focus on tests involving no difference between the two population proportions. In this case, the three forms for a hypothesis test are as follows:

All hypotheses considered use 0 as the difference of interest.

$$H_0: p_1 - p_2 \geq 0 \qquad H_0: p_1 - p_2 \leq 0 \qquad H_0: p_1 - p_2 = 0$$
$$H_a: p_1 - p_2 < 0 \qquad H_a: p_1 - p_2 > 0 \qquad H_a: p_1 - p_2 \neq 0$$

When we assume H_0 is true as an equality, we have $p_1 - p_2 = 0$, which is the same as saying that the population proportions are equal, $p_1 = p_2$.

We will base the test statistic on the sampling distribution of the point estimator $\bar{p}_1 - \bar{p}_2$. In equation (11.2), we showed that the standard error of $\bar{p}_1 - \bar{p}_2$ is given by

$$\sigma_{\bar{p}_1 - \bar{p}_2} = \sqrt{\frac{p_1(1 - p_1)}{n_1} + \frac{p_2(1 - p_2)}{n_2}}$$

Under the assumption H_0 is true as an equality, the population proportions are equal and $p_1 = p_2 = p$. In this case, $\sigma_{\bar{p}_1 - \bar{p}_2}$ becomes

STANDARD ERROR OF $\bar{p}_1 - \bar{p}_2$ WHEN $p_1 = p_2 = p$

$$\sigma_{\bar{p}_1 - \bar{p}_2} = \sqrt{\frac{p(1-p)}{n_1} + \frac{p(1-p)}{n_2}} = \sqrt{p(1-p)\left(\frac{1}{n_1} + \frac{1}{n_2}\right)} \qquad (11.5)$$

With p unknown, we pool, or combine, the point estimators from the two samples ($\bar{p}_1$ and $\bar{p}_2$) to obtain a single point estimator of p as follows.

POOLED ESTIMATOR OF p WHEN $p_1 = p_2 = p$

$$\bar{p} = \frac{n_1\bar{p}_1 + n_2\bar{p}_2}{n_1 + n_2} \qquad (11.6)$$

This **pooled estimator of p** is a weighted average of $\bar{p}_1$ and $\bar{p}_2$.

Substituting $\bar{p}$ for p in equation (11.5), we obtain an estimate of the standard error of $\bar{p}_1 - \bar{p}_2$. This estimate of the standard error is used in the test statistic. The general form of the test statistic for hypothesis tests about the difference between two population proportions is the point estimator divided by the estimate of $\sigma_{\bar{p}_1 - \bar{p}_2}$.

TEST STATISTIC FOR HYPOTHESIS TESTS ABOUT $p_1 - p_2$

$$z = \frac{(\bar{p}_1 - \bar{p}_2)}{\sqrt{\bar{p}(1-\bar{p})\left(\frac{1}{n_1} + \frac{1}{n_2}\right)}} \qquad (11.7)$$

This test statistic applies to large sample situations where n_1p_1, $n_1(1 - p_1)$, n_2p_2, and $n_2(1 - p_2)$ are all greater than or equal to 5.

Let us return to the tax preparation firm example and assume that the firm wants to use a hypothesis test to determine whether the error proportions differ between the two offices. A two-tailed test is required. The null and alternative hypotheses are as follows:

$$H_0\colon p_1 - p_2 = 0$$
$$H_a\colon p_1 - p_2 \neq 0$$

If H_0 is rejected, the firm can conclude that the error rates at the two offices differ. We will use $\alpha = .10$ as the level of significance.

The sample data previously collected showed $\bar{p}_1 = .14$ for the $n_1 = 250$ returns sampled at office 1 and $\bar{p}_2 = .09$ for the $n_2 = 300$ returns sampled at office 2. We continue by computing the pooled estimate of p.

$$\bar{p} = \frac{n_1\bar{p}_1 + n_2\bar{p}_2}{n_1 + n_2} = \frac{250(.14) + 300(.09)}{250 + 300} = .1127$$

Using this pooled estimate and the difference between the sample proportions, the value of the test statistic is as follows.

$$z = \frac{(\bar{p}_1 - \bar{p}_2)}{\sqrt{\bar{p}(1-\bar{p})\left(\frac{1}{n_1} + \frac{1}{n_2}\right)}} = \frac{(.14 - .09)}{\sqrt{.1127(1 - .1127)\left(\frac{1}{250} + \frac{1}{300}\right)}} = 1.85$$

In computing the p-value for this two-tailed test, we first note that $z = 1.85$ is in the upper tail of the standard normal distribution. Using $z = 1.85$ and the standard normal distribution table, we find the area in the upper tail is $1.0000 - .9678 = .0322$. Doubling this area for a two-tailed test, we find the p-value $= 2(.0322) = .0644$. With the p-value less than $\alpha = .10$, H_0 is rejected at the .10 level of significance. The firm can conclude that the error rates differ between the two offices. This hypothesis testing conclusion is consistent with the earlier interval estimation results that showed the interval estimate of the difference between the population error rates at the two offices to be .005 to .095, with Office 1 having the higher error rate.

Using Excel to Conduct a Hypothesis Test

We can create a worksheet for conducting a hypothesis test about the difference between population proportions. Let us illustrate by testing to see whether there is a significant difference between the proportions of erroneous tax returns at the two offices of the tax preparation firm. Refer to Figure 11.2 as we describe the tasks involved. The formula worksheet is in the background; the value worksheet is in the foreground.

FIGURE 11.2 HYPOTHESIS TEST CONCERNING DIFFERENCE IN PROPORTION OF ERRONEOUS TAX RETURNS PREPARED BY TWO OFFICES

	A	B	C	D	E	F	G
1	Office 1	Office 2			Hypothesis Test Concerning Difference		
2	No	No			Between Population Proportions		
3	No	No					
4	No	No			Office 1	Office 2	
5	No	No		Sample Size	=COUNTA(A2:A251)	=COUNTA(B2:B301)	
6	No	No		Response of Interest	Yes	Yes	
7	Yes	No		Count for Response	=COUNTIF(A2:A251,E6)	=COUNTIF(B2:B301,F6)	
8	No	No		Sample Proportion	=E7/E5	=F7/F5	
9	No	No					
10	No	No		Hypothesized Value	0		
11	No	No		Point Estimate of Difference	=E8-F8		
12	No	No					
13	No	No		Pooled Estimate of *p*	=(E5*E8+F5*F8)/(E5+F5)		
14	No	No		Standard Error	=SQRT(E13*(1-E13)*(1/E5+1/F5))		
15	No	No		Test Statistic	=(E11-E10)/E14		
16	No	No					
17	No	Yes		*p*-value (Lower Tail)	=NORM.S.DIST(E15,TRUE)		
18	Yes	No		*p*-value (Upper Tail)	=1-NORM.S.DIST(E15,TRUE)		
19	No	No		*p*-value (Two Tail)	=2*MIN(E17,E18)		
250	Yes	No					
251	No	No					
300		No					
301		No					
302							

	A	B	C	D	E	F	G
1	Office 1	Office 2		Hypothesis Test Concerning Difference			
2	No	No		Between Population Proportions			
3	No	No					
4	No	No			Office 1	Office 2	
5	No	No		Sample Size	250	300	
6	No	No		Response of Interest	Yes	Yes	
7	Yes	No		Count for Response	35	27	
8	No	No		Sample Proportion	0.14	0.09	
9	No	No					
10	No	No		Hypothesized Value	0		
11	No	No		Point Estimate of Difference	0.05		
12	No	No					
13	No	No		Pooled Estimate of *p*	0.1127		
14	No	No		Standard Error	0.0271		
15	No	No		Test Statistic	1.8462		
16	No	No					
17	No	Yes		*p*-value (Lower Tail)	0.9676		
18	Yes	No		*p*-value (Upper Tail)	0.0324		
19	No	No		*p*-value (Two Tail)	0.0649		
250	Yes	No					
251	No	No					
300		No					
301		No					
302							

Note: Rows 20–249 and 252–299 are hidden.

Enter/Access Data: Open the WEBfile named TaxPrep. Columns A and B contain headings and Yes or No data that indicate which of the tax returns from each office contain an error.

Enter Functions and Formulas: The descriptive statistics needed to perform the hypothesis test are provided in cells E5:F5 and E7:F8. They are the same as the ones used for an interval estimate (see Figure 11.1). The hypothesized value of the difference between the two populations is zero; it is entered into cell E10. In cell E11, the difference in the sample proportions is used to compute a point estimate of the difference in the two population proportions. Using the two sample proportions and sample sizes, a pooled estimate of the population proportion p is computed in cell E13; its value is .1127. Then, in cell E14, an estimate of $\sigma_{\bar{p}_1 - \bar{p}_2}$ is computed using equation (11.5), with the pooled estimate of p and the sample sizes.

The formula =(E11-E10)/E14 entered into cell E15 computes the test statistic z (1.8462). The NORM.S.DIST function is then used to compute the p-value (Lower Tail) and the p-value (Upper Tail) in cells E17 and E18. The p-value (Two Tail) is computed in cell E19 as twice the minimum of the two one-tailed p-values. The value worksheet shows that p-value (Two Tail) $= .0649$. Because the p-value $= .0649$ is less than the level of significance, $\alpha = .10$, we have sufficient evidence to reject the null hypothesis and conclude that the population proportions are not equal.

The p-value here (.0649) differs from the one we found using the cumulative normal probability tables (.0644) due to rounding.

This worksheet can be used as a template for hypothesis testing problems involving differences between population proportions. The new data can be entered into columns A and B. The ranges for the new data and the response of interest need to be revised in cells E5:F7. The remainder of the worksheet will then be updated as needed to conduct the hypothesis test. If a hypothesized difference other than 0 is to be used, the new value must be entered in cell E10.

To use this worksheet for exercises in which the sample statistics are given, just type in the given values for cells E5:F5 and E7:F8. The remainder of the worksheet will then be updated to conduct the hypothesis test. If a hypothesized difference other than 0 is to be used, the new value must be entered in cell E10.

Exercises

Methods

1. Consider the following results for independent samples taken from two populations.

Sample 1	Sample 2
$n_1 = 400$	$n_2 = 300$
$\bar{p}_1 = .48$	$\bar{p}_2 = .36$

   a. What is the point estimate of the difference between the two population proportions?
   b. Develop a 90% confidence interval for the difference between the two population proportions.
   c. Develop a 95% confidence interval for the difference between the two population proportions.

2. Consider the following hypothesis test.

$$H_0: p_1 - p_2 = 0$$
$$H_a: p_1 - p_2 \neq 0$$

The following results are for independent samples taken from the two populations.

Sample 1	Sample 2
$n_1 = 100$	$n_2 = 140$
$\bar{p}_1 = .28$	$\bar{p}_2 = .20$

a. What is the pooled estimate of p?
b. What is the p-value?
c. What is your conclusion?

3. Consider the hypothesis test

$$H_0: p_1 - p_2 \leq 0$$
$$H_a: p_1 - p_2 > 0$$

The following results are for independent samples taken from the two populations.

Sample 1	Sample 2
$n_1 = 200$	$n_2 = 300$
$\bar{p}_1 = .22$	$\bar{p}_2 = .16$

a. What is the p-value?
b. With $\alpha = .05$, what is your hypothesis testing conclusion?

Applications

4. A *Bloomberg Businessweek*/Harris survey asked senior executives at large corporations their opinions about the economic outlook for the future. One question was, "Do you think that there will be an increase in the number of full-time employees at your company over the next 12 months?" In the current survey, 220 of 400 executives answered Yes, while in a previous year survey, 192 of 400 executives had answered Yes. Provide a 95% confidence interval estimate for the difference between the proportions at the two points in time. What is your interpretation of the interval estimate?

5. *Forbes* reports that women trust recommendations from Pinterest more than recommendations from any other social network platform (*Forbes* website, April 10, 2012). But does trust in Pinterest differ by gender? The following sample data show the number of women and men who stated in a recent sample that they trust recommendations made on Pinterest.

	Women	Men
Sample	150	170
Trust Recommendations Made on Pinterest	117	102

a. What is the point estimate of the proportion of women who trust recommendations made on Pinterest?
b. What is the point estimate of the proportion of men who trust recommendations made on Pinterest?
c. Provide a 95% confidence interval estimate of the difference between the proportion of women and men who trust recommendations made on Pinterest.

6. Researchers with Oceana, a group dedicated to preserving the ocean ecosystem, reported finding that 33% of fish sold in retail outlets, grocery stores, and sushi bars throughout

the United States had been mislabeled (*San Francisco Chronicle* website, February 21, 2013). Does this mislabeling differ for different species of fish? The following data show the number labeled incorrectly for samples of tuna and mahi mahi.

	Tuna	Mahi Mahi
Sample	220	160
Mislabeled	99	56

a. What is the point estimate of the proportion of tuna that is mislabeled?
b. What is the point estimate of the proportion of mahi mahi that is mislabeled?
c. Provide a 95% confidence interval estimate of the difference between the proportion of tuna and mahi mahi that is mislabeled.

7. Minnesota had the highest turnout rate of any state for the 2012 presidential election (United States Election Project website, February 9, 2013). Political analysts wonder if turnout in rural Minnesota was higher than turnout in the urban areas of the state. A sample shows that 663 of 884 registered voters from rural Minnesota voted in the 2012 presidential election, while 414 out of 575 registered voters from urban Minnesota voted.
   a. Formulate the null and alternative hypotheses that can be used to test whether registered voters in rural Minnesota were more likely than registered voters in urban Minnesota to vote in the 2012 presidential election.
   b. What is the proportion of sampled registered voters in rural Minnesota that voted in the 2012 presidential election?
   c. What is the proportion of sampled registered voters in urban Minnesota that voted in the 2012 presidential election?
   d. At $\alpha = .05$, test the political analysts' hypothesis. What is the p-value, and what conclusion do you draw from your results?

8. Oil wells are expensive to drill, and dry wells are a great concern to oil exploration companies. The domestic oil and natural gas producer Aegis Oil, LLC describes on its website how improvements in technologies such as three-dimensional seismic imaging have dramatically reduced the number of dry (nonproducing) wells it and other oil exploration companies drill. The following sample data for wells drilled in 2005 and 2012 show the number of dry wells that were drilled in each year.

	2005	2012
Wells Drilled	119	162
Dry Wells	24	18

   a. Formulate the null and alternative hypotheses that can be used to test whether the wells drilled in 2005 were more likely to be dry than wells drilled in 2012.
   b. What is the point estimate of the proportion of wells drilled in 2005 that were dry?
   c. What is the point estimate of the proportion of wells drilled in 2012 that were dry?
   d. What is the p-value of your hypothesis test? At $\alpha = .05$, what conclusion do you draw from your results?

9. The Adecco Workplace Insights Survey sampled men and women workers and asked if they expected to get a raise or promotion this year (*USA Today*, February 16, 2012). Suppose the survey sampled 200 men and 200 women. If 104 of the men replied Yes and 74 of the women replied Yes, are the results statistically significant so that you can conclude a greater proportion of men expect to get a raise or a promotion this year?

a. State the hypothesis test in terms of the population proportion of men and the population proportion of women.
b. What is the sample proportion for men? For women?
c. Use a .01 level of significance. What is the p-value and what is your conclusion?

10. Winter visitors are extremely important to the economy of Southwest Florida. Hotel occupancy is an often-reported measure of visitor volume and visitor activity (*Naples Daily News*, March 22, 2012). Hotel occupancy data for February in two consecutive years are as follows.

	Current Year	**Previous Year**
Occupied Rooms	1470	1458
Total Rooms	1750	1800

a. Formulate the hypothesis test that can be used to determine if there has been an increase in the proportion of rooms occupied over the one-year period.
b. What is the estimated proportion of hotel rooms occupied each year?
c. Using a .05 level of significance, what is your hypothesis test conclusion? What is the p-value?
d. What is the 95% confidence interval estimate of the change in occupancy for the one-year period? Do you think area officials would be pleased with the results?

11.2 Testing the Equality of Population Proportions for Three or More Populations

In Section 11.1 we introduced methods of statistical inference for population proportions with two populations where the hypothesis test conclusion was based on the standard normal (z) test statistic. We now show how the chi-square (χ^2) test statistic can be used to make statistical inferences about the equality of population proportions for three or more populations. Using the notation

$$p_1 = \text{population proportion for population 1}$$

$$p_2 = \text{population proportion for population 2}$$

and

$$p_k = \text{population proportion for population } k$$

the hypotheses for the equality of population proportions for $k \geq 3$ populations are as follows:

$$H_0\colon p_1 = p_2 = \cdots = p_k$$

$$H_a\colon \text{Not all population proportions are equal}$$

If the sample data and the chi-square test computations indicate H_0 cannot be rejected, we cannot detect a difference among the k population proportions. However, if the sample data and the chi-square test computations indicate H_0 can be rejected, we have the statistical evidence to conclude that not all k population proportions are equal; that is, one or more population proportions differ from the other population proportions. Let us demonstrate this chi-square test by considering an application.

Organizations such as J.D. Power and Associates use the proportion of owners likely to repurchase a particular automobile as an indication of customer loyalty for the automobile.

An automobile with a greater proportion of owners likely to repurchase is concluded to have greater customer loyalty. Suppose that in a particular study we want to compare the customer loyalty for three automobiles: Chevrolet Impala, Ford Fusion, and Honda Accord. The current owners of each of the three automobiles form the three populations for the study. The three population proportions of interest are as follows:

p_1 = proportion likely to repurchase an Impala for the population of Chevrolet Impala owners

p_2 = proportion likely to repurchase a Fusion for the population of Ford Fusion owners

p_3 = proportion likely to repurchase an Accord for the population of Honda Accord owners

The hypotheses are stated as follows:

$$H_0\colon p_1 = p_2 = p_3$$
$$H_a\colon \text{Not all population proportions are equal}$$

To conduct this hypothesis test we begin by taking a sample of owners from each of the three populations. Thus we will have a sample of Chevrolet Impala owners, a sample of Ford Fusion owners, and a sample of Honda Accord owners. Each sample provides categorical data indicating whether the respondents are likely or not likely to repurchase the automobile. The data for samples of 125 Chevrolet Impala owners, 200 Ford Fusion owners, and 175 Honda Accord owners are summarized in the tabular format shown in Table 11.1. This table has two rows for the responses Yes and No and three columns, one corresponding to each of the populations. The observed frequencies are summarized in the six cells of the table corresponding to each combination of the likely to repurchase responses and the three populations.

In studies such as these, we often use the same sample size for each population. We have chosen different sample sizes in this example to show that the chi-square test is not restricted to equal sample sizes for each of the k populations.

Using Table 11.1, we see that 69 of the 125 Chevrolet Impala owners indicated that they were likely to repurchase a Chevrolet Impala. One hundred and twenty of the 200 Ford Fusion owners and 123 of the 175 Honda Accord owners indicated that they were likely to repurchase their current automobile. Also, across all three samples, 312 of the 500 owners in the study indicated that they were likely to repurchase their current automobile. The question now is how do we analyze the data in Table 11.1 to determine if the hypothesis $H_0\colon p_1 = p_2 = p_3$ should be rejected?

The data in Table 11.1 are the *observed frequencies* for each of the six cells that represent the six combinations of the likely to repurchase response and the owner population. If we can determine the *expected frequencies under the assumption H_0 is true*, we can use the chi-square test statistic to determine whether there is a significant difference between the observed and expected frequencies. If a significant difference exists between the observed and expected frequencies, the null hypothesis H_0 can be rejected and there is evidence that not all the population proportions are equal.

TABLE 11.1 SAMPLE RESULTS OF LIKELY TO REPURCHASE FOR THREE POPULATIONS OF AUTOMOBILE OWNERS (OBSERVED FREQUENCIES)

WEB file AutoLoyalty

		Automobile Owners			
		Chevrolet Impala	Ford Fusion	Honda Accord	Total
Likely to Repurchase	Yes	69	120	123	312
	No	56	80	52	188
	Total	125	200	175	500

Expected frequencies for the six cells of the table are based on the following rationale. First, we assume that the null hypothesis of equal population proportions is true. Then we note that the three samples include a total of 500 owners; for this group, 312 owners indicated that they were likely to repurchase their current automobile. Thus, 312/500 = .624 is the overall proportion of owners indicating they are likely to repurchase their current automobile. If H_0: $p_1 = p_2 = p_3$ is true, .624 would be the best estimate of the proportion responding likely to repurchase for each of the automobile owner populations. So if the assumption of H_0 is true, we would expect .624 of the 125 Chevrolet Impala owners, or .624(125) = 78 owners to indicate they are likely to repurchase the Impala. Using the .624 overall sample proportion, we would expect .624(200) = 124.8 of the 200 Ford Fusion owners and .624(175) = 109.2 of the Honda Accord owners to respond that they are likely to repurchase their respective model of automobile.

Let us generalize the approach to computing expected frequencies by letting e_{ij} denote the expected frequency for the cell in row i and column j of the table. With this notation, now reconsider the expected frequency calculation for the response of likely to repurchase Yes (row 1) for Chevrolet Impala owners (column 1), that is, the expected frequency e_{11}.

Note that 312 is the total number of Yes responses (row 1 total), 125 is the total sample size for Chevrolet Impala owners (column 1 total), and 500 is the total sample size. Following the logic in the preceding paragraph, we can show

$$e_{11} = \left(\frac{\text{Row 1 Total}}{\text{Total Sample Size}}\right)(\text{Column 1 Total}) = \left(\frac{312}{500}\right)125 = (.624)125 = 78$$

Starting with the first part of the above expression, we can write

$$e_{11} = \frac{(\text{Row 1 Total})(\text{Column 1 Total})}{\text{Total Sample Size}}$$

Generalizing this expression shows that the following formula can be used to provide the expected frequencies under the assumption H_0 is true.

EXPECTED FREQUENCIES UNDER THE ASSUMPTION H_0 IS TRUE

$$e_{ij} = \frac{(\text{Row } i \text{ Total})(\text{Column } j \text{ Total})}{\text{Total Sample Size}} \tag{11.8}$$

Using equation (11.8), we see that the expected frequency of Yes responses (row 1) for Honda Accord owners (column 3) would be e_{13} = (Row 1 Total)(Column 3 Total)/(Total Sample Size) = (312)(175)/500 = 109.2. Use equation (11.8) to verify the other expected frequencies are as shown in Table 11.2.

TABLE 11.2 EXPECTED FREQUENCIES FOR LIKELY TO REPURCHASE FOR THREE POPULATIONS OF AUTOMOBILE OWNERS IF H_0 IS TRUE

		Automobile Owners			
		Chevrolet Impala	**Ford Fusion**	**Honda Accord**	**Total**
Likely to Repurchase	**Yes**	78	124.8	109.2	312
	No	47	75.2	65.8	188
	Total	125	200.0	175.0	500

The test procedure for comparing the observed frequencies of Table 11.1 with the expected frequencies of Table 11.2 involves the computation of the following chi-square statistic:

CHI-SQUARE TEST STATISTIC

$$\chi^2 = \sum_i \sum_j \frac{(f_{ij} - e_{ij})^2}{e_{ij}} \tag{11.9}$$

where

f_{ij} = observed frequency for the cell in row i and column j

e_{ij} = expected frequency for the cell in row i and column j under the assumption H_0 is true

Note: In a chi-square test involving the equality of k population proportions, the above test statistic has a chi-square distribution with $k - 1$ degrees of freedom provided the expected frequency is 5 *or more* for each cell.

Reviewing the expected frequencies in Table 11.2, we see that the expected frequency is at least five for each cell in the table. We therefore proceed with the computation of the chi-square test statistic. The calculations necessary to compute the value of the test statistic are shown in Table 11.3. In this case, we see that the value of the test statistic is $\chi^2 = 7.89$.

In order to understand whether or not $\chi^2 = 7.89$ leads us to reject H_0: $p_1 = p_2 = p_3$, you will need to understand and refer to values of the chi-square distribution. The graph at the top of Table 11.4 shows the general shape of the chi-square distribution, but the shape of a specific chi-square distribution depends upon the number of degrees of freedom. The table shows the upper tail areas of .10, .05, .025, .01, and .005 for chi-square distributions with up to 15 degrees of freedom. This version of the chi-square table will enable us to conduct the hypothesis tests presented in this chapter.

Since the expected frequencies shown in Table 11.2 are based on the assumption that H_0: $p_1 = p_2 = p_3$ is true, observed frequencies, f_{ij}, that are in agreement with expected

TABLE 11.3 COMPUTATION OF THE CHI-SQUARE TEST STATISTIC FOR THE TEST OF EQUAL POPULATION PROPORTIONS

Likely to Repurchase?	Automobile Owner	Observed Frequency (f_{ij})	Expected Frequency (e_{ij})	Difference ($f_{ij} - e_{ij}$)	Squared Difference $(f_{ij} - e_{ij})^2$	Squared Difference Divided by Expected Frequency $(f_{ij} - e_{ij})^2/e_{ij}$
Yes	Impala	69	78.0	−9.0	81.00	1.04
Yes	Fusion	120	124.8	−4.8	23.04	0.18
Yes	Accord	123	109.2	13.8	190.44	1.74
No	Impala	56	47.0	9.0	81.00	1.72
No	Fusion	80	75.2	4.8	23.04	0.31
No	Accord	52	65.8	−13.8	190.44	2.89
	Total	500	500.0			$\chi^2 = 7.89$

TABLE 11.4 SELECTED VALUES OF THE CHI-SQUARE DISTRIBUTION

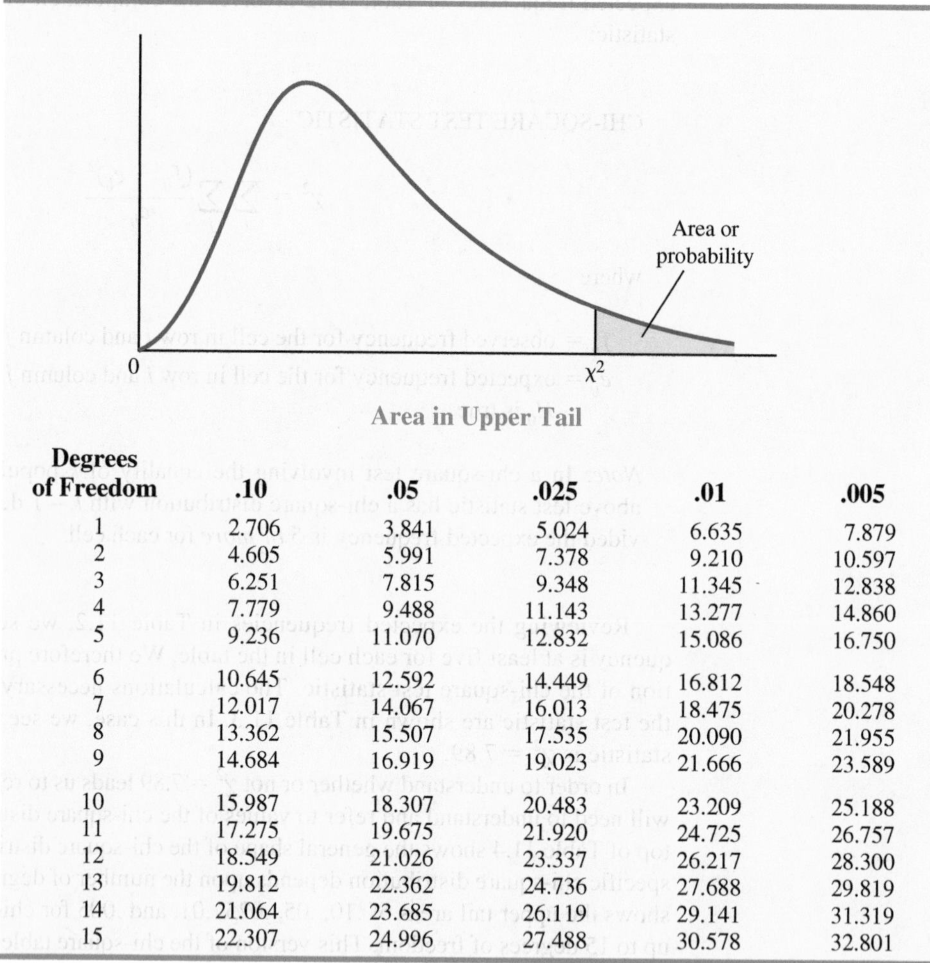

Degrees of Freedom	Area in Upper Tail .10	.05	.025	.01	.005
1	2.706	3.841	5.024	6.635	7.879
2	4.605	5.991	7.378	9.210	10.597
3	6.251	7.815	9.348	11.345	12.838
4	7.779	9.488	11.143	13.277	14.860
5	9.236	11.070	12.832	15.086	16.750
6	10.645	12.592	14.449	16.812	18.548
7	12.017	14.067	16.013	18.475	20.278
8	13.362	15.507	17.535	20.090	21.955
9	14.684	16.919	19.023	21.666	23.589
10	15.987	18.307	20.483	23.209	25.188
11	17.275	19.675	21.920	24.725	26.757
12	18.549	21.026	23.337	26.217	28.300
13	19.812	22.362	24.736	27.688	29.819
14	21.064	23.685	26.119	29.141	31.319
15	22.307	24.996	27.488	30.578	32.801

frequencies, e_{ij}, provide small values of $(f_{ij} - e_{ij})^2$ in equation (11.9). If this is the case, the value of the chi-square test statistic will be relatively small and H_0 cannot be rejected. On the other hand, if the differences between the observed and expected frequencies are *large*, values of $(f_{ij} - e_{ij})^2$ and the computed value of the test statistic will be large. In this case, the null hypothesis of equal population proportions can be rejected. Thus a chi-square test for equal population proportions will always be an upper tail test with rejection of H_0 occurring when the test statistic is in the upper tail of the chi-square distribution.

The chi-square test presented in this section is always a one-tailed test with the rejection of H_0 occurring in the upper tail of the chi-square distribution.

We can use the upper tail area of the appropriate chi-square distribution and the *p*-value approach to determine whether the null hypothesis can be rejected. In the automobile brand loyalty study, the three owner populations indicate that the appropriate chi-square distribution has $k - 1 = 3 - 1 = 2$ degrees of freedom. Using row two of the chi-square distribution table, we have the following:

Area in Upper Tail	.10	.05	.025	.01	.005
χ^2 Value (2 *df*)	4.605	5.991	7.378	9.210	10.597

↑ $\chi^2 = 7.89$

We see the upper tail area at $\chi^2 = 7.89$ is between .025 and .01. Thus, the corresponding upper tail area or p-value must be between .025 and .01. With p-value $\leq .05$, we reject H_0 and conclude that the three population proportions are not all equal and thus there is a difference in brand loyalties among the Chevrolet Impala, Ford Fusion, and Honda Accord owners. In the Using Excel subsection that follows, we will see that the p-value $= .0193$.

Instead of using the p-value, we could use the critical value approach to draw the same conclusion. With $\alpha = .05$ and 2 degrees of freedom, the critical value for the chi-square test statistic is $\chi^2 = 5.991$. The upper tail rejection region becomes

$$\text{Reject } H_0 \text{ if } \chi^2 \geq 5.991$$

With $7.89 \geq 5.991$, we reject H_0. Thus, the p-value approach and the critical value approach provide the same hypothesis-testing conclusion.

Let us summarize the general steps that can be used to conduct a chi-square test for the equality of the population proportions for three or more populations.

A CHI-SQUARE TEST FOR THE EQUALITY OF POPULATION PROPORTIONS FOR $k \geq 3$ POPULATIONS

1. State the null and alternative hypotheses.

$$H_0\colon p_1 = p_2 = \cdots = p_k$$
$$H_a\colon \text{Not all population proportions are equal}$$

2. Select a random sample from each of the populations and record the observed frequencies, f_{ij}, in a table with 2 rows and k columns.
3. Assume the null hypothesis is true and compute the expected frequencies, e_{ij}.
4. If the expected frequency, e_{ij}, is 5 or more for each cell, compute the test statistic:

$$\chi^2 = \sum_i \sum_j \frac{(f_{ij} - e_{ij})^2}{e_{ij}}$$

5. Rejection rule:

p-value approach: Reject H_0 if p-value $\leq \alpha$
Critical value approach: Reject H_0 if $\chi^2 \geq \chi^2_\alpha$

where the chi-square distribution has $k - 1$ degrees of freedom and α is the level of significance for the test.

Using Excel to Conduct a Test of Multiple Proportions

The Excel procedure used to test for the equality of three or more population proportions uses the CHISQ.TEST function with the table of observed frequencies as one input and the table of expected frequencies as the other input. The function output is the p-value for the test. We illustrate using the automobile brand loyalty study. Refer to Figure 11.3 as we describe the tasks involved. The formula worksheet is in the background; the value worksheet is in the foreground.

FIGURE 11.3 EXCEL WORKSHEET FOR THE AUTOMOBILE LOYALTY STUDY

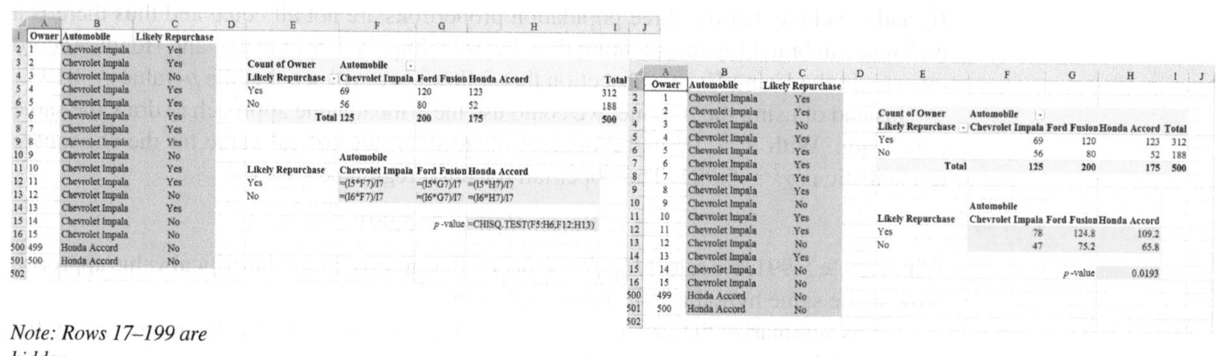

Formula worksheet:

	A	B	C	D	E	F	G	H	I
1	Owner	Automobile	Likely Repurchase						
2	1	Chevrolet Impala	Yes						
3	2	Chevrolet Impala	Yes		Count of Owner	Automobile			
4	3	Chevrolet Impala	No		Likely Repurchase	Chevrolet Impala	Ford Fusion	Honda Accord	Total
5	4	Chevrolet Impala	Yes		Yes	69	120	123	312
6	5	Chevrolet Impala	Yes		No	56	80	52	188
7	6	Chevrolet Impala	Yes		Total	125	200	175	500
8	7	Chevrolet Impala	Yes						
9	8	Chevrolet Impala	Yes						
10	9	Chevrolet Impala	No			Automobile			
11	10	Chevrolet Impala	Yes		Likely Repurchase	Chevrolet Impala	Ford Fusion	Honda Accord	
12	11	Chevrolet Impala	Yes		Yes	=(I5*F7)/I7	=(I5*G7)/I7	=(I5*H7)/I7	
13	12	Chevrolet Impala	No		No	=(I6*F7)/I7	=(I6*G7)/I7	=(I6*H7)/I7	
14	13	Chevrolet Impala	Yes						
15	14	Chevrolet Impala	No				*p*-value	=CHISQ.TEST(F5:H6,F12:H13)	
16	15	Chevrolet Impala	No						
500	499	Honda Accord	No						
501	500	Honda Accord	No						
502									

Value worksheet:

	A	B	C	D	E	F	G	H	I
1	Owner	Automobile	Likely Repurchase						
2	1	Chevrolet Impala	Yes						
3	2	Chevrolet Impala	Yes		Count of Owner	Automobile			
4	3	Chevrolet Impala	No		Likely Repurchase	Chevrolet Impala	Ford Fusion	Honda Accord	Total
5	4	Chevrolet Impala	Yes		Yes	69	120	123	312
6	5	Chevrolet Impala	Yes		No	56	80	52	188
7	6	Chevrolet Impala	Yes		Total	125	200	175	500
8	7	Chevrolet Impala	Yes						
9	8	Chevrolet Impala	Yes						
10	9	Chevrolet Impala	No			Automobile			
11	10	Chevrolet Impala	Yes		Likely Repurchase	Chevrolet Impala	Ford Fusion	Honda Accord	
12	11	Chevrolet Impala	Yes		Yes	78	124.8	109.2	
13	12	Chevrolet Impala	No		No	47	75.2	65.8	
14	13	Chevrolet Impala	Yes						
15	14	Chevrolet Impala	No				*p*-value	0.0193	
16	15	Chevrolet Impala	No						
500	499	Honda Accord	No						
501	500	Honda Accord	No						
502									

Note: Rows 17–199 are hidden.

WEB file
AutoLoyalty

Enter/Access Data: Open the WEBfile named AutoLoyalty. The data are in cells B2:C501 and labels are in column A and cells B1:C1.

Apply Tools: The observed frequencies have been computed in cells F5:H6 using Excel's PivotTable tool (see Section 2.3 for details regarding how to use this tool).

Enter Functions and Formulas: The Excel formulas in cells F12:H13 were used to compute the expected frequencies for each category. Once the observed and expected frequencies have been computed, Excel's CHISQ.TEST function has been used in cell H15 to compute the *p*-value for the test. The value worksheet shows that the resulting *p*-value is .0193. With $\alpha = .05$, we reject the null hypothesis that the three population proportions are equal.

NOTES AND COMMENTS

1. In Section 11.1, we used the standard normal distribution and the z test statistic to conduct hypothesis tests about the proportions of two populations. The chi-square test introduced in this section can also be used to conduct the hypothesis test that the proportions of two populations are equal. The results will be the same under both test procedures and the value of the test statistic χ^2 will be equal to the square of the value of the test statistic z. An advantage of the methodology in Section 11.1, however, is that it can be used for either a one-tailed or a two-tailed hypothesis about the proportions of two populations whereas the chi-square test in this section can be used only for two-tailed tests. Exercise 16 will give you a chance to use the chi-square test for the hypothesis that the proportions of two populations are equal.
2. Each of the k populations in this section had two response outcomes, Yes or No. In effect, each population had a binomial distribution with parameter p, the population proportion of Yes responses. An extension of the chi-square procedure in this section applies when each of the k populations has three or more possible responses. In this case, each population is said to be a **multinomial population**; that is, each of the k populations has a multinomial distribution. The chi-square calculations for the expected frequencies, e_{ij}, and the test statistic, χ^2, are the same as shown in expressions (11.8) and (11.9). The only difference is that the null hypothesis assumes that the multinomial distribution for the response variable is the same for all populations. With r responses for each of the k populations, the chi-square test statistic has $(r - 1)(k - 1)$ degrees of freedom. Exercise 18 will give you a chance to use the chi-square test to compare three populations with multinomial distributions.

Exercises

Methods

11. Use the sample data below to test the hypotheses

$$H_0: p_1 = p_2 = p_3$$
$$H_a: \text{Not all population proportions are equal}$$

where p_i is the population proportion of Yes responses for population i. Using a .05 level of significance, what is the p-value and what is your conclusion?

	Populations		
Response	**1**	**2**	**3**
Yes	150	150	96
No	100	150	104

12. Reconsider the observed frequencies in exercise 11.
    a. Compute the sample proportion for each population.
    b. Which population proportion is the largest?

Applications

13. The following sample data represent the number of late and on time flights for Delta, United, and US Airways (Bureau of Transportation Statistics, March 2012).

	Airline		
Flight	**Delta**	**United**	**US Airways**
Late	39	51	56
On Time	261	249	344

    a. Formulate the hypotheses for a test that will determine if the population proportion of late flights is the same for all three airlines.
    b. Conduct the hypothesis test with a .05 level of significance. What is the p-value and what is your conclusion?
    c. Compute the sample proportion of late flights for each airline. What is the overall proportion of late flights for the three airlines?

SELF test

14. Benson Manufacturing is considering ordering electronic components from three different suppliers. The suppliers may differ in terms of quality in that the proportion or percentage of defective components may differ among the suppliers. To evaluate the proportion of defective components for the suppliers, Benson has requested a sample shipment of 500 components from each supplier. The number of defective components and the number of good components found in each shipment are as follows.

	Supplier		
Component	**A**	**B**	**C**
Defective	15	20	40
Good	485	480	460

a. Formulate the hypotheses that can be used to test for equal proportions of defective components provided by the three suppliers.
b. Using a .05 level of significance, conduct the hypothesis test. What is the p-value and what is your conclusion?

15. Kate Sanders, a researcher in the department of biology at IPFW University, studied the effect of agriculture contaminants on the fish population for streams in Northeastern Indiana (April 2012). Specially designed traps collected samples of fish at each of four stream locations. A research question was, Did the differences in agricultural contaminants found at the four locations alter the proportion of the fish population by gender? Observed frequencies were as follows.

	Stream Locations			
Gender	A	B	C	D
Male	49	44	49	39
Female	41	46	36	44

a. Focusing on the proportion of male fish at each location, test the hypothesis that the population proportions are equal for all four locations. Use a .05 level of significance. What is the p-value and what is your conclusion?
b. Does it appear that differences in agricultural contaminants found at the four locations altered the fish population by gender?

Exercise 16 shows a chi-square test can be used when the hypothesis is about the equality of two population proportions.

16. A tax preparation firm is interested in comparing the quality of work at two of its regional offices. The observed frequencies showing the number of sampled returns with errors and the number of sampled returns that were correct are as follows.

	Regional Office	
Return	Office 1	Office 2
Error	35	27
Correct	215	273

a. What are the sample proportions of returns with errors at the two offices?
b. Use the chi-square test procedure to see if there is a significant difference between the population proportion of error rates for the two offices. Test the null hypothesis H_0: $p_1 = p_2$ with a .10 level of significance. What is the p-value and what is your conclusion? *Note*: We generally use the chi-square test of equal proportions when there are three or more populations, but this example shows that the same chi-square test can be used for testing equal proportions with two populations.
c. In Section 11.1, a z test was used to conduct the above test. Either a χ^2 test statistic or a z test statistic may be used to test the hypothesis. However, when we want to make inferences about the proportions for two populations, we generally prefer the z test statistic procedure. Refer to the Notes and Comments at the end of this section and comment on why the z test statistic provides the user with more options for inferences about the proportions of two populations.

17. Social networking is becoming more and more popular around the world. Pew Research Center used a survey of adults in several countries to determine the percentage of adults who use social networking sites (*USA Today,* February 8, 2012). Assume that the results for surveys in Great Britain, Israel, Russia, and United States are as follows.

	Country			
Use Social Networking Sites	**Great Britain**	**Israel**	**Russia**	**United States**
Yes	344	265	301	500
No	456	235	399	500

a. Conduct a hypothesis test to determine whether the proportion of adults using social networking sites is equal for all four countries. What is the p-value? Using a .05 level of significance, what is your conclusion?

b. What are the sample proportions for each of the four countries? Which country has the largest proportion of adults using social networking sites?

Exercise 18 shows a chi-square test can also be used for multiple population tests when the categorical response variable has three or more outcomes.

18. A manufacturer is considering purchasing parts from three different suppliers. The parts received from the suppliers are classified as having a minor defect, having a major defect, or being good. Test results from samples of parts received from each of the three suppliers are shown below. Note that any test with these data is no longer a test of proportions for the three supplier populations because the categorical response variable has three outcomes: minor defect, major defect, and good.

	Supplier		
Part Tested	**A**	**B**	**C**
Minor Defect	15	13	21
Major Defect	5	11	5
Good	130	126	124

Using the data above, conduct a hypothesis test to determine if the distribution of defects is the same for the three suppliers. Use the chi-square test calculations as presented in this section with the exception that a table with r rows and c columns results in a chi-square test statistic with $(r - 1)(c - 1)$ degrees of freedom. Using a .05 level of significance, what is the p-value and what is your conclusion?

11.3 Test of Independence

An important application of a chi-square test involves using sample data to test for the independence of two categorical variables. For this test we take one sample from a single population and record the observations for two categorical variables. We will summarize the data by counting the number of responses for each combination of a category for variable 1 and a category for variable 2. The null hypothesis for this test is that the two categorical variables are independent. Thus, the test is referred to as a **test of independence**. We will illustrate this test with the following example.

A beer industry association conducts a survey to determine the preferences of beer drinkers for light, regular, and dark beers. A sample of 200 beer drinkers is taken with each person in the sample asked to indicate a preference for one of the three types of beers: light, regular, or dark. At the end of the survey questionnaire, the respondent is asked to provide information on a variety of demographics including gender: male or female. A research question of interest to the association is whether preference for the three types of beer is independent of the gender of the beer drinker. If the two categorical variables, beer preference and gender, are independent, beer preference does not depend on gender and the preference for light, regular, and dark beer can be expected to be the same for male and female beer drinkers. However, if the test conclusion is that the two categorical variables are not independent, we have evidence that beer preference is associated with or dependent upon the gender of the beer drinker. As a result, we can expect beer preferences to differ for male and female beer drinkers. In this case, a beer manufacturer could use this information to customize its promotions and advertising for the different target markets of male and female beer drinkers.

The hypotheses for this test of independence are as follows:

$$H_0\text{: Beer preference is independent of gender}$$
$$H_a\text{: Beer preference is not independent of gender}$$

The sample data will be summarized in a two-way table with beer preferences of light, regular, and dark as one of the variables and gender of male and female as the other variable. Since an objective of the study is to determine if there is difference between the beer preferences for male and female beer drinkers, we consider gender an explanatory variable and follow the usual practice of making the explanatory variable the column variable in the observed frequency table. The beer preference is the categorical response variable and is shown as the row variable. The sample results of the 200 beer drinkers in the study are summarized in Table 11.5.

Because we have listed all possible combinations of beer preference and gender (that is, listed all contingencies for these two variables), tables such as Table 11.5 are called contingency tables.

The sample data are summarized based on the combination of beer preference and gender for the individual respondents. For example, 51 individuals in the study were males who preferred light beer, 56 individuals in the study were males who preferred regular beer, and so on. Let us now analyze the data in the table and test for independence of beer preference and gender.

First of all, since we selected a sample of beer drinkers, summarizing the data for each variable separately will provide some insights into the characteristics of the beer drinker population. For the categorical variable gender, we see 132 of the 200 in the sample were male. This gives us the estimate that 132/200 = .66, or 66%, of the beer drinker population is male. Similarly we estimate that 68/200 = .34, or 34%, of the beer drinker population is female. Thus male beer drinkers appear to outnumber female beer drinkers approximately 2 to 1. Sample proportions or percentages for the three types of beer are

Prefer Light Beer	90/200 = .450, or 45.0%
Prefer Regular Beer	77/200 = .385, or 38.5%
Prefer Dark Beer	33/200 = .165, or 16.5%

TABLE 11.5 SAMPLE RESULTS FOR BEER PREFERENCES OF MALE AND FEMALE BEER DRINKERS (OBSERVED FREQUENCIES)

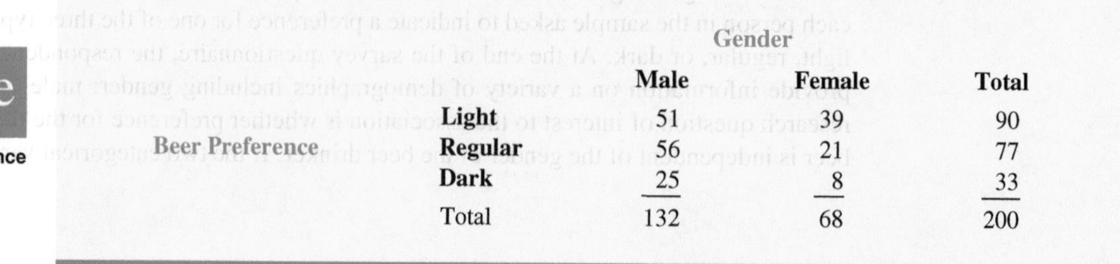

WEB file BeerPreference

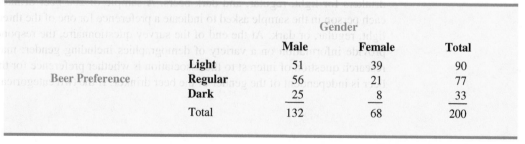

		Gender		
		Male	**Female**	**Total**
Beer Preference	**Light**	51	39	90
	Regular	56	21	77
	Dark	25	8	33
	Total	132	68	200

Across all beer drinkers in the sample, light beer is preferred most often and dark beer is preferred least often.

Let us now conduct the chi-square test to determine if beer preference and gender are independent. The computations and formulas used are the same as those used for the chi-square test in Section 11.2. Utilizing the observed frequencies in Table 11.5 for row i and column j, f_{ij}, we compute the expected frequencies, e_{ij}, under the assumption that the beer preferences and gender are independent. The computation of the expected frequencies follows the same logic and formula used in Section 11.2. Thus the expected frequency for row i and column j is given by

$$e_{ij} = \frac{(\text{Row } i \text{ Total})(\text{Column } j \text{ Total})}{\text{Sample Size}} \tag{11.10}$$

For example, $e_{11} = (90)(132)/200 = 59.40$ is the expected frequency for male beer drinkers who would prefer light beer if beer preference is independent of gender. Show that equation (11.10) can be used to find the other expected frequencies shown in Table 11.6.

Following the chi-square test procedure discussed in Section 11.2, we use the following expression to compute the value of the chi-square test statistic.

$$\chi^2 = \sum_i \sum_j \frac{(f_{ij} - e_{ij})^2}{e_{ij}} \tag{11.11}$$

With r rows and c columns in the table, the chi-square distribution will have $(r - 1)(c - 1)$ degrees of freedom provided the expected frequency is at least 5 for each cell. Thus, in this application we will use a chi-square distribution with $(3 - 1)(2 - 1) = 2$ degrees of freedom. The complete steps to compute the chi-square test statistic are summarized in Table 11.7.

We can use the upper tail area of the chi-square distribution with 2 degrees of freedom and the p-value approach to determine whether the null hypothesis that beer preference is independent of gender can be rejected. Using row 2 of the chi-square distribution table shown in Table 11.4, we have the following:

Area in Upper Tail	**.10**	**.05**	**.025**	**.01**	**.005**
χ^2 Value (2 *df*)	4.605	5.991	7.378	9.210	10.597

↑ $\chi^2 = 6.45$ (between 5.991 and 7.378)

TABLE 11.6 EXPECTED FREQUENCIES IF BEER PREFERENCE IS INDEPENDENT OF THE GENDER OF THE BEER DRINKER

		Gender		
		Male	**Female**	**Total**
Beer Preference	**Light**	59.40	30.60	90
	Regular	50.82	26.18	77
	Dark	21.78	11.22	33
	Total	132.00	68.00	200

TABLE 11.7 COMPUTATION OF THE CHI-SQUARE TEST STATISTIC FOR THE TEST OF INDEPENDENCE BETWEEN BEER PREFERENCE AND GENDER

Beer Preference	Gender	Observed Frequency f_{ij}	Expected Frequency e_{ij}	Difference $(f_{ij} - e_{ij})$	Squared Difference $(f_{ij} - e_{ij})^2$	Squared Difference Divided by Expected Frequency $(f_{ij} - e_{ij})^2/e_{ij}$
Light	Male	51	59.40	−8.40	70.56	1.19
Light	Female	39	30.60	8.40	70.56	2.31
Regular	Male	56	50.82	5.18	26.83	.53
Regular	Female	21	26.18	−5.18	26.83	1.02
Dark	Male	25	21.78	3.22	10.37	.48
Dark	Female	8	11.22	−3.22	10.37	.92
	Total	200	200.00			$\chi^2 = 6.45$

Thus, we see the upper tail area at $\chi^2 = 6.45$ is between .05 and .025, and so the corresponding upper tail area or p-value must be between .05 and .025. With p-value $\leq .05$, we reject H_0 and conclude that beer preference is not independent of the gender of the beer drinker. Stated another way, the study shows that beer preference can be expected to differ for male and female beer drinkers. In the Using Excel subsection that follows, we will see that the p-value $= .0398$.

Instead of using the p-value, we could use the critical value approach to draw the same conclusion. With $\alpha = .05$ and 2 degrees of freedom, the critical value for the chi-square test statistic is $\chi^2_{.05} = 5.991$. The upper tail rejection region becomes

$$\text{Reject } H_0 \text{ if} \geq 5.991$$

With $6.45 \geq 5.991$, we reject H_0. Again we see that the p-value approach and the critical value approach provide the same conclusion.

While we now have evidence that beer preference and gender are not independent, we will need to gain additional insight from the data to assess the nature of the association between these two variables. One way to do this is to compute the probability of the beer preference responses for males and females separately. These calculations are as follows:

Beer Preference	Male	Female
Light	51/132 = .3864, or 38.64%	39/68 = .5735, or 57.35%
Regular	56/132 = .4242, or 42.42%	21/68 = .3088, or 30.88%
Dark	25/132 = .1894, or 18.94%	8/68 = .1176, or 11.76%

The bar chart for male and female beer drinkers of the three kinds of beer is shown in Figure 11.4.

What observations can you make about the association between beer preference and gender? For female beer drinkers in the sample, the highest preference is for light beer at 57.35%. For male beer drinkers in the sample, regular beer is most frequently preferred at 42.42%. While female beer drinkers have a higher preference for light beer than males, male beer drinkers have a higher preference for both regular beer and dark beer. Data visualization through bar charts such as shown in Figure 11.4 is helpful in gaining insight as to how two categorical variables are associated.

Before we leave this discussion, we summarize the steps for a test of independence.

FIGURE 11.4 BAR CHART COMPARISON OF BEER PREFERENCE BY GENDER

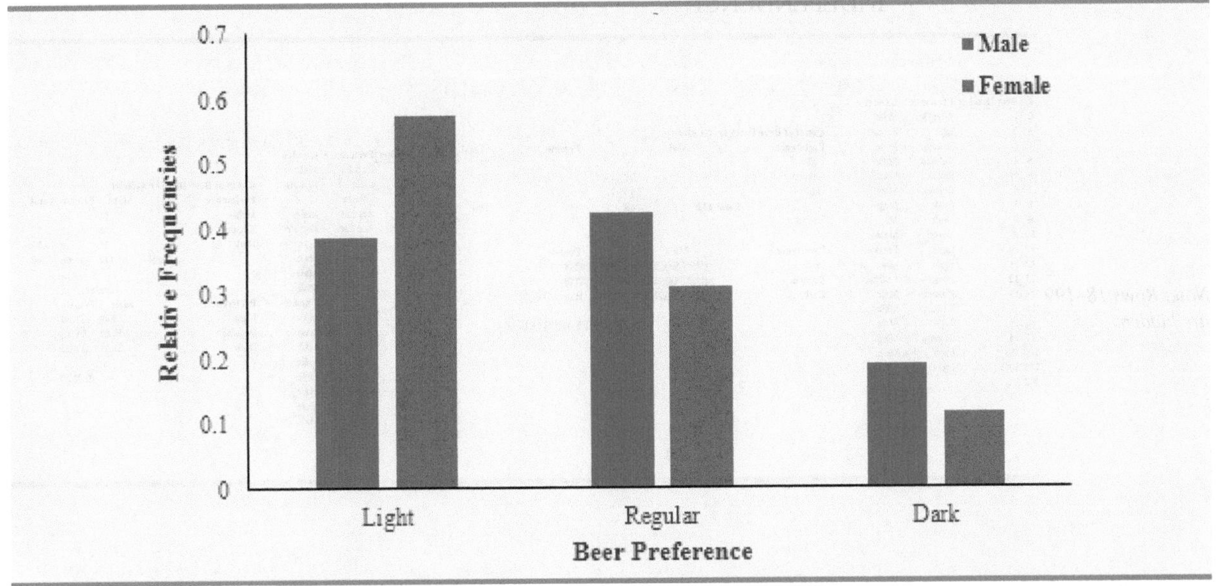

CHI-SQUARE TEST FOR INDEPENDENCE OF TWO CATEGORICAL VARIABLES

The expected frequencies must all be 5 or more for the chi-square test to be valid.

1. State the null and alternative hypotheses.

   H_0: The two categorical variables are independent

   H_a: The two categorical variables are not independent

2. Select a random sample from the population and collect data for both variables for every element in the sample. Record the observed frequencies, f_{ij}, in a table with r rows and c columns.
3. Assume the null hypothesis is true and compute the expected frequencies, e_{ij}.
4. If the expected frequency, e_{ij}, is 5 or more for each cell, compute the test statistic:

$$\chi^2 = \sum_i \sum_j \frac{(f_{ij} - e_{ij})^2}{e_{ij}}$$

This chi-square test is also a one-tailed test with rejection of H_0 occurring in the upper tail of a chi-square distribution with $(r - 1)(c - 1)$ degrees of freedom.

5. Rejection rule:

   p-value approach: Reject H_0 if p-value $\leq \alpha$

   Critical value approach: Reject H_0 if $\chi^2 \geq \chi^2_\alpha$

   where the chi-square distribution has $(r - 1)(c - 1)$ degrees of freedom and α is the level of significance for the test.

Finally, if the null hypothesis of independence is rejected, summarizing the probabilities as shown in the above example will help the analyst determine where the association or dependence exists for the two categorical variables.

Using Excel to Conduct a Test of Independence

Excel can be used to conduct a test of independence for the beer preference example. Refer to Figure 11.5 as we describe the tasks involved. The formula worksheet is in the background; the value worksheet is in the foreground.

FIGURE 11.5 EXCEL WORKSHEET FOR THE BEER PREFERENCE TEST OF INDEPENDENCE

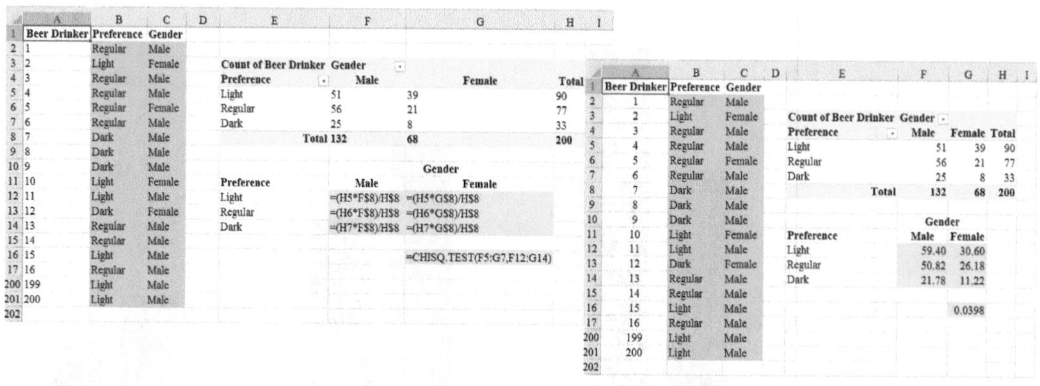

	A	B	C	D	E	F	G	H
1	Beer Drinker	Preference	Gender					
2	1	Regular	Male					
3	2	Light	Female		Count of Beer Drinker	Gender		
4	3	Regular	Male		Preference	Male	Female	Total
5	4	Regular	Male		Light	51	39	90
6	5	Regular	Female		Regular	56	21	77
7	6	Regular	Male		Dark	25	8	33
8	7	Dark	Male		Total	132	68	200
9	8	Dark	Male					
10	9	Dark	Male				Gender	
11	10	Light	Female		Preference	Male	Female	
12	11	Light	Male		Light	=(H5*F$8)/H$8	=(H5*G$8)/H$8	
13	12	Dark	Female		Regular	=(H6*F$8)/H$8	=(H6*G$8)/H$8	
14	13	Regular	Male		Dark	=(H7*F$8)/H$8	=(H7*G$8)/H$8	
15	14	Regular	Male					
16	15	Light	Male				=CHISQ.TEST(F5:G7,F12:G14)	
17	16	Regular	Male					
200	199	Light	Male					
201	200	Light	Male					
202								

	A	B	C	D	E	F	G	H
1	Beer Drinker	Preference	Gender					
2	1	Regular	Male					
3	2	Light	Female		Count of Beer Drinker	Gender		
4	3	Regular	Male		Preference	Male	Female	Total
5	4	Regular	Male		Light	51	39	90
6	5	Regular	Female		Regular	56	21	77
7	6	Regular	Male		Dark	25	8	33
8	7	Dark	Male		Total	132	68	200
9	8	Dark	Male					
10	9	Dark	Male			Gender		
11	10	Light	Female		Preference	Male	Female	
12	11	Light	Male		Light	59.40	30.60	
13	12	Dark	Female		Regular	50.82	26.18	
14	13	Regular	Male		Dark	21.78	11.22	
15	14	Regular	Male					
16	15	Light	Male				0.0398	
17	16	Regular	Male					
200	199	Light	Male					
201	200	Light	Male					
202								

Note: Rows 18–199 are hidden.

BeerPreference

Enter/Access Data: Open the WEBfile named BeerPreference. The data are in cells B2:C201 and labels are in column A and cells B1:C1.

Apply Tools: Cells E3:H8 show the contingency table resulting from using Excel's PivotTable tool (see Section 2.3 for details regarding how to use this tool) to construct a two-way table with beer preferences of light, regular, and dark as one of the variables and gender of male and female as the other variable.

Enter Functions and Formulas: The Excel formulas in cells F12:G14 were used to compute the expected frequencies for each row and column. Once the observed and expected frequencies have been computed, Excel's CHISQ.TEST function can be used to compute the p-value for a test of independence. The inputs to the CHISQ.TEST function are the range of values for the observed and expected frequencies. To compute the p-value for this test of independence, we entered the following function into cell G16:

=CHISQ.TEST(F5:G7,F12:G14)

The value worksheet shows that the resulting p-value is .0398. Thus, with $\alpha = .05$, we reject H_0 and conclude that beer preference is not independent of the gender of the beer drinker.

Exercises

Methods

19. The following table contains observed frequencies for a sample of 200. Test for independence of the row and column variables using $\alpha = .05$.

	Column Variable		
Row Variable	A	B	C
P	20	44	50
Q	30	26	30

20. The following table contains observed frequencies for a sample of 240. Test for independence of the row and column variables using $\alpha = .05$.

	Column Variable		
Row Variable	A	B	C
P	20	30	20
Q	30	60	25
R	10	15	30

Applications

21. A *Bloomberg Businessweek* subscriber study asked, "In the past 12 months, when traveling for business, what type of airline ticket did you purchase most often?" A second question asked if the type of airline ticket purchased most often was for domestic or international travel. Sample data obtained are shown in the following table.

	Type of Flight	
Type of Ticket	Domestic	International
First Class	29	22
Business Class	95	121
Economy Class	518	135

a. Using a .05 level of significance, is the type of ticket purchased independent of the type of flight? What is your conclusion?
b. Discuss any dependence that exists between the type of ticket and type of flight.

WorkforcePlan

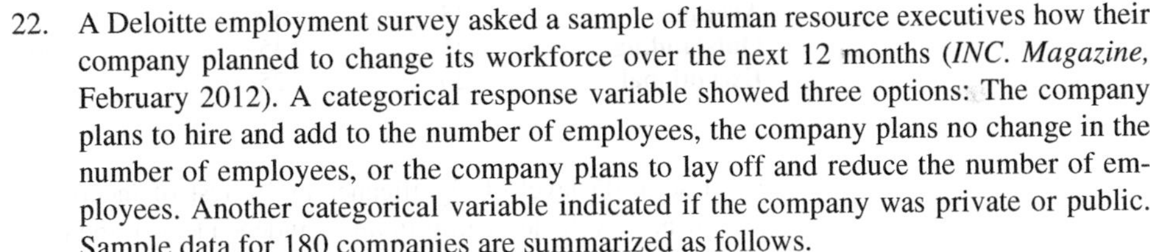

22. A Deloitte employment survey asked a sample of human resource executives how their company planned to change its workforce over the next 12 months (*INC. Magazine,* February 2012). A categorical response variable showed three options: The company plans to hire and add to the number of employees, the company plans no change in the number of employees, or the company plans to lay off and reduce the number of employees. Another categorical variable indicated if the company was private or public. Sample data for 180 companies are summarized as follows.

	Company	
Employment Plan	Private	Public
Add Employees	37	32
No Change	19	34
Lay Off Employees	16	42

a. Conduct a test of independence to determine if the employment plan for the next 12 months is independent of the type of company. At a .05 level of significance, what is your conclusion?
b. Discuss any differences in the employment plans for private and public companies over the next 12 months.

23. Health insurance benefits vary by the size of the company (*Atlanta Business Chronicle,* December 31, 2010). The sample data below show the number of companies providing health insurance for small, medium, and large companies. For purposes of this study, small

companies are companies that have fewer than 100 employees. Medium-sized companies have 100 to 999 employees, and large companies have 1000 or more employees. The questionnaire sent to 225 employees asked whether or not the employee had company-sponsored health insurance and then asked the employee to indicate the size of the company.

	Size of the Company		
Health Insurance	**Small**	**Medium**	**Large**
Yes	36	65	88
No	14	10	12

a. Conduct a test of independence to determine whether company-sponsored health insurance coverage is independent of the size of the company. What is the *p*-value? Using a .05 level of significance, what is your conclusion?

b. A newspaper article indicated employees of small companies are more likely to lack company-sponsored health insurance coverage. Use percentages based on the above data to support this conclusion.

AutoQuality

24. A vehicle quality survey asked new owners a variety of questions about their recently purchased automobile (J.D. Power and Associates, March 2012). One question asked for the owner's rating of the vehicle using categorical responses of average, outstanding, and exceptional. Another question asked for the owner's education level with the categorical responses some high school, high school graduate, some college, and college graduate. Assume the sample data below are for 500 owners who had recently purchased an automobile.

	Education			
Quality Rating	**Some HS**	**HS Grad**	**Some College**	**College Grad**
Average	35	30	20	60
Outstanding	45	45	50	90
Exceptional	20	25	30	50

a. Use a .05 level of significance and a test of independence to determine if a new owner's vehicle quality rating is independent of the owner's education. What is the *p*-value and what is your conclusion?

b. Use the overall percentage of average, outstanding, and exceptional ratings to comment upon how new owners rate the quality of their recently purchased automobiles.

25. *The Wall Street Journal* Corporate Perceptions Study 2011 surveyed readers and asked how each rated the quality of management and the reputation of the company for over 250 worldwide corporations. Both the quality of management and the reputation of the company were rated on an excellent, good, and fair categorical scale. Assume the following sample data for 200 respondents applies to this study.

	Reputation of Company		
Quality of Management	**Excellent**	**Good**	**Fair**
Excellent	40	25	5
Good	35	35	10
Fair	25	10	15

a. Use a .05 level of significance and test for independence of the quality of management and the reputation of the company. What is the p-value and what is your conclusion?
b. If there is a dependence or association between the two ratings, discuss and use probabilities to justify your answer.

26. The race for the 2013 Academy Award for Actress in a Leading Role was extremely tight, featuring several worthy performances (ABC News online, February 22, 2013). The nominees were Jessica Chastain for *Zero Dark Thirty*, Jennifer Lawrence for *Silver Linings Playbook*, Emmanuelle Riva for *Amour*, Quvenzhané Wallis for *Beasts of the Southern Wild*, and Naomi Watts for *The Impossible*. In a survey, movie fans who had seen each of the movies for which these five actresses had been nominated were asked to select the actress who was most deserving of the 2013 Academy Award for Actress in a Leading Role. The responses follow.

	18–30	31–44	45–58	Over 58
Jessica Chastain	51	50	41	42
Jennifer Lawrence	63	55	37	50
Emmanuelle Riva	15	44	56	74
Quvenzhané Wallis	48	25	22	31
Naomi Watts	36	65	62	33

a. How large was the sample in this survey?
b. Jennifer Lawrence received the 2013 Academy Award for Actress in a Leading Role for her performance in *Silver Linings Playbook*. Did the respondents favor Ms. Lawrence?
c. At $\alpha = .05$, conduct a hypothesis test to determine whether people's attitude toward the actress who was most deserving of the 2013 Academy Award for Actress in a Leading Role is independent of respondent age. What is your conclusion?

27. The National Sleep Foundation used a survey to determine whether hours of sleep per night are independent of age. A sample of individuals was asked to indicate the number of hours of sleep per night with categorical options: fewer than 6 hours, 6 to 6.9 hours, 7 to 7.9 hours, and 8 hours or more. Later in the survey, the individuals were asked to indicate their age with categorical options: age 39 or younger and age 40 or older. Sample data follow.

	Age Group	
Hours of Sleep	39 or Younger	40 or Older
Fewer Than 6	38	36
6 to 6.9	60	57
7 to 7.9	77	75
8 or More	65	92

a. Conduct a test of independence to determine whether hours of sleep are independent of age. Using a .05 level of significance, what is the p-value and what is your conclusion?
b. What is your estimate of the percentages of individuals who sleep fewer than 6 hours, 6 to 6.9 hours, 7 to 7.9 hours, and 8 hours or more per night?

28. On a syndicated television show the two hosts often create the impression that they strongly disagree about which movies are best. Each movie review is categorized as Pro ("thumbs up"), Con ("thumbs down"), or Mixed. The results of 160 movie ratings by the two hosts are shown here.

	Host B		
Host A	**Con**	**Mixed**	**Pro**
Con	24	8	13
Mixed	8	13	11
Pro	10	9	64

Use a test of independence with a .01 level of significance to analyze the data. What is your conclusion?

Summary

In this chapter, we described statistical procedures for comparisons involving proportions and the contingency table test for independence of two variables. In the first section, we compared a proportion for one population with the same proportion from another population. We described how to construct an interval estimate for the difference between the proportions and how to conduct a hypothesis test to learn whether the difference between the proportions was statistically significant.

In Section 11.2 we focused on testing the equality of population proportions for three or more populations. There we saw that this test is based on independent random samples selected from each of the populations. The sample data show the counts for each of two categorical responses for each population. The null hypothesis is that the population proportions are equal. Rejection of the null hypothesis supports the conclusion that the population proportions are not all equal. A chi-square test statistic is used to test this null hypothesis; this chi-square test is based on the differences between observed frequencies and expected frequencies. Expected frequencies are computed under the assumption that the null hypothesis is true. This chi-square test is an upper tail test; large differences between observed and expected frequencies provide a large value for the chi-square test statistic and indicate that the null hypothesis should be rejected.

Section 11.3 was concerned with tests of independence for two variables. A test of independence for two variables is an extension of the methodology employed in the goodness of fit test for a multinomial population. A contingency table is used to determine the observed and expected frequencies. Then a chi-square value is computed. Large chi-square values, caused by large differences between observed and expected frequencies, lead to the rejection of the null hypothesis of independence.

Glossary

Pooled estimator of *p* An estimator of a population proportion obtained by computing a weighted average of the sample proportions obtained from two independent samples.

Multinomial population A population in which each element is assigned to one and only one of several categories. The multinomial distribution extends the binomial distribution from two to three or more outcomes.

Test of independence A method of assessing whether two categorical variables are associated or dependent.

Contingency table A table used to summarize observed and expected frequencies for a test of independence.

Key Formulas

Point Estimator of the Difference Between Two Population Proportions

$$\bar{p}_1 - \bar{p}_2 \tag{11.1}$$

Standard Error of $\bar{p}_1 - \bar{p}_2$

$$\sigma_{\bar{p}_1 - \bar{p}_2} = \sqrt{\frac{p_1(1 - p_1)}{n_1} + \frac{p_2(1 - p_2)}{n_2}} \tag{11.2}$$

Interval Estimate of the Difference Between Two Population Proportions

$$\bar{p}_1 - \bar{p}_2 \pm z_{\alpha/2}\sqrt{\frac{\bar{p}_1(1 - \bar{p}_1)}{n_1} + \frac{\bar{p}_2(1 - \bar{p}_2)}{n_2}} \tag{11.4}$$

Standard Error of $\bar{p}_1 - \bar{p}_2$ when $p_1 = p_2 = p$

$$\sigma_{\bar{p}_1 - \bar{p}_2} = \sqrt{p(1 - p)\left(\frac{1}{n_1} + \frac{1}{n_2}\right)} \tag{11.5}$$

Pooled Estimator of p when $p_1 = p_2 = p$

$$\bar{p} = \frac{n_1\bar{p}_1 + n_2\bar{p}_2}{n_1 + n_2} \tag{11.6}$$

Test Statistic for Hypothesis Tests About $p_1 - p_2$

$$z = \frac{(\bar{p}_1 - \bar{p}_2)}{\sqrt{\bar{p}(1 - \bar{p})\left(\frac{1}{n_1} + \frac{1}{n_2}\right)}} \tag{11.7}$$

Expected Frequencies: Test for Equality of Three or More Population Proportions and for Test of Independence

$$e_{ij} = \frac{(\text{Row } i \text{ Total})(\text{Column } j \text{ Total})}{\text{Total Sample Size}} \tag{11.8}$$

Chi-Square Test Statistic

$$\chi^2 = \sum_i \sum_j \frac{(f_{ij} - e_{ij})^2}{e_{ij}} \tag{11.9}$$

Supplementary Exercises

29. Sudoku puzzles have become very popular in recent years; 31.1% of members of households with annual income of at least $100,000 worked Sudoku puzzles in 2012 (Statistica.com, March 10, 2013). Are there differences between the genders? The proportion of women and men from these households who worked Sudoku puzzles in 2012 can be estimated from the following sample data.

Gender	Sample Size	Worked Sudoku Puzzles
Men	1200	312
Women	1600	512

   a. State the hypotheses that can be used to test for a difference between the proportion for the population of men and the proportion for the population of women who worked Sudoku puzzles.
   b. What is the sample proportion of men who worked Sudoku puzzles? What is the sample proportion of women?
   c. Conduct the hypothesis test and compute the p-value. At a .05 level of significance, what is your conclusion?
   d. What is the margin of error and 95% confidence interval estimate of the difference between the population proportions?

30. A large automobile insurance company selected samples of single and married male policyholders and recorded the number who made an insurance claim over the preceding three-year period.

Single Policyholders	Married Policyholders
$n_1 = 400$	$n_2 = 900$
Number making claims = 76	Number making claims = 90

   a. Use $\alpha = .05$. Test to determine whether the claim rates differ between single and married male policyholders.
   b. Provide a 95% confidence interval for the difference between the proportions for the two populations.

31. Medical tests were conducted to learn about drug-resistant tuberculosis. Of 142 cases tested in New Jersey, 9 were found to be drug-resistant. Of 268 cases tested in Texas, 5 were found to be drug-resistant. Do these data suggest a statistically significant difference between the proportions of drug-resistant cases in the two states? Use a .02 level of significance. What is the p-value, and what is your conclusion?

Occupancy

32. Vacation occupancy rates were expected to be up during March 2008 in Myrtle Beach, South Carolina (*The Sun News*, February 29, 2008). Data in the file named Occupancy will allow you to replicate the findings presented in the newspaper. The data show units rented and not rented for a random sample of vacation properties during the first week of March 2007 and March 2008.
   a. Estimate the proportion of units rented during the first week of March 2007 and the first week of March 2008.
   b. Provide a 95% confidence interval for the difference in proportions.
   c. On the basis of your findings, does it appear March rental rates for 2008 will be up from those a year earlier?

33. The bullish sentiment of individual investors was 27.6% (*AAII Journal*, February 2009). The bullish sentiment was reported to be 48.7% one week earlier and 39.7% one month earlier. The sentiment measures were based on a poll conducted by the American Association

of Individual Investors. Assume that each bullish sentiment measure was based on a sample of 240 investors.

a. Develop a 95% confidence interval for the difference between the bullish sentiment measures for the most recent two weeks.
b. Develop hypotheses so that rejection of the null hypothesis will allow us to conclude that the most recent bullish sentiment is weaker than that of one month earlier.
c. Conduct a hypothesis test of part (b) using $\alpha = .01$. What is your conclusion?

34. Phoenix Marketing International identified Bridgeport, Connecticut, Los Alamos, New Mexico, Naples, Florida, and Washington, D.C., as the four U.S. cities with the highest percentage of millionaires (*USA Today*, December 7, 2011). Data consistent with that study show the following number of millionaires for samples of individuals from each of the four cities.

	City			
Milionaire	**Bridgeport**	**Los Alamos**	**Naples**	**Washington, DC**
Yes	44	35	36	34
No	456	265	364	366

a. What is the estimate of the percentage of millionaires in each of these cities?
b. Using a .05 level of significance, test for the equality of the population proportion of millionaires for these four cities. What is the *p*-value and what is your conclusion?

35. In a quality control test of parts manufactured at Dabco Corporation, an engineer sampled parts produced on the first, second, and third shifts. The research study was designed to determine if the population proportion of good parts was the same for all three shifts. Sample data follow.

	Production Shift		
Quality	**First**	**Second**	**Third**
Good	285	368	176
Defective	15	32	24

Using a .05 level of significance, conduct a hypothesis test to determine if the population proportion of good parts is the same for all three shifts. What is the *p*-value and what is your conclusion?

36. Efforts by airlines to improve on-time arrival rates are showing results. Boston.com (December 22, 2012) reports that in the first 10 months of 2012 on-time arrival rates at U.S. airports were the highest they have been since 2003; during this period 82% of flights landed within 15 minutes of their scheduled time. Are there differences among the major airlines? The following data show the number of on-time arrivals for samples of flights taken from seven major U.S. airlines (American Airlines, Continental Airlines, Delta Air Lines, JetBlue Airways, Southwest Airlines, United Airlines, and US Airways) in 2012.

Arrivals	American Airlines	Continental Airlines	Delta Air Lines	JetBlue Airways	Southwest Airlines	United Airlines	US Airways
On-Time	83	54	96	60	69	66	68
Late	16	18	21	22	23	15	12

a. Use the sample data to calculate the point estimate of the population proportion of on-time arrivals for each of these seven airlines.

b. Conduct a hypothesis test to determine if the population proportion of on-time flights in 2012 is equal for these seven airlines. Using a .05 level of significance, what is the p-value and what is your conclusion?

37. The five most popular art museums in the world are Musée du Louvre, the Metropolitan Museum of Art, British Museum, National Gallery, and Tate Modern (*The Art Newspaper*, April 2012). Which of these five museums would visitors most frequently rate as spectacular? Samples of recent visitors of each of these museums were taken, and the results of these samples follow.

	Musée du Louvre	Metropolitan Museum of Art	British Museum	National Gallery	Tate Modern
Rated Spectacular	113	94	96	78	88
Did Not Rate Spectacular	37	46	64	42	22

a. Use the sample data to calculate the point estimate of the population proportion of visitors who rated each of these museums as spectacular.
b. Conduct a hypothesis test to determine if the population proportion of visitors who rated the museum as spectacular is equal for these five museums. Using a .05 level of significance, what is the p-value and what is your conclusion?

38. The Golden Snow Globe website shows that four U.S. cities with a population of at least 100,000 (Rochester, NY; Salt Lake City, UT; Madison, WI; Bridgeport, CT) had recorded between 60 and 70 inches of snow for the winter of 2012–13 as of the evening of March 9, 2013 (Golden Snow Globe website, March 13, 2013). Such large amounts of snowfall can make the local roads difficult to navigate. Is there a difference in how well these four cities keep streets clear of snow? A sample of truck drivers who drive in each of these four cities was taken, and the drivers were asked whether the city does a satisfactory job in keeping its streets clear of snow. The results of these samples follow.

	Rochester, NY	Salt Lake City, UT	Madison, WI	Bridgeport, CT
Satisfactory	27	35	29	24
Not Satisfactory	21	21	18	21

a. Use the sample data to calculate the point estimate of the population proportion of truck drivers who rated each of these cities as satisfactory in keeping its streets clear of snow.
b. Conduct a hypothesis test to determine if the population proportion of truck drivers who rate whether the city does a satisfactory job of keeping its streets clear of snow is equal for these four cities. Using a .05 level of significance, what is the p-value and what is your conclusion?

39. A sample of parts provided the following contingency table data on part quality by production shift.

Shift	Number Good	Number Defective
First	368	32
Second	285	15
Third	176	24

Use $\alpha = .05$ and test the hypothesis that part quality is independent of the production shift. What is your conclusion?

40. *The Wall Street Journal* Subscriber Study showed data on the employment status of subscribers. Sample results corresponding to subscribers of the eastern and western editions are shown here.

	Region	
Employment Status	**Eastern Edition**	**Western Edition**
Full-Time	1105	574
Part-Time	31	15
Self-Employed/Consultant	229	186
Not Employed	485	344

Use $\alpha = .05$ and test the hypothesis that employment status is independent of the region. What is your conclusion?

41. A lending institution supplied the following data on loan approvals by four loan officers. Use $\alpha = .05$ and test to determine whether the loan approval decision is independent of the loan officer reviewing the loan application.

	Loan Approval Decision	
Loan Officer	**Approved**	**Rejected**
Miller	24	16
McMahon	17	13
Games	35	15
Runk	11	9

42. A Pew Research Center survey asked respondents if they would rather live in a place with a slower pace of life or a place with a faster pace of life (*USA Today*, February 13, 2009). Consider the following data showing a sample of preferences expressed by 150 men and 150 women.

	Preferred Pace of Life		
Respondent	**Slower**	**No Preference**	**Faster**
Men	102	9	39
Women	111	12	27

a. Combine the samples of men and women. What is the overall percentage of respondents who prefer to live in a place with a slower pace of life? What is the overall percentage of respondents who prefer to live in a place with a faster pace of life? What is your conclusion?
b. Is the preferred pace of life independent of the respondent? Use $\alpha = .05$. What is your conclusion? What is your recommendation?

43. According to Ezine@rticles, the most popular flavors of ice cream in the United States are vanilla, chocolate, butter pecan, and strawberry (Ezine@rticles website, March 9, 2013), but are these preferences and age of the consumer independent? In a random survey 1000

consumers were asked their age and which of these four flavors of ice cream they preferred. The survey yielded the following results.

	Under 18	18–30	31–44	45–58	Over 58
Vanilla	155	108	99	100	129
Chocolate	39	53	47	28	30
Butter Pecan	12	15	21	20	43
Strawberry	23	14	13	17	34

Do these data suggest that consumer preference for these four flavors of ice cream and age of the consumer are independent? Use a .05 level of significance. What is your conclusion?

44. The office occupancy rates were reported for four California metropolitan areas. Do the following data suggest that the office vacancies were independent of metropolitan area? Use a .05 level of significance. What is your conclusion?

Occupancy Status	Los Angeles	San Diego	San Francisco	San Jose
Occupied	160	116	192	174
Vacant	40	34	33	26

Case Problem 1 A Bipartisan Agenda for Change

In a study conducted by Zogby International for the *Democrat and Chronicle,* more than 700 New Yorkers were polled to determine whether the New York state government works. Respondents surveyed were asked questions involving pay cuts for state legislators, restrictions on lobbyists, terms limits for legislators, and whether state citizens should be able to put matters directly on the state ballot for a vote. The results regarding several proposed reforms had broad support, crossing all demographic and political lines.

Suppose that a follow-up survey of 100 individuals who live in the western region of New York was conducted. The party affiliation (Democrat, Independent, Republican) of each individual surveyed was recorded, as well as the responses to the following three questions.

1. Should legislative pay be cut for every day the state budget is late?
   Yes ____ No ____
2. Should there be more restrictions on lobbyists?
   Yes ____ No ____
3. Should there be term limits requiring that legislators serve a fixed number of years?
   Yes ____ No ____

NYReform

The responses were coded using 1 for a Yes response and 2 for a No response. The complete data set is available on the website in the WEBfile named NYReform.

Managerial Report

1. Use descriptive statistics to summarize the data from this study. What are your preliminary conclusions about the independence of the response (Yes or No) and party affiliation for each of the three questions in the survey?
2. With regard to question 1, test for the independence of the response (Yes and No) and party affiliation. Use $\alpha = .05$.

3. With regard to question 2, test for the independence of the response (Yes and No) and party affiliation. Use $\alpha = .05$.
4. With regard to question 3, test for the independence of the response (Yes and No) and party affiliation. Use $\alpha = .05$.
5. Does it appear that there is broad support for change across all political lines? Explain.

Chapter 1

Introduction

CONTENTS

1.1 DECISION MAKING

1.2 BUSINESS ANALYTICS DEFINED

1.3 A CATEGORIZATION OF ANALYTICAL METHODS AND MODELS
- Descriptive Analytics
- Predictive Analytics
- Prescriptive Analytics

1.4 BIG DATA
- Volume
- Velocity
- Variety
- Veracity

1.5 BUSINESS ANALYTICS IN PRACTICE
- Financial Analytics
- Human Resource (HR) Analytics
- Marketing Analytics
- Health Care Analytics
- Supply-Chain Analytics
- Analytics for Government and Nonprofits
- Sports Analytics
- Web Analytics

You apply for a loan for the first time. How does the bank assess the riskiness of the loan it might make to you? How does Amazon.com know which books and other products to recommend to you when you log in to their web site? How do airlines determine what price to quote to you when you are shopping for a plane ticket? How can doctors better diagnose and treat you when you are ill or injured?

You may be applying for a loan for the first time, but millions of people around the world have applied for loans before. Many of these loan recipients have paid back their loans in full and on time, but some have not. The bank wants to know whether you are more like those who have paid back their loans or more like those who defaulted. By comparing your credit history, financial situation, and other factors to the vast database of previous loan recipients, the bank can effectively assess how likely you are to default on a loan.

Similarly, Amazon.com has access to data on millions of purchases made by customers on its web site. Amazon.com examines your previous purchases, the products you have viewed, and any product recommendations you have provided. Amazon.com then searches through its huge database for customers who are similar to you in terms of product purchases, recommendations, and interests. Once similar customers have been identified, their purchases form the basis of the recommendations given to you.

Prices for airline tickets are frequently updated. The price quoted to you for a flight between New York and San Francisco today could be very different from the price that will be quoted tomorrow. These changes happen because airlines use a pricing strategy known as revenue management. Revenue management works by examining vast amounts of data on past airline customer purchases and using these data to forecast future purchases. These forecasts are then fed into sophisticated optimization algorithms that determine the optimal price to charge for a particular flight and when to change that price. Revenue management has resulted in substantial increases in airline revenues.

Finally, consider the case of being evaluated by a doctor for a potentially serious medical issue. Hundreds of medical papers may describe research studies done on patients facing similar diagnoses, and thousands of data points exist on their outcomes. However, it is extremely unlikely that your doctor has read every one of these research papers or is aware of all previous patient outcomes. Instead of relying only on her medical training and knowledge gained from her limited set of previous patients, wouldn't it be better for your doctor to have access to the expertise and patient histories of thousands of doctors around the world?

A group of IBM computer scientists initiated a project to develop a new decision technology to help in answering these types of questions. That technology is called Watson, named after the founder of IBM, Thomas J. Watson. The team at IBM focused on one aim: how the vast amounts of data now available on the Internet can be used to make more data-driven, smarter decisions.

Watson became a household name in 2011, when it famously won the television game show, *Jeopardy!* Since that proof of concept in 2011, IBM has reached agreements with the health insurance provider WellPoint (now part of Anthem), the financial services company Citibank, and Memorial Sloan-Kettering Cancer Center to apply Watson to the decision problems that they face.

Watson is a system of computing hardware, high-speed data processing, and analytical algorithms that are combined to make data-based recommendations. As more and more data are collected, Watson has the capability to learn over time. In simple terms, according to IBM, Watson gathers hundreds of thousands of possible solutions from a huge data bank, evaluates them using analytical techniques, and proposes only the best solutions for consideration. Watson provides not just a single solution, but rather a range of good solutions with a confidence level for each.

For example, at a data center in Virginia, to the delight of doctors and patients, Watson is already being used to speed up the approval of medical procedures. Citibank is beginning to explore how to use Watson to better serve its customers, and cancer specialists at more than a dozen hospitals in North America are using Watson to assist with the diagnosis and treatment of patients.[1]

This book is concerned with data-driven decision making and the use of analytical approaches in the decision-making process. Three developments spurred recent explosive growth in the use of analytical methods in business applications. First, technological advances—such as improved point-of-sale scanner technology and the collection of data through e-commerce, Internet social networks, and data generated from personal electronic devices—produce incredible amounts of data for businesses. Naturally, businesses want to use these data to improve the efficiency and profitability of their operations, better understand their customers, price their products more effectively, and gain a competitive advantage. Second, ongoing research has resulted in numerous methodological developments, including advances in computational approaches to effectively handle and explore massive amounts of data, faster algorithms for optimization and simulation, and more effective approaches for visualizing data. Third, these methodological developments were paired with an explosion in computing power and storage capability. Better computing hardware, parallel computing, and, more recently, cloud computing (the remote use of hardware and software over the Internet) have enabled businesses to solve big problems more quickly and more accurately than ever before.

In summary, the availability of massive amounts of data, improvements in analytic methodologies, and substantial increases in computing power have all come together to result in a dramatic upsurge in the use of analytical methods in business and a reliance on the discipline that is the focus of this text: business analytics. Figure 1.1 shows the job trend for analytics from 2006 to 2015. The chart from indeed.com shows the percentage of job ads that contain the word *analytics* and illustrates that demand has grown and continues to be strong for analytical skills.

It is difficult to know for sure the cause of the large spike in analytics job ads in 2008. We do note, however, that the thought-provoking book Competing on Analytics *by Davenport and Harris was published in 2007.*

Business analytics is a crucial area of study for students looking to enhance their employment prospects. It has been predicted that by 2018 there will be a shortage of more than 1.5 million business managers with adequate training in analytics in the United States alone.[2] As stated in the Preface, the purpose of this text is to provide

FIGURE 1.1 Analytics Job Trend According to Indeed.com

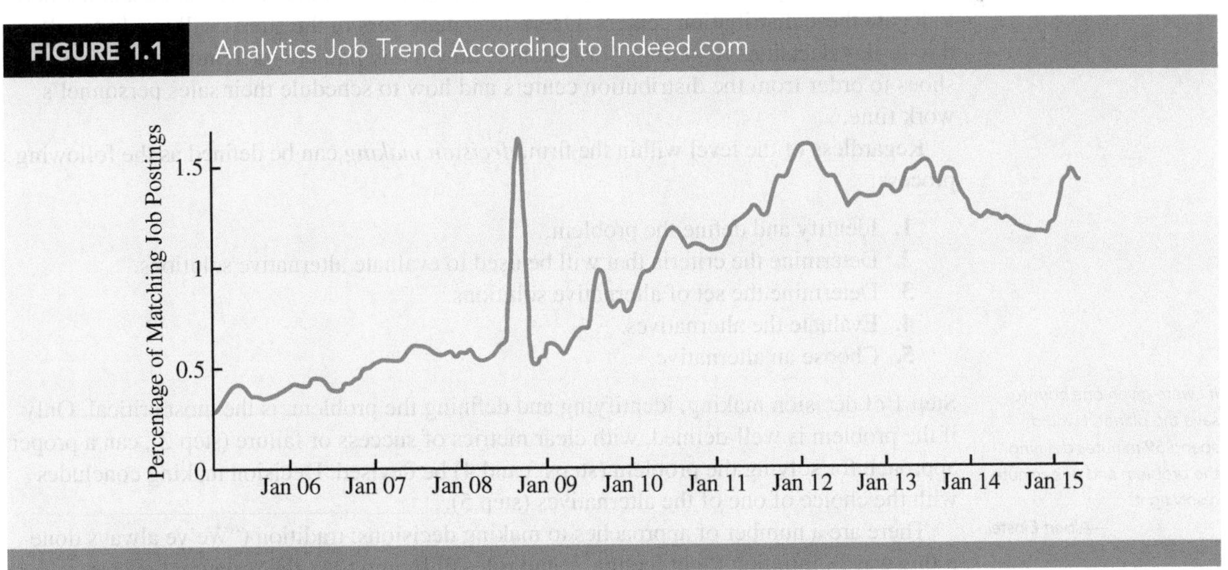

[1] "IBM's Watson Is Learning Its Way to Saving Lives," Fastcompany web site, December 8, 2012; "IBM's Watson Targets Cancer and Enlists Prominent Providers in the Fight," ModernHealthcare web site, May 5, 2015.

[2] J. Manyika et al., "Big Data: The Next Frontier for Innovation, Competition and Productivity," McKinsey Global Institute Report, 2011.

students with a sound conceptual understanding of the role that business analytics plays in the decision-making process. To reinforce the applications orientation of the text and to provide a better understanding of the variety of applications in which analytical methods have been used successfully, Analytics in Action articles are presented throughout the book. Each Analytics in Action article summarizes an application of analytical methods in practice.

1.1 Decision Making

It is the responsibility of managers to plan, coordinate, organize, and lead their organizations to better performance. Ultimately, managers' responsibilities require that they make strategic, tactical, or operational decisions. **Strategic decisions** involve higher-level issues concerned with the overall direction of the organization; these decisions define the organization's overall goals and aspirations for the future. Strategic decisions are usually the domain of higher-level executives and have a time horizon of three to five years. **Tactical decisions** concern how the organization should achieve the goals and objectives set by its strategy, and they are usually the responsibility of midlevel management. Tactical decisions usually span a year and thus are revisited annually or even every six months. **Operational decisions** affect how the firm is run from day to day; they are the domain of operations managers, who are the closest to the customer.

Consider the case of the Thoroughbred Running Company (TRC). Historically, TRC had been a catalog-based retail seller of running shoes and apparel. TRC sales revenues grew quickly as it changed its emphasis from catalog-based sales to Internet-based sales. Recently, TRC decided that it should also establish retail stores in the malls and downtown areas of major cities. This strategic decision will take the firm in a new direction that it hopes will complement its Internet-based strategy. TRC middle managers will therefore have to make a variety of tactical decisions in support of this strategic decision, including how many new stores to open this year, where to open these new stores, how many distribution centers will be needed to support the new stores, and where to locate these distribution centers. Operations managers in the stores will need to make day-to-day decisions regarding, for instance, how many pairs of each model and size of shoes to order from the distribution centers and how to schedule their sales personnel's work time.

Regardless of the level within the firm, *decision making* can be defined as the following process:

1. Identify and define the problem.
2. Determine the criteria that will be used to evaluate alternative solutions.
3. Determine the set of alternative solutions.
4. Evaluate the alternatives.
5. Choose an alternative.

If I were given one hour to save the planet, I would spend 59 minutes defining the problem and one minute resolving it.

—Albert Einstein

Step 1 of decision making, identifying and defining the problem, is the most critical. Only if the problem is well-defined, with clear metrics of success or failure (step 2), can a proper approach for solving the problem (steps 3 and 4) be devised. Decision making concludes with the choice of one of the alternatives (step 5).

There are a number of approaches to making decisions: tradition ("We've always done it this way"), intuition ("gut feeling"), and rules of thumb ("As the restaurant owner, I schedule twice the number of waiters and cooks on holidays"). The power of each of these approaches should not be underestimated. Managerial experience and intuition are valuable inputs to making decisions, but what if relevant data were available to help us make more informed decisions? With the vast amounts of data now generated and stored electronically, it is estimated that the amount of data stored by businesses more than doubles every two years. How can managers convert these data into knowledge that they can use to be more efficient and effective in managing their businesses?

1.2 Business Analytics Defined

What makes decision making difficult and challenging? Uncertainty is probably the number one challenge. If we knew how much the demand will be for our product, we could do a much better job of planning and scheduling production. If we knew exactly how long each step in a project will take to be completed, we could better predict the project's cost and completion date. If we knew how stocks will perform, investing would be a lot easier.

Another factor that makes decision making difficult is that we often face such an enormous number of alternatives that we cannot evaluate them all. What is the best combination of stocks to help me meet my financial objectives? What is the best product line for a company that wants to maximize its market share? How should an airline price its tickets so as to maximize revenue?

Some firms and industries use the simpler term, analytics. *Analytics is often thought of as a broader category than business analytics, encompassing the use of analytical techniques in the sciences and engineering as well. In this text, we use* business analytics *and* analytics *synonymously.*

Business analytics is the scientific process of transforming data into insight for making better decisions.[3] Business analytics is used for data-driven or fact-based decision making, which is often seen as more objective than other alternatives for decision making.

As we shall see, the tools of business analytics can aid decision making by creating insights from data, by improving our ability to more accurately forecast for planning, by helping us quantify risk, and by yielding better alternatives through analysis and optimization. A study based on a large sample of firms that was conducted by researchers at MIT's Sloan School of Management and the University of Pennsylvania, concluded that firms guided by data-driven decision making have higher productivity and market value and increased output and profitability.[4]

1.3 A Categorization of Analytical Methods and Models

Business analytics can involve anything from simple reports to the most advanced optimization techniques (methods for finding the best course of action). Analytics is generally thought to comprise three broad categories of techniques: descriptive analytics, predictive analytics, and prescriptive analytics.

Descriptive Analytics

Descriptive analytics encompasses the set of techniques that describes what has happened in the past. Examples are data queries, reports, descriptive statistics, data visualization including data dashboards, some data-mining techniques, and basic what-if spreadsheet models.

Appendix B at the end of this book describes how to use Microsoft Access to conduct data queries.

A **data query** is a request for information with certain characteristics from a database. For example, a query to a manufacturing plant's database might be for all records of shipments to a particular distribution center during the month of March. This query provides descriptive information about these shipments: the number of shipments, how much was included in each shipment, the date each shipment was sent, and so on. A report summarizing relevant historical information for management might be conveyed by the use of descriptive statistics (means, measures of variation, etc.) and data-visualization tools (tables, charts, and maps). Simple descriptive statistics and data-visualization techniques can be used to find patterns or relationships in a large database.

[3]We adopt the definition of analytics developed by the Institute for Operations Research and the Management Sciences (INFORMS).

[4]E. Brynjolfsson, L. M. Hitt, and H. H. Kim, "Strength in Numbers: How Does Data-Driven Decisionmaking Affect Firm Performance?" (April 18, 2013). Available at SSRN, http://papers.ssrn.com/sol3/papers.cfm?abstract_id=1819486.

Data dashboards are collections of tables, charts, maps, and summary statistics that are updated as new data become available. Dashboards are used to help management monitor specific aspects of the company's performance related to their decision-making responsibilities. For corporate-level managers, daily data dashboards might summarize sales by region, current inventory levels, and other company-wide metrics; front-line managers may view dashboards that contain metrics related to staffing levels, local inventory levels, and short-term sales forecasts.

Data mining is the use of analytical techniques for better understanding patterns and relationships that exist in large data sets. For example, by analyzing text on social network platforms like Twitter, data-mining techniques (including cluster analysis and sentiment analysis) are used by companies to better understand their customers. By categorizing certain words as positive or negative and keeping track of how often those words appear in tweets, a company like Apple can better understand how its customers are feeling about a product like the Apple Watch.

Predictive Analytics

Predictive analytics consists of techniques that use models constructed from past data to predict the future or ascertain the impact of one variable on another. For example, past data on product sales may be used to construct a mathematical model to predict future sales. This mode can factor in the product's growth trajectory and seasonality based on past patterns. A packaged-food manufacturer may use point-of-sale scanner data from retail outlets to help in estimating the lift in unit sales due to coupons or sales events. Survey data and past purchase behavior may be used to help predict the market share of a new product. All of these are applications of predictive analytics.

Linear regression, time series analysis, some data-mining techniques, and simulation, often referred to as risk analysis, all fall under the banner of predictive analytics. We discuss all of these techniques in greater detail later in this text.

Data mining, previously discussed as a descriptive analytics tool, is also often used in predictive analytics. For example, a large grocery store chain might be interested in developing a targeted marketing campaign that offers a discount coupon on potato chips. By studying historical point-of-sale data, the store may be able to use data mining to predict which customers are the most likely to respond to an offer on discounted chips by purchasing higher-margin items such as beer or soft drinks in addition to the chips, thus increasing the store's overall revenue.

Simulation involves the use of probability and statistics to construct a computer model to study the impact of uncertainty on a decision. For example, banks often use simulation to model investment and default risk in order to stress-test financial models. Simulation is also often used in the pharmaceutical industry to assess the risk of introducing a new drug.

Prescriptive Analytics

Prescriptive analytics differs from descriptive or predictive analytics in that **prescriptive analytics** indicates a best course of action to take; that is, the output of a prescriptive model is a best decision. The airline industry's use of revenue management is an example of a prescriptive analytics. Airlines use past purchasing data as inputs into a model that recommends the best pricing strategy across all flights in order to maximize revenue.

Other examples of prescriptive analytics are portfolio models in finance, supply network design models in operations, and price-markdown models in retailing. Portfolio models use historical investment return data to determine which mix of investments will yield the highest expected return while controlling or limiting exposure to risk. Supply-network design models provide data about plant and distribution center locations that will

TABLE 1.1 Coverage of Business Analytics Topics in This Text

Chapter	Title	Descriptive	Predictive	Prescriptive
1	Introduction	●	●	●
2	Descriptive Statistics	●		
3	Data Visualization	●		
4	Descriptive Data Mining	●		
5	Probability: An Introduction to Modeling Uncertainty	●		
6	Statistical Inference	●		
7	Linear Regression		●	
8	Time Series and Forecasting		●	
9	Predictive Data Mining		●	
10	Spreadsheet Models	●		
11	Linear Optimization Models			●
12	Integer Optimization Models			●
13	Nonlinear Optimization Models			●
14	Simulation		●	●
15	Decision Analysis			●

minimize costs while still meeting customer service requirements. Given historical data, retail price markdown models yield revenue-maximizing discount levels and the timing of discount offers when goods have not sold as planned. All of these models are known as **optimization models**, that is, models that give the best decision subject to the constraints of the situation.

Another type of modeling in the prescriptive analytics category is **simulation optimization**, which combines the use of probability and statistics to model uncertainty with optimization techniques to find good decisions in highly complex and highly uncertain settings. Finally, the techniques of **decision analysis** can be used to develop an optimal strategy when a decision maker is faced with several decision alternatives and an uncertain set of future events. Decision analysis also employs **utility theory**, which assigns values to outcomes based on the decision maker's attitude toward risk, loss, and other factors.

In this text we cover all three areas of business analytics: descriptive, predictive, and prescriptive. Table 1.1 shows how the chapters cover the three categories.

1.4 Big Data

Walmart handles over 1 million purchase transactions per hour. Facebook processes more than 250 million picture uploads per day. Six billion cell-phone owners around the world generate vast amounts of data by calling, texting, tweeting, and browsing the web on a daily basis.[5] As Google CEO Eric Schmidt has noted, the amount of data currently created every 48 hours is equivalent to the entire amount of data created from the dawn of civilization until the year 2003. It is through technology that we have truly been thrust into the data age. Because data can now be collected electronically, the amounts of it available are staggering. The Internet, cell phones, retail checkout scanners, surveillance video, and sensors on everything from aircraft to cars to bridges allow us to collect and store vast amounts of data in real time.

[5]SAS White Paper, "Big Data Meets Big Data Analytics," SAS Institute, 2012.

FIGURE 1.2 The 4 Vs of Big Data

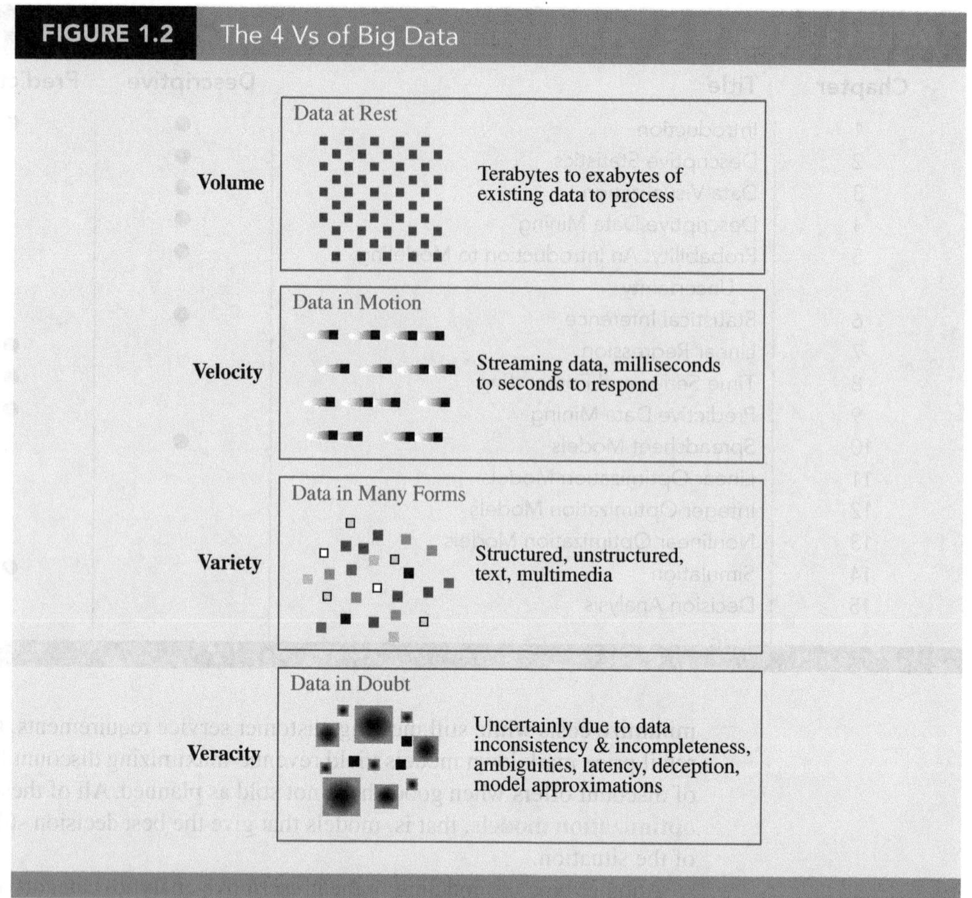

Source: *IBM*

In the midst of all of this data collection, the new term *big data* has been created. There is no universally accepted definition of big data. However, probably the most accepted and most general definition is that **big data** is any set of data that is too large or too complex to be handled by standard data-processing technics and typical desktop software. IBM describes the phenomenon of big data through the four Vs: volume, velocity, variety, and veracity, as shown in Figure 1.2.[6]

Volume

Because data are collected electronically, we are able to collect more of it. To be useful, these data must be stored, and this storage has led to vast quantities of data. Many companies now store in excess of 100 terabytes of data (a terabyte of data is 100,000 gigabytes).

Velocity

Real-time capture and analysis of data present unique challenges both in how data are stored and the speed with which those data can be analyzed for decision making. For example, the New York Stock Exchange collects 1 terabyte of data in a single trading session, and having current data and real-time rules for trades and predictive modeling are important for managing stock portfolios.

[6]IBM web site: http://www.ibmbigdatahub.com/sites/default/files/infographic_file/4-Vs-of-big-data.jpg.

Variety

In addition to the sheer volume and speed with which companies now collect data, more complicated types of data are now available and are proving to be of great value to businesses. Text data are collected by monitoring what is being said about a company's products or services on social media platforms such as Twitter. Audio data are collected from service calls (on a service call, you will often hear "this call may be monitored for quality control"). Video data collected by in-store video cameras are used to analyze shopping behavior. Analyzing information generated by these nontraditional sources is more complicated in part because of the processing required to transform the data into a numerical form that can be analyzed.

Veracity

Veracity has to do with how much uncertainty is in the data. For example, the data could have many missing values, which makes reliable analysis a challenge. Inconsistencies in units of measure and the lack of reliability of responses in terms of bias also increase the complexity of the data.

Businesses have realized that understanding big data can lead to a competitive advantage. Although big data represents opportunities, it also presents challenges in terms of data storage and processing, security and available analytical talent.

The four Vs indicate that big data creates challenges in terms of how these complex data can be captured, stored, and processed; secured; and then analyzed. Traditional databases more or less assume that data fit into nice rows and columns, but that is not always the case with big data. Also, the sheer volume (the first V) often means that it is not possible to store all of the data on a single computer. This has led to new technologies like **Hadoop**—an open-source programming environment that supports big data processing through distributed storage and distributed processing on clusters of computers. Essentially, Hadoop provides a divide-and-conquer approach to handling massive amounts of data, dividing the storage and processing over multiple computers. **MapReduce** is a programming model used within Hadoop that performs the two major steps for which it is named: the map step and the reduce step. The map step divides the data into manageable subsets and distributes it to the computers in the cluster (often termed nodes) for storing and processing. The reduce step collects answers from the nodes and combines them into an answer to the original problem. Without technologies like Hadoop and MapReduce, and relatively inexpensive computer power, processing big data would not be cost-effective; in some cases, processing might not even be possible.

While some sources of big data are publicly available (Twitter, weather data, etc.), much of it is private information. Medical records, bank account information, and credit card transactions, for example, are all highly confidential and must be protected from computer hackers. **Data security**, the protection of stored data from destructive forces or unauthorized users, is of critical importance to companies. For example, credit card transactions are potentially very useful for understanding consumer behavior, but compromise of these data could lead to unauthorized use of the credit card or identity theft. Data security company Datacastle estimated that the average cost of a data breach for a company in 2012 was $7.2 million. Since 2014, companies such as Target, Anthem, JPMorgan Chase, and Home Depot have faced major data breaches costing millions of dollars.

The complexities of the 4 Vs have increased the demand for analysts, but a shortage of qualified analysts has made hiring more challenging. More companies are searching for **data scientists**, who know how to effectively process and analyze massive amounts of data because they are well trained in both computer science and statistics. Next we discuss three examples of how companies are collecting big data for competitive advantage.

Kroger Understands Its Customers[7] Kroger is the largest retail grocery chain in the United States. It sends over 11 million pieces of direct mail to its customers each quarter. The quarterly mailers each contain 12 coupons that are tailored to each household based on several years of shopping data obtained through its customer loyalty card program. By collecting and analyzing consumer behavior at the individual household level and better matching its coupon offers to shopper interests, Kroger has been able to realize a far higher redemption rate on its coupons. In the six-week period following distribution of the mailers, over 70% of households redeem at least one coupon, leading to an estimated coupon revenue of $10 billion for Kroger.

MagicBand at Disney[8] The Walt Disney Company has begun offering a wristband to visitors to its Orlando, Florida, Disney World theme park. Known as the MagicBand, the wristband contains technology that can transmit more than 40 feet and can be used to track each visitor's location in the park in real time. The band can link to information that allows Disney to better serve its visitors. For example, prior to the trip to Disney World, a visitor might be asked to fill out a survey on his or her birth date and favorite rides, characters, and restaurant table type and location. This information, linked to the MagicBand, can allow Disney employees using smartphones to greet you by name as you arrive, offer you products they know you prefer, wish you a happy birthday, have your favorite characters show up as you wait in line or have lunch at your favorite table. The MagicBand can be linked to your credit card, so there is no need to carry cash or a credit card. And during your visit, your movement throughout the park can be tracked and the data can be analyzed to better serve you during your next visit to the park.

General Electric and the Internet of Things[9] The **Internet of Things (IoT)** is the technology that allows data, collected from sensors in all types of machines, to be sent over the Internet to repositories where it can be stored and analyzed. This ability to collect data from products has enabled the companies that produce and sell those products to better serve their customers and offer new services based on analytics. For example, each day General Electric (GE) gathers nearly 50 million pieces of data from 10 million sensors on medical equipment and aircraft engines it has sold to customers throughout the world. In the case of aircraft engines, through a service agreement with its customers, GE collects data each time an airplane powered by its engines takes off and lands. By analyzing these data, GE can better predict when maintenance is needed, which helps customers to avoid unplanned maintenance and downtime and helps ensure safe operation. GE can also use the data to better control how the plane is flown, leading to a decrease in fuel cost by flying more efficiently. In 2014, GE realized approximately $1.1 billion in revenue from the IoT.

Although big data is clearly one of the drivers for the strong demand for analytics, it is important to understand that in some sense big data issues are a subset of analytics. Many very valuable applications of analytics do not involve big data, but rather traditional data sets that are very manageable by traditional database and analytics software. The key to analytics is that it provides useful insights and better decision making using the data that are available—whether those data are "big" or "small."

[7]Based on "Kroger Knows Your Shopping Patterns Better Than You Do," Forbes.com, October 23, 2013.
[8]Based on "Disney's $1 Billion Bet on a Magical Wristband," Wired.com, March 10, 2015.
[9]Based on "G.E. Opens Its Big Data Platform," NYTimes.com, October 9, 2014.

1.5 Business Analytics in Practice

Business analytics involves tools as simple as reports and graphs to those that are as sophisticated as optimization, data mining, and simulation. In practice, companies that apply analytics often follow a trajectory similar to that shown in Figure 1.3. Organizations start with basic analytics in the lower left. As they realize the advantages of these analytic techniques, they often progress to more sophisticated techniques in an effort to reap the derived competitive advantage. Therefore, predictive and prescriptive analytics are sometimes referred to as **advanced analytics**. Not all companies reach that level of usage, but those that embrace analytics as a competitive strategy often do.

Analytics has been applied in virtually all sectors of business and government. Organizations such as Procter & Gamble, IBM, UPS, Netflix, Amazon.com, Google, the Internal Revenue Service, and General Electric have embraced analytics to solve important problems or to achieve a competitive advantage. In this section, we briefly discuss some of the types of applications of analytics by application area.

Financial Analytics

Applications of analytics in finance are numerous and pervasive. Predictive models are used to forecast financial performance, to assess the risk of investment portfolios and projects, and to construct financial instruments such as derivatives. Prescriptive models are used to construct optimal portfolios of investments, to allocate assets, and to create optimal capital budgeting plans. For example, GE Asset Management uses optimization models to decide how to invest its own cash received from insurance policies and other financial products, as well as the cash of its clients, such as Genworth Financial. The estimated benefit from the optimization models was \$75 million over a five-year period.[10] Simulation is also often used to assess risk in the financial sector; one example is the deployment by

FIGURE 1.3 The Spectrum of Business Analytics

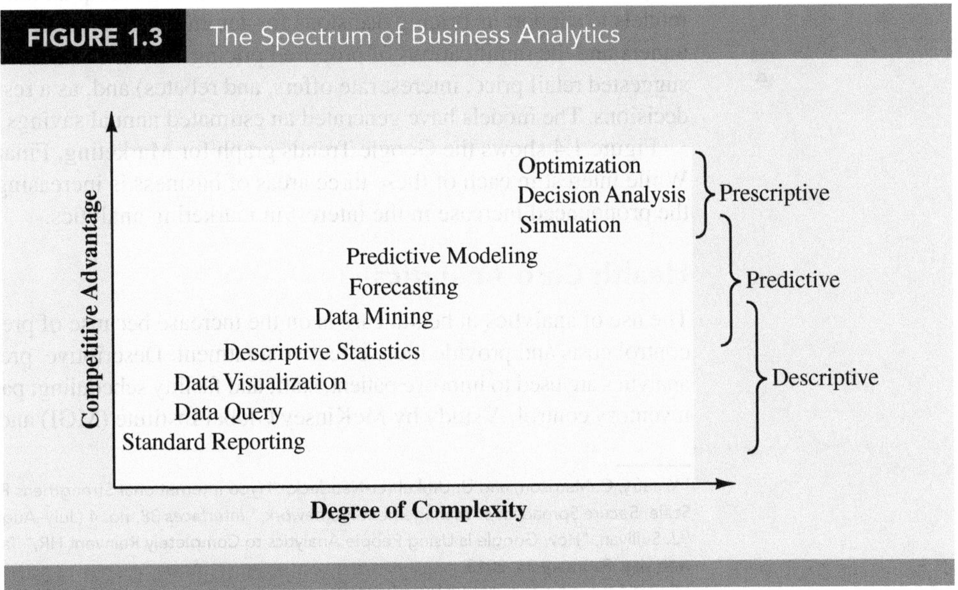

Source: *Adapted from SAS.*

[10] L. C. Chalermkraivuth et al., "GE Asset Management, Genworth Financial, and GE Insurance Use a Sequential-Linear Programming Algorithm to Optimize Portfolios," *Interfaces* 35, no. 5 (September–October 2005): 370–80.

Hypo Real Estate International of simulation models to successfully manage commercial real estate risk.[11]

Human Resource (HR) Analytics

A relatively new area of application for analytics is the management of an organization's human resources (HR). The HR function is charged with ensuring that the organization: (1) has the mix of skill sets necessary to meet its needs, (2) is hiring the highest-quality talent and providing an environment that retains it, and (3) achieves its organizational diversity goals. Google refers to its HR Analytics function as "people analytics." Google has analyzed substantial data on their own employees to determine the characteristics of great leaders, to assess factors that contribute to productivity, and to evaluate potential new hires. Google also uses predictive analytics to continually update their forecast of future employee turnover and retention.[12]

Marketing Analytics

Marketing is one of the fastest-growing areas for the application of analytics. A better understanding of consumer behavior through the use of scanner data and data generated from social media has led to an increased interest in marketing analytics. As a result, descriptive, predictive, and prescriptive analytics are all heavily used in marketing. A better understanding of consumer behavior through analytics leads to the better use of advertising budgets, more effective pricing strategies, improved forecasting of demand, improved product-line management, and increased customer satisfaction and loyalty. For example, each year, NBCUniversal uses a predictive model to help support its annual upfront market—a period in late May when each television network sells the majority of its on-air advertising for the upcoming television season. Over 200 NBC sales and finance personnel use the results of the forecasting model to support pricing and sales decisions.[13]

In another example of high-impact marketing analytics, automobile manufacturer Chrysler teamed with J.D. Power and Associates to develop an innovative set of predictive models to support its pricing decisions for automobiles. These models help Chrysler to better understand the ramifications of proposed pricing structures (a combination of manufacturer's suggested retail price, interest rate offers, and rebates) and, as a result, to improve its pricing decisions. The models have generated an estimated annual savings of $500 million.[14]

Figure 1.4 shows the Google Trends graph for Marketing, Financial, and HR Analytics. While interest in each of these three areas of business is increasing, the graph clearly shows the pronounced increase in the interest in marketing analytics.

Health Care Analytics

The use of analytics in health care is on the increase because of pressure to simultaneously control costs and provide more effective treatment. Descriptive, predictive, and prescriptive analytics are used to improve patient, staff, and facility scheduling; patient flow; purchasing; and inventory control. A study by McKinsey Global Institute (MGI) and McKinsey & Company[15]

---

[11]Y. Jafry, C. Marrison, and U. Umkehrer-Neudeck, "Hypo International Strengthens Risk Management with a Large-Scale, Secure Spreadsheet-Management Framework," *Interfaces* 38, no. 4 (July–August 2008): 281–88.

[12]J. Sullivan, "How Google Is Using People Analytics to Completely Reinvent HR," Talent Management and HR web site, February 26, 2013.

[13]S. Bollapragada et al., "NBC-Universal Uses a Novel Qualitative Forecasting Technique to Predict Advertising Demand," *Interfaces* 38, no. 2 (March–April 2008): 103–11.

[14]J. Silva-Risso et al., "Chrysler and J. D. Power: Pioneering Scientific Price Customization in the Automobile Industry," *Interfaces* 38, no. 1 (January–February 2008): 26–39.

[15]J. Manyika et al., "Big Data: The Next Frontier for Innovation, Competition and Productivity," McKinsey Global Institute Report, 2011.

FIGURE 1.4 Google Trends for Marketing, Financial, and Human Resource (HR) Analytics, 2006–2015

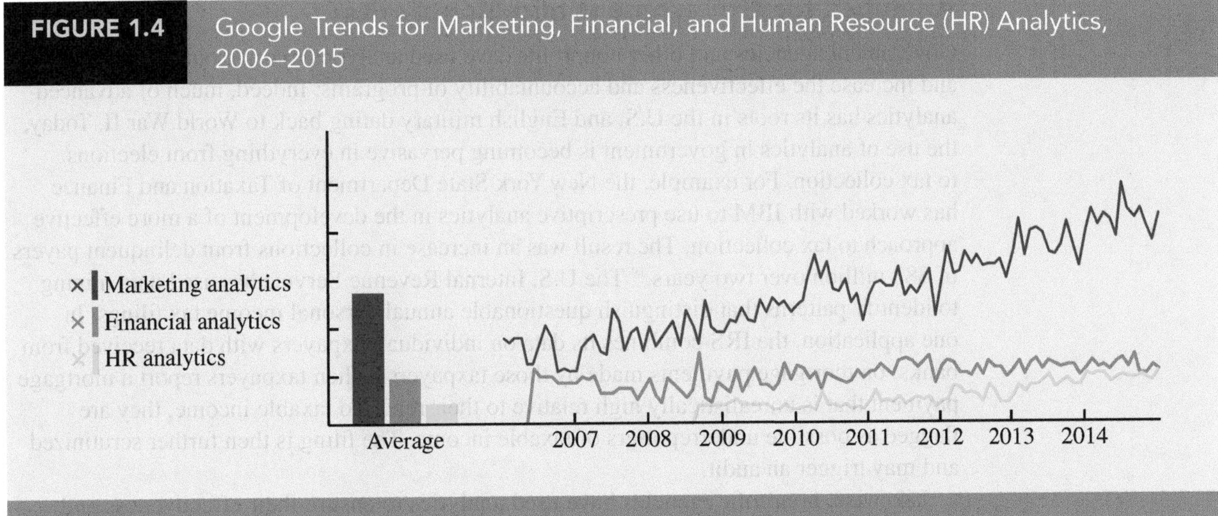

estimates that the health care system in the United States could save more than $300 billion per year by better utilizing analytics; these savings are approximately the equivalent of the entire gross domestic product of countries such as Finland, Singapore, and Ireland.

The use of prescriptive analytics for diagnosis and treatment is relatively new, but it may prove to be the most important application of analytics in health care. For example, working with the Georgia Institute of Technology, Memorial Sloan-Kettering Cancer Center developed a real-time prescriptive model to determine the optimal placement of radioactive seeds for the treatment of prostate cancer.[16] Using the new model, 20–30% fewer seeds are needed, resulting in a faster and less invasive procedure.

Supply-Chain Analytics

One of the earliest applications of analytics was in logistics and supply-chain management. The core service of companies such as UPS and FedEx is the efficient delivery of goods, and analytics has long been used to achieve efficiency. The optimal sorting of goods, vehicle and staff scheduling, and vehicle routing are all key to profitability for logistics companies such as UPS and FedEx.

Companies can benefit from better inventory and processing control and more efficient supply chains. Analytic tools used in this area span the entire spectrum of analytics. For example, the women's apparel manufacturer Bernard Claus, Inc., has successfully used descriptive analytics to provide its managers a visual representation of the status of its supply chain.[17] ConAgra Foods uses predictive and prescriptive analytics to better plan capacity utilization by incorporating the inherent uncertainty in commodities pricing. ConAgra realized a 100% return on their investment in analytics in under three months—an unheard of result for a major technology investment.[18]

[16]E. Lee and M. Zaider, "Operations Research Advances Cancer Therapeutics," *Interfaces* 38, no. 1 (January–February 2008): 5–25.

[17]T. H. Davenport, ed., *Enterprise Analytics* (Upper Saddle River, NJ: Pearson Education Inc., 2013).

[18]"ConAgra Mills: Up-to-the-Minute Insights Drive Smarter Selling Decisions and Big Improvements in Capacity Utilization," IBM Smarter Planet Leadership Series. Available at: http://www.ibm.com/smarterplanet/us/en/leadership/conagra/, retrieved December 1, 2012.

Analytics for Government and Nonprofits

Government agencies and other nonprofits have used analytics to drive out inefficiencies and increase the effectiveness and accountability of programs. Indeed, much of advanced analytics has its roots in the U.S. and English military dating back to World War II. Today, the use of analytics in government is becoming pervasive in everything from elections to tax collection. For example, the New York State Department of Taxation and Finance has worked with IBM to use prescriptive analytics in the development of a more effective approach to tax collection. The result was an increase in collections from delinquent payers of $83 million over two years.[19] The U.S. Internal Revenue Service has used data mining to identify patterns that distinguish questionable annual personal income tax filings. In one application, the IRS combines its data on individual taxpayers with data received from banks, on mortgage payments made by those taxpayers. When taxpayers report a mortgage payment that is unrealistically high relative to their reported taxable income, they are flagged as possible underreporters of taxable income. The filing is then further scrutinized and may trigger an audit.

Likewise, nonprofit agencies have used analytics to ensure their effectiveness and accountability to their donors and clients. Catholic Relief Services (CRS) is the official international humanitarian agency of the U.S. Catholic community. The CRS mission is to provide relief for the victims of both natural and human-made disasters and to help people in need around the world through its health, educational, and agricultural programs. CRS uses an analytical spreadsheet model to assist in the allocation of its annual budget based on the impact that its various relief efforts and programs will have in different countries.[20]

Sports Analytics

The use of analytics in sports has gained considerable notoriety since 2003 when renowned author Michael Lewis published *Moneyball.* Lewis' book tells the story of how the Oakland Athletics used an analytical approach to player evaluation in order to assemble a competitive team with a limited budget. The use of analytics for player evaluation and on-field strategy is now common, especially in professional sports. Professional sports teams use analytics to assess players for the amateur drafts and to decide how much to offer players in contract negotiations;[21] professional motorcycle racing teams use sophisticated optimization for gearbox design to gain competitive advantage; [22] and teams use analytics to assist with on-field decisions such as which pitchers to use in various games of a Major League Baseball playoff series.

The use of analytics for off-the-field business decisions is also increasing rapidly. Ensuring customer satisfaction is important for any company, and fans are the customers of sports teams. The Cleveland Indians professional baseball team used a type of predictive modeling known as conjoint analysis to design its premium seating offerings at Progressive Field based on fan survey data. Using prescriptive analytics, franchises across several major sports dynamically adjust ticket prices throughout the season to reflect the relative attractiveness and potential demand for each game.

[19]G. Miller et al., "Tax Collection Optimization for New York State," *Interfaces* 42, no. 1 (January–February 2013): 74–84.

[20]I. Gamvros, R. Nidel, and S. Raghavan, "Investment Analysis and Budget Allocation at Catholic Relief Services," *Interfaces* 36. no. 5 (September–October 2006): 400–406.

[21]N. Streib, S. J. Young, and J. Sokol, "A Major League Baseball Team Uses Operations Research to Improve Draft Preparation," *Interfaces* 42, no. 2 (March–April 2012): 119–30.

[22]J. Amoros, L. F. Escudero, J. F. Monge, J. V. Segura, and O. Reinoso, "TEAM ASPAR Uses Binary Optimization to Obtain Optimal Gearbox Ratios in Motorcycle Racing," *Interfaces* 42, no. 2 (March–April 2012): 191–98.

Web Analytics

Web analytics is the analysis of online activity, which includes, but is not limited to, visits to web sites and social media sites such as Facebook and LinkedIn. Web analytics obviously has huge implications for promoting and selling products and services via the Internet. Leading companies apply descriptive and advanced analytics to data collected in online experiments to determine the best way to configure web sites, position ads, and utilize social networks for the promotion of products and services. Online experimentation involves exposing various subgroups to different versions of a web site and tracking the results. Because of the massive pool of Internet users, experiments can be conducted without risking the disruption of the overall business of the company. Such experiments are proving to be invaluable because they enable the company to use trial-and-error in determining statistically what makes a difference in their web site traffic and sales.

SUMMARY

This introductory chapter began with a discussion of decision making. Decision making can be defined as the following process: (1) identify and define the problem; (2) determine the criteria that will be used to evaluate alternative solutions; (3) determine the set of alternative solutions; (4) evaluate the alternatives; and (5) choose an alternative. Decisions may be strategic (high-level, concerned with the overall direction of the firm), tactical (midlevel, concerned with how to achieve the strategic goals of the firm), or operational (day-to-day decisions that must be made to run the company).

Uncertainty and an overwhelming number of alternatives are two key factors that make decision making difficult. Business analytics approaches can assist by identifying and mitigating uncertainty and by prescribing the best course of action from a very large number of alternatives. In short, business analytics can help us make better-informed decisions.

There are three categories of analytics: descriptive, predictive, and prescriptive. Descriptive analytics describes what has happened and includes tools such as reports, data visualization, data dashboards, descriptive statistics, and some data-mining techniques. Predictive analytics consists of techniques that use past data to predict future events and include regression, data mining, forecasting, and simulation. Prescriptive analytics uses data to determine a best course of action. This class of analytical techniques includes simulation, decision analysis, and optimization. Descriptive and predictive analytics can help us better understand the uncertainty and risk associated with our decision alternatives. Predictive and prescriptive analytics, also often referred to as advanced analytics, can help us make the best decision when facing a myriad of alternatives.

Big data is a set of data that is too large or too complex to be handled by standard data-processing techniques or typical desktop software. The increasing prevalence of big data is leading to an increase in the use of analytics. The Internet, retail scanners, and cell phones are making huge amounts of data available to companies, and these companies want to better understand these data. Business analytics is helping them understand these data and use them to make better decisions.

We concluded this chapter with a discussion of various application areas of analytics. Our discussion focused on financial analytics, human resource analytics, marketing analytics, health care analytics, supply-chain analytics, analytics for government and nonprofit organizations, sports analytics, and web analytics. However, the use of analytics is rapidly spreading to other sectors, industries, and functional areas of organizations. Each remaining chapter in this text will provide a real-world vignette in which business analytics is applied to a problem faced by a real organization.

GLOSSARY

Advanced analytics Predictive and prescriptive analytics.
Big data Any set of data that is too large or too complex to be handled by standard data-processing technics and typical desktop software.
Business analytics The scientific process of transforming data into insight for making better decisions.
Data dashboard A collection of tables, charts, and maps to help management monitor selected aspects of the company's performance.
Data mining The use of analytical techniques for better understanding patterns and relationships that exist in large data sets.
Data query A request for information with certain characteristics from a database.
Data scientists Analysts trained in both computer science and statistics who know how to effectively process and analyze massive amounts of data.
Data security Protecting stored data from destructive forces or unauthorized users.
Decision analysis A technique used to develop an optimal strategy when a decision maker is faced with several decision alternatives and an uncertain set of future events.
Descriptive analytics Analytical tools that describe what has happened.
Hadoop An open-source programming environment that supports big data processing through distributed storage and distributed processing on clusters of computers.
Internet of Things (IoT) The technology that allows data collected from sensors in all types of machines to be sent over the Internet to repositories where it can be stored and analyzed.
MapReduce Programming model used within Hadoop that performs the two major steps for which it is named: the map step and the reduce step. The map step divides the data into manageable subsets and distributes it to the computers in the cluster for storing and processing. The reduce step collects answers from the nodes and combines them into an answer to the original problem.
Operational decision A decision concerned with how the organization is run from day to day.
Optimization model A mathematical model that gives the best decision, subject to the situation's constraints.
Predictive analytics Techniques that use models constructed from past data to predict the future or to ascertain the impact of one variable on another.
Prescriptive analytics Techniques that analyze input data and yield a best course of action.
Simulation The use of probability and statistics to construct a computer model to study the impact of uncertainty on the decision at hand.
Simulation optimization The use of probability and statistics to model uncertainty, combined with optimization techniques, to find good decisions in highly complex and highly uncertain settings.
Strategic decision A decision that involves higher-level issues and that is concerned with the overall direction of the organization, defining the overall goals and aspirations for the organization's future.
Tactical decision A decision concerned with how the organization should achieve the goals and objectives set by its strategy.
Utility theory The study of the total worth or relative desirability of a particular outcome that reflects the decision maker's attitude toward a collection of factors such as profit, loss, and risk.

Chapter 4

Descriptive Data Mining

CONTENTS

4.1 DATA PREPARATION
Treatment of Missing Data
Identification of Outliers and Erroneous Data
Variable Representation

4.2 CLUSTER ANALYSIS
Measuring Similarity Between Observations
Hierarchical Clustering
k-Means Clustering
Hierarchical Clustering Versus *k*-Means Clustering

4.3 ASSOCIATION RULES
Evaluating Association Rules

APPENDIX 4.1: HIERARCHICAL CLUSTERING WITH XLMINER
APPENDIX 4.2: *k*-MEANS CLUSTERING WITH XLMINER
APPENDIX 4.3: ASSOCIATION RULES WITH XLMINER

ANALYTICS IN ACTION

Advice from a Machine[1]

The proliferation of data and increase in computing power have sparked the development of automated *recommender systems*, which provide consumers with suggestions for movies, music, books, clothes, restaurants, online dating, and whom to follow on Twitter. The sophisticated, proprietary algorithms guiding recommender systems measure the degree of similarity between users or items to identify recommendations of potential interest to a user.

Netflix, a company that provides media content via DVD-by-mail or Internet streaming, provides its users with recommendations for movies and television shows based on each user's expressed interests and feedback on previously viewed content. As its business has shifted from renting DVDs by mail to streaming content online, Netflix has been able to track its customers' viewing behavior more closely. This allows Netflix's recommendations to account for differences in viewing behavior based on the day of the week, the time of day, the device used (computer, phone, television), and even the viewing location.

The use of recommender systems is prevalent in e-commerce. Using attributes detailed by the Music Genome Project, Pandora Internet Radio plays songs with properties similar to songs that a user "likes." In the online dating world, web sites such as eHarmony, Match.com, and OKCupid use different "formulas" to take into account hundreds of different behavioral traits to propose date "matches." Stitch Fix, a personal shopping service for women, combines recommendation algorithms and human input from its fashion experts to match its inventory of fashion items to its clients.

[1]"The Science Behind the Netflix Algorithms That Decide What You'll Watch Next," http://www.wired.com/2013/08/qq_netflix-algorithm. Retrieved on August 7, 2013; E. Colson, "Using Human and Machine Processing in Recommendation Systems," *First AAAI Conference on Human Computation and Crowdsourcing* (2013); K. Zhao, X. Wang, M. Yu, and B. Gao, "User Recommendation in Reciprocal and Bipartite Social Networks—A Case Study of Online Dating," *IEEE Intelligent Systems* 29, no. 2 (2014).

Over the past few decades, technological advances have led to a dramatic increase in the amount of recorded data. The use of smartphones, radio-frequency identification (RFID) tags, electronic sensors, credit cards, and the Internet has facilitated the collection of data from phone conversations, e-mails, business transactions, product and customer tracking, business transactions, and web browsing. The increase in the use of data-mining techniques in business has been caused largely by three events: the explosion in the amount of data being produced and electronically tracked, the ability to electronically warehouse these data, and the affordability of computer power to analyze the data. In this chapter, we discuss the analysis of large quantities of data in order to gain insight on customers and to uncover patterns to improve business processes.

We define an **observation**, or record, as the set of recorded values of variables associated with a single entity. An observation is often displayed as a row of values in a spreadsheet or database in which the columns correspond to the variables. For example, in a university's database of alumni, an observation may correspond to an alumnus's age, gender, marital status, employer, position title, as well as size and frequency of donations to the university.

Predictive data mining is discussed in Chapter 9.

In this chapter, we focus on descriptive data-mining methods, also called **unsupervised learning** techniques. In an unsupervised learning application, there is no outcome variable to predict; rather, the goal is to use the variable values to identify relationships between observations. Unsupervised learning approaches can be thought of as high-dimensional descriptive analytics because they are designed to describe patterns and relationships in large data sets with many observations of many variables. Without an explicit outcome (or one that is objectively known), there is no definitive measure of accuracy. Instead, qualitative assessments, such as how well the results match expert judgment, are used to assess and compare the results from an unsupervised learning method.

4.1 Data Preparation

The data in a data set are often said to be "dirty" and "raw" before they have been put into a form that is best suited for a data-mining algorithm. Data preparation makes heavy use of the descriptive statistics and data-visualization methods described in Chapters 2 and 3 to gain an understanding of the data. Common tasks include treating missing data, identifying erroneous data and outliers, and defining the appropriate way to represent variables.

Treatment of Missing Data

It is common to have observations with missing values for one or more variables. The primary options for addressing missing data are: (1) to discard observations (rows) with any missing values, (2) to discard any variable (column) with missing values, (3) to fill in missing entries with estimated values, or (4) to apply a data-mining algorithm (such as classification and regression trees) that can handle missing values.

*XLMiner, data-mining software discussed in the chapter appendix provides a **Missing Data Handling** procedure under **Transform** in the **Data Analysis** group.*

How to deal with missing data requires some understanding of why the data are missing and the impact these missing values might have on the analysis. If the missing value is truly a random occurrence, it is called a data value **missing completely at random** (MCAR). However, the occurrence of some missing values might not be completely at random—they might be correlated with the values of some other variables. These missing values are called **missing at random** (MAR). For data that is MAR, the reason for the missing values may determine its importance. For example if the responses to one survey question collected by a specific employee were lost due to a data entry error, then the treatment of the missing data may be less critical. However, in a health care study, suppose observations corresponding to patient visits are missing the results of a diagnostic tests whenever the doctor deems the patient too sick to undergo the procedure. In this case, the absence of a variable measurement actually provides the additional information about the patient's condition, which may be helpful in understanding other relationships in the data. A third category of missing data is **missing not at random** (MNAR). Data is MNAR if the reason that the value is missing is related to the value of the variable. As an example of MNAR, a survey of households on spending habits and wealth might reveal that records with missing values for annual property taxes paid seem to be associated with expensive house values (and therefore large property taxes).

If a variable is missing measurements for a large number of observations, removing this variable from consideration may be an option. In particular, if the variable to be dropped is highly correlated with another variable that is known for a majority of observations, the loss of information may be minimal. If the number of observations with missing values is small and the missing values seem to be MCAR, discarding these incomplete observations may be a reasonable option.

If a considerable number of observations have missing values, then replacing them with a value that seems reasonable may be useful, as it does not decrease the number of observations. Options for replacing the missing entries for a variable include replacing the missing value with the variable's mode, mean, or median. Imputing values in this manner is truly valid only if variable values are MCAR; otherwise, we may be introducing misleading information into the data. If missing values are particularly troublesome and MAR, it may be possible to build a model to predict a variable with missing values and then to use these predictions in place of the missing entries. How to deal with missing values is fairly subjective, and caution must be used to not induce bias by replacing missing values.

Identification of Outliers and Erroneous Data

Examining the variables in the data set by means of summary statistics, histograms, PivotTables, scatter plots, and other tools can uncover data-quality issues and outliers. For example, negative values for sales may result from a data-entry error or may actually denote a missing value. Closer examination of outliers may reveal an error or a need for further investigation to determine whether the observation is relevant to the current analysis. A conservative approach is to create two data sets, one with and one without outliers, and then construct a model on both data sets. If a model's implications depend on the inclusion or exclusion of outliers, then you should spend additional time to track down the cause of the outliers.

Variable Representation

In many data-mining applications, it may be prohibitive to analyze the data because of the number of variables recorded. In such cases, the analyst may have to first identify variables that can be safely omitted from further analysis before proceeding with a data-mining technique. **Dimension reduction** is the process of removing variables from the analysis without losing any crucial information. One simple method for reducing the number of variables is to examine pairwise correlations to detect variables or groups of variables that may supply similar information. Such variables can be aggregated or removed to allow more parsimonious model development.

*XLMiner provides a **Transform Categorical** procedure under **Transform** in the **Data Analysis** group. This procedure provides options to create dummy variables, create ordinal category scores, and reduce categories by combining them into similar groups.*

A critical part of data mining is determining how to represent the measurements of the variables and which variables to consider. The treatment of categorical variables is particularly important. Typically, it is best to encode categorical variables with 0–1 dummy variables. Consider a data set that contains the variable Language to track the language preference of callers to a call center. The variable Language with the possible values of English, German, and Spanish would be replaced with three binary variables called English, German, and Spanish. An entry of German would be captured using a 0 for the English dummy variable, a 1 for the German dummy variable, and a 0 for the Spanish dummy variable. Using 0–1 dummy variables to encode categorical variables with many different categories results in a large number of variables. In these cases, the use of PivotTables is helpful in identifying categories that are similar and can possibly be combined to reduce the number of 0–1 dummy variables. For example, some categorical variables (zip code, product model number) may have many possible categories such that, for the purpose of model building, there is no substantive difference between multiple categories, and therefore the number of categories may be reduced by combining categories.

Often data sets contain variables that, considered separately, are not particularly insightful but that, when appropriately combined, result in a new variable that reveals an important relationship. Financial data supplying information on stock price and company earnings may be as useful as the derived variable representing the price/earnings (PE) ratio. A variable tabulating the dollars spent by a household on groceries may not be interesting because this value may depend on the size of the household. Instead, considering the *proportion* of total household spending on groceries may be more informative.

NOTES + COMMENTS

1. In some cases, it may be desirable to transform a numerical variable into categories. For example, if we wish to analyze the circumstances in which a numerical outcome variable exceeds a certain value, it may be helpful to create a binary categorical variable that is 1 for observations with the variable value greater than the threshold and 0 otherwise. In another case, if a variable has a skewed distribution, it may be helpful to categorize the values into quantiles. To facilitate such categorization, XLMiner provides a **Bin Continuous Data** procedure under **Transform** in the **Data Analysis** group on the **XLMINER Platform** tab. However, in general, we advise caution when transforming numerical variables into categories because this causes a loss of information (a numerical variable's category is less informative than a specific numeric value) and increases the number of variables.
2. XLMiner provides functionality to apply a more sophisticated dimension-reduction approach called *principal components analysis*. The **Principal Components** procedure can be found on the **XLMiner Platform** tab under **Transform** in the **Data Analysis** group. Principal-components analysis creates a collection of metavariables (components) that are weighted sums of the original variables. These components are not correlated with each other, and often only a few of them are needed to convey the same information as the large set of original variables. In many cases, only one or two components are necessary to explain the majority of the variance in the original variables. Then the analyst can continue to build a data-mining model using just a few of the most explanatory components rather than the entire set of original variables. Although principal-components analysis can reduce the number of variables in this manner, it may be harder to explain the results of the model because the interpretation of a component that is a linear combination of variables can be unintuitive.

4.2 Cluster Analysis

The goal of clustering is to segment observations into similar groups based on the observed variables. Clustering can be employed during the data-preparation step to identify variables or observations that can be aggregated or removed from consideration. Cluster analysis is commonly used in marketing to divide consumers into different homogeneous groups, a process known as *market segmentation*. Identifying different clusters of consumers allows a firm to tailor marketing strategies for each segment. Cluster analysis can also be used to identify outliers, which in a manufacturing setting may represent quality-control problems and in financial transactions may represent fraudulent activity.

In this section, we consider the use of cluster analysis to assist a company called Know Thy Customer (KTC), a financial advising company that provides personalized financial advice to its clients. As a basis for developing this tailored advising, KTC would like to segment its customers into several groups (or clusters) so that the customers within a group are similar with respect to key characteristics and are dissimilar to customers that are not in the group. For each customer, KTC has an observation consisting of the following variables:

Age = age of the customer in whole years
Female = 1 if female, 0 if male
Income = annual income in dollars
Married = 1 if married, 0 if not
Children = number of children
Car Loan = 1 if customer has a car loan, 0 if not
Mortgage = 1 if customer has a mortgage, 0 if not

We present two clustering methods using a small sample of data from KTC. We first consider bottom-up **hierarchical clustering** that starts with each observation belonging to its own cluster and then sequentially merges the most similar clusters to create a series of nested clusters. The second method, ***k*-means clustering**, assigns each observation to one of k clusters in a manner such that the observations assigned to the same cluster are as similar as possible. Because both methods depend on how two observations are similar, we first discuss how to measure similarity between observations.

Measuring Similarity Between Observations

The goal of cluster analysis is to group observations into clusters such that observations within a cluster are similar and observations in different clusters are dissimilar. Therefore, to formalize this process, we need explicit measurements of similarity or, conversely, dissimilarity. Some metrics track similarity between observations, and a clustering method using such a metric would seek to maximize the similarity between observations. Other metrics measure dissimilarity, or distance, between observations, and a clustering method using one of these metrics would seek to minimize the distance between observations in a cluster.

When observations include numerical variables, **Euclidean distance** is the most common method to measure dissimilarity between observations. Let observations $u = (u_1, u_2, \ldots, u_q)$ and $v = (v_1, v_2, \ldots, v_q)$ each comprise measurements of q variables. The Euclidean distance between observations u and v is

$$d_{uv} = \sqrt{(u_1 - v_1)^2 + (u_2 - v_2)^2 + \cdots + (u_q - v_q)^2}$$

Figure 4.1 depicts Euclidean distance for two observations consisting of two variable measurements. Euclidean distance becomes smaller as a pair of observations become more similar with respect to their variable values. Euclidean distance is highly influenced by the scale on which variables are measured. For example, consider the task of clustering customers on the basis of the variables Age and Income. Let observation u = (23, \$20,375) correspond to a 23-year old customer with an annual income of \$20,375 and observation v = (36, \$19,475) correspond to a 36-year old with an annual income of \$19,475. As measured by Euclidean distance, the dissimilarity between these two observations is:

$$d_{uv} = \sqrt{(23 - 36)^2 + (20{,}375 - 19{,}475)^2} = \sqrt{169 + 811{,}441} = 901$$

FIGURE 4.1 Euclidean Distance

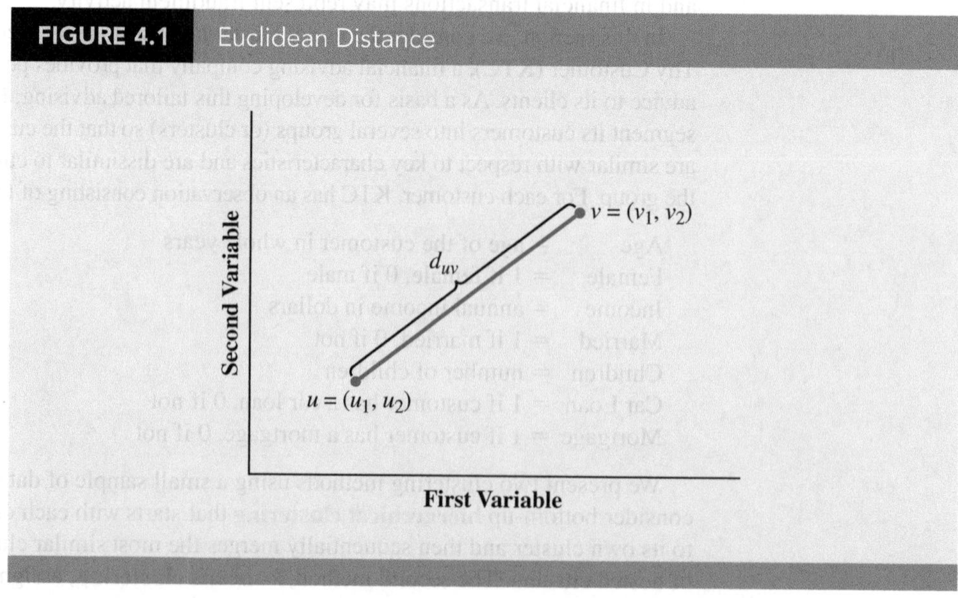

Refer to Chapter 2 for a discussion of z-scores.

Thus, we see that when using the raw variable values, the dissimilarity between observations is dominated by the Income variable because of the difference in the magnitude of the measurements. Therefore, it is common to standardize the units of each variable j of each observation u. That is, u_j, the value of variable j in observation u, is replaced with its z-score z_j. For the data in *DemoKTC*, the standardized (or normalized) values of observations u and v are $(-1.76, -0.56)$ and $(-0.76, -0.62)$, respectively. The dissimilarity between these two observations based on standardized values is:

$$(standardized)\ d_{uv} = \sqrt{(-1.76 - (-0.76))^2 + (-0.56 - (-0.62))^2}$$
$$= \sqrt{0.994 + 0.004} = 0.998$$

Based on standardized variable values, we observe that observations u and v are actually much more different in age than in income.

Scaling and weighting variable values can be particularly helpful when clustering observations with respect to both numerical and categorical variables.

The conversion to z-scores also makes it easier to identify outlier measurements, which can distort the Euclidean distance between observations. After conversion to z-scores, unequal weighting of variables can also be considered by multiplying the variables of each observation by a selected set of weights. For instance, after standardizing the units on customer observations so that income and age are expressed as their respective z-scores (instead of expressed in dollars and years), we can multiply the income z-scores by 2 if we wish to treat income with twice the importance of age. In other words, standardizing removes bias due to the difference in measurement units, and variable weighting allows the analyst to introduce appropriate bias based on the business context.

When clustering observations solely on the basis of categorical variables encoded as 0–1 (or dummy variables), a better measure of similarity between two observations can be achieved by counting the number of variables with matching values. The simplest overlap measure is called the **matching coefficient** and is computed by

MATCHING COEFFICIENT

$$\frac{\text{number of variables with matching value for observations } u \text{ and } v}{\text{total number of variables}}$$

One weakness of the matching coefficient is that if two observations both have a 0 entry for a categorical variable, this is counted as a sign of similarity between the two observations. However, matching 0 entries do not necessarily imply similarity. For instance, if the categorical variable is Own A Minivan, then a 0 entry in two different observations does not mean that these two people own the same type of car; it means only that neither owns a minivan. To avoid misstating similarity due to the absence of a feature, a similarity measure called **Jaccard's coefficient** does not count matching zero entries and is computed by

JACCARD'S COEFFICIENT

$$\frac{\text{number of variables with matching nonzero value for observations } u \text{ and } v}{(\text{total number of variables}) - (\text{number of variables with matching zero values for observations } u \text{ and } v)}$$

For five customer observations from the file *DemoKTC*, Table 4.1 contains observations of the binary variables Female, Married, Car Loan, and Mortgage and the distance matrixes corresponding to the matching coefficient and Jaccard's coefficient, respectively. Based on the matching coefficient, Observation 1 and Observation 4 are more similar (0.75) than Observation 2 and Observation 3 (0.5) because 3 out of 4 variable values match

TABLE 4.1 Comparison of Similarity Matrixes for Observations with Binary Variables

Observation	Female	Married	Car Loan	Mortgage
1	1	0	0	0
2	0	1	1	1
3	1	1	1	0
4	1	1	0	0
5	1	1	0	0

Similarity Matrix Based on Matching Coefficient

	1	2	3	4	5
1	1				
2	0	1			
3	0.5	0.5	1		
4	0.75	0.25	0.75	1	
5	0.75	0.25	0.75	1	1

Similarity Matrix Based on Jaccard's Coefficient

	1	2	3	4	5
1	1				
2	0	1			
3	0.333	0.5	1		
4	0.5	0.25	0.667	1	
5	0.5	0.25	0.667	1	1

between Observation 1 and Observation 4 versus just 2 matching values out of 4 for Observation 2 and Observation 3. However, based on Jaccard's coefficient, Observation 1 and Observation 4 are equally similar (0.5) as Observation 2 and Observation 3 (0.5) as Jaccard's coefficient discards the matching zero values for the Car Loan and Mortgage variables for Observation 1 and Observation 4. In the context of this example, choice of the matching coefficient or Jaccard's coefficient depends on whether KTC believes that matching 0 entries imply similarity or not. That is, KTC must gauge whether meaningful similarity is implied if a pair of observations are not female, not married, do not have a car loan, or do not have a mortgage.

Hierarchical Clustering

We consider a bottom-up hierarchical clustering approach that starts with each observation in its own cluster and then iteratively combines the two clusters that are the most similar into a single cluster. Each iteration corresponds to an increased level of aggregation by decreasing the number of distinct clusters. Hierarchical clustering determines the similarity of two clusters by considering the similarity between the observations composing either cluster. Given a way to measure similarity between observations (Euclidean distance, matching coefficients, or Jaccard's coefficients), there are several clustering method alternatives for comparing observations in two clusters to obtain a cluster similarity measure. Using Euclidean distance to illustrate, Figure 4.2 provides a two-dimensional depiction of four methods we will discuss.

When using the **single linkage** clustering method, the similarity between two clusters is defined by the similarity of the pair of observations (one from each cluster) that are the most similar. Thus, single linkage will consider two clusters to be close if an observation in one of the clusters is close to at least one observation in the other cluster. However, a cluster formed by merging two clusters that are close with respect to single linkage may also consist of pairs of observations that are very different. The reason is that there is no consideration of how different an observation may be from other observations in a cluster as long as it is similar to at least one observation in that cluster.

In two dimensions, single linkage clustering can result in long, elongated clusters rather than compact circular clusters. This can occur because single linkage favors merging two different clusters as long as at least one observation in a cluster is very similar to an observation in another cluster.

The **complete linkage** clustering method defines the similarity between two clusters as the similarity of the pair of observations (one from each cluster) that are the most different. Thus, complete linkage will consider two clusters to be close if their most different pair of observations are close. This method produces clusters such that all member observations of a cluster are relatively close to each other. However, clustering created with complete linkage can be distorted by outlier observations.

The single linkage and complete linkage methods define between-cluster similarity based on the single pair of observations in two different clusters that are most similar or least

FIGURE 4.2 Measuring Similarity Between Clusters

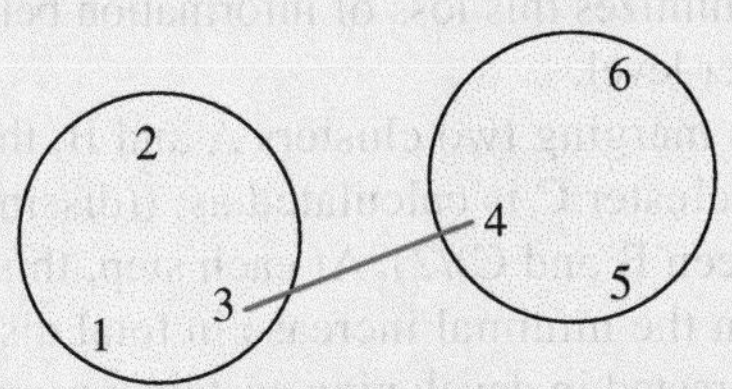

Single Linkage, $d_{3,4}$

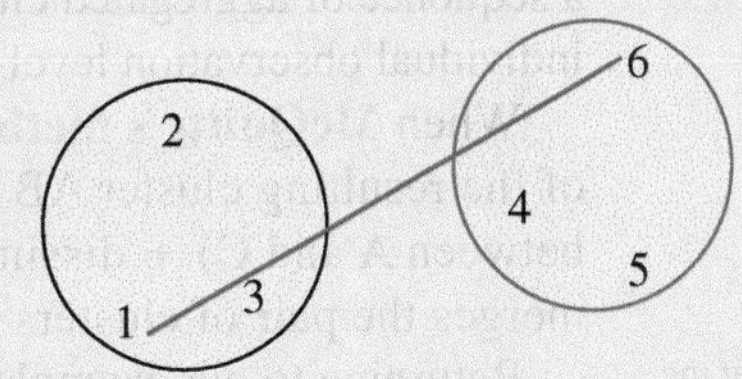

Complete Linkage, $d_{1,6}$

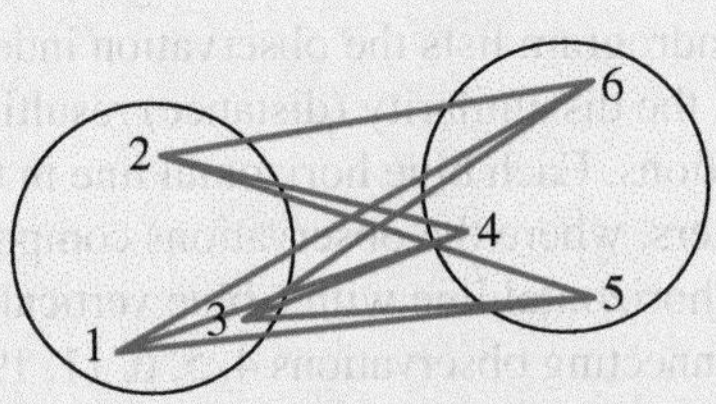

Group Average Linkage,

$$\frac{d_{1,4}+d_{1,5}+d_{1,6}+d_{2,4}+d_{2,5}+d_{2,6}+d_{3,4}+d_{3,5}+d_{3,6}}{9}$$

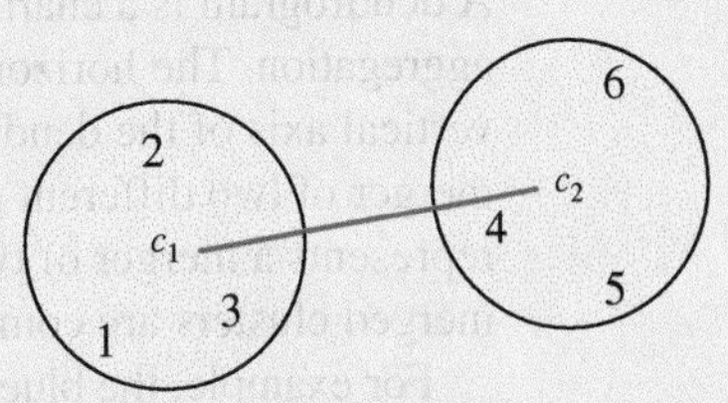

Centroid Linkage, d_{c_1,c_2}

similar. In contrast, the **group average linkage** clustering method defines the similarity between two clusters to be the average similarity computed over *all* pairs of observations between the two clusters. If Cluster 1 consists of n_1 observations and Cluster 2 consists of n_2 observations, the similarity of these clusters would be the average of $n_1 \times n_2$ similarity measures. This method produces clusters that are less dominated by the similarity between single pairs of observations. The **median linkage** method is analogous to group average linkage except that it uses the median of the similarities computed between all pairs of observations between the two clusters. The use of the median reduces the effect of outliers.

Centroid linkage uses the averaging concept of cluster centroids to define between-cluster similarity. The centroid for cluster k, denoted c_k, is found by calculating the average value for each variable across all observations in a cluster; that is, a centroid is the average observation of a cluster. The similarity between two clusters is then defined as the similarity of the centroids of the two clusters.

Ward's method merges two clusters such that the dissimilarity of the observations within the resulting single cluster increases as little as possible. It tends to produce clearly defined clusters of similar size. For a pair of clusters under consideration for aggregation, Ward's method computes the sum of the squared dissimilarity between each individual observation in the union of the two clusters and the centroid of the resulting merged cluster. Representing observations within a cluster with the centroid can be viewed as a loss of information in the sense that the individual differences in these observations will not be captured by the cluster centroid. Hierarchical clustering using Ward's method results in a sequence of aggregated clusters that minimizes this loss of information between the individual observation level and the cluster level.

When **McQuitty's method** considers merging two clusters A and B, the dissimilarity of the resulting cluster AB to any other cluster C is calculated as: ((dissimilarity between A and C) + dissimilarity between B and C)/2). At each step, this method then merges the pair of clusters that results in the minimal increase in total dissimilarity.

Refer to Appendix 4.1 at the end of this chapter for step-by-step instructions on how to execute hierarchical clustering with XLMiner.

Returning to our example, KTC is interested in developing customer segments based on gender, marital status, and whether the customer is repaying a car loan and a mortgage. Using data in the file *DemoKTC*, we base the clusters on a collection of 0–1 categorical variables (Female, Married, Car Loan, and Mortgage). We use the matching coefficient to measure similarity between observations and the group average linkage clustering method to measure similarity between clusters.

Figure 4.3 depicts a **dendrogram** to visually summarize the output from a hierarchical clustering using the matching coefficient to measure similarity between observations and the group average linkage clustering method to measure similarity between clusters. A dendrogram is a chart that depicts the set of nested clusters resulting at each step of aggregation. The horizontal axis of the dendrogram lists the observation indexes. The vertical axis of the dendrogram represents the dissimilarity (distance) resulting from a merger of two different groups of observations. Each blue horizontal line in the dendrogram represents a merger of two (or more) clusters, where the observations composing the merged clusters are connected to the blue horizontal line with a blue vertical line.

For example, the blue horizontal line connecting observations 4, 5, 6, 11, 19, and 28 conveys that these six observations are grouped together and the resulting cluster has a dissimilarity measure of 0. A dissimilarity of 0 results from this merger because these six observations have identical values for the Female, Married, Car Loan, and Mortgage variables. Following the blue vertical line up from the cluster of {4, 5, 6, 11, 19}, another blue horizontal line connects this cluster with the cluster consisting solely of Observation 1. Thus, the cluster {4, 5, 6, 11, 19} and cluster {1} are merged resulting in a dissimilarity of 0.25.

To interpret a dendrogram at a specific level of aggregation, it is helpful to visualize a horizontal line such as one of the black dashed lines we have drawn across Figure 4.3. The

FIGURE 4.3 Dendrogram for KTC

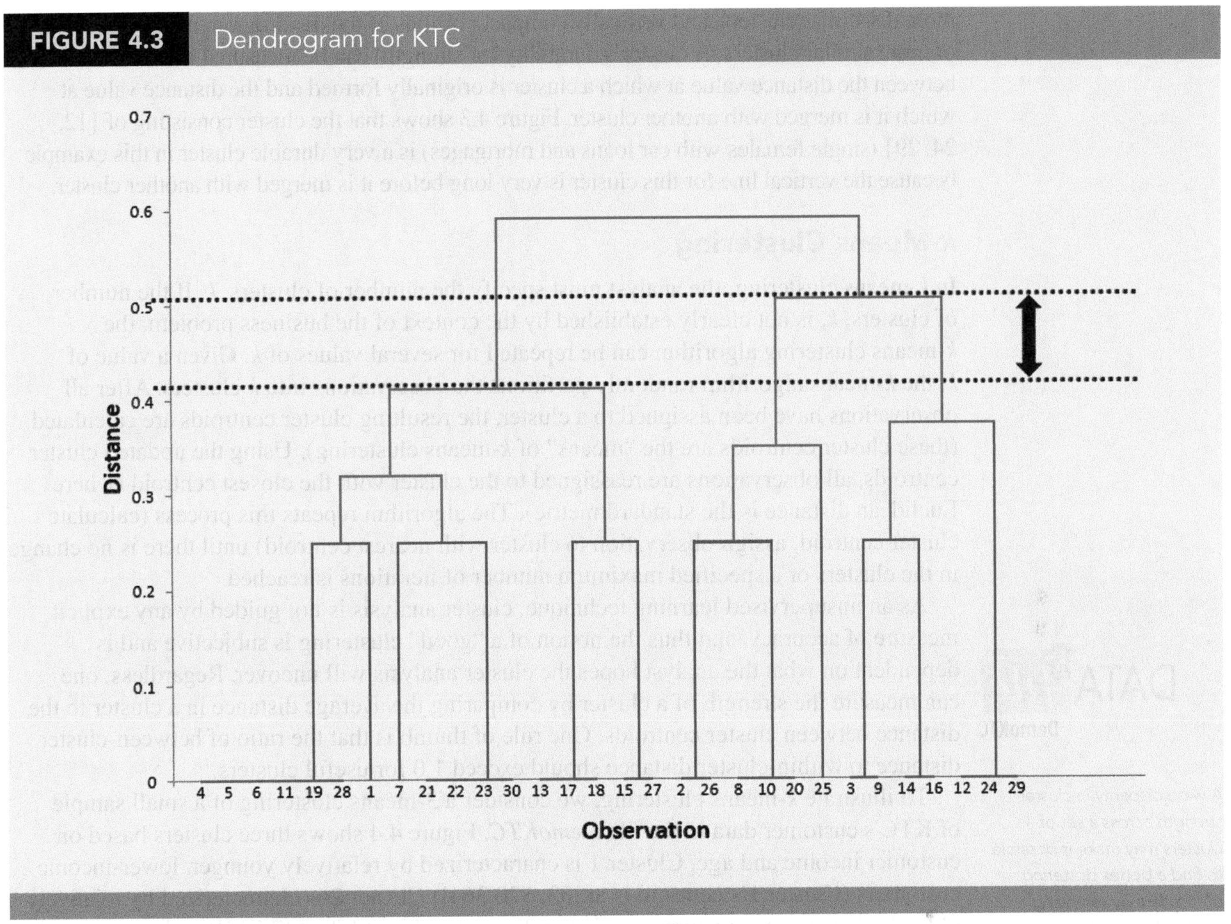

bottom horizontal black dashed line intersects with the vertical branches in the dendrogram three times; each intersection corresponds to a cluster containing the observations connected by the vertical branch that is intersected. The composition of these three clusters is

Cluster 1: {4, 5, 6, 11, 19, 28, 1, 7, 21, 22, 23, 30, 13, 17, 18, 15, 27}
= mix of males and females, 15 out of 17 married, no car loans, 5 out of 17 with mortgages

Cluster 2: {2, 26, 8, 10, 20, 25}
= all males with car loans, 5 out of 6 married, 2 out of 6 with mortgages

Cluster 3: {3, 9, 14, 16, 12, 24, 29}
= all females with car loans, 4 out of 7 married, 5 out of 7 with mortgages

These clusters segment KTC's customers into three groups that could possibly indicate varying levels of responsibility—an important factor to consider when providing financial advice.

The nested construction of the hierarchical clusters allows KTC to identify different numbers of clusters and assess (often qualitatively) the implications. By sliding a horizontal line up or down the vertical axis of a dendrogram and observing the intersection of the horizontal line with the vertical dendrogram branches, an analyst can extract varying numbers of clusters. Note that sliding up to the position of the top horizontal black line in Figure 4.3 results in merging Cluster 2 with Cluster 3 into a single, more dissimilar, cluster. The vertical distance between the points of agglomeration is the "cost" of merging clusters in terms of decreased homogeneity within clusters. Thus, vertically elongated portions of the dendrogram represent mergers of more dissimilar clusters, and vertically compact portions of the dendrogram represent mergers of more similar clusters. A cluster's durability (or strength) can be measured by the difference between the distance value at which a cluster is originally formed and the distance value at which it is merged with another cluster. Figure 4.3 shows that the cluster consisting of {12, 24, 29} (single females with car loans and mortgages) is a very durable cluster in this example because the vertical line for this cluster is very long before it is merged with another cluster.

k-Means Clustering

In *k*-means clustering, the analyst must specify the number of clusters, *k*. If the number of clusters, *k*, is not clearly established by the context of the business problem, the *k*-means clustering algorithm can be repeated for several values of *k*. Given a value of *k*, the *k*-means algorithm randomly partitions the observations into *k* clusters. After all observations have been assigned to a cluster, the resulting cluster centroids are calculated (these cluster centroids are the "means" of *k*-means clustering). Using the updated cluster centroids, all observations are reassigned to the cluster with the closest centroid (where Euclidean distance is the standard metric). The algorithm repeats this process (calculate cluster centroid, assign observation to cluster with nearest centroid) until there is no change in the clusters or a specified maximum number of iterations is reached.

As an unsupervised learning technique, cluster analysis is not guided by any explicit measure of accuracy, and thus the notion of a "good" clustering is subjective and is dependent on what the analyst hopes the cluster analysis will uncover. Regardless, one can measure the strength of a cluster by comparing the average distance in a cluster to the distance between cluster centroids. One rule of thumb is that the ratio of between-cluster distance to within-cluster distance should exceed 1.0 for useful clusters.

A wide disparity in cluster strength across a set of clusters may make it possible to find a better clustering of the data by removing all members of the strong clusters and then continuing the clustering process on the remaining observations.

To illustrate *k*-means clustering, we consider a 3-means clustering of a small sample of KTC's customer data in the file *DemoKTC*. Figure 4.4 shows three clusters based on customer income and age. Cluster 1 is characterized by relatively younger, lower-income customers (Cluster 1's centroid is at [33, $20,364]).Cluster 2 is characterized by relatively older, higher-income customers (Cluster 2's centroid is at [58, $47,729]). Cluster 3 is characterized by relatively older, lower-income customers (Cluster 3's centroid is at [53, $21,416]). As visually corroborated by Figure 4.4, Table 4.2 shows that Cluster 2 is the

Cluster centroids are depicted by circles in Figure 4.4.

Although Figure 4.4 is plotted in the original scale of the variables, the clustering was based on the variables after standardizing (normalizing) their values.

FIGURE 4.4 Clustering Observations by Age and Income Using *k*-Means Clustering with $k = 3$

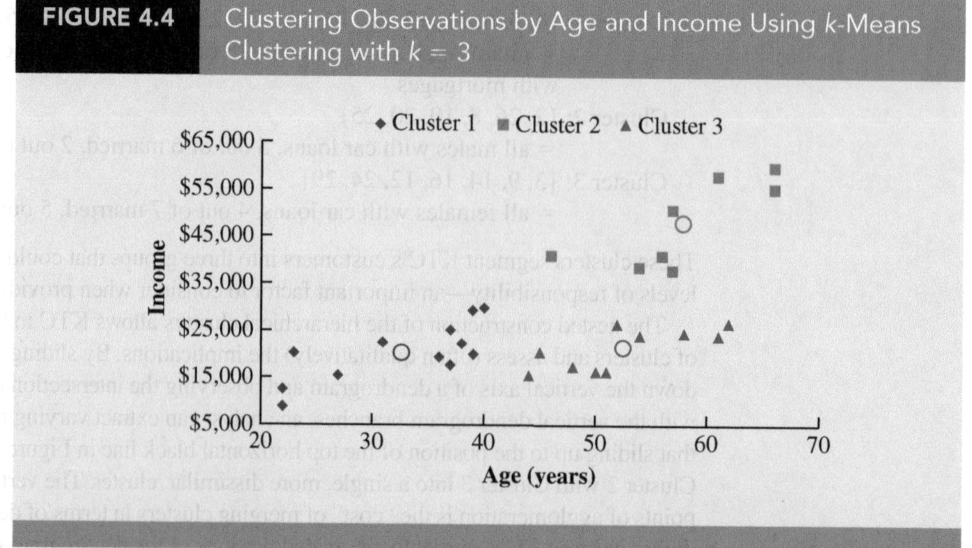

Tables 4.2 and 4.3 are expressed in terms of normalized coordinates in order to eliminate any distortion resulting from differences in the scale of the input variables.

TABLE 4.2 Average Distances within Clusters

	No. of Observations	Average Distance Between Observations in Cluster
Cluster 1	12	0.622
Cluster 2	8	0.739
Cluster 3	10	0.520

TABLE 4.3 Distances Between Cluster Centroids

Distance Between Cluster Centroids	Cluster 1	Cluster 2	Cluster 3
Cluster 1	0	2.784	1.529
Cluster 2	2.784	0	1.964
Cluster 3	1.529	1.964	0

smallest, but most heterogeneous cluster. We also observe that Cluster 1 is the largest cluster and Cluster 3 is the most homogeneous cluster. Table 4.3 displays the distance between each pair of cluster centroids to demonstrate how distinct the clusters are from each other. Cluster 1 and Cluster 2 are the most distinct from each other. To evaluate the strength of the clusters, we compare the average distance within each cluster (Table 4.2) to the average distances between clusters (Table 4.3). For example, although Cluster 2 is the most heterogeneous, with an average distance between observations of 0.739, comparing this to the distance between the Cluster 2 and Cluster 3 centroids (1.964) reveals that on average an observation in Cluster 2 is approximately 2.66 times closer to the Cluster 2 centroid than to the Cluster 3 centroid. In general, the larger the ratio of the distance between a pair of cluster centroids and the within-cluster distance, the more distinct the clustering is for the observations in the two clusters in the pair. Although qualitative considerations should take priority in evaluating clusters, using the ratios of between-cluster distance and within-cluster distance provides some guidance in determining k, the number of clusters.

Hierarchical Clustering Versus *k*-Means Clustering

If you have a small data set (e.g., fewer than 500 observations) and want to easily examine solutions with increasing numbers of clusters, you may want to use hierarchical clustering. Hierarchical clusters are also convenient if you want to observe how clusters are nested. However, hierarchical clustering can be very sensitive to outliers, and clusters may change dramatically if observations are eliminated from (or added to) the data set. If you know how many clusters you want and you have a larger data set (e.g., more than 500 observations), you may choose to use k-means clustering. Recall that k-means clustering partitions the observations, which is appropriate if you are trying to summarize the data with k "average" observations that describe the data with the minimum amount of error. However, k-means clustering is generally not appropriate for binary or ordinal data, for which an "average" is not meaningful.

4.3 Association Rules

In marketing, analyzing consumer behavior can lead to insights regarding the location and promotion of products. Specifically, marketers are interested in examining transaction data on customer purchases to identify the products commonly purchased together. In this section, we discuss the development of if–then statements, called **association rules**, which convey the likelihood of certain items being purchased together. Although association rules are an important tool in **market basket analysis**, they are also applicable to disciplines other than marketing. For example, association rules can assist medical researchers in understanding which treatments have been commonly prescribed to certain patient symptoms (and the resulting effects).

Hy-Vee grocery store would like to gain insight into its customers' purchase patterns to possibly improve its in-aisle product placement and cross-product promotions. Table 4.4 contains a small sample of data in which each transaction comprises the items purchased by a shopper in a single visit to a Hy-Vee. An example of an association rule from this data would be "if {bread, jelly}, then {peanut butter}," meaning that "if a transaction includes bread and jelly it also includes peanut butter." The collection of items (or item set) corresponding to the *if* portion of the rule, {bread, jelly}, is called the **antecedent**. The item set corresponding to the *then* portion of the rule, {peanut butter}, is called the **consequent**. Typically, only association rules for which the consequent consists of a single item are considered because these are more actionable. Although the number of possible association rules can be overwhelming, we typically investigate only association rules that involve antecedent and consequent item sets that occur together frequently. To formalize the notion of "frequent," we define the **support count** of an item set as the number of transactions in the data that include that item set. In Table 4.4, the support count of {bread, jelly} is 4. A rule of thumb is to consider only association rules with a support count of at least 20% of the total number of transactions.

If an item set is particularly valuable, then the minimum support count used to filter rules is often lowered.

Support is also sometimes expressed as the percentage of total transactions containing an item set.

The potential impact of an association rule is often governed by the number of transactions it may affect, which is measured by computing the support count of the item set consisting of the union of its antecedent and consequent. Investigating the rule "if {bread, jelly}, then {peanut butter}" from the Table 4.4, we see the support count of {bread, jelly, peanut butter} is 2. By only considering rules involving item sets with a support above a minimum level, inexplicable rules capturing random noise in the data can generally be avoided.

The data in Table 4.4 are in item list format; that is, each transaction row corresponds to a list of item names. Alternatively, the data can be represented in binary matrix format, in which each row is a transaction record and the columns correspond to each distinct item. This is equivalent to encoding each item name with a 0–1 dummy variable.

TABLE 4.4 Shopping-Cart Transactions

Transaction	Shopping Cart
1	bread, peanut butter, milk, fruit, jelly
2	bread, jelly, soda, potato chips, milk, fruit, vegetables, peanut butter
3	whipped cream, fruit, chocolate sauce, beer
4	steak, jelly, soda, potato chips, bread, fruit
5	jelly, soda, peanut butter, milk, fruit
6	jelly, soda, potato chips, milk, bread, fruit
7	fruit, soda, potato chips, milk
8	fruit, soda, peanut butter, milk
9	fruit, cheese, yogurt
10	yogurt, vegetables, beer

To help identify reliable association rules, we define the measure of **confidence** of a rule, which is computed as

CONFIDENCE

$$\frac{\text{support of \{antecedent and consequent\}}}{\text{support of antecedent}}$$

This measure of confidence can be viewed as the conditional probability of the consequent item set occurring given that the antecedent item set occurs. A high value of confidence suggests a rule in which the consequent is frequently true when the antecedent is true, but a high value of confidence can be misleading. For example, if the support of the consequent is high—that is, the item set corresponding to the *then* part is very frequent—then the confidence of the association rule could be high even if there is little or no association between the items. In Table 4.4, the rule "if {cheese}, then {fruit}" has a confidence of 1.0 (or 100%). This is misleading because {fruit} is a frequent item; the confidence of *almost any* rule with {fruit} as the consequent will have high confidence. Therefore, to evaluate the efficiency of a rule, we compute the **lift ratio** of the rule by accounting for the frequency of the consequent:

Adjusting the data by aggregating items into more general categories (or splitting items into more specific categories) so that items occur in roughly the same number of transactions often yields better association rules.

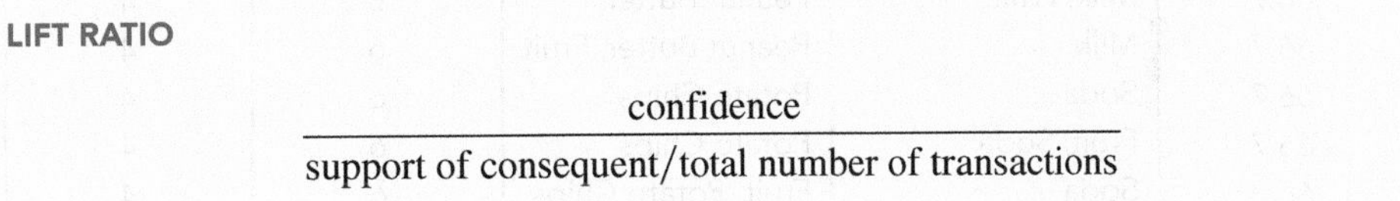

LIFT RATIO

$$\frac{\text{confidence}}{\text{support of consequent/total number of transactions}}$$

A lift ratio greater than 1 suggests that there is some usefulness to the rule and that it is better at identifying cases when the consequent occurs than is no rule at all. In other words, a lift ratio greater than 1 suggests that the level of association between the antecedent and consequent is higher than would be expected if these item sets were independent.

For the data in Table 4.4, the rule "if {bread, jelly}, then {peanut butter}" has confidence = 2/4 = 0.5 and a lift ratio = 0.5/(4/10) = 1.25. In other words, identifying a customer who purchased both bread and jelly as one who also purchased peanut butter is 25% better than just guessing that a random customer purchased peanut butter.

An association rule with a high lift ratio and low support may still be useful if the consequent represents a very valuable opportunity.

The utility of a rule depends on both its support and its lift ratio. Although a high lift ratio suggests that the rule is very efficient at finding when the consequent occurs, if it has a very low support, the rule may not be as useful as another rule that has a lower lift ratio but affects a large number of transactions (as demonstrated by a high support).

Based on the data in Table 4.4, Table 4.5 shows the list of association rules that achieve a lift ratio of at least 1.39 while satisfying a minimum support of 4 transactions (out of 10) and a minimum confidence of 50%. The top rules in Table 4.5 suggest that bread, fruit, and jelly are commonly associated items. For example, the sixth rule listed in Table 4.5 states, "If Jelly is purchased, then Bread and Fruit are also purchased." Perhaps Hy-Vee could consider a promotion and/or product placement to leverage this perceived relationship.

Evaluating Association Rules

Although explicit measures such as support, confidence, and lift ratio can help filter association rules, an association rule is ultimately judged on how actionable it is and how well it explains the relationship between item sets. For example, Walmart mined its transactional data to uncover strong evidence of the association rule, "If a customer purchases a Barbie doll, then a customer also purchases a candy bar." Walmart could leverage this relationship in product placement decisions as well as in advertisements and promotions, perhaps by placing a high-margin candy-bar display near the Barbie dolls. However, we must be aware that association rule mining often results in obvious relationships

TABLE 4.5 Association Rules for Hy-Vee

Confidence (%)	Antecedent (A)	Consequent (C)	Support for A	Support for C	Support for A & C	Lift Ratio
100.0	Bread	Jelly	4	5	4	2.00
100.0	Bread, Fruit	Jelly	4	5	4	2.00
100.0	Bread	Fruit, Jelly	4	5	4	2.00
80.0	Jelly	Bread	5	4	4	2.00
80.0	Fruit, Jelly	Bread	5	4	4	2.00
80.0	Jelly	Bread, Fruit	5	4	4	2.00
100.0	Peanut Butter	Milk	4	6	4	1.67
100.0	Peanut Butter, Fruit	Milk	4	6	4	1.67
100.0	Peanut Butter	Milk, Fruit	4	6	4	1.67
100.0	Potato Chips	Soda	4	6	4	1.67
100.0	Fruit, Potato Chips	Soda	4	6	4	1.67
100.0	Potato Chips	Fruit, Soda	4	6	4	1.67
66.7	Milk	Peanut Butter	6	4	4	1.67
66.7	Milk, Fruit	Peanut Butter	6	4	4	1.67
66.7	Milk	Peanut Butter, Fruit	6	4	4	1.67
66.7	Soda	Potato Chips	6	4	4	1.67
66.7	Fruit, Soda	Potato Chips	6	4	4	1.67
66.7	Soda	Fruit, Potato Chips	6	4	4	1.67
83.3	Soda	Milk	6	6	5	1.39
83.3	Milk	Soda	6	6	5	1.39
83.3	Fruit, Soda	Milk	6	6	5	1.39
83.3	Milk, Fruit	Soda	6	6	5	1.39
83.3	Soda	Milk, Fruit	6	6	5	1.39
83.3	Milk	Fruit, Soda	6	6	5	1.39

such as "If a customer purchases hamburger patties, then a customer also purchases hamburger buns," which may be true but provide no new insight. Association rules with a weak support measure often are inexplicable. For an association rule to be useful, it must be well supported *and* explain an important previously unknown relationship. The support of an association rule can generally be improved by basing it on less specific antecedent and consequent item sets. Unfortunately, association rules based on less specific item sets tend to yield less insight.

SUMMARY

We introduced the descriptive data-mining methods and related concepts. We began with a discussion about preparing data for analysis, including how to handle data errors and missing data. We also presented the issue of reducing or redefining the set of variables to analyze when faced with a data set that includes measurements for an overwhelming number of variables. After introducing similarity measures, we presented two different methods for grouping observations based on the similarity of their respective variable values: hierarchical clustering and *k*-means clustering. Hieararchical clustering begins with each observation in its own cluster and iteratively aggregates clusters. In *k*-means clustering, the analyst specifies *k*, the number of clusters, and then observations are placed into these clusters in an attempt to minimize the dissimilarity within the clusters. We explained the use association rules to identify patterns across transactions.

GLOSSARY

Antecedent The item set corresponding to the *if* portion of an if–then association rule.
Association rule An if–then statement describing the relationship between item sets.
Centroid linkage Uses the averaging concept of cluster centroids to define between-cluster similarity.
Complete linkage Measure of calculating dissimilarity between clusters by considering only the two most dissimilar observations between the two clusters.
Confidence The conditional probability that the consequent of an association rule occurs given the antecedent occurs.
Consequent The item set corresponding to the *then* portion of an if–then association rule.
Dendrogram A tree diagram used to illustrate the sequence of nested clusters produced by hierarchical clustering.
Dimension reduction Process of reducing the number of variables to consider in a data-mining approach.
Euclidean distance Geometric measure of dissimilarity between observations based on the Pythagorean theorem.
Group average linkage Measure of calculating dissimilarity between clusters by considering the distance between each pair of observations between two clusters.
Hierarchical clustering Process of agglomerating observations into a series of nested groups based on a measure of similarity.
Jaccard's coefficient Measure of similarity between observations consisting solely of binary categorical variables that considers only matches of nonzero entries.
***k*-Means clustering** Process of organizing observations into one of k groups based on a measure of similarity.
Lift ratio The ratio of the confidence of an association rule to the benchmark confidence.
Market basket analysis Analysis of items frequently co-occuring in transactions (such as purchases).
Matching coefficient Measure of similarity between observations based on the number of matching values of categorical variables.
McQuitty's method Measure that computes the dissimilarity between a cluster AB (formed by merging clusters A and B) and a cluster C by averaging the distance between A and C and the distance between B and C.
Median linkage Method that computes the similarity between two clusters as the median of the similarities between each pair of observations in the two clusters.
Missing at random The case when data for a variable is missing due to a relationship a relationship between other variables.
Missing completely at random The case when data for a variable is missing purely due to random chance.
Missing not at random The case when data for a variable is missing due to its unrecorded value.
Observation A set of observed values of variables associated with a single entity, often displayed as a row in a spreadsheet or database.
Single linkage Measure of calculating dissimilarity between clusters by considering only the two most similar observations between the two clusters.
Support count The number of times that a collection of items occurs together in a transaction data set.
Unsupervised learning Category of data-mining techniques in which an algorithm explains relationships without an outcome variable to guide the process.
Ward's method Procedure that partitions observations in a manner to obtain clusters with the least amount of information loss due to the aggregation.

PROBLEMS

Problem descriptions may include XLMiner directions. If using alternative software, steps may vary and results may differ depending on algorithm implementation. Due to the realistic size of these data sets, XLMiner may take several minutes to complete execution for some of these problems. Where relevant, we used the default seed of 12345 when applying XLMiner.

1. The Football Bowl Subdivision (FBS) level of the National Collegiate Athletic Association (NCAA) consists of over 100 schools. Most of these schools belong to one of several conferences, or collections of schools, that compete with each other on a regular basis in collegiate sports. Suppose the NCAA has commissioned a study that will propose the formation of conferences based on the similarities of the constituent schools. The file *FBS* contains data on schools belong to the Football Bowl Subdivision (FBS). Each row in this file contains information on a school. The variables include football stadium capacity, latitude, longitude, athletic department revenue, endowment, and undergraduate enrollment.
   a. Apply k-means clustering with $k = 10$ using football stadium capacity, latitude, longitude, endowment, and enrollment as variables. Be sure to **Normalize Input Data** and specify 50 iterations and 10 random starts in Step 2 of the XLMiner k-Means Clustering procedure. Analyze the resultant clusters. What is the smallest cluster? What is the least dense cluster (as measured by the average distance in the cluster)? What makes the least dense cluster so diverse?
   b. What problems do you see with the plan with defining the school membership of the 10 conferences directly with the 10 clusters?
   c. Repeat part a, but this time do not **Normalize Input Data** in Step 2 of the XLMiner k-Means Clustering procedure. Analyze the resultant clusters. How and why do they differ from those in part a? Identify the dominating factor(s) in the formation of these new clusters.

2. Refer to the clustering problem involving the file *FBS* described in Problem 1. Apply hierarchical clustering with 10 clusters using football stadium capacity, latitude, longitude, endowment, and enrollment as variables. Be sure to **Normalize Input Data** in Step 2 of the XLMiner Hierarchical Clustering procedure. Use Ward's method as the clustering method.
   a. Use a PivotTable on the data in the *HC_Clusters* worksheet to compute the cluster centers for the clusters in the hierarchical clustering.
   b. Identify the cluster with the largest average football stadium capacity. Using all the variables, how would you characterize this cluster?
   c. Examine the smallest cluster. What makes this cluster unique?
   d. By examining the sequence of clustering stages in *HC_Output* worksheet (and the accompanying dendrogram on the *HC_Dendrogram* worksheet), recommend the number of clusters that seems to be the most natural fit based on the distance. By comparing the total distance at the stage with eight clusters to the total distance at the stage with seven clusters, compute the increase in distance if 7 clusters are used instead of 8 clusters.
3. Refer to the clustering problem involving the file *FBS* described in Problem 1. Apply hierarchical clustering with 10 clusters using latitude and longitude as variables. Be sure to **Normalize Input Data** in Step 2 of the XLMiner Hierarchical Clustering procedure. Execute the clustering two times – once with single linkage as the clustering method and once with group average linkage as the clustering method. Use a PivotTable on the data in the respective *HC_Clusters* worksheets to compute the cluster sizes, as well as the minimum and maximum of the latitude and longitude within each cluster. To visualize the clusters, create a scatter plot with longitude as the x-variable and latitude as the y-variable. Compare the results of the two approaches.

4. Refer to the clustering problem involving the file *FBS* described in Problem 1. Apply hierarchical clustering with 10 clusters using latitude and longitude as variables. Be sure to **Normalize Input Data** in Step 2 of the XLMiner Hierarchical Clustering procedure. Execute the clustering two times – once with Ward's method as the clustering method and once with group average linkage as the clustering method. Use a PivotTable on the data in the respective *HC_Clusters* worksheets to compute the cluster sizes, as well as the minimum and maximum of the latitude and longitude within each cluster. To visualize the clusters, create a scatter plot with longitude as the x-variable and latitude as the y-variable. Compare the results of the two approaches.
5. Refer to the clustering problem involving the file *FBS* described in Problem 1. Apply hierarchical clustering with 10 clusters using latitude and longitude as variables. Be sure to **Normalize Input Data** in Step 2 of the XLMiner Hierarchical Clustering procedure. Execute the clustering two times – once with complete linkage as the clustering method and once with Ward's method as the clustering method. Use a PivotTable on the data in the respective *HC_Clusters* worksheets to compute the cluster sizes, as well as the minimum and maximum of the latitude and longitude within each cluster. To visualize the clusters, create a scatter plot with longitude as the x-variable and latitude as the y-variable. Compare the results of the two approaches.
6. Refer to the clustering problem involving the file *FBS* described in Problem 1. Apply hierarchical clustering with 10 clusters using latitude and longitude as variables. Be sure to **Normalize Input Data** in Step 2 of the XLMiner Hierarchical Clustering procedure. Execute the clustering two times – once with centroid linkage as the clustering method and once with group average linkage as the clustering method. Use a PivotTable on the data in the respective *HC_Clusters* worksheets to compute the cluster sizes, as well as the minimum and maximum of the latitude and longitude within each cluster. To visualize the clusters, create a scatter plot with longitude as the x-variable and latitude as the y-variable. Compare the results of the two approaches.
7. Refer to the clustering problem involving the file *FBS* described in Problem 1. Apply hierarchical clustering with 10 clusters using latitude and longitude as variables. Be sure to **Normalize Input Data** in Step 2 of the XLMiner Hierarchical Clustering procedure. Execute the clustering two times – once with median linkage as the clustering method and once with centroid linkage as the clustering method. Use a PivotTable on the data in the respective *HC_Clusters* worksheets to compute the cluster sizes, as well as the minimum and maximum of the latitude and longitude within each cluster. To visualize the clusters, create a scatter plot with longitude as the x-variable and latitude as the y-variable. Compare the results of the two approaches.
8. Refer to the clustering problem involving the file *FBS* described in Problem 1. Apply hierarchical clustering with 10 clusters using latitude and longitude as variables. Be sure to **Normalize Input Data** in Step 2 of the XLMiner Hierarchical Clustering procedure. Execute the clustering two times – once with McQuitty's method as the clustering method and once with group average linkage as the clustering method. Use a PivotTable on the data in the respective *HC_Clusters* worksheets to compute the cluster sizes, as well as the minimum and maximum of the latitude and longitude within each cluster. To visualize the clusters, create a scatter plot with longitude as the x-variable and latitude as the y-variable. Compare the results of the two approaches.

9. From 1946 to 1990, the Big Ten Conference consisted of the University of Illinois, Indiana University, University of Iowa, University of Michigan, Michigan State University, University of Minnesota, Northwestern University, Ohio State University, Purdue University, and University of Wisconsin. In 1990, the conference added Pennsylvania State University. In 2011, the conference added the University of

Nebraska. Even more recently, the University of Maryland and Rutgers University have been added to the conference with speculation of more schools being added. The file *BigTen* contains the similar information as the file *FBS* (see Problem 1 description), except that the variable values for the original 10 schools in the Big 10 conference have been replaced with the respective averages of these variables over these 10 schools.

Apply hierarchical clustering with 2 clusters using football stadium capacity, latitude, longitude, endowment, and enrollment as variables. Be sure to **Normalize Input Data** in Step 2 of the XLMiner Hierarchical Clustering procedure. Use complete linkage as the clustering method. By referencing the *HC_Output* worksheet or the *HC_Dendrogram* worksheet, which schools does the clustering suggest would have been the most appropriate to be the eleventh school in the Big Ten? The twelfth and thirteenth schools? What is the problem with using this method to identify the fourteenth school to add to the Big Ten?

10. Refer to the clustering problem involving the file *FBS* described in Problem 1. The NCAA has a preference for conferences consisting of similar schools with respect to their endowment, enrollment, and football stadium capacity, but these conferences must be in the same geographic region to reduce traveling costs. Follow the following steps to address this desire. Apply k-means clustering using latitude and longitude as variables with $k = 3$. Be sure to **Normalize Input Data** and specify 50 iterations and 10 random starts in Step 2 of the XLMiner k-Means Clustering procedure. Using the cluster assignments, separate the original data in the Data worksheet into three separate data sets – one data set for each of the three "regional" clusters.
    a. For Region 1 data set, apply hierarchical clustering with Ward's method to form four clusters using football stadium capacity, endowment, and enrollment as variables. Be sure to **Normalize Input Data** in Step 2 of the XLMiner Hierarchical Clustering procedure. Using a PivotTable on the data in the corresponding *HC_Clusters* worksheet, report the characteristics of each cluster.
    b. For the Region 2 data set, apply hierarchical clustering with Ward's method to form three clusters using football stadium capacity, endowment, and enrollment as variables. Be sure to **Normalize Input Data** in Step 2 of the XLMiner Hierarchical Clustering procedure. Using a PivotTable on the data in the corresponding *HC_Clusters* worksheet, report the characteristics of each cluster.
    c. For the Region 3 data set, apply hierarchical clustering with Ward's method to form two clusters using football stadium capacity, endowment, and enrollment as variables. Be sure to **Normalize Input Data** in Step 2 of the XLMiner Hierarchical Clustering procedure. Using a PivotTable on the data in the corresponding *HC_Clusters* worksheet, report the characteristics of each cluster.
    d. What problems do you see with the plan with defining the school membership of nine conferences directly with the nine total clusters formed from the regions? How could this approach be tweaked to solve this problem?

11. IBM employs a network of expert analytics consultants for various projects. To help it determine how to distribute its bonuses, IBM wants to form groups of employees with similar performance according to key performance metrics. Each observation (corresponding to an employee) in the file *BigBlue* consists of values for: (1) *UsageRate* which corresponds to the proportion of time that the employee has been actively working on high priority projects, (2) *Recognition* which is the number of projects for which the employee was specifically requested, and (3) *Leader* which is the number of projects on which the employee has served as project leader.
Apply *k*-means clustering with for values of $k = 2, \ldots, 7$. Be sure to **Normalize Input Data** and specify 50 iterations and 10 random starts in Step 2 of the XLMiner *k*-Means

Clustering procedure. How many clusters do you recommend using to categorize the employees? Why?

12. Use the data file *DemoKTC* to conduct the following analysis.
    a. Use hierarchical clustering with the matching coefficient as the similarity measure and the group average linkage as the clustering method to create nested clusters based on the Female, Married, Car Loan, and Mortgage variables as shown in Appendix 4.1. Specify the construction of 3 clusters. Use a PivotTable on the data in *HC_Clusters* to characterize the cluster centers.
    b. Repeat part a, but use Jaccard's coefficient as the similarity measure.
    c. Compare the clusters and explain your observations.
13. Use the data file *DemoKTC* file to conduct the following analysis.
    a. Use k-means clustering with a value of $k = 3$ to cluster based on the Age, Income, and Children variables to reproduce the results in Appendix 4.2.
    b. Repeat the k-means clustering for values of $k = 2, 4, 5$.
    c. How many clusters do you recommend? Why?

14. Attracted by the possible returns from a portfolio of movies, hedge funds have invested in the movie industry by financially backing individual films and/or studios. The hedge fund Gelt Star is currently conducting some research involving movies involving Adam Sandler, an American actor, screenwriter, and film producer. As a first step, Gelt Star would like to cluster Adam Sandler movies based on their gross box office returns and movie critic ratings. Using the data in the file *Sandler*, apply k-means clustering with $k = 3$ to characterize three different types of Adam Sandler movies. Based the clusters on the variables *Rating* and *Box Office*. *Rating* corresponds to movie ratings provided by critics (a higher score represents a movie receiving better reviews). *Box Office* represents the gross box office earnings in 2015 dollars. Be sure to **Normalize Input Data** and specify 50 iterations and 10 random starts in Step 2 of the XLMiner k-Means Clustering procedure. Use the resulting clusters to characterize Adam Sandler movies.

15. Josephine Mater works for a market research firm that specializes in the food industry. She currently is analyzing Trader Joe's, a national chain of specialty grocery stores. Specifically, Josephine would like to gain insight on Trader Joe's future expansion plans (which are closely guarded by the company). Josephine knows that Trader Joe's replenishes its inventory at its retail stores with frequent trucking shipments from its distribution centers. The file *TraderJoes* contains data on the location of Trader Joe's retail stores. To keep costs low, retail stores are typically located near a distribution center. Josephine would like to use k-means clustering to estimate the location and number of Trader Joe's distribution centers (information on Trader Joe's distribution centers is not publicly disclosed). How large must k be so that the average distance to each cluster centroid is less than 8 distance units as measured in the original (non-normalized) coordinates? Be sure to **Normalize Input Data** and specify 50 iterations and 10 random starts in Step 2 of the XLMiner k-Means Clustering procedure.

16. Apple Inc. tracks online transactions at its iStore and is interested in learning about the purchase patterns of its customers in order to provide recommendations as a customer browses its web site. A sample of the "shopping cart" data in binary matrix format resides in the file *AppleCart*. Each row indicates which iPad features and accessories a customer selected.
    Using a minimum support of 10% of the total number of transactions and a minimum confidence of 50%, use XLMiner to generate a list of association rules.
    a. Interpret what the rule with the largest lift ratio is saying about the relationship between the antecedent item set and consequent item set.
    b. Interpret the support count of the item set involved in the rule with the largest lift ratio.
    c. Interpret the confidence of the rule with the largest lift ratio.

d. Interpret the lift ratio of the rule with the largest lift ratio.
e. Review the top 15 rules and summarize what the rules suggest.

17. Cookie Monster Inc. is a company that specializes in the development of software that tracks web browsing history of individuals. A sample of browser histories is provided in the file *CookieMonster*. Using binary matrix format, the entry in row i and column j indicates whether web site j was visited by user i.
Using a minimum support of 800 transactions and a minimum confidence of 50%, use XLMiner to generate a list of association rules. Review the top 14 rules. What information does this analysis provide Cookie Monster regarding the online behavior of individuals?

18. A grocery store introducing items from Italy is interested in analyzing buying trends of these new "international" items, namely prosciutto, peroni, risotto, and gelato. The file *GroceryStore* provides data on a collection of transactions in item-list format.
a. Using a minimum support of 100 transactions and a minimum confidence of 50%, use XLMiner to generate a list of association rules. How many rules satisfy this criterion?
b. Using a minimum support of 250 transactions and a minimum confidence of 50%, use XLMiner to generate a list of association rules. How many rules satisfy this criterion? Why may the grocery store want to increase the minimum support required for their analysis? What is the risk of increasing the minimum support required?
c. Using the list of rules from part b, consider the rule with the largest lift ratio that involves an Italian item. Interpret what this rule is saying about the relationship between the antecedent item set and consequent item set.
d. Interpret the support count of the item set involved in the rule with the largest lift ratio that involves an Italian item.
e. Interpret the confidence of the rule with the largest lift ratio that involves an Italian item.
f. Interpret the lift ratio of the rule with the largest lift ratio that involves an Italian item.
g. What insight can the grocery store obtain about its purchasers of the Italian fare?
h. How would you characterize this cluster?
i. Examine the smallest cluster. What makes this cluster unique?
j. By examining the dendrogram on the *HC_Dendrogram* worksheet and the sequence of clustering stages in *HC_Output*, what number of clusters seems to be the most natural fit based on the distance? What is the increase in distance if 7 clusters were used instead of 8 clusters?
k. How many clusters do you recommend? Why?

CASE PROBLEM: KNOW THY CUSTOMER

Know Thy Customer (KTC) is a financial consulting company that provides personalized financial advice to its clients. As a basis for developing this tailored advising, KTC would like to segment its customers into several representative groups based on key characteristics.

Peyton Avery, the director of KTC's fledging analytics division, plans to establish the set of representative customer profiles based on 600 customer records in the file *KnowThyCustomer*. Each customer record contains data on age, gender, annual income, marital status, number of children, whether the customer has a car loan, and whether the customer has a home mortgage. KTC's market research staff has determined that these seven characteristics should form the basis of the customer clustering.

Peyton has invited a summer intern, Danny Riles, into her office so they can discuss how to proceed. As they review the data on the computer screen, Peyton's brow furrows as she realizes that this task may not be trivial. The data contains both categorical variables (Female, Married, Car, Mortgage) and interval variables (Age, Income, and Children).

Managerial Report

Playing the role of Peyton, you must write a report documenting the construction of the representative customer profiles. Because Peyton would like to use this report as a training reference for interns such as Danny, your report should experiment with several approaches and explain the strengths and weaknesses of each. In particular, your report should include the following analyses:

KnowThyCustomer

1. Using k-means clustering on all seven variables, experiment with different values of k. Recommend a value of k and describe these k clusters according to their "average" characteristics. Why might k-means clustering not be a good method to use for these seven variables?
2. Using hierarchical clustering on all seven variables, experiment with using complete linkage and group average linkage as the clustering method. Recommend a set of customer profiles (clusters). Describe these clusters according to their "average" characteristics. Why might hierarchical clustering not be a good method to use for these seven variables?
3. Apply a two-step clustering method:
   a. Apply hierarchical clustering on the binary variables Female, Married, Car, and Mortgage to recommend a set of clusters. Use matching coefficients as the similarity measure and group average linkage as the clustering method.
   b. Based on the clusters from part (a), split the original 600 observations into m separate data sets, where m is the number of clusters recommended from part (a). For each of these m data sets, apply 2-means clustering using Age, Income, and Children as variables. This will generate a total of $2m$ clusters. Describe these $2m$ clusters according to their "average" characteristics.

   What benefit does this two-step clustering approach have over the approaches in parts (1) and (2)? What weakness does it have?

Chapter 4 Appendix

DemoKTC

Appendix 4.1 Hierarchical Clustering with XLMiner

KTC is interested in developing customer segments based on the gender, marital status, and whether the customer is repaying a car loan and a mortgage. Using the file *DemoKTC*, the following steps and Figure 4.5 demonstrate how to use XLMiner to construct hierarchical clusters. We base the clusters on a collection of 0–1 categorical variables (Female, Married, Car Loan, and Mortgage). We use the matching coefficient to measure similarity between observations and the group average linkage clustering method to measure similarity between clusters.

Typically, clustering is executed on "raw" data consisting of observations of variable measurements. However, in some cases, a precomputed distance matrix of pairwise dissimilarity between each pair of observations is used to cluster observations. For these cases, in the Hierarchical Clustering—Step 1 of 3 dialog box, you should select Distance matrix for the Data type: in the Clustering Options area

Step 1. Select any cell in the range of the data
Step 2. Click the **XLMiner Platform** tab in the Ribbon
Step 3. Click **Cluster** in the **Data Analysis** group
Step 4. Click **Hierarchical Clustering**
Step 5. When the **Hierarchical Clustering—Step 1 of 3** dialog box appears:
In the **Data source** area, confirm that the **Worksheet:**, **Workbook:**, and **Data range:** entries correspond to the appropriate data

FIGURE 4.5 XLMiner Steps for Hierarchical Clustering

*Double-clicking on the variable names Female, Married, Car Loan, and Mortage in the **Variables** box will also move these variables into the **Selected variables** box.*

In the **Variables** area, select the checkbox for **First Row Contains Headers**
In the **Variables In Input Data** box of the **Variables** area, select the variables **Female**, **Married**, **Car Loan**, and **Mortage**, and click the > button to populate the **Selected Variables** box
In the **Clustering Options** area, select **Raw data** from the drop down window next to **Data type:**
Click **Next >**

Step 6. In the **Hierarchical Clustering—Step 2 of 3** dialog box:
In the **Similarity Measure** area, select **Matching coefficients**
In the **Clustering Method** area, select **Group Average Linkage**
Click **Next >**

FIGURE 4.6 HC_Output Worksheet

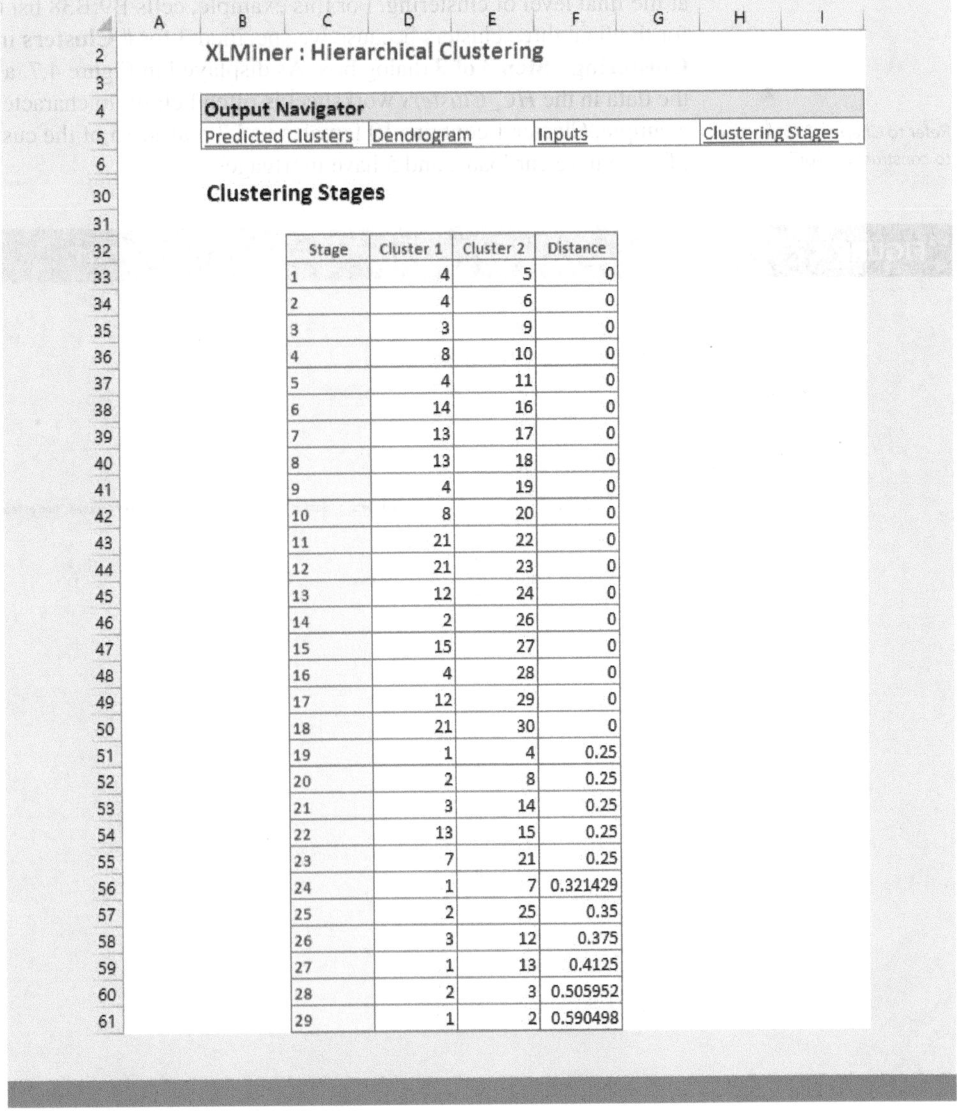

XLMiner : Hierarchical Clustering

Output Navigator			
Predicted Clusters	Dendrogram	Inputs	Clustering Stages

Clustering Stages

Stage	Cluster 1	Cluster 2	Distance
1	4	5	0
2	4	6	0
3	3	9	0
4	8	10	0
5	4	11	0
6	14	16	0
7	13	17	0
8	13	18	0
9	4	19	0
10	8	20	0
11	21	22	0
12	21	23	0
13	12	24	0
14	2	26	0
15	15	27	0
16	4	28	0
17	12	29	0
18	21	30	0
19	1	4	0.25
20	2	8	0.25
21	3	14	0.25
22	13	15	0.25
23	7	21	0.25
24	1	7	0.321429
25	2	25	0.35
26	3	12	0.375
27	1	13	0.4125
28	2	3	0.505952
29	1	2	0.590498

Step 7. In the **Hierarchical Clustering—Step 3 of 3** dialog box:
Select the checkboxes for **Draw dendrogram** and **Show cluster membership**
In the box next to **# Clusters**, enter *3*
Click **Finish**

This procedure generates three worksheets: *HC_Output*, *HC_Clusters*, and *HC_Dendrogram*. As Figure 4.6 shows, *HC_Output* lists the sequence in which clusters are aggregated and the increase in dissimilarity resulting from each merger. For example, at stage 1, Cluster 4 (containing only observation 4) and Cluster 5 (containing only observation 5) are aggregated and the resulting cluster results in a zero increase in dissimilarity because these clusters contain identical observations. When two clusters are merged, the resulting cluster is indexed with the smaller index of the two cluster indices involved in the merger. So when Cluster 4 and Cluster 5 are aggregated, the resulting cluster {4, 5} is labeled Cluster 4 for the next stage.

As Figure 4.7 shows, *HC_Clusters* contains a table showing each observation's cluster at the final level of clustering. For this example, cells B9:B38 list the cluster membership for the final three clusters because we specified 3 for **# Clusters** in the **Hierarchical Clustering - Step 3 of 3** dialog box. As displayed in Figure 4.7, a PivotTable based on the data in the *HC_Clusters* worksheet is often helpful to characterize the clusters. For example, Cluster 1 contains 10 females and 7 males, 15 of the customers are married, none of them have car loans, and 5 have mortgages.

Refer to Chapter 3 to see how to construct a PivotTable.

FIGURE 4.7 HC_Clusters Worksheet

XLMiner : Hierarchical Clustering - Predicted Clusters

Output Navigator			
Predicted Clusters	Dendrogram	Inputs	Clustering Stages

Cluster ID	Sub-Cluster	Female	Married	Car Loan	Mortgage
1	1	1	0	0	0
2	2	0	1	1	1
3	3	1	1	1	0
1	4	1	1	0	0
1	5	1	1	0	0
1	6	1	1	0	0
1	7	0	0	0	0
2	8	0	1	1	0
3	9	1	1	1	0
2	10	0	1	1	0
1	11	1	1	0	0
3	12	1	0	1	1
1	13	1	1	0	1
3	14	1	1	1	1
1	15	0	1	0	1
3	16	1	1	1	1
1	17	1	1	0	1
1	18	1	1	0	1
1	19	1	1	0	0
2	20	0	1	1	0
1	21	0	1	0	0
1	22	0	1	0	0
1	23	0	1	0	0
3	24	1	0	1	1
2	25	0	0	1	0
2	26	0	1	1	1
1	27	0	1	0	1
1	28	1	1	0	0
3	29	1	0	1	1
1	30	0	1	0	0

Row Labels	Sum of Female	Sum of Married	Sum of Car Loan	Sum of Mortgage	Count of Cluster ID
1	10	15	0	5	17
2	0	5	6	2	6
3	7	4	7	5	7
Grand Total	17	24	13	12	30

FIGURE 4.8 HC_Dendrogram Worksheet

XLMiner : Hierarchical Clustering - Dendrogram

Output Navigator			
Predicted Clusters	Dendrogram	Inputs	Clustering Stages

Dendrogram

Distance

0.7 0.6 0.5 0.4 0.3 0.2 0.1 0

4 5 6 11 19 28 1 7 21 22 23 30 13 17 18 15 27 2 26 8 10 20 25 3 9 14 16 12 24 29

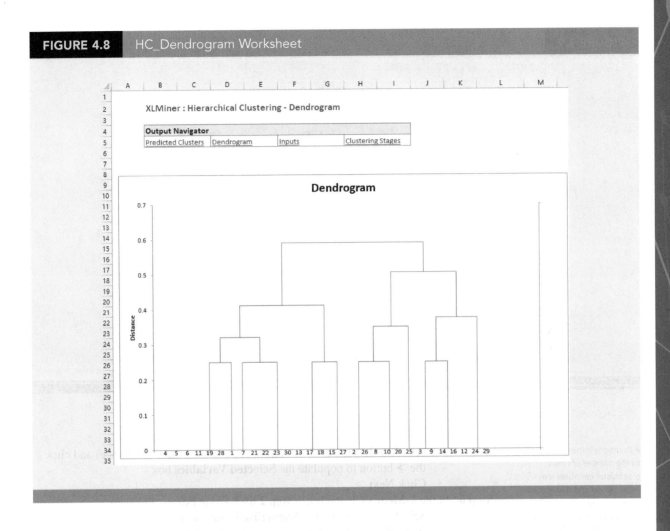

Figure 4.8 shows the dendrogram from *HC_Dendrogram*, visually summarizing the clustering output.

Appendix 4.2 *k*-Means Clustering with XLMiner

DemoKTC

KTC is interested in developing customer segments based on age, income, and number of children. Using the file *DemoKTC*, the following steps and Figure 4.9 demonstrate how to execute *k*-means clustering with XLMiner.

Step 1. Select any cell in the range of the data
Step 2. Click the **XLMiner Platform** tab in the Ribbon
Step 3. Click **Cluster** in the **Data Analysis** group
Step 4. Click ***k*-Means Clustering**
Step 5. When the ***k*-Means Clustering—Step 1 of 3** dialog box appears:
In the **Data source** area, confirm the **Worksheet:**, **Workbook:**, and **Data range**: entries correspond to the appropriate data
In the **Variables** area, select the checkbox for **First Row Contains Headers**
In the **Variables In Input Data** box of the **Variables** area, select the variables **Age**, **Income**, and **Children** (pressing the Crtl key while

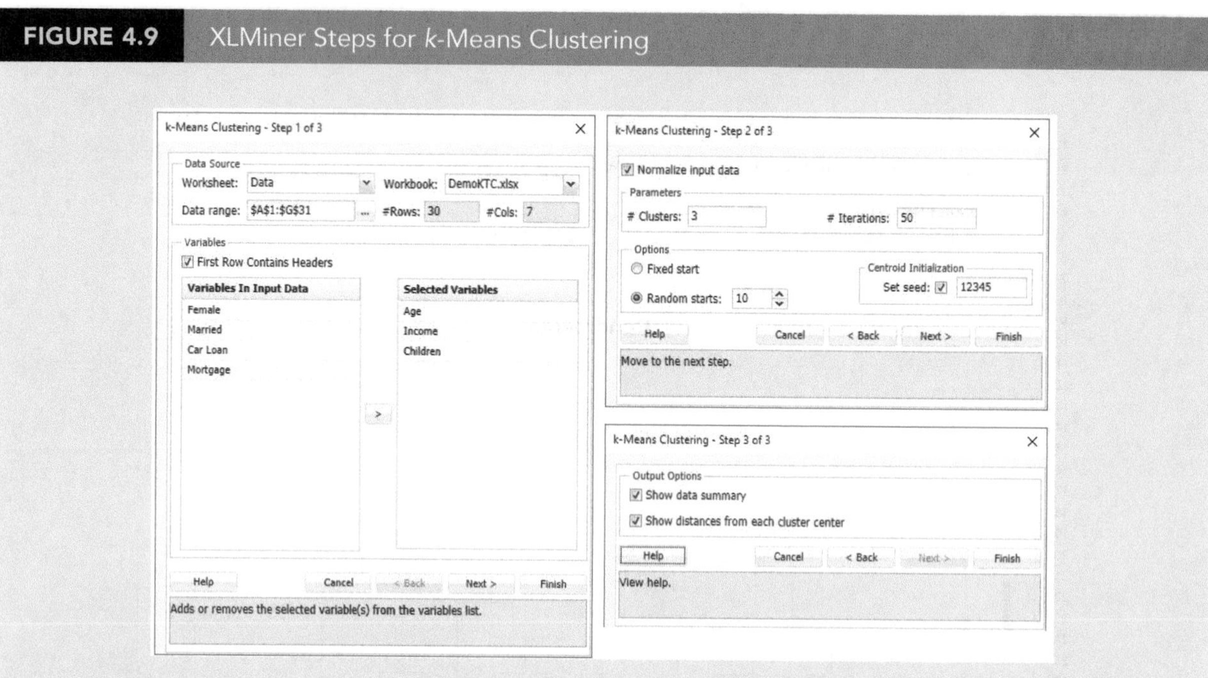

FIGURE 4.9 XLMiner Steps for *k*-Means Clustering

selecting the variables will allow you to select them all at once) and click the **>** button to populate the **Selected Variables** box

Click **Next >**

Step 6. In the ***k*-Means Clustering—Step 2 of 3** dialog box:

Select the checkbox for **Normalize input data**

In the **Parameters** area, enter *3* in the **# Clusters** box, and enter *50* in the **# Iterations** box

In the **Options** area, select **Random Starts:** and enter *10* in the adjacent box

In the **Centroid Initialization** box within the **Options** area, select the checkbox for **Set Seed:** and enter *12345* in the adjacent box

Click **Next >**

Step 7. In the ***k*-Means Clustering—Step 3 of 3** dialog box, click **Finish:**

In the **Output Options** area, select the checkboxes for **Show data summary** and **Show distances from each cluster center**

Click **Finish**

 # Iterations corresponds to the number of times that cluster centroids are recalculated and observations are reassigned to clusters. By choosing ***Random Starts*** *and increasing* ***No. Of Starts****, the k-means algorithm is repeated on multiple randomly generated initial clusters and the best-found cluster set is reported. If the additional run time is not prohibitive, better clusters may result from a larger number of iterations and from a larger number of starts. Setting the seed for* ***Centroid Initialization*** *allows the clustering experiment to be reproduced. If a seed is not set, the clustering results may vary each time the clustering is performed.*

This procedure generates two worksheets, *KMC_Output* and *KMC_Clusters*. Of particular interest on the *KM_Output* worksheet is the **Cluster Centers** information. As shown in Figure 4.10, clicking on the **Cluster Centers** link in the **Output Navigator** area at the top of the *KMC_Output* worksheet brings information describing the clusters into view. In the **Cluster Centers** area, there are two sets of tables. In the first set of tables, the left table lists the cluster centroids in the original units of the input variables and the right table lists the cluster centroids in the normalized units of the input variables. Cluster 1 consists of the youngest customers with largest families and the lowest incomes. Cluster 2 consists of the

FIGURE 4.10 KMC_Output Worksheet

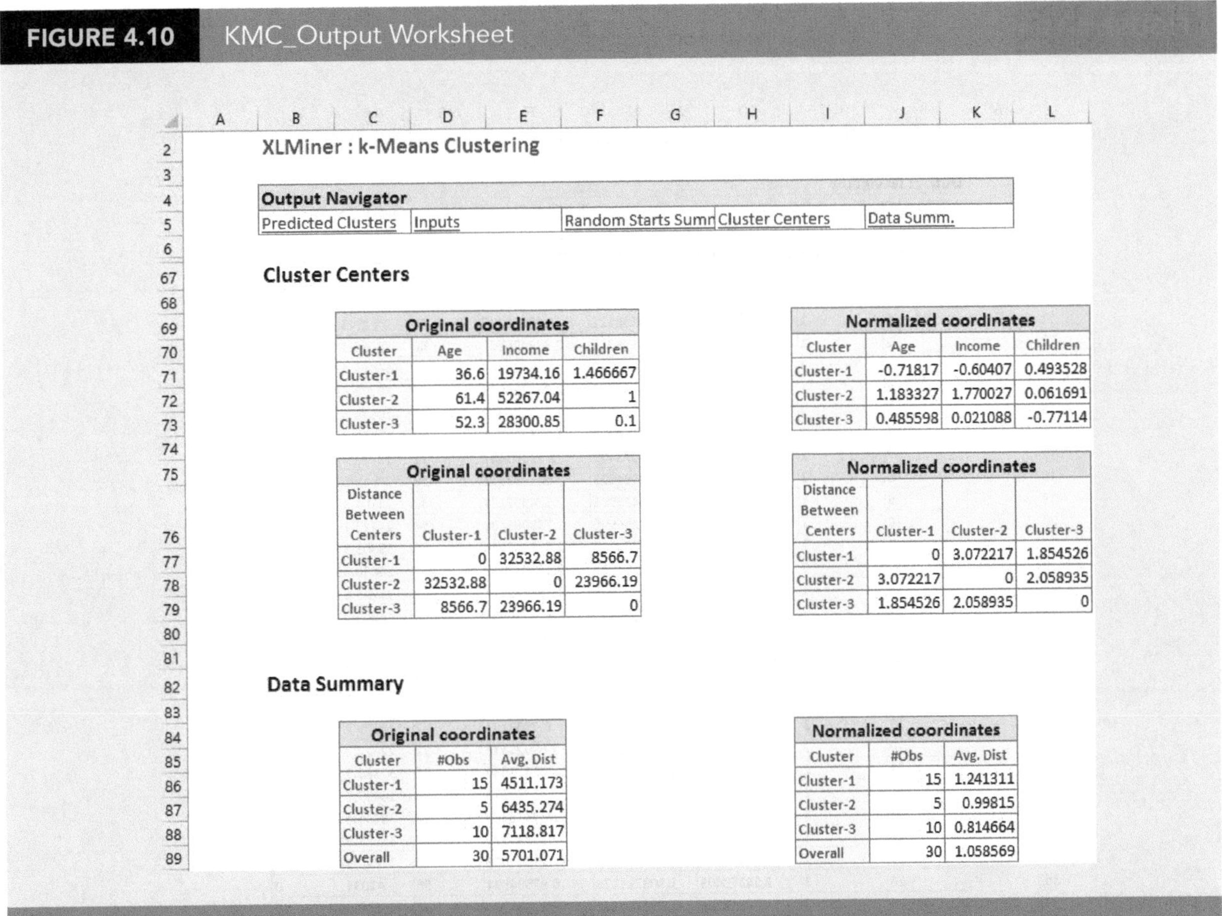

XLMiner : k-Means Clustering

Output Navigator				
Predicted Clusters	Inputs	Random Starts Sumr	Cluster Centers	Data Summ.

Cluster Centers

Original coordinates			
Cluster	Age	Income	Children
Cluster-1	36.6	19734.16	1.466667
Cluster-2	61.4	52267.04	1
Cluster-3	52.3	28300.85	0.1

Normalized coordinates			
Cluster	Age	Income	Children
Cluster-1	-0.71817	-0.60407	0.493528
Cluster-2	1.183327	1.770027	0.061691
Cluster-3	0.485598	0.021088	-0.77114

Original coordinates			
Distance Between Centers	Cluster-1	Cluster-2	Cluster-3
Cluster-1	0	32532.88	8566.7
Cluster-2	32532.88	0	23966.19
Cluster-3	8566.7	23966.19	0

Normalized coordinates			
Distance Between Centers	Cluster-1	Cluster-2	Cluster-3
Cluster-1	0	3.072217	1.854526
Cluster-2	3.072217	0	2.058935
Cluster-3	1.854526	2.058935	0

Data Summary

Original coordinates		
Cluster	#Obs	Avg. Dist
Cluster-1	15	4511.173
Cluster-2	5	6435.274
Cluster-3	10	7118.817
Overall	30	5701.071

Normalized coordinates		
Cluster	#Obs	Avg. Dist
Cluster-1	15	1.241311
Cluster-2	5	0.99815
Cluster-3	10	0.814664
Overall	30	1.058569

oldest customers with the highest incomes and an average of one child. Cluster 3 consists of older customers with moderate incomes and few children. If KTC decides these clusters are appropriate, they can use them as a basis for creating financial advising plans based on the characteristics of each cluster.

The second set of tables under **Cluster Centers** in Figure 4.10 displays the between-cluster distances between the three cluster centers. The left and right tables express the inter-cluster distances in the original and normalized units of the input variables, respectively. Cluster 1 and Cluster 3 are the most distinct pair of clusters, with a distance of 3.07 units between their respective centroids. Cluster 2 and Cluster 3 are the second most distinct pair of clusters (between-centroid distance of 2.06). Cluster 1 and Cluster 3 are the least distinct (between-centroid distance of 1.85).

Typically, distance measurements based on the normalized coordinates should be used when making cluster comparisons to avoid the original scale of the input variables skewing the analysis.

The **Data Summary** area of Figure 4.10 displays the within-cluster distances in both the original and normalized units of the input variables, respectively. Referring to the right table expressed in normalized units, we observe that Cluster 3 is the most homogeneous and Cluster 1 is the most heterogeneous. By comparing the normalized between-cluster distance in the bottom right table under **Cluster Centers** to the normalized within-cluster distance in the right table under **Data Summary**, we observe that the observations within clusters are more similar than the observations between clusters. By conducting *k*-means clusters for other values of *k*, we can evaluate how the choice of *k* affects the strength of the clustering as measured by the ratio between the between-cluster and within-cluster distances.

FIGURE 4.11 KMC_Clusters Worksheet

XLMiner : k-Means Clustering - Predicted Clusters

Output Navigator

Predicted Clusters	Inputs	Random Starts Summ.	Cluster Centers	Data Summ.

Distances from cluster centers are in normalized coordinates

Record ID	Cluster ID	Dist. Clust-1	Dist. Clust-2	Dist. Clust-3	Age	Income	Children
1	1	0.98792311	2.734158512	1.19091227	48	17546	1
2	1	1.628430379	2.955969211	2.847426201	40	30085.1	3
3	3	1.7646987	2.876825512	0.866409367	51	16575.4	0
4	1	1.761473809	4.18451778	3.547235929	23	20375.4	3
5	2	3.058468348	0.992641041	1.667590968	57	50576.3	0
6	2	2.107506821	1.440136304	1.925798731	57	37869.6	2
7	1	1.929471674	4.473073409	2.72305407	22	8877.07	0
8	3	2.163086915	2.213404825	0.509393351	58	24946.6	0
9	1	0.640107623	2.868415901	2.124907137	37	25304.3	2
10	1	1.459528629	2.317266996	1.788088108	54	24212.1	2
11	2	3.933670152	1.132783988	2.529248044	66	59803.9	0
12	3	1.868574302	2.206364327	0.153137437	52	26658.8	0
13	1	0.770417673	2.981067897	1.392612112	44	15735.8	1
14	2	3.459490964	0.412738412	2.377310051	66	55204.7	1
15	1	1.35811263	3.221133108	1.409030639	36	19474.6	0
16	3	1.374677024	2.97391956	1.183135173	38	22342.1	0
17	1	0.515659563	3.272391017	2.250001888	37	17729.8	2
18	3	2.184811721	1.710157265	1.050178654	46	41016	0
19	3	2.430828697	2.069479576	0.7563163	62	26909.2	0
20	1	1.437973295	3.316736333	1.68923513	31	22522.8	0
21	2	3.390112135	1.012452306	2.862821636	61	57880.7	2
22	1	1.164029752	2.904135826	1.965780278	50	16497.3	2
23	3	2.342344286	1.481686946	0.757448363	54	38446.6	0
24	1	1.574013642	3.872571031	2.15380573	27	15538.8	0
25	1	1.328415143	4.283068598	3.129630608	22	12640.3	2
26	3	2.54373403	1.303721224	0.97594334	56	41034	0
27	3	1.504315206	2.776198332	0.787839774	45	20809.7	0
28	1	0.470226791	2.907788582	1.445834508	39	20114	1
29	1	1.593881128	3.028130438	2.871818915	39	29359.1	3
30	3	1.948348711	2.043313711	1.10683836	61	24270.1	1

The *KMC_Clusters* worksheet (Figure 4.11) lists each observation's assigned cluster in the Cluster ID column as well as the distance (dissimilarity) from the observation to each respective cluster centroid (in normalized units of the input variable). We can use this table to evaluate how well an individual observation fits its assigned cluster relative to the other clusters. For example, Observation 9's assignment to Cluster 1 is quite solid as it is only 0.64 units from Cluster 1's centroid, but 2.12 and 2.87 units from the centroids of Cluster 3 and Cluster 2, respectively. However, Observation 15's assignment to Cluster 1 is not as resolute as it is 1.36 units from Cluster 1's centroid and 1.41 units from Cluster 3's centroid.

Appendix 4.3 Association Rules with XLMiner

HyVeeDemo

Using the file *HyVeeDemo*, the following steps and Figure 4.12 demonstrate how to examine association rules using XLMiner.

Step 1. Select any cell in the range of the data

Step 2. Click the **XLMiner Platform** tab in the Ribbon

FIGURE 4.12 XLMiner Association Rules Dialog Box

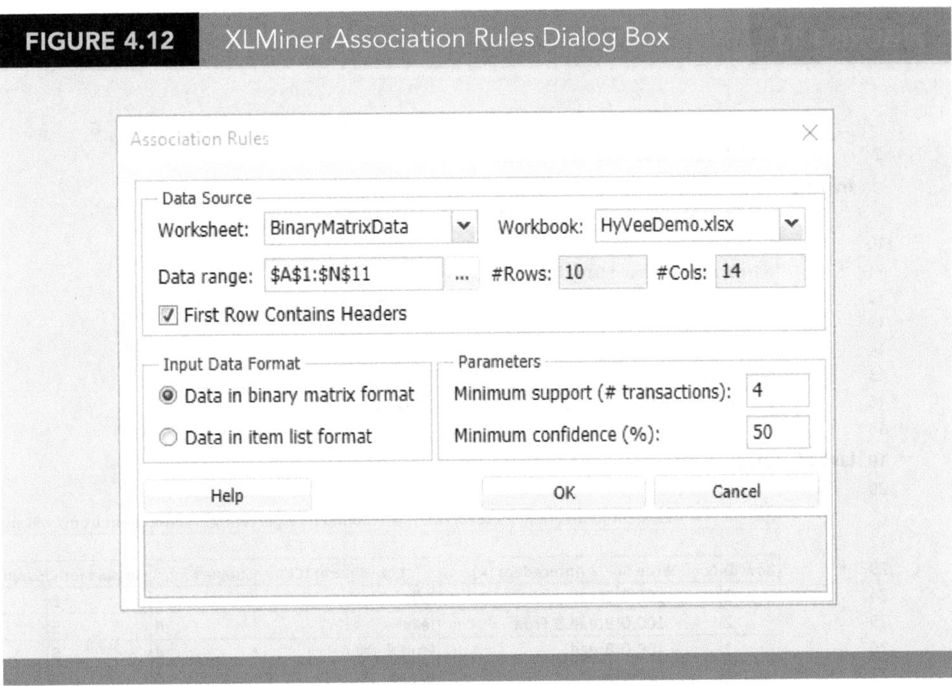

Step 3. Click **Associate** in the **Data Mining** group
Step 4. Click **Association Rules**
Step 5. When the **Association Rules** dialog box appears, in the **Data source** area, confirm that the **Worksheet:**, **Workbook:**, and **Data range:** entries correspond to the appropriate data
Step 6. In the **Data source** area, select the checkbox for **First Row Contains Headers**
Step 7. In the **Input Data Format** area, select **Data in binary matrix format**
Step 8. In the **Parameters** area, enter *4* in the box next to **Minimum support (# transactions)**, and enter *50* in the box next to **Minimum confidence (%)**
Step 9. Click **OK**

Figure 4.13 illustrates a portion of the *AssocRules_Output* worksheet generated by this procedure. For this data, the 52 rules satisfying the minimum support rule of 4 transactions (out of 10) and the minimum confidence of 50% are displayed in decreasing order of lift ratio.

FIGURE 4.13 XLMiner Association Rules Output

XLMiner : Association Rules

Inputs

Data	
# Transactions in Input Data	10
# Columns in Input Data	14
# Items in Input Data	14
# Association Rules	52
Minimum Support	4
Minimum Confidence	50.00%

List of Rules

Rule: If all Antecedent items are purchased, then with Confidence percentage Consequent items will also be purchased.

Row ID	Confidence %	Antecedent (A)	Consequent (C)	Support for A	Support for C	Support for A & C	Lift Ratio
1	100.0	Bread	Jelly	4	5	4	2.00
2	100.0	Bread & Fruit	Jelly	4	5	4	2.00
3	100.0	Bread	Fruit & Jelly	4	5	4	2.00
4	80.0	Jelly	Bread	5	4	4	2.00
5	80.0	Fruit & Jelly	Bread	5	4	4	2.00
6	80.0	Jelly	Bread & Fruit	5	4	4	2.00
7	100.0	Peanut Butter	Milk	4	6	4	1.67
8	100.0	Peanut Butter & Fruit	Milk	4	6	4	1.67
9	100.0	Peanut Butter	Milk & Fruit	4	6	4	1.67
10	100.0	Potato Chips	Soda	4	6	4	1.67
11	100.0	Fruit & Potato Chips	Soda	4	6	4	1.67
12	100.0	Potato Chips	Fruit & Soda	4	6	4	1.67
13	66.7	Milk	Peanut Butter	6	4	4	1.67
14	66.7	Milk & Fruit	Peanut Butter	6	4	4	1.67
15	66.7	Milk	Peanut Butter & Fruit	6	4	4	1.67
16	66.7	Soda	Potato Chips	6	4	4	1.67
17	66.7	Fruit & Soda	Potato Chips	6	4	4	1.67
18	66.7	Soda	Fruit & Potato Chips	6	4	4	1.67

Chapter 7

Linear Regression

CONTENTS

7.1 THE SIMPLE LINEAR REGRESSION MODEL
- Regression Model
- Estimated Regression Equation

7.2 LEAST SQUARES METHOD
- Least Squares Estimates of the Regression Parameters
- Using Excel's Chart Tools to Compute the Estimated Regression Equation

7.3 ASSESSING THE FIT OF THE SIMPLE LINEAR REGRESSION MODEL
- The Sums of Squares
- The Coefficient of Determination
- Using Excel's Chart Tools to Compute the Coefficient of Determination

7.4 THE MULTIPLE REGRESSION MODEL
- Regression Model
- Estimated Multiple Regression Equation
- Least Squares Method and Multiple Regression
- Butler Trucking Company and Multiple Regression
- Using Excel's Regression Tool to Develop the Estimated Multiple Regression Equation

7.5 INFERENCE AND REGRESSION
- Conditions Necessary for Valid Inference in the Least Squares Regression Model
- Testing Individual Regression Parameters
- Addressing Nonsignificant Independent Variables
- Multicollinearity
- Inference and Very Large Samples

7.6 CATEGORICAL INDEPENDENT VARIABLES
- Butler Trucking Company and Rush Hour
- Interpreting the Parameters
- More Complex Categorical Variables

7.7 MODELING NONLINEAR RELATIONSHIPS
- Quadratic Regression Models
- Piecewise Linear Regression Models
- Interaction Between Independent Variables

7.8 MODEL FITTING
- Variable Selection Procedures
- Overfitting

ANALYTICS IN ACTION

Alliance Data Systems*

DALLAS, TEXAS

Alliance Data Systems (ADS) provides transaction processing, credit services, and marketing services for clients in the rapidly growing customer relationship management (CRM) industry. ADS clients are concentrated in four industries: retail, petroleum/convenience stores, utilities, and transportation. In 1983, Alliance began offering end-to-end credit-processing services to the retail, petroleum, and casual dining industries; today the company employs more than 6,500 employees who provide services to clients around the world. Operating more than 140,000 point-of-sale terminals in the United States alone, ADS processes in excess of 2.5 billion transactions annually. The company ranks second in the United States in private-label credit services by representing 49 private label programs with nearly 72 million cardholders. In 2001, ADS made an initial public offering and is now listed on the New York Stock Exchange.

As one of its marketing services, ADS designs direct mail campaigns and promotions. With its database containing information on the spending habits of more than 100 million consumers, ADS can target consumers who are the most likely to benefit from a direct mail promotion. The Analytical Development Group uses regression analysis to build models that measure and predict the responsiveness of consumers to direct market campaigns. Some regression models predict the probability of purchase for individuals receiving a promotion, and others predict the amount spent by consumers who make purchases.

For one campaign, a retail store chain wanted to attract new customers. To predict the effect of the campaign, ADS analysts selected a sample from the consumer database, sent the sampled individuals promotional materials, and then collected transaction data on the consumers' responses. Sample data were collected on the amount of purchases made by the consumers responding to the campaign, as well as on a variety of consumer-specific variables thought to be useful in predicting sales. The consumer-specific variable that contributed most to predicting the amount purchased was the total amount of credit purchases at related stores over the past 39 months. ADS analysts developed an estimated regression equation relating the amount of purchase to the amount spent at related stores:

$$\hat{y} = 26.7 + 0.00205x,$$

where

$\hat{y}$ = predicted amount of purchase
x = amount spent at related stores

Using this equation, we could predict that someone spending $10,000 over the past 39 months at related stores would spend $47.20 when responding to the direct mail promotion. In this chapter, you will learn how to develop this type of estimated regression equation. The final model developed by ADS analysts also included several other variables that increased the predictive power of the preceding equation. Among these variables was the absence or presence of a bank credit card, estimated income, and the average amount spent per trip at a selected store. In this chapter, we will also learn how such additional variables can be incorporated into a multiple regression model.

*The authors are indebted to Philip Clemance, Director of Analytical Development at Alliance Data Systems, for providing this Analytics in Action.

Managerial decisions are often based on the relationship between two or more variables. For example, after considering the relationship between advertising expenditures and sales, a marketing manager might attempt to predict sales for a given level of advertising expenditures. In another case, a public utility might use the relationship between the daily high temperature and the demand for electricity to predict electricity usage on the basis of next month's anticipated daily high temperatures. Sometimes a manager will rely on intuition to judge how two variables are related. However, if data can be obtained, a statistical procedure called **regression analysis** can be used to develop an equation showing how the variables are related.

The statistical methods used in studying the relationship between two variables were first employed by Sir Francis Galton (1822–1911). Galton found that the heights of the sons of unusually tall or unusually short fathers tend to move, or "regress," toward the average height of the male population. Karl Pearson (1857–1936), a disciple of Galton, later confirmed this finding in a sample of 1,078 pairs of fathers and sons.

In regression terminology, the variable being predicted is called the **dependent variable**, or *response*, and the variables being used to predict the value of the dependent variable are called the **independent variables**, or *predictor variables*. For example, in analyzing the effect of advertising expenditures on sales, a marketing manager's desire to predict sales would suggest making sales the dependent variable. Advertising expenditure would be the independent variable used to help predict sales.

In this chapter, we begin by considering **simple linear regression**, in which the relationship between one dependent variable (denoted by y) and one independent variable (denoted by x) is approximated by a straight line. We then extend this concept to higher dimensions by introducing **multiple linear regression** to model the relationship between a dependent variable (y) and two or more independent variables ($x_1, x_2, \ldots, x_q$).

7.1 Simple Linear Regression Model

Butler Trucking Company is an independent trucking company in southern California. A major portion of Butler's business involves deliveries throughout its local area. To develop better work schedules, the managers want to estimate the total daily travel times for their drivers. The managers believe that the total daily travel times (denoted by y) are closely related to the number of miles traveled in making the daily deliveries (denoted by x). Using regression analysis, we can develop an equation showing how the dependent variable y is related to the independent variable x.

Regression Model

In the Butler Trucking Company example, a simple linear regression model hypothesizes that the travel time of a driving assignment (y) is linearly related to the number of miles traveled (x) as follows:

SIMPLE LINEAR REGRESSION MODEL

$$y = \beta_0 + \beta_1 x + \varepsilon \quad \textbf{(7.1)}$$

In equation (7.1), β_0 and β_1 are population parameters that describe the y-intercept and slope of the line relating y and x. The error term ε (Greek letter epsilon) accounts for the variability in y that cannot be explained by the linear relationship between x and y. The simple linear regression model assumes that the error term is a normally distributed random variable with a mean of zero and constant variance for all observations.

Estimated Regression Equation

In practice, the values of the population parameters β_0 and β_1 are not known and must be estimated using sample data. Sample statistics (denoted b_0 and b_1) are computed as estimates of the population parameters β_0 and β_1. Substituting the values of the sample statistics b_0 and b_1 for β_0 and β_1 in equation (7.1) and dropping the error term (because its expected value is zero), we obtain the **estimated regression** for simple linear regression:

ESTIMATED SIMPLE LINEAR REGRESSION EQUATION

$$\hat{y} = b_0 + b_1 x \quad \textbf{(7.2)}$$

The estimation of β_0 and β_1 is a statistical process much like the estimation of the population mean, μ, discussed in Chapter 6. β_0 and β_1 are the unknown parameters of interest, and b_0 and b_1 are the sample statistics used to estimate the parameters.

FIGURE 7.1 The Estimation Process in Simple Linear Regression

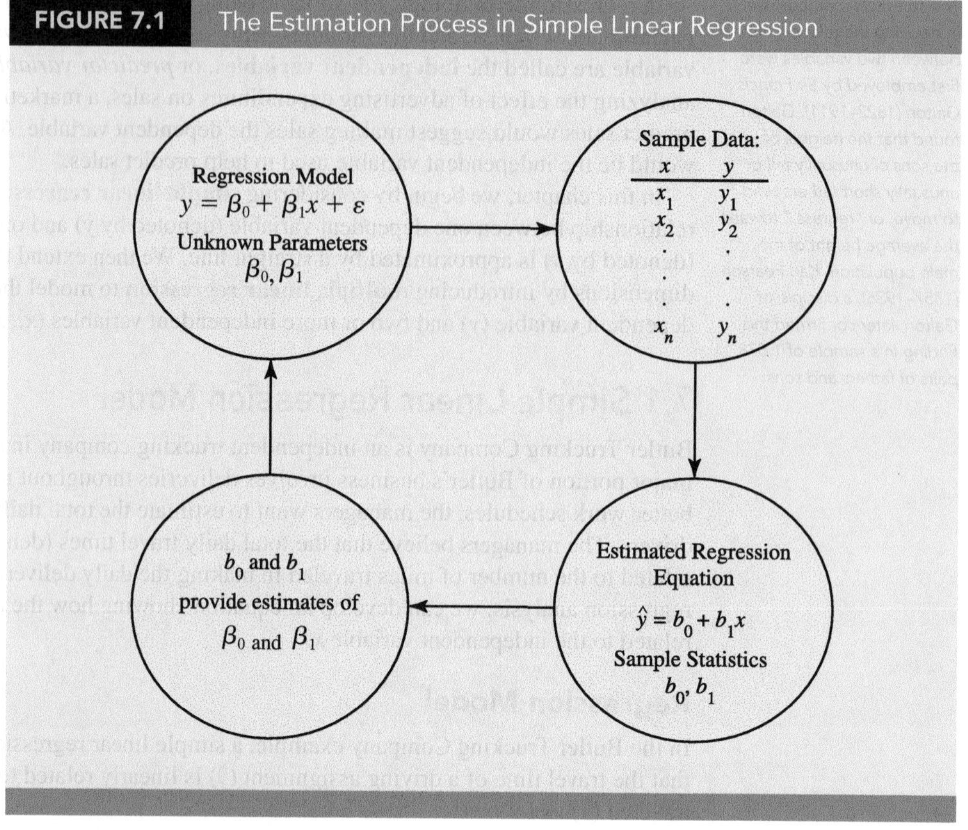

Figure 7.1 provides a summary of the estimation process for simple linear regression. Using equation (7.2), $\hat{y}$ provides an estimate for the mean value of y corresponding to a given value of x.

The graph of the estimated simple linear regression equation is called the *estimated regression line*; b_0 is the estimated y-intercept, and b_1 is the estimated slope. In the next section, we show how the least squares method can be used to compute the values of b_0 and b_1 in the estimated regression equation.

Examples of possible regression lines are shown in Figure 7.2. The regression line in Panel A shows that the estimated mean value of y is related positively to x, with larger values of $\hat{y}$ associated with larger values of x. In Panel B, the estimated mean value of y is related negatively to x, with smaller values of $\hat{y}$ associated with larger values of x. In Panel C, the estimated mean value of y is not related to x; that is, $\hat{y}$ is the same for every value of x.

In general, $\hat{y}$ is the **point estimator** of $E(y|x)$, the mean value of y for a given value of x. Thus, to estimate the mean or expected value of travel time for a driving assignment of 75 miles, Butler trucking would substitute the value of 75 for x in equation (7.2). In some cases, however, Butler Trucking may be more interested in predicting travel time for an upcoming driving assignment of a particular length. For example, suppose Butler Trucking would like to predict travel time for a new 75-mile driving assignment the company is considering. As it turns out, the best predictor of y for a given value of x is also provided by $\hat{y}$. Thus, to predict travel time for a new 75-mile driving assignment, Butler Trucking would also substitute the value of 75 for x in equation (7.3). The value of $\hat{y}$ provides both

A point estimator is a single value used as an estimate of the corresponding population parameter.

FIGURE 7.2 Possible Regression Lines in Simple Linear Regression

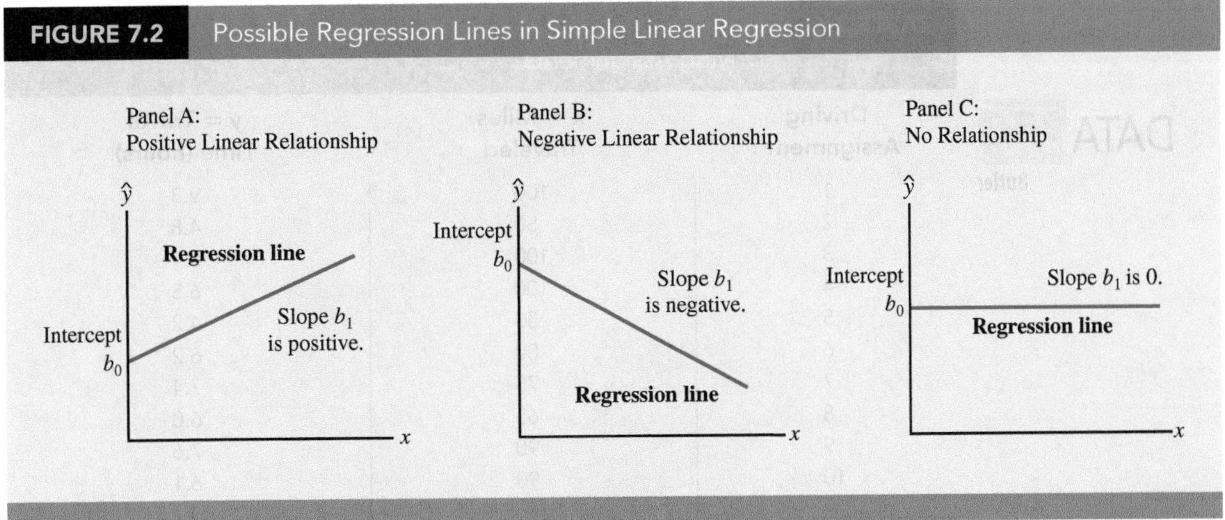

a point estimate of $E(y|x)$ for a given value of x and a prediction of an individual value of y for a given value of x. In most cases, we will refer to $\hat{y}$ simply as the predicted value of y.

7.2 Least Squares Method

The **least squares method** is a procedure for using sample data to find the estimated regression equation. To illustrate the least squares method, suppose data were collected from a sample of 10 Butler Trucking Company driving assignments. For the ith observation or driving assignment in the sample, x_i is the miles traveled and y_i is the travel time (in hours). The values of x_i and y_i for the 10 driving assignments in the sample are summarized in Table 7.1. We see that driving assignment 1, with $x_1 = 100$ and $y_1 = 9.3$, is a driving assignment of 100 miles and a travel time of 9.3 hours. Driving assignment 2, with $x_2 = 50$ and $y_2 = 4.8$, is a driving assignment of 50 miles and a travel time of 4.8 hours. The shortest travel time is for driving assignment 5, which requires 50 miles with a travel time of 4.2 hours.

Figure 7.3 is a scatter chart of the data in Table 7.1. Miles traveled is shown on the horizontal axis, and travel time (in hours) is shown on the vertical axis. Scatter charts for regression analysis are constructed with the independent variable x on the horizontal axis and the dependent variable y on the vertical axis. The scatter chart enables us to observe the data graphically and to draw preliminary conclusions about the possible relationship between the variables.

What preliminary conclusions can be drawn from Figure 7.3? Longer travel times appear to coincide with more miles traveled. In addition, for these data, the relationship between the travel time and miles traveled appears to be approximated by a straight line; indeed, a positive linear relationship is indicated between x and y. We therefore choose the simple linear regression model to represent this relationship. Given that choice, our next task is to use the sample data in Table 7.1 to determine the values of b_0 and b_1 in the estimated simple linear regression equation. For the ith driving assignment, the estimated regression equation provides:

$$\hat{y}_i = b_0 + b_1 x_i, \qquad (7.3)$$

where

$\hat{y}_i$ = predicted travel time (in hours) for the ith driving assignment
b_0 = the y-intercept of the estimated regression line

TABLE 7.1 Miles Traveled and Travel Time for 10 Butler Trucking Company Driving Assignments

Driving Assignment i	x = Miles Traveled	y = Travel Time (hours)
1	100	9.3
2	50	4.8
3	100	8.9
4	100	6.5
5	50	4.2
6	80	6.2
7	75	7.4
8	65	6.0
9	90	7.6
10	90	6.1

b_1 = the slope of the estimated regression line
x_i = miles traveled for the ith driving assignment

With y_i denoting the observed (actual) travel time for driving assignment i and $\hat{y}_i$ in equation (7.3) representing the predicted travel time for driving assignment i, every driving assignment in the sample will have an observed travel time y_i and a predicted travel time $\hat{y}_i$. For the estimated regression line to provide a good fit to the data, the differences between the observed travel times y_i and the predicted travel times $\hat{y}_i$ should be small.

The least squares method uses the sample data to provide the values of b_0 and b_1 that minimize the sum of the squares of the deviations between the observed values of the

FIGURE 7.3 Scatter Chart of Miles Traveled and Travel Time for Sample of 10 Butler Trucking Company Driving Assignments

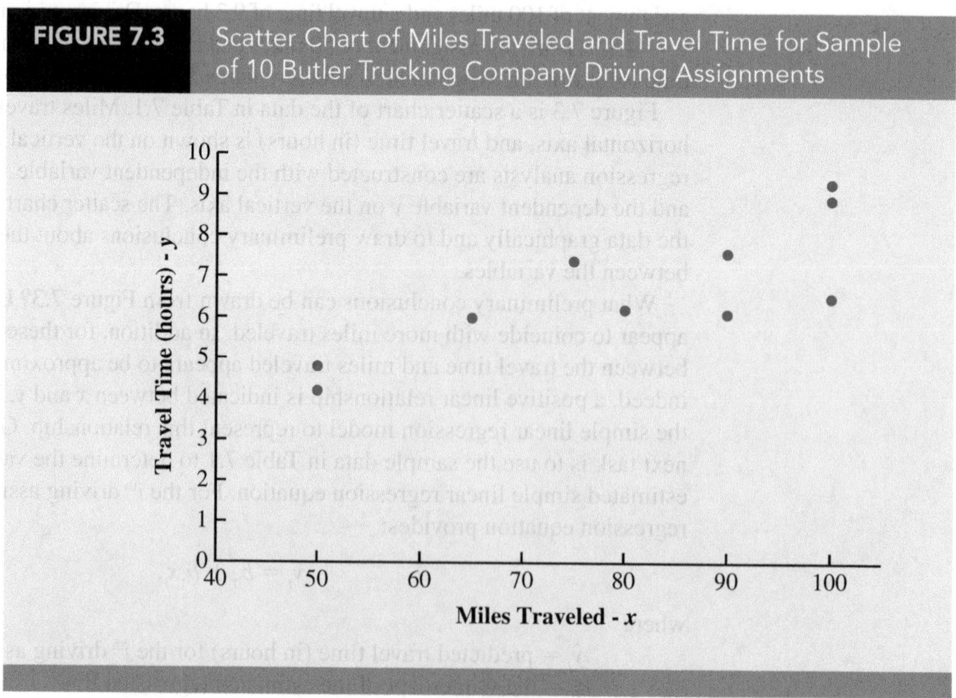

dependent variable y_i and the predicted values of the dependent variable $\hat{y}_i$. The criterion for the least squares method is given by equation (7.4).

LEAST SQUARES EQUATION

$$\min \sum_{i=1}^{n} (y_i - \hat{y}_i)^2 = \min \sum_{i=1}^{n} (y_1 - b_0 - b_1 x_i)^2 \tag{7.4}$$

where

y_i = observed value of the dependent variable for the ith observation
$\hat{y}_i$ = predicted value of the dependent variable for the ith observation
n = total number of observations

This is known as the least squares method for estimating the regression equation.

The error we make using the regression model to estimate the mean value of the dependent variable for the ith observation is often written as $e_i = y_i - \hat{y}_i$ and is referred to as the ith **residual**. Using this notation, equation (7.4) can be rewritten as:

$$\min \sum_{i=1}^{n} e_i^2$$

and we say that we are finding the regression that minimizes the sum of squared errors.

Least Squares Estimates of the Regression Parameters

Although the values of b_0 and b_1 that minimize equation (7.3) can be calculated manually with equations (see note at end of this section), computer software such as Excel or XLMiner is generally used to calculate b_1 and b_0. For the Butler Trucking Company data in Table 7.1, an estimated slope of $b_1 = 0.0678$ and a y-intercept of $b_0 = 1.2739$ minimize the sum of squared errors (in the next section we show how to use Excel to obtain these values). Thus, our estimated simple linear regression model is $\hat{y} = 1.2739 + 0.0678x_1$.

We interpret b_1 and b_0 as we would the y-intercept and slope of any straight line. The slope b_1 is the estimated change in the mean of the dependent variable y that is associated with a one-unit increase in the independent variable x. For the Butler Trucking Company model, we therefore estimate that, if the length of a driving assignment were 1 unit (1 mile) longer, the mean travel time for that driving assignment would be 0.0678 unit (0.0678 hour, or approximately 4 minutes) longer. The y-intercept b_0 is the estimated value of the dependent variable y when the independent variable x is equal to 0. For the Butler Trucking Company model, we estimate that if the driving distance for a driving assignment was 0 units (0 miles), the mean travel time would be 1.2739 units (1.2739 hours, or approximately 76 minutes). Can we find a plausible explanation for this? Perhaps the 76 minutes represent the time needed to prepare, load, and unload the vehicle, which is required for all trips regardless of distance and which therefore does not depend on the distance traveled. However, we must use caution: To estimate the travel time for a driving distance of 0 miles, we have to extend the relationship we have found with simple linear regression well beyond the range of values for driving distance in our sample. Those sample values range from 50 to 100 miles, and this range represents the only values of driving distance for which we have empirical evidence of the relationship between driving distance and our estimated travel time.

It is important to note that the regression model is valid only over the **experimental region**, which is the range of values of the independent variables in the data used to estimate the model. Prediction of the value of the dependent variable outside the experimental region is called **extrapolation** and is risky. Because we have no empirical evidence that the relationship we have found holds true for values of x outside of the range of values of x in

The estimated value of the y-intercept often results from extrapolation.

the data used to estimate the relationship, extrapolation is risky and should be avoided if possible. For Butler Trucking, this means that any prediction outside the travel time for a driving distance less than 50 miles or greater than 100 miles is not a reliable estimate, and so for this model the estimate of β_0 is meaningless. However, if the experimental region for a regression problem includes zero, the *y*-intercept will have a meaningful interpretation.

We can now also use this model and our known values for miles traveled for a driving assignment (x) to estimate mean travel time in hours. For example, the first driving assignment in Table 7.1 has a value for miles traveled of $x = 100$. We estimate the mean travel time in hours for this driving assignment to be:

The point estimate $\hat{y}$ provided by the regression equation does not give us any information about the precision associated with the prediction. For that we must develop an interval estimate around the point estimate. In the appendix at the end of the chapter, we demonstrate how to generate interval estimates around the point estimates provided by a regression equation.

$$\hat{y}_i = 1.2739 + 0.0678(100) = 8.0539.$$

Since the travel time for this driving assignment was 9.3 hours, this regression estimate would have resulted in a residual of:

$$e_1 = y_1 - \hat{y}_i = 9.3 - 8.0539 = 1.2461.$$

The simple linear regression model underestimated travel time for this driving assignment by 1.2461 hours (approximately 74 minutes). Table 7.2 shows the predicted mean travel times, the residuals, and the squared residuals for all 10 driving assignments in the sample data.

Note in Table 7.2 that:

- The sum of predicted values $\hat{y}_i$ is equal to the sum of the values of the dependent variable y.
- The sum of the residuals e_i is 0.
- The sum of the squared residuals e_i^2 has been minimized.

These three points will always be true for a simple linear regression that is determined by equations (7.6) and (7.7). Figure 7.4 shows the simple linear regression line $\hat{y}_i = 1.2739 + 0.0678x_i$ superimposed on the scatter chart for the Butler Trucking Company data in Table 7.1. This figure, which also highlights the residuals for driving assignment 3 (e_3) and driving assignment 5 (e_5), shows that the regression model underpredicts travel time for some driving assignments (such as driving assignment 3) and overpredicts travel time for others (such as driving assignment 5), but in general appears to fit the data relatively well.

TABLE 7.2 Predicted Travel Time and Residuals for 10 Butler Trucking Company Driving Assignments

Driving Assignment i	x = Miles Traveled	y = Travel Time (hours)	$\hat{y}_i = b_0 + b_1x_i$	$e_i = y_i - \hat{y}_i$	e_i^2
1	100	9.3	8.0565	1.2435	1.5463
2	50	4.8	4.6652	0.1348	0.0182
3	100	8.9	8.0565	0.8435	0.7115
4	100	6.5	8.0565	−1.5565	2.4227
5	50	4.2	4.6652	−0.4652	0.2164
6	80	6.2	6.7000	−0.5000	0.2500
7	75	7.4	6.3609	1.0391	1.0797
8	65	6.0	5.6826	0.3174	0.1007
9	90	7.6	7.3783	0.2217	0.0492
10	90	6.1	7.3783	−1.2783	1.6341
	Totals	67.0	67.0000	0.0000	8.0288

FIGURE 7.4 Scatter Chart of Miles Traveled and Travel Time for Butler Trucking Company Driving Assignments with Regression Line Superimposed

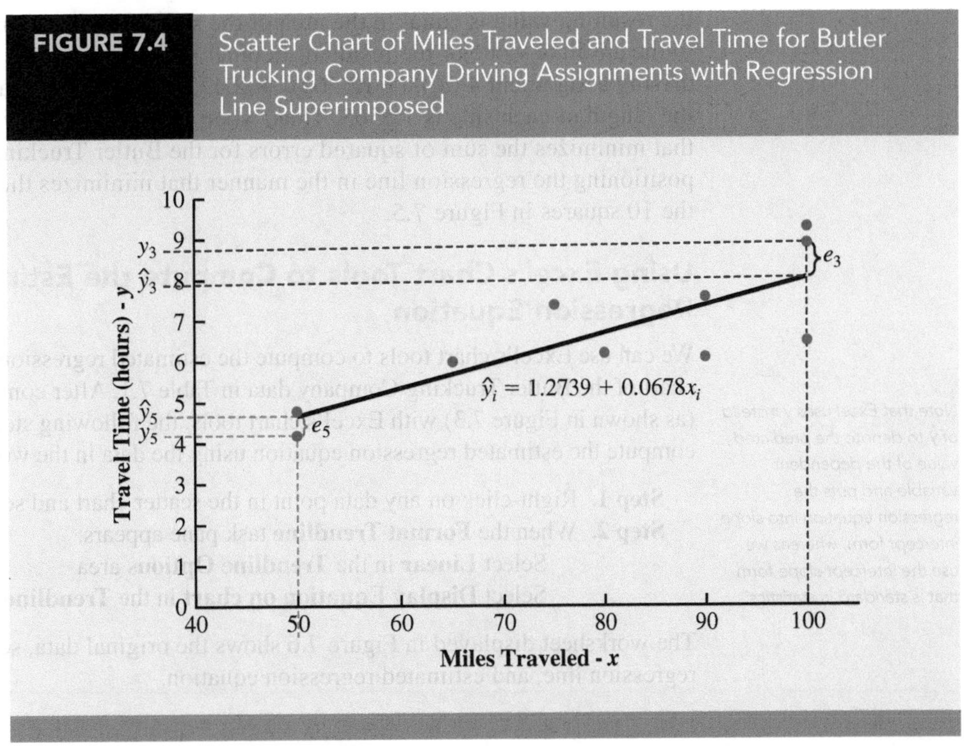

In Figure 7.5, a vertical line is drawn from each point in the scatter chart to the linear regression line. Each of these vertical lines represents the difference between the actual driving time and the driving time we predict using linear regression for one of the assignments in our data. The length of each vertical line is equal to the absolute value of the residual for one of the driving assignments. When we square a residual,

FIGURE 7.5 A Geometric Interpretation of the Least Squares Method

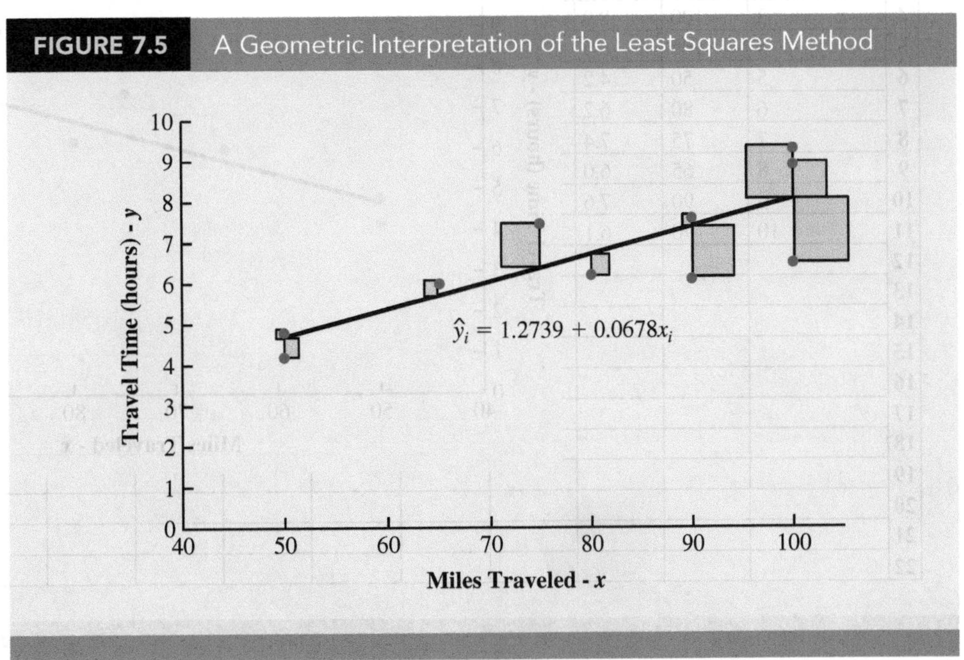

the resulting value is equal to the area of the square with the length of each side equal to the absolute value of the residual. In other words, the square of the residual for driving assignment 4 (e_4), $(-1.5565)^2 = 2.4227$, is the area of a square for which the length of each side is 1.5565. Thus, when we find the linear regression model that minimizes the sum of squared errors for the Butler Trucking example, we are positioning the regression line in the manner that minimizes the sum of the areas of the 10 squares in Figure 7.5.

Using Excel's Chart Tools to Compute the Estimated Regression Equation

Note that Excel uses y instead of $\hat{y}$ to denote the predicted value of the dependent variable and puts the regression equation into slope-intercept form, whereas we use the intercept-slope form that is standard in statistics.

We can use Excel's chart tools to compute the estimated regression equation on a scatter chart of the Butler Trucking Company data in Table 7.1. After constructing a scatter chart (as shown in Figure 7.3) with Excel's chart tools, the following steps describe how to compute the estimated regression equation using the data in the worksheet:

Step 1. Right-click on any data point in the scatter chart and select **Add Trendline . . .**
Step 2. When the **Format Trendline** task pane appears:
Select **Linear** in the **Trendline Options** area
Select **Display Equation on chart** in the **Trendline Options** area

The worksheet displayed in Figure 7.6 shows the original data, scatter chart, estimated regression line, and estimated regression equation.

FIGURE 7.6 Scatter Chart and Estimated Regression Line for Butler Trucking Company

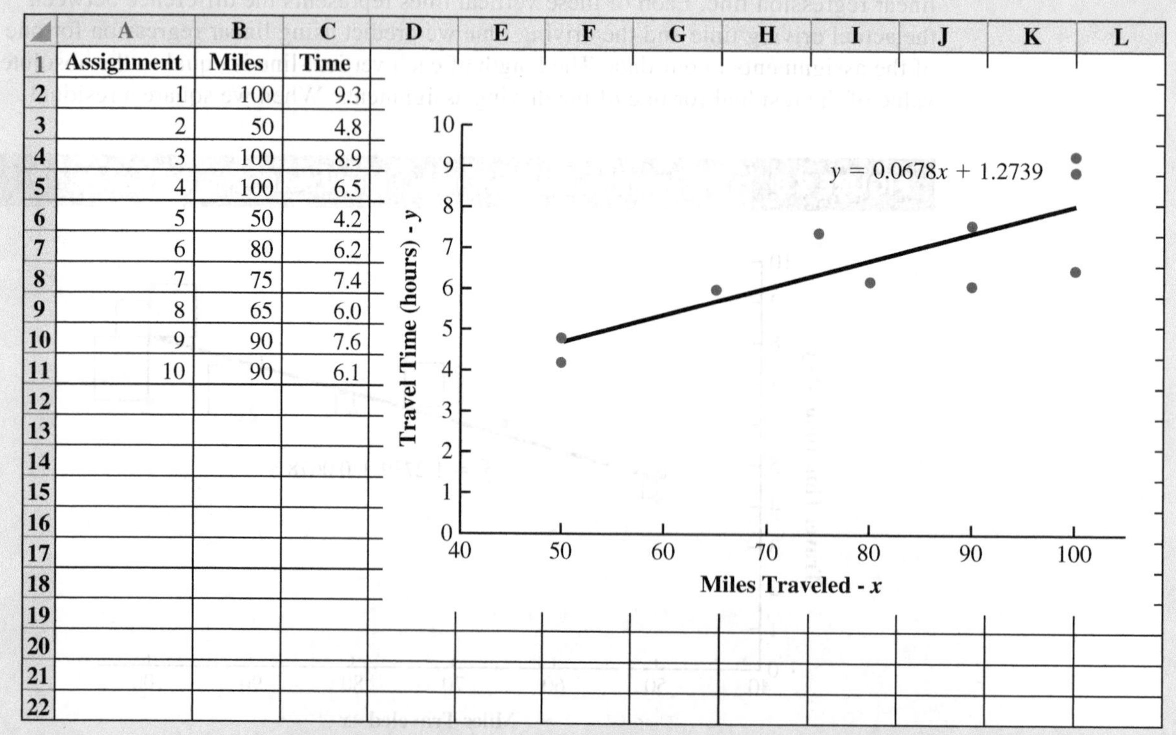

	A	B	C
1	Assignment	Miles	Time
2	1	100	9.3
3	2	50	4.8
4	3	100	8.9
5	4	100	6.5
6	5	50	4.2
7	6	80	6.2
8	7	75	7.4
9	8	65	6.0
10	9	90	7.6
11	10	90	6.1

NOTES + COMMENTS

1. Differential calculus can be used to show that the values of b_0 and b_1 that minimize expression (7.5) are given by:

SLOPE EQUATION

$$b_1 = \frac{\sum_{i=1}^{n}(x_i - \bar{x})(y_i - \bar{y})}{\sum_{i=1}^{n}(x_i - \bar{x})^2}$$

***y*-INTERCEPT EQUATION**

$$b_0 = \bar{y} - b_1\bar{x}$$

where

x_i = value of the independent variable for the ith observation
y_i = value of the dependent variable for the ith observation
$\bar{x}$ = mean value for the independent variable
$\bar{y}$ = mean value for the dependent variable
n = total number of observations

2. Equation 7.5 minimizes the sum of the squared deviations between the observed values of the dependent variable y_i and the predicted values of the dependent variable $\hat{y}_i$. One alternative is to simply minimize the sum of the deviations between the observed values of the dependent variable y_i and the predicted values of the dependent variable $\hat{y}_i$. This is not a viable option because then negative deviations (observations for which the regression forecast exceeds the actual value) and positive deviations (observations for which the regression forecast is less than the actual value) offset each other. Another alternative is to minimize the sum of the absolute value of the deviations between the observed values of the dependent variable y_i and the predicted values of the dependent variable $\hat{y}_i$. It is possible to compute estimated regression parameters that minimize this sum of the absolute value of the deviations, but this approach is more difficult than the least squares approach.

7.3 Assessing the Fit of the Simple Linear Regression Model

For the Butler Trucking Company example, we developed the estimated regression equation $\hat{y}_i = 1.2739 + 0.0678x_i$ to approximate the linear relationship between the miles traveled x and travel time in hours y. We now wish to assess how well the estimated regression equation fits the sample data. We begin by developing the intermediate calculations, referred to as sums of squares.

The Sums of Squares

Recall that we found our estimated regression equation for the Butler Trucking Company example by minimizing the sum of squares of the residuals. This quantity, also known as the *sum of squares due to error*, is denoted by SSE.

SUM OF SQUARES DUE TO ERROR

$$\text{SSE} = \sum_{i=1}^{n}(y_i - \hat{y}_i)^2 \quad \textbf{(7.5)}$$

The value of SSE is a measure of the error (in the same units as the dependent variable) that results from using the estimated regression equation to predict the values of the dependent variable in the sample.

We have already shown the calculations required to compute the sum of squares due to error for the Butler Trucking Company example in Table 7.2. The squared residual or error for each observation in the data is shown in the last column of that table. After computing and squaring

FIGURE 7.7 The Sample Mean $\bar{y}$ as a Predictor of Travel Time for Butler Trucking Company

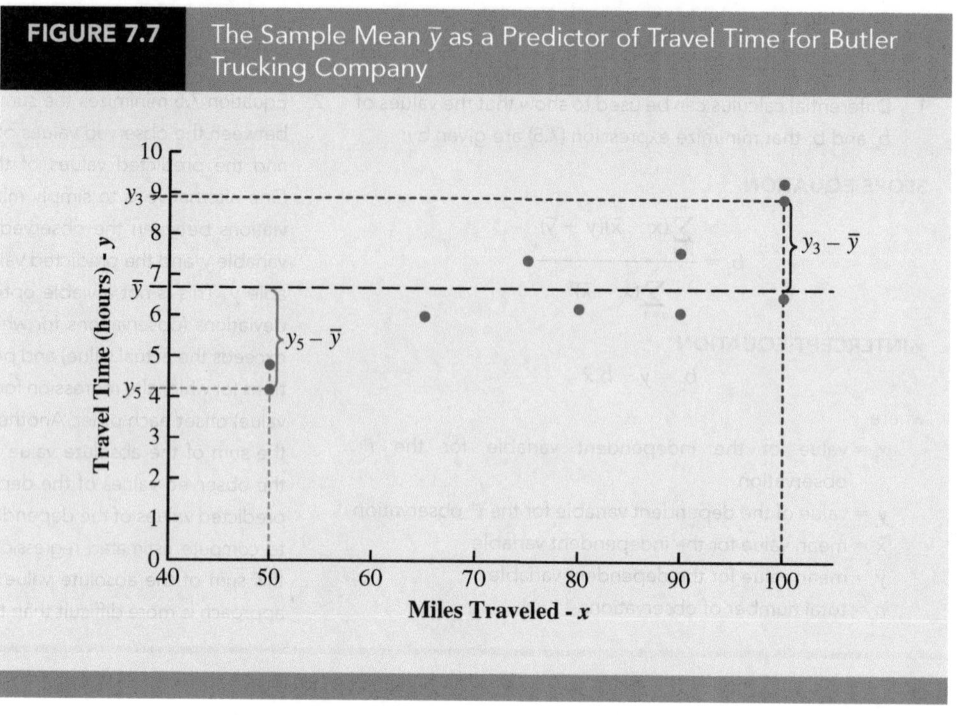

the residuals for each driving assignment in the sample, we sum them to obtain SSE = 8.0288 hours. Thus, SSE = 8.0288 measures the error in using the estimated regression equation $\hat{y}_i = 1.2739 + 0.0678x_i$ to predict travel time for the driving assignments in the sample.

Now suppose we are asked to predict travel time in hours without knowing the miles traveled for a driving assignment. Without knowledge of any related variables, we would use the sample mean $\bar{y}$ as a predictor of travel time for any given driving assignment. To find $\bar{y}$, we divide the sum of the actual driving times y_i from Table 7.2 (67) by the number of observations n in the data (10); this yields $\bar{y} = 6.7$.

Figure 7.7 provides insight on how well we would predict the values of y_i in the Butler Trucking company example using $\bar{y} = 6.7$. From this figure, which again highlights the residuals for driving assignments 3 and 5, we can see that $\bar{y}$ tends to overpredict travel times for driving assignments that have relatively small values for miles traveled (such as driving assignment 5) and tends to underpredict travel times for driving assignments that have relatively large values for miles traveled (such as driving assignment 3).

In Table 7.3 we show the sum of squared deviations obtained by using the sample mean $\bar{y} = 6.7$ to predict the value of travel time in hours for each driving assignment in the sample. For the ith driving assignment in the sample, the difference $y_i - \bar{y}$ provides a measure of the error involved in using $\bar{y}$ to predict travel time for the ith driving assignment. The corresponding sum of squares, called the total sum of squares, is denoted SST.

TOTAL SUM OF SQUARES, SST

$$\text{SST} = \sum_{i=1}^{n} (y_i - \bar{y})^2 \tag{7.6}$$

TABLE 7.3 Calculations for the Sum of Squares Total for the Butler Trucking Simple Linear Regression

Driving Assignment i	x = Miles Traveled	y = Travel Time (hours)	$y_i - \bar{y}$	$(y_i - \bar{y})^2$
1	100	9.3	2.6	6.76
2	50	4.8	−1.9	3.61
3	100	8.9	2.2	4.84
4	100	6.5	−0.2	0.04
5	50	4.2	−2.5	6.25
6	80	6.2	−0.5	0.25
7	75	7.4	0.7	0.49
8	65	6.0	−0.7	0.49
9	90	7.6	0.9	0.81
10	90	6.1	2.6	6.76
	Totals	67.0	0	23.9

The sum at the bottom of the last column in Table 7.3 is the total sum of squares for Butler Trucking Company: SST = 23.9.

Now we put it all together. In Figure 7.8 we show the estimated regression line $\hat{y}_i = 1.2739 + 0.0678x_i$ and the line corresponding to $\bar{y} = 6.7$. Note that the points cluster more closely around the estimated regression line $\hat{y}_i = 1.2739 + 0.0678x_i$ than they do about the horizontal line $\bar{y} = 6.7$. For example, for the third driving assignment in the sample, we see that the error is much larger when $\bar{y} = 6.7$ is used to predict y_3 than when $\hat{y}_3 = 1.2739 + 0.0678\,(100) = 8.0539$ is used. We can think of SST as a measure of

FIGURE 7.8 Deviations About the Estimated Regression Line and the Line $y = \bar{y}$ for the Third Butler Trucking Company Driving Assignment

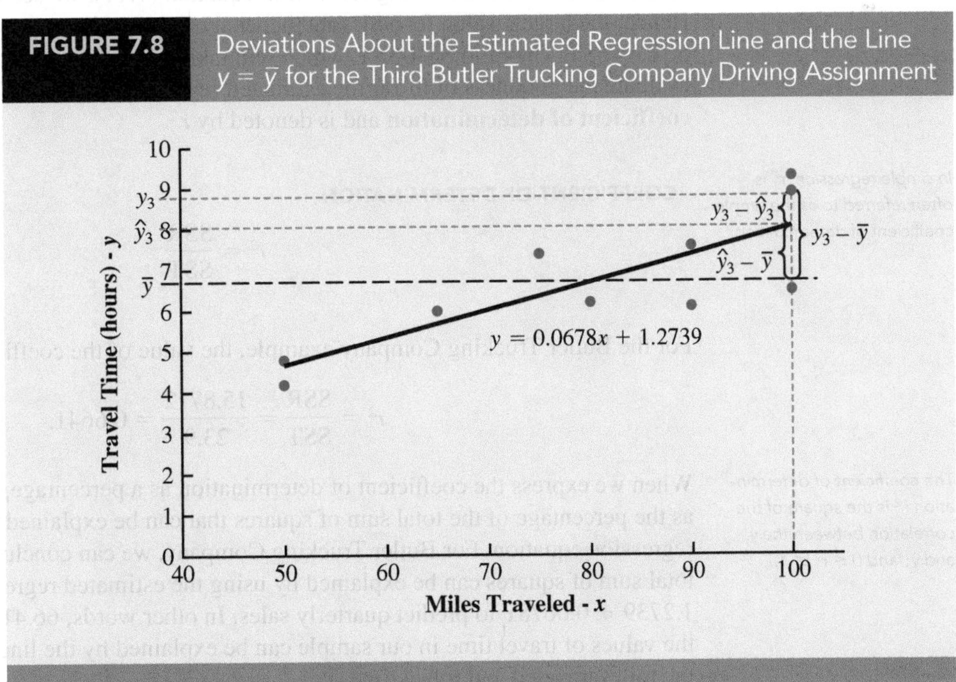

how well the observations cluster about the $\bar{y}$ line and SSE as a measure of how well the observations cluster about the $\hat{y}$ line.

To measure how much the $\hat{y}$ values on the estimated regression line deviate from $\bar{y}$, another sum of squares is computed. This sum of squares, called the *sum of squares due to regression*, is denoted SSR.

SUM OF SQUARES DUE TO REGRESSION, SSR

$$SSR = \sum_{i=1}^{n} (\hat{y}_i - \bar{y})^2 \tag{7.7}$$

From the preceding discussion, we should expect that SST, SSR, and SSE are related. Indeed, the relationship among these three sums of squares is:

$$SST = SSR + SSE, \tag{7.8}$$

where

SST = total sum of squares
SSR = sum of squares due to regression
SSE = sum of squares due to error

The Coefficient of Determination

Now let us see how the three sums of squares, SST, SSR, and SSE, can be used to provide a measure of the goodness of fit for the estimated regression equation. The estimated regression equation would provide a perfect fit if every value of the dependent variable y_i happened to lie on the estimated regression line. In this case, $y_i - \hat{y}$ would be zero for each observation, resulting in SSE = 0. Because SST = SSR + SSE, we see that for a perfect fit SSR must equal SST, and the ratio (SSR/SST) must equal one. Poorer fits will result in larger values for SSE. Solving for SSE in equation (7.11), we see that SSE = SST − SSR. Hence, the largest value for SSE (and hence the poorest fit) occurs when SSR = 0 and SSE = SST. The ratio SSR/SST, which will take values between zero and one, is used to evaluate the goodness of fit for the estimated regression equation. This ratio is called the **coefficient of determination** and is denoted by r^2.

In simple regression, r^2 is often referred to as the simple coefficient of determination.

COEFFICIENT OF DETERMINATION

$$r^2 = \frac{SSR}{SST} \tag{7.9}$$

For the Butler Trucking Company example, the value of the coefficient of determination is:

$$r^2 = \frac{SSR}{SST} = \frac{15.8712}{23.9} = 0.6641.$$

The coefficient of determination r^2 is the square of the correlation between the y_i and $\hat{y}_i$, and $0 \le r^2 \le 1$.

When we express the coefficient of determination as a percentage, r^2 can be interpreted as the percentage of the total sum of squares that can be explained by using the estimated regression equation. For Butler Trucking Company, we can conclude that 66.41% of the total sum of squares can be explained by using the estimated regression equation $\hat{y}_i = 1.2739 + 0.0678x_i$ to predict quarterly sales. In other words, 66.41% of the variability in the values of travel time in our sample can be explained by the linear relationship between the miles traveled and travel time.

FIGURE 7.9 Scatter Chart and Estimated Regression Line with Coefficient of Determination r^2 for Butler Trucking Company

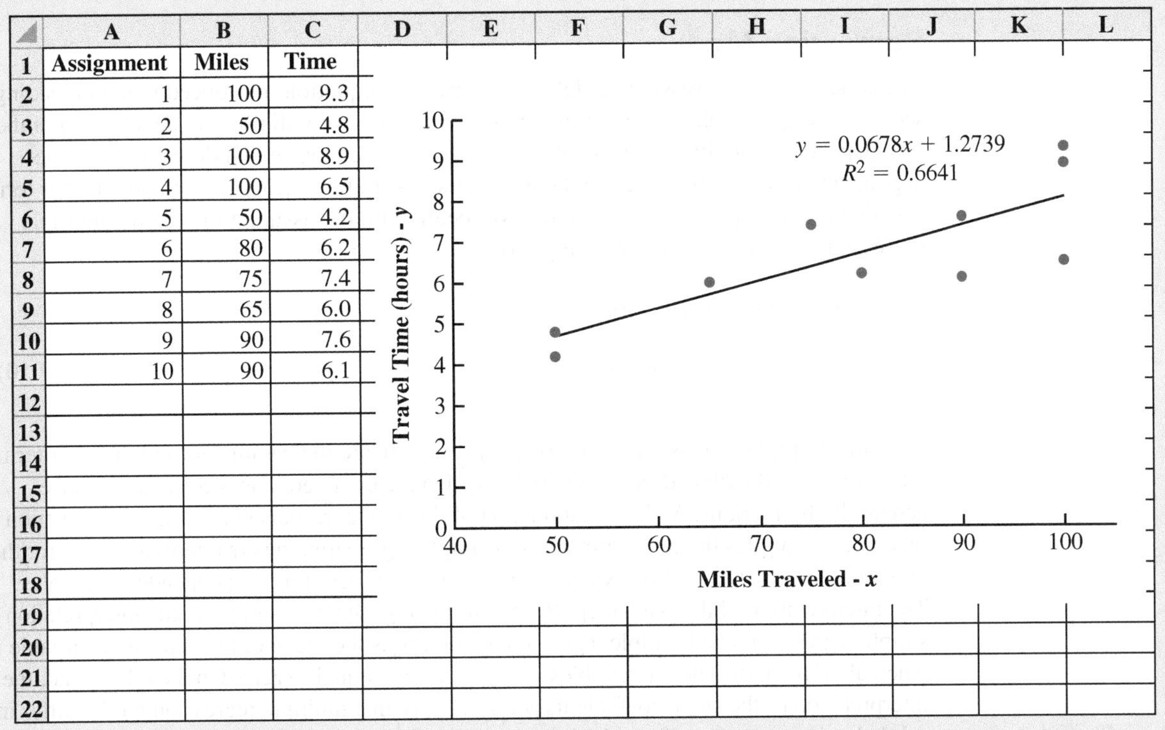

	A	B	C
1	Assignment	Miles	Time
2	1	100	9.3
3	2	50	4.8
4	3	100	8.9
5	4	100	6.5
6	5	50	4.2
7	6	80	6.2
8	7	75	7.4
9	8	65	6.0
10	9	90	7.6
11	10	90	6.1

Using Excel's Chart Tools to Compute the Coefficient of Determination

In Section 7.1 we used Excel's chart tools to construct a scatter chart and compute the estimated regression equation for the Butler Trucking Company data. We will now describe how to compute the coefficient of determination using the scatter chart in Figure 7.3.

Step 1. Right-click on any data point in the scatter chart and select **Add Trendline. . .**
Step 2. When the **Format Trendline** task pane appears:
Select **Display R-squared value on chart** in the **Trendline Options** area

Note that Excel notates the coefficient of determination as R^2.

Figure 7.9 displays the scatter chart, the estimated regression equation, the graph of the estimated regression equation, and the coefficient of determination for the Butler Trucking Company data. We see that $r^2 = 0.6641$.

NOTES + COMMENTS

As a practical matter, for typical data in the social and behavioral sciences, values of r^2 as low as 0.25 are often considered useful. For data in the physical and life sciences, r^2 values of 0.60 or greater are often found; in fact, in some cases, r^2 values greater than 0.90 can be found. In business applications, r^2 values vary greatly, depending on the unique characteristics of each application.

7.4 The Multiple Regression Model

We now extend our discussion to the study of how a dependent variable y is related to two or more independent variables.

Regression Model

The concepts of a regression model and a regression equation introduced in the preceding sections are applicable in the multiple regression case. We will use q to denote the number of independent variables in the regression model. The equation that describes how the dependent variable y is related to the independent variables $x_1, x_2, \ldots, x_q$ and an error term is called the multiple regression model. We begin with the assumption that the multiple regression model takes the following form:

MULTIPLE REGRESSION MODEL

$$y = \beta_0 + \beta_1 x_1 + \beta_2 x_2 + \cdots + \beta_q x_q + \varepsilon \quad \textbf{(7.10)}$$

In the multiple regression model, $\beta_0, \beta_1, \beta_2, \ldots, \beta_q$ are the parameters and the error term ε is a normally distributed random variable with a mean of zero and a constant variance across all observations. A close examination of this model reveals that y is a linear function of $x_1, x_2, \ldots, x_q$ plus the error term ε. As in simple regression, the error term accounts for the variability in y that cannot be explained by the linear effect of the q independent variables. The interpretation of the y-intercept β_0 in multiple regression is similar to the interpretation in simple regression; in a multiple regression model, β_0 is the mean of the dependent variable y when all of the independent variables $x_1, x_2, \ldots, x_q$ are equal to zero. On the other hand, the interpretation of the slope coefficients $\beta_1, \beta_2, \ldots, \beta_q$ in a multiple regression model differ in a subtle but important way from the interpretation of the slope β_1 in a simple regression model. In a multiple regression model the slope coefficient β_j represents the change in the mean value of the dependent variable y that corresponds to a one-unit increase in the independent variable x_j, *holding the values of all other independent variables in the model constant.* Thus, in a multiple regression model, the slope coefficient β_1 represents the change in the mean value of the dependent variable y that corresponds to a one-unit increase in the independent variable x_1, holding the values of $x_2, x_3, \ldots, x_q$ constant. Similarly, the slope coefficient β_2 represents the change in the mean value of the dependent variable y that corresponds to a one-unit increase in the independent variable x_2, holding the values of $x_1, x_3, \ldots, x_q$ constant.

Estimated Multiple Regression Equation

In practice, the values of the population parameters $\beta_0, \beta_1, \beta_2, \ldots, \beta_q$ are not known and so must be estimated from sample data. A simple random sample is used to compute sample statistics $b_0, b_1, b_2, \ldots, b_q$ that are then used as the point estimators of the parameters $\beta_0, \beta_1, \beta_2, \ldots, \beta_q$. These sample statistics provide the following estimated multiple regression equation.

ESTIMATED MULTIPLE REGRESSION EQUATION

$$\hat{y} = b_0 + b_1 x_1 + b_2 x_2 + \cdots + b_q x_q, \quad \textbf{(7.11)}$$

where

$b_0, b_1, b_2, \ldots, b_q$ = the point estimates of $\beta_0, \beta_1, \beta_2, \ldots, \beta_q$

$\hat{y}$ = estimated mean value of y given values for $x_1, \ldots, x_q$

Least Squares Method and Multiple Regression

As with simple linear regression, in multiple regression we wish to find a model that results in small errors over the sample data. We continue to use the least squares method to develop the estimated multiple regression equation; that is, we find b_0, b_1, b_2, . . . , b_q that minimize the sum of squared residuals (the deviations between the observed values of the dependent variable y_i and the estimated values of the dependent variable $\hat{y}$):

$$\min \sum_{i=1}^{n} (y_i - \hat{y}_i)^2 = \min \sum_{i=1}^{n} (y_i - b_0 - b_1x_1 - \cdots - b_qx_q)^2 = \min \sum_{i=1}^{n} e_i^2. \tag{7.12}$$

The estimation process for multiple regression is shown in Figure 7.10.

The estimated values of the dependent variable y are computed by substituting values of the independent variables $x_1, x_2, \ldots, x_q$ into the estimated multiple regression equation (7.11).

As in simple regression, it is possible to derive formulas that determine the values of the regression coefficients that minimize equation (7.12). However, these formulas involve the use of matrix algebra and are outside the scope of this text. Therefore, in presenting multiple regression, we focus on how computer software packages can be used to obtain the estimated regression equation and other information. The emphasis will be on how to construct and interpret a regression model.

FIGURE 7.10 The Estimation Process for Multiple Regression

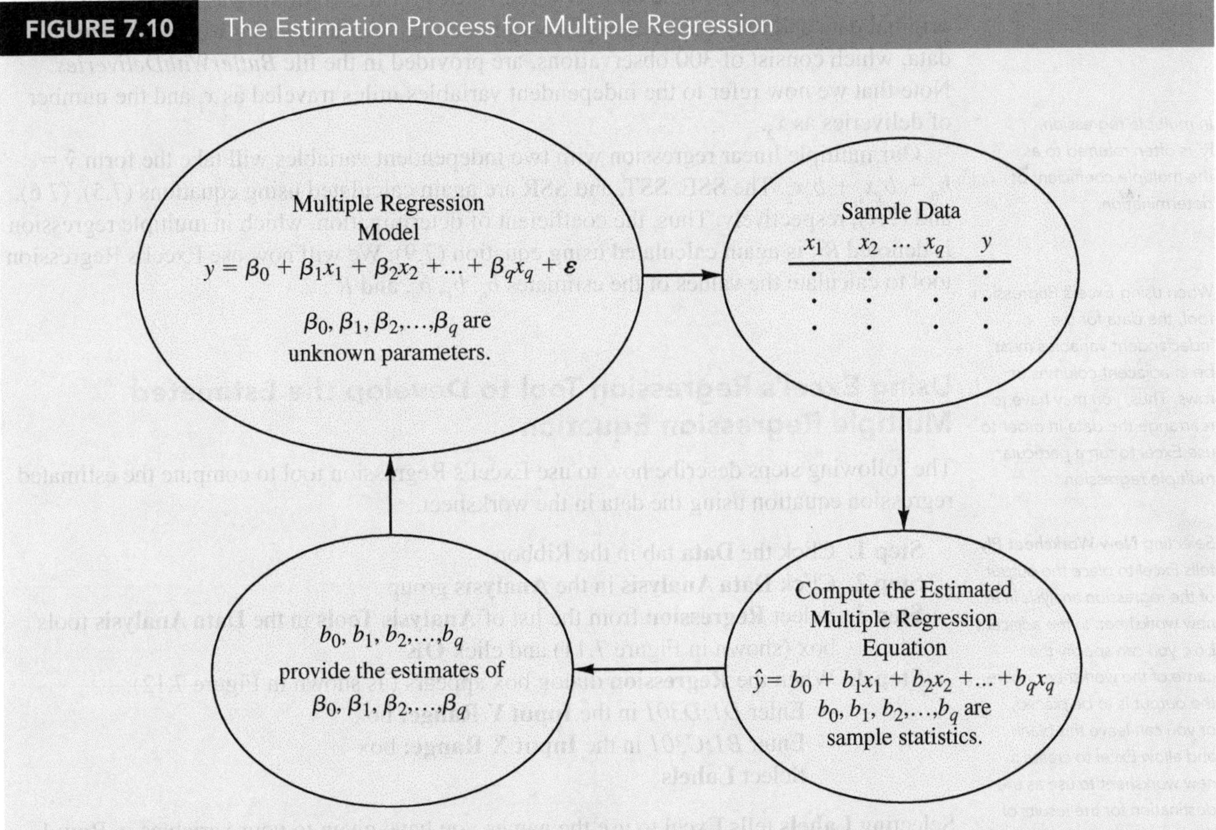

Butler Trucking Company and Multiple Regression

As an illustration of multiple regression analysis, recall that a major portion of Butler Trucking Company's business involves deliveries throughout its local area and that the managers want to estimate the total daily travel time for their drivers in order to develop better work schedules for the company's drivers.

Initially, the managers believed that the total daily travel time would be closely related to the number of miles traveled in making the daily deliveries. Based on a simple random sample of 10 driving assignments, we explored the simple linear regression model $y = \beta_0 + \beta_1 x + \varepsilon$ to describe the relationship between travel time (y) and number of miles (x). As Figure 7.9 shows, we found that the estimated simple linear regression equation for our sample data is $\hat{y}_i = 1.2739 + 0.0678x_i$. With a coefficient of determination $r^2 = 0.6641$, the linear effect of the number of miles traveled explains 66.41% of the variability in travel time in the sample data, and so 33.59% of the variability in sample travel times remains unexplained. This result suggests to Butler's managers that other factors may contribute to the travel times for driving assignments. The managers might want to consider adding one or more independent variables to the model to explain some of the remaining variability in the dependent variable.

ButlerWithDeliveries

In considering other independent variables for their model, the managers felt that the number of deliveries made on a driving assignment also contributes to the total travel time. To support the development of a multiple regression model that includes both the number of miles traveled and the number of deliveries, they augment their original data with information on the number of deliveries for the 10 driving assignments in the original data and they collect new observations over several ensuing weeks. The new data, which consist of 300 observations, are provided in the file *ButlerWithDeliveries*. Note that we now refer to the independent variables miles traveled as x_1 and the number of deliveries as x_2.

In multiple regression, R^2 is often referred to as the multiple coefficient of determination.

Our multiple linear regression with two independent variables will take the form $\hat{y} = b_0 + b_1x_1 + b_2x_2$. The SSE, SST, and SSR are again calculated using equations (7.5), (7.6), and (7.7), respectively. Thus, the coefficient of determination, which in multiple regression is denoted R^2, is again calculated using equation (7.9). We will now use Excel's Regression tool to calculate the values of the estimates b_0, b_1, b_2, and R^2.

When using Excel's Regression tool, the data for the independent variables must be in adjacent columns or rows. Thus, you may have to rearrange the data in order to use Excel to run a particular multiple regression.

Using Excel's Regression Tool to Develop the Estimated Multiple Regression Equation

The following steps describe how to use Excel's Regression tool to compute the estimated regression equation using the data in the worksheet.

*Selecting **New Worksheet Ply:** tells Excel to place the output of the regression analysis in a new worksheet. In the adjacent box, you can specify the name of the worksheet where the output is to be placed, or you can leave this blank and allow Excel to create a new worksheet to use as the destination for the results of this regression analysis (as we are doing here).*

Step 1. Click the **Data** tab in the Ribbon
Step 2. Click **Data Analysis** in the **Analysis** group
Step 3. Select **Regression** from the list of **Analysis Tools** in the **Data Analysis** tools box (shown in Figure 7.11) and click **OK**
Step 4. When the **Regression** dialog box appears (as shown in Figure 7.12):
Enter *D1:D301* in the **Input Y Range:** box
Enter *B1:C301* in the **Input X Range:** box
Select **Labels**

Selecting **Labels** tells Excel to use the names you have given to your variables in Row 1 when displaying the regression model output.

If Data Analysis does not appear in your Analysis group, you will have to load the Analysis ToolPak add-in into Excel. To do so, click the ***FILE*** *tab in the Ribbon, and click* ***Options****. When the* ***Excel Options*** *dialog box appears, click* ***Add-Ins*** *from the menu. Next to* ***Manage:****, select* ***Excel Add-ins****, and click* ***Go. . .*** *at the bottom of the dialog box. When the* ***Add-Ins*** *dialog box appears, select* ***Analysis ToolPak*** *and click* ***Go.*** *When the* ***Add-Ins*** *dialog box appears, check the box next to* ***Analysis Toolpak*** *and click* ***OK.***

FIGURE 7.11 Data Analysis Tools Box

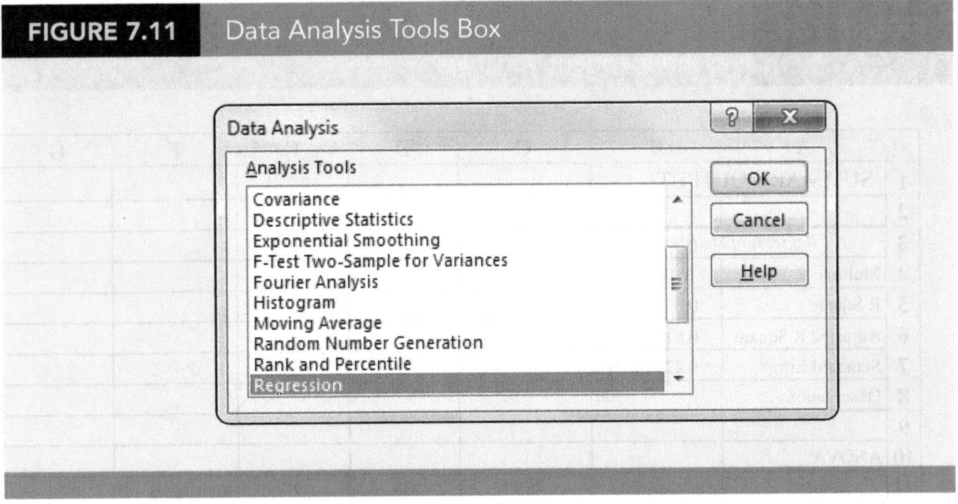

Select **Confidence Level:**
Enter *99* in the **Confidence Level:** box
Select **New Worksheet Ply:**
Click **OK**

In the Excel output shown in Figure 7.13, the label for the independent variable x_1 is Miles (see cell A18), and the label for the independent variable x_2 is Deliveries (see cell A19). The estimated regression equation is:

$$\hat{y} = 0.1273 + 0.0672x_1 + 0.6900x_2 \tag{7.13}$$

FIGURE 7.12 Regression Dialog Box

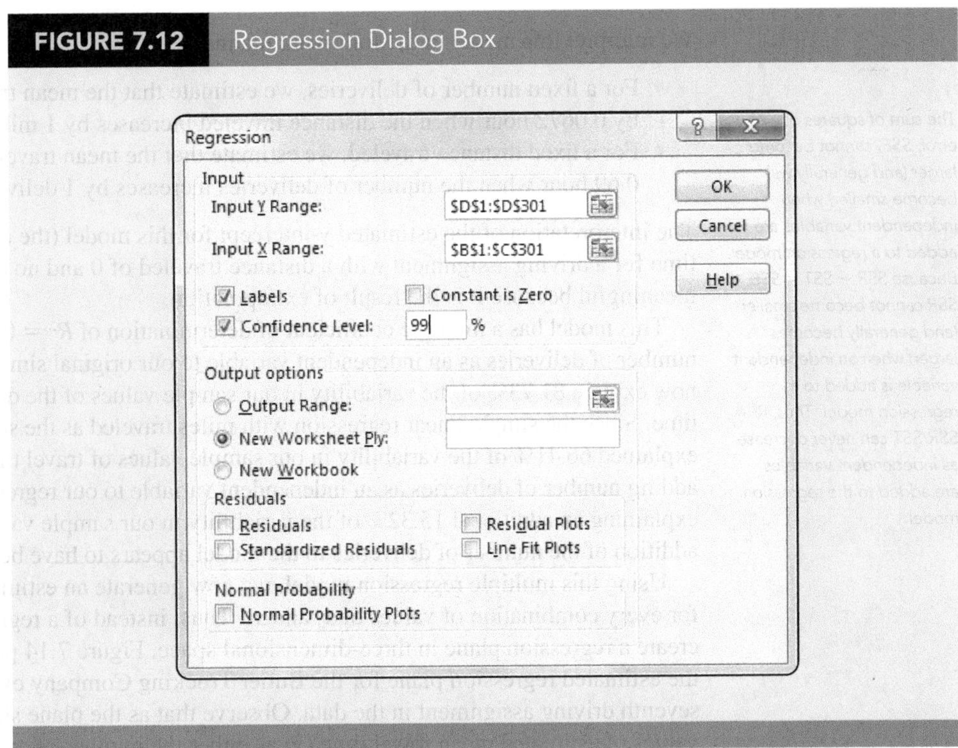

FIGURE 7.13 Excel Regression Output for the Butler Trucking Company with Miles and Deliveries as Independent Variables

	A	B	C	D	E	F	G	H	I
1	SUMMARY OUTPUT								
2									
3	*Regression Statistics*								
4	Multiple R	0.90407397							
5	R Square	0.817349743							
6	Adjusted R Square	0.816119775							
7	Standard Error	0.829967216							
8	Observations	300							
9									
10	ANOVA								
11		*df*	*SS*	*MS*	*F*	*Significance F*			
12	Regression	2	915.5160626	457.7580313	664.5292419	2.2419E-110			
13	Residual	297	204.5871374	0.68884558					
14	Total	299	1120.1032						
15									
16		*Coefficients*	*Standard Error*	*t Stat*	*P-value*	*Lower 95%*	*Upper 95%*	*Lower 99.0%*	*Upper 99.0%*
17	Intercept	0.127337137	0.20520348	0.620540826	0.53537766	−0.276499931	0.531174204	−0.404649592	0.659323866
18	Miles	0.067181742	0.002454979	27.36551071	3.5398E-83	0.062350385	0.072013099	0.06081725	0.073546235
19	Deliveries	0.68999828	0.029521057	23.37308852	2.84826E-69	0.631901326	0.748095234	0.613465414	0.766531147

We interpret this model in the following manner:

- For a fixed number of deliveries, we estimate that the mean travel time will increase by 0.0672 hour when the distance traveled increases by 1 mile.
- For a fixed distance traveled, we estimate that the mean travel time will increase by 0.69 hour when the number of deliveries increases by 1 delivery.

The sum of squares due to error, SSE, cannot become larger (and generally will become smaller) when independent variables are added to a regression model. Because SSR − SST = SSE, the SSR cannot become smaller (and generally becomes larger) when an independent variable is added to a regression model. Thus, R^2 = SSR/SST can never decrease as independent variables are added to the regression model.

The interpretation of the estimated y-intercept for this model (the expected mean travel time for a driving assignment with a distance traveled of 0 and no deliveries) is not meaningful because it is the result of extrapolation.

This model has a multiple coefficient of determination of $R^2 = 0.8173$. By adding the number of deliveries as an independent variable to our original simple linear regression, we now explain 81.73% of the variability in our sample values of the dependent variable, travel time. Since the simple linear regression with miles traveled as the sole independent variable explained 66.41% of the variability in our sample values of travel time, we can see that adding number of deliveries as an independent variable to our regression model resulted in explaining an additional 15.32% of the variability in our sample values of travel time. The addition of the number of deliveries to the model appears to have been worthwhile.

Using this multiple regression model, we now generate an estimated mean value of y for every combination of values of x_1 and x_2. Thus, instead of a regression line, we now create a regression plane in three-dimensional space. Figure 7.14 provides the graph of the estimated regression plane for the Butler Trucking Company example and shows the seventh driving assignment in the data. Observe that as the plane slopes upward to larger values of estimated mean travel time ($\hat{y}$) as either the number of miles traveled (x_1) or

FIGURE 7.14 Graph of the Regression Equation for Multiple Regression Analysis with Two Independent Variables

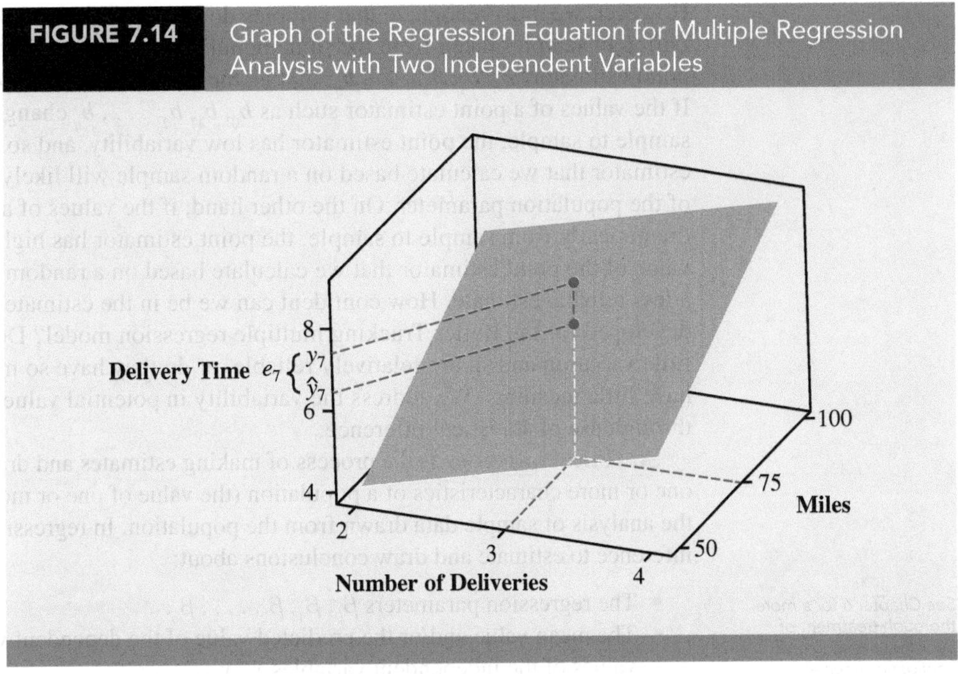

the number of deliveries (x_2) increases. Further, observe that the residual for a driving assignment when $x_1 = 75$ and $x_2 = 3$ is the difference between the observed y value and the estimated mean value of y given $x_1 = 75$ and $x_2 = 3$. Note that in Figure 7.14, the observed value lies above the regression plane, indicating that the regression model underestimates the expected driving time for the seventh driving assignment.

NOTES + COMMENTS

Although we use regression analysis to estimate relationships between independent variables and the dependent variable, it does not provide information on whether these are cause-and-effect relationships. The analyst can conclude that a cause-and-effect relationship exists between an independent variable and the dependent variable only if there is a theoretical justification that the relationship is in fact causal. In the Butler Trucking Company multiple regression, through regression analysis we have found evidence of a relationship between distance traveled and travel time and evidence of a relationship between number of deliveries and travel time. Nonetheless, we cannot conclude from the regression model that changes in distance traveled x_1 cause changes in travel time y, and we cannot conclude that changes in number of deliveries x_2 cause changes in travel time y. The appropriateness of such cause-and-effect conclusions are left to supporting practical justification and to good judgment on the part of the analyst. Based on their practical experience, Butler Trucking's managers felt that increases in distance traveled and number of deliveries were likely causes of increased travel time. However, it is important to realize that the regression model itself provides no information about cause-and-effect relationships.

7.5 Inference and Regression

The statistics $b_0, b_1, b_2, \ldots, b_q$ are point estimators of the population parameters $\beta_0, \beta_1, \beta_2, \ldots, \beta_q$; that is, each of these $q + 1$ estimates is a single value used as an estimate of the corresponding population parameter. Similarly, we use $\hat{y}$ as a point estimator of $E(y \mid x_1, x_2, \ldots, x_q)$, the conditional expectation of y given values of $x_1, x_2, \ldots, x_q$.

However, we must recognize that samples do not replicate the population exactly. Different samples taken from the same population will result in different values of the point estimators $b_0, b_1, b_2, \ldots, b_q$; that is, the point estimators are random variables. If the values of a point estimator such as $b_0, b_1, b_2, \ldots, b_q$ change relatively little from sample to sample, the point estimator has low variability, and so the value of the point estimator that we calculate based on a random sample will likely be a reliable estimate of the population parameter. On the other hand, if the values of a point estimator change dramatically from sample to sample, the point estimator has high variability, and so the value of the point estimator that we calculate based on a random sample will likely be a less reliable estimate. How confident can we be in the estimates b_0, b_1, and b_2 that we developed for the Butler Trucking multiple regression model? Do these estimates have little variation and so are relatively reliable, or do they have so much variation that they have little meaning? We address the variability in potential values of the estimators through use of statistical inference.

Statistical inference is the process of making estimates and drawing conclusions about one or more characteristics of a population (the value of one or more parameters) through the analysis of sample data drawn from the population. In regression, we commonly use inference to estimate and draw conclusions about:

See Chapter 6 for a more thorough treatment of hypothesis testing and confidence intervals.

- The regression parameters $\beta_0, \beta_1, \beta_2, \ldots, \beta_q$.
- The mean value and/or the predicted value of the dependent variable y for specific values of the independent variables $x_1, x_2, \ldots, x_q$.

In our discussion of inference and regression, we will consider both **hypothesis testing** and **interval estimation**.

Conditions Necessary for Valid Inference in the Least Squares Regression Model

In conducting a regression analysis, we begin by making an assumption about the appropriate model for the relationship between the dependent and independent variable(s). For the case of linear regression, the assumed multiple regression model is:

$$y = \beta_0 + \beta_1 x_1 + \beta_2 x_2 + \cdots + \beta_q x_q + \varepsilon.$$

The least squares method is used to develop values for $b_1, b_2, \ldots, b_q$, the estimates of the model parameters $\beta_0, \beta_1, \beta_2, \ldots, \beta_p$, respectively. The resulting estimated multiple regression equation is:

$$\hat{y} = b_0 + b_1 x_1 + b_2 x_2 + \cdots + b_q x_q.$$

Although inference can provide greater understanding of the nature of relationships estimated through regression analysis, our inferences are valid only if the error term ε behaves in a certain way. Specifically, the validity of inferences in regression analysis depends on how well the following two conditions about the error term ε are met:

1. For any given combination of values of the independent variables $x_1, x_2, \ldots, x_q$, the population of potential error terms ε is normally distributed with a mean of 0 and a constant variance.
2. The values of ε are statistically independent.

The practical implication of normally distributed errors with a mean of zero and a constant variation for any given combination of values of $x_1, x_2, \ldots, x_q$ is that the regression estimates are unbiased (i.e., do not tend to over- or underpredict), possess

FIGURE 7.15 Illustration of the Conditions for Valid Inference in Regression

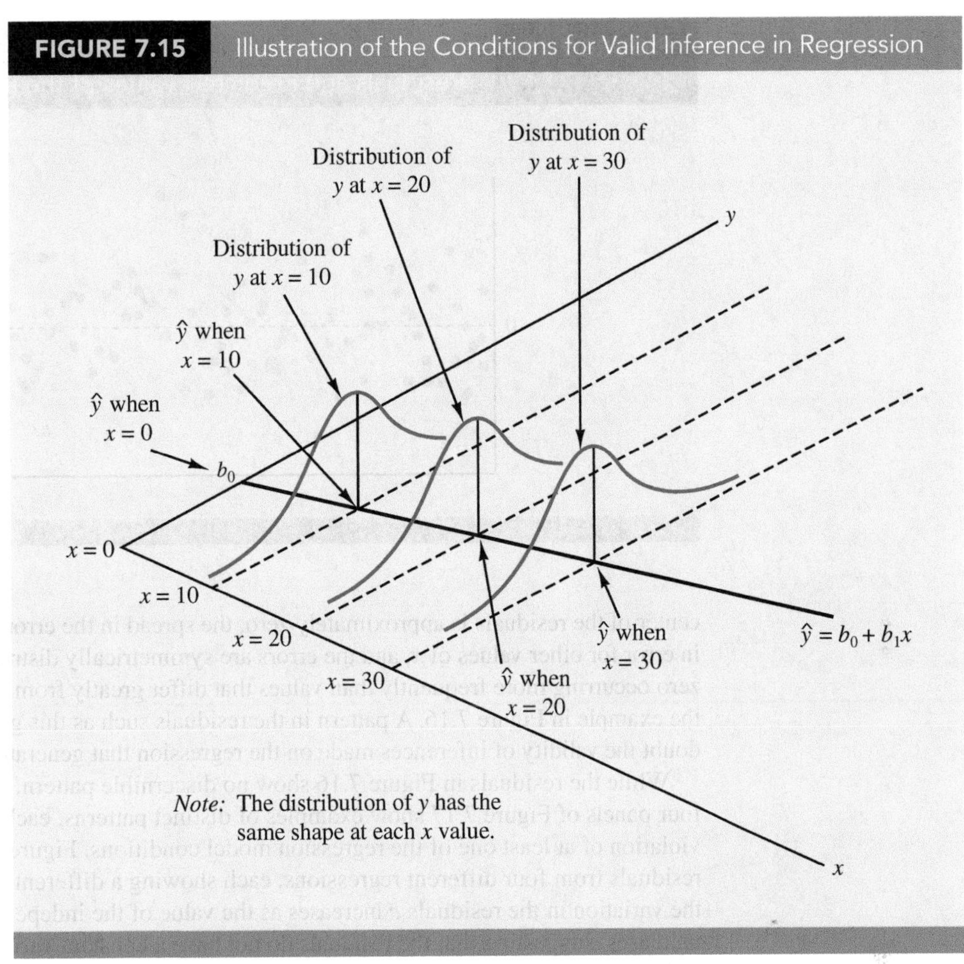

consistent accuracy, and tend to err in small amounts rather than in large amounts. This first condition must be met for statistical inference in regression to be valid. The second condition is generally a concern when we collect data from a single entity over several periods of time and must also be met for statistical inference in regression to be valid in these instances. However, inferences in regression are generally reliable unless there are marked violations of these conditions.

Keep in mind that we are also making an assumption or hypothesis about the form of the relationship between x and y. We assume that a straight line represented by $\beta_0 + \beta_1 x$ is the basis for the relationship between the variables. We must not lose sight of the fact that some other model, for instance $y = \beta_0 + \beta_1 x_1 + \beta_2 x_2 + \varepsilon$, may actually provide a better representation for the underlying population relationship.

Figure 7.15 illustrates these model conditions and their implications for a simple linear regression; note that in this graphical interpretation, the value of $E(y|x)$ changes linearly according to the specific value of x considered, and so the mean error is zero at each value of x. However, regardless of the x value, the error term ε and hence the dependent variable y are normally distributed, each with the same variance.

To evaluate whether the error of an estimated regression equation reasonably meets the two conditions, the sample residuals ($e_i = y_i - \hat{y}_i$ for observations $i = 1, \ldots n$) need to be analyzed. There are many sophisticated diagnostic procedures for detecting whether the sample errors violate these conditions, but simple scatter charts of the residuals and independent variables are an extremely effective method for assessing whether these conditions are violated. We should review the scatter chart for patterns in the residuals indicating that one or more of the conditions have been violated. At any given value of x, the

FIGURE 7.16 Example of a Random Error Pattern in a Scatter Chart of Residuals and Predicted Values of the Dependent Variable

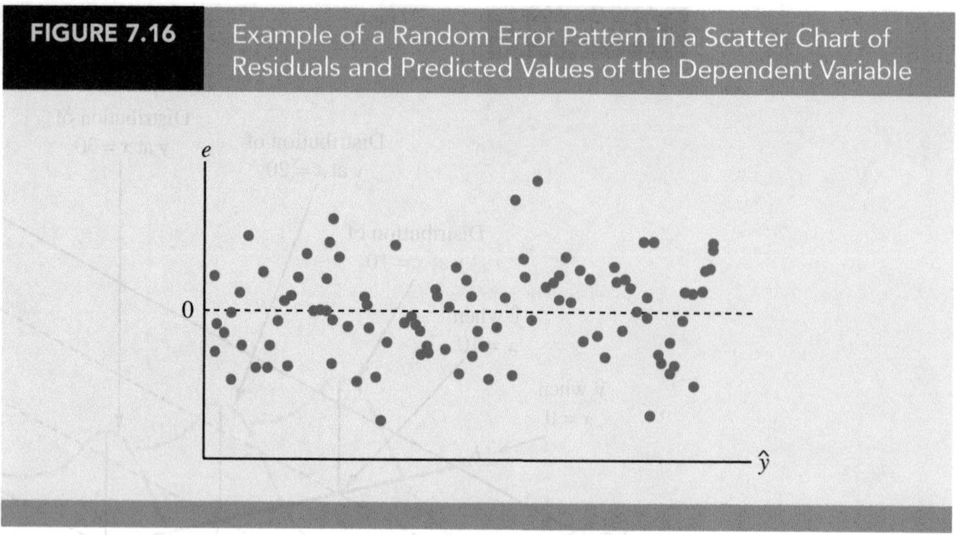

center of the residuals is approximately zero, the spread in the errors is similar to the spread in error for other values of x, and the errors are symmetrically distributed with values near zero occurring more frequently than values that differ greatly from zero. This is shown in the example in Figure 7.16. A pattern in the residuals such as this gives us little reason to doubt the validity of inferences made on the regression that generated the residuals.

While the residuals in Figure 7.16 show no discernible pattern, the residuals in the four panels of Figure 7.17 show examples of distinct patterns, each of which suggests a violation of at least one of the regression model conditions. Figure 7.17 shows plots of residuals from four different regressions, each showing a different pattern. In panel (a), the variation in the residuals e increases as the value of the independent variable x increases, suggesting that the residuals do not have a constant variance. In panel (b), the residuals are positive for small and large values of the independent variable x but are negative for moderate values of the independent variable. This pattern suggests that the linear regression model underpredicts the value of dependent variable for small and large values of the independent variable and overpredicts the value of the dependent variable for intermediate values of the independent variable. In this case, the regression model does not adequately capture the relationship between the independent variable x and the dependent variable y. The residuals in panel (c) are not symmetrically distributed around 0; many of the negative residuals are relatively close to zero, while the relatively few positive residuals tend to be far from zero. This skewness suggests that the residuals are not normally distributed. Finally, the residuals in panel (d) are plotted over time t, which generally serves as an independent variable; that is, an observation is made at each of several (usually equally spaced) points in time. In this case, connected consecutive residuals allow us to see a distinct pattern across every set of four residuals; the second residual is consistently larger than the first and smaller than the third, whereas the fourth residual is consistently the smallest. This pattern, which occurs consistently over each set of four consecutive residuals in the chart in panel (d), suggests that the residuals generated by this model are not independent. A residual pattern such as this generally occurs when we have collected quarterly data and have not captured seasonal effects in the model. In each of these four instances, any inferences based on our regression will likely not be reliable.

Frequently, the residuals do not meet these conditions either because an important independent variable has been omitted from the model or because the functional form of

FIGURE 7.17 Examples of Diagnostic Scatter Charts of Residuals from Four Regressions

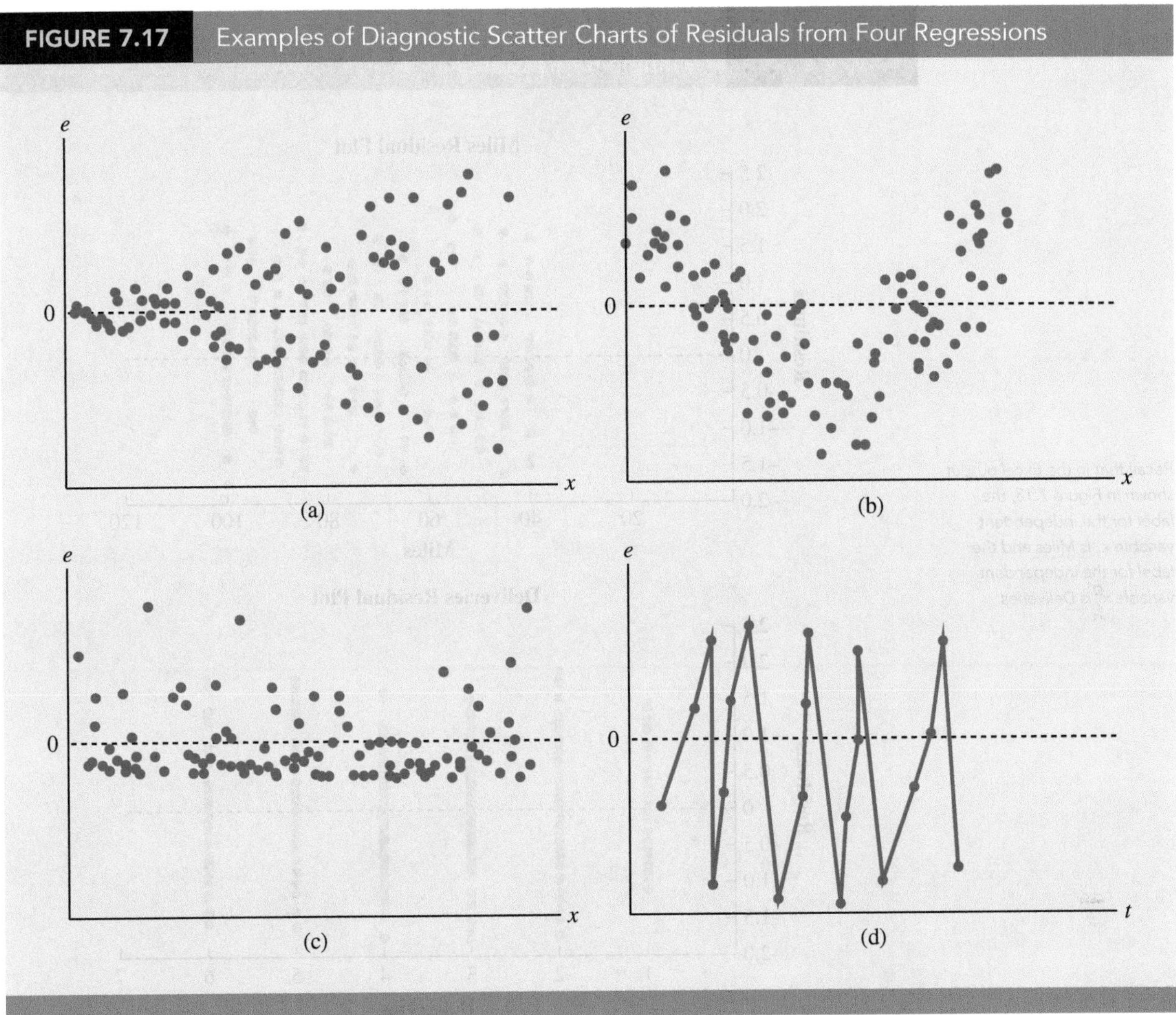

the model is inadequate to explain the relationships between the independent variables and the dependent variable. It is important to note that calculating the values of the estimates $b_0, b_1, b_2, \ldots, b_q$ does not require the errors to satisfy these conditions. However, the errors must satisfy these conditions in order for inferences (interval estimates for predicted values of the dependent variable and confidence intervals and hypothesis tests of the regression parameters $\beta_0, \beta_1, \beta_2, \ldots, \beta_q$) to be reliable.

You can generate scatter charts of the residuals against each independent variable in the model when using Excel's Regression tool; to do so, select the **Residual Plots** option in the **Residuals** area of the **Regression** dialog box. Figure 7.18 shows residual plots produced by Excel for the Butler Trucking Company example for which the independent variables are miles (x_1) and deliveries (x_2).

The residuals at each value of miles appear to have a mean of zero, to have similar variances, and to be concentrated around zero. The residuals at each value of deliveries also appear to have a mean of zero, to have similar variances, and to be concentrated around zero. Although there appears to be a slight pattern in the residuals across values of

Recall that in the Excel output shown in Figure 7.13, the label for the independent variable x_1 is Miles and the label for the independent variable x_2 is Deliveries.

FIGURE 7.18 Excel Residual Plots for the Butler Trucking Company Multiple Regression

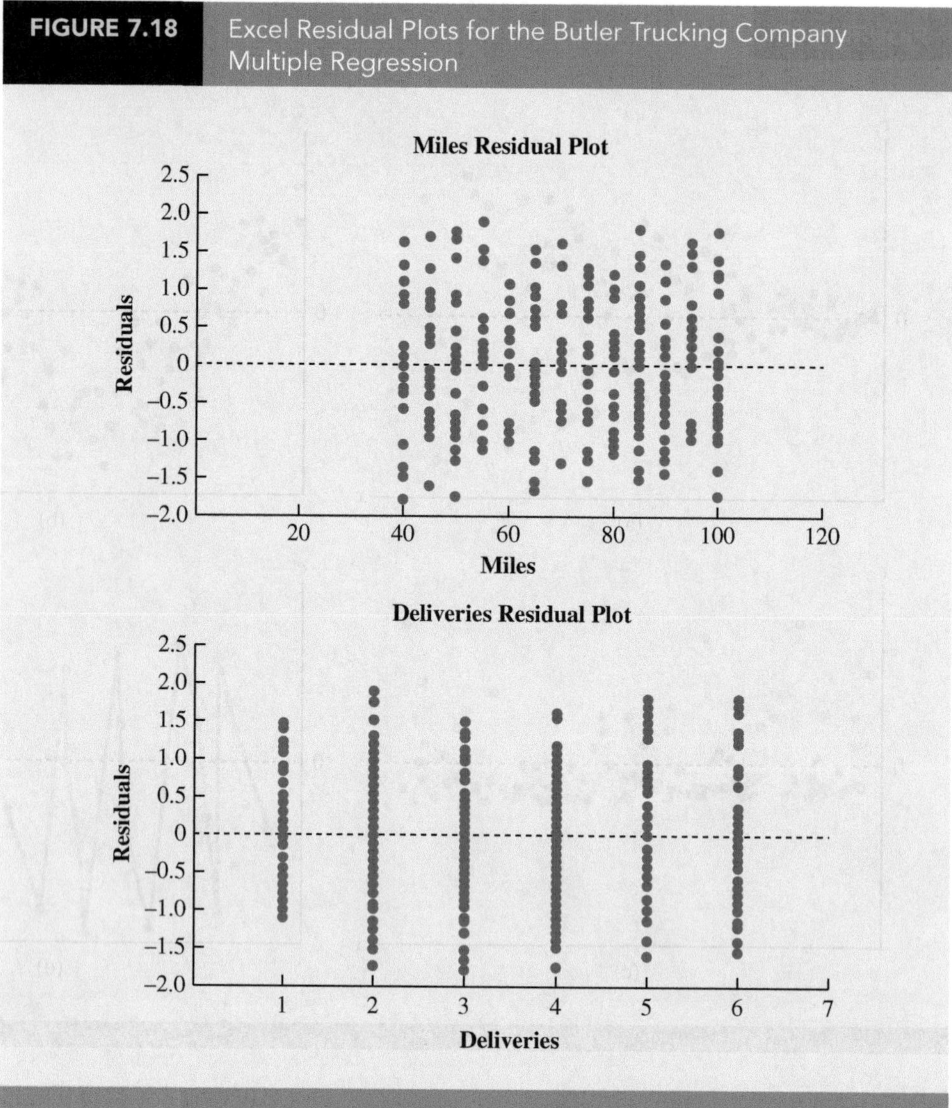

deliveries, it is negligible and could conceivably be the result of random variation. Thus, this evidence provides little reason for concern over the validity of inferences about the regression model that we may perform.

A scatter chart of the residuals e against the predicted values of the dependent variables is also commonly used to assess whether the residuals of the regression model satisfy the conditions necessary for valid inference. To obtain the data to construct a scatter chart of the residuals against the predicted values of the dependent variable using Excel's Regression tool, select the **Residuals** option in the **Residuals** area of the **Regression** dialog box (shown in Figure 7.12). This generates a table of predicted values of the dependent variable and residuals for the observations in the data; a partial list for the Butler Trucking multiple regression example is shown in Figure 7.19.

We can then use the Excel chart tool to create a scatter chart of these predicted values and residuals similar to the chart in Figure 7.20. The figure shows that the residuals at

FIGURE 7.19 Table of the First Several Predicted Values $\hat{y}$ and Residuals e Generated by the Excel Regression Tool

23	RESIDUAL OUTPUT		
24			
25	*Observation*	*Predicted Time*	*Residuals*
26	1	9.605504464	−0.305504464
27	2	5.556419081	−0.756419081
28	3	9.605504464	−0.705504464
29	4	8.225507903	−1.725507903
30	5	4.8664208	−0.6664208
31	6	6.881873062	−0.681873062
32	7	7.235932632	0.164037368
33	8	7.254143492	−1.254143492
34	9	8.243688763	−0.643688763
35	10	7.553690482	−1.453690482
36	11	6.936415641	0.063584359
37	12	7.290505212	−0.290505212
38	13	9.287776613	0.312223387
39	14	5.874146931	0.625853069
40	15	6.954596501	0.245403499
41	16	5.556419081	0.443580919

FIGURE 7.20 Scatter Chart of Predicted Values $\hat{y}$ and Residuals e

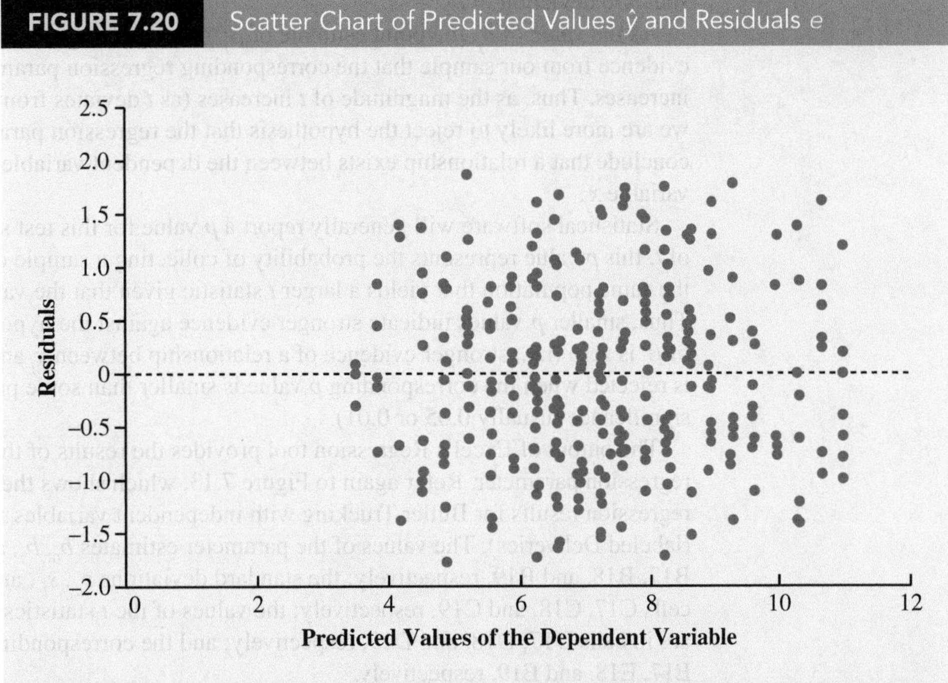

each predicted value of the dependent variable appear to have a mean of zero, to have similar variances, and to be concentrated around zero. This leads us to the same conclusion we reached when looking at the residuals plotted against the independent variables: The residuals provide little evidence that our regression model violates the conditions necessary for reliable inference. We can trust the inferences that we may wish to perform on our regression model.

Testing Individual Regression Parameters

Once we ascertain that our regression model satisfies the conditions necessary for reliable inference reasonably well, we can begin testing hypotheses and building confidence intervals. Specifically, we may then wish to determine whether statistically significant relationships exist between the dependent variable y and each of the independent variables $x_1, x_2, \ldots, x_q$ individually. Note that if a β_j is zero, then the dependent variable y does not change when the independent variable x_j changes, and there is no linear relationship between y and x_j. Alternatively, if a β_j is not zero, there is a linear relationship between the dependent variable y and the independent variable x_j.

See Chapter 6 for a more in-depth discussion of hypothesis testing.

We use a ***t* test** to test the hypothesis that a regression parameter β_j is zero. The corresponding null and alternative hypotheses are:

$$H_0: \beta = 0$$
$$H_a: \beta \neq 0$$

The standard deviation of b_j is often referred to as the standard error of b_j. Thus, s_{b_j} provides an estimate of the standard error of b_j.

The test statistic for this t test is:

$$t = \frac{b_j}{s_{b_j}}, \tag{7.14}$$

where b_j is the point estimate of the regression parameter β_j and s_{b_j} is the estimated standard deviation of b_j.

As the value of b_j, the point estimate of β_j, deviates from zero in either direction, the evidence from our sample that the corresponding regression parameter β_j is not zero increases. Thus, as the magnitude of t increases (as t deviates from zero in either direction), we are more likely to reject the hypothesis that the regression parameter β_j is zero and so conclude that a relationship exists between the dependent variable y and the independent variable x_j.

Statistical software will generally report a p value for this test statistic; for a given value of t, this p value represents the probability of collecting a sample of the same size from the same population that yields a larger t statistic given that the value of β_j is actually zero. Thus, smaller p values indicate stronger evidence against the hypothesis that the value of β_j is zero (i.e., stronger evidence of a relationship between x_j and y). The hypothesis is rejected when the corresponding p value is smaller than some predetermined level of significance (usually 0.05 or 0.01).

The output of Excel's Regression tool provides the results of the t tests for each regression parameter. Refer again to Figure 7.13, which shows the multiple linear regression results for Butler Trucking with independent variables x_1 (labeled Miles) and x_2 (labeled Deliveries). The values of the parameter estimates b_0, b_1, and b_2 are located in cells B17, B18, and B19, respectively; the standard deviations s_{b_0}, s_{b_1}, and s_{b_2} are contained in cells C17, C18, and C19, respectively; the values of the t statistics for the hypothesis tests are in cells D17, D18, and D19, respectively; and the corresponding p values are in cells E17, E18, and E19, respectively.

Let's use these results to test the hypothesis that β_1 is zero. If we do not reject this hypothesis, we conclude that the mean value of y does not change when the value of x_1 changes, and so there is no relationship between driving time and miles traveled. We see in the Excel output in Figure 7.13 that the *s*tatistic for this test is 27.3655 and that the associated p value is 3.5398E-83. This p value tells us that if the value of β_1 is actually zero, the probability we could collect a random sample of 300 observations from the population of Butler Trucking driving assignments that yields a t statistic with an absolute value greater than 27.3655 is practically zero. Such a small probability represents a highly unlikely scenario; thus, the small p value allows us to conclude that a relationship exists between driving time and miles traveled. (The p value is small enough to justify rejecting the hypothesis that $\beta_1 = 0$ for the Butler Trucking multiple regression example at a 0.01 level of significance or even at a far smaller level of significance.) Thus, this p value is sufficiently small to allow us to reject the hypothesis that there is no relationship between driving time and miles traveled at the 0.05 level of significance.

Similarly, we can test the hypothesis that β_2 is zero. If we do not reject this hypothesis, we conclude that the mean value of y does not change when the value of x_2 changes, and so there is no relationship between driving time and number of deliveries. We see in the Excel output in Figure 7.13 that the t statistic for this test is 23.3731 and that the associated p value is 2.84826E-69. This p value tells us that if the value of β_2 is actually zero, the probability we could collect a random sample of 300 observations from the population of Butler Trucking driving assignments that yields a t statistic with an absolute value greater than 23.3731 is practically zero. This is highly unlikely, and so the p value is sufficiently small to allow us to conclude that a relationship exists between driving time and number of deliveries. (The p value is small enough to justify rejecting the hypothesis that $\beta_2 = 0$ for the Butler Trucking multiple regression example at a 0.01 level of significance or even at a far smaller level of significance.) Thus, this p value is sufficiently small to allow us to reject the hypothesis that there is no relationship between driving time and number of deliveries at the 0.05 level of significance.

Finally, we can test the hypothesis that β_0 is zero in a similar fashion. If we do not reject this hypothesis, we conclude that the mean value of y is zero when the values of x_1 and x_2 are both zero, and so there is no driving time when a driving assignment is 0 miles and has 0 deliveries. We see in the Excel output that the t statistic for this test is 0.6205 and the associated p value is 0.5358. This p value tells us that if the value of β_0 is actually zero, the probability we could collect a random sample of 300 observations from the population of Butler Trucking driving assignments that yields a t statistic with an absolute value greater than 0.6205 is 0.5358. Thus, we do not reject the hypothesis that mean driving time is zero when a driving assignment is 0 miles and has 0 deliveries. However, the range of values for the independent variable distance traveled for the Butler Trucking multiple regression is 40 to 100, and the range of values for the independent variable number of deliveries is 1 to 6. Any prediction outside these ranges, such as the y-intercept for this model, is not a reliable estimate, and so a hypothesis test of β_0 is meaningless for this model. However, if the experimental region for a regression problem includes the origin, a hypothesis test of β_0 will be meaningful.

The estimated value of the y-intercept often results from extrapolation.

We can also execute each of these hypothesis tests through confidence intervals. A **confidence interval** for a regression parameter β_i is an estimated interval believed to contain the true value of β_i at some level of confidence. The level of confidence, or **confidence level**, indicates how frequently interval estimates based on samples of the same size taken from the same population using identical sampling techniques will contain the true value of β_i. Thus, when building a 95% confidence interval, we can expect that if we took samples of the same size from the same population using identical sampling

*See Chapter 6 for a more in-depth discussion of **confidence intervals**.*

techniques, the corresponding interval estimates would contain the true value of β_i for 95% of the samples.

Although the confidence intervals for $\beta_0, \beta_1, \beta_2, \ldots, \beta_q$ convey information about the variation in the estimates $b_1, b_2, \ldots, b_q$ that can be expected across repeated samples, they can also be used to test whether each of the regression parameters $\beta_0, \beta_1, \beta_2, \ldots, \beta_q$ is equal to zero in the following manner. To test that β_j is zero (i.e., there is no linear relationship between x_j and y) at some predetermined level of significance (say 0.05), first build a confidence interval at the $(1 - 0.05)100\%$ confidence level. If the resulting confidence interval does not contain zero, we conclude that β_j differs from zero at the predetermined level of significance.

The form of a confidence interval for β_j is as follows:

$$b_j \pm t_{\alpha/2} s_{b_j},$$

where b_j is the point estimate of the regression parameter β_j, s_{b_j} is the estimated standard deviation of b_j, and $t_{\alpha/2}$ is a multiplier term based on the sample size and specified $100(1 - \alpha)\%$ confidence level of the interval. More specifically, $t_{\alpha/2}$ is the t value that provides an area of $\alpha/2$ in the upper tail of a t distribution with $n - 2$ degrees of freedom.

Most software that is capable of regression analysis can also produce these confidence intervals. For example, the output of Excel's Regression tool for Butler Trucking, given in Figure 7.13, provides confidence intervals for β_1 (the slope coefficient associated with the independent variable x_1, labeled Miles) and β_2 (the slope coefficient associated with the independent variable x_2, labeled Deliveries), as well as the y-intercept β_0. The 95% confidence intervals for β_0, β_1, and β_2 are shown in cells F17:G17, F18:G18, and F19:G19, respectively; these 95% confidence intervals are automatically generated. Neither of the 95% confidence intervals for β_1 and β_2 includes zero, so we can conclude that β_1 and β_2 each differ from zero at the 0.05 level of significance. On the other hand, the 95% confidence interval for β_0 does include zero, so we conclude that β_0 does not differ from zero at the 0.05 level of significance. Again note that, for the Butler Trucking example, the estimated y-intercept results from extrapolation, and so the confidence interval for β_0 is meaningless. However, if the experimental region for a regression problem includes the origin, the confidence interval for β_0 will be meaningful.

The Regression tool dialog box offers the user the opportunity to generate confidence intervals for β_0, β_1, and β_2 at a confidence level other than 95%. In this example, we chose to create 99% confidence intervals for β_0, β_1, and β_2, which in Figure 7.13 are given in cells H17:I17, H18:I18, and H19:I19, respectively. Neither of the 99% confidence intervals for β_1 and β_2 includes zero, so we can conclude that β_1 and β_2 each differs from zero at the 0.01 level of significance. On the other hand, the 99% confidence interval for β_0 does include zero, so we conclude that β_0 does not differ from zero at the 0.01 level of significance.

Addressing Nonsignificant Independent Variables

If the data do not support rejection of the hypothesis that a β_j is zero, we conclude that there is no linear relationship between y and x_j. This leads to the question of how to handle the corresponding independent variable. Do we use the model as originally formulated with the nonsignificant independent variable, or do we rerun the regression without the nonsignificant independent variable and use the new result? The approach to be taken depends on a number of factors, but ultimately whatever model we use should have a theoretical basis. If practical experience dictates that the nonsignificant independent variable has a relationship with the dependent variable, the independent variable should be left in the model. On the other hand, if the model sufficiently explains the dependent variable without the nonsignificant independent variable, then we should consider rerunning the regression without the nonsignificant independent variable. Note that it is possible that the estimates of the other regression coefficients and their p values may change considerably when we remove the nonsignificant independent variable from the model.

The appropriate treatment of the inclusion or exclusion of the y-intercept when b_0 is not statistically significant may require special consideration. For example, in the Butler Trucking multiple regression model, recall that the p value for b_0 is 0.5354, suggesting that this estimate of β_0 is not statistically significant. Should we remove the y-intercept from this model because it is not statistically significant? Excel provides functionality to remove the y-intercept from the model by selecting **Constant is zero** in Excel's Regression tool. This will force the y-intercept to go through the origin (when the independent variables $x_1, x_2, \ldots, x_q$ all equal zero, the estimated value of the dependent variable will be zero). However, doing this can substantially alter the estimated slopes in the regression model and result in a less effective regression that yields less accurate predicted values of the dependent variable. The primary purpose of the regression model is to explain or predict values of the dependent variable for values of the independent variables that lie within the experimental region on which the model is based. Therefore, regression through the origin should not be forced unless there are strong *a priori* reasons for believing that the dependent variable is equal to zero when the values of all independent variables in the model are equal to zero. A common business example of regression through the origin is a model for which output in a labor-intensive production process is the dependent variable and hours of labor is the independent variable; because the production process is labor intense, we would expect no output when the value of labor hours is zero.

Multicollinearity

We use the term *independent variable* in regression analysis to refer to any variable used to predict or explain the value of the dependent variable. The term does not mean, however, that the independent variables themselves are independent in any statistical sense. On the contrary, most independent variables in a multiple regression problem are correlated with one another to some degree. For example, in the Butler Trucking example involving the two independent variables x_1 (miles traveled) and x_2 (number of deliveries), we could compute the sample correlation coefficient r_{x_1,x_2} to determine the extent to which these two variables are related. Doing so yields $r_{x_1,x_2} = 0.16$. Thus, we find some degree of linear association between the two independent variables. In multiple regression analysis, **multicollinearity** refers to the correlation among the independent variables.

To gain a better perspective of the potential problems of multicollinearity, let us consider a modification of the Butler Trucking example. Instead of x_2 being the number of deliveries, let x_2 denote the number of gallons of gasoline consumed. Clearly, x_1 (the miles traveled) and x_2 are now related; that is, we know that the number of gallons of gasoline used depends to a large extent on the number of miles traveled. Hence, we would conclude logically that x_1 and x_2 are highly correlated independent variables and that multicollinearity is present in the model. The data for this example are provided in the file *ButlerWithGasConsumption*.

ButlerWithGasConsumption

Using Excel's Regression tool, we obtain the results shown in Figure 7.21 for our multiple regression. When we conduct a t test to determine whether β_1 is equal to zero, we find a p value of 3.1544E-07, and so we reject this hypothesis and conclude that travel time is related to miles traveled. On the other hand, when we conduct a t test to determine whether β_2 is equal to zero, we find a p value of 0.6588, and so we do not reject this hypothesis. Does this mean that travel time is not related to gasoline consumption? Not necessarily.

FIGURE 7.21 Excel Regression Output for the Butler Trucking Company with Miles and Gasoline Consumption as Independent Variables

	A	B	C	D	E	F	G	H	I
1	SUMMARY OUTPUT								
2									
3	*Regression Statistics*								
4	Multiple R	0.69406354							
5	R Square	0.481724198							
6	Adjusted R Square	0.478234125							
7	Standard Error	1.398077545							
8	Observations	300							
9									
10	ANOVA								
11		*df*	*SS*	*MS*	*F*	*Significance F*			
12	Regression	2	539.5808158	269.7904079	138.0269794	4.09542E-43			
13	Residual	297	580.5223842	1.954620822					
14	Total	299	1120.1032						
15									
16		*Coefficients*	*Standard Error*	*t Stat*	*P-value*	*Lower 95%*	*Upper 95%*	*Lower 99.0%*	*Upper 99.0%*
17	Intercept	2.493095385	0.33669895	7.404523781	1.36703E-12	1.830477398	3.155713373	1.620208758	3.365982013
18	Miles	0.074701825	0.014274552	5.233216928	3.15444E-07	0.046609743	0.102793908	0.037695279	0.111708371
19	Gasoline Consumption	−0.067506102	0.152707928	−0.442060235	0.658767336	−0.368032789	0.233020584	−0.463398955	0.328386751

What it probably means in this instance is that, with x_1 already in the model, x_2 does not make a significant marginal contribution to predicting the value of y. This interpretation makes sense within the context of the Butler Trucking example; if we know the miles traveled, we do not gain much new information that would be useful in predicting driving time by also knowing the amount of gasoline consumed. We can see this in the scatter chart in Figure 7.22; miles traveled and gasoline consumed are strongly related.

Note that, even though we rejected the hypothesis that β_1 is equal to zero for this model, the value of the t statistic is much smaller and the p value substantially larger than in the multiple regression model that includes miles driven and number of deliveries as the independent variables. The evidence against the hypothesis that β_1 is equal to zero is weaker in the multiple regression that includes miles driven and gasoline consumed as the independent variables because of the high correlation between these two independent variables.

If any estimated regression parameters $b_1, b_2, \ldots, b_q$ or associated p values change dramatically when a new independent variable is added to the model (or an existing independent variable is removed from the model), multicollinearity is likely present. Looking for changes such as these is sometimes used as a way to detect multicollinearity.

To summarize, in t tests for the significance of individual parameters, the difficulty caused by multicollinearity is that it is possible to conclude that a parameter associated with one of the multicollinear independent variables is not significantly different from zero when the independent variable actually has a strong relationship with the dependent variable. This problem is avoided when there is little correlation among the independent variables.

Statisticians have developed several tests for determining whether multicollinearity is strong enough to cause problems. In addition to the initial understanding of the nature of the relationships between the various pairs of variables that we can gain through scatter charts such as the chart shown in Figure 7.22, correlations between pairs of independent

FIGURE 7.22 Scatter Chart of Miles and Gasoline Consumed for Butler Trucking Company

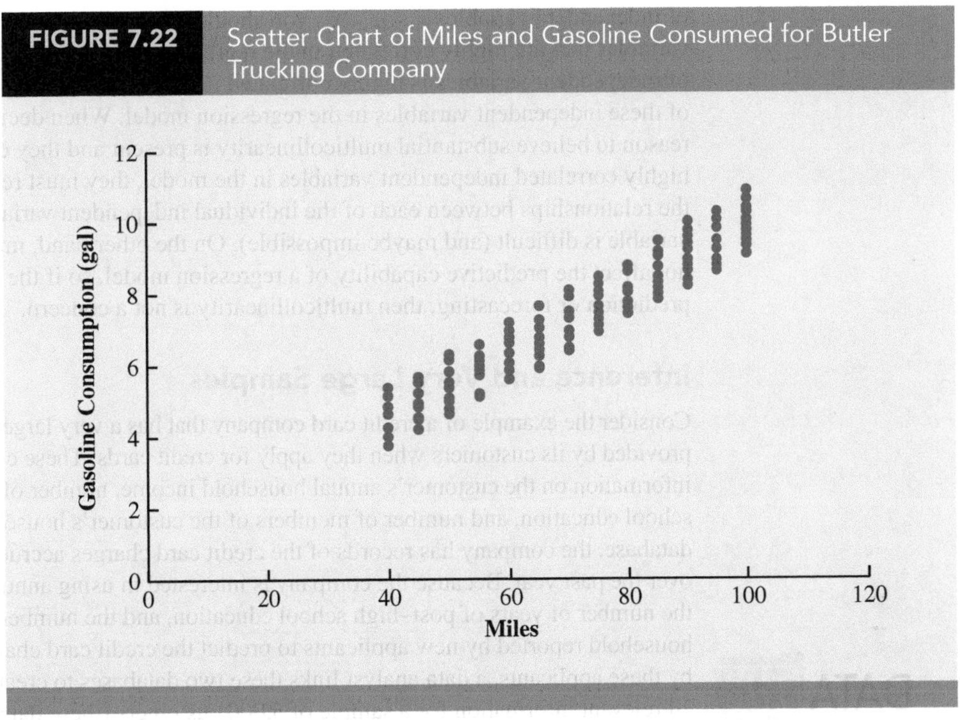

See Chapter 2 for a more in-depth discussion of correlation and how to compute it with Excel.

variables can be used to identify potential problems. According to a common rule-of-thumb test, multicollinearity is a potential problem if the absolute value of the sample correlation coefficient exceeds 0.7 for any two of the independent variables. We can place the Excel function:

=CORREL(B2:B301, C2:C301)

into any empty cell of the file *ButlerWithGasConsumption* to find that the correlation between Miles (in column B) and Gasoline Consumed (in column C) for the sample Butler Trucking data is $r_{\text{Miles, Gasoline Consumed}} = 0.9572$, which supports the conclusion that Miles and Gasoline Consumed are multicollinear. Similarly, by placing the Excel function:

=CORREL(B2:B301, D2:D301)

into any empty cell of the file *ButlerWithGasConsumption* shows that the correlation between Miles (in column B) and Deliveries (in column D) for the sample data is $r_{\text{Miles, Deliveries}} = 0.0258$. This supports the conclusion that Miles and Deliveries are not multicollinear. Other tests for multicollinearity are more advanced and beyond the scope of this text.

The primary consequence of multicollinearity is that it increases the standard deviation of $b_0, b_1, \ldots, b_q$ and predicted values of the dependent variable, and so inference based on these estimates is less precise than it should be. This means that confidence intervals for $\beta_0, \beta_1, \beta_2, \ldots, \beta_q$ and predicted values of the dependent variable are wider than they should be. Thus, we are less likely to reject the hypothesis that an individual parameter b_j is equal to zero than we otherwise would be, and multicollinearity leads us to conclude that an independent variable x_j is not related to the dependent variable y when they in fact are related. In addition, multicollinearity can result in confusing or misleading regression parameters $b_1, b_2, \ldots, b_q$. Therefore, if a primary objective of the regression analysis is inference, to explain the relationship between a dependent variable y and a set of independent variables $x_1, \ldots, x_q$, you should, if possible, avoid including independent variables that are highly correlated in the regression model. For example, when a pair of independent variables is highly correlated it is common to simply include only one of these independent variables in the regression model. When decision makers have reason to believe substantial multicollinearity is present and they choose to retain the highly correlated independent variables in the model, they must realize that separating the relationships between each of the individual independent variables and the dependent variable is difficult (and maybe impossible). On the other hand, multicollinearity does not affect the predictive capability of a regression model, so if the primary objective is prediction or forecasting, then multicollinearity is not a concern.

Inference and Very Large Samples

Consider the example of a credit card company that has a very large database of information provided by its customers when they apply for credit cards. These customer records include information on the customer's annual household income, number of years of post–high school education, and number of members of the customer's household. In a second database, the company has records of the credit card charges accrued by each customer over the past year. Because the company is interested in using annual household income, the number of years of post–high school education, and the number of members of the household reported by new applicants to predict the credit card charges that will be accrued by these applicants, a data analyst links these two databases to create one data set containing all relevant information for a sample of 5,000 customers (these data are available in the file *LargeCredit*).

LargeCredit

The company has decided to apply multiple regression to these data to develop a model for predicting annual credit card charges for its new applicants. The dependent variable in the model is credit card charges accrued by a customer in the data set over the past year (y); the independent variables are the customer's annual household income (x_1), number of members of the household (x_2), and number of years of post–high school education (x_3). Figure 7.23 provides Excel output for the multiple regression model estimated using the data set the company has created.

The model has a coefficient of determination of 0.3635 (see cell B5 in Figure 7.23), indicating that this model explains approximately 36% of the variation in credit card charges accrued by the customers in the sample over the past year. The p value for each test of the individual regression parameters is also very small (see cells E18 through E20), indicating that for each independent variable we can reject the hypothesis of no relationship with the dependent variable. The estimated slopes associated with the dependent variables are all highly significant. The model estimates that:

- For a fixed number of members of the household and number of years of post–high school education, accrued credit card charges increase by \$120.63 when a customer's annual household income increases by \$1,000. This is shown in cell B18 of Figure 7.23.
- For a fixed annual household income and number of years of post–high school education, accrued credit card charges increase by \$533.85 when a customer's household increases by one member. This is shown in cell B19 of Figure 7.23.
- For a fixed annual household income and number of members of the household, accrued credit card charges decrease by \$505.63 when a customer's number of years of post–high school education increases by one year. This is shown in cell B20 of Figure 7.23.

Because the y-intercept is an obvious result of extrapolation (no customer in the data has values of zero for annual household income, number of members of the household, *and*

FIGURE 7.23 Excel Regression Output for Credit Card Company Example

	A	B	C	D	E	F	G	H	I
1	SUMMARY OUTPUT								
2									
3	*Regression Statistics*								
4	Multiple R	0.602946393							
5	R Square	0.363544353							
6	Adjusted R Square	0.363162174							
7	Standard Error	4847.563495							
8	Observations	5000							
9									
10	ANOVA								
11		*df*	*SS*	*MS*	*F*	*Significance F*			
12	Regression	3	67059251577	22353083859	951.2407238	0			
13	Residual	4996	1.174E+11	23498871.84					
14	Total	4999	1.8446E+11						
15									
16		*Coefficients*	*Standard Error*	*t Stat*	*P-value*	*Lower 95%*	*Upper 95%*	*Lower 99.0%*	*Upper 99.0%*
17	Intercept	2051.638735	258.2118129	7.945564971	2.37056E-15	1545.430245	2557.847226	1386.274984	2717.002486
18	Annual Income ($1000)	120.6315397	2.439500895	49.44927054	0	115.8490472	125.4140323	114.3454003	126.9176792
19	Household Size	533.8460243	33.07739782	16.13929932	3.6874E-57	468.9998058	598.6922428	448.6117306	619.080318
20	Years of Post-High School Education	–505.632418	45.54182323	–11.10259498	2.60612E-28	–594.9143812	–416.3504547	–622.9852144	–388.2796215

number of years of post–high school education), the estimated regression parameter b_0 is meaningless.

The small p values associated with a model that is fit on an extremely large sample do not imply that an extremely large sample solves all problems. Virtually all relationships between independent variables and the dependent variable will be statistically significant if the sample size is sufficiently large. That is, if the sample size is very large, there will be little difference in the b_j values generated by different random samples. Because we address the variability in potential values of our estimators through the use of statistical inference, and variability of our estimates b_j essentially disappears as the sample size grows very large, inference is of little use for estimates generated from very large samples. Thus, we generally are not concerned with the conditions a regression model must satisfy in order for inference to be reliable when we use a very large sample. Multicollinearity, on the other hand, can result in confusing or misleading regression parameters $b_1, b_2, \ldots, b_q$ and so is still a concern when we use a large data set to estimate a regression model that is to be used for explanatory purposes.

The phenomenon by which the value of an estimate generally becomes closer to the value of parameter being estimated as the sample size grows is called the Law of Large Numbers.

How much does sample size matter? Table 7.4 provides the regression parameter estimates and the corresponding p values for multiple regression models estimated on the first 50 observations, the second 50 observations, and so on for the *LargeCredit* data. Note that, even though the means of the parameter estimates for the regressions based on 50 observations are similar to the parameter estimates based on the full sample of 5,000 observations, the individual values of the estimated regression parameters in the regressions based on 50 observations show a great deal of variation. In these 10 regressions, the estimated values

TABLE 7.4 Regression Parameter Estimates and the Corresponding *p* values for 10 Multiple Regression Models, Each Estimated on 50 Observations from the *LargeCredit* Data

Observations	b_0	*p* value	b_1	*p* value	b_2	*p* value	b_3	*p* value
1–50	−805.182	0.7814	154.488	1.45E-06	234.664	0.5489	207.828	0.6721
51–100	894.407	0.6796	125.343	2.23E-07	822.675	0.0070	−355.585	0.3553
101–150	−2,191.590	0.4869	155.187	3.56E-07	674.961	0.0501	−25.309	0.9560
151–200	2,294.023	0.3445	114.734	1.26E-04	297.011	0.3700	−537.063	0.2205
201–250	8,994.040	0.0289	103.378	6.89E-04	−489.932	0.2270	−375.601	0.5261
251–300	7,265.471	0.0234	73.207	1.02E-02	−77.874	0.8409	−405.195	0.4060
301–350	2,147.906	0.5236	117.500	1.88E-04	390.447	0.3053	−374.799	0.4696
351–400	−504.532	0.8380	118.926	8.54E-07	798.499	0.0112	45.259	0.9209
401–450	1,587.067	0.5123	81.532	5.06E-04	1,267.041	0.0004	−891.118	0.0359
451–500	−315.945	0.9048	148.860	1.07E-05	1,000.243	0.0053	−974.791	0.0420
Mean	1,936.567		119.316		491.773		−368.637	

of b_0 range from −2,191.590 to 8,994.040, the estimated values of b_1 range from 73.207 to 155.187, the estimated values of b_2 range from −489.932 to 1,267.041, and the estimated values of b_3 range from −974.791 to 207.828. This is reflected in the *p* values corresponding to the parameter estimates in the regressions based on 50 observations, which are substantially larger than the corresponding *p* values in the regression based on 5,000 observations. These results underscore the impact that a very large sample size can have on inference.

For another example, suppose the credit card company also has a separate database of information on shopping and lifestyle characteristics that it has collected from its customers during a recent Internet survey. The data analyst notes in the results in Figure 7.23 that the original regression model fails to explain almost 65% of the variation in credit card charges accrued by the customers in the data set. In an attempt to increase the variation in the dependent variable explained by the model, the data analyst decides to augment the original regression with a new independent variable, number of hours per week spent watching television (which we will designate as x_4). After linking the databases so that all necessary information for each of the 5,000 customers is in a single data set, the analyst runs the new multiple regression and achieves the results shown in Figure 7.24.

The new model has a coefficient of determination of 0.3669 (see cell B5 in Figure 7.24), indicating the addition of number of hours per week spent watching television increased the explained variation in sample values of accrued credit card charges by less than 1%. The estimated regression parameters and associated *p* values for annual household income, number of members of the household, and number of years of post–high school education changed little after introducing into the model the number of hours per week spent watching television.

The estimated regression parameter for number of hours per week spent watching television is 20.44 (see cell B21 in Figure 7.24), suggesting a that 1-hour increase coincides with an increase of $20.44 in credit card charges accrued by each customer over the past year. The *p* value associated with this estimate is 2.3744E-07 (see cell E21 in Figure 7.24), so we can reject the hypothesis that there is no relationship between the number of hours per week spent watching television and credit card charges accrued. However, when the model is based on a very large sample, almost all relationships will be significant whether they are real or not, and statistical significance does not necessarily imply that a relationship is meaningful or useful.

FIGURE 7.24 Excel Regression Output for Credit Card Company Example after Adding Number of Hours per Week Spent Watching Television to the Model

	A	B	C	D	E	F	G	H	I
1	SUMMARY OUTPUT								
2									
3	*Regression Statistics*								
4	Multiple R	0.605753974							
5	R Square	0.366937877							
6	Adjusted R Square	0.36643092							
7	Standard Error	4835.106762							
8	Observations	5000							
9									
10	ANOVA								
11		*df*	*SS*	*MS*	*F*	*Significance F*			
12	Regression	4	67685219598	16921304900	723.8052269	0			
13	Residual	4995	1.16774E+11	23378257.4					
14	Total	4999	1.8446E+11						
15									
16		*Coefficients*	*Standard Error*	*t Stat*	*P-value*	*Lower 95%*	*Upper 95%*	*Lower 99.0%*	*Upper 99.0%*
17	Intercept	1440.385909	283.3464635	5.083479398	3.84109E-07	884.9024443	1995.869374	710.2547892	2170.51703
18	Annual Income ($1000)	120.4937794	2.433377775	49.51708715	0	115.7232906	125.2642681	114.2234176	126.7641412
19	Household Size	538.2043625	33.00314865	16.30766713	2.72804E-58	473.5037019	602.9050231	453.1613886	623.2473364
20	Years of Post-High School Education	-509.7777354	45.43185836	-11.22071062	7.12888E-29	-598.8441236	-420.7113472	-626.8471819	-392.7082889
21	Hours Per Week Watching Television	20.4413308	3.950382611	5.174519234	2.37441E-07	12.69684656	28.18581504	10.26192978	30.62073183

Is it reasonable to expect that the credit card charges accrued by a customer are related to the number of hours per week the consumer watches television? If not, the model that includes number of hours per week the consumer watches television as an independent variable may provide inaccurate or unreliable predictions of the credit card charges that will be accrued by new customers, even though we have found a significant relationship between these two variables. If the model is to be used to predict future amounts of credit charges, then the usefulness of including the number of hours per week the consumer watches television is best evaluated by measuring the accuracy of predictions for observations not included in the sample data used to construct the model. This use of out-of-sample data is common in data-mining applications and is covered in detail in Chapter 9.

NOTES + COMMENTS

1. In multiple regression we can test the null hypothesis that the regression parameters $b_1, b_2, \ldots, b_q$ are all equal to zero (H_0: $\beta_1 = \beta_2 = \cdots = \beta_q = 0$, H_a: at least one $b_j \neq 0$ for $j = 1, \ldots, q$) with an F test based on the F probability distribution. The test statistic generated by the sample data for this test is:

$$F = \frac{SSR/q}{SSE/(n - q - 1)},$$

where SSR and SSE are as defined by equations (7.5) and (7.7), q is the number of independent variables in the regression model, and n is the number of observations in the sample. If the p value corresponding to the F statistic is smaller than some predetermined level of significance (usually 0.05 or 0.01), this leads us to reject the hypothesis that the values of $b_1, b_2, \ldots, b_q$ are all zero, and we would conclude that there is an overall regression relationship; otherwise, we conclude that there is no overall regression relationship.

The output of Excel's Regression tool provides the results of the F test; in Figure 7.13, which shows the multiple linear regression results for Butler Trucking with independent variables x_1 (labeled Miles) and x_2 (labeled Deliveries), the value of the F statistic and the corresponding p value are in cells E24 and F24, respectively. From the Excel output in Figure 7.13 we see tht the p value for the F test is essentially 0 (2.2419E-110, or 2.2419 with the decimal moved 110 places to the left). Thus, the p value is sufficiently small to allow us to reject the hypothesis that no overall regression relationship exists at the 0.05 level of significance.

2. Finding a significant relationship between an independent variable x_j and a dependent variable y in a linear regression does not enable us to conclude that the relationship is linear. We can state only that x_j and y are related and that a linear relationship explains a statistically significant portion of the variability in y over the range of values for x_j observed in the sample.
3. Note that a review of the correlations of pairs of independent variables is not always sufficient to entirely uncover multicollinearity. The problem is that sometimes one independent variable is highly correlated with some combination of several other independent variables. If you suspect that one independent variable is highly correlated with a combination of several other independent variables, you can use multiple regression to assess whether the sample data support your suspicion. Suppose that your original regression model includes the independent variables $x_1, x_2, \ldots, x_q$ and that you suspect that x_1 is highly correlated with a subset of the other independent variables $x_2, \ldots, x_q$. Estimate the multiple linear regression for which x_1 is now the dependent variable; the subset of the independent variables $x_2, \ldots, x_q$ that you suspect are highly correlated with x_1 are now the independent variables. The coefficient of determination R^2 for this regression provides an estimate of the strength of the relationship between x_1 and the subset of the other independent variables $x_2, \ldots, x_q$ that you suspect are highly correlated with x_1. As a rule of thumb, if the coefficient of determination R^2 for this regression exceeds 0.50, multicollinearity between x_1 and the subset of the other independent variables $x_2, \ldots, x_q$ is a concern.
4. When working with a small number of observations, assessing the conditions necessary for inference to be valid in regression can be extremely difficult. Similarly, when working with a small number of observations, assessing multicollinearity can also be difficult. Under these conditions we generally proceed with inference unless we find strong evidence of a violation of the conditions necessary for inference to be valid in regression or a strong multicollinearity.
5. To determine the independent variables to be included in a regression model when working with an extremely large sample, one can partition the sample into a training set and a validation set. The training set is used to estimate the regression coefficients and the validation set is then used to estimate the accuracy of the model.

7.6 Categorical Independent Variables

Thus far, the examples we have considered have involved quantitative independent variables such as distance traveled and number of deliveries. In many situations, however, we must work with categorical independent variables such as sex (male, female), method of payment (cash, credit card, check), and so on. The purpose of this section is to show how categorical variables are handled in regression analysis. To illustrate the use and interpretation of a categorical independent variable, we will again consider the Butler Trucking Company example.

Butler Trucking Company and Rush Hour

Several of Butler Trucking's driving assignments require the driver to travel on a congested segment of a highway during the afternoon rush hour. Management believes this factor may also contribute substantially to variability in the travel times across driving assignments.

Dummy variables are sometimes referred to as indicator variables.

How do we incorporate information on which driving assignments include travel on a congested segment of a highway during the afternoon rush hour into a regression model?

The previous independent variables we have considered (such as miles traveled and number of deliveries) have been quantitative, but this new variable is categorical and will require us to define a new type of variable called a **dummy variable**. To incorporate a variable that indicates whether a driving assignment included travel on this congested segment of a highway during the afternoon rush hour into a model that currently includes the independent variables miles traveled (x_1) and number of deliveries (x_2), we define the following variable:

$$x_3 = \begin{cases} 0 \text{ if an assignment did not include travel on the congested segment of highway} \\ \text{during afternoon rush hour} \\ 1 \text{ if an assignment included travel on the congested segment of highway} \\ \text{during afternoon rush hour} \end{cases}$$

Once a value of one is input for each of the driving assignments that included travel on a congested segment of a highway during the afternoon rush hour and a value of zero is input for each of the remaining driving assignments in the sample data, the independent variable x_3 can be included in the model. The file *ButlerHighway* includes this dummy variable.

See Chapter 2 for step-by-step descriptions of how to construct charts in Excel.

Will this dummy variable add valuable information to the current Butler Trucking regression model? A review of the residuals produced by the current model may help us make an initial assessment. Using Excel chart tools, we can create a frequency distribution and a histogram of the residuals for driving assignments that included travel on a congested segment of a highway during the afternoon rush hour period. We then create a frequency distribution and a histogram of the residuals for driving assignments that did not include travel on a congested segment of a highway during the afternoon rush hour period. The two histograms are shown in Figure 7.25.

Recall that the residual for the ith observation is $e_i = y_i - \hat{y}_i$, which is the difference between the observed and predicted values of the dependent variable. The histograms in Figure 7.25 show that driving assignments that included travel on a congested segment of a highway during the afternoon rush hour period tend to have positive residuals, which means we are generally underpredicting the travel times for those driving assignments. Conversely, driving assignments that did not include travel on a congested segment of a highway during the afternoon rush hour period tend to have negative residuals, which means we are generally overpredicting the travel times for those driving assignments. These results suggest that the dummy variable could potentially explain a substantial proportion of the variance in travel time that is unexplained by the current model, and so we proceed by adding the dummy variable x_3 to the current Butler Trucking multiple regression model. Using Excel's Regression tool to develop the estimated regression equation, we obtained the Excel output in Figure 7.26. The estimated regression equation is:

ButlerHighway

$$\hat{y} = -0.3302 + 0.0672x_1 + 0.6735x_2 + 0.9980x_3. \tag{7.15}$$

Interpreting the Parameters

After checking to make sure this regression satisfies the conditions for inference and the model does not suffer from serious multicollinearity, we can consider inference on our results. The p values for the t tests of miles traveled (p value = 4.7852E-105), number of deliveries (p value = 6.7480E-87), and the rush hour driving dummy variable (p value = 6.4982E-31) are all extremely small, indicating that each of these independent variables has

FIGURE 7.25 Histograms of the Residuals for Driving Assignments That Included Travel on a Congested Segment of a Highway During the Afternoon Rush Hour and Residuals for Driving Assignments That Did Not

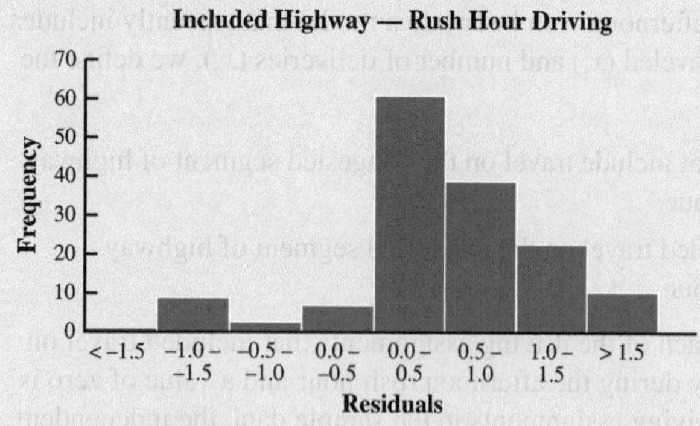

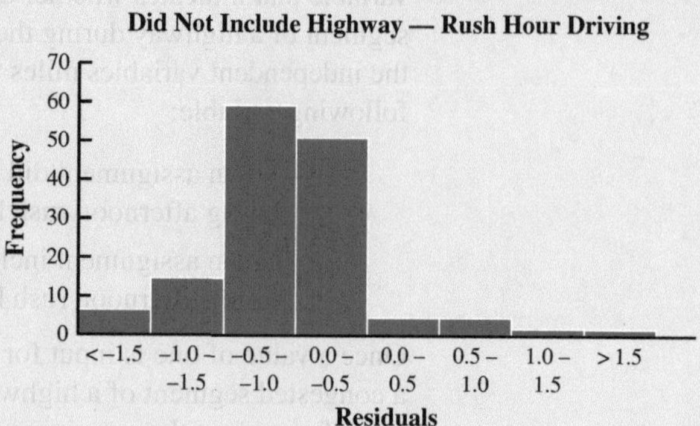

FIGURE 7.26 Excel Data and Output for Butler Trucking with Miles Traveled (x_1), Number of Deliveries (x_2), and the Highway Rush Hour Dummy Variable (x_3) as the Independent Variables

	A	B	C	D	E	F	G	H	I
1	SUMMARY OUTPUT								
2									
3	*Regression Statistics*								
4	Multiple R	0.940107228							
5	R Square	0.8838016							
6	Adjusted R Square	0.882623914							
7	Standard Error	0.663106426							
8	Observations	300							
9									
10	ANOVA								
11		*df*	*SS*	*MS*	*F*	*Significance F*			
12	Regression	3	989.9490008	329.9830003	750.455757	5.7766E–138			
13	Residual	296	130.1541992	0.439710132					
14	Total	299	1120.1032						
15									
16		*Coefficients*	*Standard Error*	*t Stat*	*P-value*	*Lower 95%*	*Upper 95%*	*Lower 99.0%*	*Upper 99.0%*
17	Intercept	–0.330229304	0.167677925	–1.969426232	0.04983651	–0.66022126	–0.000237349	–0.764941128	0.104482519
18	Miles	0.067220302	0.00196142	34.27125147	4.7852E-105	0.063360208	0.071080397	0.062135243	0.072305362
19	Deliveries	0.67351584	0.023619993	28.51465081	6.74797E-87	0.627031441	0.720000239	0.612280051	0.734751629
20	Highway	0.9980033	0.076706582	13.0106605	6.49817E-31	0.847043924	1.148962677	0.799138374	1.196868226

a statistical relationship with travel time. The model estimates that the mean travel time of a driving assignment increases by:

- 0.0672 hour for every increase of 1 mile traveled, holding constant the number of deliveries and whether the driving assignment route requires the driver to travel on the congested segment of a highway during the afternoon rush hour.
- 0.6735 hour for every delivery, holding constant the number of miles traveled and whether the driving assignment route requires the driver to travel on the congested segment of a highway during the afternoon rush hour.
- 0.9980 hour if the driving assignment route requires the driver to travel on the congested segment of a highway during the afternoon rush hour, holding constant the number of miles traveled and the number of deliveries.

In addition, $R^2 = 0.8838$ indicates that the regression model explains approximately 88.4% of the variability in travel time for the driving assignments in the sample. Thus, equation (7.15) should prove helpful in estimating the travel time necessary for the various driving assignments.

To understand how to interpret the regression when a categorical variable is present, let's compare the regression model for the case when $x_3 = 0$ (the driving assignment does not include travel on congested highways) and when $x_3 = 1$ (the driving assignment does include travel on congested highways). In the case that $x_3 = 0$, we have:

$$\begin{aligned}\hat{y} &= -0.3302 + 0.0672x_1 + 0.6735x_2 + 0.9980(0)\\ &= -0.3302 + 0.0672x_1 + 0.6735x_2.\end{aligned} \tag{7.16}$$

In the case that $x_3 = 1$, we have:

$$\begin{aligned}\hat{y} &= -0.3302 + 0.0672x_1 + 0.6735x_2 + 0.9980(1)\\ &= 0.6678 + 0.0672x_1 + 0.6735x_2.\end{aligned} \tag{7.17}$$

Comparing equations (7.16) and (7.17), we see that the mean travel time has the same linear relationship with x_1 and x_2 for both driving assignments that include travel on the congested segment of highway during the afternoon rush hour period and driving assignments that do not. However, the y-intercept is -0.3302 in equation (7.16) and $(-0.3302 + 0.9980)$ in equation (7.17). That is, 0.9980 is the difference between the mean travel time for driving assignments that include travel on the congested segment of highway during the afternoon rush hour and the mean travel time for driving assignments that do not.

In effect, the use of a dummy variable provides two estimated regression equations that can be used to predict the travel time: One that corresponds to driving assignments that include travel on the congested segment of highway during the afternoon rush hour period, and one that corresponds to driving assignments that do not include such travel.

More Complex Categorical Variables

The categorical variable for the Butler Trucking Company example had two levels: (1) driving assignments that include travel on the congested segment of highway during the afternoon rush hour, and (2) driving assignments that do not. As a result, defining a dummy variable with a value of zero indicating a driving assignment that does not include travel on the congested segment of highway during the afternoon rush hour and a value of one indicating a driving assignment that includes such travel was sufficient. However, when a categorical variable has more than two levels, care must be taken in both defining and interpreting the dummy variables. As we will show, if a categorical variable has k levels,

$k - 1$ dummy variables are required, with each dummy variable corresponding to one of the levels of the categorical variable and coded as 0 or 1.

For example, suppose a manufacturer of vending machines organized the sales territories for a particular state into three regions: A, B, and C. The managers want to use regression analysis to help predict the number of vending machines sold per week. With the number of units sold as the dependent variable, they are considering several independent variables (the number of sales personnel, advertising expenditures, etc.). Suppose the managers believe that sales region is also an important factor in predicting the number of units sold. Because sales region is a categorical variable with three levels (A, B, and C), we will need $3 - 1 = 2$ dummy variables to represent the sales region. Selecting Region A to be the "reference" region, each dummy variable can be coded 0 or 1 as follows:

$$x_1 = \begin{cases} 1 \text{ if sales Region B} \\ 0 \text{ otherwise} \end{cases}, \quad x_2 = \begin{cases} 1 \text{ if sales Region C} \\ 0 \text{ otherwise} \end{cases}$$

With this definition, we have the following values of x_1 and x_2:

Region	x_1	x_2
A	0	0
B	1	0
C	0	1

The regression equation relating the estimated mean number of units sold to the dummy variables is written as:

$$\hat{y} = b_0 + b_1x_1 + b_2x_2.$$

Observations corresponding to Region A correspond to $x_1 = 0$, $x_2 = 0$, so the estimated mean number of units sold in Region A is:

$$\hat{y} = b_0 + b_1(0) + b_2(0) = b_0.$$

Observations corresponding to Region B are coded $x_1 = 1$, $x_2 = 0$, so the estimated mean number of units sold in Region B is:

$$\hat{y} = b_0 + b_1(1) + b_2(0) = b_0 + b_1.$$

Observations corresponding to Region C are coded $x_1 = 0$, $x_2 = 1$, so the estimated mean number of units sold in Region C is:

$$\hat{y} = b_0 + b_1(0) + b_2(1) = b_0 + b_2.$$

Thus, b_0 is the estimated mean sales for Region A, b_1 is the estimated difference between the mean number of units sold in Region B and the mean number of units sold in Region A, and b_2 is the estimated difference between the mean number of units sold in Region C and the mean number of units sold in Region A.

Dummy variables are often used to model seasonal effects in sales data. If the data are collected quarterly, we may use three dummy variables defined in the following manner:

$$x_1 = \begin{cases} 1 \text{ if spring;} \\ 0 \text{ otherwise} \end{cases}$$

$$x_2 = \begin{cases} 1 \text{ if summer;} \\ 0 \text{ otherwise} \end{cases}$$

$$x_3 = \begin{cases} 1 \text{ if fall} \\ 0 \text{ otherwise} \end{cases}$$

Two dummy variables were required because sales region is a categorical variable with three levels. But the assignment of $x_1 = 0$ and $x_2 = 0$ to indicate Region A, $x_1 = 1$ and $x_2 = 0$ to indicate Region B, and $x_1 = 0$ and $x_2 = 1$ to indicate Region C was arbitrary. For example, we could have chosen to let $x_1 = 1$ and $x_2 = 0$ indicate Region A, $x_1 = 0$ and $x_2 = 0$ indicate Region B, and $x_1 = 0$ and $x_2 = 1$ indicate Region C. In this case, b_0 is the mean or expected value of sales for Region B, b_1 is the difference between the mean number of units sold in Region A and the mean number of units sold in Region B, and b_2 is the difference between the mean number of units sold in Region C and the mean number of units sold in Region B.

The important point to remember is that when a categorical variable has k levels, $k - 1$ dummy variables are required in the multiple regression analysis. Thus, if the sales region example had a fourth region, labeled D, three dummy variables would be necessary. For example, these three dummy variables could then be coded as follows:

$$x_1 = \begin{cases} 1 \text{ if sales Region B} \\ 0 \text{ otherwise} \end{cases}, \; x_2 = \begin{cases} 1 \text{ if sales Region C} \\ 0 \text{ otherwise} \end{cases}, \; x_3 = \begin{cases} 1 \text{ if sales Region D} \\ 0 \text{ otherwise} \end{cases}$$

NOTES + COMMENTS

Detecting multicollinearity when a categorical variable is involved is difficult. The correlation coefficient that we used in Section 7.5 is appropriate only when assessing the relationship between two quantitative variables. However, recall that if any estimated regression parameters $b_1, b_2, \ldots, b_q$ or associated p values change dramatically when a new independent variable is added to the model (or an existing independent variable is removed from the model), multicollinearity is likely present. We can use our understanding of these ramifications of multicollinearity to assess whether there is multicollinearity that involves a dummy variable. We estimate the regression model twice; once with the dummy variable included as an independent variable and once with the dummy variable omitted from the regression model. If we see relatively little change in the estimated regression parameters $b_1, b_2, \ldots, b_q$ or associated p values for the independent variables that have been included in both regression models, we can be confident there is not a strong multicollinearity involving the dummy variable.

7.7 Modeling Nonlinear Relationships

Regression may be used to model more complex types of relationships. To illustrate, let us consider the problem facing Reynolds, Inc., a manufacturer of industrial scales and laboratory equipment. Managers at Reynolds want to investigate the relationship between length of employment of their salespeople and the number of electronic laboratory scales sold. The file *Reynolds* gives the number of scales sold by 15 randomly selected salespeople for the most recent sales period and the number of months each salesperson has been employed by the firm. Figure 7.27, the scatter chart for these data, indicates a possible curvilinear relationship between the length of time employed and the number of units sold.

FIGURE 7.27 Scatter Chart for the Reynolds Example

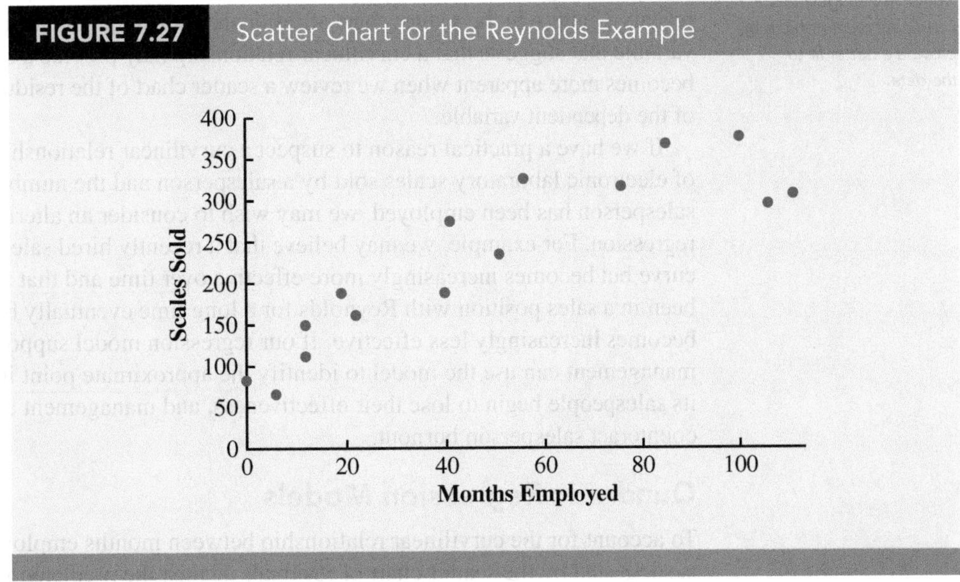

FIGURE 7.28 Excel Regression Output for the Reynolds Example

	A	B	C	D	E	F	G	H	I
1	SUMMARY OUTPUT								
2									
3	*Regression Statistics*								
4	Multiple R	0.888897515							
5	R Square	0.790138792							
6	Adjusted R Square	0.773995622							
7	Standard Error	48.49087146							
8	Observations	15							
9									
10	ANOVA								
11		*df*	*SS*	*MS*	*F*	*Significance F*			
12	Regression	1	115089.1933	115089.1933	48.94570268	9.39543E–06			
13	Residual	13	30567.74	2351.364615					
14	Total	14	145656.9333						
15									
16		*Coefficients*	*Standard Error*	*t Stat*	*P-value*	*Lower 95%*	*Upper 95%*	*Lower 95.0%*	*Upper 95.0%*
17	Intercept	113.7452874	20.81345608	5.464987985	0.000108415	68.78054927	158.7100256	68.78054927	158.7100256
18	Months Employed	2.367463621	0.338396631	6.996120545	9.39543E-06	1.636402146	3.098525095	1.636402146	3.098525095

Before considering how to develop a curvilinear relationship for Reynolds, let us consider the Excel output in Figure 7.28 for a simple linear regression; the estimated regression is:

$$\text{Sales} = 113.7453 + 2.3675 \text{ Months Employed.}$$

The scatter chart of residuals against the independent variable Months Employed would also suggest that a curvilinear relationship may provide a better fit to the data.

The computer output shows that the relationship is significant (p value = 9.3954E-06 in cell E18 of Figure 7.28 for the t test that $\beta_1 = 0$) and that a linear relationship explains a high percentage of the variability in sales ($r^2 = 0.7901$ in cell B5). However, Figure 7.29 reveals a pattern in the scatter chart of residuals against the predicted values of the dependent variable that suggests that a curvilinear relationship may provide a better fit to the data. This becomes more apparent when we review a scatter chart of the residuals and predicted values of the dependent variable.

If we have a practical reason to suspect a curvilinear relationship between number of electronic laboratory scales sold by a salesperson and the number of months the salesperson has been employed, we may wish to consider an alternative to simple linear regression. For example, we may believe that a recently hired salesperson faces a learning curve but becomes increasingly more effective over time and that a salesperson who has been in a sales position with Reynolds for a long time eventually becomes burned out and becomes increasingly less effective. If our regression model supports this theory, Reynolds management can use the model to identify the approximate point in employment when its salespeople begin to lose their effectiveness, and management can plan strategies to counteract salesperson burnout.

Quadratic Regression Models

To account for the curvilinear relationship between months employed and scales sold that is suggested by the scatter chart of residuals against the predicted values of the dependent

FIGURE 7.29 Scatter Chart of the Residuals and Predicted Values of the Dependent Variable for the Reynolds Simple Linear Regression

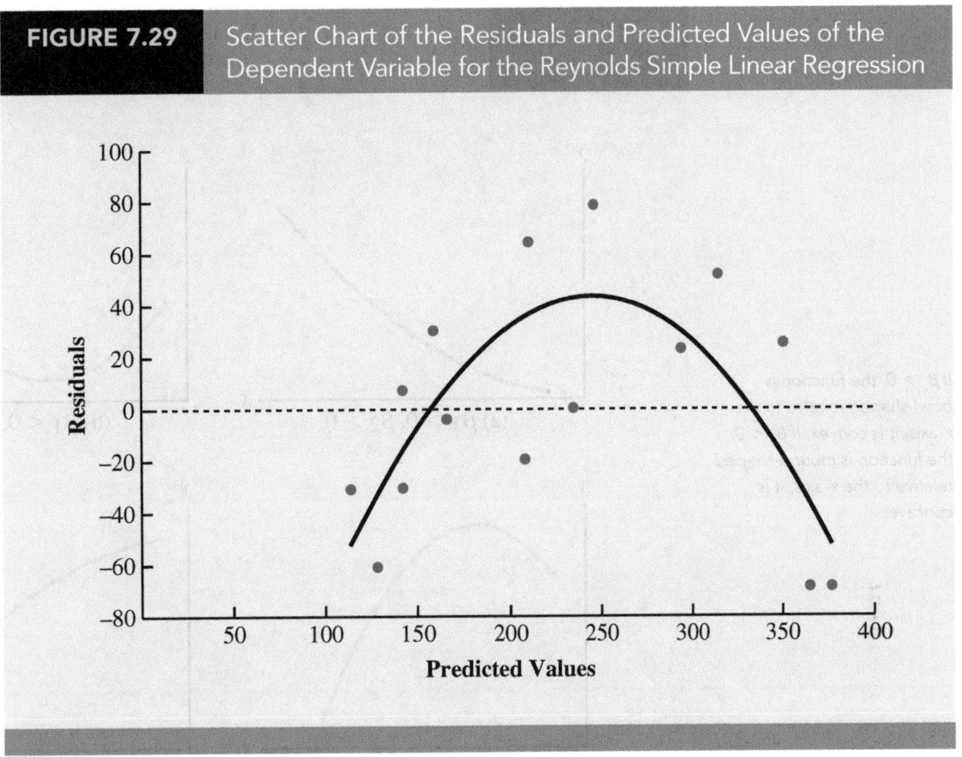

variable, we could include the square of the number of months the salesperson has been employed in the model as a second independent variable:

$$y = b_0 + b_1x_1 + b_2x_1^2 + e. \tag{7.18}$$

As we can see in Figure 7.30, quadratic regression models are flexible and are capable of representing a wide variety of nonlinear relationships between an independent variable and the dependent variable.

To develop an estimated regression equation corresponding to this model, referred to as a **quadratic regression model**, the statistical software package we are using needs the original data as well as the square of the number of months the employee has been with the firm. Figure 7.31 shows the Excel spreadsheet that includes the square of the number of months the employee has been with the firm. To create the variable, which we will call MonthsSq, we create a new column and set each cell in that column equal to the square of the associated value of the variable Months. These values are shown in Column B of Figure 7.31.

The regression output for the model in equation (7.18) is shown in Figure 7.32. The estimated regression equation is:

$$\text{Sales} = 61.4299 + 5.8198 \text{ Months Employed} - 0.0310 \text{ MonthsSq},$$

where MonthsSq is the square of the number of months the salesperson has been employed. Because the value of b_1 (5.8198) is positive, and the value of b_2 (−0.0310) is negative, $\hat{y}$ will initially increase as the number of months the salesperson has been employed increases. As the value of the independent variable Months Employed increases, its squared value increases more rapidly, and eventually $\hat{y}$ will decrease as the number of months the salesperson has been employed increases.

The R^2 of 0.9013 indicates that this regression model explains approximately 90.2% of the variation in Scales Sold for our sample data. The lack of a distinct pattern in the scatter

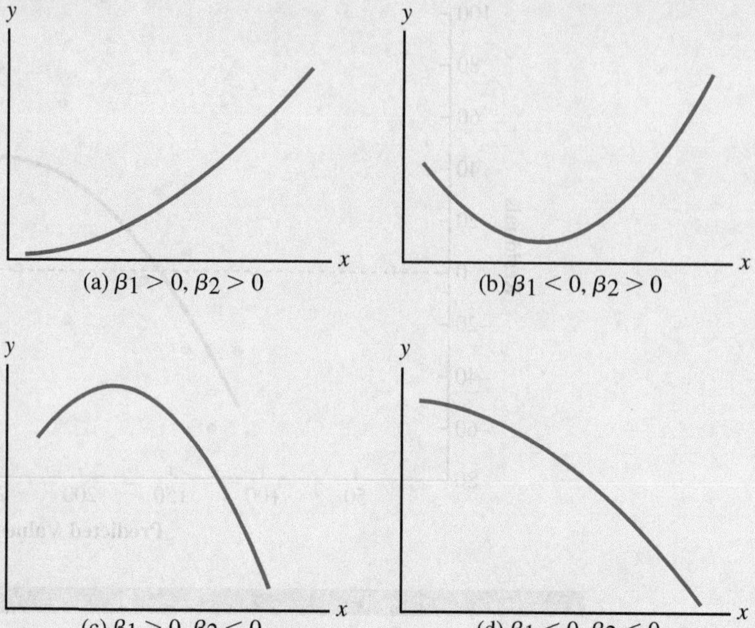

If $\beta_2 > 0$, the function is bowl-shaped relative to the x-axis, it is convex; if $\beta_2 < 0$, the function is mound-shaped relative to the x-axis, it is concave.

FIGURE 7.30 Relationships That Can Be Fit with a Quadratic Regression Model

FIGURE 7.31 Excel Data for the Reynolds Quadratic Regression Model

	A	B	C
1	Months Employed	MonthsSq	Scales Sold
2	41	1,681	275
3	106	11,236	296
4	76	5,776	317
5	100	10,000	376
6	22	484	162
7	12	144	150
8	85	7,225	367
9	111	12,321	308
10	40	1,600	189
11	51	2,601	235
12	0	0	83
13	12	144	112
14	6	36	67
15	56	3,136	325
16	19	361	189

FIGURE 7.32 Excel Output for the Reynolds Quadratic Regression Model

	A	B	C	D	E	F	G	H	I
1	SUMMARY OUTPUT								
2									
3	*Regression Statistics*								
4	Multiple R	0.949361402							
5	R Square	0.901287072							
6	Adjusted R Square	0.884834917							
7	Standard Error	34.61481184							
8	Observations	15							
9									
10	ANOVA								
11		*df*	*SS*	*MS*	*F*	*Significance F*			
12	Regression	2	131278.711	65639.35548	54.78231208	9.25218E-07			
13	Residual	12	14378.22238	1198.185199					
14	Total	14	145656.9333						
15									
16		*Coefficients*	*Standard Error*	*t Stat*	*P-value*	*Lower 95%*	*Upper 95%*	*Lower 99.0%*	*Upper 99.0%*
17	Intercept	61.42993467	20.57433536	2.985755485	0.011363561	16.60230882	106.2575605	−1.415187222	124.2750566
18	Months Employed	5.819796648	0.969766536	6.001234761	6.20497E-05	3.706856877	7.93273642	2.857606371	8.781986926
19	MonthsSq	−0.031009589	0.008436087	−3.675826286	0.003172962	−0.049390243	−0.012628935	−0.05677795	−0.005241228

The scatter chart of residuals against the independent variable Months Employed would also lead us to this conclusion.

chart of residuals against the predicted values of the dependent variable (Figure 7.33) suggests that the quadratic model fits the data better than the simple linear regression in the Reynolds example.

Although it is difficult to assess from a sample as small as this whether the regression model satisfies the conditions necessary for reliable inference, we see no marked violations of these conditions, so we will proceed with hypothesis tests of the regression parameters β_0, β_1, and β_2 for our quadratic regression model.

From the Excel output for the model in equation (7.18) provided in Figure 7.32, we see that the p values corresponding to the t statistics for Months Employed (6.2050E-05) and MonthsSq (0.0032) are both substantially less than 0.05, and hence we can conclude that adding MonthsSq to the model involving Months is significant. There is a nonlinear relationship between months and sales.

Note that if the estimated regression parameters b_1 and b_2 corresponding to the linear term x and the squared term x^2 are of the same sign, the estimated value of the dependent variable is either increasing over the experimental range of x (when $b_1 > 0$ and $b_2 > 0$) or decreasing over the experimental range of x (when $b_1 < 0$ and $b_2 < 0$). If the estimated regression parameters b_1 and b_2 corresponding to the linear term x and the squared term x^2 have different signs, the estimated value of the dependent variable has a maximum over the experimental range of x (when $b_1 > 0$ and $b_2 < 0$) or a minimum over the experimental range of x (when $b_1 < 0$ and $b_2 > 0$). In these instances, we can find the estimated maximum or minimum over the experimental range of x by finding the value of x at which the estimated value of the dependent variable stops increasing and begins decreasing (when a maximum exists) or stops decreasing and begins increasing (when a minimum exists).

FIGURE 7.33 Scatter Chart of the Residuals and Predicted Values of the Dependent Variable for the Reynolds Quadratic Regression Model

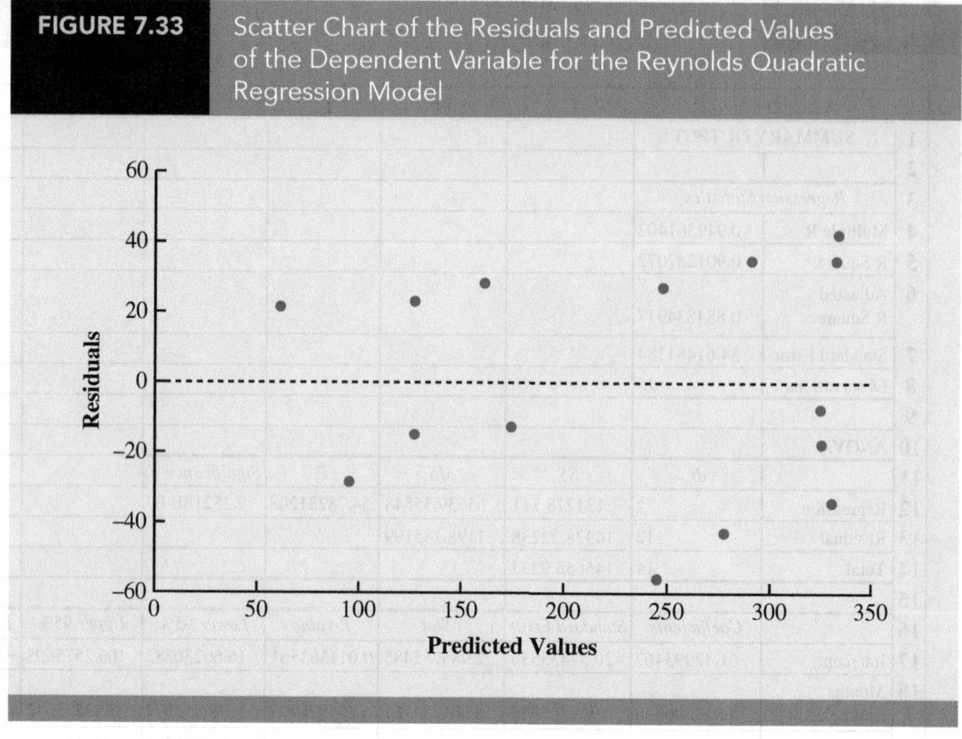

For example, we estimate that when months employed increases by 1 from some value x $(x + 1)$, sales changes by:

$$\begin{aligned} &5.8198\,[(x+1)-x]-0.0310\,[(x+1)^2-x^2]\\ &= 5.8198\,(x-x+1)-0.0310\,(x^2+2x+1-x^2)\\ &= 5.8198-0.0310\,(2x+1)\\ &= 5.7888-0.0620x. \end{aligned}$$

That is, estimated Sales initially increases as Months Employed increases and then eventually decreases as Months Employed increases. Solving this result for x:

$$\begin{aligned} 5.7888-0.0620x &= 0\\ -0.0620x &= -5.7888\\ x &= \frac{-5.7888}{-0.0620} = 93.3387 \end{aligned}$$

tells us that estimated maximum sales occurs at approximately 93 months (in about seven years nine months). We can then find the estimated maximum value of the dependent variable Sales by substituting this value of x into the estimated regression equation:

In business analytics applications, polynomial regression models of higher than second or third order are rarely used.

$$\text{Sales} = 61.58198 + 5.8198\,(93.3387) - 0.0310\,(93.3387^2) = 334.4909.$$

At approximately 93 months, the maximum estimated sales of approximately 334 scales occurs.

Piecewise Linear Regression Models

A piecewise linear regression model is sometimes referred to as a segment regression or a spline model.

As an alternative to a quadratic regression model, we can recognize that below some value of Months Employed, the relationship between Months Employed and Sales appears to be positive and linear, whereas the relationship between Months Employed and Sales appears to be negative and linear for the remaining observations. A **piecewise linear regression model**

FIGURE 7.34 Possible Position of Knot $x^{(k)}$

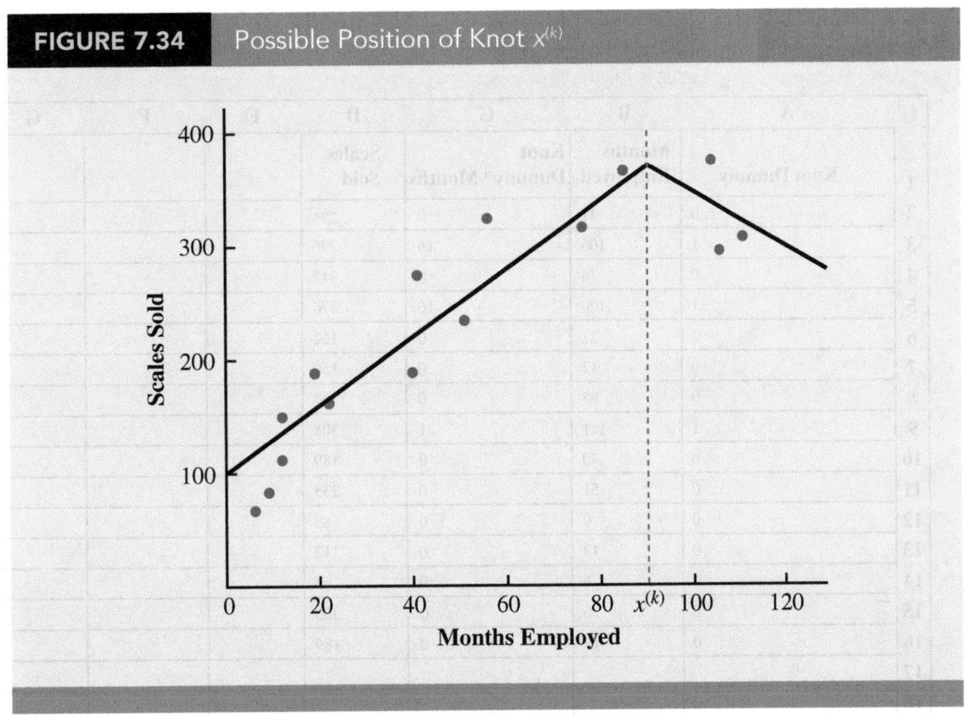

will allow us to fit these relationships as two linear regressions that are joined at the value of Months at which the relationship between Months Employed and Sales changes.

Our first step in fitting a piecewise linear regression model is to identify the value of the independent variable Months Employed at which the relationship between Months Employed and Sales changes; this point is called the **knot**, or *breakpoint*. Although theory should determine this value, analysts often use the sample data to aid in the identification of this point. Figure 7.34 provides the scatter chart for the Reynolds data with an indication of the possible location of the knot, which we have denoted $x^{(k)}$. From this scatter chart, it appears the knot is at approximately 90 months.

Once we have decided on the location of the knot, we define a dummy variable that is equal to zero for any observation for which the value of Months Employed is less than or equal to the value of the knot, and equal to one for any observation for which the value of Months Employed is greater than the value of the knot:

$$x_k = \begin{cases} 0 \text{ if } x_1 \leq x^{(k)} \\ 1 \text{ if } x_1 > x^{(k)} \end{cases} \tag{7.19}$$

where

x_1 = Months

$x^{(k)}$ = the value of the knot (90 months for the Reynolds example)

x_k = the knot dummy variable

We then fit the following regression model:

$$y = b_0 + b_1x_1 + b_2(x_1 - x^{(k)})x_k + e. \tag{7.20}$$

The data and Excel output for the Reynolds piecewise linear regression model are provided in Figure 7.35. Because we placed the knot at $x^{(k)} = 90$, the estimated regression model is

$$\hat{y} = 87.2172 + 3.4094x_1 - 7.8726(x_1 - 90)x_k$$

FIGURE 7.35 Data and Excel Output for the Reynolds Piecewise Linear Regression Model

	A	B	C	D	E	F	G	H	I
1	Knot Dummy	Months Employed	Knot Dummy* Months	Scales Sold					
2	0	41	0	275					
3	1	106	16	296					
4	0	76	0	317					
5	1	100	10	376					
6	0	22	0	162					
7	0	12	0	150					
8	0	85	0	367					
9	1	111	21	308					
10	0	40	0	189					
11	0	51	0	235					
12	0	0	0	83					
13	0	12	0	112					
14	0	6	0	67					
15	0	56	0	325					
16	0	19	0	189					
17									
18									
19	SUMMARY OUTPUT								
20									
21	*Regression Statistics*								
22	Multiple R	0.955796127							
23	R Square	0.913546237							
24	Adjusted R Square	0.899137276							
25	Standard Error	32.3941739							
26	Observations	15							
27									
28	ANOVA								
29		*df*	*SS*	*MS*	*F*	*Significance F*			
30	Regression	2	133064.3433	66532.17165	63.4012588	4.17545E-07			
31	Residual	12	12592.59003	1049.382502					
32	Total	14	145656.9333						
33									
34		*Coefficients*	*Standard Error*	*t Stat*	*P-value*	*Lower 95%*	*Upper 95%*	*Lower 99.0%*	*Upper 99.0%*
35	Intercept	87.21724231	15.31062519	5.696517369	9.9677E-05	53.85825572	120.5762289	40.45033153	133.9841531
36	Months Employed	3.409431979	0.338360666	10.07632484	3.2987E-07	2.67220742	4.146656538	2.375895931	4.442968028
37	Knot Dummy* Months	-7.872553259	1.902156543	-4.138751508	0.00137388	-12.01699634	-3.728110179	-13.68276572	-2.062340794

The output shows that the p value corresponding to the t statistic for knot term ($p = 0.0014$) is less than 0.05, and hence we can conclude that adding the knot to the model with Months Employed as the independent variable is significant.

But what does this model mean? For any value of Months less than or equal to 90, the knot term $7.8726(x_1 - 90)x_k$ is zero because the knot dummy variable $x_k = 0$, so the regression model is:

$$\hat{y} = 87.2172 + 3.4094x_1.$$

*The variable Knot Dummy*Months is the product of the corresponding values of Knot Dummy and the difference between Months Employed and the knot value, i.e., C2 = A2 * (B2 − 90) in this Excel spreadsheet.*

For any value of Months Employed greater than 90, the knot term is $-7.87(x_1 - 90)$ because the knot dummy variable $x_k = 1$, so the regression model is:

$$\begin{aligned}\hat{y} &= 87.2172 + 3.4094x_1 - 7.8726(x_1 - 90)\\ &= 87.2172 - 7.8726(-90) + (3.4094 - 7.8726)x_1 = 795.7512 - 4.4632x_1.\end{aligned}$$

Note that if Months Employed is equal to 90, both regressions yield the same value of $\hat{y}$:

$$\hat{y} = 87.2172 + 3.4094(90) = 795.7512 - 4.4632(90) = 394.06.$$

So the two regression segments are joined at the knot.

Multiple knots can be used to fit complex piecewise linear regressions.

The interpretation of this model is similar to the interpretation of the quadratic regression model. A salesperson's sales are expected to increase by 3,409.4 electronic laboratory scales for each month of employment until the salesperson has been employed for 90 months. At that point the salesperson's sales are expected to decrease by 4,463.1 (because 3,409.4 − 7,872.5 = −4,463.1) electronic laboratory scales for each additional month of employment.

Should we use the quadratic regression model or the piecewise linear regression model? These models fit the data equally well, and both have reasonable interpretations, so we cannot differentiate between the models on either of these criteria. Thus, we must consider whether the abrupt change in the relationship between Sales and Months Employed that is suggested by the piecewise linear regression model captures the real relationship between Sales and Months Employed better than the smooth change in the relationship between Sales and Months Employed suggested by the quadratic model.

Interaction Between Independent Variables

Often the relationship between the dependent variable and one independent variable is different at various values of a second independent variable. When this occurs, it is called an **interaction**. If the original data set consists of observations for y and two independent variables x_1 and x_2, we can incorporate an x_1x_2 interaction into the multiple linear regression in the following manner:

$$y = b_0 + b_1x_1 + b_2x_2 + b_3x_1x_2 + e. \quad \textbf{(7.21)}$$

To provide an illustration of interaction and what it means, let us consider the regression study conducted by Tyler Personal Care for one of its new shampoo products. The two factors believed to have the most influence on sales are unit selling price and advertising expenditure. To investigate the effects of these two variables on sales, prices of \$2.00, \$2.50, and \$3.00 were paired with advertising expenditures of \$50,000 and \$100,000 in 24 test markets.

Tyler

The data collected by Tyler are provided in the file *Tyler*. Figure 7.36 shows the sample mean sales for the six price advertising expenditure combinations. Note that the sample mean sales corresponding to a price of \$2.00 and an advertising expenditure of \$50,000 is 461,000 units and that the sample mean sales corresponding to a price of \$2.00 and an advertising expenditure of \$100,000 is 808,000 units. Hence, with price held constant at \$2.00, the difference in mean sales between advertising expenditures of \$50,000 and \$100,000 is 808,000 − 461,000 = 347,000 units. When the price of the product is \$2.50, the difference in mean sales between advertising expenditures of \$50,000 and \$100,000 is 646,000 − 364,000 = 282,000 units. Finally, when the price is \$3.00, the difference in mean sales between advertising expenditures of \$50,000 and \$100,000 is 375,000 − 332,000 = 43,000 units. Clearly, the difference in mean sales between advertising expenditures of \$50,000 and \$100,000 depends on the price of the product. In other words, at higher selling prices, the effect of increased advertising expenditure diminishes. These

FIGURE 7.36 Mean Unit Sales (1,000s) as a Function of Selling Price and Advertising Expenditures

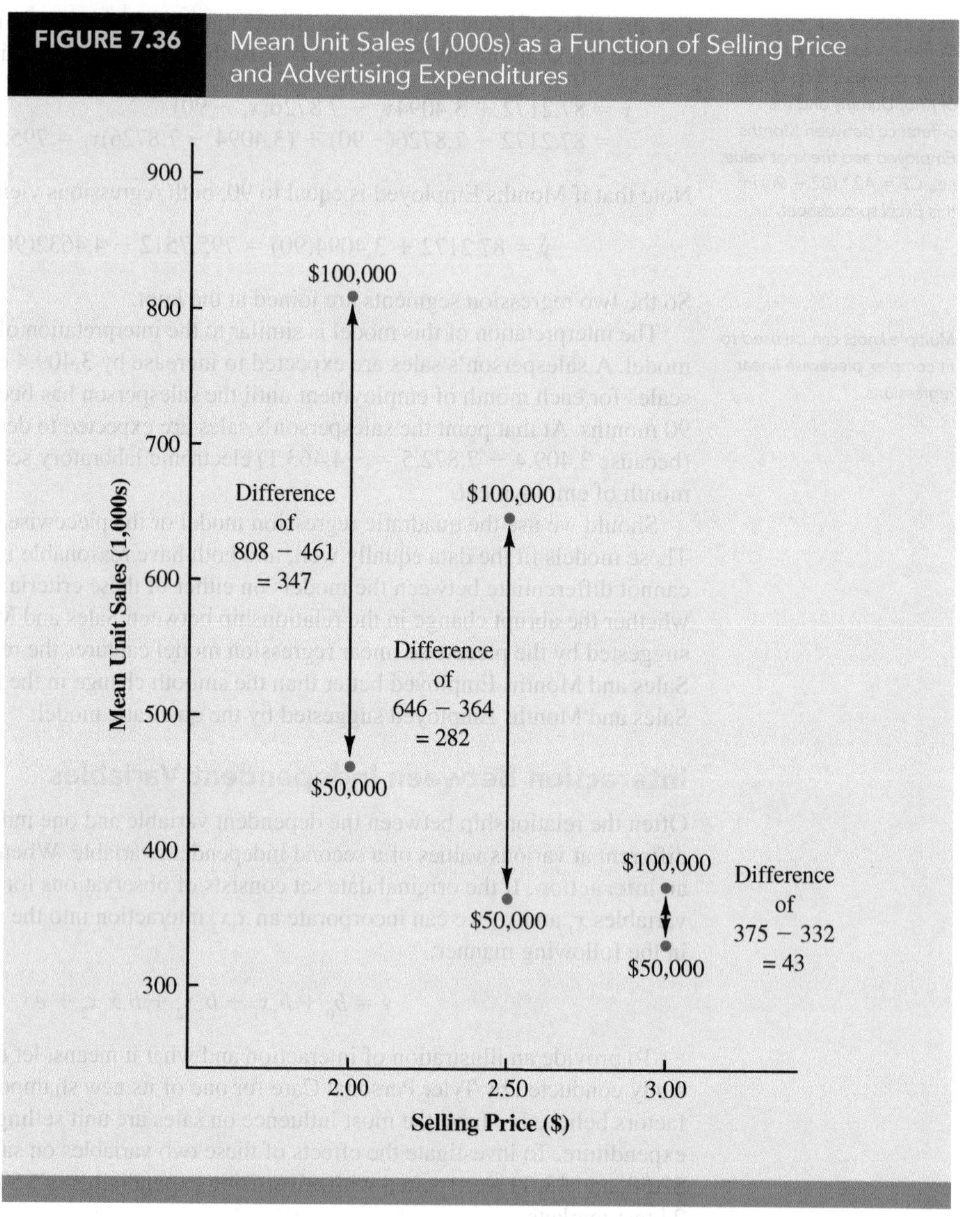

*In the file Tyler, the data for the independent variable Price is in column A, the independent variable Advertising Expenditures is in column B, and the dependent variable Sales is in column D. We created the interaction variable Price*Advertising in column C by entering the function A2*B2 in cell C2, and then copying cell C2 into cells C3 through C25.*

observations provide evidence of interaction between the price and advertising expenditure variables.

When interaction between two variables is present, we cannot study the relationship between one independent variable and the dependent variable y independently of the other variable. In other words, meaningful conclusions can be developed only if we consider the joint relationship that both independent variables have with the dependent variable. To account for the interaction, we use the regression model in equation (7.21), where:

$$y = \text{Unit Sales (1,000s)}$$
$$x_1 = \text{Price (\$)}$$
$$x_2 = \text{Advertising Expenditure (\$1,000s)}$$

FIGURE 7.37 Excel Output for the Tyler Personal Care Linear Regression Model with Interaction

	A	B	C	D	E	F	G	H	I
1	SUMMARY OUTPUT								
2									
3	*Regression Statistics*								
4	Multiple R	0.988993815							
5	R Square	0.978108766							
6	Adjusted R Square	0.974825081							
7	Standard Error	28.17386496							
8	Observations	24							
9									
10	ANOVA								
11		*df*	*SS*	*MS*	*F*	*Significance F*			
12	Regression	3	709316	236438.6667	297.8692	9.25881E-17			
13	Residual	20	15875.33333	793.7666667					
14	Total	23	725191.3333						
15									
16		*Coefficients*	*Standard Error*	*t Stat*	*P-value*	*Lower 95%*	*Upper 95%*	*Lower 99.0%*	*Upper 99.0%*
17	Intercept	–275.8333333	112.8421033	-2.444418575	0.023898351	-511.2178361	-40.44883053	-596.9074508	45.24078413
18	Price	175	44.54679188	3.928453489	0.0008316	82.07702045	267.9229796	48.24924412	301.7507559
19	Advertising Expenditure ($1,000s)	19.68	1.42735225	13.78776683	1.1263E-11	16.70259538	22.65740462	15.61869796	23.74130204
20	Price*Advertising	–6.08	0.563477299	-10.79014187	8.67721E-10	-7.255393049	-4.904606951	-7.683284335	-4.476715665

Note that the regression model in equation (7.21) reflects Tyler's belief that the number of units sold is related to selling price and advertising expenditure (accounted for by the $\beta_1 x_1$ and $\beta_2 x_2$ terms) and an interaction between the two variables (accounted for by the $\beta_3 x_1 x_2$ term).

The Excel output corresponding to the interaction model for the Tyler Personal Care example is provided in Figure 7.37.

The resulting estimated regression equation is:

$$\text{Sales} = -275.8333 + 175\ \text{Price} + 19.68\ \text{Advertising} - 6.08\ \text{Price*Advertising}.$$

Because the p value corresponding to the t test for Price*Advertising is 8.6772E-10, we conclude that interaction is significant. Thus, the regression results show that the relationship between advertising expenditure and sales depends on the price (and the relationship between advertising expenditures and price depends on sales).

Our initial review of these results may alarm us: How can price have a positive estimated regression coefficient? With the exception of luxury goods, we expect sales to decrease as price increases. Although this result appears counterintuitive, we can make sense of this model if we work through the interpretation of the interaction. In other words, the relationship between the independent variable Price and the dependent variable Sales is different at various values of Advertising (and the relationship between the independent variable Advertising and the dependent variable Sales is different at various values of Price).

It becomes easier to see how the predicted value of Sales depends on Price by using the estimated regression model to consider the effect when Price increases by $1:

$$\text{Sales After \$1 Price Increase} = -275.8333 + 175\ (\text{Price} + 1) + 19.68\ \text{Advertising} - 6.08\ (\text{Price} + 1) * \text{Advertising}.$$

Thus,

$$\text{Sales After \$1 Price Increase} - \text{Sales Before \$1 Price Increase} = 175 - 6.08\ \text{Advertising Expenditure}.$$

So the change in the predicted value of the dependent variable that occurs when the independent variable Price increases by $1 depends on how much was spent on advertising.

Consider a concrete example. If Advertising Expenditures is $50,000 when price is $2.00, we estimate sales to be:

$$\text{Sales} = -275.8333 + 175\ (2) + 19.68\ (50) - 6.08\ (2)\ (50) = 450.1667, \text{ or } 450{,}167 \text{ units.}$$

At the same level of Advertising Expenditures ($50,000) when price is $3.00, we estimate sales to be:

$$\text{Sales} = -275.8333 + 175\ (3) + 19.68\ (50) - 6.08\ (3)\ (50) = 321.1667, \text{ or } 321{,}167 \text{ units.}$$

So when Advertising Expenditures is $50,000, a change in price from $2.00 to $3.00 results in a 450,167 − 321,167 = 129,000-unit decrease in estimated sales. However, if Advertising Expenditures is $100,000 when price is $2.00, we estimate sales to be:

$$\text{Sales} = -275.8333 + 175\ (2) + 19.68\ (100) - 6.08\ (2)\ (100) = 826.1667, \text{ or } 826{,}167 \text{ units.}$$

At the same level of Advertising Expenditures ($100,000) when price is $3.00, we estimate sales to be:

$$\text{Sales} = -275.8333 + 175\ (3) + 19.68\ (100) - 6.08\ (3)\ (100) = 393.1667, \text{ or } 393{,}167 \text{ units.}$$

So when Advertising Expenditures is $100,000, a change in price from $2.00 to $3.00 results in a 826,167 − 393,167 = 433,000-unit decrease in estimated sales. When Tyler spends more on advertising, its sales are more sensitive to changes in price. Perhaps at larger Advertising Expenditures, Tyler attracts new customers who have been buying the product from another company and so are more aware of the prices charged for the product by Tyler's competitors.

There is a second and equally valid interpretation of the interaction; it tells us that the relationship between the independent variable Advertising Expenditure and the dependent variable Sales is different at various values of Price. Using the estimated regression model to consider the effect when Advertising Expenditure increases by $1,000:

$$\text{Sales After \$1K Advertising Increase} = -275.8333 + 175\ \text{Price} + 19.68\ (\text{Advertising} + 1) - 6.08\ \text{Price} * (\text{Advertising} + 1).$$

Thus,

$$\text{Sales After \$1K Advertising Increase} - \text{Sales Before \$1K Advertising Increase} = 19.68 - 6.08\ \text{Price}.$$

So the change in the predicted value of the dependent variable that occurs when the independent variable Advertising Expenditure increases by $1,000 depends on the price.

Thus, if Price is \$2.00 when Advertising Expenditures is \$50,000, we estimate sales to be:

Sales $= -275.8333 + 175\,(2) + 19.68\,(50) - 6.08\,(2)\,(50) = 450.1667$, or 450,167 units.

At the same level of Price (\$2.00) when Advertising Expenditures is \$100,000, we estimate sales to be:

Sales $= -275.8333 + 175\,(2) + 19.68\,(100) - 6.08\,(2)\,(100) = 826.1667$, or 826,167 units.

So when Price is \$2.00, a change in Advertising Expenditures from \$50,000 to \$100,000 results in a $826{,}167 - 450{,}167 = 376{,}000$-unit increase in estimated sales. However, if Price is \$3.00 when Advertising Expenditures is 50,000, we estimate sales to be:

Sales $= -275.8333 + 175\,(3) + 19.68\,(50) - 6.08\,(3)\,(50) = 321.1667$, or 321,167 units.

At the same level of Price (\$3.00) when Advertising Expenditures is \$100,000, we estimate sales to be:

Sales $= -275.8333 + 175\,(3) + 19.68\,(100) - 6.08\,(3)\,(100) = 393.1667$, or 393,167 units.

So when Price is \$3.00, a change in Advertising Expenditure from \$50,000 to \$100,000 results in a $393{,}167 - 321{,}167 = 72{,}000$-unit increase in estimated sales. When the price of Tyler's product is high, its sales are less sensitive to changes in advertising expenditure. Perhaps as Tyler increases its price, it must advertise more to convince potential customers that its product is a good value.

Note that we can combine a quadratic effect with interaction to produce a second-order polynomial model with interaction between the two independent variables. The model obtained is:

$$y = b_0 + b_1x_1 + b_2x_2 + b_3x_1^2 + b_4x_2^2 + b_5x_1x_2 + e. \tag{7.22}$$

This model provides a great deal of flexibility in capturing nonlinear effects.

NOTES + COMMENTS

1. Just as a dummy variable can be used to allow for different y-intercepts for the two groups represented by the dummy, we can use an interaction between a dummy variable and a quantitative independent variable to allow for different relationships between independent and dependent variables for the two groups represented by the dummy. Consider the Butler Trucking example: Travel time is the dependent variable y, miles traveled and number of deliveries are the quantitative independent variables x_1 and x_2, and the dummy variable x_3 differentiates between driving assignments that included travel on a congested segment of a highway and driving assignments that did not. If we believe that the relationship between miles traveled and travel time differs for driving assignments that included travel on a congested segment of a highway and those that did not, we could create a new variable that is the interaction between miles traveled and the dummy variable ($x_4 = x_1{*}x_3$) and estimate the following model:

$$\hat{y} = b_0 + b_1x_1 + b_2x_2 + b_3x_4.$$

If a driving assignment does not include travel on a congested segment of a highway, $x_4 = x_1{*}x_3 = x_1{*}(0) = 0$ and the regression model is:

$$\hat{y} = b_0 + b_1x_1 + b_2x_2.$$

If a driving assignment does include travel on a congested segment of a highway, $x_4 = x_1{*}x_3 = x_1{*}(1) = x_1$ and the regression model is:

$$\begin{aligned}\hat{y} &= b_0 + b_1x_1 + b_2x_2 + b_3x_1(1)\\ &= b_0 + (b_1 + b_3)x_1 + b_2x_2.\end{aligned}$$

So in this regression model b_1 is the estimate of the relationship between miles traveled and travel time for driving assignments that do not include travel on a congested segment of a highway, and $b_1 + b_3$ is the estimate of the relationship between miles traveled and travel time for driving assignments that do include travel on a congested segment of a highway.

2. Multicollinearity can be divided into two types. *Data-based multicollinearity* occurs when separate independent variables that are related are included in the model, whereas *structural multicollinearity* occurs when a new independent variable is created by taking a function of one or more existing independent variables. If we use ratings that consumers give on bread's aroma and taste as independent variables in a model for which the dependent variable is the overall rating of the bread, the multicollinearity that would exist between the aroma and taste ratings is an example of data-based multicollinearity. If we build a quadratic model for which the independent variables are ratings that consumers give on bread's aroma and the square of the ratings that consumers give on bread's aroma, the multicollinearity that would exist is an example of structural multicollinearity.

3. Structural multicollinearity occurs naturally in polynomial regression models and regression models with interactions. You can greatly reduce the structural multicollinearity in a polynomial regression by centering the independent variable x (using $x - \bar{x}$ in place of x). In a regression model with interaction, you can greatly reduce the structural multicollinearity by centering both independent variables that interact. However, quadratic regression models and regression models with interactions are frequently used only for prediction; in these instances centering independent variables is not necessary because we are not concerned with inference.

7.8 Model Fitting

Finding an effective regression model can be challenging. Although we rely on theory to guide us, often we are faced with a large number of potential independent variables from which to choose. In this section we discuss common algorithms for building a regression model and the potential hazards of these and other similar algorithms.

Variable Selection Procedures

When there are many independent variables to consider, special procedures are sometimes employed to select the independent variables to include in the regression model. These variable selection procedures include **backward elimination**, **forward selection**, **stepwise selection**, and the **best subsets** procedure. Given a data set with several possible independent variables, we can use these procedures to identify which independent variables provide a model that best satisfies some criterion. The first four procedures are iterative; at each step of the procedure a single independent variable is added or removed and the new model is evaluated. The process continues until a stopping criterion indicates that the procedure cannot find a superior model. The best subsets procedure is not a one-variable-at-a-time procedure; it evaluates regression models involving different subsets of the independent variables.

The backward elimination procedure begins with the regression model that includes all of the independent variables under consideration. At each step of the procedure, backward elimination considers the removal of an independent variable according to some criterion. For example, if any independent variables currently in the model are not significant at a preselected level of significance, XLMiner removes the least significant of these independent variables from the model. The regression model is then refit with the remaining independent variables and statistical significance is reexamined. The backward elimination procedure stops when all independent variables in the model are significant at a preselected level of significance.

The forward selection procedure begins with none of the independent variables under consideration included in the regression model. At each step of the procedure, forward selection considers the addition of an independent variable according to some criterion. For example, if any independent variables currently not in the model are significant at a preselected level of significance, XLMiner adds the most significant of these independent variables to the model. The regression model is then refit with the additional independent variable and statistical significance is reexamined. The forward selection procedure stops when all of the independent variables not in the model are not significant at a preselected level of significance.

The stepwise procedure requires that the criterion for an independent variable to enter the regression model is more difficult to satisfy than the criterion for an independent variable to be removed from the regression model. This requirement prevents the same independent variable from exiting and then reentering the regression model in the same step.

Similar to the forward selection procedure, the stepwise procedure begins with none of the independent variables under consideration included in the regression model. The analyst establishes both a criterion for allowing independent variables to enter the model and a criterion for allowing independent variables to remain in the model. For example, XLMiner adds the most significant variable and removes the least significant variable at each iteration. In the first step of the procedure, the most significant independent variable is added to the current model if its level of significance satisfies the entering threshold. Each subsequent step involves two intermediate steps. First, the remaining independent variables not in the current model are evaluated, and the most significant one is added to the model if its significance satisfies the entering threshold. Then the independent variables in the resulting model are evaluated, and the least significant variable is removed if its level of significance fails to satisfy the exiting threshold. The procedure stops when no independent variable not currently in the model has a level of significance that satisfies the entering threshold, and no independent variable currently in the model has a level of significance that fails to satisfy the exiting threshold.

XLMiner also provides a sequential replacement algorithm in which, for a given number of independent variables, individual independent variables are sequentially replaced and replacements that improve performance are retained.

In the best subsets procedure, simple linear regressions for each of the independent variables under consideration are generated, and then the multiple regressions with all combinations of two independent variables under consideration are generated, and so on. Once a regression model has been generated for every possible subset of the independent variables under consideration, the entire collection of regression models can be compared and evaluated by the analyst.

Although these algorithms are potentially useful when dealing with a large number of potential independent variables, they do not necessarily provide useful models. Once the procedure terminates, you should deliberate whether the combination of independent variables included in the final regression model makes sense from a practical standpoint and consider whether you can create a more useful regression model with more meaningful interpretation through the addition or removal of independent variables. Use your own judgment and intuition about your data to refine the results of these algorithms.

Overfitting

The objective in building a regression model (or any other type of mathematical model) is to provide the simplest accurate representation of the population. A model that is relatively simple will be easy to understand, interpret, and use, and a model that accurately represents the population will yield meaningful results.

When we base a model on sample data, we must be wary. Sample data generally do not perfectly represent the population from which they are drawn; if we attempt to fit a model too closely to the sample data, we risk capturing behavior that is idiosyncratic to the sample data rather than representative of the population. When the model is too closely fit to sample data and as a result does not accurately reflect the population, the model is said to have been overfit.

The principle of using the simplest meaningful model possible without sacrificing accuracy is referred to as Ockham's razor, the law of parsimony, or the law of economy.

Overfitting generally results from creating an overly complex model to explain idiosyncrasies in the sample data. In regression analysis, this often results from the use of complex functional forms or independent variables that do not have meaningful relationships with the dependent variable. If a model is overfit to the sample data, it will perform better on the sample data used to fit the model than it will on other data from the population. Thus, an overfit model can be misleading with regard to its predictive capability and its interpretation.

Overfitting is a difficult problem to detect and avoid. The following list summarizes one way to avoid overfitting and one way to determine how well a model will may generalize to new data.

- Use only independent variables that you expect to have real and meaningful relationships with the dependent variable.
- Use complex models, such as quadratic models and piecewise linear regression models, only when you have a reasonable expectation that such complexity provides a more accurate depiction of what you are modeling.
- Do not let software dictate your model. Use iterative modeling procedures, such as the stepwise and best-subsets procedures, only for guidance and not to generate your final model. Use your own judgment and intuition about your data and what you are modeling to refine your model.
- If you have access to a sufficient quantity of data, assess your model on data other than the sample data that were used to generate the model (this is referred to as **cross-validation**. The following list contains three possible ways to execute cross-validation.

Validation data sets are sometimes referred to as holdout samples. XLMiner allows the user to easily divide data sets into training and validation sets for use with regression models.

  Holdout method: The sample data are randomly divided into mutually exclusive and collectively exhaustive training and validation sets. The **training set** is the data set used to build the candidate models that appear to make practical sense. The **validation set** is the set of data used to compare model performances and ultimately select a model for predicting values of the dependent variable. For example, we might randomly select half of the data for use in developing regression models. We could use these data as our training set to estimate a model or a collection of models that appear to perform well. Then we use the remaining half of the data as a validation set to assess and compare the models' performances and ultimately select the model that minimizes some measure of overall error when applied to the validation set. The advantages of the holdout method are that it is simple and quick. However, results of a holdout sample can vary greatly depending on which observations are randomly selected for the training set, the number of observations in the sample, and the number of observations that are randomly selected for the training and validation sets.

  ***k*-fold cross-validation:** The sample data set are randomly divided into k equal-sized, mutually exclusive, and collectively exhaustive subsets called folds, and k iterations are executed. For each iteration, a different subset is designated as the validation set and the remaining $k - 1$ subsets are combined and designated as the training set. The model is estimated using the respective training set data and evaluated using the respective validation set. The results of the k iterations are then combined and evaluated. A common choice for the number of folds is $k = 10$. The k-fold cross-validation method is more complex and time consuming than the holdout method, but the results of the k-fold cross-validation method are less sensitive to how the observations are randomly assigned to the training validation sets.

  Leave-one-out cross-validation: For a sample of n observations, an iteration consists of estimating the model on $n - 1$ observations and evaluating the model on the single observation that was omitted from the training data. This procedure is repeated for n total iterations so that the model is trained on each possible combination of $n - 1$ observations and evaluated on the single remaining observation in each case.

Observing these guidelines will reduce the risk of overfitting, but one must always be wary of the potential for overfitting when interpreting and assessing a model.

SUMMARY

In this chapter we showed how regression analysis can be used to determine how a dependent variable y is related to an independent variable x. In simple linear regression, the regression model is $y = \beta_0 + \beta_1 x_1 + \varepsilon$. We use sample data and the least squares method to develop the estimated regression equation $\hat{y} = b_0 + b_1 x_1$. In effect, b_0 and b_1 are the sample statistics used to estimate the unknown model parameters.

The coefficient of determination r^2 was presented as a measure of the goodness of fit for the estimated regression equation; it can be interpreted as the proportion of the variation in the sample values of the dependent variable y that can be explained by the estimated regression equation. We then extended our discussion to include multiple independent variables and reviewed how to use Excel to find the estimated multiple regression equation $\hat{y} = b_0 + b_1 x_1 + b_2 x_2 + \cdots + b_q x_q$, and we considered the interpretations of the parameter estimates in multiple regression and the ramifications of multicollinearity.

The assumptions related to the regression model and its associated error term ε were discussed. We reviewed the t test for determining whether there is a statistically significant relationship between the dependent variable and an individual independent variable given the other independent variables in the regression model. We showed how to use Excel to develop confidence interval estimates of the regression parameters $\beta_0, \beta_1, \ldots, \beta_q$, and we discussed the special case of inference with very large samples.

We showed how to incorporate categorical independent variables into a regression model through the use of dummy variables, and we discussed a variety of ways to use multiple regression to fit nonlinear relationships between independent variables and the dependent variable. We concluded with a discussion of various automated procedures for selecting independent variables to include in a regression model and consideration of the problem of overfitting a regression model.

GLOSSARY

Backward elimination An iterative variable selection procedure that starts with a model with all independent variables and considers removing an independent variable at each step.

Best subsets A variable selection procedure that constructs and compares all possible models with up to a specified number of independent variables.

Coefficient of determination A measure of the goodness of fit of the estimated regression equation. It can be interpreted as the proportion of the variability in the dependent variable y that is explained by the estimated regression equation.

Confidence interval An estimate of a population parameter that provides an interval believed to contain the value of the parameter at some level of confidence.

Confidence level An indication of how frequently interval estimates based on samples of the same size taken from the same population using identical sampling techniques will contain the true value of the parameter we are estimating.

Cross-validation Assessment of the performance of a model on data other than the data that were used to generate the model.

Dependent variable The variable that is being predicted or explained. It is denoted by y and is often referred to as the response.

Dummy variable A variable used to model the effect of categorical independent variables in a regression model; generally takes only the value zero or one.

Estimated regression The estimate of the regression equation developed from sample data by using the least squares method. The estimated simple linear regression equation is $\hat{y} = b_0 + b_1 x$, and the estimated multiple linear regression equation is $\hat{y} = b_0 + b_1 x_1 + b_2 x_2 + \cdots + b_q x_q$.

Experimental region The range of values for the independent variables $x_1, x_2, \ldots, x_q$ for the data that are used to estimate the regression model.
Extrapolation Prediction of the mean value of the dependent variable y for values of the independent variables $x_1, x_2, \ldots, x_q$ that are outside the experimental range.
Forward selection an iterative variable selection procedure that starts with a model with no variables and considers adding an independent variable at each step.
Holdout method Method of cross-validation in which sample data are randomly divided into mutually exclusive and collectively exhaustive sets, then one set is used to build the candidate models and the other set is used to compare model performances and ultimately select a model.
Hypothesis testing The process of making a conjecture about the value of a population parameter, collecting sample data that can be used to assess this conjecture, measuring the strength of the evidence against the conjecture that is provided by the sample, and using these results to draw a conclusion about the conjecture.
Independent variable(s) The variable(s) used for predicting or explaining values of the dependent variable. It is denoted by x and is often referred to as the predictor variable.
Interaction The relationship between the dependent variable and one independent variable is different at different values of a second independent variable.
Interval estimation The use of sample data to calculate a range of values that is believed to include the unknown value of a population parameter.
***k*-fold cross validation** Method of cross-validation in which sample data set are randomly divided into k equal sized, mutually exclusive and collectively exhaustive subsets. In each of k iterations, one of the k subsets is used to build a candidate model and the remaining $k - 1$ sets are used evaluate the candidate model.
Knot The prespecified value of the independent variable at which its relationship with the dependent variable changes in a piecewise linear regression model; also called the breakpoint or the joint.
Least squares method A procedure for using sample data to find the estimated regression equation.
Leave-one-out cross validation Method of cross-validation in which candidate models are repeatedly fit using $n - 1$ observations and evaluated with the remaining observation.
Linear regression Regression analysis in which relationships between the independent variables and the dependent variable are approximated by a straight line.
Multicollinearity The degree of correlation among independent variables in a regression model.
Multiple linear regression Regression analysis involving one dependent variable and more than one independent variable.
Overfitting Fitting a model too closely to sample data, resulting in a model that does not accurately reflect the population.
***p* value** The probability that a random sample of the same size collected from the same population using the same procedure will yield stronger evidence against a hypothesis than the evidence in the sample data given that the hypothesis is actually true.
Parameter A measurable factor that defines a characteristic of a population, process, or system.
Piecewise linear regression model Regression model in which one linear relationship between the independent and dependent variables is fit for values of the independent variable below a prespecified value of the independent variable, a different linear relationship between the independent and dependent variables is fit for values of the independent variable above the prespecified value of the independent variable, and the two regressions have the same estimated value of the dependent variable (i.e., are joined) at the prespecified value of the independent variable.
Point estimator A single value used as an estimate of the corresponding population parameter.
Quadratic regression model Regression model in which a nonlinear relationship between the independent and dependent variables is fit by including the independent variable and

the square of the independent variable in the model: $\hat{y} = b_0 + b_1x_1 + b_2x_1^2$; also referred to as a second-order polynomial model.
Random variable The outcome of a random experiment (such as the drawing of a random sample) and so represents an uncertain outcome.
Regression analysis A statistical procedure used to develop an equation showing how the variables are related.
Regression model The equation that describes how the dependent variable y is related to an independent variable x and an error term; the *simple linear regression model* is $y = \beta_0 + \beta_1x_1 + \varepsilon$, and the *multiple linear regression model* is $y = \beta_0 + \beta_1x_1 + \beta_2x_2 + \cdots + \beta_qx_q + \varepsilon$.
Residual The difference between the observed value of the dependent variable and the value predicted using the estimated regression equation; for the ith observation, the ith residual is $y_i - \hat{y}_i$.
Simple linear regression Regression analysis involving one dependent variable and one independent variable.
Statistical inference The process of making estimates and drawing conclusions about one or more characteristics of a population (the value of one or more parameters) through analysis of sample data drawn from the population.
Stepwise selection an iterative variable selection procedure that considers adding an independent variable and removing an independent variable at each step.
***t* test** Statistical test based on the Student's t probability distribution that can be used to test the hypothesis that a regression parameter β_j is zero; if this hypothesis is rejected, we conclude that there is a regression relationship between the jth independent variable and the dependent variable.
Training set The data set used to build the candidate models.
Validation set The data set used to compare model forecasts and ultimately pick a model for predicting values of the dependent variable.

PROBLEMS

1. *Bicycling World*, a magazine devoted to cycling, reviews hundreds of bicycles throughout the year. Its Road-Race category contains reviews of bicycles used by riders primarily interested in racing. One of the most important factors in selecting a bicycle for racing is its weight. The following data show the weight (pounds) and price ($) for ten racing bicycles reviewed by the magazine:

BicyclingWorld

Model	Weight (lb)	Price ($)
Fierro 7B	17.9	2,200
HX 5000	16.2	6,350
Durbin Ultralight	15.0	8,470
Schmidt	16.0	6,300
WSilton Advanced	17.3	4,100
bicyclette vélo	13.2	8,700
Supremo Team	16.3	6,100
XTC Racer	17.2	2,680
D'Onofrio Pro	17.7	3,500
Americana #6	14.2	8,100

a. Develop a scatter chart with weight as the independent variable. What does the scatter chart indicate about the relationship between the weight and price of these bicycles?
b. Use the data to develop an estimated regression equation that could be used to estimate the price for a bicycle, given its weight. What is the estimated regression model?

c. Test whether each of the regression parameters β_0 and β_1 is equal to zero at a 0.05 level of significance. What are the correct interpretations of the estimated regression parameters? Are these interpretations reasonable?
d. How much of the variation in the prices of the bicycles in the sample does the regression model you estimated in part (b) explain?
e. The manufacturers of the D'Onofrio Pro plan to introduce the 15-lb D'Onofrio Elite bicycle later this year. Use the regression model you estimated in part (a) to predict the price of the D'Ononfrio Elite.

2. In a manufacturing process the assembly line speed (feet per minute) was thought to affect the number of defective parts found during the inspection process. To test this theory, managers devised a situation in which the same batch of parts was inspected visually at a variety of line speeds. They collected the following data:

Line Speed (ft/min)	No. of Defective Parts Found
20	21
20	19
40	15
30	16
60	14
40	17

a. Develop a scatter chart with line speed as the independent variable. What does the scatter chart indicate about the relationship between line speed and the number of defective parts found?
b. Use the data to develop an estimated regression equation that could be used to predict the number of defective parts found, given the line speed. What is the estimated regression model?
c. Test whether each of the regression parameters β_0 and β_1 is equal to zero at a 0.01 level of significance. What are the correct interpretations of the estimated regression parameters? Are these interpretations reasonable?
d. How much of the variation in the number of defective parts found for the sample data does the model you estimated in part (b) explain?

3. Jensen Tire & Auto is deciding whether to purchase a maintenance contract for its new computer wheel alignment and balancing machine. Managers feel that maintenance expense should be related to usage, and they collected the following information on weekly usage (hours) and annual maintenance expense (in hundreds of dollars).

Weekly Usage (hours)	Annual Maintenance Expense ($100s)
13	17.0
10	22.0
20	30.0
28	37.0
32	47.0
17	30.5
24	32.5
31	39.0
40	51.5
38	40.0

a. Develop a scatter chart with weekly usage hours as the independent variable. What does the scatter chart indicate about the relationship between weekly usage and annual maintenance expense?
b. Use the data to develop an estimated regression equation that could be used to predict the annual maintenance expense for a given number of hours of weekly usage. What is the estimated regression model?
c. Test whether each of the regression parameters β_0 and β_1 is equal to zero at a 0.05 level of significance. What are the correct interpretations of the estimated regression parameters? Are these interpretations reasonable?
d. How much of the variation in the sample values of annual maintenance expense does the model you estimated in part (b) explain?
e. If the maintenance contract costs $3,000 per year, would you recommend purchasing it? Why or why not?

4. A sociologist was hired by a large city hospital to investigate the relationship between the number of unauthorized days that employees are absent per year and the distance (miles) between home and work for the employees. A sample of 10 employees was chosen, and the following data were collected.

DATA *file*
Absent

Distance to Work (miles)	No. of Days Absent
1	8
3	5
4	8
6	7
8	6
10	3
12	5
14	2
14	4
18	2

a. Develop a scatter chart for these data. Does a linear relationship appear reasonable? Explain.
b. Use the data to develop an estimated regression equation that could be used to predict the number of days absent given the distance to work. What is the estimated regression model?
c. What is the 99% confidence interval for the regression parameter β_1? Based on this interval, what conclusion can you make about the hypotheses that the regression parameter β_1 is equal to zero?
d. What is the 99% confidence interval for the regression parameter β_0? Based on this interval, what conclusion can you make about the hypotheses that the regression parameter β_0 is equal to zero?
e. How much of the variation in the sample values of number of days absent does the model you estimated in part (b) explain?

5. The regional transit authority for a major metropolitan area wants to determine whether there is a relationship between the age of a bus and the annual maintenance cost. A sample of 10 buses resulted in the following data:

AgeCost

Age of Bus (years)	Annual Maintenance Cost ($)
1	350
2	370

(Continued)

Age of Bus (years)	Annual Maintenance Cost ($)
2	480
2	520
2	590
3	550
4	750
4	800
5	790
5	950

a. Develop a scatter chart for these data. What does the scatter chart indicate about the relationship between age of a bus and the annual maintenance cost?
b. Use the data to develop an estimated regression equation that could be used to predict the annual maintenance cost given the age of the bus. What is the estimated regression model?
c. Test whether each of the regression parameters β_0 and β_1 is equal to zero at a 0.05 level of significance. What are the correct interpretations of the estimated regression parameters? Are these interpretations reasonable?
d. How much of the variation in the sample values of annual maintenance cost does the model you estimated in part (b) explain?
e. What do you predict the annual maintenance cost to be for a 3.5-year-old bus?

6. A marketing professor at Givens College is interested in the relationship between hours spent studying and total points earned in a course. Data collected on 156 students who took the course last semester are provided in the file *MktHrsPts*.

MktHrsPts

a. Develop a scatter chart for these data. What does the scatter chart indicate about the relationship between total points earned and hours spent studying?
b. Develop an estimated regression equation showing how total points earned is related to hours spent studying. What is the estimated regression model?
c. Test whether each of the regression parameters β_0 and β_1 is equal to zero at a 0.01 level of significance. What are the correct interpretations of the estimated regression parameters? Are these interpretations reasonable?
d. How much of the variation in the sample values of total point earned does the model you estimated in part (b) explain?
e. Mark Sweeney spent 95 hours studying. Use the regression model you estimated in part (b) to predict the total points Mark earned.

7. The Dow Jones Industrial Average (DJIA) and the Standard & Poor's 500 (S&P 500) indexes are used as measures of overall movement in the stock market. The DJIA is based on the price movements of 30 large companies; the S&P 500 is an index composed of 500 stocks. Some say the S&P 500 is a better measure of stock market performance because it is broader based. The closing price for the DJIA and the S&P 500 for 15 weeks, beginning with January 6, 2012, follow (*Barron's* web site, April 17, 2012).

DJIAS&P500

Date	DJIA	S&P
January 6	12,360	1,278
January 13	12,422	1,289
January 20	12,720	1,315
January 27	12,660	1,316
February 3	12,862	1,345

February 10	12,801	1,343
February 17	12,950	1,362
February 24	12,983	1,366
March 2	12,978	1,370
March 9	12,922	1,371
March 16	13,233	1,404
March 23	13,081	1,397
March 30	13,212	1,408
April 5	13,060	1,398
April 13	12,850	1,370

a. Develop a scatter chart for these data with DJIA as the independent variable. What does the scatter chart indicate about the relationship between DJIA and S&P 500?
b. Develop an estimated regression equation showing how S&P 500 is related to DJIA. What is the estimated regression model?
c. What is the 95% confidence interval for the regression parameter β_1? Based on this interval, what conclusion can you make about the hypotheses that the regression parameter β_1 is equal to zero?
d. What is the 95% confidence interval for the regression parameter β_0? Based on this interval, what conclusion can you make about the hypotheses that the regression parameter β_0 is equal to zero?
e. How much of the variation in the sample values of S&P 500 does the model estimated in part (b) explain?
f. Suppose that the closing price for the DJIA is 13,500. Estimate the closing price for the S&P 500.
g. Should we be concerned that the DJIA value of 13,500 used to predict the S&P 500 value in part (f) is beyond the range of the DJIA used to develop the estimated regression equation?

8. The Toyota Camry is one of the best-selling cars in North America. The cost of a previously owned Camry depends on many factors, including the model year, mileage, and condition. To investigate the relationship between the car's mileage and the sales price for Camrys, the following data show the mileage and sale price for 19 sales (PriceHub web site, February 24, 2012).

Miles (1,000s)	Price ($1,000s)
22	16.2
29	16.0
36	13.8
47	11.5
63	12.5
77	12.9
73	11.2
87	13.0
92	11.8
101	10.8
110	8.3
28	12.5

(Continued)

Miles (1,000s)	Price ($1,000s)
59	11.1
68	15.0
68	12.2
91	13.0
42	15.6
65	12.7
110	8.3

a. Develop a scatter chart for these data with miles as the independent variable. What does the scatter chart indicate about the relationship between price and miles?
b. Develop an estimated regression equation showing how price is related to miles. What is the estimated regression model?
c. Test whether each of the regression parameters β_0 and β_1 is equal to zero at a 0.01 level of significance. What are the correct interpretations of the estimated regression parameters? Are these interpretations reasonable?
d. How much of the variation in the sample values of price does the model estimated in part (b) explain?
e. For the model estimated in part (b), calculate the predicted price and residual for each automobile in the data. Identify the two automobiles that were the biggest bargains.
f. Suppose that you are considering purchasing a previously owned Camry that has been driven 60,000 miles. Use the estimated regression equation developed in part (b) to predict the price for this car. Is this the price you would offer the seller?

9. Dixie Showtime Movie Theaters, Inc., owns and operates a chain of cinemas in several markets in the southern United States. The owners would like to estimate weekly gross revenue as a function of advertising expenditures. Data for a sample of eight markets for a recent week follow:

DixieShowtime

Market	Weekly Gross Revenue ($100s)	Television Advertising ($100s)	Newspaper Advertising ($100s)
Mobile	101.3	5.0	1.5
Shreveport	51.9	3.0	3.0
Jackson	74.8	4.0	1.5
Birmingham	126.2	4.3	4.3
Little Rock	137.8	3.6	4.0
Biloxi	101.4	3.5	2.3
New Orleans	237.8	5.0	8.4
Baton Rouge	219.6	6.9	5.8

a. Develop an estimated regression equation with the amount of television advertising as the independent variable. Test for a significant relationship between television advertising and weekly gross revenue at the 0.05 level of significance. What is the interpretation of this relationship?
b. How much of the variation in the sample values of weekly gross revenue does the model in part (a) explain?

c. Develop an estimated regression equation with both television advertising and newspaper advertising as the independent variables. Test whether each of the regression parameters β_0, β_1, and β_2 is equal to zero at a 0.05 level of significance. What are the correct interpretations of the estimated regression parameters? Are these interpretations reasonable?
d. How much of the variation in the sample values of weekly gross revenue does the model in part (c) explain?
e. Given the results in parts (a) and (c), what should your next step be? Explain.
f. What are the managerial implications of these results?

10. *Resorts & Spas,* a magazine devoted to upscale vacations and accommodations, published its Reader's Choice List of the top 20 independent beachfront boutique hotels in the world. The data shown are the scores received by these hotels based on the results from *Resorts & Spas'* annual Readers' Choice Survey. Each score represents the percentage of respondents who rated a hotel as excellent or very good on one of three criteria (comfort, amenities, and in-house dining). An overall score was also reported and used to rank the hotels. The highest ranked hotel, the Muri Beach Odyssey, has an overall score of 94.3, the highest component of which is 97.7 for in-house dining.

BeachFrontHotels

Hotel	Overall	Comfort	Amenities	In-House Dining
Muri Beach Odyssey	94.3	94.5	90.8	97.7
Pattaya Resort	92.9	96.6	84.1	96.6
Sojourner's Respite	92.8	99.9	100.0	88.4
Spa Carribe	91.2	88.5	94.7	97.0
Penang Resort and Spa	90.4	95.0	87.8	91.1
Mokihana Hōkele	90.2	92.4	82.0	98.7
Theo's of Cape Town	90.1	95.9	86.2	91.9
Cap d'Agde Resort	89.8	92.5	92.5	88.8
Spirit of Mykonos	89.3	94.6	85.8	90.7
Turismo del Mar	89.1	90.5	83.2	90.4
Hotel Iguana	89.1	90.8	81.9	88.5
Sidi Abdel Rahman Palace	89.0	93.0	93.0	89.6
Sainte-Maxime Quarters	88.6	92.5	78.2	91.2
Rotorua Inn	87.1	93.0	91.6	73.5
Club Lapu-Lapu	87.1	90.9	74.9	89.6
Terracina Retreat	86.5	94.3	78.0	91.5
Hacienda Punta Barco	86.1	95.4	77.3	90.8
Rendezvous Kolocep	86.0	94.8	76.4	91.4
Cabo de Gata Vista	86.0	92.0	72.2	89.2
Sanya Deluxe	85.1	93.4	77.3	91.8

a. Determine the estimated multiple linear regression equation that can be used to predict the overall score given the scores for comfort, amenities, and in-house dining.
b. Use the *t* test to determine the significance of each independent variable. What is the conclusion for each test at the 0.01 level of significance?
c. Remove all independent variables that are not significant at the 0.01 level of significance from the estimated regression equation. What is your recommended estimated regression equation?

11. The American Association of Individual Investors (AAII) On-Line Discount Broker Survey polls members on their experiences with electronic trades handled by discount brokers. As part of the survey, members were asked to rate their satisfaction with the trade price and the speed of execution, as well as provide an overall satisfaction rating. Possible responses (scores) were no opinion (0), unsatisfied (1), somewhat satisfied (2), satisfied (3), and very satisfied (4). For each broker, summary scores were computed by computing a weighted average of the scores provided by each respondent. A portion the survey results follow (AAII web site, February 7, 2012).

Brokerage	Satisfaction with Trade Price	Satisfaction with Speed of Execution	Overall Satisfaction with Electronic Trades
Scottrade, Inc.	3.4	3.4	3.5
Charles Schwab	3.2	3.3	3.4
Fidelity Brokerage Services	3.1	3.4	3.9
TD Ameritrade	2.9	3.6	3.7
E*Trade Financial	2.9	3.2	2.9
(Not listed)	2.5	3.2	2.7
Vanguard Brokerage Services	2.6	3.8	2.8
USAA Brokerage Services	2.4	3.8	3.6
Thinkorswim	2.6	2.6	2.6
Wells Fargo Investments	2.3	2.7	2.3
Interactive Brokers	3.7	4.0	4.0
Zecco.com	2.5	2.5	2.5
Firstrade Securities	3.0	3.0	4.0
Banc of America Investment Services	4.0	1.0	2.0

a. Develop an estimated regression equation using trade price and speed of execution to predict overall satisfaction with the broker. Interpret the coefficient of determination.
b. Use the *t* test to determine the significance of each independent variable. What are your conclusions at the 0.05 level of significance?
c. Interpret the estimated regression parameters. Are the relationships indicated by these estimates what you would expect?
d. Finger Lakes Investments has developed a new electronic trading system and would like to predict overall customer satisfaction assuming they can provide satisfactory service levels (3) for both trade price and speed of execution. Use the estimated regression equation developed in part (a) to predict overall satisfaction level for Finger Lakes Investments if they can achieve these performance levels.
e. What concerns (if any) do you have with regard to the possible responses the respondents could select on the survey.

12. The National Football League (NFL) records a variety of performance data for individuals and teams. To investigate the importance of passing on the percentage of games won by a team, the following data show the conference (Conf), average number of passing yards per attempt (Yds/Att), the number of interceptions thrown per attempt

(Int/Att), and the percentage of games won (Win%) for a random sample of 16 NFL teams for the 2011 season (NFL web site, February 12, 2012).

Team	Conf	Yds/Att	Int/Att	Win%
Arizona Cardinals	NFC	6.5	0.042	50.0
Atlanta Falcons	NFC	7.1	0.022	62.5
Carolina Panthers	NFC	7.4	0.033	37.5
Cincinnati Bengals	AFC	6.2	0.026	56.3
Detroit Lions	NFC	7.2	0.024	62.5
Green Bay Packers	NFC	8.9	0.014	93.8
Houston Texans	AFC	7.5	0.019	62.5
Indianapolis Colts	AFC	5.6	0.026	12.5
Jacksonville Jaguars	AFC	4.6	0.032	31.3
Minnesota Vikings	NFC	5.8	0.033	18.8
New England Patriots	AFC	8.3	0.020	81.3
New Orleans Saints	NFC	8.1	0.021	81.3
Oakland Raiders	AFC	7.6	0.044	50.0
San Francisco 49ers	NFC	6.5	0.011	81.3
Tennessee Titans	AFC	6.7	0.024	56.3
Washington Redskins	NFC	6.4	0.041	31.3

a. Develop the estimated regression equation that could be used to predict the percentage of games won, given the average number of passing yards per attempt. What proportion of variation in the sample values of proportion of games won does this model explain?
b. Develop the estimated regression equation that could be used to predict the percentage of games won, given the number of interceptions thrown per attempt. What proportion of variation in the sample values of proportion of games won does this model explain?
c. Develop the estimated regression equation that could be used to predict the percentage of games won, given the average number of passing yards per attempt and the number of interceptions thrown per attempt. What proportion of variation in the sample values of proportion of games won does this model explain?
d. The average number of passing yards per attempt for the Kansas City Chiefs during the 2011 season was 6.2, and the team's number of interceptions thrown per attempt was 0.036. Use the estimated regression equation developed in part (c) to predict the percentage of games won by the Kansas City Chiefs during the 2011 season. Compare your prediction to the actual percentage of games won by the Kansas City Chiefs. (*Note:* For the 2011 season, the Kansas City Chiefs' record was 7 wins and 9 losses.)
e. Did the estimated regression equation that uses only the average number of passing yards per attempt as the independent variable to predict the percentage of games won provide a good fit?

13. Johnson Filtration, Inc., provides maintenance service for water filtration systems throughout southern Florida. Customers contact Johnson with requests for maintenance service on their water filtration systems. To estimate the service time and the service cost, Johnson's managers want to predict the repair time necessary for each maintenance request. Hence, repair time in hours is the dependent variable. Repair time is believed to be related to three factors: the number of months since the last

maintenance service, the type of repair problem (mechanical or electrical), and the repairperson who performs the repair (Donna Newton or Bob Jones). Data for a sample of 10 service calls are reported in the following table:

Repair Time in Hours	Months Since Last Service	Type of Repair	Repairperson
2.9	2	Electrical	Donna Newton
3.0	6	Mechanical	Donna Newton
4.8	8	Electrical	Bob Jones
1.8	3	Mechanical	Donna Newton
2.9	2	Electrical	Donna Newton
4.9	7	Electrical	Bob Jones
4.2	9	Mechanical	Bob Jones
4.8	8	Mechanical	Bob Jones
4.4	4	Electrical	Bob Jones
4.5	6	Electrical	Donna Newton

a. Develop the simple linear regression equation to predict repair time given the number of months since the last maintenance service, and use the results to test the hypothesis that no relationship exists between repair time and the number of months since the last maintenance service at the 0.05 level of significance. What is the interpretation of this relationship? What does the coefficient of determination tell you about this model?
b. Using the simple linear regression model developed in part (a), calculate the predicted repair time and residual for each of the 10 repairs in the data. Sort the data in ascending order by value of the residual. Do you see any pattern in the residuals for the two types of repair? Do you see any pattern in the residuals for the two repairpersons? Do these results suggest any potential modifications to your simple linear regression model? Now create a scatter chart with months since last service on the x-axis and repair time in hours on the y-axis for which the points representing electrical and mechanical repairs are shown in different shapes and/or colors. Create a similar scatter chart of months since last service and repair time in hours for which the points representing repairs by Bob Jones and Donna Newton are shown in different shapes and/or colors, Do these charts and the results of your residual analysis suggest the same potential modifications to your simple linear regression model?
c. Create a new dummy variable that is equal to zero if the type of repair is mechanical and one if the type of repair is electrical. Develop the multiple regression equation to predict repair time, given the number of months since the last maintenance service and the type of repair. What are the interpretations of the estimated regression parameters? What does the coefficient of determination tell you about this model?
d. Create a new dummy variable that is equal to zero if the repairperson is Bob Jones and one if the repairperson is Donna Newton. Develop the multiple regression equation to predict repair time, given the number of months since the last maintenance service and the repairperson. What are the interpretations of the estimated regression parameters? What does the coefficient of determination tell you about this model?
e. Develop the multiple regression equation to predict repair time, given the number of months since the last maintenance service, the type of repair, and the repairperson. What are the interpretations of the estimated regression parameters? What does the coefficient of determination tell you about this model?
f. Which of these models would you use? Why?

14. A study investigated the relationship between audit delay (the length of time from a company's fiscal year-end to the date of the auditor's report) and variables that describe the client and the auditor. Some of the independent variables that were included in this study follow:

Industry	A dummy variable coded 1 if the firm was an industrial company or 0 if the firm was a bank, savings and loan, or insurance company.
Public	A dummy variable coded 1 if the company was traded on an organized exchange or over the counter; otherwise coded 0.
Quality	A measure of overall quality of internal controls, as judged by the auditor, on a 5-point scale ranging from "virtually none" (1) to "excellent" (5).
Finished	A measure ranging from 1 to 4, as judged by the auditor, where 1 indicates "all work performed subsequent to year-end" and 4 indicates "most work performed prior to year-end."

A sample of 40 companies provided the following data:

Delay (Days)	Industry	Public	Quality	Finished
62	0	0	3	1
45	0	1	3	3
54	0	0	2	2
71	0	1	1	2
91	0	0	1	1
62	0	0	4	4
61	0	0	3	2
69	0	1	5	2
80	0	0	1	1
52	0	0	5	3
47	0	0	3	2
65	0	1	2	3
60	0	0	1	3
81	1	0	1	2
73	1	0	2	2
89	1	0	2	1
71	1	0	5	4
76	1	0	2	2
68	1	0	1	2
68	1	0	5	2
86	1	0	2	2
76	1	1	3	1
67	1	0	2	3
57	1	0	4	2
55	1	1	3	2
54	1	0	5	2
69	1	0	3	3
82	1	0	5	1
94	1	0	1	1
74	1	1	5	2
75	1	1	4	3

(Continued)

Delay (Days)	Industry	Public	Quality	Finished
69	1	0	2	2
71	1	0	4	4
79	1	0	5	2
80	1	0	1	4
91	1	0	4	1
92	1	0	1	4
46	1	1	4	3
72	1	0	5	2
85	1	0	5	1

a. Develop the estimated regression equation using all of the independent variables included in the data.

b. How much of the variation in the sample values of delay does this estimated regression equation explain? What other independent variables could you include in this regression model to improve the fit?

c. Test the relationship between each independent variable and the dependent variable at the 0.05 level of significance, and interpret the relationship between each of the independent variables and the dependent variable.

d. On the basis of your observations about the relationships between the dependent variable Delay and the independent variables Quality and Finished, suggest an alternative model for the regression equation developed in part (a) to explain as much of the variability in Delay as possible.

15. The U.S. Department of Energy's Fuel Economy Guide provides fuel efficiency data for cars and trucks. A portion of the data for 311 compact, midsized, and large cars follows. The Class column identifies the size of the car: Compact, Midsize, or Large. The Displacement column shows the engine's displacement in liters. The FuelType column shows whether the car uses premium (P) or regular (R) fuel, and the HwyMPG column shows the fuel efficiency rating for highway driving in terms of miles per gallon. The complete data set is contained in the file *FuelData*:

DATA *file*
FuelData

Car	Class	Displacement	FuelType	HwyMPG
1	Compact	3.1	P	25
2	Compact	3.1	P	25
3	Compact	3.0	P	25
⋮	⋮	⋮	⋮	⋮
161	Midsize	2.4	R	30
162	Midsize	2.0	P	29
⋮	⋮	⋮	⋮	⋮
310	Large	3.0	R	25

a. Develop an estimated regression equation that can be used to predict the fuel efficiency for highway driving given the engine's displacement. Test for significance using the 0.05 level of significance. How much of the variation in the sample values of HwyMPG does this estimated regression equation explain?

b. Create a scatter chart with HwyMPG on the y-axis and displacement on the x-axis for which the points representing compact, midsize, and large automobiles are shown in different shapes and/or colors. What does this chart suggest about the relationship between the class of automobile (compact, midsize, and large) and HwyMPG?

c. Now consider the addition of the dummy variables ClassMidsize and ClassLarge to the simple linear regression model in part (a). The value of ClassMidsize is 1 if the car is a midsize car and 0 otherwise; the value of ClassLarge is 1 if the car is a large car and 0 otherwise. Thus, for a compact car, the value of ClassMidsize and the value of ClassLarge are both 0. Develop the estimated regression equation that can be used to predict the fuel efficiency for highway driving, given the engine's displacement and the dummy variables ClassMidsize and ClassLarge. How much of the variation in the sample values of HwyMPG is explained by this estimated regression equation?

d. Use significance level of 0.05 to determine whether the dummy variables added to the model in part (c) are significant.

e. Consider the addition of the dummy variable FuelPremium, where the value of FuelPremium is 1 if the car uses premium fuel and 0 if the car uses regular fuel. Develop the estimated regression equation that can be used to predict the fuel efficiency for highway driving given the engine's displacement, the dummy variables ClassMidsize and ClassLarge, and the dummy variable FuelPremium. How much of the variation in the sample values of HwyMPG does this estimated regression equation explain?

f. For the estimated regression equation developed in part (e), test for the significance of the relationship between each of the independent variables and the dependent variable using the 0.05 level of significance for each test.

16. A highway department is studying the relationship between traffic flow and speed during rush hour on Highway 193. The data in the file *TrafficFlow* were collected on Highway 193 during 100 recent rush hours.

a. Develop a scatter chart for these data. What does the scatter chart indicate about the relationship between vehicle speed and traffic flow?

b. Develop an estimated simple linear regression equation for the data. How much variation in the sample values of traffic flow is explained by this regression model? Use a 0.05 level of significance to test the relationship between vehicle speed and traffic flow. What is the interpretation of this relationship?

c. Develop an estimated quadratic regression equation for the data. How much variation in the sample values of traffic flow is explained by this regression model? Test the relationship between each of the independent variables and the dependent variable at a 0.05 level of significance. How would you interpret this model? Is this model superior to the model you developed in part (b)?

d. As an alternative to fitting a second-order model, fit a model using a piecewise linear regression with a single knot. What value of vehicle speed appears to be a good point for the placement of the knot? Does the estimated piecewise linear regression provide a better fit than the estimated quadratic regression developed in part (c)? Explain.

e. Separate the data into two sets such that one data set contains the observations of vehicle speed less than the value of the knot from part (d) and the other data set contains the observations of vehicle speed greater than or equal to the value of the knot from part (d). Then fit a simple linear regression equation to each data set. How does this pair of regression equations compare to the single piecewise linear regression with the single knot from part (d)? In particular, compare predicted values of traffic flow for values of the speed slightly above and slightly below the knot value from part (d).

f. What other independent variables could you include in your regression model to explain more variation in traffic flow?

17. A sample containing years to maturity and (percent) yield for 40 corporate bonds is contained in the file named *CorporateBonds* (*Barron's*, April 2, 2012).
    a. Develop a scatter chart of the data using years to maturity as the independent variable. Does a simple linear regression model appear to be appropriate?
    b. Develop an estimated quadratic regression equation with years to maturity and squared values of years to maturity as the independent variables. How much variation in the sample values of yield is explained by this regression model? Test the relationship between each of the independent variables and the dependent variable at a 0.05 level of significance. How would you interpret this model?
    c. Create a plot of the linear and quadratic regression lines overlaid on the scatter chart of years to maturity and yield. Does this helps you better understand the difference in how the quadratic regression model and a simple linear regression model fit the sample data? Which model does this chart suggest provides a superior fit to the sample data?
    d. What other independent variables could you include in your regression model to explain more variation in yield?
18. In 2011, home prices and mortgage rates fell so far that in a number of cities the monthly cost of owning a home was less expensive than renting. The following data show the average asking rent for 10 markets and the monthly mortgage on the median priced home (including taxes and insurance) for 10 cites where the average monthly mortgage payment was less than the average asking rent (*The Wall Street Journal*, November 26–27, 2011).

City	Rent ($)	Mortgage ($)
Atlanta	840	539
Chicago	1,062	1,002
Detroit	823	626
Jacksonville	779	711
Las Vegas	796	655
Miami	1,071	977
Minneapolis	953	776
Orlando	851	695
Phoenix	762	651
St. Louis	723	654

    a. Develop a scatter chart for these data, treating the average asking rent as the independent variable. Does a simple linear regression model appear to be appropriate?
    b. Use a simple linear regression model to develop an estimated regression equation to predict the monthly mortgage on the median priced home given the average asking rent. Construct a plot of the residuals against the independent variable rent. Based on this residual plot, does a simple linear regression model appear to be appropriate?
    c. Using a quadratic regression model, develop an estimated regression equation to predict the monthly mortgage on the median-priced home, given the average asking rent.
    d. Do you prefer the estimated regression equation developed in part (a) or part (c)? Create a plot of the linear and quadratic regression lines overlaid on the scatter chart of the monthly mortgage on the median-priced home and the average asking rent to help you assess the two regression equations. Explain your conclusions.

19. A recent 10-year study conducted by a research team at the Great Falls Medical School was conducted to assess how age, systolic blood pressure, and smoking relate to the risk of strokes. Assume that the following data are from a portion of this study. Risk is interpreted as the probability (times 100) that the patient will have a stroke over the next 10-year period. For the smoking variable, define a dummy variable with 1 indicating a smoker and 0 indicating a nonsmoker.

Risk	Age	Systolic Blood Pressure	Smoker
12	57	152	No
24	67	163	No
13	58	155	No
56	86	177	Yes
28	59	196	No
51	76	189	Yes
18	56	155	Yes
31	78	120	No
37	80	135	Yes
15	78	98	No
22	71	152	No
36	70	173	Yes
15	67	135	Yes
48	77	209	Yes
15	60	199	No
36	82	119	Yes
8	66	166	No
34	80	125	Yes
3	62	117	No
37	59	207	Yes

a. Develop an estimated multiple regression equation that relates risk of a stroke to the person's age, systolic blood pressure, and whether the person is a smoker.
b. Is smoking a significant factor in the risk of a stroke? Explain. Use a 0.05 level of significance.
c. What is the probability of a stroke over the next 10 years for Art Speen, a 68-year-old smoker who has a systolic blood pressure of 175? What action might the physician recommend for this patient?
d. What other factors could be included in the model as independent variables?

20. The Scholastic Aptitude Test (or SAT) is a standardized college entrance test that is used by colleges and universities as a means for making admission decisions. The critical reading and mathematics components of the SAT are reported on a scale from 200 to 800. Several universities believe these scores are strong predictors of an incoming student's potential success, and they use these scores as important inputs when making admission decisions on potential freshman. The file *RugglesCollege* contains freshman year GPA and the critical reading and mathematics SAT scores for a random sample of 200 students who recently completed their freshman year at Ruggles College.
a. Develop an estimated multiple regression equation that includes critical reading and mathematics SAT scores as independent variables. How much variation in freshman GPA is explained by this model? Test whether each of the regression parameters

β_0, β_1, and β_2 is equal to zero at a 0.05 level of significance. What are the correct interpretations of the estimated regression parameters? Are these interpretations reasonable?

b. Using the multiple linear regression model you developed in part (a), what is the predicted freshman GPA of Bobby Engle, a student who has been admitted to Ruggles College with a 660 SAT score on critical reading and at a 630 SAT score on mathematics?

c. The Ruggles College Director of Admissions believes that the relationship between a student's scores on the critical reading component of the SAT and the student's freshman GPA varies with the student's score on the mathematics component of the SAT. Develop an estimated multiple regression equation that includes critical reading and mathematics SAT scores and their interaction as independent variables. How much variation in freshman GPA is explained by this model? Test whether each of the regression parameters β_0, β_1, β_2, and β_3 is equal to zero at a 0.05 level of significance. What are the correct interpretations of the estimated regression parameters? Do these results support the conjecture made by the Ruggles College Director of Admissions?

d. Do you prefer the estimated regression model developed in part (a) or part (c)? Explain.

e. What other factors could be included in the model as independent variables?

21. Consider again the example introduced in Section 7.5 of a credit card company that has a database of information provided by its customers when they apply for credit cards. An analyst has created a multiple regression model for which the dependent variable in the model is credit card charges accrued by a customer in the data set over the past year (y), and the independent variables are the customer's annual household income (x_1), number of members of the household (x_2), and number of years of post–high school education (x_3). Figure 7.23 provides Excel output for a multiple regression model estimated using a data set the company created.

a. Estimate the corresponding simple linear regression with the customer's annual household income as the independent variable and credit card charges accrued by a customer over the past year as the dependent variable. Interpret the estimated relationship between the customer's annual household income and credit card charges accrued over the past year. How much variation in credit card charges accrued by a customer over the past year is explained by this simple linear regression model?

b. Estimate the corresponding simple linear regression with the number of members in the customer's household as the independent variable and credit card charges accrued by a customer over the past year as the dependent variable. Interpret the estimated relationship between the number of members in the customer's household and credit card charges accrued over the past year. How much variation in credit card charges accrued by a customer over the past year is explained by this simple linear regression model?

c. Estimate the corresponding simple linear regression with the customer's number of years of post–high school education as the independent variable and credit card charges accrued by a customer over the past year as the dependent variable. Interpret the estimated relationship between the customer's number of years of post–high school education and credit card charges accrued over the past year. How much variation in credit card charges accrued by a customer over the past year is explained by this simple linear regression model?

d. Recall the multiple regression in Figure 7.23 with credit card charges accrued by a customer over the past year as the dependent variable and customer's annual household income (x_1), number of members of the household (x_2), and number of years of post–high school education (x_3) as the independent variables. Do the estimated slopes differ substantially from the corresponding slopes that were estimated using simple linear regression in parts (a), (b), and (c)? What does this tell you about multicollinearity in the multiple regression model in Figure 7.23?

e. Add the coefficients of determination for the simple linear regression in parts (a), (b), and (c), and compare the result to the coefficient of determination for the multiple regression model in Figure 7.23. What does this tell you about multicollinearity in the multiple regression model in Figure 7.23?

f. Add age, a dummy variable for sex, and a dummy variable for whether a customer has exceeded his or her credit limit in the past 12 months as independent variables to the multiple regression model in Figure 7.23. Code the dummy variable for sex as 1 if the customer is female and 0 if male, and code the dummy variable for whether a customer has exceeded his or her credit limit in the past 12 months as 1 if the customer has exceeded his or her credit limit in the past 12 months and 0 otherwise. Do these variables substantially improve the fit of your model?

CASE PROBLEM ALUMNI GIVING

Alumni donations are an important source of revenue for colleges and universities. If administrators could determine the factors that could lead to increases in the percentage of alumni who make a donation, they might be able to implement policies that could lead to increased revenues. Research shows that students who are more satisfied with their contact with teachers are more likely to graduate. As a result, one might suspect that smaller class sizes and lower student/faculty ratios might lead to a higher percentage of satisfied graduates, which in turn might lead to increases in the percentage of alumni who make a donation. The following table shows data for 48 national universities. The Graduation Rate column is the percentage of students who initially enrolled at the university and graduated. The % of Classes Under 20 column shows the percentages of classes with fewer than 20 students that are offered. The Student/Faculty Ratio column is the number of students enrolled divided by the total number of faculty. Finally, the Alumni Giving Rate column is the percentage of alumni who made a donation to the university.

	State	Graduation Rate	% of Classes Under 20	Student/ Faculty Ratio	Alumni Giving Rate
Boston College	MA	85	39	13	25
Brandeis University	MA	79	68	8	33
Brown University	RI	93	60	8	40
California Institute of Technology	CA	85	65	3	46
Carnegie Mellon University	PA	75	67	10	28
Case Western Reserve Univ.	OH	72	52	8	31
College of William and Mary	VA	89	45	12	27
Columbia University	NY	90	69	7	31
Cornell University	NY	91	72	13	35
Dartmouth College	NH	94	61	10	53
Duke University	NC	92	68	8	45
Emory University	GA	84	65	7	37

(Continued)

	State	Graduation Rate	% of Classes Under 20	Student/ Faculty Ratio	Alumni Giving Rate
Georgetown University	DC	91	54	10	29
Harvard University	MA	97	73	8	46
Johns Hopkins University	MD	89	64	9	27
Lehigh University	PA	81	55	11	40
Massachusetts Institute of Technology	MA	92	65	6	44
New York University	NY	72	63	13	13
Northwestern University	IL	90	66	8	30
Pennsylvania State Univ.	PA	80	32	19	21
Princeton University	NJ	95	68	5	67
Rice University	TX	92	62	8	40
Stanford University	CA	92	69	7	34
Tufts University	MA	87	67	9	29
Tulane University	LA	72	56	12	17
University of California–Berkeley	CA	83	58	17	18
University of California–Davis	CA	74	32	19	7
University of California–Irvine	CA	74	42	20	9
University of California–Los Angeles	CA	78	41	18	13
University of California–San Diego	CA	80	48	19	8
University of California–Santa Barbara	CA	70	45	20	12
University of Chicago	IL	84	65	4	36
University of Florida	FL	67	31	23	19
University of Illinois–Urbana Champaign	IL	77	29	15	23
University of Michigan–Ann Arbor	MI	83	51	15	13
University of North Carolina–Chapel Hill	NC	82	40	16	26
University of Notre Dame	IN	94	53	13	49
University of Pennsylvania	PA	90	65	7	41
University of Rochester	NY	76	63	10	23
University of Southern California	CA	70	53	13	22
University of Texas–Austin	TX	66	39	21	13
University of Virginia	VA	92	44	13	28
University of Washington	WA	70	37	12	12
University of Wisconsin–Madison	WI	73	37	13	13
Vanderbilt University	TN	82	68	9	31
Wake Forest University	NC	82	59	11	38
Washington University–St. Louis	MO	86	73	7	33
Yale University	CT	94	77	7	50

Managerial Report

1. Use methods of descriptive statistics to summarize the data.
2. Develop an estimated simple linear regression model that can be used to predict the alumni giving rate, given the graduation rate. Discuss your findings.
3. Develop an estimated multiple linear regression model that could be used to predict the alumni giving rate using the Graduation Rate, % of Classes Under 20, and Student/Faculty Ratio as independent variables. Discuss your findings.
4. Based on the results in parts (2) and (3), do you believe another regression model may be more appropriate? Estimate this model, and discuss your results.
5. What conclusions and recommendations can you derive from your analysis? What universities are achieving a substantially higher alumni giving rate than would be expected, given their Graduation Rate, % of Classes Under 20, and Student/Faculty Ratio? What universities are achieving a substantially lower alumni giving rate than would be expected, given their Graduation Rate, % of Classes Under 20, and Student/Faculty Ratio? What other independent variables could be included in the model?

Chapter 8

Time Series Analysis and Forecasting

CONTENTS

8.1 TIME SERIES PATTERNS
- Horizontal Pattern
- Trend Pattern
- Seasonal Pattern
- Trend and Seasonal Pattern
- Cyclical Pattern
- Identifying Time Series Patterns

8.2 FORECAST ACCURACY

8.3 MOVING AVERAGES AND EXPONENTIAL SMOOTHING
- Moving Averages
- Forecast Accuracy
- Exponential Smoothing
- Forecast Accuracy

8.4 USING REGRESSION ANALYSIS FOR FORECASTING
- Linear Trend Projection
- Seasonality
- Seasonality Without Trend
- Seasonality with Trend
- Using Regression Analysis as a Causal Forecasting Method
- Combining Causal Variables with Trend and Seasonality Effects
- Considerations in Using Regression in Forecasting

8.5 DETERMINING THE BEST FORECASTING MODEL TO USE

ANALYTICS IN ACTION

ACCO Brands*

ACCO Brands Corporation is one of the world's largest suppliers of branded office and consumer products and print finishing solutions. The company's brands include AT-A-GLANCE®, Day-Timer®, Five Star®, GBC®, Hilroy®, Kensington®, Marbig®, Mead®, NOBO, Quartet®, Rexel, Swingline®, Tilibra®, Wilson Jones®, and many others.

Because it produces and markets a wide array of products with myriad demand characteristics, ACCO Brands relies heavily on sales forecasts in planning its manufacturing, distribution, and marketing activities. By viewing its relationship in terms of a supply chain, ACCO Brands and its customers (which are generally retail chains) establish close collaborative relationships and consider each other to be valued partners. As a result, ACCO Brands' customers share valuable information and data that serve as inputs into ACCO Brands' forecasting process.

In her role as a forecasting manager for ACCO Brands, Vanessa Baker appreciates the importance of this additional information. "We do separate forecasts of demand for each major customer," said Baker, "and we generally use twenty-four to thirty-six months of history to generate monthly forecasts twelve to eighteen months into the future. While trends are important, several of our major product lines, including school, planning and organizing, and decorative calendars, are heavily seasonal, and seasonal sales make up the bulk of our annual volume."

Daniel Marks, one of several account-level strategic forecast managers for ACCO Brands, adds,

> The supply chain process includes the total lead time from identifying opportunities to making or procuring the product to getting the product on the shelves to align with the forecasted demand; this can potentially take several months, so the accuracy of our forecasts is critical throughout each step of the supply chain. Adding to this challenge is the risk of obsolescence. We sell many dated items, such as planners and calendars, which have a natural, built-in obsolescence. In addition, many of our products feature designs that are fashion-conscious or contain pop culture images, and these products can also become obsolete very quickly as tastes and popularity change. An overly optimistic forecast for these products can be very costly, but an overly pessimistic forecast can result in lost sales potential and give our competitors an opportunity to take market share from us.

In addition to looking at trends, seasonal components, and cyclical patterns, Baker and Marks must contend with several other factors. Baker notes, "We have to adjust our forecasts for upcoming promotions by our customers." Marks agrees and adds:

> We also have to go beyond just forecasting consumer demand; we must consider the retailer's specific needs in our order forecasts, such as what type of display will be used and how many units of a product must be on display to satisfy their presentation requirements. Current inventory is another factor—if a customer is carrying either too much or too little inventory, that will affect their future orders, and we need to reflect that in our forecasts. Will the product have a short life because it is tied to a cultural fad? What are the retailer's marketing and markdown strategies? Our knowledge of the environments in which our supply chain partners are competing helps us to forecast demand more accurately, and that reduces waste and makes our customers, as well as ACCO Brands, far more profitable.

*The authors are indebted to Vanessa Baker and Daniel Marks of ACCO Brands for providing input for this Analytics in Action.

The purpose of this chapter is to provide an introduction to time series analysis and forecasting. Suppose we are asked to provide quarterly **forecasts** of sales for one of our company's products over the coming one-year period. Production schedules, raw materials purchasing, inventory policies, marketing plans, and cash flows will all be affected by the quarterly forecasts we provide. Consequently, poor forecasts may result in poor planning and increased costs for the company. How should we go about providing the quarterly sales forecasts? Good judgment, intuition, and an awareness of the state of the economy may give us a rough idea, or feeling, of what is likely to happen in the future, but converting that feeling into a number that can be used as next year's sales forecast is challenging.

A forecast is simply a prediction of what will happen in the future. Managers must accept that regardless of the technique used, they will not be able to develop perfect forecasts.

Forecasting methods can be classified as qualitative or quantitative. Qualitative methods generally involve the use of expert judgment to develop forecasts. Such methods are appropriate when historical data on the variable being forecast are either unavailable or not applicable. Quantitative forecasting methods can be used when: (1) past information about the variable being forecast is available, (2) the information can be quantified, and (3) it is reasonable to assume that past is prologue (i.e., that the pattern of the past will continue into the future). We will focus exclusively on quantitative forecasting methods in this chapter.

If the historical data are restricted to past values of the variable to be forecast, the forecasting procedure is called a time series method and the historical data are referred to as *time series*. The objective of time series analysis is to uncover a pattern in the time series and then extrapolate the pattern to forecast the future; the forecast is based solely on past values of the variable and/or on past forecast errors.

Causal or exploratory forecasting methods are based on the assumption that the variable we are forecasting has a cause-and-effect relationship with one or more other variables. These methods help explain how the value of one variable impacts the value of another. For instance, the sales volume for many products is influenced by advertising expenditures, so regression analysis may be used to develop an equation showing how these two variables are related. Then, once the advertising budget is set for the next period, we could substitute this value into the equation to develop a prediction or forecast of the sales volume for that period. Note that if a time series method was used to develop the forecast, advertising expenditures would not be considered; that is, a time series method would base the forecast solely on past sales.

Modern data-collection technologies have enabled individuals, businesses, and government agencies to collect vast amounts of data that may be used for causal forecasting. For example, supermarket scanners allow retailers to collect point-of-sale data that can then be used to help aid in planning sales, coupon targeting, and other marketing and planning efforts. These data can help answer important questions like, "Which products tend to be purchased together?" One of the techniques used to answer such questions is regression analysis. In this chapter we discuss the use of regression analysis as a causal forecasting method.

In Section 8.1 we discuss the various kinds of time series that a forecaster might be faced with in practice. These include a constant or horizontal pattern, a trend, a seasonal pattern, both a trend and a seasonal pattern, and a cyclical pattern. To build a quantitative forecasting model it is also necessary to have a measurement of forecast accuracy. Different measurements of forecast accuracy, as well as their respective advantages and disadvantages, are discussed in Section 8.2. In Section 8.3 we consider the simplest case, which is a horizontal or constant pattern. For this pattern, we develop the classical moving average, weighted moving average, and exponential smoothing models. Many time series have a trend, and taking this trend into account is important; in Section 8.4 we provide regression models for finding the best model parameters when a linear trend is present, when the data show a seasonal pattern, or when the variable to be predicted has a causal relationship with other variables. Finally, in Section 8.5 we discuss considerations to be made when determining the best forecasting model to use.

NOTES + COMMENTS

Virtually all large companies today rely on enterprise resource planning (ERP) software to aid in their planning and operations. These software systems help the business run smoothly by collecting and efficiently storing company data, enabling it to be shared company-wide for planning at all levels: strategically, tactically, and operationally. Most ERP systems include a forecasting module to help plan for the future. SAP, one of the most widely used ERP systems, includes a forecasting component. This module allows the user to select from a number of forecasting techniques and/or have the system find a "best" model. The various forecasting methods and ways to measure the quality of a forecasting model discussed in this chapter are routinely available in software that supports forecasting.

8.1 Time Series Patterns

We limit our discussion to time series for which the values of the series are recorded at equal intervals. Cases in which the observations are made at unequal intervals are beyond the scope of this text.

A **time series** is a sequence of observations on a variable measured at successive points in time or over successive periods of time. The measurements may be taken every hour, day, week, month, year, or at any other regular interval. The pattern of the data is an important factor in understanding how the time series has behaved in the past. If such behavior can be expected to continue in the future, we can use it to guide us in selecting an appropriate forecasting method.

In Chapter 2 we discussed line charts, which are often used to graph time series.

To identify the underlying pattern in the data, a useful first step is to construct a *time series plot*, which is a graphical presentation of the relationship between time and the time series variable; time is represented on the horizontal axis and values of the time series variable are shown on the vertical axis. Let us first review some of the common types of data patterns that can be identified in a time series plot.

Horizontal Pattern

Gasoline

A horizontal pattern exists when the data fluctuate randomly around a constant mean over time. To illustrate a time series with a horizontal pattern, consider the 12 weeks of data in Table 8.1. These data show the number of gallons of gasoline (in 1,000s) sold by a gasoline distributor in Bennington, Vermont, over the past 12 weeks. The average value, or mean, for this time series is 19.25 or 19,250 gallons per week. Figure 8.1 shows a time series plot for these data. Note how the data fluctuate around the sample mean of 19,250 gallons. Although random variability is present, we would say that these data follow a horizontal pattern.

The term **stationary time series** is used to denote a time series whose statistical properties are independent of time. In particular this means that:

1. The process generating the data has a constant mean.
2. The variability of the time series is constant over time.

For a formal definition of stationarity, see K. Ord and R. Fildes, Principles of Business Forecasting (Mason, OH: Cengage Learning, 2012), p. 155.

A time series plot for a stationary time series will always exhibit a horizontal pattern with random fluctuations. However, simply observing a horizontal pattern is not sufficient evidence to conclude that the time series is stationary. More advanced texts on forecasting

TABLE 8.1 Gasoline Sales Time Series

Week	Sales (1,000s of gallons)
1	17
2	21
3	19
4	23
5	18
6	16
7	20
8	18
9	22
10	20
11	15
12	22

FIGURE 8.1 Gasoline Sales Time Series Plot

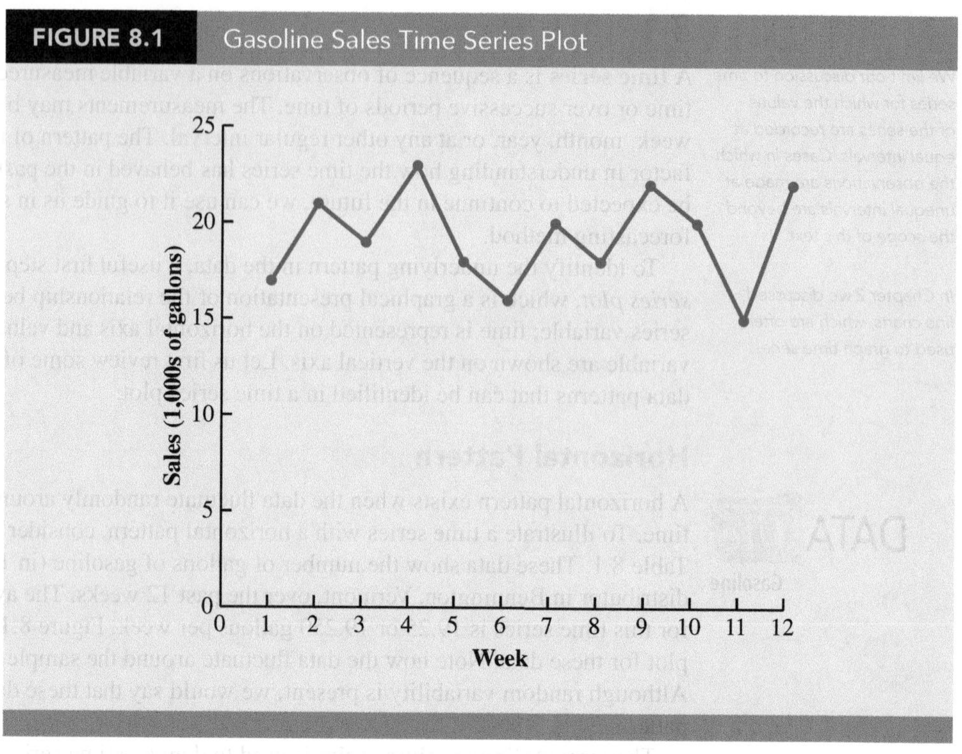

discuss procedures for determining whether a time series is stationary and provide methods for transforming a nonstationary time series into a stationary series.

Changes in business conditions often result in a time series with a horizontal pattern that shifts to a new level at some point in time. For instance, suppose the gasoline distributor signs a contract with the Vermont State Police to provide gasoline for state police cars located in southern Vermont beginning in week 13. With this new contract, the distributor naturally expects to see a substantial increase in weekly sales starting in week 13. Table 8.2

GasolineRevised

TABLE 8.2 Gasoline Sales Time Series after Obtaining the Contract with the Vermont State Police

Week	Sales (1,000s of gallons)	Week	Sales (1,000s of gallons)
1	17	12	22
2	21	13	31
3	19	14	34
4	23	15	31
5	18	16	33
6	16	17	28
7	20	18	32
8	18	19	30
9	22	20	29
10	20	21	34
11	15	22	33

FIGURE 8.2 Gasoline Sales Time Series Plot after Obtaining the Contract with the Vermont State Police

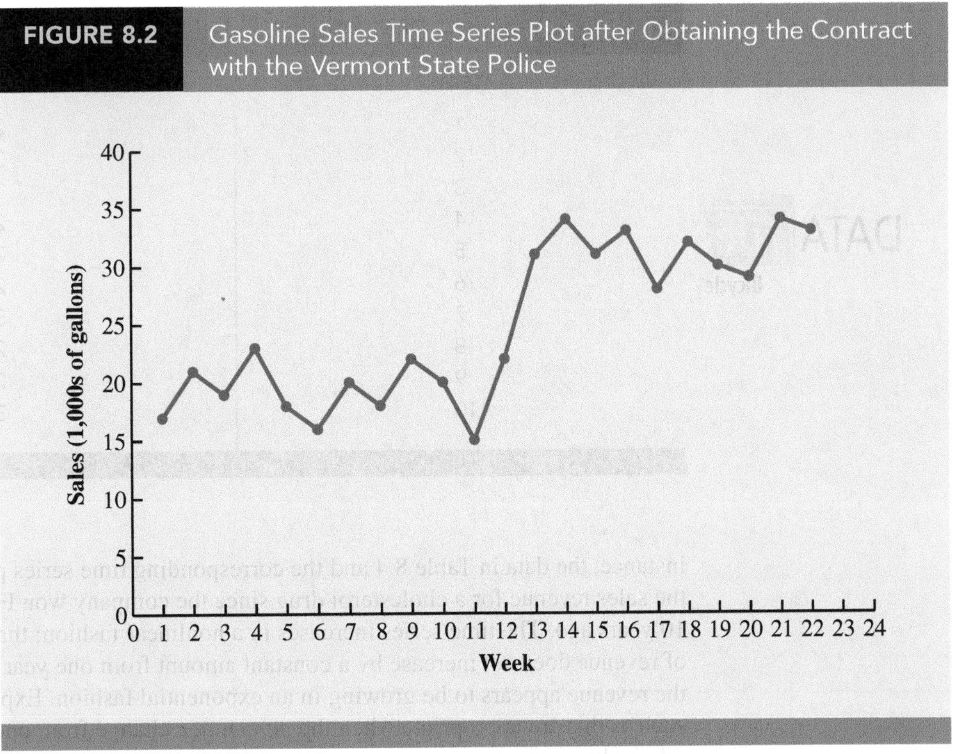

shows the number of gallons of gasoline sold for the original time series and for the 10 weeks after signing the new contract. Figure 8.2 shows the corresponding time series plot. Note the increased level of the time series beginning in week 13. This change in the level of the time series makes it more difficult to choose an appropriate forecasting method. Selecting a forecasting method that adapts well to changes in the level of a time series is an important consideration in many practical applications.

Trend Pattern

Although time series data generally exhibit random fluctuations, a time series may also show gradual shifts or movements to relatively higher or lower values over a longer period of time. If a time series plot exhibits this type of behavior, we say that a **trend** pattern exists. A trend is usually the result of long-term factors such as population increases or decreases, shifting demographic characteristics of the population, improving technology, changes in the competitive landscape, and/or changes in consumer preferences.

To illustrate a time series with a linear trend pattern, consider the time series of bicycle sales for a particular manufacturer over the past 10 years, as shown in Table 8.3 and Figure 8.3. Note that a total of 21,600 bicycles were sold in year 1, a total of 22,900 in year 2, and so on. In year 10, the most recent year, 31,400 bicycles were sold. Visual inspection of the time series plot shows some up-and-down movement over the past 10 years, but the time series seems also to have a systematically increasing, or upward, trend.

The trend for the bicycle sales time series appears to be linear and increasing over time, but sometimes a trend can be described better by other types of patterns. For

TABLE 8.3 Bicycle Sales Time Series

Year	Sales (1,000s)
1	21.6
2	22.9
3	25.5
4	21.9
5	23.9
6	27.5
7	31.5
8	29.7
9	28.6
10	31.4

instance, the data in Table 8.4 and the corresponding time series plot in Figure 8.4 show the sales revenue for a cholesterol drug since the company won FDA approval for the drug 10 years ago. The time series increases in a nonlinear fashion; that is, the rate of change of revenue does not increase by a constant amount from one year to the next. In fact, the revenue appears to be growing in an exponential fashion. Exponential relationships such as this are appropriate when the *percentage* change from one period to the next is relatively constant.

FIGURE 8.3 Bicycle Sales Time Series Plot

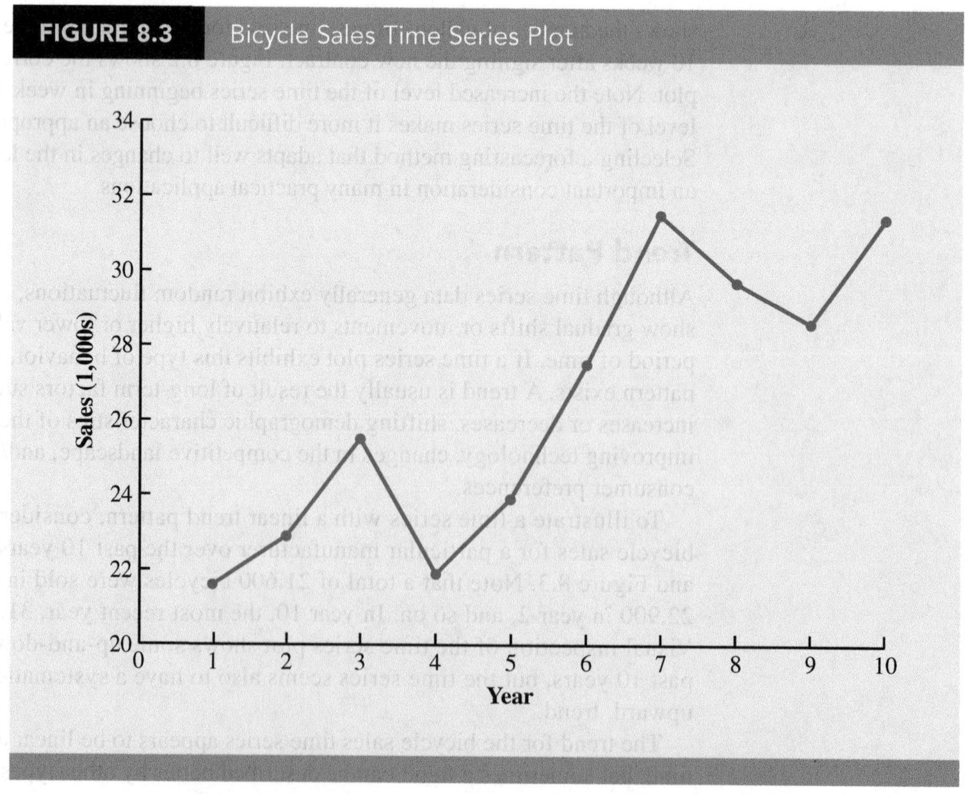

TABLE 8.4 Cholesterol Drug Revenue Time Series

Year	Revenue ($ millions)
1	23.1
2	21.3
3	27.4
4	34.6
5	33.8
6	43.2
7	59.5
8	64.4
9	74.2
10	99.3

Seasonal Pattern

The trend of a time series can be identified by analyzing movements in historical data over multiple time periods. **Seasonal patterns** are recognized by observing recurring patterns over successive periods of time. For example, a retailer who sells bathing suits expects low sales activity in the fall and winter months, with peak sales in the spring and summer months to occur every year. Retailers who sell snow removal equipment and heavy clothing, however, expect the opposite yearly pattern. Not surprisingly, the pattern for a time series plot that exhibits a recurring pattern over a one-year period due to seasonal influences is called a seasonal pattern. Although we generally think of seasonal movement in a time series as occurring within one year, time series data can also exhibit seasonal patterns of less than one year in duration. For example, daily traffic volume shows within-the-day "seasonal" behavior, with peak levels occurring during rush hours, moderate flow during the rest of the day and early evening, and light flow from midnight to early morning.

FIGURE 8.4 Cholesterol Drug Revenue Times Series Plot ($ Millions)

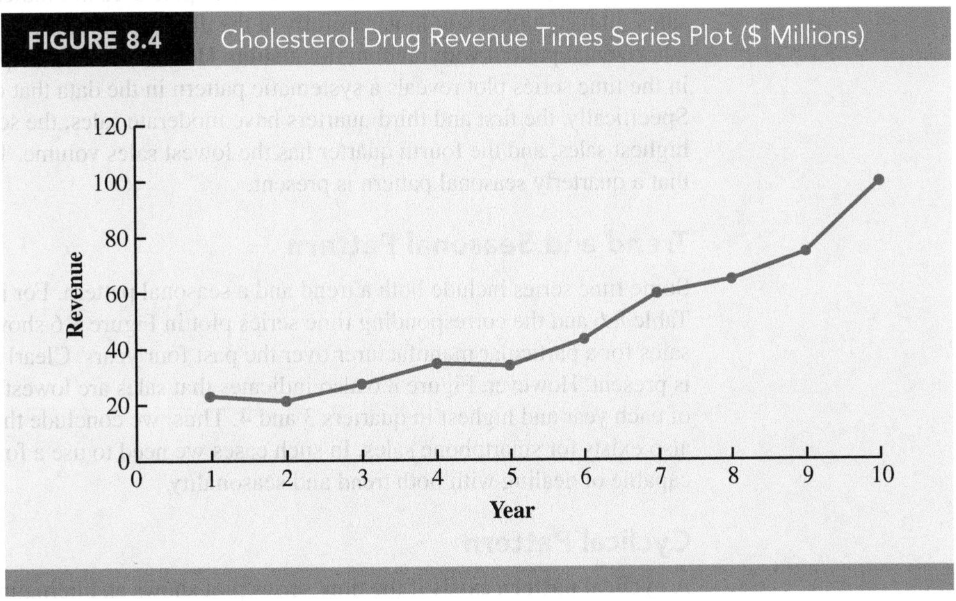

TABLE 8.5 Umbrella Sales Time Series

Year	Quarter	Sales
1	1	125
	2	153
	3	106
	4	88
2	1	118
	2	161
	3	133
	4	102
3	1	138
	2	144
	3	113
	4	80
4	1	109
	2	137
	3	125
	4	109
5	1	130
	2	165
	3	128
	4	96

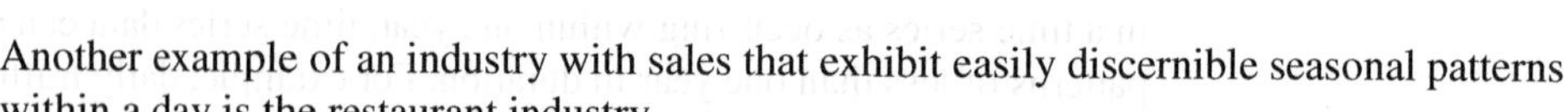

Another example of an industry with sales that exhibit easily discernible seasonal patterns within a day is the restaurant industry.

As an example of a seasonal pattern, consider the number of umbrellas sold at a clothing store over the past five years. Table 8.5 shows the time series and Figure 8.5 shows the corresponding time series plot. The time series plot does not indicate a long-term trend in sales. In fact, unless you look carefully at the data, you might conclude that the data follow a horizontal pattern with random fluctuation. However, closer inspection of the fluctuations in the time series plot reveals a systematic pattern in the data that occurs within each year. Specifically, the first and third quarters have moderate sales, the second quarter has the highest sales, and the fourth quarter has the lowest sales volume. Thus, we would conclude that a quarterly seasonal pattern is present.

Trend and Seasonal Pattern

Some time series include both a trend and a seasonal pattern. For instance, the data in Table 8.6 and the corresponding time series plot in Figure 8.6 show quarterly smartphone sales for a particular manufacturer over the past four years. Clearly an increasing trend is present. However, Figure 8.6 also indicates that sales are lowest in the second quarter of each year and highest in quarters 3 and 4. Thus, we conclude that a seasonal pattern also exists for smartphone sales. In such cases we need to use a forecasting method that is capable of dealing with both trend and seasonality.

Cyclical Pattern

A **cyclical pattern** exists if the time series plot shows an alternating sequence of points below and above the trendline that lasts for more than one year. Many economic time series

FIGURE 8.5 Umbrella Sales Time Series Plot

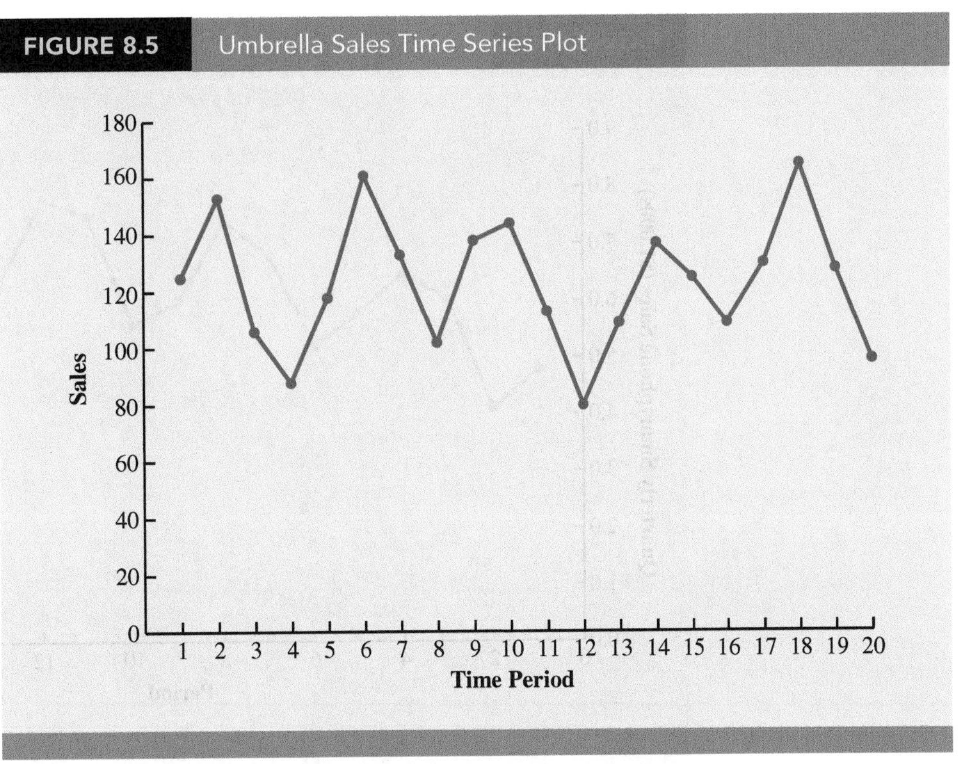

exhibit cyclical behavior with regular runs of observations below and above the trendline. Often the cyclical component of a time series is due to multiyear business cycles. For example, periods of moderate inflation followed by periods of rapid inflation can lead to a time series that alternates below and above a generally increasing trendline (e.g., a time series for housing costs). Business cycles are extremely difficult, if not impossible, to

SmartPhoneSales

TABLE 8.6 Quarterly Smartphone Sales Time Series

Year	Quarter	Sales ($1,000s)
1	1	4.8
	2	4.1
	3	6.0
	4	6.5
2	1	5.8
	2	5.2
	3	6.8
	4	7.4
3	1	6.0
	2	5.6
	3	7.5
	4	7.8
4	1	6.3
	2	5.9
	3	8.0
	4	8.4

FIGURE 8.6 Quarterly Smartphone Sales Time Series Plot

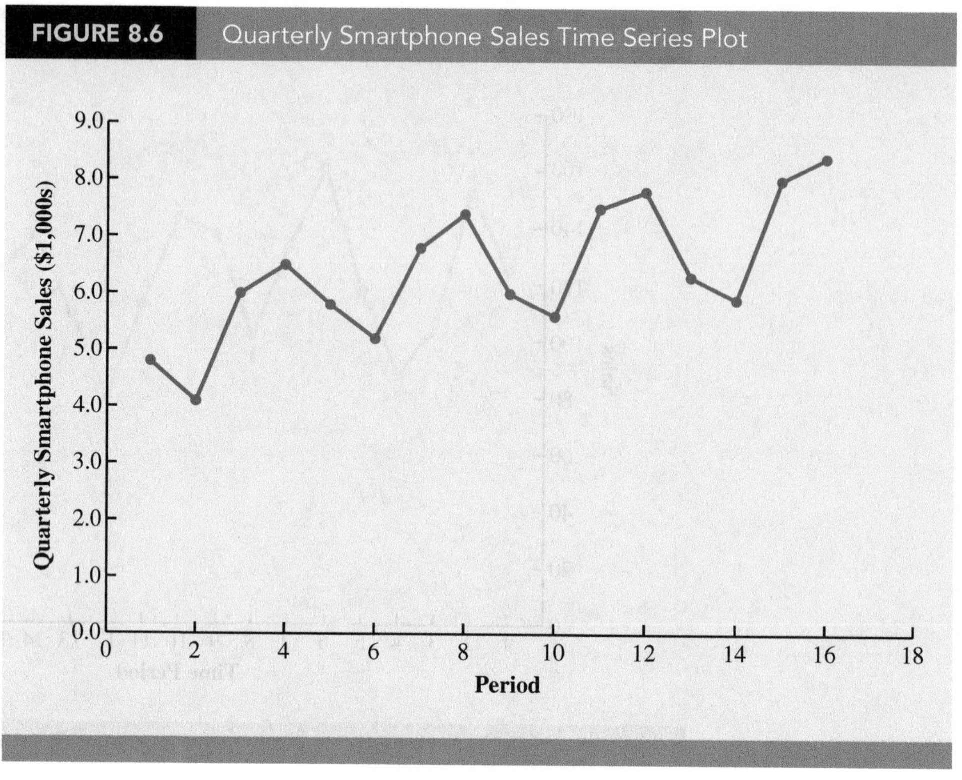

forecast. As a result, cyclical effects are often combined with long-term trend effects and referred to as *trend-cycle effects*. In this chapter we do not deal with cyclical effects that may be present in the time series.

Identifying Time Series Patterns

The underlying pattern in the time series is an important factor in selecting a forecasting method. Thus, a time series plot should be one of the first analytic tools employed when trying to determine which forecasting method to use. If we see a horizontal pattern, then we need to select a method appropriate for this type of pattern. Similarly, if we observe a trend in the data, then we need to use a forecasting method that is capable of handling a trend effectively. In the next section we discuss methods for assessing forecast accuracy. We then consider forecasting models that can be used in situations for which the underlying pattern is horizontal; in other words, no trend or seasonal effects are present. We then consider methods appropriate when trend and/or seasonality are present in the data.

8.2 Forecast Accuracy

In this section we begin by developing forecasts for the gasoline time series shown in Table 8.1 using the simplest of all the forecasting methods. We use the most recent week's sales volume as the forecast for the next week. For instance, the distributor sold 17 thousand gallons of gasoline in week 1; this value is used as the forecast for week 2. Next, we use 21, the actual value of sales in week 2, as the forecast for week 3, and so on. The forecasts obtained for the historical data using this method are shown in Table 8.7 in

TABLE 8.7 Computing Forecasts and Measures of Forecast Accuracy Using the Most Recent Value as the Forecast for the Next Period

Week	Time Series Value	Forecast	Forecast Error	Absolute Value of Forecast Error	Squared Forecast Error	Percentage Error	Absolute Value of Percentage Error
1	17						
2	21	17	4	4	16	19.05	19.05
3	19	21	−2	2	4	−10.53	10.53
4	23	19	4	4	16	17.39	17.39
5	18	23	−5	5	25	−27.78	27.78
6	16	18	−2	2	4	−12.50	12.50
7	20	16	4	4	16	20.00	20.00
8	18	20	−2	2	4	−11.11	11.11
9	22	18	4	4	16	18.18	18.18
10	20	22	−2	2	4	−10.00	10.00
11	15	20	−5	5	25	−33.33	33.33
12	22	15	7	7	49	31.82	31.82
		Totals	5	41	179	1.19	211.69

the Forecast column. Because of its simplicity, this method is often referred to as a **naïve forecasting method**.

How accurate are the forecasts obtained using this naïve forecasting method? To answer this question, we will introduce several measures of forecast accuracy. These measures are used to determine how well a particular forecasting method is able to reproduce the time series data that are already available. By selecting the method that is most accurate for the data already known, we hope to increase the likelihood that we will obtain more accurate forecasts for future time periods. The key concept associated with measuring forecast accuracy is **forecast error**. If we denote y_t and $\hat{y}_t$ as the actual and forecasted values of the time series for period t, respectively, the forecasting error for period t is:

FORECAST ERROR

$$e_t = y_t - \hat{y}_t \tag{8.1}$$

That is, the forecast error for time period t is the difference between the actual and the forecasted values for period t.

For instance, because the distributor actually sold 21 thousand gallons of gasoline in week 2, and the forecast, using the sales volume in week 1, was 17 thousand gallons, the forecast error in week 2 is:

$$e_2 = y_2 - \hat{y}_2 = 21 - 17 = 4.$$

A positive error such as this indicates that the forecasting method underestimated the actual value of sales for the associated period. Next we use 21, the actual value of sales in week 2, as the forecast for week 3. Since the actual value of sales in week 3 is 19, the forecast error for week 3 is $e_3 = 19 - 21 = -2$. In this case, the negative forecast error indicates that the forecast overestimated the actual value for week 3. Thus, the forecast error may be positive or negative, depending on whether the forecast is too low or too high.

A complete summary of the forecast errors for this naïve forecasting method is shown in Table 8.7 in the Forecast Error column. It is important to note that because we are using a past value of the time series to produce a forecast for period t, we do not have sufficient data to produce a naïve forecast for the first week of this time series.

A simple measure of forecast accuracy is the mean or average of the forecast errors. If we have n periods in our time series and k is the number of periods at the beginning of the time series for which we cannot produce a naïve forecast, the mean forecast error (MFE) is:

MEAN FORECAST ERROR (MFE)

$$\text{MFE} = \frac{\sum_{t=k+1}^{n} e_t}{n-k} \tag{8.2}$$

Table 8.7 shows that the sum of the forecast errors for the gasoline sales time series is 5; thus, the mean, or average, error is $5/11 = 0.45$. Because we do not have sufficient data to produce a naïve forecast for the first week of this time series, we must adjust our calculations in both the numerator and denominator accordingly. This is common in forecasting; we often use k past periods from the time series to produce forecasts, and so we frequently cannot produce forecasts for the first k periods. In those instances the summation in the numerator starts at the first value of t for which we have produced a forecast (so we begin the summation at $t = k + 1$), and the denominator (which is the number of periods in our time series for which we are able to produce a forecast) will also reflect these circumstances. In the gasoline example, although the time series consists of $n = 12$ values, to compute the mean error we divided the sum of the forecast errors by 11 because there are only 11 forecast errors (we cannot generate forecast sales for the first week using this naïve forecasting method).

Also note that in the gasoline time series, the mean forecast error is positive, implying that the method is generally underforecasting; in other words, the observed values tend to be greater than the forecasted values. Because positive and negative forecast errors tend to offset one another, the mean error is likely to be small; thus, the mean error is not a very useful measure of forecast accuracy.

The **mean absolute error (MAE)** is a measure of forecast accuracy that avoids the problem of positive and negative forecast errors offsetting one another. As you might expect given its name, MAE is the average of the absolute values of the forecast errors:

The MAE is also referred to as the mean absolute deviation (MAD).

MEAN ABSOLUTE ERROR (MAE)

$$\text{MAE} = \frac{\sum_{t=k+1}^{n} |e_t|}{n-k} \tag{8.3}$$

Table 8.7 shows that the sum of the absolute values of the forecast errors is 41; thus:

$$\text{MAE} = \text{average of the absolute value of the forecast errors} = \frac{41}{11} = 3.73.$$

Another measure that avoids the problem of positive and negative errors offsetting each other is obtained by computing the average of the squared forecast errors. This measure of forecast accuracy is referred to as the **mean squared error (MSE)**:

MEAN SQUARED ERROR (MSE)

$$\text{MSE} = \frac{\sum_{t=k+1}^{n} e_t^2}{n-k} \tag{8.4}$$

From Table 8.7, the sum of the squared errors is 179; hence:

$$\text{MSE} = \text{average of the square of the forecast errors} = \frac{179}{11} = 16.27.$$

The size of the MAE or MSE depends on the scale of the data. As a result, it is difficult to make comparisons for different time intervals (such as comparing a method of forecasting monthly gasoline sales to a method of forecasting weekly sales) or to make comparisons across different time series (such as monthly sales of gasoline and monthly sales of oil filters). To make comparisons such as these we need to work with relative or percentage error measures. The **mean absolute percentage error (MAPE)** is such a measure. To calculate MAPE we use the formula:

MEAN ABSOLUTE PERCENTAGE ERROR (MAPE)

$$\text{MAPE} = \frac{\sum_{t=k+1}^{n} \left| \left(\frac{e_t}{y_t}\right) 100 \right|}{n-k} \tag{8.5}$$

Table 8.7 shows that the sum of the absolute values of the percentage errors is:

$$\sum_{t=1+1}^{12} \left| \left(\frac{e_t}{y_t}\right) 100 \right| = 211.69.$$

Thus, the MAPE, which is the average of the absolute value of percentage forecast errors, is:

$$\frac{211.69}{11} = 19.24\%.$$

In summary, using the naïve (most recent observation) forecasting method, we obtain the following measures of forecast accuracy:

$$\text{MAE} = 3.73$$
$$\text{MSE} = 16.27$$
$$\text{MAPE} = 19.24\%$$

These measures of forecast accuracy simply measure how well the forecasting method is able to forecast historical values of the time series. Now, suppose we want to forecast sales for a future time period, such as week 13. The forecast for week 13 is 22, the actual value of the time series in week 12. Is this an accurate estimate of sales for week 13? Unfortunately, there is no way to address the issue of accuracy associated with forecasts for future time periods. However, if we select a forecasting method that works well for the historical data, and we have reason to believe the historical pattern will continue into the future, we should obtain forecasts that will ultimately be shown to be accurate.

Before closing this section, let us consider another method for forecasting the gasoline sales time series in Table 8.1. Suppose we use the average of all the historical data available as the forecast for the next period. We begin by developing a forecast for week 2. Because there is only one historical value available prior to week 2, the forecast for week 2 is just the time series value in week 1; thus, the forecast for week 2 is 17 thousand gallons of gasoline. To compute the forecast for week 3, we take the average of the sales values in weeks 1 and 2. Thus:

$$\hat{y}_3 = \frac{17 + 21}{2} = 19.$$

Similarly, the forecast for week 4 is:

$$\hat{y}_4 = \frac{17 + 21 + 19}{3} = 19.$$

The forecasts obtained using this method for the gasoline time series are shown in Table 8.8 in the Forecast column. Using the results shown in Table 8.8, we obtain the following values of MAE, MSE, and MAPE:

$$\text{MAE} = \frac{26.81}{11} = 2.44$$

$$\text{MSE} = \frac{89.07}{11} = 8.10$$

$$\text{MAPE} = \frac{141.34}{11} = 12.85\%$$

We can now compare the accuracy of the two forecasting methods we have considered in this section by comparing the values of MAE, MSE, and MAPE for each method.

TABLE 8.8 Computing Forecasts and Measures of Forecast Accuracy Using the Average of All the Historical Data as the Forecast for the Next Period

Week	Time Series Value	Forecast	Forecast Error	Absolute Value of Forecast Error	Squared Forecast Error	Percentage Error	Absolute Value of Percentage Error
1	17						
2	21	17.00	4.00	4.00	16.00	19.05	19.05
3	19	19.00	0.00	0.00	0.00	0.00	0.00
4	23	19.00	4.00	4.00	16.00	17.39	17.39
5	18	20.00	−2.00	2.00	4.00	−11.11	11.11
6	16	19.60	−3.60	3.60	12.96	−22.50	22.50
7	20	19.00	1.00	1.00	1.00	5.00	5.00
8	18	19.14	−1.14	1.14	1.31	−6.35	6.35
9	22	19.00	3.00	3.00	9.00	13.64	13.64
10	20	19.33	0.67	0.67	0.44	3.33	3.33
11	15	19.40	−4.40	4.40	19.36	−29.33	29.33
12	22	19.00	3.00	3.00	9.00	13.64	13.64
		Totals	4.52	26.81	89.07	2.75	141.34

	Naïve Method	Average of Past Values
MAE	3.73	2.44
MSE	16.27	8.10
MAPE	19.24%	12.85%

For each of these measures, the average of past values provides more accurate forecasts for the next period than using the most recent observation.

Evaluating different forecasts based on historical accuracy is helpful only if historical patterns continue into the future. As we note in Section 8.1, the 12 observations of Table 8.1 comprise a stationary time series. In Section 8.1 we also mentioned that changes in business conditions often result in a time series that is not stationary. We discussed a situation in which the gasoline distributor signed a contract with the Vermont State Police to provide gasoline for state police cars located in southern Vermont. Table 8.2 shows the number of gallons of gasoline sold for the original time series and for the 10 weeks after signing the new contract, and Figure 8.2 shows the corresponding time series plot. Note the change in level in week 13 for the resulting time series. When a shift to a new level such as this occurs, it takes several periods for the forecasting method that uses the average of all the historical data to adjust to the new level of the time series. However, in this case the simple naïve method adjusts very rapidly to the change in level because it uses only the most recent observation as the forecast.

Measures of forecast accuracy are important factors in comparing different forecasting methods, but we have to be careful not to rely too heavily on them. Good judgment and knowledge about business conditions that might affect the value of the variable to be forecast also have to be considered carefully when selecting a method. Historical forecast accuracy is not the sole consideration, especially if the pattern exhibited by the time series is likely to change in the future.

In the next section, we will introduce more sophisticated methods for developing forecasts for a time series that exhibits a horizontal pattern. Using the measures of forecast accuracy developed here, we will be able to assess whether such methods provide more accurate forecasts than we obtained using the simple approaches illustrated in this section. The methods that we will introduce also have the advantage that they adapt well to situations in which the time series changes to a new level. The ability of a forecasting method to adapt quickly to changes in level is an important consideration, especially in short-term forecasting situations.

8.3 Moving Averages and Exponential Smoothing

In this section we discuss two forecasting methods that are appropriate for a time series with a horizontal pattern: moving averages and exponential smoothing. These methods are capable of adapting well to changes in the level of a horizontal pattern such as the one we saw with the extended gasoline sales time series (Table 8.2 and Figure 8.2). However, without modification they are not appropriate when considerable trend, cyclical, or seasonal effects are present. Because the objective of each of these methods is to smooth out random fluctuations in the time series, they are referred to as *smoothing methods*. These methods are easy to use and generally provide a high level of accuracy for short-range forecasts, such as a forecast for the next time period.

Moving Averages

The **moving averages method** uses the average of the most recent k data values in the time series as the forecast for the next period. Mathematically, a moving average forecast of order k is:

MOVING AVERAGE FORECAST

$$\hat{y}_{t+1} = \frac{\sum(\text{most recent } k \text{ data values})}{k} = \frac{\sum_{i=t-k+1}^{t} y_i}{k}$$

$$= \frac{y_{t-k+1} + \cdots + y_{t-1} + y_t}{k} \tag{8.6}$$

where

$\hat{y}_{t+1}$ = forecast of the time series for period $t + 1$

y_t = actual value of the time series in period t

k = number of periods of time series data used to generate the forecast

The term *moving* is used because every time a new observation becomes available for the time series, it replaces the oldest observation in the equation and a new average is computed. Thus, the periods over which the average is calculated change, or move, with each ensuing period.

To illustrate the moving averages method, let us return to the original 12 weeks of gasoline sales data in Table 8.1 and Figure 8.1. The time series plot in Figure 8.1 indicates that the gasoline sales time series has a horizontal pattern. Thus, the smoothing methods of this section are applicable.

To use moving averages to forecast a time series, we must first select the order k, or the number of time series values to be included in the moving average. If only the most recent values of the time series are considered relevant, a small value of k is preferred. If a greater number of past values are considered relevant, then we generally opt for a larger value of k. As previously mentioned, a time series with a horizontal pattern can shift to a new level over time. A moving average will adapt to the new level of the series and continue to provide good forecasts in k periods. Thus a smaller value of k will track shifts in a time series more quickly (the naïve approach discussed earlier is actually a moving average for $k = 1$). On the other hand, larger values of k will be more effective in smoothing out random fluctuations. Thus, managerial judgment based on an understanding of the behavior of a time series is helpful in choosing an appropriate value of k.

To illustrate how moving averages can be used to forecast gasoline sales, we will use a three-week moving average ($k = 3$). We begin by computing the forecast of sales in week 4 using the average of the time series values in weeks 1 to 3:

$$\hat{y}_4 = \text{average for weeks 1 to 3} = \frac{17 + 21 + 19}{3} = 19.$$

Thus, the moving average forecast of sales in week 4 is 19, or 19,000 gallons of gasoline. Because the actual value observed in week 4 is 23, the forecast error in week 4 is $e_4 = 23 - 19 = 4$.

We next compute the forecast of sales in week 5 by averaging the time series values in weeks 2 to 4:

$$\hat{y}_5 = \text{average for weeks 2 to 4} = \frac{21 + 19 + 23}{3} = 21.$$

Hence, the forecast of sales in week 5 is 21 and the error associated with this forecast is $e_5 = 18 - 21 = -3$. A complete summary of the three-week moving average forecasts for the gasoline sales time series is provided in Table 8.9. Figure 8.7 shows the original time series plot and the three-week moving average forecasts. Note how the graph of the moving average forecasts has tended to smooth out the random fluctuations in the time series.

TABLE 8.9 Summary of Three-Week Moving Average Calculations

Week	Time Series Value	Forecast	Forecast Error	Absolute Value of Forecast Error	Squared Forecast Error	Percentage Error	Absolute Value of Percentage Error
1	17						
2	21						
3	19						
4	23	19	4	4	16	17.39	17.39
5	18	21	−3	3	9	−16.67	16.67
6	16	20	−4	4	16	−25.00	25.00
7	20	19	1	1	1	5.00	5.00
8	18	18	0	0	0	0.00	0.00
9	22	18	4	4	16	18.18	18.18
10	20	20	0	0	0	0.00	0.00
11	15	20	−5	5	25	−33.33	33.33
12	22	19	3	3	9	13.64	13.64
		Totals	0	24	92	−20.79	129.21

To forecast sales in week 13, the next time period in the future, we simply compute the average of the time series values in weeks 10, 11, and 12:

Gasoline

$$\hat{y}_{13} = \text{average for weeks 10 to 12} = \frac{20 + 15 + 22}{3} = 19.$$

Thus, the forecast for week 13 is 19, or 19,000 gallons of gasoline.

FIGURE 8.7 Gasoline Sales Time Series Plot and Three-Week Moving Average Forecasts

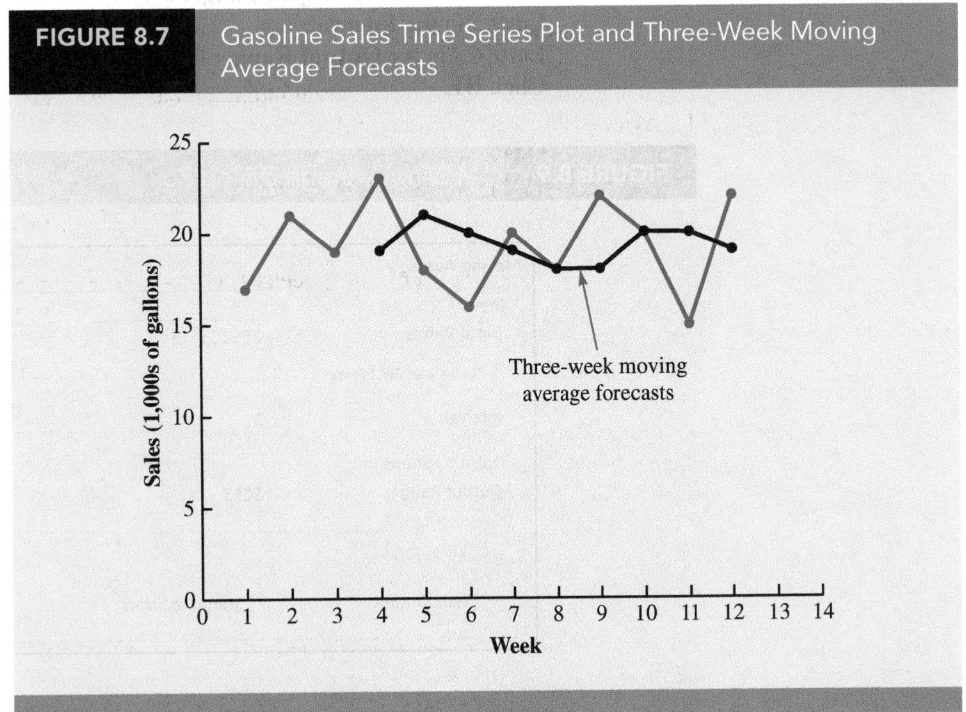

FIGURE 8.8 Data Analysis Dialog Box

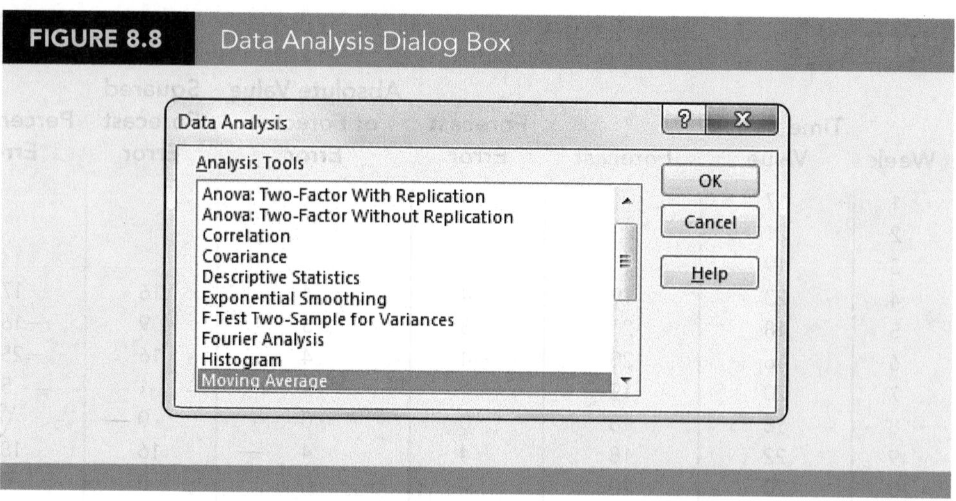

To show how Excel can be used to develop forecasts using the moving averages method, we develop a forecast for the gasoline sales time series in Table 8.1 and Figure 8.1. We assume that the user has entered the week into rows 2 through 13 of column A and the sales data for the 12 weeks into worksheet rows 2 through 13 of column B.

The following steps can be used to produce a three-week moving average:

In versions of Excel prior to Excel 2016, the **Data Analysis** *tool can be found in the* **Analysis** *group.*

Step 1. Click the **Data** tab in the Ribbon

Step 2. Click **Data Analysis** in the **Analyze** group

Step 3. When the **Data Analysis** dialog box appears (Figure 8.8), select **Moving Average** and click **OK**

Step 4. When the **Moving Average** dialog box appears (Figure 8.9):
Enter *B2:B13* in the **Input Range:** box
Enter *3* in the **Interval:** box
Enter *C3* in the **Output Range:** box
Click **OK**

FIGURE 8.9 Moving Average Dialog Box

Moving Average
Input
Input Range: $B$2:$B$13
Labels in First Row
Interval: 3
Output options
Output Range: $C$3
New Worksheet Ply:
New Workbook
Chart Output
Standard Errors
OK
Cancel
Help

FIGURE 8.10 Excel Output for Moving Average Forecast for Gasoline Data

	A	B	C
1	Week	Sales (1,000s of gallons)	
2	1	17	
3	2	21	#N/A
4	3	19	#N/A
5	4	23	19
6	5	18	21
7	6	16	20
8	7	20	19
9	8	18	18
10	9	22	18
11	10	20	20
12	11	15	20
13	12	22	19
14	13		19

Once you have completed this step, the three-week moving average forecasts will appear in column C of the worksheet as shown in Figure 8.10. Note that forecasts for periods of other lengths can be computed easily by entering a different value in the **Interval:** box.

If **Data Analysis** does not appear in your **Analyze** group for Step 1 (or in the **Analysis** group in versions of Excel prior to Excel 2016), you will have to load the Analysis ToolPak add-in into Excel. To do so, click the **File** tab in the Ribbon and click **Options**. When the **Excel Options** dialog box appears, click **Add-Ins** from the menu. Next to **Manage**, select **Excel Add-ins** and click **Go…** at the bottom of the dialog box. When the **Add-Ins** dialog box appears select **Analysis ToolPak** and click **OK**.

Forecast Accuracy

In Section 8.2 we discussed three measures of forecast accuracy: mean absolute error (MAE), mean squared error (MSE), and mean absolute percentage error (MAPE). Using the three-week moving average calculations in Table 8.9, the values for these three measures of forecast accuracy are:

$$\text{MAE} = \frac{\sum_{t=k+1}^{n} |e_t|}{n-k} = \frac{24}{9} = 2.67$$

$$\text{MSE} = \frac{\sum_{t=k+1}^{n} e_t^2}{n-k} = \frac{92}{9} = 10.22$$

$$\text{MAPE} = \frac{\sum_{t=k+1}^{n} \left|\left(\frac{e_t}{y_t}\right)100\right|}{n-k} = \frac{129.21}{9} = 14.36\%$$

In Section 8.2 we showed that using the most recent observation as the forecast for the next week (a moving average of order $k = 1$) resulted in values of MAE = 3.73, MSE = 16.27, and MAPE = 19.24%. Thus, in each case the three-week moving average approach has provided more accurate forecasts than simply using the most recent observation as the forecast. Also note how we have revised the formulas for the MAE, MSE, and MAPE to reflect that our use of a three-week moving average leaves us with insufficient data to generate forecasts for the first three weeks of our time series.

If a large amount of data are available to build the forecast models, we suggest dividing the data into training and validation sets, and then determining the best value of k as the value that minimizes the MSE for the validation set. We discuss the use of training and validation sets in more detail in Section 8.5.

To determine whether a moving average with a different order k can provide more accurate forecasts, we recommend using trial and error to determine the value of k that minimizes the MSE. For the gasoline sales time series, it can be shown that the minimum value of MSE corresponds to a moving average of order $k = 6$ with MSE = 6.79. If we are willing to assume that the order of the moving average that is best for the historical data will also be best for future values of the time series, the most accurate moving average forecasts of gasoline sales can be obtained using a moving average of order $k = 6$.

Exponential Smoothing

Exponential smoothing uses a weighted average of past time series values as a forecast. The exponential smoothing model is:

EXPONENTIAL SMOOTHING FORECAST

$$\hat{y}_{t+1} = \alpha y_t + (1 - \alpha)\hat{y}_t \tag{8.7}$$

where

$\hat{y}_{t+1}$ = forecast of the time series for period $t + 1$
y_t = actual value of the time series in period t
$\hat{y}_t$ = forecast of the time series for period t
α = smoothing constant $(0 \le \alpha \le 1)$

Equation (8.7) shows that the forecast for period $t + 1$ is a weighted average of the actual value in period t and the forecast for period t. The weight given to the actual value in period t is the **smoothing constant** α, and the weight given to the forecast in period t is $1 - \alpha$. It turns out that the exponential smoothing forecast for any period is actually a weighted average of all the previous actual values of the time series. Let us illustrate by working with a time series involving only three periods of data: y_1, y_2, and y_3.

To initiate the calculations, we let $\hat{y}_1$ equal the actual value of the time series in period 1; that is, $\hat{y}_1 = y_1$. Hence, the forecast for period 2 is:

$$\begin{aligned}\hat{y}_2 &= \alpha y_1 + (1 - \alpha)\hat{y}_1 \\ &= \alpha y_1 + (1 - \alpha)y_1 \\ &= y_1.\end{aligned}$$

We see that the exponential smoothing forecast for period 2 is equal to the actual value of the time series in period 1.

The forecast for period 3 is:

$$\hat{y}_3 = \alpha y_2 + (1 - \alpha)\hat{y}_2 = \alpha y_2 + (1 - \alpha)y_1.$$

Finally, substituting this expression for $\hat{y}_3$ into the expression for $\hat{y}_4$, we obtain:

$$\begin{aligned}\hat{y}_4 &= \alpha y_3 + (1 - \alpha)\hat{y}_3 \\ &= \alpha y_3 + (1 - \alpha)(\alpha y_2 + (1 - \alpha)y_1) \\ &= \alpha y_3 + \alpha(1 - \alpha)y_2 + (1 - \alpha)^2 y_1.\end{aligned}$$

We now see that $\hat{y}_4$ is a weighted average of the first three time series values. The sum of the coefficients, or weights, for y_1, y_2, and y_3 equals 1. A similar argument can be made to show that, in general, any forecast $\hat{y}_{t+1}$ is a weighted average of all the t previous time series values.

Despite the fact that exponential smoothing provides a forecast that is a weighted average of all past observations, all past data do not need to be retained to compute the forecast for the next period. In fact, equation (8.7) shows that once the value for the smoothing constant α is selected, only two pieces of information are needed to compute the forecast for period $t + 1$: y_t, the actual value of the time series in period t; and $\hat{y}_t$, the forecast for period t.

To illustrate the exponential smoothing approach to forecasting, let us again consider the gasoline sales time series in Table 8.1 and Figure 8.1. As indicated previously, to initialize the calculations we set the exponential smoothing forecast for period 2 equal to the actual value of the time series in period 1. Thus, with $y_1 = 17$, we set $\hat{y}_2 = 17$ to initiate the computations. Referring to the time series data in Table 8.1, we find an actual time series value in period 2 of $y_2 = 21$. Thus, in period 2 we have a forecast error of $e_2 = 21 - 17 = 4$.

Continuing with the exponential smoothing computations using a smoothing constant of $\alpha = 0.2$, we obtain the following forecast for period 3:

$$\hat{y}_3 = 0.2y_2 + 0.8\hat{y}_2 = 0.2(21) + 0.8(17) = 17.8.$$

Once the actual time series value in period 3, $y_3 = 19$, is known, we can generate a forecast for period 4 as follows:

$$\hat{y}_4 = 0.2y_3 + 0.8\hat{y}_3 = 0.2(19) + 0.8(17.8) = 18.04.$$

Continuing the exponential smoothing calculations, we obtain the weekly forecast values shown in Table 8.10. Note that we have not shown an exponential smoothing forecast or a forecast error for week 1 because no forecast was made (we used actual sales for week 1 as the forecasted sales for week 2 to initialize the exponential smoothing process). For week 12, we have $y_{12} = 22$ and $\hat{y}_{12} = 18.48$. We can we use this information to generate a forecast for week 13:

$$\hat{y}_{13} = 0.2y_{12} + 0.8\hat{y}_{12} = 0.2(22) + 0.8(18.48) = 19.18.$$

Thus, the exponential smoothing forecast of the amount sold in week 13 is 19.18, or 19,180 gallons of gasoline. With this forecast, the firm can make plans and decisions accordingly.

Figure 8.11 shows the time series plot of the actual and forecasted time series values. Note in particular how the forecasts smooth out the irregular or random fluctuations in the time series.

To show how Excel can be used for exponential smoothing, we again develop a forecast for the gasoline sales time series in Table 8.1 and Figure 8.1. We use the file *Gasoline,* which has the week in rows 2 through 13 of column A and the sales data for the 12 weeks in rows 2 through 13 of column B. We use $\alpha = 0.2$. The following steps can be used to produce a forecast.

TABLE 8.10 Summary of the Exponential Smoothing Forecasts and Forecast Errors for the Gasoline Sales Time Series with Smoothing Constant $\alpha = 0.2$

Week	Time Series Value	Forecast	Forecast Error	Squared Forecast Error
1	17			
2	21	17.00	4.00	16.00
3	19	17.80	1.20	1.44
4	23	18.04	4.96	24.60
5	18	19.03	−1.03	1.06
6	16	18.83	−2.83	8.01
7	20	18.26	1.74	3.03
8	18	18.61	−0.61	0.37
9	22	18.49	3.51	12.32
10	20	19.19	0.81	0.66
11	15	19.35	−4.35	18.92
12	22	18.48	3.52	12.39
		Totals	10.92	98.80

Step 1. Click the **Data** tab in the Ribbon
Step 2. Click **Data Analysis** in the **Analyze** group
Step 3. When the **Data Analysis** dialog box appears (Figure 8.12), select **Exponential Smoothing** and click **OK**

FIGURE 8.11 Actual and Forecast Gasoline Time Series with Smoothing Constant $\alpha = 0.2$

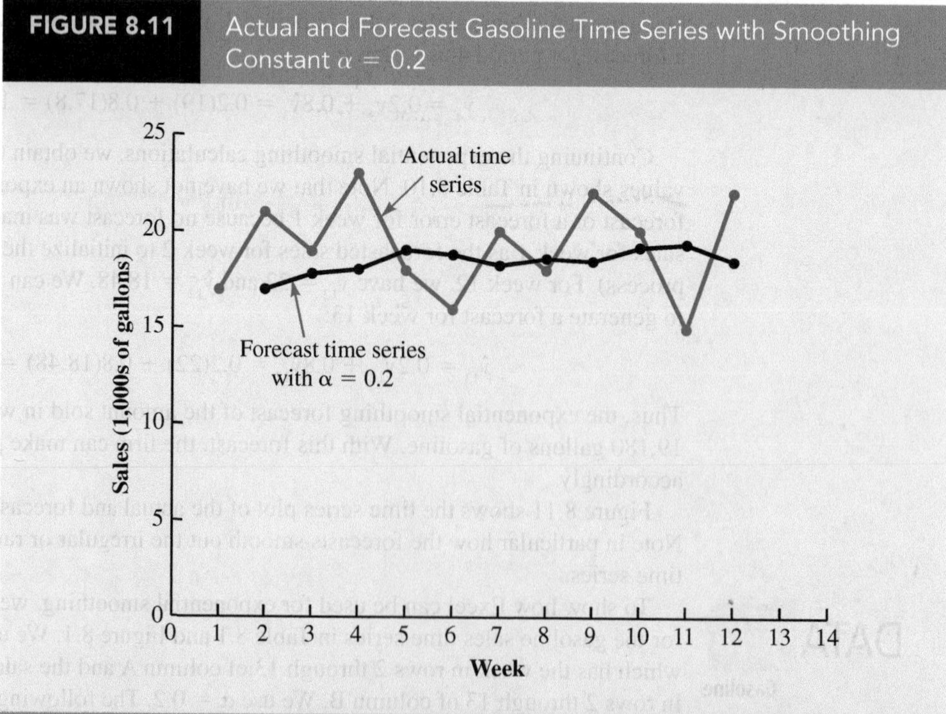

FIGURE 8.12 Data Analysis Dialog Box

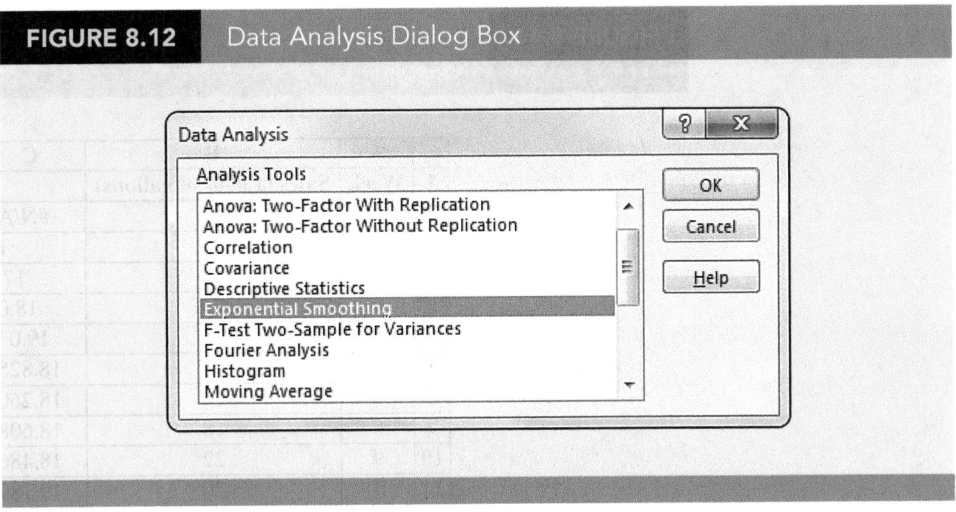

Step 4. When the **Exponential Smoothing** dialog box appears (Figure 8.13):
Enter *B2:B13* in the **Input Range:** box
Enter *0.8* in the **Damping factor:** box
Enter *C2* in the **Output Range:** box
Click **OK**

Once you have completed this step, the exponential smoothing forecasts will appear in column C of the worksheet as shown in Figure 8.14. Note that the value we entered in the **Damping factor:** box is $1 - \alpha$; forecasts for other smoothing constants can be computed easily by entering a different value for $1 - \alpha$ in the **Damping factor:** box.

Forecast Accuracy

In the preceding exponential smoothing calculations, we used a smoothing constant of $\alpha = 0.2$. Although any value of α between 0 and 1 is acceptable, some values will yield

FIGURE 8.13 Exponential Smoothing Dialog Box

Exponential Smoothing
Input
Input Range: $B$2:$B$13
Damping factor: 0.8
Labels
Output options
Output Range: $C$2
New Worksheet Ply:
New Workbook
Chart Output
Standard Errors
OK
Cancel
Help

FIGURE 8.14 Excel Output for Exponential Smoothing Forecast for Gasoline Data

	A	B	C
1	Week	Sales (1,000s of gallons)	
2	1	17	#N/A
3	2	21	17
4	3	19	17.8
5	4	23	18.04
6	5	18	19.032
7	6	16	18.8256
8	7	20	18.2605
9	8	18	18.6084
10	9	22	18.4867
11	10	20	19.1894
12	11	15	19.3515
13	12	22	18.4812

more accurate forecasts than others. Insight into choosing a good value for α can be obtained by rewriting the basic exponential smoothing model as follows:

$$\begin{aligned}\hat{y}_{t+1} &= \alpha y_t + (1-\alpha)\hat{y}_t \\ &= \alpha y_t + \hat{y}_t - \alpha\hat{y}_t \\ &= \hat{y}_t + \alpha(y_t - \hat{y}_t) = \hat{y}_t + \alpha e_t.\end{aligned}$$

Thus, the new forecast $\hat{y}_{t+1}$ is equal to the previous forecast $\hat{y}_t$ plus an adjustment, which is the smoothing constant α times the most recent forecast error, $e_t = y_t - \hat{y}_t$. In other words, the forecast in period $t + 1$ is obtained by adjusting the forecast in period t by a fraction of the forecast error from period t. If the time series contains substantial random variability, a small value of the smoothing constant is preferred. The reason for this choice is that if much of the forecast error is due to random variability, we do not want to overreact and adjust the forecasts too quickly. For a time series with relatively little random variability, a forecast error is more likely to represent a real change in the level of the series. Thus, larger values of the smoothing constant provide the advantage of quickly adjusting the forecasts to changes in the time series, thereby allowing the forecasts to react more quickly to changing conditions.

Similar to our note related to moving averages, if enough data are available, then α should be chosen to minimize the MSE of the validation set.

The criterion we will use to determine a desirable value for the smoothing constant α is the same as that proposed for determining the order or number of periods of data to include in the moving averages calculation; that is, we choose the value of α that minimizes the MSE. A summary of the MSE calculations for the exponential smoothing forecast of gasoline sales with $\alpha = 0.2$ is shown in Table 8.10. Note that there is one less squared error term than the number of time periods; this is because we had no past values with which to make a forecast for period 1. The value of the sum of squared forecast errors is 98.80; hence, MSE $= 98.80/11 = 8.98$. Would a different value of α provide better results in terms of a lower MSE value? Trial and error is often used to determine whether a different smoothing constant α can provide more accurate forecasts, but we can avoid trial and error and determine the value of α that minimizes MSE through the use of nonlinear optimization. Nonlinear optimization is discussed in Chapter 13.

NOTES + COMMENTS

1. Spreadsheet packages are effective tools for implementing exponential smoothing. With the time series data and the forecasting formulas in a spreadsheet such as the one shown in Table 8.10, you can use the MAE, MSE, and MAPE to evaluate different values of the smoothing constant α.
2. Moving averages and exponential smoothing provide the foundation for much of time series analysis, and many more sophisticated refinements of these methods have been developed. These include but are not limited to weighted moving averages, double moving averages, Brown's method for double exponential smoothing, and Holt-Winters exponential smoothing. Appendix 8.1 explains how to implement the Holt-Winters method using a new tool in Excel 2016 called Forecast Sheet. Appendix 8.2 demonstrates the use of the Excel add-in Analytic Solver Platform which allows for the use of additional forecasting models.

8.4 Using Regression Analysis for Forecasting

As we saw in Chapter 7, regression analysis is a statistical technique that can be used to develop a mathematical equation showing how variables are related. In regression terminology, the variable that is being predicted is called the *dependent*, or *response*, *variable*, and the variable or variables being used to predict the value of the dependent variable are called the *independent*, or *predictor*, *variables*. Regression analysis involving one independent variable and one dependent variable for which the relationship between the variables is approximated by a straight line is called *simple linear regression*. Regression analysis involving two or more independent variables is called *multiple regression analysis*. In this section we will show how to use regression analysis to develop forecasts for a time series that has a trend, a seasonal pattern, and both a trend and a seasonal pattern. We will also show how to use regression analysis to develop forecast models that include causal variables.

Linear Trend Projection

We now consider forecasting methods that are appropriate for time series that exhibit trend patterns and show how regression analysis can be used to forecast a time series with a linear trend. In Section 8.1 we used the bicycle sales time series in Table 8.3 and Figure 8.3 to illustrate a time series with a trend pattern. Let us now use this time series to illustrate how regression analysis can be used to forecast a time series with a linear trend. Although the time series plot in Figure 8.3 shows some up-and-down movement over the past 10 years, we might agree that the linear trendline shown in Figure 8.3 provides a reasonable approximation of the long-run movement in the series. We can use regression analysis to develop such a linear trendline for the bicycle sales time series.

Because simple linear regression analysis yields the linear relationship between the independent variable and the dependent variable that minimizes the MSE, we can use this approach to find a best-fitting line to a set of data that exhibits a linear trend. In finding a linear trend, the variable to be forecasted (y_t, the actual value of the time series in period t) is the dependent variable and the trend variable (time period t) is the independent variable. We will use the following notation for our linear trendline:

$$\hat{y}_t = b_0 + b_1 t, \tag{8.8}$$

where

$\hat{y}_t$ = forecast of sales in period t
t = time period
b_0 = the y-intercept of the linear trendline
b_1 = the slope of the linear trendline

FIGURE 8.15 Excel Simple Linear Regression Output for Trendline Model for Bicycle Sales Data

	A	B	C	D	E	F	G	H	I
1	SUMMARY OUTPUT								
2									
3	*Regression Statistics*								
4	Multiple R	0.874526167							
5	R Square	0.764796016							
6	Adjusted R Square	0.735395518							
7	Standard Error	1.958953802							
8	Observations	10							
9									
10	ANOVA								
11		*df*	*SS*	*MS*	*F*	*Significance F*			
12	Regression	1	99.825	99.825	26.01302932	0.000929509			
13	Residual	8	30.7	3.8375					
14	Total	9	130.525						
15									
16		*Coefficients*	*Standard Error*	*t Stat*	*P-value*	*Lower 95%*	*Upper 95%*	*Lower 99.0%*	*Upper 99.0%*
17	Intercept	20.4	1.338220211	15.24412786	3.39989E-07	17.31405866	23.48594134	15.90975286	24.89024714
18	Year	1.1	0.215673715	5.100296983	0.000929509	0.60265552	1.59734448	0.376331148	1.823668852

In equation (8.8), the time variable begins at $t = 1$, corresponding to the first time series observation (year 1 for the bicycle sales time series). The time variable then continues until $t = n$, corresponding to the most recent time series observation (year 10 for the bicycle sales time series). Thus, for the bicycle sales time series $t = 1$ corresponds to the oldest time series value, and $t = 10$ corresponds to the most recent year.

Excel can be used to compute the estimated intercept b_0 and slope b_1. The Excel output for a regression analysis of the bicycle sales data is provided in Figure 8.15.

We see in this output that the estimated intercept b_0 is 20.4 (shown in cell B17) and the estimated slope b_1 is 1.1 (shown in cell B18). Thus,

$$\hat{y}_t = 20.4 + 1.1t \tag{8.9}$$

is the regression equation for the linear trend component for the bicycle sales time series. The slope of 1.1 in this trend equation indicates that over the past 10 years the firm has experienced an average growth in sales of about 1,100 units per year. If we assume that the past 10-year trend in sales is a good indicator for the future, we can use equation (8.9) to project the trend component of the time series. For example, substituting $t = 11$ into equation (8.9) yields next year's trend projection, $\hat{y}_{11}$:

$$\hat{y}_{11} = 20.4 + 1.1(11) = 32.5.$$

Thus, the linear trend model yields a sales forecast of 32,500 bicycles for the next year.

We can also use the trendline to forecast sales farther into the future. Using equation (8.9), we develop annual forecasts of bicycle sales for two and three years into the future as follows:

$$\hat{y}_{12} = 20.4 + 1.1(12) = 33.6$$

$$\hat{y}_{13} = 20.4 + 1.1(13) = 34.7$$

The forecasted value increases by 1,100 bicycles in each year.

Note that in this example we are not using past values of the time series to produce forecasts, so we can produce a forecast for each period of the time series; that is, $k = 0$ in equations (8.3), (8.4), and (8.5) to calculate the MAE, MSE, and MAPE.

We can also use more complex regression models to fit nonlinear trends. For example, if we also include t^2 and t^3 as independent variables in our model, the estimated regression equation would become:

$$\hat{y}_t = b_0 + b_1 t + b_2 t^2 + b_3 t^3.$$

This model provides a forecast of a time series with curvilinear characteristics over time.

Another type of regression-based forecasting model occurs whenever all the independent variables are previous values of the same time series. For example, if the time series values are denoted $y_1, y_2, \ldots, y_n$, we might try to find an estimated regression equation relating y_t to the most recent time series values, y_{t-1}, y_{t-2}, and so on. If we use the actual values of the time series for the three most recent periods as independent variables, the estimated regression equation would be:

$$\hat{y}_t = b_0 + b_1 y_{t-1} + b_2 y_{t-2} + b_3 y_{t-3}.$$

Because autoregressive models typically violate the conditions necessary for inference in least squares regression, you must be careful when testing hypotheses or estimating confidence intervals in autoregressive models. There are special methods for constructing autoregressive models, but they are beyond the scope of this book.

Regression models such as this in which the independent variables are previous values of the time series are referred to as **autoregressive models**.

Seasonality

To the extent that seasonality exists, we need to incorporate it into our forecasting models to ensure accurate forecasts. We begin by considering a seasonal time series with no trend and then discuss how to model seasonality with a linear trend.

Seasonality Without Trend

Let us consider again the data from Table 8.5, the number of umbrellas sold at a clothing store over the past five years. As we see in the time series plot provided in Figure 8.5, the data do not suggest any long-term trend in sales. In fact, unless you look carefully at the data, you might conclude that the data follow a horizontal pattern with random fluctuation and that single exponential smoothing could be used to forecast sales. However, closer inspection of the time series plot reveals a pattern in the fluctuations. The first and third quarters have moderate sales, the second quarter the highest sales, and the fourth quarter the lowest sales. Thus, we conclude that a quarterly seasonal pattern is present.

We can model a time series with a seasonal pattern by treating the season as a dummy variable. As indicated in Chapter 7, categorical variables are data used to categorize observations of data, and $k - 1$ dummy variables are required to model a categorical variable that has k levels. Thus, we need three dummy variables to model four seasons. For instance, in the umbrella sales time series, the quarter to which each observation corresponds is treated as a season; it is a categorical variable with four levels: quarter 1, quarter 2, quarter 3, and quarter 4. Thus, to model the seasonal effects in the umbrella time series we need $4 - 1 = 3$ dummy variables. The three dummy variables can be coded as follows:

$$\text{Qtr1}_t = \begin{cases} 1 \text{ if period } t \text{ is a quarter 1} \\ 0 \text{ otherwise} \end{cases}$$

$$\text{Qtr2}_t = \begin{cases} 1 \text{ if period } t \text{ is a quarter 2} \\ 0 \text{ otherwise} \end{cases}$$

$$\text{Qtr3}_t = \begin{cases} 1 \text{ if period } t \text{ is a quarter 3} \\ 0 \text{ otherwise} \end{cases}$$

Using $\hat{y}_t$ to denote the forecasted value of sales for period t, the general form of the equation relating the number of umbrellas sold to the quarter the sales take place is as follows:

$$\hat{y}_t = b_0 + b_1\text{Qtr1}_t + b_2\text{Qtr2}_t + b_3\text{Qtr3}_t. \tag{8.10}$$

Note that the fourth quarter will be denoted by setting all three dummy variables to 0.

Table 8.11 shows the umbrella sales time series with the coded values of the dummy variables shown. We can use a multiple linear regression model to find the values of b_0, b_1, b_2, and b_3 that minimize the sum of squared errors. For this regression model, y_t is the dependent variable, and the quarterly dummy variables Qtr1_t, Qtr2_t, and Qtr3_t are the independent variables.

Using the data in Table 8.11 and regression analysis, we obtain the following equation:

$$\hat{y}_t = 95.0 + 29.0\text{Qtr1}_t + 57.0\text{Qtr2}_t + 26.0\text{Qtr3}_t. \tag{8.11}$$

We can use equation (8.11) to forecast sales of every quarter for next year:

Quarter 1: Sales = 95.0 + 29.0(1) + 57.0(0) + 26.0(0) = 124

Quarter 2: Sales = 95.0 + 29.0(0) + 57.0(1) + 26.0(0) = 152

Quarter 3: Sales = 95.0 + 29.0(0) + 57.0(0) + 26.0(1) = 121

Quarter 4: Sales = 95.0 + 29.0(0) + 57.0(0) + 26.0(0) = 95

It is interesting to note that we could have obtained the quarterly forecasts for next year by simply computing the average number of umbrellas sold in each quarter. Nonetheless, for more complex problem situations, such as dealing with a time series that has both trend and seasonal effects, this simple averaging approach will not work.

TABLE 8.11 Umbrella Sales Time Series with Dummy Variables

Period	Year	Quarter	Qtr1	Qtr2	Qtr3	Sales
1	1	1	1	0	0	125
2		2	0	1	0	153
3		3	0	0	1	106
4		4	0	0	0	88
5	2	1	1	0	0	118
6		2	0	1	0	161
7		3	0	0	1	133
8		4	0	0	0	102
9	3	1	1	0	0	138
10		2	0	1	0	144
11		3	0	0	1	113
12		4	0	0	0	80
13	4	1	1	0	0	109
14		2	0	1	0	137
15		3	0	0	1	125
16		4	0	0	0	109
17	5	1	1	0	0	130
18		2	0	1	0	165
19		3	0	0	1	128
20		4	0	0	0	96

Seasonality with Trend

We now consider situations for which the time series contains both seasonal effects and a linear trend by showing how to forecast the quarterly sales of smartphones introduced in Section 8.1. The data for the smartphone time series are shown in Table 8.6. The time series plot in Figure 8.6 indicates that sales are lowest in the second quarter of each year and increase in quarters 3 and 4. Thus, we conclude that a seasonal pattern exists for smartphone sales. However, the time series also has an upward linear trend that will need to be accounted for in order to develop accurate forecasts of quarterly sales. This is easily done by combining the dummy variable approach for handling seasonality with the approach for handling a linear trend discussed earlier in this section.

The general form of the regression equation for modeling both the quarterly seasonal effects and the linear trend in the smartphone time series is:

$$\hat{y}_t = b_0 + b_1\text{Qtr1}_t + b_2\text{Qtr2}_t + b_3\text{Qtr3}_t + b_4t, \tag{8.12}$$

where

$\hat{y}_t$ = forecast of sales in period t

Qtr1_t = 1 if time period t corresponds to the first quarter of the year; 0 otherwise

Qtr2_t = 1 if time period t corresponds to the second quarter of the year; 0 otherwise

Qtr3_t = 1 if time period t corresponds to the third quarter of the year; 0 otherwise

t = time period (quarter)

For this regression model y_t is the dependent variable and the quarterly dummy variables Qtr1_t, Qtr2_t, and Qtr3_t and the time period t are the independent variables.

Table 8.12 shows the revised smartphone sales time series that includes the coded values of the dummy variables and the time period t. Using the data in Table 8.12 with

TABLE 8.12 Smartphone Sales Time Series with Dummy Variables and Time Period

Period	Year	Quarter	Qtr1	Qtr2	Qtr3	Sales (1,000s)
1	1	1	1	0	0	4.8
2		2	0	1	0	4.1
3		3	0	0	1	6.0
4		4	0	0	0	6.5
5	2	1	1	0	0	5.8
6		2	0	1	0	5.2
7		3	0	0	1	6.8
8		4	0	0	0	7.4
9	3	1	1	0	0	6.0
10		2	0	1	0	5.6
11		3	0	0	1	7.5
12		4	0	0	0	7.8
13	4	1	1	0	0	6.3
14		2	0	1	0	5.9
15		3	0	0	1	8.0
16		4	0	0	0	8.4

the regression model that includes both the seasonal and trend components, we obtain the following equation that minimizes our sum of squared errors:

$$\hat{y}_t = 6.07 - 1.36\text{Qtr1}_t - 2.03\text{Qtr2}_t - 0.304\text{Qtr3}_t + 0.146t. \tag{8.13}$$

We can now use equation (8.13) to forecast quarterly sales for next year. Next year is year 5 for the smartphone sales time series, that is, time periods 17, 18, 19, and 20.

Forecast for time period 17 (quarter 1 in year 5):

$$\hat{y}_{17} = 6.07 - 1.36(1) - 2.03(0) - 0.304(0) + 0.146(17) = 7.19.$$

Forecast for time period 18 (quarter 2 in year 5):

$$\hat{y}_{18} = 6.07 - 1.36(0) - 2.03(1) - 0.304(0) + 0.146(18) = 6.67.$$

Forecast for time period 19 (quarter 3 in year 5):

$$\hat{y}_{19} = 6.07 - 1.36(0) - 2.03(0) - 0.304(1) + 0.146(19) = 8.54.$$

Forecast for time period 20 (quarter 4 in year 5):

$$\hat{y}_{20} = 6.07 - 1.36(0) - 2.03(0) - 0.304(0) + 0.146(20) = 8.99.$$

Thus, accounting for the seasonal effects and the linear trend in smartphone sales, the estimates of quarterly sales in year 5 are 7,190, 6,670, 8,540, and 8,990.

The dummy variables in the equation actually provide four equations, one for each quarter. For instance, if time period t corresponds to quarter 1, the estimate of quarterly sales is:

$$\text{Quarter 1: Sales} = 6.07 - 1.36(1) - 2.03(0) - 0.304(0) + 0.146t = 4.71 + 0.146t.$$

Similarly, if time period t corresponds to quarters 2, 3, and 4, the estimates of quarterly sales are:

$$\text{Quarter 2: Sales} = 6.07 - 1.36(0) - 2.03(1) - 0.304(0) + 0.146t = 4.04 + 0.146t$$

$$\text{Quarter 3: Sales} = 6.07 - 1.36(0) - 2.03(0) - 0.304(1) + 0.146t = 5.77 + 0.146t$$

$$\text{Quarter 4: Sales} = 6.07 - 1.36(0) - 2.03(0) - 0.304(0) + 0.146t = 6.07 + 0.146t$$

The slope of the trendline for each quarterly forecast equation is 0.146, indicating a consistent growth in sales of about 146 phones per quarter. The only difference in the four equations is that they have different intercepts.

In the smartphone sales example, we showed how dummy variables can be used to account for the quarterly seasonal effects in the time series. Because there were four levels for the categorical variable season, three dummy variables were required. However, many businesses use monthly rather than quarterly forecasts. For monthly data, season is a categorical variable with 12 levels, and thus $12 - 1 = 11$ dummy variables are required to capture monthly seasonal effects. For example, the 11 dummy variables could be coded as follows:

$$\text{Month1}_t = \begin{cases} 1 \text{ if period } t \text{ is January} \\ 0 \text{ otherwise} \end{cases}$$

$$\text{Month2}_t = \begin{cases} 1 \text{ if period } t \text{ is February} \\ 0 \text{ otherwise} \end{cases}$$

$$\vdots$$

$$\text{Month11}_t = \begin{cases} 1 \text{ if period } t \text{ is November} \\ 0 \text{ otherwise} \end{cases}$$

Other than this change, the approach for handling seasonality remains the same. Time series data collected at other intervals can be handled in a similar manner.

Using Regression Analysis as a Causal Forecasting Method

The methods discussed for estimating linear trends and seasonal effects make use of patterns in historical values of the variable to be forecast; these methods are classified as time series methods because they rely on past values of the variable to be forecast when developing the model. However, the relationship of the variable to be forecast with other variables may also be used to develop a forecasting model. Generally such models include only variables that are believed to cause changes in the variable to be forecast, such as:

- Advertising expenditures when sales is to be forecast.
- The mortgage rate when new housing construction is to be forecast.
- Grade point average when starting salaries for recent college graduates is to be forecast.
- The price of a product when the demand for the product is to be forecast.
- The value of the Dow Jones Industrial Average when the value of an individual stock is to be forecast.
- Daily high temperature when electricity usage is to be forecast.

Because these variables are used as independent variables when we believe they cause changes in the value of the dependent variable, forecasting models that include such variables as independent variables are referred to as **causal models**. It is important to note here that the forecasting model provides evidence only of association between an independent variable and the variable to be forecast. The model does not provide evidence of a causal relationship between an independent variable and the variable to be forecast; the conclusion that a causal relationship exists must be based on practical experience.

To illustrate how regression analysis is used as a causal forecasting method, we consider the sales forecasting problem faced by Armand's Pizza Parlors, a chain of Italian restaurants doing business in a five-state area. Historically, the most successful locations have been near college campuses. The managers believe that quarterly sales for these restaurants (denoted by y) are related positively to the size of the student population (denoted by x); that is, restaurants near campuses with a large population tend to generate more sales than those located near campuses with a small population.

Using regression analysis we can develop an equation showing how the dependent variable y is related to the independent variable x. This equation can then be used to forecast quarterly sales for restaurants located near college campuses given the size of the student population. This is particularly helpful for forecasting sales for new restaurant locations. For instance, suppose that management wants to forecast sales for a new restaurant that it is considering opening near a college campus. Because no historical data are available on sales for a new restaurant, Armand's cannot use time series data to develop the forecast. However, as we will now illustrate, regression analysis can still be used to forecast quarterly sales for this new location.

To develop the equation relating quarterly sales to the size of the student population, Armand's collected data from a sample of 10 of its restaurants located near college campuses. These data are summarized in Table 8.13. For example, restaurant 1, with $y = 58$ and $x = 2$, had \$58,000 in quarterly sales and is located near a campus with 2,000 students. Figure 8.16 shows a scatter chart of the data presented in Table 8.13, with the size of the student population shown on the horizontal axis and quarterly sales shown on the vertical axis.

What preliminary conclusions can we draw from Figure 8.16? Sales appear to be higher at locations near campuses with larger student populations. Also, it appears that the relationship

TABLE 8.13 Student Population and Quarterly Sales Data for 10 Armand's Pizza Parlors

DATA *file* Armand's

Restaurant	Student Population (1,000s)	Quarterly Sales ($1,000s)
1	2	58
2	6	105
3	8	88
4	8	118
5	12	117
6	16	137
7	20	157
8	20	169
9	22	149
10	26	202

between the two variables can be approximated by a straight line. In Figure 8.17, we can draw a straight line through the data that appears to provide a good linear approximation of the relationship between the variables. Observe that the relationship is not perfect. Indeed, few, if any, of the data fall exactly on the line. However, if we can develop the mathematical expression for this line, we may be able to use it to forecast the value of y corresponding to

FIGURE 8.16 Scatter Chart of Student Population and Quarterly Sales for Armand's Pizza Parlors

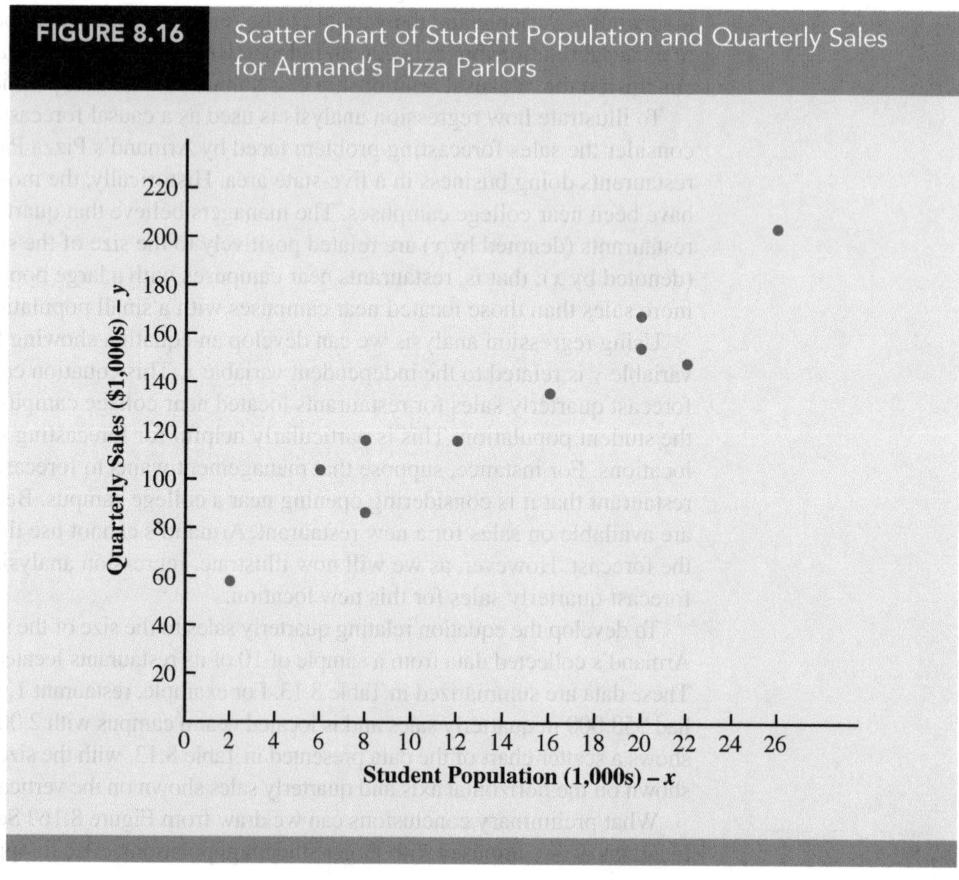

FIGURE 8.17 Graph of the Estimated Regression Equation for Armand's Pizza Parlors: $y = 60 + 5x$

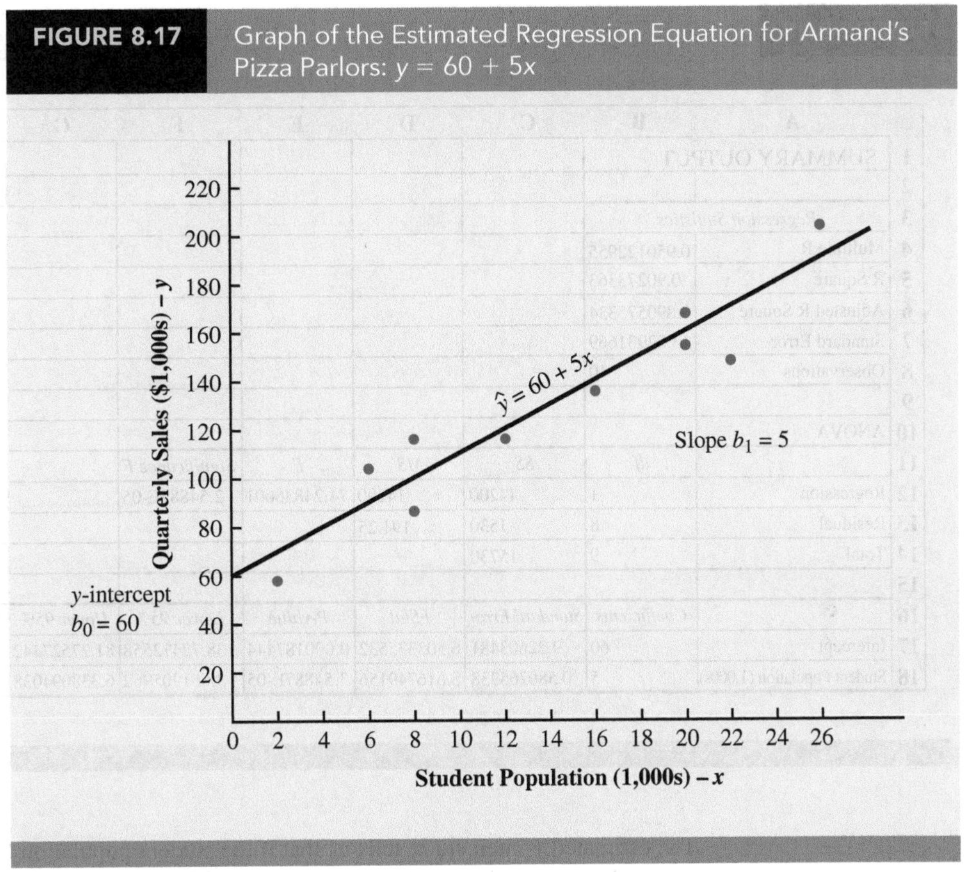

each possible value of x. The resulting equation of the line is called the estimated regression equation.

Using the least-squares method of estimation, the estimated regression equation is:

$$\hat{y}_i = b_0 + b_1 x_i, \tag{8.14}$$

where

$\hat{y}_i$ = estimated value of the dependent variable (quarterly sales) for the ith observation
b_0 = intercept of the estimated regression equation
b_1 = slope of the estimated regression equation
x_i = value of the independent variable (student population) for the ith observation

The Excel output for a simple linear regression analysis of the Armand's Pizza data is provided in Figure 8.18.

We see in this output that the estimated intercept b_0 is 60 and the estimated slope b_1 is 5. Thus, the estimated regression equation is:

Note that the values of the independent variable range from 2,000 to 26,000; thus, as discussed in Chapter 7, the y-intercept in such cases is an extrapolation of the regression line and must be interpreted with caution.

$$\hat{y}_i = 60 + 5x_i.$$

The slope of the estimated regression equation ($b_1 = 5$) is positive, implying that, as student population increases, quarterly sales increase. In fact, we can conclude (because sales are measured in thousands of dollars and student population in thousands) that an increase in the student population of 1,000 is associated with an increase of $5,000 in expected quarterly sales; that is, quarterly sales are expected to increase by $5 per student.

FIGURE 8.18 Excel Simple Linear Regression Output for Armand's Pizza Parlors

	A	B	C	D	E	F	G	H	I
1	SUMMARY OUTPUT								
2									
3	*Regression Statistics*								
4	Multiple R	0.950122955							
5	R Square	0.90273363							
6	Adjusted R Square	0.890575334							
7	Standard Error	13.82931669							
8	Observations	10							
9									
10	ANOVA								
11		*df*	*SS*	*MS*	*F*	*Significance F*			
12	Regression	1	14200	14200	74.24836601	2.54887E-05			
13	Residual	8	1530	191.25					
14	Total	9	15730						
15									
16		*Coefficients*	*Standard Error*	*t Stat*	*P-value*	*Lower 95%*	*Upper 95%*	*Lower 99.0%*	*Upper 99.0%*
17	Intercept	60	9.22603481	6.503335532	0.000187444	38.72472558	81.27527442	29.04307968	90.95692032
18	Student Population (1,000s)	5	0.580265238	8.616749156	2.54887E-05	3.661905962	6.338094038	3.052985371	6.947014629

The estimated y-intercept b_0 tells us that if the student population for the location of an Armand's pizza parlor was 0 students, we would expect sales of $60,000.

If we believe that the least squares estimated regression equation adequately describes the relationship between x and y, using the estimated regression equation to forecast the value of y for a given value of x seems reasonable. For example, if we wanted to forecast quarterly sales for a new restaurant to be located near a campus with 16,000 students, we would compute:

$$\begin{aligned}\hat{y} &= 60 + 5(16)\\ &= 140.\end{aligned}$$

Hence, we would forecast quarterly sales of $140,000.

The sales forecasting problem facing Armand's Pizza Parlors illustrates how simple linear regression analysis can be used to develop forecasts when a causal variable is available.

Combining Causal Variables with Trend and Seasonality Effects

The value of an independent variable from the prior period is referred to as a lagged variable.

Regression models are very flexible and can incorporate both causal variables and time series effects. Suppose we had a time series of several years of quarterly sales data and advertising expenditures for a single Armand's restaurant. If we suspected that sales were related to the causal variable advertising expenditures and that sales showed trend and seasonal effects, we could incorporate each into a single model by combining the approaches we have outlined. If we believe that the effect of advertising is not immediate, we might also try to find a relationship between sales in period t and advertising in the previous period, $t - 1$.

Multiple regression analysis also can be applied in these situations if additional data for other independent variables are available. For example, suppose that the management of Armand's Pizza Parlors also believes that the number of competitors near the college campus is related to quarterly sales. Intuitively, management believes that restaurants located near campuses with fewer competitors generate more sales revenue than those located near campuses with more competitors. With additional data, multiple regression analysis could be used to develop an equation relating quarterly sales to the size of the student population and the number of competitors.

Considerations in Using Regression in Forecasting

Although regression analysis allows for the estimation of complex forecasting models, we must be cautious about using such models and guard against the potential for overfitting our model to the sample data. Spyros Makridakis, a noted forecasting expert, conducted research showing that simple techniques usually outperform more complex procedures for short-term forecasting. Using a more sophisticated and expensive procedure will not guarantee better forecasts. However, many research studies, including those done by Makridakis, have also shown that quantitative forecasting models such as those presented in this chapter commonly outperform qualitative forecasts made by "experts." Thus, there is good reason to use quantitative forecasting methods whenever data are available.

Whether a regression approach provides a good forecast depends largely on how well we are able to identify and obtain data for independent variables that are closely related to the time series. Generally, during the development of an estimated regression equation, we will want to consider many possible sets of independent variables. Thus, part of the regression analysis procedure should focus on the selection of the set of independent variables that provides the best forecasting model.

NOTES + COMMENTS

Many different software packages can be used to estimate regression models. Section 7.4 in this textbook explains how Excel's Regression tool can be used to perform regression analysis. Appendix 7.1 demonstrates the use of Analytic Solver Platform to estimate regression models.

8.5 Determining the Best Forecasting Model to Use

Given the variety of forecasting models and approaches, the obvious question is, "For a given forecasting study, how does one choose an appropriate model?" As discussed throughout this text, it is always a good idea to get descriptive statistics on the data and graph the data so that they can be visually inspected. In the case of times series data, a visual inspection can indicate whether seasonality appears to be a factor and whether a linear or nonlinear trend seems to exist. For causal modeling, scatter charts can indicate whether strong linear or nonlinear relationships exist between the independent and dependent variables. If certain relationships appear totally random, this may lead you to exclude these variables from the model.

As in regression analysis, you may be working with large data sets when generating a forecasting model. In such cases, it is recommended to divide your data into training and validation sets. For example, you might have five years of monthly data available to produce a time series forecast. You could use the first three years of data as a training set to estimate a model or a collection of models that appear to provide good forecasts. You might develop exponential smoothing models and regression models for the training set. You could then use the last two years as a validation set to assess and compare the models' performances. Based on the errors produced by the different models for the validation set, you could ultimately pick the model that minimizes some forecast error measure, such as MAE, MSE or MAPE. However, you must exercise caution in using the older portion of a time series for the training set and the more recent portion of the time series as the validation set; if the behavior of the time series has changed recently, the older portion of the time series may no longer show patterns similar to the more recent values of the time series, and a forecasting model based on such data will not perform well.

Some software packages try many different forecasting models on time series data (those included in this chapter and more) and report back optimal model parameters and error measures for each model tested. Although some of these software packages will even automatically select the best model to use, ultimately the user should decide which model to use going forward based on a combination of the software output and the user's managerial knowledge.

SUMMARY

This chapter provided an introduction to the basic methods of time series analysis and forecasting. First, we showed that to explain the behavior of a time series, it is often helpful to graph the time series and identify whether trend, seasonal, and/or cyclical components are present in the time series. The methods we have discussed are based on assumptions about which of these components are present in the time series.

We discussed how smoothing methods can be used to forecast a time series that exhibits no significant trend, seasonal, or cyclical effect. The moving averages approach consists of computing an average of past data values and then using that average as the forecast for the next period. In the exponential smoothing method, a weighted average of past time series values is used to compute a forecast.

For time series that have only a long-term trend, we showed how regression analysis could be used to make trend projections. For time series with seasonal influences, we showed how to incorporate the seasonality for more accurate forecasts. We described how regression analysis can be used to develop causal forecasting models that relate values of the variable to be forecast (the dependent variable) to other independent variables that are believed to explain (cause) the behavior of the dependent variable. Finally, we have provided guidance on how to select an appropriate model from the models discussed in this chapter.

GLOSSARY

Autoregressive model A regression model in which a regression relationship based on past time series values is used to predict the future time series values.
Causal models Forecasting methods that relate a time series to other variables that are believed to explain or cause its behavior.
Cyclical pattern The component of the time series that results in periodic above-trend and below-trend behavior of the time series lasting more than one year.

Exponential smoothing A forecasting technique that uses a weighted average of past time series values as the forecast.
Forecast A prediction of future values of a time series.
Forecast error The amount by which the forecasted value $\hat{y}_t$ differs from the observed value y_t, denoted $e_t = y_t - \hat{y}_t$.
Mean absolute error (MAE) A measure of forecasting accuracy; the average of the values of the forecast errors. Also referred to as mean absolute deviation (MAD).
Mean absolute percentage error (MAPE) A measure of the accuracy of a forecasting method; the average of the absolute values of the errors as a percentage of the corresponding forecast values.
Mean squared error (MSE) A measure of the accuracy of a forecasting method; the average of the sum of the squared differences between the forecast values and the actual time series values.
Moving averages method A method of forecasting or smoothing a time series that uses the average of the most recent n data values in the time series as the forecast for the next period.
Naïve forecasting method A forecasting technique that uses the value of the time series from the most recent period as the forecast for the current period.
Seasonal pattern The component of the time series that shows a periodic pattern over one year or less.
Smoothing constant A parameter of the exponential smoothing model that provides the weight given to the most recent time series value in the calculation of the forecast value.
Stationary time series A time series whose statistical properties are independent of time.
Time series A set of observations on a variable measured at successive points in time or over successive periods of time.
Trend The long-run shift or movement in the time series observable over several periods of time.

PROBLEMS

1. Consider the following time series data:

Week	1	2	3	4	5	6
Value	18	13	16	11	17	14

Using the naïve method (most recent value) as the forecast for the next week, compute the following measures of forecast accuracy:
   a. Mean absolute error
   b. Mean squared error
   c. Mean absolute percentage error
   d. What is the forecast for week 7?
2. Refer to the time series data in Problem 1. Using the average of all the historical data as a forecast for the next period, compute the following measures of forecast accuracy:
   a. Mean absolute error
   b. Mean squared error
   c. Mean absolute percentage error
   d. What is the forecast for week 7?
3. Problems 1 and 2 used different forecasting methods. Which method appears to provide the more accurate forecasts for the historical data? Explain.

4. Consider the following time series data:

Month	1	2	3	4	5	6	7
Value	24	13	20	12	19	23	15

a. Compute MSE using the most recent value as the forecast for the next period. What is the forecast for month 8?
b. Compute MSE using the average of all the data available as the forecast for the next period. What is the forecast for month 8?
c. Which method appears to provide the better forecast?

5. Consider the following time series data:

Week	1	2	3	4	5	6
Value	18	13	16	11	17	14

a. Construct a time series plot. What type of pattern exists in the data?
b. Develop a three-week moving average for this time series. Compute MSE and a forecast for week 7.
c. Use $\alpha = 0.2$ to compute the exponential smoothing values for the time series. Compute MSE and a forecast for week 7.
d. Compare the three-week moving average forecast with the exponential smoothing forecast using $\alpha = 0.2$. Which appears to provide the better forecast based on MSE? Explain.
e. Use trial and error to find a value of the exponential smoothing coefficient α that results in a smaller MSE than what you calculated for $\alpha = 0.2$.

6. Consider the following time series data:

Month	1	2	3	4	5	6	7
Value	24	13	20	12	19	23	15

a. Construct a time series plot. What type of pattern exists in the data?
b. Develop a three-week moving average for this time series. Compute MSE and a forecast for week 8.
c. Use $\alpha = 0.2$ to compute the exponential smoothing values for the time series. Compute MSE and a forecast for week 8.
d. Compare the three-week moving average forecast with the exponential smoothing forecast using $\alpha = 0.2$. Which appears to provide the better forecast based on MSE?
e. Use trial and error to find a value of the exponential smoothing coefficient α that results in a smaller MSE than what you calculated for $\alpha = 0.2$.

Gasoline

7. Refer to the gasoline sales time series data in Table 8.1.
a. Compute four-week and five-week moving averages for the time series.
b. Compute the MSE for the four-week and five-week moving average forecasts.
c. What appears to be the best number of weeks of past data (three, four, or five) to use in the moving average computation? Recall that the MSE for the three-week moving average is 10.22.

Gasoline

8. With the gasoline time series data from Table 8.1, show the exponential smoothing forecasts using $\alpha = 0.1$.
a. Applying the MSE measure of forecast accuracy, would you prefer a smoothing constant of $\alpha = 0.1$ or $\alpha = 0.2$ for the gasoline sales time series?
b. Are the results the same if you apply MAE as the measure of accuracy?
c. What are the results if MAPE is used?

9. With a smoothing constant of $\alpha = 0.2$, equation (8.7) shows that the forecast for week 13 of the gasoline sales data from Table 8.1 is given by $\hat{y}_{13} = 0.2y_{12} + 0.8\hat{y}_{12}$. However, the forecast for week 12 is given by $\hat{y}_{12} = 0.2y_{11} + 0.8\hat{y}_{11}$. Thus, we could combine these two results to show that the forecast for week 13 can be written as:

$$\hat{y}_{13} = 0.2y_{12} + 0.8(0.2y_{11} + 0.8\hat{y}_{11}) = 0.2y_{12} + 0.16y_{11} + 0.64\hat{y}_{11}.$$

   a. Making use of the fact that $\hat{y}_{11} = 0.2y_{10} + 0.8\hat{y}_{10}$ (and similarly for $\hat{y}_{10}$ and $\hat{y}_9$), continue to expand the expression for $\hat{y}_{13}$ until it is written in terms of the past data values $y_{12}, y_{11}, y_{10}, y_9, y_8$, and the forecast for period 8, $\hat{y}_8$.
   b. Refer to the coefficients or weights for the past values $y_{12}, y_{11}, y_{10}, y_9, y_8$. What observation can you make about how exponential smoothing weights past data values in arriving at new forecasts? Compare this weighting pattern with the weighting pattern of the moving averages method.

10. United Dairies, Inc., supplies milk to several independent grocers throughout Dade County, Florida. Managers at United Dairies want to develop a forecast of the number of half gallons of milk sold per week. Sales data for the past 12 weeks are:

Week	Sales	Week	Sales
1	2,750	7	3,300
2	3,100	8	3,100
3	3,250	9	2,950
4	2,800	10	3,000
5	2,900	11	3,200
6	3,050	12	3,150

   a. Construct a time series plot. What type of pattern exists in the data?
   b. Use exponential smoothing with $\alpha = 0.4$ to develop a forecast of demand for week 13. What is the resulting MSE?

DATA file
Hawkins

11. For the Hawkins Company, the monthly percentages of all shipments received on time over the past 12 months are 80, 82, 84, 83, 83, 84, 85, 84, 82, 83, 84, and 83.

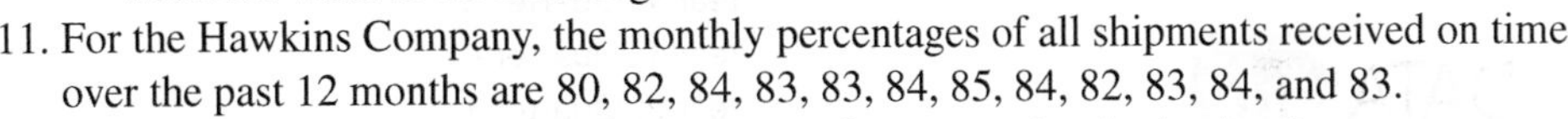

   a. Construct a time series plot. What type of pattern exists in the data?
   b. Compare a three-month moving average forecast with an exponential smoothing forecast for $\alpha = 0.2$. Which provides the better forecasts using MSE as the measure of model accuracy?
   c. What is the forecast for next month?

DATA file
TripleABond

12. Corporate triple A bond interest rates for 12 consecutive months are as follows:

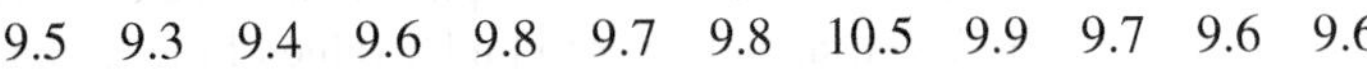

9.5 9.3 9.4 9.6 9.8 9.7 9.8 10.5 9.9 9.7 9.6 9.6

   a. Construct a time series plot. What type of pattern exists in the data?
   b. Develop three-month and four-month moving averages for this time series. Does the three-month or the four-month moving average provide the better forecasts based on MSE? Explain.
   c. What is the moving average forecast for the next month?

13. The values of Alabama building contracts (in millions of dollars) for a 12-month period are as follows:

240 350 230 260 280 320 220 310 240 310 240 230

   a. Construct a time series plot. What type of pattern exists in the data?
   b. Compare a three-month moving average forecast with an exponential smoothing forecast. Use $\alpha = 0.2$. Which provides the better forecasts based on MSE?
   c. What is the forecast for the next month using exponential smoothing with $\alpha = 0.2$?

14. The following time series shows the sales of a particular product over the past 12 months.

DATA file
MonthlySales

Month	Sales	Month	Sales
1	105	7	145
2	135	8	140
3	120	9	100
4	105	10	80
5	90	11	100
6	120	12	110

a. Construct a time series plot. What type of pattern exists in the data?
b. Use $\alpha = 0.3$ to compute the exponential smoothing values for the time series.
c. Use trial and error to find a value of the exponential smoothing coefficient α that results in a relatively small MSE.

15. Ten weeks of data on the Commodity Futures Index are:

CommodityFutures

7.35 7.40 7.55 7.56 7.60 7.52 7.52 7.70 7.62 7.55

a. Construct a time series plot. What type of pattern exists in the data?
b. Use trial and error to find a value of the exponential smoothing coefficient α that results in a relatively small MSE.

16. The following table reports the percentage of stocks in a portfolio for nine quarters:

Portfolio

Quarter	Stock (%)
Year 1, Quarter 1	29.8
Year 1, Quarter 2	31.0
Year 1, Quarter 3	29.9
Year 1, Quarter 4	30.1
Year 2, Quarter 1	32.2
Year 2, Quarter 2	31.5
Year 2, Quarter 3	32.0
Year 2, Quarter 4	31.9
Year 3, Quarter 1	30.0

a. Construct a time series plot. What type of pattern exists in the data?
b. Use trial and error to find a value of the exponential smoothing coefficient α that results in a relatively small MSE.
c. Using the exponential smoothing model you developed in part (b), what is the forecast of the percentage of stocks in a typical portfolio for the second quarter of year 3?

17. Consider the following time series:

t	1	2	3	4	5
y_t	6	11	9	14	15

a. Construct a time series plot. What type of pattern exists in the data?
b. Use simple linear regression analysis to find the parameters for the line that minimizes MSE for this time series.
c. What is the forecast for $t = 6$?

18. Consider the following time series:

t	1	2	3	4	5	6	7
y_t	120	110	100	96	94	92	88

a. Construct a time series plot. What type of pattern exists in the data?
b. Use simple linear regression analysis to find the parameters for the line that minimizes MSE for this time series.
c. What is the forecast for $t = 8$?

19. Because of high tuition costs at state and private universities, enrollments at community colleges have increased dramatically in recent years. The following data show the enrollment for Jefferson Community College for the nine most recent years:

Jefferson

Year	Period (t)	Enrollment (1,000s)
2001	1	6.5
2002	2	8.1
2003	3	8.4
2004	4	10.2
2005	5	12.5
2006	6	13.3
2007	7	13.7
2008	8	17.2
2009	9	18.1

a. Construct a time series plot. What type of pattern exists in the data?
b. Use simple linear regression analysis to find the parameters for the line that minimizes MSE for this time series.
c. What is the forecast for year 10?

20. The Seneca Children's Fund (SCF) is a local charity that runs a summer camp for disadvantaged children. The fund's board of directors has been working very hard over recent years to decrease the amount of overhead expenses, a major factor in how charities are rated by independent agencies. The following data show the percentage of the money SCF has raised that was spent on administrative and fund-raising expenses over the past seven years:

Seneca

Period (t)	Expense (%)
1	13.9
2	12.2
3	10.5
4	10.4
5	11.5
6	10.0
7	8.5

a. Construct a time series plot. What type of pattern exists in the data?
b. Use simple linear regression analysis to find the parameters for the line that minimizes MSE for this time series.
c. Forecast the percentage of administrative expenses for year 8.
d. If SCF can maintain its current trend in reducing administrative expenses, how long will it take SCF to achieve a level of 5% or less?

21. The president of a small manufacturing firm is concerned about the continual increase in manufacturing costs over the past several years. The following figures provide a time series of the cost per unit for the firm's leading product over the past eight years:

ManufacturingCosts

Year	Cost/Unit ($)	Year	Cost/Unit ($)
1	20.00	5	26.60
2	24.50	6	30.00
3	28.20	7	31.00
4	27.50	8	36.00

a. Construct a time series plot. What type of pattern exists in the data?
b. Use simple linear regression analysis to find the parameters for the line that minimizes MSE for this time series.
c. What is the average cost increase that the firm has been realizing per year?
d. Compute an estimate of the cost/unit for next year.

22. Consider the following time series:

Quarter	Year 1	Year 2	Year 3
1	71	68	62
2	49	41	51
3	58	60	53
4	78	81	72

a. Construct a time series plot. What type of pattern exists in the data? Is there an indication of a seasonal pattern?
b. Use a multiple linear regression model with dummy variables as follows to develop an equation to account for seasonal effects in the data: Qtr1 $= 1$ if quarter 1, 0 otherwise; Qtr2 $= 1$ if quarter 2, 0 otherwise; Qtr3 $= 1$ if quarter 3, 0 otherwise.
c. Compute the quarterly forecasts for next year.

23. Consider the following time series data:

Quarter	Year 1	Year 2	Year 3
1	4	6	7
2	2	3	6
3	3	5	6
4	5	7	8

a. Construct a time series plot. What type of pattern exists in the data?
b. Use a multiple regression model with dummy variables as follows to develop an equation to account for seasonal effects in the data: Qtr1 $= 1$ if quarter 1, 0 otherwise; Qtr2 $= 1$ if quarter 2, 0 otherwise; Qtr3 $= 1$ if quarter 3, 0 otherwise.
c. Compute the quarterly forecasts for next year based on the model you developed in part (b).
d. Use a multiple regression model to develop an equation to account for trend and seasonal effects in the data. Use the dummy variables you developed in part (b) to capture seasonal effects and create a variable t such that $t = 1$ for quarter 1 in year 1, $t = 2$ for quarter 2 in year 1, . . . $t = 12$ for quarter 4 in year 3.
e. Compute the quarterly forecasts for next year based on the model you developed in part (d).
f. Is the model you developed in part (b) or the model you developed in part (d) more effective? Justify your answer.

24. The quarterly sales data (number of copies sold) for a college textbook over the past three years are as follows:

TextbookSales

Year	1	1	1	1	2	2	2	2	3	3	3	3
Quarter	1	2	3	4	1	2	3	4	1	2	3	4
Sales	1,690	940	2,625	2,500	1,800	900	2,900	2,360	1,850	1,100	2,930	2,615

a. Construct a time series plot. What type of pattern exists in the data?
b. Use a regression model with dummy variables as follows to develop an equation to account for seasonal effects in the data: Qtr1 = 1 if quarter 1, 0 otherwise; Qtr2 = 1 if quarter 2, 0 otherwise; Qtr3 = 1 if quarter 3, 0 otherwise.
c. Based on the model you developed in part (b), compute the quarterly forecasts for next year.
d. Let $t = 1$ to refer to the observation in quarter 1 of year 1; $t = 2$ to refer to the observation in quarter 2 of year 1; . . . ; and $t = 12$ to refer to the observation in quarter 4 of year 3. Using the dummy variables defined in part (b) and t, develop an equation to account for seasonal effects and any linear trend in the time series.
e. Based upon the seasonal effects in the data and linear trend, compute the quarterly forecasts for next year.
f. Is the model you developed in part (b) or the model you developed in part (d) more effective? Justify your answer.

25. Air pollution control specialists in southern California monitor the amount of ozone, carbon dioxide, and nitrogen dioxide in the air on an hourly basis. The hourly time series data exhibit seasonality, with the levels of pollutants showing patterns that vary over the hours in the day. On July 15, 16, and 17, the following levels of nitrogen dioxide were observed for the 12 hours from 6:00 a.m. to 6:00 p.m.:

Pollution

July 15	25	28	35	50	60	60	40	35	30	25	25	20
July 16	28	30	35	48	60	65	50	40	35	25	20	20
July 17	35	42	45	70	72	75	60	45	40	25	25	25

a. Construct a time series plot. What type of pattern exists in the data?
b. Use a multiple linear regression model with dummy variables as follows to develop an equation to account for seasonal effects in the data:

Hour1 = 1 if the reading was made between 6:00 a.m. and 7:00a.m.; 0 otherwise;
Hour2 = 1 if the reading was made between 7:00 a.m. and 8:00 a.m.; 0 otherwise;
⋮
Hour11 = 1 if the reading was made between 4:00 p.m. and 5:00 p.m., 0 otherwise.

Note that when the values of the 11 dummy variables are equal to 0, the observation corresponds to the 5:00 p.m. to 6:00 p.m. hour.
c. Using the equation developed in part (b), compute estimates of the levels of nitrogen dioxide for July 18.
d. Let $t = 1$ to refer to the observation in hour 1 on July 15; $t = 2$ to refer to the observation in hour 2 of July 15; . . . ; and $t = 36$ to refer to the observation in hour 12 of July 17. Using the dummy variables defined in part (b) and t_s, develop an equation to account for seasonal effects and any linear trend in the time series.

e. Based on the seasonal effects in the data and linear trend estimated in part (d), compute estimates of the levels of nitrogen dioxide for July 18.
f. Is the model you developed in part (b) or the model you developed in part (d) more effective? Justify your answer.

26. South Shore Construction builds permanent docks and seawalls along the southern shore of Long Island, New York. Although the firm has been in business only five years, revenue has increased from $308,000 in the first year of operation to $1,084,000 in the most recent year. The following data show the quarterly sales revenue in thousands of dollars:

SouthShore

Quarter	Year 1	Year 2	Year 3	Year 4	Year 5
1	20	37	75	92	176
2	100	136	155	202	282
3	175	245	326	384	445
4	13	26	48	82	181

a. Construct a time series plot. What type of pattern exists in the data?
b. Use a multiple regression model with dummy variables as follows to develop an equation to account for seasonal effects in the data: Qtr1 = 1 if quarter 1, 0 otherwise; Qtr2 = 1 if quarter 2, 0 otherwise; Qtr3 = 1 if quarter 3, 0 otherwise.
c. Based on the model you developed in part (b), compute estimates of quarterly sales for year 6.
d. Let Period = 1 refer to the observation in quarter 1 of year 1; Period = 2 refer to the observation in quarter 2 of year 1; . . . and Period = 20 refer to the observation in quarter 4 of year 5. Using the dummy variables defined in part (b) and the variable Period, develop an equation to account for seasonal effects and any linear trend in the time series.
e. Based on the seasonal effects in the data and linear trend estimated in part (c), compute estimates of quarterly sales for year 6.
f. Is the model you developed in part (b) or the model you developed in part (d) more effective? Justify your answer.

27. Hogs & Dawgs is an ice cream parlor on the border of north-central Louisiana and southern Arkansas that serves 43 flavors of ice creams, sherbets, frozen yogurts, and sorbets. During the summer Hogs & Dawgs is open from 1:00 p.m. to 10:00 p.m. on Monday through Saturday, and the owner believes that sales change systematically from hour to hour throughout the day. She also believes her sales increase as the outdoor temperature increases. Hourly sales and the outside temperature at the start of each hour for the last week are provided in the file *IceCreamSales*.

IceCreamSales

a. Construct a time series plot of hourly sales and a scatter plot of outdoor temperature and hourly sales. What types of relationships exist in the data?
b. Use a simple regression model with outside temperature as the causal variable to develop an equation to account for the relationship between outside temperature and hourly sales in the data. Based on this model, compute an estimate of hourly sales for today from 2:00 p.m. to 3:00 p.m. if the temperature at 2:00 p.m. is 93°F.
c. Use a multiple linear regression model with the causal variable outside temperature and dummy variables as follows to develop an equation to account for both seasonal effects and the relationship between outside temperature and hourly sales in the data in the data:

Hour1 = 1 if the sales were recorded between 1:00 p.m. and 2:00 p.m., 0 otherwise;
Hour2 = 1 if the sales were recorded between 2:00 p.m. and 3:00 p.m., 0 otherwise;
⋮
Hour8 = 1 if the sales were recorded between 8:00 p.m. and 9:00 p.m., 0 otherwise.

Note that when the values of the 8 dummy variables are equal to 0, the observation corresponds to the 9:00-to-10:00-p.m. hour.

Based on this model, compute an estimate of hourly sales for today from 2:00 p.m. to 3:00 p.m. if the temperature at 2:00 p.m. is 93°F.

d. Is the model you developed in part (b) or the model you developed in part (c) more effective? Justify your answer.

GasStation

28. Donna Nickles manages a gasoline station on the corner of Bristol Avenue and Harpst Street in Arcata, California. Her station is a franchise, and the parent company calls her station every day at midnight to give her the prices for various grades of gasoline for the upcoming day. Over the past eight weeks Donna has recorded the price and sales (in gallons) of regular-grade gasoline at her station as well as the price of regular-grade gasoline charged by her competitor across the street. She is curious about the sensitivity of her sales to the price of regular gasoline she charges and the price of regular gasoline charged by her competitor across the street. She also wonders whether her sales differ systematically by day of the week and whether her station has experienced a trend in sales over the past eight weeks. The data collected by Donna for each day of the past eight weeks are provided in the file *GasStation*.

a. Construct a time series plot of daily sales, a scatter plot of the price Donna charges for a gallon of regular gasoline and daily sales at Donna's station, and a scatter plot of the price Donna's competitor charges for a gallon of regular gasoline and daily sales at Donna's station. What types of relationships exist in the data?

b. Use a multiple regression model with the price Donna charges for a gallon of regular gasoline and the price Donna's competitor charges for a gallon of regular gasoline as causal variables to develop an equation to account for the relationships between these prices and Donna's daily sales in the data. Based on this model, compute an estimate of sales for a day on which Donna is charging $3.50 for a gallon for regular gasoline and her competitor is charging $3.45 for a gallon of regular gasoline.

c. Use a multiple linear regression model with the trend and dummy variables as follows to develop an equation to account for both trend and seasonal effects in the data:

Monday = 1 if the sales were recorded on a Monday, 0 otherwise;
Tuesday = 1 if the sales were recorded on a Tuesday, 0 otherwise;
⋮
Saturday = 1 if the sales were recorded on a Saturday, 0 otherwise;

Note that when the values of the six dummy variables are equal to 0, the observation corresponds to Sunday.

Based on this model, compute an estimate of sales for Tuesday of the first week after Donna collected her data.

d. Use a multiple regression model with the price Donna charges for a gallon of regular gasoline and the price Donna's competitor charges for a gallon of regular gasoline as causal variables and the trend and dummy variables from part (c) to create an equation to account for the relationships between these prices and daily sales as well as the trend and seasonal effects in the data. Based on this model, compute an estimate of sales for Tuesday of the first week after Donna collected her data a day if Donna is charging $3.50 for a gallon for regular gasoline and her competitor is charging $3.45 for a gallon of regular gasoline.

e. Which of the three models you developed in parts (b), (c), and (d) is most effective? Justify your answer.

CASE PROBLEM: FORECASTING FOOD AND BEVERAGE SALES

The Vintage Restaurant, on Captiva Island near Fort Myers, Florida, is owned and operated by Karen Payne. The restaurant just completed its third year of operation. During those three years, Karen sought to establish a reputation for the restaurant as a high-quality dining establishment that specializes in fresh seafood. Through the efforts of Karen and her staff, her restaurant has become one of the best and fastest-growing restaurants on the island.

To better plan for future growth of the restaurant, Karen needs to develop a system that will enable her to forecast food and beverage sales by month for up to one year in advance. The following table shows the value of food and beverage sales ($1,000s) for the first three years of operation:

Month	First Year	Second Year	Third Year
January	242	263	282
February	235	238	255
March	232	247	265
April	178	193	205
May	184	193	210
June	140	149	160
July	145	157	166
August	152	161	174
September	110	122	126
October	130	130	148
November	152	167	173
December	206	230	235

Managerial Report

Perform an analysis of the sales data for the Vintage Restaurant. Prepare a report for Karen that summarizes your findings, forecasts, and recommendations. Include the following:

1. A time series plot. Comment on the underlying pattern in the time series.
2. Using the dummy variable approach, forecast sales for January through December of the fourth year.

How would you explain this model to Karen?

Assume that January sales for the fourth year turn out to be $295,000. What was your forecast error? If this error is large, Karen may be puzzled about the difference between your forecast and the actual sales value. What can you do to resolve her uncertainty about the forecasting procedure?

Chapter 9

Predictive Data Mining

CONTENTS

9.1 DATA SAMPLING

9.2 DATA PARTITIONING

9.3 ACCURACY MEASURES
- Evaluating the Classification of Categorical Outcomes
- Evaluating the Estimation of Continuous Outcomes

9.4 LOGISTIC REGRESSION

9.5 *k*-NEAREST NEIGHBORS
- Classifying Categorical Outcomes with *k*-Nearest Neighbors
- Estimating Continuous Outcomes with *k*-Nearest Neighbors

9.6 CLASSIFICATION AND REGRESSION TREES
- Classifying Categorical Outcomes with a Classification Tree
- Estimating Continuous Outcomes with a Regression Tree
- Ensemble Methods

APPENDIX 9.1: DATA PARTITIONING WITH XLMINER

APPENDIX 9.2: LOGISTIC REGRESSION CLASSIFICATION WITH XLMINER

APPENDIX 9.3: *k*-NEAREST NEIGHBOR CLASSIFICATION AND ESTIMATION WITH XLMINER

APPENDIX 9.4: SINGLE CLASSIFICATION AND REGRESSION TREES WITH XLMINER

APPENDIX 9.5: RANDOM FORESTS OF CLASSIFICATION OR REGRESSION TREES WITH XLMINER

ANALYTICS IN ACTION

Orbitz*

Although they might not see their customers face to face, online retailers are getting to know their patrons to tailor the offerings on their virtual shelves. By mining web-browsing data collected in "cookies"—files that web sites use to track people's web-browsing behavior, online retailers identify trends that can potentially be used to improve customer satisfaction and boost online sales.

For example, consider Orbitz, an online travel agency that books flights, hotels, car rentals, cruises, and other travel activities for its customers. Tracking its patrons' online activities, Orbitz discovered that people who use Mac computers spend as much as 30% more per night on hotels. Orbitz's analytics team has uncovered other factors that affect purchase behavior, including how the shopper arrived at the Orbitz site (Did the user visit Orbitz directly or was he or she referred from another site?), previous booking history on Orbitz, and the shopper's geographic location. Orbitz can act on this and other information gleaned from the vast amount of web data to differentiate the recommendations for hotels, car rentals, flight bookings, etc.

*"On Orbitz, Mac Users Steered to Pricier Hotels" *Wall Street Journal* (2012, June 26).

In Chapter 4, we describe descriptive data-mining methods, such as clustering and association rules, that explore relationships between observations and/or variables.

Organizations are collecting an increasing amount of data, and one of the most pressing tasks is converting this data into actionable insights. A common challenge is to analyze this data to extract information on patterns and trends that can be used to assist decision makers in predicting future events. In this chapter, we discuss predictive methods that can be applied to leverage data to gain customer insights and to establish new business rules to guide managers.

We define an **observation**, or *record*, as the set of recorded values of **variables** associated with a single entity. An observation is often displayed as a row of values in a spreadsheet or database in which the columns correspond to the variables. For example, in direct-marketing data, an observation may correspond to a customer and contain information regarding her response to an e-mail advertisement as well as information regarding her demographic characteristics.

Estimation methods are also referred to as regression methods or prediction methods.

In this chapter, we focus on data-mining methods for predicting an outcome based on a set of input variables, or **features**. These methods are also referred to as **supervised learning**. Linear regression is a well-known supervised learning approach from classical statistics in which observations of a quantitative outcome (the dependent y variable) and one or more corresponding features (the independent variables $x_1, x_2, \ldots, x_q$) are used to create an equation for estimating y values. That is, in supervised learning the outcome variable "supervises" or guides the process of "learning" how to predict future outcomes. In this chapter, we focus on supervised learning methods for the **estimation** of a continuous outcome (e.g., sales revenue) and for **classification** of a categorical outcomes (e.g., whether or not a customer defaults on a loan).

See Chapter 7 for a discussion of linear regression.

The data-mining process comprises the following steps:

1. *Data sampling.* Extract a sample of data that are relevant to the business problem under consideration.
2. *Data preparation.* Manipulate the data to put it in a form suitable for formal modeling. This step includes addressing missing and erroneous data, reducing the number of variables, and defining new variables. Data exploration is an important part of this step and may involve descriptive statistics, data visualization, and clustering.
3. *Data partitioning.* Divide the sample data into three sets for the training, validation, and testing of the data-mining algorithm performance.
4. *Data exploration.* Apply descriptive statistics and data visualization to the training set to understand the data and assist in the selection of an appropriate technique.

Chapter 4 discusses the data-preparation process as well as clustering techniques often used to redefine variables. Chapters 2 and 3 discuss descriptive statistics and data-visualization techniques.

5. *Model construction.* Apply the appropriate data-mining technique (e.g., *k*-nearest neighbors, regression trees) to the training data set to accomplish the desired data-mining task (classification or estimation).
6. *Model assessment.* Evaluate models by comparing performance on the training and validation data sets. Apply the chosen model to the test data as a final evaluation of model performance.

9.1 Data Sampling

Upon identifying a business problem, data on relevant variables must be obtained for analysis. Although access to large amounts of data offers the potential to unlock insight and improve decision making, it comes with the risk of drowning in a sea of data. Data repositories with millions of observations over hundreds of measured variables are now common. If the volume of relevant data is extremely large (thousands of observations or more), it is unnecessary (and computationally difficult) to use all the data in order to perform a detailed analysis. When dealing with large volumes of data (with hundreds of thousands or millions of observations), best practice is to extract a representative sample (with thousands or tens of thousands of observations) for analysis. A sample is representative if the analyst can make the same conclusions from it as from the entire population of data.

For a more detailed description of sampling techniques, Appendix 9.1 illustrates how to create data sets for data mining analysis by sampling data from a larger volume using XLMiner.

There are no definite rules to determine the size of a sample. The sample of data must be large enough to contain significant information, yet small enough to manipulate quickly. If the sample is too small, relationships in the data may be missed or spurious relationships may be suggested. Perhaps the best advice is to use enough data to eliminate any doubt about whether the sample size is sufficient; data-mining algorithms typically are more effective given more data. If we are investigating a rare event (e.g., click-through on an advertisement posted on a web site), the sample should be large enough to ensure several hundred to thousands of observations that correspond to click-throughs. That is, if the click-through rate is only 1%, then a representative sample would need to be approximately 50,000 observations in order to have about 500 observations corresponding to situations in which a person clicked on an ad.

When obtaining a representative sample, it is also important not to carelessly discard variables. It is generally best to include as many variables as possible in the sample. After exploring the data with descriptive statistics and visualization, the analyst can eliminate "uninteresting" variables.

NOTES + COMMENTS

1. XLMiner provides functionality to create data sets for data-mining analysis by sampling data from the larger volume residing in an Excel worksheet or a database (e.g., Access, SQL Server) by clicking the **Get Data** icon in the Data group of the **XLMiner Platform** ribbon and then choosing the appropriate source, **Worksheet**, **Database**, **File Folder** (to get data from a collection of files—often used in text mining), or **Big Data** (to get data from the Apache Spark cluster computing system).
2. After selecting from where to sample data, XLMiner offers several **Sampling Options** in its **Sampling** window. Users can specify a **Desired sample size**, and different random samples can be generated by varying the random seed in the box next to **Set seed**. XLMiner supports **Simple random sampling** with or without replacement. In simple random sampling without replacement, each observation is equally likely to be selected for the sample and an observation can be selected for the sample at most once. If **Sample with replacement** is selected, each observation is equally likely to be picked for the sample and an observation can be inserted more than once into the sample. One reason to sample with replacement is to artificially generate a larger sample in cases for which the number of observations observed is not large enough for the analysis desired. XLMiner also provides an option to execute **Stratified random sampling,** which allows the user to control the number of observations in the sample with certain values of a specified variable, called the *stratum variable*. One use of stratified sampling is to ensure that rare events of interest are adequately represented in the sample.

9.2 Data Partitioning

We begin by discussing how to partition a data set in order to appropriately evaluate the future accuracy of a predictive data-mining method. Consider a situation in which an analyst has relatively few data points from which to build a multiple regression model. To maintain the sample size necessary to obtain reliable estimates of slope coefficients, an analyst may have no choice but to use the entire data set to build a model. Even if measures such as R^2 and the standard error of the estimate suggest that the resulting linear regression model may fit the data set well, these measures only explain how well the model fits data it has "seen," and the analyst has little idea how well this model will fit other "unobserved" data points.

Multiple regression models are discussed in Chapter 7.

Classical statistics deals with a scarcity of data by determining the minimum sample size needed to draw legitimate inferences about the population. In contrast, data-mining applications deal with an abundance of data that simplifies the process of assessing the accuracy of data-based estimates of variable effects. However, the wealth of data can tempt the analyst the overfit the model. **Model overfitting** occurs when the analyst builds a model that does a great job of explaining the sample of data on which it is based, but fails to accurately predict outside the sample data. We can use the abundance of data to guard against the potential for overfitting by decomposing the data set into three partitions: the training set, the validation set, and the test set.

The **training set** consists of the data used to build the candidate models. For example, a training set may be used to estimate the slope coefficients in a multiple regression model. We use measures of accuracy of these models on the training set to identify a promising initial subset of models. However, since the training set consists of the data used to build the models, it cannot be used to clearly identify the best model for prediction when applied to new data (data outside the training set). Therefore, the promising subset of models is then applied to the **validation set** to identify which model may be the most accurate at predicting observations that were not used to build the model.

If the validation set is used to identify a "best" model through either comparison with other models or the tuning of model parameters. then the estimates of model accuracy are also biased (we tend to overestimate accuracy). Thus, the final model must be applied to the **test set** in order to conservatively estimate this model's effectiveness when applied to data that have not been used to build or select the model.

For example, suppose we have identified four models that fit the training set reasonably well. To evaluate how these models will handle predictions when applied to new data, we apply these four models to the validation set. After identifying the best of the four models, we apply this "best" model to the test set in order to obtain an unbiased estimate of this model's accuracy on future applications.

There are no definite rules for the size of the three partitions, but the training set is typically the largest. For estimation tasks, a rule of thumb is to have at least 10 times as many observations as variables. For classification tasks, a rule of thumb is to have at least $6 \times m \times q$ observations, where m is the number of outcome categories and q is the number of variables. When we are interested in predicting a rare event, such as a click-through on an advertisement posted on a web site or a fraudulent credit-card transaction, it is recommended that the training set oversample the number of observations corresponding to the rare events to provide the data-mining algorithm sufficient data to "learn" about the rare events. For example, if only one out of every 10,000 users clicks on an advertisement posted on a web site, we would not have sufficient information to distinguish between users who do not click-through and those who do if we constructed a representative training set consisting of one observation corresponding to a click-through and 9,999 observations with no click-through. In these cases, the training set should contain equal or nearly equal numbers of observations corresponding to the different values of the outcome variable. Note that we do not oversample the validation set and test sets; these samples should be representative of the overall population so that accuracy measures evaluated on these data sets appropriately reflect future performance of the data-mining model.

9.3 Accuracy Measures

There are different accuracy measures for methods classifying categorical outcomes than for methods estimating continuous outcomes. We describe each of these in the context of an example from the financial services industry. Optiva Credit Union wants to better understand its personal lending process and its loan customers. The file *Optiva* contains over 40,000 customer observations with information on whether the customer defaulted on a loan, customer age, average checking account balance, whether the customer had a mortgage, the customer's job status, the customer's marital status, and the customer's level of education. We will use these data to demonstrate the use of supervised learning methods to classify customers who are likely to default and to predict the average balance in a customer's bank accounts.

Evaluating the Classification of Categorical Outcomes

In our treatment of classification problems, we restrict our attention to problems for which we want to classify observations into one of two possible classes (e.g., loan default or no default), but the concepts generally extend to cases with more than two classes. A natural way to evaluate the performance of a classification method, or classifier, is to count the number of times that an observation is predicted to be in the wrong class. By counting the classification errors on a sufficiently large validation set and/or test set that is representative of the population, we will generate an accurate measure of classification performance of our model.

Classification error is commonly displayed in a **classification confusion matrix**, which displays a model's correct and incorrect classifications. Table 9.1 illustrates a classification confusion matrix resulting from an attempt to classify the customer observations in a subset of data from the file *Optiva*. In this table, Class 1 = loan default and Class 0 = no default. The classification confusion matrix is a cross-tabulation of the actual class of each observation and the predicted class of each observation. From the first row of the matrix in Table 9.1, we see that 146 observations corresponding to loan defaults were correctly identified as such, but another 89 actual loan defaults were classified as nondefault observations. From the second row, we observe that 5,244 actual nondefault observations were incorrectly classified as loan defaults, while 7,479 nondefaults were correctly identified.

TABLE 9.1 Classification Confusion Matrix

	Predicted Class	
Actual Class	**1**	**0**
1	$n_{11} = 146$	$n_{10} = 89$
0	$n_{01} = 5{,}244$	$n_{00} = 7{,}479$

Many measures of classification accuracy are based on the classification confusion matrix. The percentage of misclassified observations is expressed as the **overall error rate** and is computed as:

$$\text{overall error rate} = \frac{n_{10} + n_{01}}{n_{11} + n_{10} + n_{01} + n_{00}}$$

The overall error rate of the classification in Table 9.1 is (89 + 5,244)/(146 + 89 + 5,244 + 7,479) = 41.2%. One minus the overall error rate is often referred to as the **accuracy** of the model. The model accuracy based on Table 9.1 is 58.8%.

In Table 9.1, n_{01} is the number of false positives and n_{10} is the number of false negatives.

While overall error rate conveys an aggregate measure of misclassification, it counts misclassifying an actual Class 0 observation as a Class 1 observation (a **false positive**) the same as misclassifying an actual Class 1 observation as a Class 0 observation (a **false negative**). In many situations, the cost of making these two types of errors is not equivalent. For example, suppose we are classifying patient observations into two categories: Class 1 is cancer and Class 0 is healthy. The cost of incorrectly classifying a healthy patient observation as "cancer" will likely be limited to the expense (and stress) of additional testing. The cost of incorrectly classifying a cancer patient observation as "healthy" may result in an indefinite delay in treatment of the cancer and premature death of the patient.

To account for the assymetric costs in misclassification, we define the error rate with respect to the individual classes:

$$\textbf{Class 1 error rate} = \frac{n_{10}}{n_{11} + n_{10}}$$

$$\textbf{Class 0 error rate} = \frac{n_{01}}{n_{01} + n_{00}}$$

The Class 1 error rate of the classification in Table 9.1 is 89/(146 + 89) = 37.9%. The Class 0 error rate of the classification in Table 9.1 is (5,244)/(5,244 + 7,479) = 41.2%. That is, the model that produced the classifications in Table 9.1 is slightly better at predicting Class 1 observations than Class 0 observations.

To understand the tradeoff between Class 1 error rate and Class 0 error rate, we must be aware of the criteria generally used by classification algorithms to classify observations. Most classification algorithms first estimate an observation's probability of Class 1 membership and then classify the observation into Class 1 if this probability meets or exceeds a specified **cutoff value** (default cutoff value, 0.5). The choice of cutoff value affects the type of classification error. As we decrease the cutoff value, more observations will be classified as Class 1, thereby increasing the likelihood that a Class 1 observation will be correctly classified as Class 1; that is, Class 1 error will decrease. However, as a side effect, more Class 0 observations will be incorrectly classified as Class 1; that is, Class 0 error will rise.

To demonstrate how the choice of cutoff value affects classification error, Table 9.2 shows a list of 50 observations (11 of which are actual Class 1 members) and an estimated probability of Class 1 membership produced by the classification algorithm. Table 9.3 shows classification confusion matrix and corresponding Class 1 error rates, Class 0 error rates, and overall error rates for cutoff values of 0.75, 0.5, and 0.25, respectively. As we decrease the cutoff value, more observations will be classified as Class 1, thereby increasing the likelihood that a Class 1 observation will be correctly classified as Class 1 (decreasing the Class 1 error rate). However, as a side effect, more Class 0 observations will be incorrectly classified as Class 1 (increasing the Class 0 error rate). That is, we can accurately identify more of the actual Class 1 observations by lowering the cutoff value, but we do so at a cost of misclassifying more actual Class 0 observations as Class 1

TABLE 9.2 Classification Probabilities

Actual Class	Probability of Class 1	Actual Class	Probability of Class 1
1	1.00	0	0.66
1	1.00	0	0.65
0	1.00	1	0.64
1	1.00	0	0.62
0	1.00	0	0.60
0	0.90	0	0.51
1	0.90	0	0.49
0	0.88	0	0.49
0	0.88	1	0.46
1	0.88	0	0.46
0	0.87	1	0.45
0	0.87	1	0.45
0	0.87	0	0.45
0	0.86	0	0.44
1	0.86	0	0.44
0	0.86	0	0.30
0	0.86	0	0.28
0	0.85	0	0.26
0	0.84	1	0.25
0	0.84	0	0.22
0	0.83	0	0.21
0	0.68	0	0.04
0	0.67	0	0.04
0	0.67	0	0.01
0	0.67	0	0.00

observations. Figure 9.1 shows the Class 1 and Class 0 error rates for cutoff values ranging from 0 to 1. One common approach to handling the tradeoff between Class 1 and Class 0 error is to set the cutoff value to minimize the Class 1 error rate subject to a threshold on the maximum Class 0 error rate. Specifically, Figure 9.1 illustrates that for a maximum allowed Class 0 error rate of 70%, a cutoff value of 0.45 (depicted by the vertical dashed line) achieves a Class 1 error rate of 20%.

As we have mentioned, identifying Class 1 members is often more important than identifying Class 0 members. One way to evaluate a classifier's value is to compare its effectiveness in identifying Class 1 observations as compared with random classification. To gauge a classifier's added value, a **cumulative lift chart** compares the number of actual Class 1 observations identified if considered in decreasing order of their estimated probability of being in Class 1 and compares this to the number of actual Class 1 observations identified if randomly selected. The left panel of Figure 9.2 illustrates a cumulative lift chart. The point (10, 5) on the blue curve means that if the 10 observations with the largest estimated probabilities of being in Class 1 were selected from Table 9.2, 5 of these observations correspond to actual Class 1 members. In contrast, the point (10, 2.2) on the red curve means that if 10 observations were randomly selected, only $(11/50) \times 10 = 2.2$ of these

TABLE 9.3 Classification Confusion Matrices for Various Cutoff Values

Cutoff Value = 0.75

Actual Class	**Predicted Class** 1	0
1	$n_{11} = 6$	$n_{10} = 5$
0	$n_{01} = 15$	$n_{00} = 24$

Actual Class	**No. of Cases**	**No. of Errors**	**Error Rate (%)**
1	$n_{11} + n_{10} = 11$	$n_{10} = 5$	45.45
0	$n_{01} + n_{00} = 39$	$n_{01} = 15$	38.46
Overall	$n_{11} + n_{10} + n_{01} + n_{00} = 50$	$n_{10} + n_{01} = 20$	40.00

Cutoff Value = 0.50

Actual Class	**Predicted Class** 1	0
1	$n_{11} = 7$	$n_{10} = 4$
0	$n_{01} = 24$	$n_{00} = 15$

Actual Class	**No. of Cases**	**No. of Errors**	**Error Rate (%)**
1	11	4	36.36
0	39	24	61.54
Overall	50	28	56.00

Cutoff Value = 0.25

Actual Class	**Predicted Class** 1	0
1	$n_{11} = 10$	$n_{10} = 1$
0	$n_{01} = 33$	$n_{00} = 6$

Actual Class	**No. of Cases**	**No. of Errors**	**Error Rate (%)**
1	11	1	9.09
0	39	33	84.62
Overall	50	34	68.00

observations would be Class 1 members. Thus, the better the classifier is at identifying responders, the larger the vertical gap between points on the red and blue curves.

A decile is one of nine values that divide ordered data into ten equal parts. The deciles determine the values for 10%, 20%, 30% . . . 90% of the data.

Another way to view how much better a classifier is at identifying Class 1 observations than random classification is to construct a **decile-wise lift chart**. For a decile-wise lift chart, observations are ordered in decreasing probability of Class 1 membership and then considered in 10 equal-sized groups. For the data in Table 9.2, the first decile group corresponds to the

Figure 9.1 was created using a data table that varied the cutoff value and tracked the Class 1 error rate and Class 0 error rate. For instructions on how to construct data tables in Excel, see Chapter 10.

FIGURE 9.1 Classification Error Rates vs. Cutoff Value

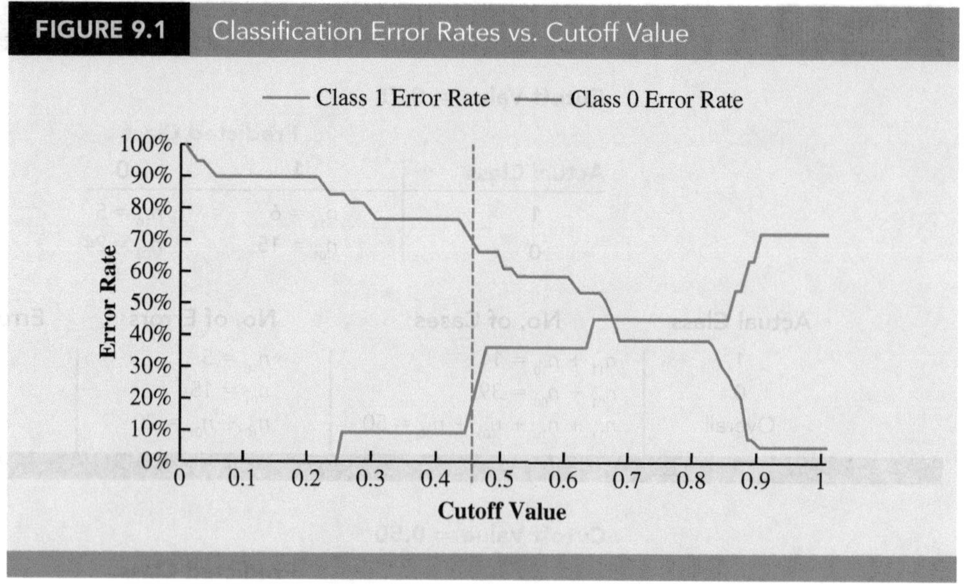

$0.1 \times 50 = 5$ observations most likely to be in Class 1, the second decile group corresponds to the 6th through the 10th observations most likely to be in Class 1, and so on. For each of these deciles, the decile-wise lift chart compares the number of actual Class 1 observations to the number of Class 1 responders in a randomly selected group of $0.1 \times 50 = 5$ observations. In the first decile group from Table 9.2 (the top 10% of observations believed by the classifier to most likely to be in Class 1), there are three Class 1 observations. A random sample of 5 observations would be expected to have $5 \times (11/50) = 1.1$ observations in Class 1. Thus the first-decile lift of this classification is $3/1.1 = 2.73$, which corresponds to the height of the first bar in the chart in the right panel of Figure 9.2. The interpratation of this ratio is that in the first decile, the model correctly predicted three observations, whereas random sampling would, on average, correctly classify only 1.1. Visually, the taller the bar in a decile-wise lift chart, the better the classifier is at identifying responders in the respective decile group. The height of the bars for the 2nd through 10th deciles is computed and intepreted in a similar manner.

Lift charts are prominently used in direct-marketing applications that seek to identify customers who are likely to respond to a direct-mail promotion. In these applications, it is

FIGURE 9.2 Cumulative and Decile-Wise Lift Charts

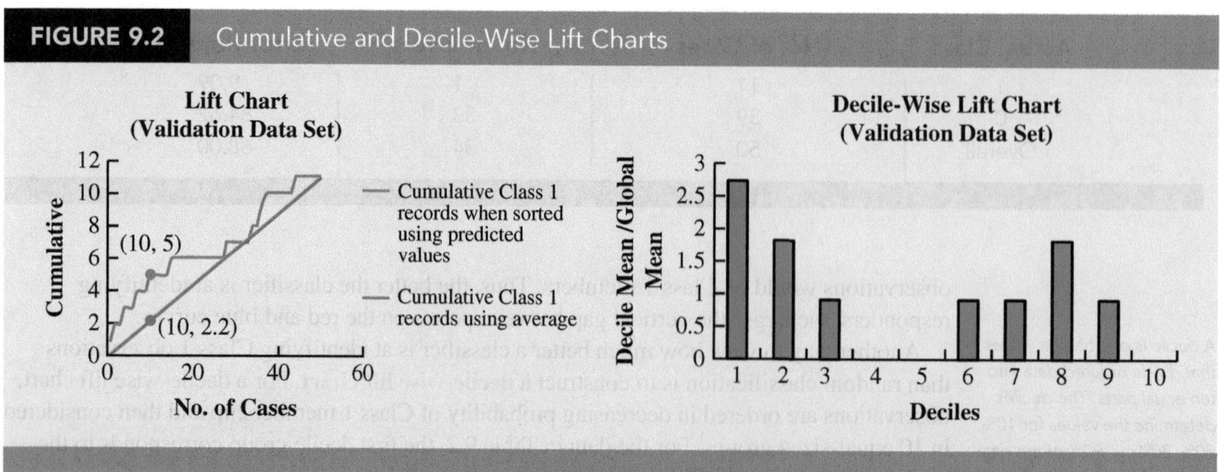

common to have a fixed budget and, therefore, a fixed number of customers to target. Lift charts identify how much better a data-mining model does at identifying responders than a mailing to a random set of customers.

In addition to the overall error rate, Class 1 error rate, and Class 0 error rate, there are a few other measures that express a classifier's performance. The ability to correctly predict Class 1 (positive) observations is commonly expressed by subtracting the Class 1 error rate from one. The resulting measure is referred to as the **sensitivity**, or **recall**, which is calculated as:

$$\text{Sensitivity} = 1 - \text{Class 1 error rate} = \frac{n_{11}}{n_{11} + n_{10}}.$$

Similarly, the ability to correctly predict Class 0 (negative) observations is commonly expressed by subtracting the Class 0 error rate from one. The resulting measure is referred to as the **specificity**, which is calculated as:

$$\text{Specificity} = 1 - \text{Class 0 error rate} = \frac{n_{00}}{n_{11} + n_{10}}.$$

The sensitivity of the model that produced the classifications in Table 9.1 is 146/(146 + 89) = 62.1%. The specificity of the model that produced the classifications in Table 9.1 is 7,479/(5,244 + 7,479) = 58.8%.

Precision is a measure that corresponds to the proportion of observations predicted to be Class 1 by a classifier that are actually in Class 1:

$$\text{Precision} = \frac{n_{11}}{n_{11} + n_{01}}.$$

The **F1 Score** combines precision and sensitivity into a single measure and is defined as:

$$\text{F1 Score} = \frac{2n_{11}}{2n_{11} + n_{01} + n_{10}}.$$

As we illustrated in Figure 9.1, decreasing the cutoff value will decrease the number of actual Class 1 observations misclassified as Class 0, but at the cost of increasing the number of Class 0 observations that are misclassfied as Class 1. The **receiver operating characteristic (ROC) curve** is an alternative graphical approach for displaying this tradeoff between a classifier's ability to correctly identify Class 1 observations and its Class 0 error rate. In a ROC curve, the vertical axis is the sensitivity of the classifier, and the horizontal axis is the Class 0 error rate (which is equal to 1 − specificity).

In Figure 9.3, the blue curve depicts the ROC curve corresponding to the classification probabilities in Table 9.2. The red diagonal line in Figure 9.3 represents random classification of observations. The point (0, 0) on the curve occurs when the cutoff value is set so that all observations are classified as Class 0; for this set of 50 observations, a cutoff value greater than 1.0 will achieve this. That is, for a cutoff value greater than 1, for the observations in Table 9.2, sensitivity = 0/(0 + 50) = 0 and the Class 0 error rate = 0/(0 + 50) = 0. The point (1, 1) on the curve occurs when the cutoff value is set so that all observations are classified as Class 1; for this set of 50 observations, a cutoff value of zero will achieve this. That is, for a cutoff value of 0, sensitivity = 11/(11 + 0) = 1 and the Class 0 error rate = 39/(39 + 0) = 1. Repeating these calculations for varying cutoff values and recording the resulting sensitivity and Class 0 error rate values, we can construct the ROC curve in Figure 9.3.

In general, we can evaluate the quality of a classifier by computing the area under the ROC curve. The more area under the ROC curve, the better the classifier performs. To understand why, suppose there exists a cutoff value such that a classifier correctly identifies each observation's actual class. Then, the ROC curve will pass through the point (0, 1), which represents the case in which the Class 0 error rate is zero and the sensitivity is equal to one (which means that the Class 1 error rate is zero). In this case, the area under

FIGURE 9.3 Receiver Operating Characteristic (ROC) Curve

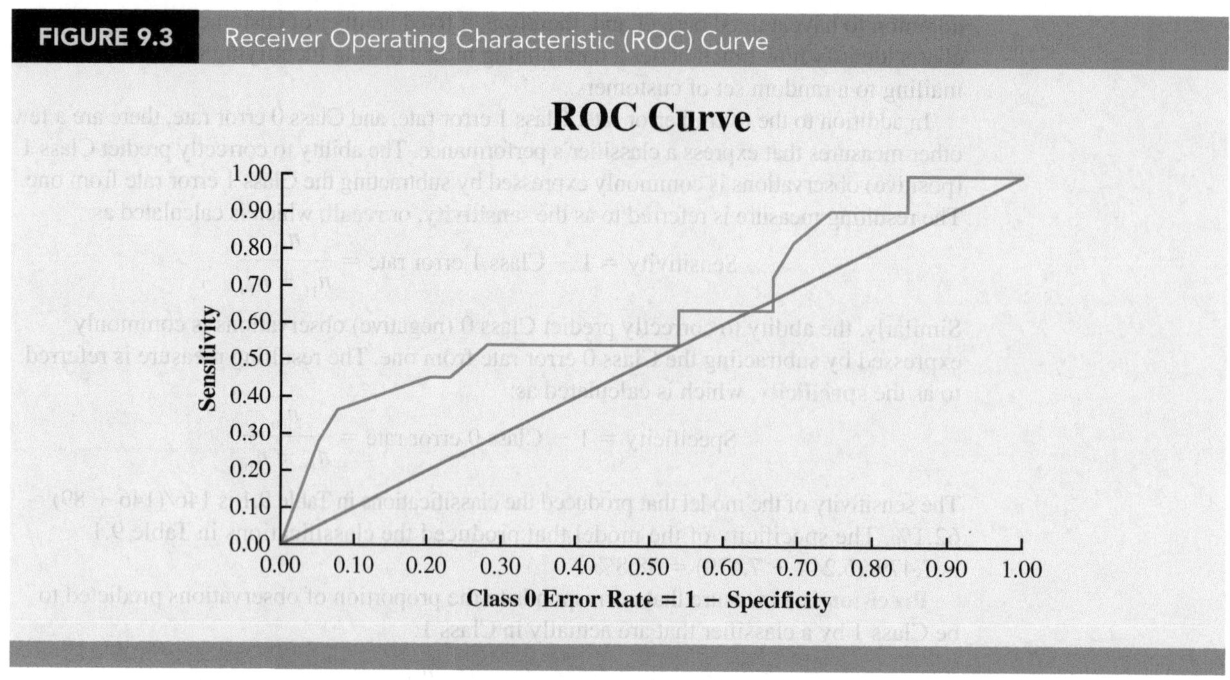

the ROC curve would be equal to one as the curve would extend from (0, 0) to (0, 1) to (1, 1). In Figure 9.3, note that the area under the red diagonal line representing random classification results is 0.5. In Figure 9.3, we observe that the classifier is providing value over a random classification, as the area under its ROC curve is greater than 0.5.

Evaluating the Estimation of Continuous Outcomes

There are several ways to measure accuracy when estimating a continuous outcome variable, but each of these measures is some function of the error in estimating an outcome for an observation *i*. Let e_i be the error in estimating an outcome for observation *i*, defined as $e_i = y_i - \hat{y}_i$, where y_i is the actual outcome for observation *i* and $\hat{y}_i$ is the predicted outcome for observation *i*. Two common measures are the **average error** $= \sum_{i=1}^{n} e_i/n$ and the **root mean squared error** (RMSE) $= \sqrt{\sum_{i=1}^{n} e_i^2/n}$. The average error estimates the **bias** in a model's predictions. If the average error is negative, then the model tends to overestimate the value of the outcome variable; if the average error is positive, the model tends to underestimate. The RMSE is similar to the standard error of the estimate for a regression model; it has the same units as the outcome variable predicted and provides a measure of how much the predicted value varies from the actual value.

Chapter 8 discusses additional measures, such as mean absolute error, mean absolute percentage error, and mean squared error, that also can be used to evaluate the accuracy of predictions.

Applying these measures (or others) to the model's predictions on the training set estimates the retrodictive accuracy or goodness-of-fit of the model, not the predictive accuracy. In estimating future performance, we are most interested in applying the accuracy measures to the model's predictions on the validation and test sets.

To demonstrate the computation and interpretation of average error and RMSE, we consider the challenge of predicting the average balance of Optiva Credit Union customers based on their features. Table 9.4 shows the error and squared error resulting from the predictions of the average balance for 10 observations. Using Table 9.4, we compute average error $= -80.1$ and the RSME $= 774$. Because the average error is negative, we observe that the model overestimates the actual balance of these 10 customers. Furthermore, if the performance of the model on these 10 observations is indicative of

TABLE 9.4 Computing Error in Estimates of Average Balance for 10 Customers

Actual Average Balance	Estimated Average Balance	Error (e_i)	Squared Error (e_i^2)
3,793	3,784	9	9,054,081
1,800	1,460	340	16,384
900	1,381	−481	1,666,681
1,460	566	894	176,400
6,288	5,487	801	641,601
341	605	−264	69,696
506	760	−254	64,516
621	1,593	−972	944,784
1,442	3,050	−1,608	1,292,769
944	210	734	538,756

the accuracy on a larger set of observations, we should investigate improvements to the estimation model, as the RMSE of 774 is 43% of the average actual balance.

NOTES + COMMENTS

Lift charts analogous to those constructed for classification methods can also be applied to the continuous outcomes when using estimation methods. A lift chart for a continuous outcome variable is relevant for evaluating a model's effectiveness in identifying observations with the largest values of the outcome variable. This is similar to the way a lift chart for a categorical outcome variable helps evaluate a model's effectiveness in identifying observations that are most likely to be Class 1 members.

9.4 Logistic Regression

Similar to how multiple linear regression predicts a continuous outcome variable, y, with a collection of explanatory variables, $x_1, x_2, \ldots, x_q$, via the linear equation $\hat{y} = b_0 + b_1x_1 + \cdots + b_qx_q$, **logistic regression** attempts to classify a categorical outcome ($y = 0$ or 1) as a linear function of explanatory variables. However, directly trying to explain a categorical outcome via a linear function of the explanatory variables is not effective. To understand this, consider the task of predicting whether a movie wins the Academy Award for Best Picture using information on the total number of other Oscar nominations that a movie has received. Figure 9.4 shows a scatter chart of a sample of movie data found in the file *OscarsDemo*; each data point corresponds to the total number of Oscar nominations that a movie received and whether the movie won the best picture award (1 = movie won, 0 = movie lost). The diagonal line in Figure 9.4 corresponds to the simple linear regression fit. This linear function can be thought of as predicting the probability p of a movie winning the Academy Award for best picture via the equation $\hat{p} = -0.4054 + (0.0836 \times \text{total number of Oscar nominations})$. As Figure 9.4 shows, a linear regression model fails to appropriately explain a categorical outcome variable. This model predicts that a movie with fewer than 5 total Oscar nominations has a negative probability of winning the best picture award. For a movie with more than 17 total Oscar nominations, this model predicts a probability greater than 1.0 of winning the best picture award. Furthermore, the residual plot in

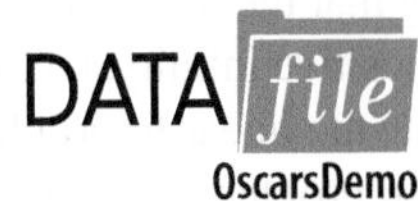

OscarsDemo

FIGURE 9.4 Scatter Chart and Simple Linear Regression Fit for Oscars Example

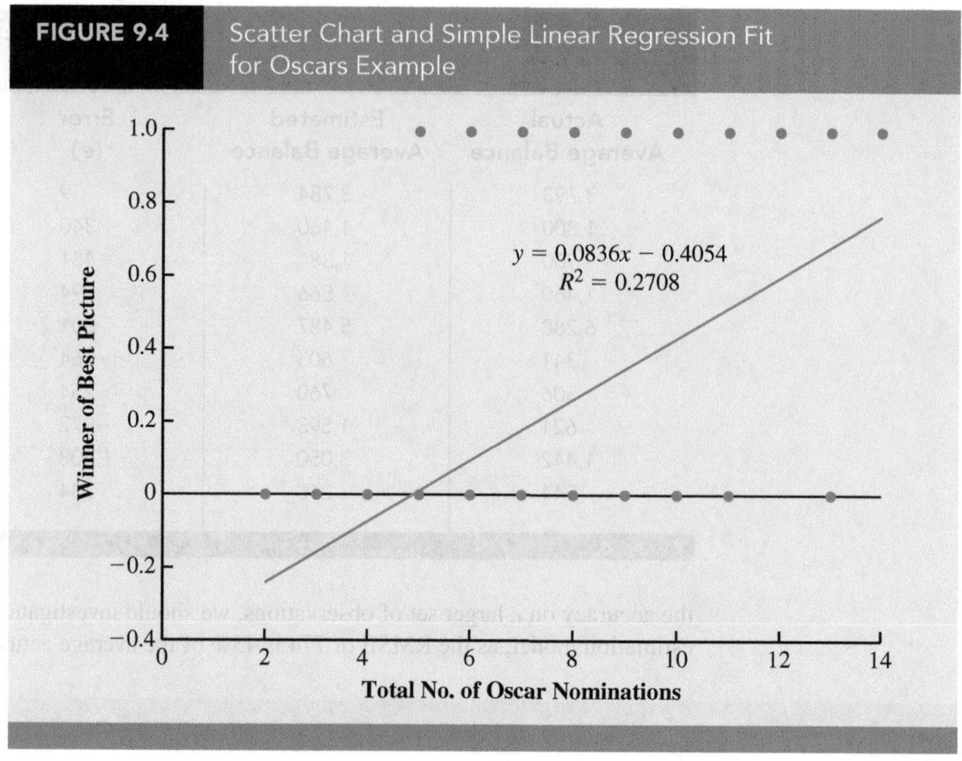

As discussed in Chapter 7, if a linear regression model is appropriate, the residuals should appear randomly dispersed with no discernible pattern.

Figure 9.5 shows an unmistakable pattern of systematic misprediction, suggesting that the simple linear regression model is not appropriate.

Estimating the probability p with the linear function $\hat{p} = b_0 + b_1x_1 + \cdots + b_qx_q$ does not fit well because, although p is a continuous measure, it is restricted to the range [0, 1]; that is, a probability cannot be less than zero or larger than one. Figure 9.6 shows an S-shaped curve that appears to better explain the relationship between the probability p of winning the best picture award and the total number of Oscar nominations. Instead of extending off to positive and negative infinity, the S-shaped curve flattens and never goes above one or below zero. We can achieve this S-shaped curve by estimating an appropriate function of the probability p of winning the best picture award with a linear function rather than directly estimating p with a linear function.

As a first step, we note that there is a measure related to probability known as *odds* that is very prominent in gambling and epidemiology. If an estimate of the probability of an event is $\hat{p}$ then the equivalent odds measure is $\hat{p}/(1 - \hat{p})$. For example, if the probability of an event is $\hat{p} = 2/3$, then the odds measure would be $(2/3)/(1/3) = 2$, meaning that the odds are 2 to 1 that the event will occur. The odds metric ranges between zero and positive infinity, so by considering the odds measure rather than the probability $\hat{p}$, we eliminate the linear fit problem resulting from the upper bound on the probability $\hat{p}$. To eliminate the fit problem resulting from the remaining lower bound on $\hat{p}/(1 - \hat{p})$, we observe that the natural log of the odds for an event, also known as "log odds" or logit, $\ln(\hat{p}/(1 - \hat{p}))$, ranges from negative infinity to positive infinity. Estimating the logit with a linear function results in a logistic regression model:

$$\ln\left(\frac{\hat{p}}{1-\hat{p}}\right) = b_0 + b_1x_1 + \cdots + b_qx_q. \quad \textbf{(9.1)}$$

Given a training set of observations consisting of values for a set of explanatory variables, $x_1, x_2, \ldots, x_q$, and whether or not an event of interest occurred ($y = 0$ or 1), the logistic

FIGURE 9.5 Residuals for Simple Linear Regression on Oscars Data

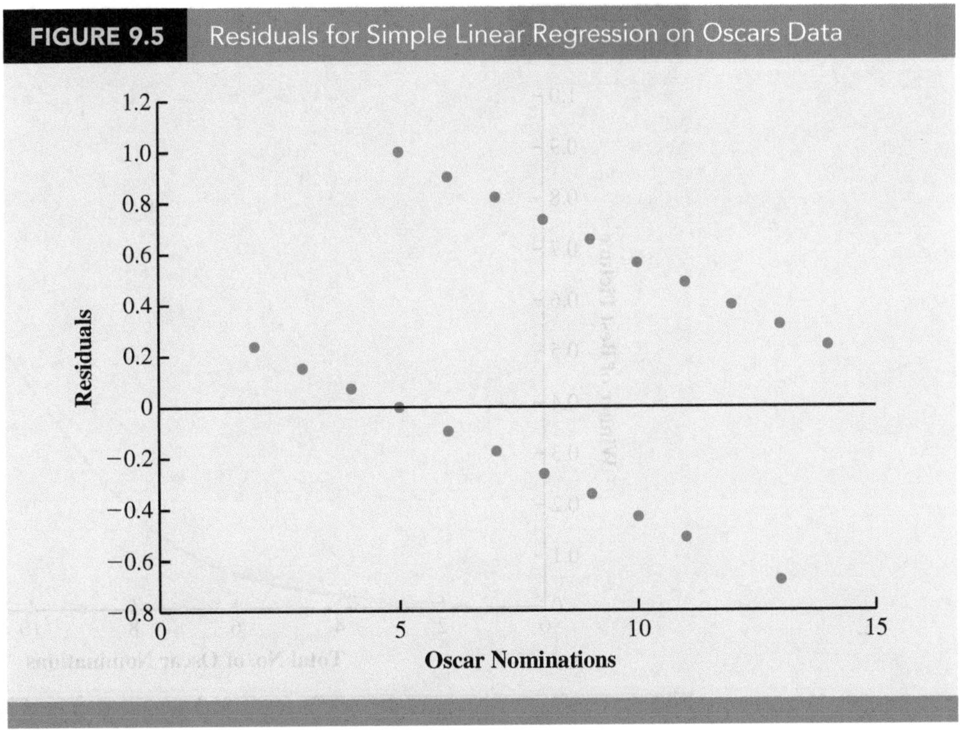

regression model fits values of $b_0, b_1, \ldots, b_q$ that best estimate the log odds of the event occurring. Fitting the logistic regression model to the data in the file *OscarsDemo* results in estimates of $b_0 = -6.214$ and $b_1 = 0.596$; that is, the log odds of a movie winning the best picture award is given by:

$$\ln\left(\frac{\hat{p}}{1-\hat{p}}\right) = -6.214 + 0.596 \times \text{total number of Oscar nominations.} \quad \textbf{(9.2)}$$

Software such as XLMiner is necessary to compute the estimates for the coefficients $b_0, b_1, b_2, \ldots, b_q$, of a logistic regression mode l that result in the best fit of the training data.

Unlike the coefficients in a multiple linear regression, the coefficients in a logistic regression do not have an intuitive interpretation. For example, $b_1 = 0.596$ means that for every additional Oscar nomination that a movie receives, its log odds of winning the best picture award increase by 0.596. In other words, the total number of Oscar nominations is linearly related to the log odds of a movie winning the best picture award. Unfortunately, a change in the log odds of an event is not as easy as to interpret as a change in the probability of an event. Algebraically solving equation (9.1) for p, we can express the relationship between the estimated probability of an event and the explanatory variables with an equation known as the logistic function:

LOGISTIC FUNCTION

$$\hat{p} = \frac{1}{1 + e^{-(b_0 + b_1x_1 + \cdots + b_qx_q)}} \quad \textbf{(9.3)}$$

For the *OscarsDemo* data, equation (9.3) is

$$\hat{p} = \frac{1}{1 + e^{-(-6.214 + 0.596 \times \text{total number of Oscar nominations})}} \quad \textbf{(9.4)}$$

Plotting equation (9.4), we obtain the S-shaped curve of Figure 9.6. Clearly, the logistic regression fit implies a nonlinear relationship between the probability of winning the best picture award and the total number of Oscar nominations. The effect of increasing the total number of Oscar nominations on the probability of winning the best picture award

FIGURE 9.6 Logistic S-Curve for Oscars Example

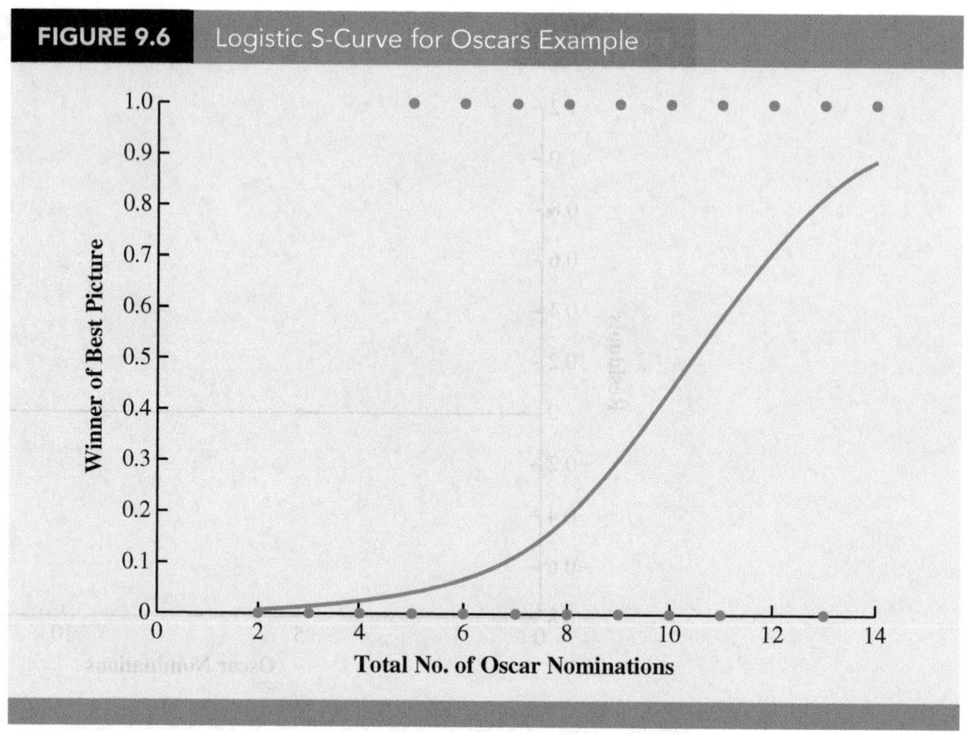

depends on the original number of Oscar nominations. For instance, if the total number of Oscar nominations is four, an additional Oscar nomination increases the estimated probability of winning the best picture award from $\hat{p} = \frac{1}{1 + e^{-(-6.214 + 0.596 \times 4)}} = 0.021$ to $\hat{p} = \frac{1}{1 + e^{-(-6.214 + 0.596 \times 5)}} = 0.038$, an increase of 0.017. But if the total number of Oscar nominations is eight, an additional Oscar nomination increases the estimated probability of winning the best picture award from $\hat{p} = \frac{1}{1 + e^{-(-6.214 + 0.596 \times 8)}} = 0.191$ to $\hat{p} = \frac{1}{1 + e^{-(-6.214 + 0.596 \times 9)}} = 0.299$, an increase of 0.108.

As with other classification methods, logistic regression classifies an observation by using equation (9.3) to compute the probability of an observation belonging to Class 1 and then comparing this probability to a cutoff value. If the probability exceeds the cutoff value (a typical value is 0.5), the observation is classified as Class 1 and otherwise it is classified as Class 0. Table 9.5 shows a subsample of the predicted probabilities computed using equation (9.3) and the subsequent classification.

See Chapter 7 for an in-depth discussion of variable selection in multiple regression models.

Appendix 9.2 demonstrates the construction of a logistic regression classifier using XLMiner.

The selection of variables to consider for a logistic regression model is similar to the approach in multiple linear regression. Especially when dealing with many variables, thorough data exploration via descriptive statistics and data visualization is essential in narrowing down viable candidates for explanatory variables. While a logistic regression model used for prediction should ultimately be judged based on its classification accuracy on validation and test sets, **Mallow's C_p statistic** is a measure commonly computed by statistical software that can be used to identify models with promising sets of variables. Models that achieve a small value of Mallow's C_p statistic tend to have smaller mean squared error and models with a value of Mallow's C_p statistic approximately equal to the number of coefficients in the model tend to have less bias (the tendency to systemically over- or under-predict).

TABLE 9.5 Predicted Probabilities by Logistic Regression for Oscars Example

Total No. of Oscar Nominations	Predicted Probability of Winning	Predicted Class	Actual Class
14	0.89	Winner	Winner
11	0.58	Winner	Loser
10	0.44	Loser	Loser
6	0.07	Loser	Winner

NOTES + COMMENTS

As with multiple linear regression, strong collinearity between the independent variables $x_1, x_2, \ldots x_q$ in a logistic regression model can distort the estimation of the coefficients $b_1, b_2, \ldots b_q$ in equation (9.1). If we are constructing a logistic regression model to explain and quantify a relationship between the set of independent variables and the log odds of an event occurring, then it is recommended to avoid models that include independent variables that are highly correlated. However, if the purpose of a logistic regression model is to classify observations, multicollinearity does not affect predictive capability so correlated independent variables are not a concern and the model should be evaluated based on its classification accuracy on validation and test sets.

Appendix 9.3 demonstrates the use of XLMiner to apply k-NN *for classification and estimation.*

9.5 *k*-Nearest Neighbors

The ***k*-Nearest Neighbor (*k*-NN)** method can be used either to classify an outcome category or estimate a continuous outcome. In a *k*-NN approach, the predicted outcome for an observation in the validation set is based on the *k* most similar observations from the training set, where similarity is typically measured with Euclidean distance.

Classifying Categorical Outcomes with *k*-Nearest Neighbors

Unlike logistic regression, which uses a training set to build a classification model (the logistic equation) to apply to the observations in the validation and test sets, a nearest-neighbor classifier is a "lazy learner" that instead directly uses the entire training set to classify observations in the validation and test sets. When *k*-NN is used as a classification method, a new observation is classified as Class 1 if the percentage of its *k* nearest neighbors in Class 1 is greater than or equal to a specified cutoff value (a typical value is 0.5).

The value of k can plausibly range from 1 to n, the number of observations in the training set. If $k = 1$, then the classification of a new observation is set to be equal to the class of the single most similar observation from the training set. At the other extreme, if $k = n$, then the new observation's class is naïvely assigned to the most common class in the training set. Typical values of k range from 1 to 20. The best value of k can be determined by building models over a typical range ($k = 1, \ldots, 20$) and then selecting the value of k^* that results in the smallest classification error. Note that the use of the validation set to identify k^* in this manner implies that the method should be applied to a test set with this value of k^* to accurately estimate the classification error on future data.

To illustrate, suppose a training set consists of the 10 observations listed in Table 9.6. For this example, we will refer to an observation with Loan Default = 1 as a Class 1

TABLE 9.6 Training Set Observations for *k*-NN Classifier

Observation	Average Balance	Age	Loan Default
1	49	38	1
2	671	26	1
3	772	47	1
4	136	48	1
5	123	40	1
6	36	29	0
7	192	31	0
8	6,574	35	0
9	2,200	58	0
10	2,100	30	0
Average:	1,285	38.2	
Standard Deviation:	2,029	10.2	

observation and an observation with Loan Default = 0 as a Class 0 observation. Our task is to classify a new observation with Average Balance = 900 and Age = 28 based on its similarity to the values of Average Balance and Age of the 10 observations in the training set.

Chapter 2 discusses z-scores.

Before computing the similarity between a new observation and the observations in the training set, it is common practice to normalize the values of all variables. By replacing the original values of each variable with the corresponding *z*-score, we avoid the computation of Euclidean distance being disproportionately affected by the scale of the variables. For example, the average value of the Average Balance variable in the training set is 1,285 and the standard deviation is 2,029. The average and standard deviation of the Age variable are 38.2 and 10.2, respectively. Thus, Observation 1's normalized value of Average Balance is $(49 - 1{,}285)/2{,}029 = -0.61$ and its normalized value of Age is $(38 - 38.2)/10.2 = -0.02$.

FIGURE 9.7 Scatter Chart for *k*-NN Classification

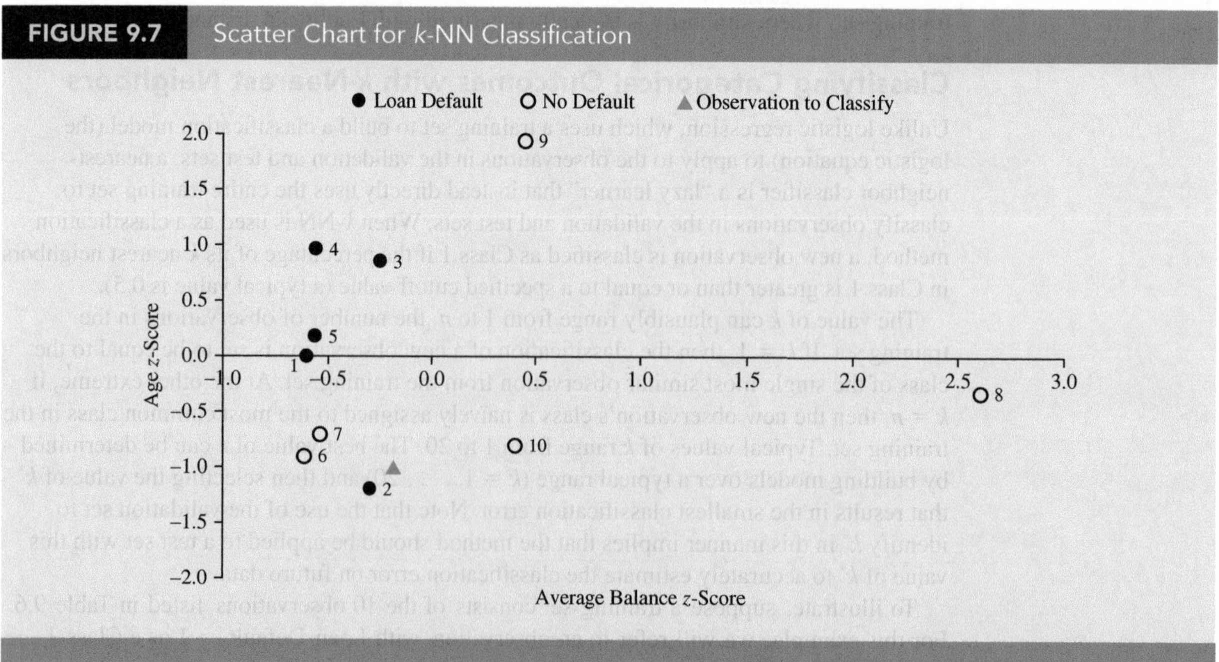

TABLE 9.7 Classification of Observation with Average Balance = 900 and Age = 28 for Different Values of k

k	% of Class 1 Neighbors	Classification
1	1.00	1
2	0.50	1
3	0.33	0
4	0.25	0
5	0.40	0
6	0.50	1
7	0.57	1
8	0.63	1
9	0.56	1
10	0.50	1

Figure 9.7 displays the 10 training-set observations and the new observation to be classified plotted according to their normalized variable values. To classify the new observation, we will use a cutoff value of 0.5. For $k = 1$, this observation is classified as a Loan Default (Class 1) because its nearest neighbor (Observation 2) is in Class 1. For $k = 2$, we see that the two nearest neighbors are Observation 2 (Class 1) and Observation 7 (Class 0). Because at least 0.5 of the $k = 2$ neighbors are Class 1, the new observation is classified as Class 1. For $k = 3$, the three nearest neighbors are Observation 2 (Class 1), Observation 7 (Class 0), and Observation 6 (Class 0). Because only 1/3 of the neighbors are Class 1, the new observation is classified as Class 0 (.33 is less than the .5 cutoff value). Table 9.7 summarizes the classification of the new observation for values of k ranging from 1 to 10.

Estimating Continuous Outcomes with *k*-Nearest Neighbors

When *k*-NN is used to estimate a continuous outcome, a new observation's outcome value is predicted to be the *average* of the outcome values of its k nearest neighbors in the training set. The value of k can plausibly range from 1 to n, the number of observations in the training set. If $k = 1$, then the estimation of a new observation's outcome value is set equal to the outcome value of the single most similar observation from the training set. At the other extreme, if $k = n$, then the new observation's outcome value is estimated by the average outcome value over the entire training set. Typical values of k range from 1 to 20. The best value of k can be determined by building models over a typical range ($k = 1, \ldots, 20$) and then selecting the value of k^* that results in the smallest estimation error. Note that the use of the validation set to identify k^* in this manner implies that the method should be applied to a test set with this value of k^* to accurately estimate the estimation error on future data.

To illustrate, we again consider the training set of 10 observations listed in Table 9.6. In this case, we are interested in estimating the value of Average Balance for a new observation based on its similarity with respect to Age to the 10 observations in the training set. Figure 9.8 displays the 10 training-set observations and a new observation with

FIGURE 9.8 Scatter Chart for *k*-NN Estimation

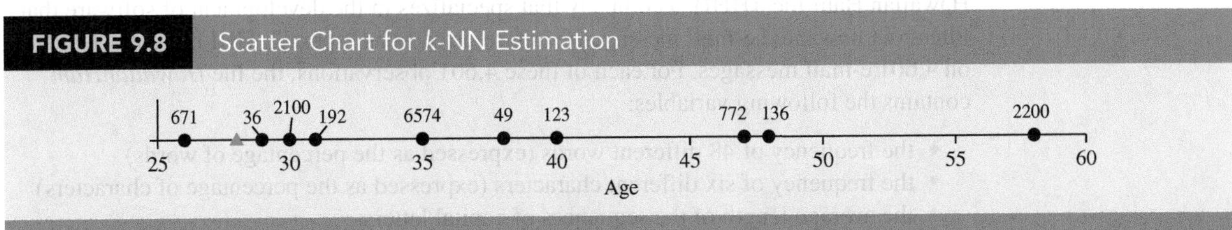

TABLE 9.8 Estimation Average Balance for Observation with Age = 28 for Different Values of k

k	Average Balance Estimate
1	$36
2	$936
3	$936
4	$750
5	$1,915
6	$1,604
7	$1,392
8	$1,315
9	$1,184
10	$1,285

Age = 28 for which we want to estimate the value of Average Balance. For $k = 1$, the new observation's average balance is estimated to be $36, which is the value of Average Balance for the nearest neighbor (Observation 6 in Table 9.6). For $k = 2$, we see that there is a tie between Observation 2 (Age = 26) and Observation 10 (Age = 30) for the second-closest observation to the new observation (Age = 28). Rather than employ an arbitrary tie-breaking rule, we will include all three observations to estimate the average balance of the new observation as (36 + 671 + 2,100)/3 = $936. Table 9.8 summarizes the estimation of the new observation's average balance for values of k ranging from 1 to 10.

9.6 Classification and Regression Trees

Appendix 9.4 demonstrates how to construct classification and regression trees using XLMiner.

Classification and regression trees (CART) successively partition a data set of observations into increasingly smaller and more homogeneous subsets. At each iteration of the CART method, a subset of observations is split into two new subsets based on the values of a single variable. The CART method can be thought of as a series of questions that successively narrow down observations into smaller and smaller groups of decreasing **impurity**, which is the measure of the heterogeneity in a group of observations' outcome classes or outcome values.

Classifying Categorical Outcomes with a Classification Tree

For **classification trees**, the impurity of a group of observations is based on the proportion of observations belonging to the same class (where there is zero impurity if all observations in a group are in the same class). After a final tree is constructed, the classification of a new observation is then based on the final partition into which the new observation belongs (based on the variable splitting rules).

To demonstrate the classification tree method, we consider an example involving Hawaiian Ham Inc. (HHI), a company that specializes in the development of software that filters out unwanted e-mail messages (often referred to as "spam"). HHI has collected data on 4,601 e-mail messages. For each of these 4,601 observations, the file *HawaiianHam* contains the following variables:

- the frequency of 48 different words (expressed as the percentage of words)
- the frequency of six different characters (expressed as the percentage of characters)
- the average length of the sequences of capital letters

- the longest sequence of capital letters
- the total number of sequences with capital letters
- whether or not the e-mail was spam

HHI would like to use these variables to classify e-mail messages as either "spam" (Class 1) or "not spam" (Class 0).

To explain how a classification tree categorizes observations, we use a small sample of data from HHI consisting of 46 observations and only two variables, Dollar and Exclamation, corresponding to the percentage of the $ character and the percentage of the ! character, respectively. The results of a classification tree analysis can be graphically displayed in a tree that explains the process of classifying a new observation. The tree outlines the values of the variables that result in an observation falling into a particular partition.

Let us consider the classification tree in Figure 9.9. At each step, the CART method identifies the split of the variable that results in the least impurity in the two resulting categories. In Figure 9.9, the number within the circle (or node) represents the value on which the variable (whose name is listed below the node) is split. The first partition is formed by splitting observations into two groups, observations with Dollar ≤ 0.0555 and observations with Dollar > 0.0555. The numbers on the left and right arc emanating from the node denote the number of observations in the Dollar ≤ 0.0555 and Dollar > 0.0555 partitions, respectively. There are 28 observations containing less than 5.55% of the '$' character and 18 observations containing more than 5.55% of the '$' character. The split on the variable

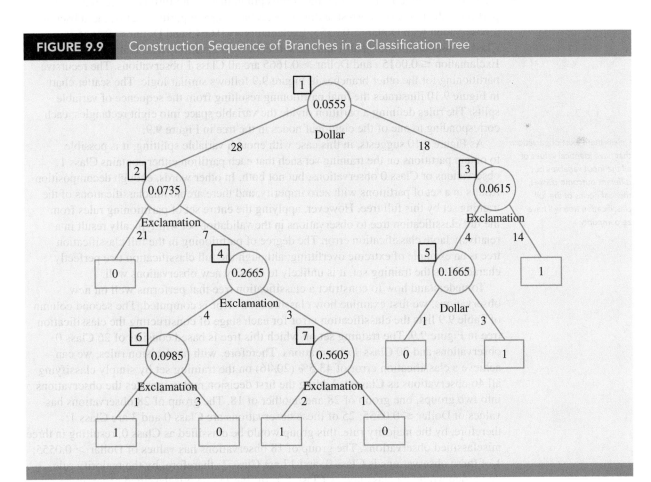

FIGURE 9.9 Construction Sequence of Branches in a Classification Tree

Dollar at the value 0.0555 is selected because it results in the two subsets of the original 46 observations with the least impurity. The splitting process is then repeated on these two newly created groups of observations in a manner that again results in an additional subset with the least impurity. In this tree, the second split is applied to the group of 28 observations with Dollar ≤ 0.0555 using the variable Exclamation; 21 of the 28 observations in this subset have Exclamation ≤ 0.0735, while 7 have Exclamation > 0.0735. After this second variable splitting, there are three total partitions of the original 46 observations. There are 21 observations with values of Dollar ≤ 0.0555 and Exclamation ≤ 0.0735, 7 observations with values of Dollar ≤ 0.0555 and Exclamation > 0.0735, and 18 observations with values of Dollar > 0.0555. No further partitioning of the 21-observation group with values of Dollar ≤ 0.0555 and Exclamation ≤ 0.0735 is necessary since this group consists entirely of Class 0 (nonspam) observations (i.e., this group has zero impurity). The 7-observation group with values of Dollar ≤ 0.0555 and Exclamation > 0.0735 and 18-observation group with values of Dollar > 0.0555 are successively partitioned in the order as denoted by the boxed numbers in Figure 9.9 until subsets with zero impurity are obtained.

For example, the group of 18 observations with Dollar > 0.0555 is further split into two groups using the variable Exclamation; 4 of the 18 observations in this subset have Exclamation ≤ 0.0615, while the other 14 observations have Exclamation > 0.0615. That is, 4 observations have Exclamation > 0.0555 and Exclamation ≤ 0.0615. This subset of 4 observations is further decomposed into 1 observation with Dollar ≤ 0.1665 and 3 observations with Dollar > 0.1665. At this point, there is no further branching in this portion of the tree since corresponding subsets have zero impurity. That is, the subset of 1 observation with Dollar > 0.0555, Exclamation ≤ 0.0615 and Dollar ≤ 0.1665 is a Class 0 observation (nonspam) and the subset of 3 observations with Dollar > 0.0555, Exclamation ≤ 0.0615 , and Dollar > 0.1665 are all Class 1 observations. The recursive partitioning for the other branches in Figure 9.9 follows similar logic. The scatter chart in Figure 9.10 illustrates the final partitioning resulting from the sequence of variable splits. The rules defining a partition divide the variable space into eight rectangles, each corresponding to one of the eight leaf nodes in the tree in Figure 9.9.

Unless there exist observations that have identical values of all the input variables but different outcome classes, the leaf nodes of the full classification tree will have zero impurity.

As Figure 9.10 suggests, in this case with enough variable splitting, it is possible to obtain partitions on the training set such that each partition either contains Class 1 observations or Class 0 observations, but not both. In other words, enough decomposition results in a set of partitions with zero impurity, and there are no misclassifications of the training set by this full tree. However, applying the entire set of partitioning rules from the full classification tree to observations in the validation set will typically result in a relatively large classification error. The degree of partitioning in the full classification tree is an example of extreme overfitting; although the full classification tree perfectly characterizes the training set, it is unlikely to classify new observations well.

To understand how to construct a classification tree that performs well on new observations, we first examine how classification error is computed. The second column of Table 9.9 lists the classification error for each stage of constructing the classification tree in Figure 9.9. The training set on which this tree is based consists of 26 Class 0 observations and 20 Class 1 observations. Therefore, with no decision rules, we can achieve a classification error of 43.5% (20/46) on the training set by simply classifying all 46 observations as Class 0. Adding the first decision node separates the observations into two groups, one group of 28 and another of 18. The group of 28 observations has values of Dollar ≤ 0.0555; 25 of these observations are Class 0 and 3 are Class 1; therefore, by the majority rule, this group would be classified as Class 0, resulting in three misclassified observations. The group of 18 observations has values of Dollar > 0.0555; 1 of these observations is Class 0, and 17 are Class 1; therefore, by the majority rule, this group would be classified as Class 1, resulting in one misclassified observation.

FIGURE 9.10 Geometric Illustration of Full Classification Tree Partitions

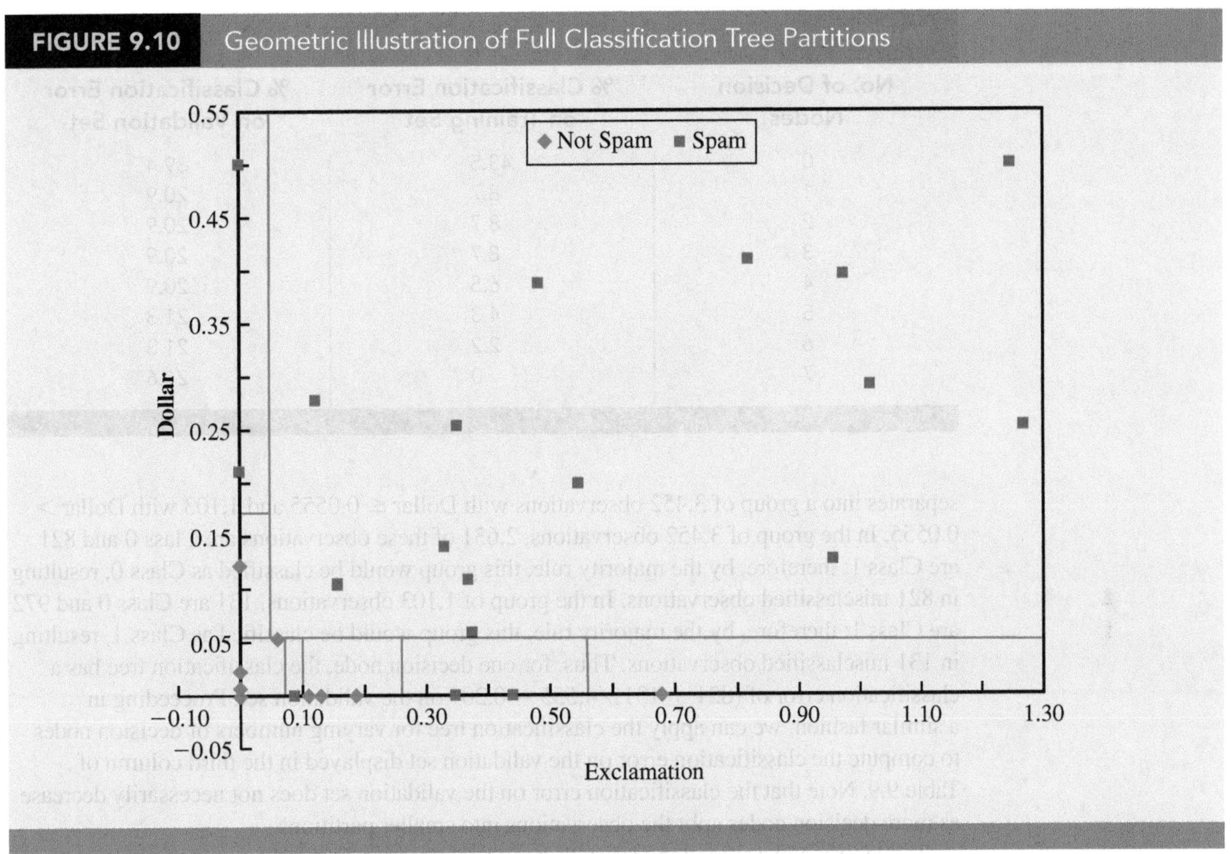

Thus, for one decision node, the classification tree has a classification error of $(3 + 1)/46 = 0.087$.

When the second decision node is added, the 28 observations with values of Dollar $\leq$ 0.0555 are further decomposed into a group of 21 observations and a group of 7 observations. The classification tree with two decision nodes has three groups: a group of 18 observations with Dollar $>$ 0.0555, a group of 21 observations with Dollar $\leq$ 0.0555 and Exclamation $\leq$ 0.0735, and a group of 7 observations with Dollar $\leq$ 0.0555 and Exclamation $>$ 0.0735. As before, the group of 18 observations would be classified as Class 1 and misclassify a single observation that is actually Class 0. In the group of 21 observations, all of these observations are Class 0, so there is no misclassification error for this group. In the group of seven observations, four are Class 0 and three are Class 1. Therefore, by the majority rule, this group would be classified as Class 0, resulting in three misclassified observations. Thus, for the classification tree with two decision nodes (and three partitions), the classification error is $(1 + 0 + 3)/46 = 0.087$. Proceeding in a similar fashion, we can compute the classification error on the training set for classification trees with varying numbers of decision nodes to complete the second column of Table 9.9. Table 9.9 shows that the classification error on the training set decreases as we add more decision nodes and split the observations into smaller partitions.

To evaluate how well the decision rules of the classification tree in Figure 9.9 established from the training set extend to other data, we apply it to a validation set of 4,555 observations consisting of 2,762 Class 0 observations and 1,793 Class 1 observations. Without any decision rules, we can achieve a classification error of 39.4% (1,793/4,555) on the training set by simply classifying all 4,555 observations as Class 0. Applying the first decision node

TABLE 9.9 Classification Error Rates on Sequence of Pruned Trees

No. of Decision Nodes	% Classification Error on Training Set	% Classification Error on Validation Set
0	43.5	39.4
1	8.7	20.9
2	8.7	20.9
3	8.7	20.9
4	6.5	20.9
5	4.3	21.3
6	2.2	21.3
7	0	21.6

separates into a group of 3,452 observations with Dollar $\leq$ 0.0555 and 1,103 with Dollar $>$ 0.0555. In the group of 3,452 observations, 2,631 of these observations are Class 0 and 821 are Class 1; therefore, by the majority rule, this group would be classified as Class 0, resulting in 821 misclassified observations. In the group of 1,103 observations, 131 are Class 0 and 972 are Class 1; therefore, by the majority rule, this group would be classified as Class 1, resulting in 131 misclassified observations. Thus, for one decision node, the classification tree has a classification error of $(821 + 131)/4{,}555 = 0.209$ on the validation set. Proceeding in a similar fashion, we can apply the classification tree for varying numbers of decision nodes to compute the classification error on the validation set displayed in the third column of Table 9.9. Note that the classification error on the validation set does not necessarily decrease as more decision nodes split the observations into smaller partitions.

To identify a classification tree with good performance on new data, we "prune" the full classification tree by removing decision nodes in the reverse order in which they were added. In this manner, we seek to eliminate the decision nodes corresponding to weaker rules. Figure 9.11 illustrates the tree resulting from pruning the last variable splitting rule (Exclamation $\leq$ 0.5605 or Exclamation $>$ 0.5605) from Figure 9.9. By pruning this rule, we obtain a partition defined by Dollar $\leq$ 0.0555, Exclamation $>$ 0.0735, and Exclamation $>$ 0.2665 that contains three observations. Two of these observations are Class 1 (spam) and one is Class 0 (nonspam), so this pruned tree classifies observations in this partition as Class 1 observations, since the proportion of Class 1 observations in this partition (two-thirds) exceeds the default cutoff value of 0.5. Therefore, the classification error of this pruned true on the training set is $1/46 = 0.022$, an increase over the zero classification error of the full tree on the training set. However, Table 9.9 shows that applying the six decision rules of this pruned tree to the validation set achieves a classification error of 0.213, which is less than the classification error of 0.216 of the full tree on the validation set. Compared to the full tree with seven decision rules, the pruned tree with six decision rules is less likely to be overfit to the training set.

Sequentially removing decision nodes, we can obtain six pruned trees. These pruned trees have one to six variable splits (decision nodes). However, while adding decision nodes at first decreases the classification error on the validation set, too many decision nodes overfits the classification tree to the training data and results in increased error on the validation set. For each of these pruned trees, each observation belongs to a single partition defined by a sequence of decision rules and is classified as Class 1 if the proportion of Class 1 observations in the partition exceeds the cutoff value (default value, 0.5) and Class 0 otherwise.

One common approach for identifying the best-pruned tree is to begin with the full classification tree and prune decision rules until the classification error on the validation set

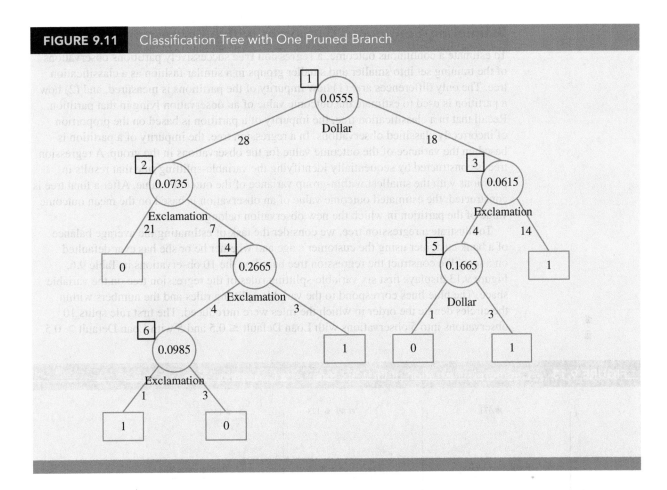

FIGURE 9.11 Classification Tree with One Pruned Branch

increases. Following this procedure, Table 9.9 suggests that a classification tree partitioning observations into two subsets with a single decision node (Dollar $\leq$ 0.0555 or Dollar $>$ 0.0555) is just as reliable at classifying the validation data as any other tree. As Figure 9.12 shows, this classification tree classifies e-mails with '!' accounting for $\leq$ 5.55% of the characters as nonspam and e-mails as spam if the '$' character accounts for more than 5.55% of the total characters in the email, otherwise the email is classified as nonspam. This best-pruned classification tree results in a classification error of 20.9% on the validation set.

FIGURE 9.12 Best-Pruned Classification Tree

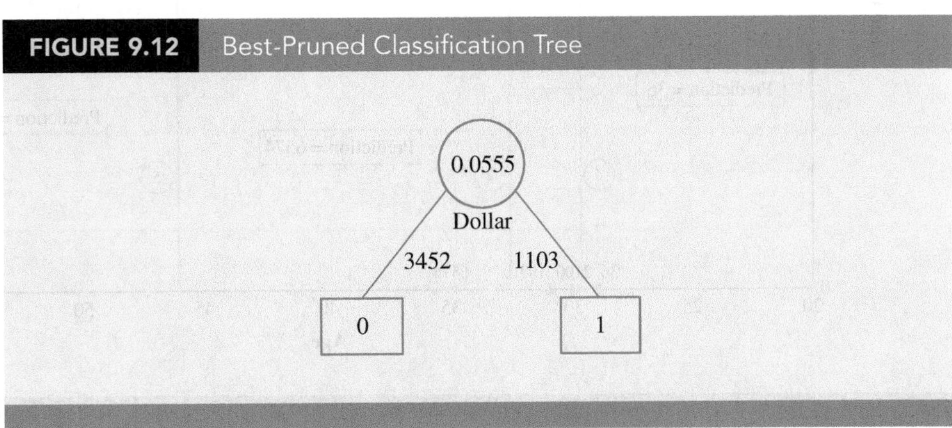

Estimating Continuous Outcomes with a Regression Tree

To estimate a continuous outcome, a **regression tree** successively partitions observations of the training set into smaller and smaller groups in a similar fashion as a classification tree. The only differences are: (1) how impurity of the partitions is measured, and (2) how a partition is used to estimate the outcome value of an observation lying in that partition. Recall that in a classification tree, the impurity of a partition is based on the proportion of incorrectly classified observations. In a regression tree, the impurity of a partition is based on the variance of the outcome value for the observations in the group. A regression tree is constructed by sequentially identifying the variable-splitting rule that results in partitions with the smallest within-group variance of the outcome value. After a final tree is constructed, the estimated outcome value of an observation is based on the mean outcome value of the partition in which the new observation belongs.

To illustrate a regression tree, we consider the task of estimating the average balance of a bank customer using the customer's age and whether he or she has ever defaulted on a loan. We construct the regression tree based on the 10 observations in Table 9.6. Figure 9.13 displays first six variable-splitting rules of the regression tree on the variable space. The blue lines correspond to the variable-splitting rules and the numbers within the circles denote the order in which the rules were introduced. The first rule splits 10 observations into 5 observations with Loan Default ≤ 0.5 and 5 with Loan Default > 0.5.

FIGURE 9.13 Geometric Illustration of First Six Rules of a Regression Tree

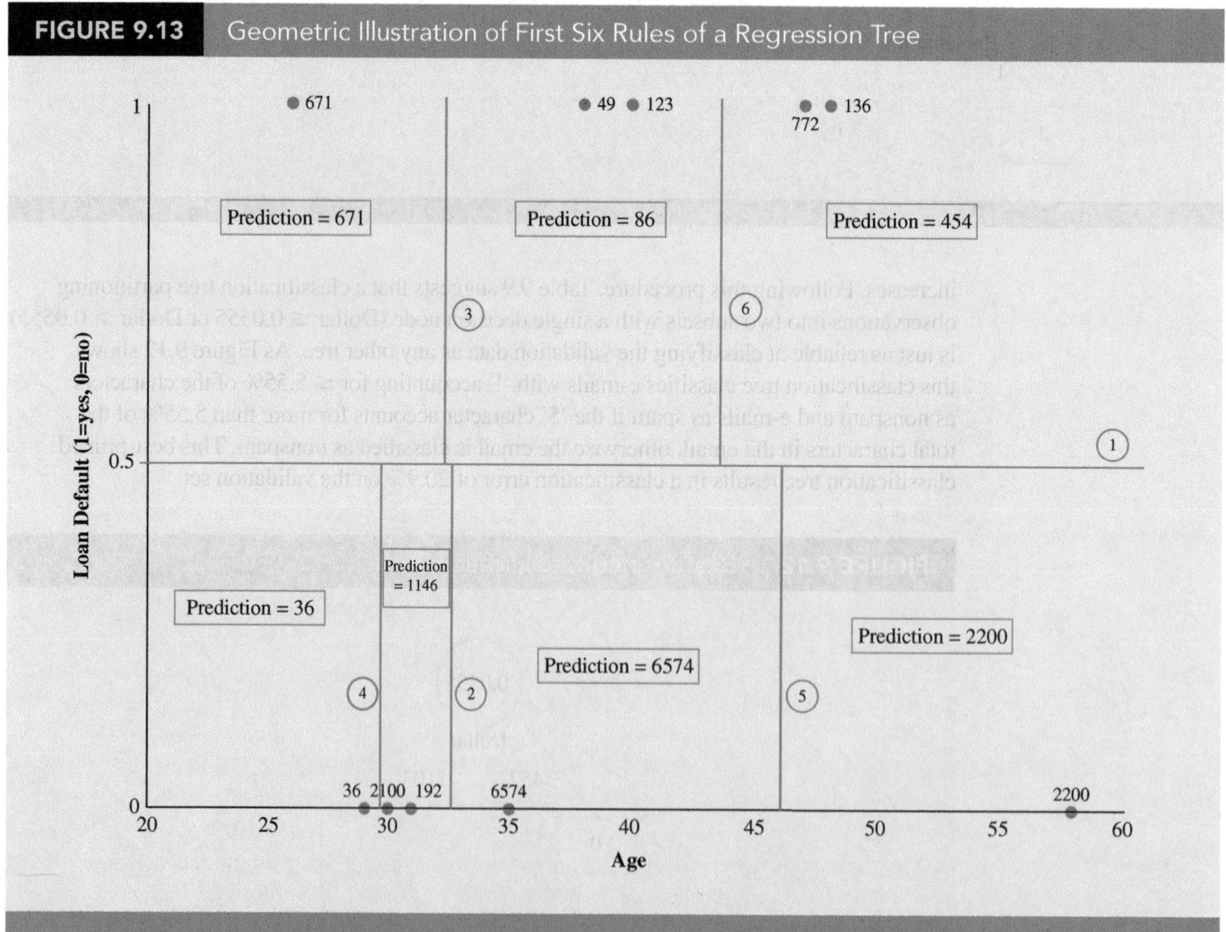

Unless there exist observations that have identical values of all the input variables but different values of the outcome variable, the leaf nodes of the full regression tree will have zero impurity.

This rule results in two groups of observations such that the variance in Average Balance within the groups is as small as possible. The second rule further splits the 5 observations with Loan Default ≤ 0.5 into a partition with 3 with Age ≤ 33 and 2 with Age > 33. Again, this rule results in the largest reduction in variance within any partition. Four more rules further split the observations into partitions with smaller Average Balance variance as illustrated by Figure 9.13. This six-rule regression tree would then sets its prediction estimate of each partition to be the average of the Average Balance variable (depicted in the red boxes in Figure 9.13).

Note that the full regression tree would continue to partition the variable space into smaller rectangles until the Average Balance variable was the same in each partition. Then, similar to the classification tree, rules are pruned from this full regression tree in order to obtain the simplest tree that obtained the least amount of prediction error.

Ensemble Methods

Up to this point, we have demonstrated the prediction of a new observation (either classification in the case of a categorical outcome or estimation in the case of a continuous outcome) based on the decision rules of a single constructed tree. In this section, we discuss the notion of ensemble methods. In an **ensemble method**, predictions are made based on the combination of a collection of models. For example, instead of basing the classification of a new observation on a single classification tree, an ensemble method generates a collection of different classification trees and then predicts the class of a new observation based on the collective voting of this collection.

To gain an intuitive grasp of why an ensemble of prediction models may outperform, on average, any single prediction model, let's consider the task of predicting the value of the S&P 500 Index one year in the future. Suppose there are 100 financial analysts independently developing their own forecast based on a variety of information. One year from now, there certainly will be one analyst (or more in the case of a tie) whose forecast will prove to be the most accurate. However, identifying beforehand which of the 100 analysts will be the most accurate may be virtually impossible. Therefore, instead of trying to pick one of the analysts and depending solely on their forecast, an ensemble approach would combine their forecasts (e.g., taking an average of the 100 forecast values) and use this as the predicted value of the S&P 500 Index. The two necessary conditions for an ensemble to perform better than a single model are: (1) The individual base models are constructed independently of each other (analysts don't base their forecasts on the forecasts of other analysts), and (2) the individual models perform better than just randomly guessing.

A neural network is also typically an unstable prediction method, but this method is beyond the scope of this book.

There are two primary steps to an ensemble approach: (1) the development of a committee of individual base models, and (2) the combination of the individual base models' predictions to form a composite prediction. While an ensemble can be composed of various individual classification or estimation models, the ensemble approach works better with an unstable prediction method. A classification or estimation method is **unstable** if relatively small changes in the training set cause its predictions to fluctuate substantially. As classification and regression trees are known to be unstable, our discussion of ensemble methods will involve CART. Specifically, we discuss three different ways to construct an ensemble of classification or regression trees: bagging, boosting, and random forests.

In the **bagging** approach, the committee of individual base models is generated by first constructing multiple training sets by repeated random sampling of the n observations in the original data *with replacement*. Because the sampling is done with replacement, some observations may appear multiple times in a single training set, while other observations will not appear at all. If each generated training set consists of n observations, then the probability of an observation from the original data *not* being selected for a specific

TABLE 9.10 Original 10-Observation Training Data

Age	29	31	35	38	47	48	53	54	58	70
Loan default	0	0	0	1	1	1	1	0	0	0

training set is $((n - 1)/n)^n$. Therefore, the average proportion of a training set of size n that are unique observations from the original data is $1 - ((n - 1)/n)^n$. The bagging approach then trains a predictive model on each of the m training sets and generates the ensemble prediction based on the average of the m individual predictions.

To demonstrate bagging, we consider the task of classifying customers as defaulting or not defaulting on their loan, using only their age. Table 9.10 contains the 10 observations in the original training data. Table 9.11 shows the results of generating 10 new training sets by randomly sampling from the original data with replacement. For each of these training sets, we construct a one-rule classification tree that minimizes the impurity of the resulting partition. The two partitions of each training set are illustrated with a vertical red line and accompanying decision rule.

Table 9.12 shows the results of applying this ensemble of 10 classification trees to a validation set consisting of 10 observations. The ensemble method bases its classification on the average of the 10 individual classifications trees; if at least half of the individual trees classify an observation as Class 1, so does the ensemble. Note from Table 9.12 that the 20% classification error rate of the ensemble is lower than any of the individual trees, illustrating the potential advantage of using ensemble methods.

Similar to bagging, the **boosting** method generates its committee of individual base models by sampling multiple training sets. However, boosting iteratively adapts how it samples the original data when constructing a new training set based on the prediction error of the models constructed on the previous training sets. To generate the first training set, each of the n observations in the original data is initially given equal weight of being selected. That is, each observation i has weight $w_i = 1/n$. A classification or estimation model is then trained on this training set and is used to predict the outcome of the n observations in the original data. The weight of each observation i is then adjusted based on the degree of its prediction error. For example, in a classification problem, if an observation i is misclassified by a classifier, then its weight w_i is increased, but if it is correctly classified, then its weight w_i is decreased. The next training set is then generated by sampling the observations according to the updated weights. In this manner, the next training set is more likely to contain observations that have been mispredicted in early iterations.

XLMiner offers three different variants of the AdaBoost boosting algorithm that differ in the weighting of individual models' predictions when they are averaged.

To combine the predictions of the m individual models from the m training sets, boosting weights the vote of each individual model based on its overall prediction error. For example, suppose that the classifier associated with the jth training set has a large prediction error and the classifier associated with the kth training set has a small prediction error. Then the classification votes of the jth classifier will be weighted less than the classification votes of the kth classifer when they are combined. Note that this method differs from bagging, in which each of the individual classifiers has an equally weighted vote.

Random forests (also called *random trees*) can be viewed as a variation of bagging specifically tailored for use with classification or regression trees. As in bagging, the random forests approach generates multiple training sets by randomly sampling (with replacement) the n observations in the original data. However, when constructing a tree model for each separate training set, each tree is restricted to using only a fixed number of randomly selected input variables. For example, suppose we are attempting to classify a

TABLE 9.11 Bagging: Generation of 10 New Training Sets and Corresponding Classification Trees

Iteration 1 — Age $\le$ 36.5

Age	29	31	31	35	38	38	47	48	58	58
Loan default	0	0	0	0	1	1	1	1	0	0
Prediction	0	0	0	0	1	1	1	1	1	1

Iteration 2 — Age $\le$ 50.5

Age	29	31	35	38	47	54	58	70	70	70
Loan default	0	0	0	1	1	0	0	0	0	0
Prediction	0	0	0	0	0	0	0	0	0	0

Iteration 3 — Age $\le$ 36.5

Age	29	31	35	38	38	47	53	53	54	58
Loan default	0	0	0	1	1	1	1	1	0	0
Prediction	0	0	0	1	1	1	1	1	1	1

Iteration 4 — Age $\le$ 34.5

Age	29	29	31	38	38	47	47	53	54	58
Loan default	0	0	0	1	1	1	1	1	0	0
Prediction	0	0	0	1	1	1	1	1	1	1

Iteration 5 — Age $\le$ 39

Age	29	29	31	47	48	48	48	70	70	70
Loan default	0	0	0	1	1	1	1	0	0	0
Prediction	0	0	0	1	1	1	1	1	1	1

Iteration 6 — Age $\le$ 53.5

Age	31	38	47	48	53	53	53	54	58	70
Loan default	0	1	1	1	1	1	1	0	0	0
Prediction	1	1	1	1	1	1	1	0	0	0

Iteration 7 — Age $\le$ 53.5

Age	29	38	38	48	53	54	58	58	58	70
Loan default	0	1	1	1	1	0	0	0	0	0
Prediction	1	1	1	1	1	0	0	0	0	0

Iteration 8 — Age $\le$ 53.5

Age	29	31	47	47	47	53	53	54	58	70
Loan default	0	0	1	1	1	1	1	0	0	0
Prediction	1	1	1	1	1	1	1	0	0	0

Iteration 9 — Age $\le$ 53.5

Age	29	35	38	38	48	53	53	54	70	70
Loan default	0	0	1	1	1	1	1	0	0	0
Prediction	1	1	1	1	1	1	1	0	0	0

Iteration 10 — Age $\le$ 14.5

Age	29	29	29	29	35	35	54	54	58	58
Loan default	0	0	0	0	0	0	0	0	0	0
Prediction	0	0	0	0	0	0	0	0	0	0

TABLE 9.12 Classification of 10 Observations from Validation Set with Bagging Ensemble

Age	26	29	30	32	34	37	42	47	48	54	**Overall Error Rate**
Loan default	1	0	0	0	0	1	0	1	1	0	
Tree 1	0	0	0	0	0	1	1	1	1	1	30%
Tree 2	0	0	0	0	0	0	0	0	0	0	40%
Tree 3	0	0	0	0	0	1	1	1	1	1	30%
Tree 4	0	0	0	0	0	1	1	1	1	1	30%
Tree 5	0	0	0	0	0	0	1	1	1	1	40%
Tree 6	1	1	1	1	1	1	1	1	1	0	50%
Tree 7	1	1	1	1	1	1	1	1	1	0	50%
Tree 8	1	1	1	1	1	1	1	1	1	0	50%
Tree 9	1	1	1	1	1	1	1	1	1	0	50%
Tree 10	0	0	0	0	0	0	0	0	0	0	40%
Average Vote	0.4	0.4	0.4	0.4	0.4	0.7	0.8	0.8	0.8	0.4	
Bagging Ensemble	0	0	0	0	0	1	1	1	1	0	20%

The default seting in XLMiner's random trees procedure is for each individual classification tree to be based on f = $\sqrt{q}$ variables and each individual regression tree to be based on f = q/3 variables.

tax return as fraudulent or not and there are q input variables. For each of the m generated training sets, a classification tree is constructed based on splitting rules based on f randomly selected input variables, where f is much smaller than q.

For most problems, the predictive accuracy of boosting ensembles exceeds the predictive accuracy of bagging ensembles. Boosting achieves its performance advantage because: (1) It evolves its committee of models by focusing on observations that are mispredicted, and (2) the member models' votes are weighted by their accuracy. However, boosting is more computationally expensive than bagging. Because there is no adaptive feedback in a bagging approach, all m training sets and corresponding models can be implemented simultaneously. However, in boosting, the first training set and predictive model guide the construction of the second training set and predictive model, and so on. The random forests approach has performance similar to boosting, but maintains the computational simplicity of bagging.

SUMMARY

In this chapter, we introduced the concepts and techniques in predictive data mining. Predictive data mining methods, also called supervised learning, classify a categorical outcome or estimate a continuous outcome. We described how to partition data into training, validation, and test sets in order to construct and evaluate predictive data mining models. We discussed various accuracy measures for classification and estimation methods. We discussed three common data mining methods: logistic regression, k-nearest neighbors, and classification/regression trees. We explained how logistic regression is analogous to multiple linear regression for the case when the outcome variable is binary. We demonstrated how to use logistic regression, as well as k-nearest neighbors and classification trees, to classify a binary categorical outcome. We also discussed the use of k-nearest neighbors and regression trees to estimate a continuous outcome. In our discussion of ensemble methods, we presented the concept of generating multiple prediction models and combining their predictions. We illustrated the use of ensemble methods within the context of classification trees

TABLE 9.13 Overview of Supervised Learning Methods

	Strengths	Weaknesses
***k*-NN**	Simple	Requires large amounts of data relative to number of variables
Classification and Regression Trees	Provides easy-to-interpret business rules; can handle data sets with missing data	May miss interactions between variables since splits occur one at a time; sensitive to changes in data entries
Multiple Linear Regression	Provides easy-to-interpret relationship between dependent and independent variables	Assumes linear relationship between outcome and variables
Logistic Regression	Classification analog of the familiar multiple regression modeling procedure	Coefficients not easily interpretable in terms of probability
Discriminant Analysis	Allows classification based on interaction effects between variables	Assumes variables are normally distributed with equal variance
Naïve Bayes	Simple and effective at classifying	Requires a large amount of data; restricted to categorical variables
Neural Networks	Flexible and often effective	Many difficult decisions to make when building the model; results cannot be easily explained, i.e., "black box"

and noted that ensemble methods based on committees of "weak" prediction models generally outperform a single "strong" prediction model. Table 9.13 provides a comparative summary of common supervised learning approaches. We provide brief descriptions of discriminant analysis, the naïve Bayes method, and neural networks in the following Notes + Comments section.

NOTES + COMMENTS

1. XLMiner provides functionality for the **Discriminant Analysis** classification procedure under **Classify** in the **Data Mining** group on the **XLMiner** Ribbon. Like logistic regression, discriminant analysis assumes a functional form to describe the probability that an observation belongs to a class and then uses data to develop estimates of the parameters of the function. Specifically, *P*(observation *i* belongs to Class 1) $= \frac{e^{c_1(i)}}{e^{c_0(i)} + e^{c_1(i)}}$, where $c_0(i)$ and $c_1(i)$ are classification scores for Class 0 and Class 1 that are computed by the algorithm. The strengths of discriminant analysis are its computational simplicity and its ability to provide estimates of the effect of each variable on the probability of class membership. However, while discriminant analysis is useful for small data sets, on large data sets its performance is typically dominated by other classification methods.
2. XLMiner provides functionality for the **Naïve Bayes** classification procedure under **Classify** in the **Data Mining** group on the **XLMiner** Ribbon. The naïve Bayes method is based on Bayes' Theorem from classical statistics. However, it is limited to using only categorical predictor variables to classify an observation and requires a very large number of observations to be effective.
3. XLMiner provides functionality for neural networks for both classification and estimation. Neural networks are based on the biological model of brain activity. Well-structured neural networks have been shown to possess accurate classification and estimation performance in many application domains. However, the use of neural networks is a "black box" method that does not provide any interpretable explanation to accompany its classifications or estimates. Adjusting the parameters to tune the neural network performance is largely trial and error guided by rules of thumb and user experience.

GLOSSARY

Accuracy Measure of classification success defined as 1 minus the overall error rate.
Average error The average difference between the actual values and the predicted values of observations in a data set.
Bagging An ensemble method that generates a committee of models based on different random samples and makes predictions based on the average prediction of the set of models.
Bias The tendency of a predictive model to overestimate or underestimate the value of a continuous outcome.
Boosting An ensemble method that iteratively samples from the original training data to generate individual models that target observations that were mispredicted in previously generated models. Its predictions are based on the weighted average of the predictions of the individual models, where the weights are proportional to the individual models' accuracy.
Class 0 error rate The percentage of Class 0 observations misclassified by a model in a data set.
Class 1 error rate The percentage of actual Class 1 observations misclassified by a model in a data set.
Classification confusion matrix A matrix showing the counts of actual versus predicted class values.
Classification tree A tree that classifies a categorical outcome variable by splitting observations into groups via a sequence of hierarchical rules.
Classification A predictive data mining task requiring the prediction of an observation's outcome class or category.
Cumulative lift chart A chart used to present how well a model performs in identifying observations most likely to be in Class 1 as compared with random classification.
Cutoff value The smallest value that the predicted probability of an observation can be for the observation to be classified as Class 1.
Decile-wise lift chart A chart used to present how well a model performs at identifying observations for each of the top *k* deciles most likely to be in Class 1 versus a random selection.
Ensemble method A predictive data-mining approach in which a committee of individual classification or estimation models are generated and a prediction is made by combining these individual predictions.
Estimation A predictive data mining task requiring the prediction of an observation's continuous outcome value.
F1 Score A measure combining precision and sensitivity into a single metric.
False negative The misclassification of a Class 1 observation as Class 0.
False positive The misclassification of a Class 0 observation as Class 1.
Features A set of input variables used to predict an observation's outcome class or continuous outcome value.
Impurity Measure of the heterogeneity of observations in a classification tree.
***k*-Nearest neighbors** A classification method that classifies an observation based on the class of the *k* observations most similar or nearest to it.
Logistic regression A generalization of linear regression for predicting a categorical outcome variable.
Mallow's C_p statistic A measure in which small values approximately equal to the number of coefficients suggest promising logistic regression models.
Model overfitting A situation in which a model explains random patterns in the data on which it is trained rather than just the relationships, resulting in training-set accuracy that far exceeds accuracy for the new data.

Observation (record) A set of observed values of variables associated with a single entity, often displayed as a row in a spreadsheet or database.
Overall error rate The percentage of observations misclassified by a model in a data set.
Precision The percentage of observations predicted to be Class 1 that actually are Class 1.
Random forests A variant of the bagging ensemble method that generates a committee of classification or regression trees based on different random samples but restricts each individual tree to a limited number of randomly selected features (variables)
Receiver operating characteristic (ROC) curve A chart used to illustrate the tradeoff between a model's ability to identify Class 1 observations and its Class 0 error rate.
Regression tree A tree that predicts values of a continuous outcome variable by splitting observations into groups via a sequence of hierarchical rules.
Root mean squared error A measure of the accuracy of an estimation method defined as the square root of the sum of squared deviations between the actual values and predicted values of observations.
Sensitivity (recall) The percentage of actual Class 1 observations correctly identified.
Specificity The percentage of actual Class 1 observations correctly identified.
Supervised learning Category of data-mining techniques in which an algorithm learns how to predict or classify an outcome variable of interest.
Test set Data set used to compute unbiased estimate of final predictive model's accuracy.
Training set Data used to build candidate predictive models.
Unstable When small changes in the training set cause its predictions to fluctuate substantially.
Validation set Data used to evaluate candidate predictive models.
Variable (feature) A characteristic or quantity of interest that can take on different values.

PROBLEMS

Due to the realistic size of these data sets, XLMiner may take several minutes to complete execution for some of these problems. Where relevant, we used the default seed of 12345 when applying XLMiner.

Salmons

1. Salmons Stores operates a national chain of women's apparel stores. Five thousand copies of an expensive four-color sales catalog have been printed, and each catalog includes a coupon that provides a $50 discount on purchases of $200 or more. Salmons would like to send the catalogs only to customers who have the highest probability of using the coupon. The file *Salmons* contains data from an earlier promotional campaign. For each of 1,000 Salmons customers, three variables are tracked: last year's total spending at Salmons, whether they have a Salmons store credit card, and whether they used the promotional coupon they were sent.

   Create a standard partition of the data with all the tracked variables and 50% of observations in the training set, 30% in the validation set, and 20% in the test set. Use logistic regression to classify observations as a promotion-responder or not by using Spending and Card as input variables and Coupon as the output variable. Perform **Variable Selection** with the best subsets procedure with the number of best subsets equal to two.

   a. Evaluate the logistic regression models based on their classification error. Recommend a final model and express the model as a mathematical equation relating the output variable to the input variables.
   b. For the model selected in part (a), interpret the meaning of the first-decile lift in the decile-wise lift chart on the test set.

c. What is the area under the ROC curve on the test set? To achieve a sensitivity of at least 0.80, how much Class 0 error rate must be tolerated?

2. Sandhills Bank would like to increase the number of customers who use payroll direct deposit as part of the rollout of its new e-banking platform. Management has proposed offering an increased interest rate on a savings account if customers sign up for direct deposit into a checking account. To determine whether this proposal is a good idea, management would like to estimate how many of the 200 current customers who do not use direct deposit would accept the offer. In the *Data* worksheet of the file *Sandhills*, the IT company that handles Sandhills Bank's e-banking has provided anonymized data from one of its other client banks that made a similar promotion to increase direct deposit participation. For 1,000 customers, this data lists the average monthly checking account balance and whether the customer signed up for direct deposit. The *Customer* worksheet contains the average monthly balance data for Sandhill's 200 customers that would be the target of the direct-deposit promotion. Sandhills would like to estimate the likelihood of these customers signing up for direct deposit.

   Create a standard partition of the data in the *Data* worksheet with 60% of observations in the training set and 40% in the validation set. Classify the data using *k*-Nearest Neighbors with up to $k = 20$. Use Balance the as input variable and Direct as the output variable. In Step 2 of XLMiner's *k*-Nearest Neighbors Classification procedure, be sure to **Normalize Input Data**, **Score on best k between 1 and specified value**, and assign prior class probabilities **According to relative occurrences in training data**. In Step 3, specify the data in the *Customer* worksheet by selecting **In Worksheet** in the **Score New Data** area.

   a. For the cutoff probability value 0.5, what value of *k* minimizes the overall error rate on the validation data?
   b. What is the area under the ROC curve on the validation set? To achieve a sensitivity of 0.80, how much Class 0 error rate must be tolerated?
   c. Using the default cutoff value of 0.5, how many of Sandhills Bank's 200 customers does *k*-Nearest Neighbors classify as enrolling in direct deposit?

3. Over the past few years the percentage of students who leave Dana College at the end of their first year has increased. Last year, Dana started voluntary one-credit hour-long seminars with faculty to help first-year students establish an on-campus connection. If Dana is able to show that the seminars have a positive effect on retention, college administrators will be convinced to continue funding this initiative. Dana's administration also suspects that first-year students with lower high school GPAs have a higher probability of leaving Dana at the end of the first year. The file *Dana* contains data on the 500 first-year students from last year. Each observation consists of a first-year student's high school GPA, whether they enrolled in a seminar, and whether they dropped out and did not return to Dana. Create a standard partition of the data with all the tracked variables and 60% of observations in the training set and 40% in the validation set. Use logistic regression to classify observations as dropped out or not dropped out by using GPA and Seminar as input variables and Dropped as the output variable. Perform **Variable Selection** with the best subsets procedure with the number of best subsets equal to two.

   a. Evaluate the logistic regression models based on their predictive accuracy on the validation set. Recommend a final model and express the model as a mathematical equation relating the output variable to the input variables.
   b. The data analyst team realized that they jumped directly into building a predictive model without exploring the data. Using descriptive statistics and charts, investigate any relationships in the data that may explain the unsatisfactory result in part (a).

For next year's first-year class, what could Dana's administration do regarding the enrollment of the seminars to better determine whether they have an effect on retention?

4. Campaign organizers for both the Republican and Democratic parties are interested in identifying individual undecided voters who would consider voting for their party in an upcoming election. The file *BlueOrRed* contains data on a sample of voters with tracked variables, including whether or not they are undecided regarding their candidate preference, age, whether they own a home, gender, marital status, household size, income, years of education, and whether they attend church.

   Create a standard partition of the data with all the tracked variables and 50% of observations in the training set, 30% in the validation set, and 20% in the test set. Classify the data using k-Nearest Neighbors with up to $k = 20$. Use Age, HomeOwner, Female, HouseholdSize, Income, Education, and Church as input variables and Undecided as the output variable. In Step 2 of XLMiner's k-Nearest Neighbors Classification procedure, be sure to **Normalize Input Data, Score on best k between 1 and specified value**, and assign prior class probabilities **According to relative occurrences in training data.**

   The k-Nearest Neighbors procedure is computationally intensive. Depending on your computer's capability, you may have to reduce the number of observations in the training set (by repartitioning the original data and reducing the percentage allocated to the training set) in order to successfully execute the k-Nearest Neighbors procedure.

   a. For $k = 1$, what is the overall error rate on the training set and the validation set, respectively? Explain the difference in magnitude of these two measures.
   b. For the cutoff probability value of 0.5, what value of k minimizes the overall error rate on the validation data? Explain the difference in the overall error rate on the training, validation, and test set.
   c. Examine the decile-wise lift chart for the test set. What is the first decile lift? Interpret this value.
   d. In the effort to identify undecided voters, a campaign is willing to accept an increase in the misclassification of decided voters as undecided if it can correctly classify more undecided voters. For cutoff probability values of 0.5, 0.4, 0.3, and 0.2, what are the corresponding Class 1 error rates and Class 0 error rates on the validation data?

5. Refer to the scenario in Problem 4 using the file *BlueOrRed*. Create a standard partition of the data with all the tracked variables and 50% of observations in the training set, 30% in the validation set, and 20% in the test set. Fit a single classification tree using Age, HomeOwner, Female, Married, HouseholdSize, Income, Education, and Church as input variables and Undecided as the output variable. In Step 2 of XLMiner's Classification Tree procedure, be sure to **Normalize Input Data** and to set the **Minimum # records in a terminal node** to 100. Generate the **Full tree** and **Best pruned tree.**
   a. From the *CT_Output* worksheet, what is the overall error rate of the full tree on the training set? Explain why this is not necessarily an indication that the full tree should be used to classify future observations and the role of the best-pruned tree.
   b. Consider a 50-year-old man who attends church, has 15 years of education, owns a home, is married, lives in a household of four people, and has an annual income of $150,000. Using the *CT_PruneTree* worksheet, does the best-pruned tree classify this observation as undecided?
   c. For the default cutoff value of 0.5, what are the overall error rate, Class 1 error rate, and Class 0 error rate of the best-pruned tree on the test set?
   d. Examine the decile-wise lift chart for the best-pruned tree on the test set. What is the first decile lift? Interpret this value.

6. Refer to scenario in Problem 4 using the file *BlueOrRed*. Create a standard partition of the data with all the tracked variables and 50% of observations in the training set,

30% in the validation set, and 20% in the test set. Apply the random trees procedure to create an ensemble of classification trees using Age, HomeOwner, Female, Married, HouseholdSize, Income, Education, and Church as input variables and Undecided as the output variable. In Step 2 of XLMiner's Random Trees Classification procedure, be sure to **Normalize Input Data**, to set **Number of weak learners** to 20, to set the **Number of randomly selected features** to 3, and to set the **Minimum # records in a terminal node** to 100.

a. What is the most important variable in terms of reducing the classification error of the ensemble?
b. For the default cutoff value of 0.5, compare the overall error rate, Class 1 error rate, and Class 0 error rate of the random trees on the test set to the corresponding measures of the single best-pruned tree from Problem 5.

7. Refer to the scenario in Problem 4 using the file *BlueOrRed*. Create a standard partition of the data with all the tracked variables and 50% of observations in the training set, 30% in the validation set, and 20% in the test set. Use logistic regression to classify observations as undecided (or decided) using Age, HomeOwner, Female, Married, HouseholdSize, Income, Education, and Church as input variables and Undecided as the output variable. Perform **Variable Selection** with the best subsets procedure with the number of best subsets equal to two.
   a. From the generated set of logistic regression models, use Mallow's C_p statistic to identify a pair of candidate models. Then evaluate these candidate models based on their classification error and decile-wise lift on the validation set. Recommend a final model and express the model as a mathematical equation relating the output variable to the input variables.
   b. Increases in which variables increase the chance of a voter being undecided? Increases in which variables decrease the chance of a voter being decided?
   c. Using the default cutoff value of 0.5 for your logistic regression model, what is the overall error rate on the test set?

8. Telecommunications companies providing cell-phone service are interested in customer retention. In particular, identifying customers who are about to churn (cancel their service) is potentially worth millions of dollars if the company can proactively address the reason that customer is considering cancellation and retain the customer. The DATAfile *Cellphone* contains customer data to be used to classify a customer as a churner or not.

   Using XLMiner's Partition with Oversampling procedure, partition the data with all the variables so there is 50% successes (churners) in the training set and 40% of the validation data are taken away as test set. Use 12345 as the seed in the randomized sampling. Classify the data using *k*-Nearest Neighbors with up to $k = 20$. Use Churn as the output variable and all the other variables as input variables. In Step 2 of XLMiner's *k*-Nearest Neighbors Classification procedure, be sure to **Normalize Input Data, Score on best k between 1 and specified value**, and specify prior probabilities that correspond to the Class 0 and Class 1 probabilities in the original data set (see cell F21 in the *Data_Partition* worksheet).
   a. Why is partitioning with oversampling advised in this case?
   b. For the cutoff probability value of 0.5, what value of *k* minimizes the overall error rate on the validation data?
   c. Referring to *KNNC_Output*, what is the overall error rate on the test set?
   d. Referring to *KNNC_Output*, what are the Class 1 and Class 0 error rates on the test set?
   e. Compute and interpret the sensitivity and specificity for the test set.

f. How many false positives and false negatives did the model commit on the test set? What percentage of predicted churners were false positives? What percentage of predicted nonchurners were false negatives?
g. Examine the decile-wise lift chart on the test set. What is the first decile lift on the test set? Interpret this value.

9. Refer to scenario in Problem 8 using the file *Cellphone*. Using XLMiner's Partition with Oversampling procedure, partition the data with all the variables so there is 50% successes (churners) in the training set and 40% of the validation data are taken away as test set. Use 12345 as the seed in the randomized sampling. Fit a single classification tree using Churn as the output variable and all the other variables as input variables. In Step 2 of XLMiner's Classification Tree procedure, be sure to **Normalize Input Data** and to set the **Minimum # records in a terminal node** to 1. Generate the **Full tree**, **Best pruned tree**, and **Minimum error tree**.
   a. Why is partitioning with oversampling advised in this case?
   b. From the *CT_Output* worksheet, what is the overall error rate of the full tree on the training set? Explain why this is not necessarily an indication that the full tree should be used to classify future observations and the role of the best pruned tree.
   c. Consider the minimum error tree in the *CT_MinErrorTree* worksheet. List and interpret the set of rules that characterize churners.
   d. For the default cutoff value of 0.5, what are the overall error rate, Class 1 error rate, and Class 0 error rate of the best-pruned tree on the test set?
   e. Examine the decile-wise lift chart for the best-pruned tree on the test set. What is the first decile lift? Interpret this value.

10. Refer to the scenario in Problem 8 using the file *Cellphone*. Using XLMiner's Partition with Oversampling procedure, partition the data with all the variables so there is 50% successes (churners) in the training set and 40% of the validation data are taken away as test set. Use 12345 as the seed in the randomized sampling. Apply the random trees ensemble approach using Churn as the output variable and all the other variables as input variables. In Step 2 of XLMiner's Random Trees Classification procedure, be sure to **Normalize Input Data**, to set **Number of weak learners** to 20, and to set the **Minimum # records in a terminal node** to 1.
   a. What is the most important variable in terms of reducing the classification error of the ensemble?
   b. For the default cutoff value of 0.5, compare the overall error rate, Class 1 error rate, and Class 0 error rate of the random trees on the test set to the corresponding measures of the single best-pruned tree from Problem 5.

11. Refer to the scenario in Problem 8 using the file *Cellphone*. In XLMiner's Partition with Oversampling procedure, partition the data with all the variables so there is 50% successes (churners) in the training set and 40% of the validation data are taken away as a test set. Use 12345 as the seed in the randomized sampling. Construct a logistic regression model using Churn as the output variable and all the other variables as input variables. Perform **Variable Selection** with the best subsets procedure with the number of best subsets equal to two.
   a. Why is partitioning with oversampling advised in this case?
   b. From the generated set of logistic regression models, use Mallow's C_p statistic to identify a pair of candidate models. Then evaluate these candidate models based on their classification error on the validation set and decile-wise lift on the validation set. Recommend a final model and express the model as a mathematical equation relating the output variable to the input variables. Do the relationships suggested by the model make sense? Try to explain them.

c. Using the default cutoff value of 0.5 for your logistic regression model, what is the overall error rate on the test set?

12. A consumer advocacy agency, Equitable Ernest, is interested in providing a service in which an individual can estimate their own credit score (a continuous measure used by banks, insurance companies, and other businesses when granting loans, quoting premiums, and issuing credit). The file *CreditScore* contains data on an individual's credit score and other variables.

    Create a standard partition of the data with all the tracked variables and 50% of observations in the training set, 30% in the validation set, and 20% in the test set. Predict the individuals' credit scores using k-Nearest Neighbors with up to $k = 20$. Use CreditScore as the output variable and all the other variables as input variables. In Step 2 of XLMiner's k-Nearest Neighbors Prediction procedure, be sure to **Normalize input data** and to **Score on best k between 1 and specified value**. Generate a **Detailed Report** for all three sets of data.

    a. What value of k minimizes the RMSE on the validation data?
    b. How does the RMSE on the test set compare to the RMSE on the validation set?
    c. What is the average error on the test set? Analyze the distribution of the residual output in the *KNNP_TestScore* worksheet by constructing a histogram.

13. Refer to the scenario in Problem 11 using the file *CreditScore*. Create a standard partition of the data with all the tracked variables and 50% of observations in the training set, 30% in the validation set, and 20% in the test set. Predict the individuals' credit scores using a single regression tree. Use CreditScore as the output variable and all the other variables as input variables. In Step 2 of XLMiner's Regression Tree procedure, be sure to **Normalize Input Data**, to specify **Using Best Pruned Tree** as the scoring option, and to set the **Minimum # records in a terminal node** to 244. Generate the **Full tree**, **Best pruned tree**, and **Minimum error tree.** Generate a **Detailed Report** for the training, validation, and test sets.

    a. What is the RMSE of the best-pruned tree on the validation data and on the test set? Discuss the implication of these calculations.
    b. Consider an individual who has had 5 credit bureau inquiries, has used 10% of her available credit, has $14,500 of total available credit, has no collection reports or missed payments, is a homeowner, has an average credit age of 6.5 years, and has worked continuously for the past 5 years. What is the best-pruned tree's predicted credit score for this individual?
    c. Repeat the construction of a single regression tree following the previous instructions, but in Step 2 of XLMiner's Regression Tree procedure, set the **Minimum # records in a terminal node** to 1. How does the RMSE of the best pruned tree on the test set compare to the analogous measure from part (a)? In terms of number of decision nodes, how does the size of the best-pruned tree compare to the size of the best-pruned tree from part (a)?

14. Refer to scenario in Problem 11 using the file *CreditScore*. Create a standard partition of the data with all the tracked variables and 50% of observations in the training set, 30% in the validation set, and 20% in the test set. Apply the random trees ensemble approach using CreditScore as the output variable and all the other variables as input variables. In Step 2 of XLMiner's Random Trees Classification procedure, be sure to **Normalize Input Data**, to set **Number of weak learners** to 20, and to set the **Minimum # records in a terminal node** to 244. Compare the root mean squared error of the random trees on the test set to the root mean squared error of the single best-pruned tree from part (a) of Problem 13.

15. Each year, the American Academy of Motion Picture Arts and Sciences recognizes excellence in the film industry by honoring directors, actors, and writers with awards (called "Oscars") in different categories. The most notable of these awards is the Oscar for Best Picture. The *Data* worksheet in the file *Oscars* contains data on a sample of movies nominated for the Best Picture Oscar. The variables include total number of Oscar nominations across all award categories, number of Golden Globe awards won (the Golden Globe award show precedes the Academy Awards), whether or not the movie is a comedy, and whether or not the movie won the Best Picture Oscar award.

    There is also a variable called ChronoPartition that specifies how to partition the data into training, validation, and test sets. The value "t" identifies observations that belong to the training set, the value "v" identifies observations that belong to the validation set, and the value "s" identifies observations that belong to the test set. Create a standard partition of the data containing all the variables (except the partition variable ChronoPartition) using XLMiner's **Standard Partition** routine by selecting **Use partition variable** in the **Partitioning options area** and specifying the variable ChronoPartition.

    Construct a logistic regression model to classify winners of the Best Picture Oscar. Use Winner as the output variable and OscarNominations, GoldenGlobeWins, and Comedy as input variables. Perform **Variable Selection** with the best subsets procedure with the number of best subsets equal to 2. Generate a **Detailed Report** for the training and validation sets.

    a. From the generated set of logistic regression models, use Mallow's C_p statistic to identify a pair of candidate models. Then evaluate these candidate models based on their classification error on the validation set. Recommend a final model and express the model as a mathematical equation relating the output variable to the input variables. Do the relationships suggested by the model make sense? Try to explain them.
    b. Using the default cutoff value of 0.5, what is the sensitivity of the logistic regression model on the validation set? Why is this a good metric to use for this problem?
    c. Note that each year there is only one winner of the Best Picture Oscar. Knowing this, what is wrong with classifying a movie based on a cutoff value? (*Hint*: Investigate the results on the *LR_ValidationScore* worksheet and investigate the predicted results on an annual basis.)
    d. What is the best way to use the model to predict the annual winner? Out of the six years in the validation data, how many does the model correctly "identify" as the winner?
    e. Use the model from part (a) to predict the 2014 nominees for Best Picture; in Step 3 of XLMiner's Logistic Regression procedure, check the box next to **In worksheet** in the **Score new data** area. In the **Match Variable in the New Range** dialog box: (1) Specify *NewDataToPredict* in the **Worksheet**: field, (2) enter the cell range C1:E9 in the **Data range:** field, and (3) click **Match By Name**. When completing the procedure, this will result in a *LR_NewScore* worksheet, which will contain the predicted probability that each 2014 nominee will win the Best Picture. What film did the model believe was the most likely to win the 2014 Academy Award for Best Picture? Was the model correct?

16. As an intern with the local home builder's association, you have been asked to analyze the state of the local housing market, which has suffered during a recent economic crisis. You have been provided two data sets in the file *HousingBubble*. The *Pre-Crisis* worksheet contains information on 1,978 single-family homes sold during the one-year period before the burst of the "housing bubble." The *Post-Crisis* worksheet contains

information on 1,657 single-family homes sold during the one-year period after the burst of the housing bubble. The *NewDataToPredict* worksheet contains information on homes currently for sale.

a. Consider the *Pre-Crisis* worksheet data. Create a standard partition of the data with all the tracked variables and 50% of observations in the training set, 30% in the validation set, and 20% in the test set. Predict the sale price using *k*-Nearest Neighbors with up to $k = 20$. Use Price as the output variable and all the other variables as input variables. In Step 2 of XLMiner's *k*-Nearest Neighbors Prediction procedure, be sure to **Normalize Input Data** and to **Score on best k between 1 and specified value**. Check the box next to **In worksheet** in the **Score New Data** area. In the **Match Variables in the New Range** dialog box: (1) Specify the *NewDataToPredict* worksheet in the **Worksheet:** field, (2) enter the cell range A1:P2001 in the **Data range:** field, and (3) click **Match By Name**. When completing the procedure, this will result in a *KNNP_NewScore* worksheet, which will contain the predicted sales price for each home in *NewDataToPredict*.
   i. What value of *k* minimizes the RMSE on the validation data?
   ii. What is the RMSE on the validation data and test set?
   iii. What is the average error on the validation data and test set? What does this suggest?

b. Repeat part (a) with the *Post-Crisis* worksheet data.

c. The *KNNP_NewScore* and *KNNP_NewScore* worksheets contain the sales price predictions for the 2,000 homes in the *NewDataToPredict* using the pre-crisis and post-crisis data, respectively. For each of these 2,000 homes, compare the two predictions by computing the percentage change in predicted price between the pre-crisis and post-crisis models. Let percentage change = (post-crisis predicted price − pre-crisis predicted price)/pre-crisis predicted price. Summarize these percentage changes with a histogram. What is the average percentage change in predicted price between the pre-crisis and post-crisis model?

17. Refer to scenario in Problem 16 using the file *HousingBubble*.

a. Consider the *Pre-Crisis* worksheet data. Create a standard partition of the data with all the tracked variables and 50% of observations in the training set, 30% in the validation set, and 20% in the test set. Predict the sale price using a single regression tree. Use Price as the output variable and all the other variables as input variables. In Step 2 of XLMiner's Regression Tree procedure, be sure to **Normalize Input Data**, to set the **Minimum # records in a terminal node** to 1, and to specify **Using Best Pruned Tree** as the scoring option. In Step 3 of XLMiner's Regression Tree procedure, generate the **Pruned tree**. Generate the **Full tree** and **Pruned tree**. Check the box next to **In worksheet** in the **Score New Data** area. In the **Match Variables in the New Range** dialog box: (1) Specify the *NewDataToPredict* worksheet in the **Worksheet:** field, (2) enter the cell range A1:P2001 in the **Data range:** field, and (3) click **Match By Name.** When completing the procedure, this will result in a *RT_NewScore1* worksheet, which will contain the predicted sales price for each home in *NewDataToPredict*.
   i. In terms of number of decision nodes, compare the size of the full tree to the size of the best-pruned tree.
   ii. What is the RMSE of the best-pruned tree on the validation data and on the test set?
   iii. What is the average error on the validation data and the test set? What does this suggest?

   iv. By examining the best-pruned tree, what are the critical variables in predicting the price of a home?

b. Repeat part (a) with the *Post-Crisis* worksheet data.

c. The *RT_NewScore1* and *RT_NewScore2* worksheets contain the sales price predictions for the 2,000 homes in the *NewDataToPredict* using the pre-crisis and post-crisis data, respectively. For each of these 2,000 homes, compare the two predictions by computing the percentage change in predicted price between the pre-crisis and post-crisis model. Let percentage change = (post-crisis predicted price − pre-crisis predicted price)/pre-crisis predicted price. Summarize these percentage changes with a histogram. What is the average percentage change in predicted price between the pre-crisis and post-crisis model? What does this suggest about the impact of the bursting of the housing bubble?

18. Refer to scenario in Problem 14 using the file *HousingBubble*.

a. Consider the *Pre-Crisis* worksheet data. Create a standard partition of the data with all the tracked variables and 50% of observations in the training set, 30% in the validation set, and 20% in the test set. Predict the sale price using multiple linear regression. Use Price as the output variable and all the other variables as input variables. Perform **Variable Selection** with the **Best Subsets** procedure with the number of best subsets equal to two.

   i. From the generated set of multiple linear regression models, select one that you believe is a good fit. Select **Choose Subset** of the corresponding model and refit the model to obtain the coefficients. In Step 2 of XLMiner's Multiple Linear Regression procedure, check the box next to **In worksheet** in the **Score New Data** area. In the **Match Variables in the New Range** dialog box: (1) Specify the *NewDataToPredict* worksheet in the **Worksheet:** field, (2) enter the cell range A1:P2001 in the **Data range:** field, and (3) click **Match By Name**.

   ii. For the model you selected, what is the RMSE on the validation data and the test set?

   iii. What is the average error on the validation data and test set? What does this suggest?

b. Repeat part (a) with the *Post-Crisis* worksheet data.

c. The *MLR_NewScore* worksheets generated in parts (a) and (b) contain the sales price predictions for the 2,000 homes in the *NewDataToPredict* using the pre-crisis and post-crisis data, respectively. For each of these 2,000 homes, compare the two predictions by computing the percentage change in predicted price between the pre-crisis and post-crisis model. Let percentage change = (post-crisis predicted price − pre-crisis predicted price)/pre-crisis predicted price. Summarize these percentage changes with a histogram. What is the average percentage change in predicted price between the pre-crisis and post-crisis model?

CASE PROBLEM: GREY CODE CORPORATION

Grey Code Corporation (GCC) is a media and marketing company involved in magazine and book publishing and in television broadcasting. GCC's portfolio of home and family magazines has been a long-running strength, but they have expanded to become a provider of a spectrum of services (market research, communications planning, web site advertising, etc.) that can enhance their clients' brands.

GCC's relational database contains over a terabyte of data encompassing 75 million customers. GCC uses the data in its database to develop campaigns for new customer acquisition, customer reactivation, and the identification of cross-selling opportunities for products. For example, GCC will generate separate versions of a monthly issue of a magazine that will differ only by the advertisements they contain. They will mail a subscribing customer the version with the print ads identified by their database as being of most interest to that customer.

One particular problem facing GCC is how to boost the customer response rate to renewal offers that it mails to its magazine subscribers. The industry response rate is about 2%, but GCC has historically performed better than that. However, GCC must update its model to correspond to recent changes. GCC's director of database marketing, Chris Grey, wants to make sure GCC maintains its place as one of the top achievers in targeted marketing. The file *GCC* contains 99 variables (columns) and 50,000 rows (distinct customers).

Play the role of Chris Grey and construct a classification model to identify customers who are likely to respond to a mailing. Write a report that documents the following steps:

1. Explore the data. This includes addressing any missing data as well as treatment of variables. Variables may need to be transformed. Also, because of the large number of variables, you must identify appropriate means to reduce the dimension of the data. In particular, it may be helpful to filter out unnecessary and redundant variables.
2. Partition the data into training, validation, and test sets.
3. Experiment with various classification methods and propose a final model for identifying customers who will respond to the targeted marketing.

   a. Your report should include a chart of the Class 1 and Class 0 error rates for various values of the cutoff probability.
   b. Recommend a cutoff probability value. For the test set, what is the overall error rate at this value? What are the Class 1 and Class 0 error rates at this value?
   c. If GCC sends the targeted marketing to the model's top decile, what is the expected response rate? How does that compare to the average industry rate?

Chapter 9 Appendix

Appendix 9.1 Data Partitioning with XLMiner

Before a classification or estimation method can be constructed, the data must be partitioned into training, validation, and test sets. We demonstrate this using the Optiva Credit Union example. In the file *Optiva* we observe that only 1.8% of the customer observations correspond to a default. Thus, the task of classifying loan customers as either "default" or "no default" involves a rare event. To provide sufficient information on loan defaults, we will create a training set with 50% loan default observations. The validation set and test set will be formed to have approximately 1.8% loan default observations in order to be representative of the overall population. The following steps and Figure 9.14 demonstrate this process. We have saved the standard partition of the Optiva data set resulting from executing the following steps in the file *OptivaPartOS*.

Optiva

Step 1. Select any cell in the range of the data
Step 2. Click the **XLMiner Platform** tab on the Ribbon
Step 3. Click **Partition** from the **Data Mining** group
Step 4. Click **Partition with Oversampling**
Step 5. In the **Data Source** area, confirm that the **Worksheet:**, **Workbook:**, and **Data range:** entries correspond to the appropriate data (see Figure 9.14)
Step 6. In the **Variables** area, select **First Row Contains Headers**
Step 7. In the **Variables** box of the **Variables** area, select **CustomerID**, **LoanDefault**, **AverageBalance**, **Age**, **Entrepreneur**, **Unemployed**, **Married**, **Divorced**, **High School**, and **College** variables and click the > button to populate the **Variables in the Partition Data** box
Step 8. Select **LoanDefault** in the **Variables in the Partition Data** box of the **Variables** area
Step 9. Click the > button to populate the **Output variable:** box
Step 10. In the **Randomization Options** area, select the box next to **Set seed:** and enter *12345*
Step 11. In the **Output options** area, select **1** from the pulldown menu of the **Specify Success class**:
Step 12. In the **Output options** area, enter *2* in the **# Classes** box, enter *50* in the **Specify % success in training set** box, and enter *40* in the **Specify % validation data to be taken away as test data**
Step 13. Click **OK**

To partition the data in the file *Optiva* for the purposes of predicting a customer's average balance, we use XLMiner's Standard Data Partition procedure. The following steps and Figure 9.15 demonstrate the process of partitioning a data set so that 23.15% of the observations compose the training set, 46.11% of the observations compose the validation set, and 30.74% of the observations compose the test set. We have saved the standard partition of the Optiva data set resulting from executing the following steps in the file *OptivaStandard*.

Step 1. Select any cell in the range of the data
Step 2. Click the **XLMiner Platform** tab on the Ribbon
Step 3. Click **Partition** from the **Data Mining** group
Step 4. Click **Standard Partition**

FIGURE 9.14 XLMiner Data Partition with Oversampling Dialog Box

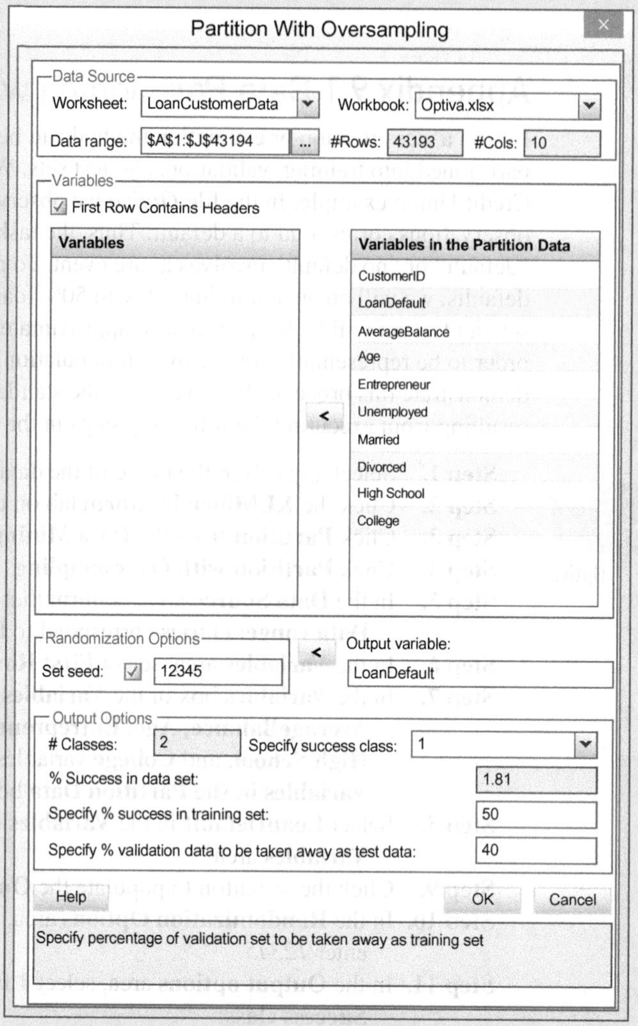

Step 5. In the **Data Source** area, confirm that the **Worksheet:**, **Workbook:**, and **Data range:** entries correspond to the appropriate data (see Figure 9.15)

Step 6. In the **Variables** area, select **First Row Contains Headers**

Step 7. In the **Variables** box of the **Variables** area, select **CustomerID**, **AverageBalance**, **Age**, **Entrepreneur**, **Unemployed**, **Married**, **Divorced**, **High School**, and **College** variables and click the > button to populate the **Variables in the partitioned data** box

Step 8. In the **Partitioning options** area, select **Pick up rows randomly**, select the box next to **Set seed:**, and enter *12345*

Step 9. In the **Partitioning percentages when picking up rows randomly** area, select **Specify percentages**, enter *23.15* in the **Training Set** box, enter *46.11* in the **Validation Set** box, and enter *30.74* in the **Test Set** box

Step 10. Click **OK**

FIGURE 9.15 XlMiner Standard Data Partition Dialog Box

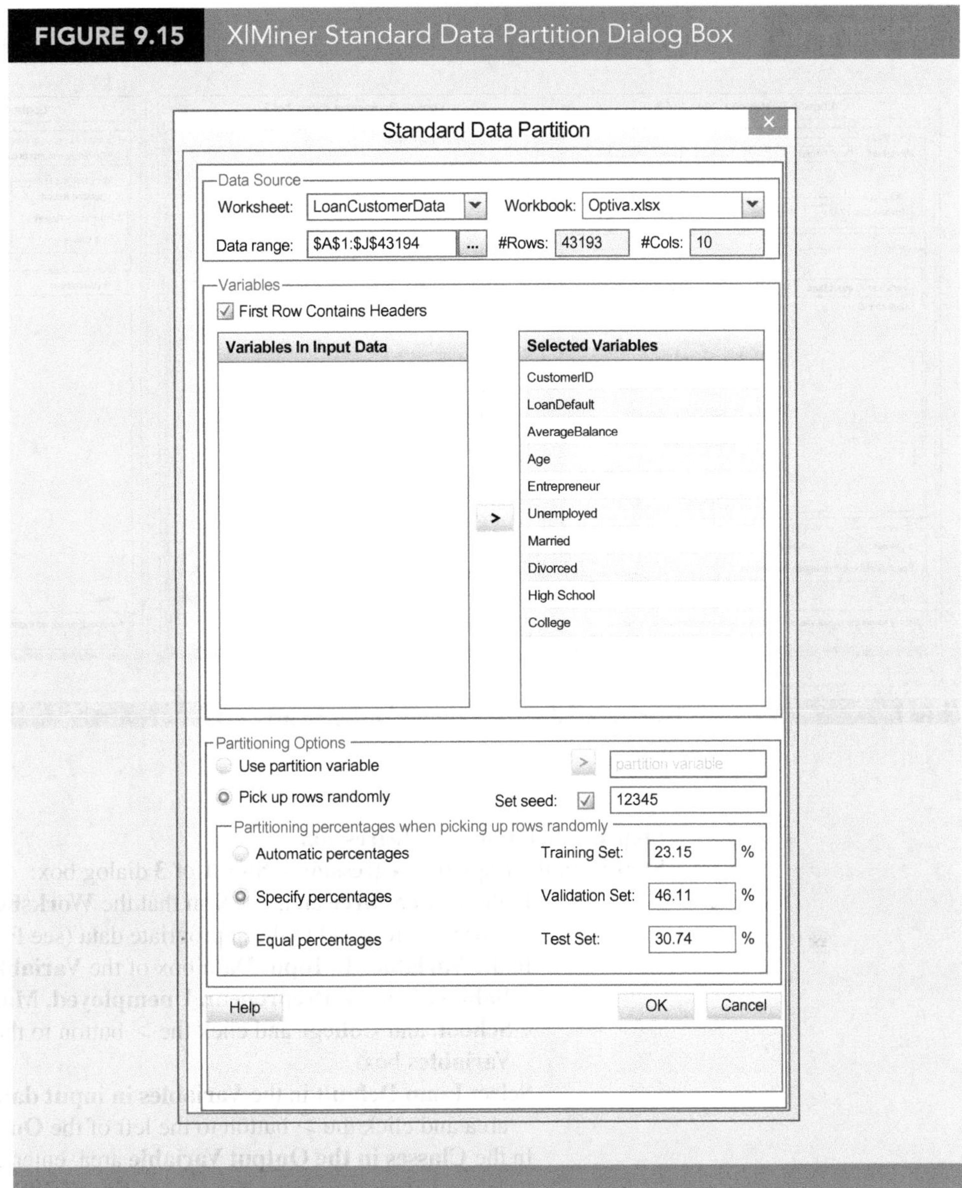

Appendix 9.2 Logistic Regression Classification with XLMiner

DATA *file* OptivaToPredict

We demonstrate how XLMiner facilitates the construction of a logistic regression model by using the Optiva Credit Union problem of classifying customer observations as either a loan default (Class 1) or no default (Class 0). The following steps and Figure 9.16 demonstrate this process.

Step 1. In the *Data_Partition* worksheet, select any cell (such as cell B26) in the range of data listed below **Selected Variables**

Step 2. Click the **XLMiner Platform** tab on the Ribbon

Step 3. Click **Classify** from the **Data Mining** group

FIGURE 9.16 XLMiner Steps for Logistic Regression

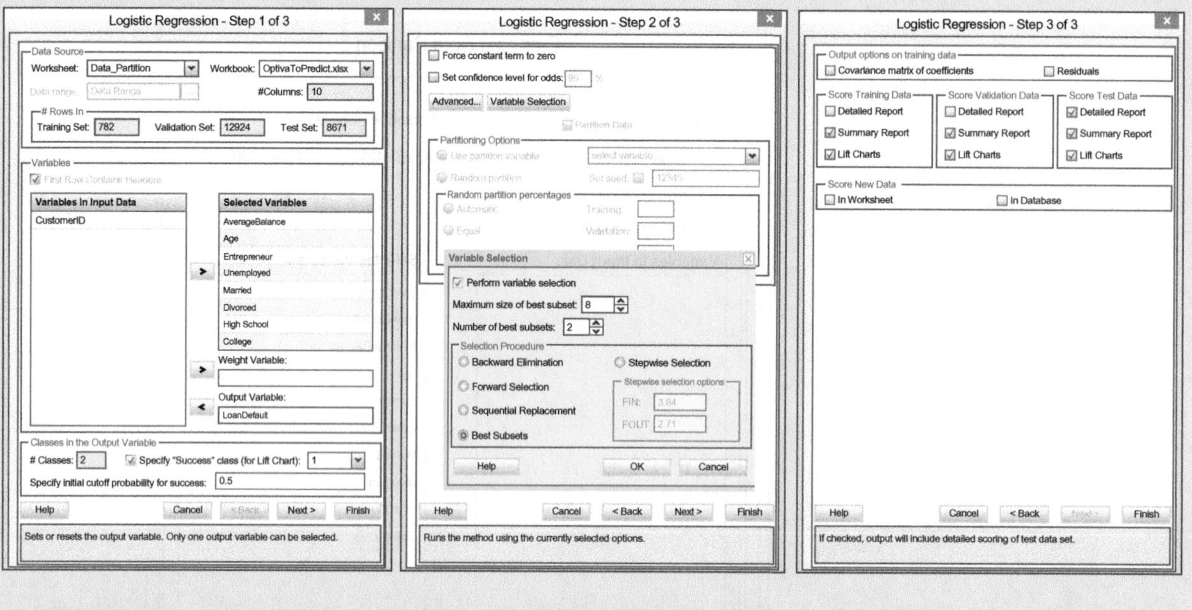

Step 4. Click **Logistic Regression**

Step 5. In the **Logistic Regression – Step 1 of 3** dialog box:

In the **Data Source** area, confirm that the **Worksheet:** and **Workbook:** entries correspond to the appropriate data (see Figure 9.16)

In the **Variables In Input Data** box of the **Variables** area, select **Average Balance, Age, Entrepreneur, Unemployed, Married, Divorced, High School,** and **College** and click the > button to the left of the **Selected Variables** box

Select **Loan Default** in the **Variables in input data** box of the **Variables** area and click the > button to the left of the **Output variable:** box

In the **Classes in the Output Variable** area, enter *2* in the **# Classes** box, select **1** from dropdown box next to **Specify "Success" class (for Lift Chart):**, and enter *0.5* in the **Specify initial cutoff probability for success:** box

Click **Next**

Step 6. In the **Logistic Regression – Step 2 of 3** dialog box:

Click **Variable Selection** and when the **Variable Selection** dialog box appears:

Select the checkbox for **Perform variable selection**

Set the **Maximum size of best subset:** box to **8**

In the **Selection Procedure** area, select **Best Subsets**

Above the **Selection Procedure area**, set the **Number of best subsets:** box to **2**

Click **OK**

Click **Next**

Step 7. In the **Logistic Regression – Step 3 of 3** dialog box:
In the **Score Test Data** area, select the checkboxes for **Detailed Report**, **Summary Report**, and **Lift Charts**. Leave all other checkboxes unchanged.
Click **Finish**

XLMiner provides several options for selecting variables to include in alternative logistic regression models. Best subsets is the most comprehensive method; it considers every possible combination of the variables but is typically appropriate only when dealing with fewer than 10 explanatory variables. When dealing with many variables, best subsets may be too computationally expensive, as it will require constructing hundreds of alternative models. In cases with a moderate number of variables, 10 to 20, backward selection is effective at eliminating the unhelpful variables. Backward elimination begins with all possible variables and sequentially removes the least useful variable (with respect to statistical significance). When dealing with more than 20 variables, forward selection is often appropriate, as it identifies the most helpful variables.

This procedure builds several logistic regression models for consideration. In the *LR_Output* worksheet displayed in Figure 9.17, the area titled **Regression Model** lists the statistical information on the logistic regression model using all of the selected explanatory variables. This information corresponds to the logistic regression fit of:

$$\ln(\hat{p}/(1-\hat{p})) = 0.6745 - 0.0005 \times \text{Average Balance} + \cdots$$
$$+ 0.5262 \times \text{Divorced} + \cdots - 0.2428 \times \text{College}$$

FIGURE 9.17 XLMiner Logistic Regression Output in *LR_Output* Worksheet

Regression Model

Input Variables	Coefficient	Std. Error	Chi2-Statistic	P-Value	Odds	CI Lower	CI Upper
Intercept	0.6745466	0.405697	2.764527047	0.096375167	1.963143	0.886384517	4.3
AverageBalance	-0.000541	8.49E-05	40.55115657	1.91535E-10	0.99946	0.999293362	1
Age	-0.006155	0.008814	0.487674461	0.484966512	0.993864	0.976842025	1
Entrepreneur	0.5773065	0.290799	3.941177957	0.047117773	1.781234	1.007377335	3.1
Unemployed	0.7756305	0.464299	2.790710517	0.09481218	2.171961	0.874259306	5.4
Married	0.0930365	0.187158	0.247108477	0.619118487	1.097502	0.76049377	1.6
Divorced	0.5261797	0.277765	3.588499313	0.05818076	1.692454	0.981935296	2.9
High School	-0.165151	0.236247	0.488685973	0.484514048	0.847766	0.533558986	1.3
College	-0.242765	0.259119	0.87775861	0.348816314	0.784456	0.472069551	1.3

Residual DF	773
Residual Dev.	988.338
# Iterations Use	4
Multiple R²	0.088318

Variable Selection

					Model								
Subset Link	#Coeffs	RSS	Cp	Probability	1	2	3	4	5	6	7	8	9
Choose Subset	1	77,986	-6.4726	0.9998	Intercept								
Choose Subset	2	77,983	-4.506	0.9995	Intercept						Divorced		
Choose Subset	2	77,944	-4.8895	1	Intercept	AverageBalance							
Choose Subset	3	77,941	-2.9217	1	Intercept	AverageBalance					Divorced		
Choose Subset	3	77,941	-2.9218	1	Intercept	AverageBalance		Entrepreneur					
Choose Subset	4	77,938	-0.9547	1	Intercept	AverageBalance		Entrepreneur	Unemployed				
Choose Subset	4	77,937	-0.9559	1	Intercept	AverageBalance		Entrepreneur			Divorced		
Choose Subset	5	77,937	1.0387	0.9998	Intercept	AverageBalance		Entrepreneur			Divorced		College
Choose Subset	5	77,934	1.0139	1	Intercept	AverageBalance		Entrepreneur	Unemployed		Divorced		
Choose Subset	6	77,934	3.0122	0.9996	Intercept	AverageBalance	Age	Entrepreneur	Unemployed		Divorced		
Choose Subset	6	77,934	3.0098	0.9997	Intercept	AverageBalance		Entrepreneur	Unemployed		Divorced		College
Choose Subset	7	77,934	5.008	0.996	Intercept	AverageBalance	Age	Entrepreneur	Unemployed		Divorced		College
Choose Subset	7	77,934	5.0055	0.9973	Intercept	AverageBalance		Entrepreneur	Unemployed		Divorced	High School	College
Choose Subset	8	77,933	7.0048	0.9446	Intercept	AverageBalance		Entrepreneur	Unemployed	Married	Divorced	High School	College
Choose Subset	8	77,933	7.0025	0.9605	Intercept	AverageBalance	Age	Entrepreneur	Unemployed		Divorced	High School	College
Choose Subset	9	77,933	9	1	Intercept	AverageBalance	Age	Entrepreneur	Unemployed	Married	Divorced	High School	College

While these coefficients do not have a direct intuitive interpretation, the sign of a coefficient in the logistic regression is meaningful. For example, the negative coefficient of the Average Balance variable means that as a customer's average balance increases, the probability of default decreases. Similarly, the positive coefficient of the binary Divorced variable means that a divorced customer is more likely to default than a nondivorced customer. The p value information reflects the statistical significance of each coefficient. While a logistic regression model used for predictive purposes should ultimately be judged by its classification error on the validation and test sets, the p value information can provide some guidance about which models to evaluate further (i.e., large p values suggest that the corresponding variable may be less helpful in accurately classifying observations).

In addition to fitting the logistic regression model with all the selected explanatory variables, XLMiner also provides summary measures on models with combinations of the variables. The **Variable Selection** area in Figure 9.17 lists (Maximum size of best subset $\times$ Number of best subsets) $= 8 \times 2 = 16$ models. To sort through these models, typically there is a preference for models with fewer coefficients (cells D92 through D107) and with a Mallow's C_p statistic value (cells F92 through F107) that is small and near the number of coefficients in the model. RSS stands for residual sum of squares and computes the sum of squared deviations between the predicted probability of success and the actual value (1 or 0). Models with a smaller RSS are preferred, but as more variables are added, the additional decrease in RSS is not as large.

After identifying one or more models for further analysis, we can then evaluate each of them with respect to how well they classify the observations in the validation set. Evaluating the models listed in Figure 9.17, we see that there appear to be several similar models. For example, the model in row 94 with 2 coefficients (the constant and the variable AverageBalance) may be a good candidate for closer examination.

Clicking on **Choose Subset** in cell C94 of the *LR_Output* worksheet activates the XLMiner procedure to refit the logistic regression model with explanatory variable AverageBalance. The following steps and Figure 9.18 explain how to construct this logistic regression model and use it to predict the loan default probability of 30 new customers.

Step 1. Click on **Choose Subset** in cell C94 of *LR_Output* worksheet
Step 2. In the **Logistic Regression – Step 1 of 3** dialog box, click **Next >**
Step 3. In the **Logistic Regression – Step 2 of 3** dialog box, click **Next**
Step 4. In the **Logistic Regression – Step 3 of 3** dialog box:
In the **Score Test Data** area, select the checkboxes for **Detailed Report, Summary Report, Lift Charts;** leave all other checkboxes unchanged
In the **Score New Data** area, select **In worksheet**
When the **Match Variables in the New Range** dialog box appears:
In the **Data Source** area, select the worksheet name **New Data To Predict** from the pulldown menu next to **Worksheet;** enter *$A$1:$J$31* in the **Data Range:** box
In the **Variables** area, select the checkbox for **First Row Contains Headers** and click **Match By Name**
Click **OK**
Click **Finish**

The preceding steps produce a worksheet titled *LR_Output1* that lists the classification confusion matrices for the logistic regression model with AverageBalance as the explanatory variable. Figure 9.19 displays the classification confusion matrices for the validation and test sets. Using the cutoff value of 0.5, we observe that the logistic

FIGURE 9.18 XLMiner Steps for Refitting the Logistic Regression Model and Predicting New Data

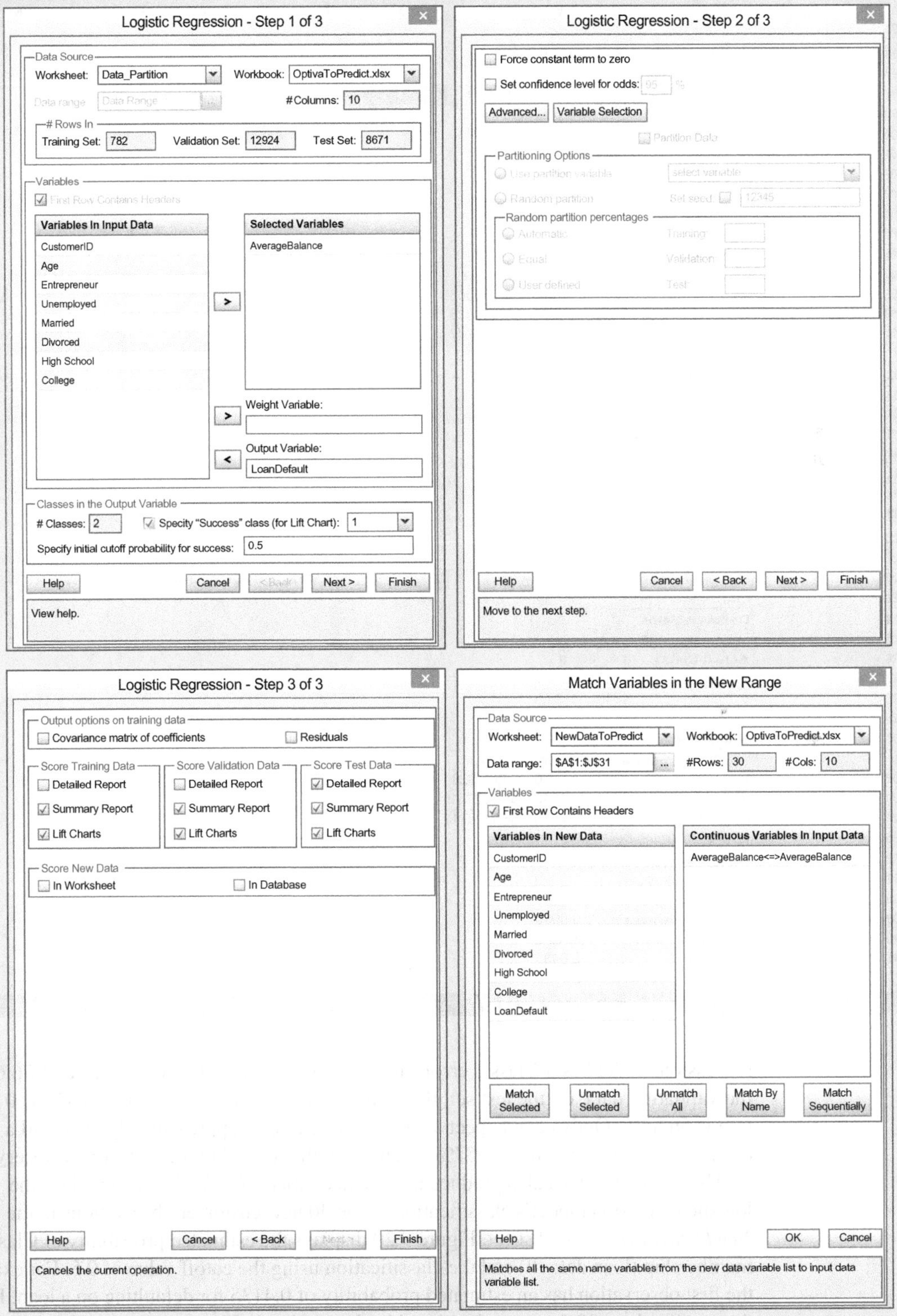

FIGURE 9.19 Classification Error for Logistic Regression Model in *LR_Output* Worksheet

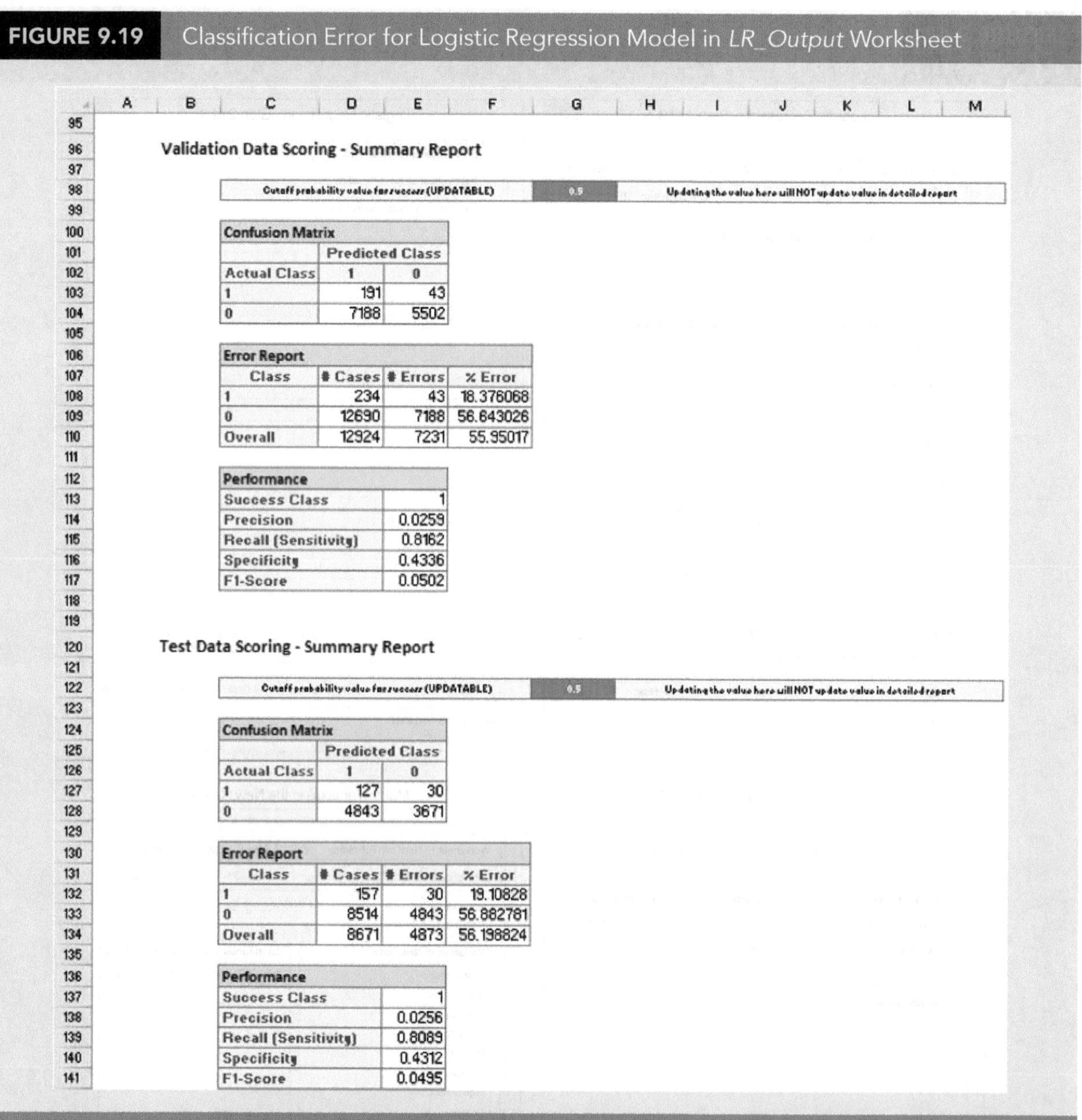

Validation Data Scoring - Summary Report

Cutoff probability value for success (UPDATABLE)	0.5	Updating the value here will NOT update value in detailed report

Confusion Matrix		
	Predicted Class	
Actual Class	1	0
1	191	43
0	7188	5502

Error Report			
Class	# Cases	# Errors	% Error
1	234	43	18.376068
0	12690	7188	56.643026
Overall	12924	7231	55.95017

Performance	
Success Class	1
Precision	0.0259
Recall (Sensitivity)	0.8162
Specificity	0.4336
F1-Score	0.0502

Test Data Scoring - Summary Report

Cutoff probability value for success (UPDATABLE)	0.5	Updating the value here will NOT update value in detailed report

Confusion Matrix		
	Predicted Class	
Actual Class	1	0
1	127	30
0	4843	3671

Error Report			
Class	# Cases	# Errors	% Error
1	157	30	19.10828
0	8514	4843	56.882781
Overall	8671	4873	56.198824

Performance	
Success Class	1
Precision	0.0256
Recall (Sensitivity)	0.8089
Specificity	0.4312
F1-Score	0.0495

regression model has a Class 1 error rate of 18.38% and a Class 0 error rate of 56.64% on the validation data; on the test set, the Class 1 error rate is 19.11% and the Class 0 error rate is 56.88%. Optiva can expect a Class 1 error rate of approximately 19% and a Class 0 error rate of approximately of 57% when using this model on new customer observations.

The preceding steps also produce a worksheet titled *LR_NewScore1* that lists the logistic regression model's classification of the 30 new customer observations in the *NewDataToPredict* worksheet. Figure 9.20 displays the estimated probability of Class 1 membership (loan default) and the classification using the cutoff value of 0.5. For example, the first observation has an estimated probability of 0.4135 for defaulting on a loan. Based on the cutoff value of 0.5, we predict that this observation is Class 0 or a nondefaulter on a loan.

FIGURE 9.20 Classification of 30 New Customer Observations (*LR_Newscore* Worksheet)

	A	B	C	D	E
13					
14		Predicted Class	Prob. for 0	Prob. for 1	AverageBalance
15		0	0.5864874	0.41351259	1467
16		1	0.438304	0.56169598	386
17		0	0.5888982	0.41110178	1485
18		1	0.4806967	0.51930328	695
19		1	0.4823527	0.51764733	707
20		1	0.3932268	0.60677317	50
21		0	0.9128765	0.08712349	5085
22		0	0.6476437	0.35235626	1936
23		0	0.7582661	0.24173389	2903
24		1	0.4682931	0.53170691	605
25		0	0.9911537	0.00884632	9372
26		1	0.4277195	0.5722805	308
27		0	0.7742013	0.22579872	3064
28		0	0.5623052	0.4376948	1288
29		0	0.5769387	0.42306135	1396
30		1	0.3890146	0.61098537	18
31		1	0.4351767	0.56482335	363
32		1	0.3969256	0.60307439	78
33		1	0.4940913	0.50590868	792
34		1	0.4080913	0.59190873	162
35		1	0.3933587	0.60664127	51
36		0	0.7255977	0.2744023	2594
37		1	0.4233956	0.57660436	276
38		0	0.9406896	0.0593104	5835
39		1	0.455106	0.54489403	509
40		1	0.3993097	0.60069035	96
41		1	0.4255561	0.57444386	292
42		1	0.4095608	0.59043924	173
43		1	0.4790412	0.52095881	683
44		1	0.4553801	0.54461987	511

NOTES + COMMENTS

1. Other XLMiner alternatives for selecting variables in a regression model include stepwise selection and sequential replacement. Stepwise selection starts with no variables, but at each step considers both the insertion and removal of a variable based on the *F*-statistics FIN and FOUT, respectively. To prevent cycling, FIN $\geq$ FOUT, with typical values of 6.5 and 3, respectively. Sequential replacement considers models with a fixed number of values by inserting a new variable whenever one is removed.
2. XLMiner provides functionality for multiple linear regression that greatly enhances the basic regression capabilities provided by Excel's Data Analysis Toolpak. The **Multiple Linear Regression** procedure is listed under **Prediction** in the **Data Mining** group on the XLMiner Ribbon. This functionality is described in the appendix to Chapter 7.

Appendix 9.3 *k*-Nearest Neighbor Classification and Estimation with XLMiner

XLMiner provides the capability to apply the *k*-Nearest Neighbors method for classifying a 0–1 categorical outcome and for estimating a continuous outcome. We begin by demonstrating how to use *k*-Nearest Neighbors as a classification method.

We apply this *k*-Nearest Neighbors method on the data partitioned with oversampling from *Optiva* to classify observations as either loan default (Class 1) or no default (Class 0). The following steps and Figure 9.21 demonstrate this process.

OptivaPartOS

Step 1. In the *Data_Partition* worksheet, select any cell (such as cell B26) in the range of data listed below **Selected Variables**

Step 2. Click the **XLMiner Platform** tab on the Ribbon

Step 3. Click **Classify** from the **Data Mining** group

Step 4. Click ***k*-Nearest Neighbors**

Step 5. In the ***k*-Nearest Neighbors Classification – Step 1 of 3** dialog box:

In the **Data Source** area, confirm that the **Worksheet:**, **Workbook:**, and **Data range:** entries correspond to the appropriate data (see Figure 9.21)

In the **Variables in Input Data** box of the **Variables** area, select **Average Balance**, **Age**, **Entrepreneur**, **Unemployed**, **Married**, and **Divorced**, **High School**, and **College** variables and click the > button to the left of the **Selected Variables** box

In the **Variables in Input Data** box of the **Variables** area, select **Loan Default** and click the > button to the left of the **Output Variable:** box

In the **Classes in the Output Variable** area, enter *2* in the **# Classes** box, select **1** from dropdown box next to **Specify "Success" class (for Lift Chart):**, and enter *0.5* in the **Specify initial cutoff probability value for success** box

Click **Next**

Step 6. In the ***k*-Nearest Neighbors Classification – Step 2 of 3** dialog box:

Select the checkbox for **Normalize input data**

Enter *20* in the **Number of nearest neighbors (k):** box

In the **Scoring Option** area, select **Score on best k between 1 and specified value**

In the **Prior Class Probabilities** area, select **User specified prior probabilities**, and enter *0.9819* for the probabilty of Class 0 and *0.0181* for the probability of Class 1 by double-clicking the corresponding entry in the table

Click **Next**

If there are not k distinct nearest neighbors of an observation because this observation has several neighboring observations equidistant from it, then the procedure must break this tie. To do this, XLMiner randomly selects from the set of equidistant neighbors, the needed number of observations to assemble a set of k-nearest neighbors. The likelihood of an equidistant neighboring observation being selected depends on the prior probability of the observation's class.

Step 7. In the ***k*-Nearest Neighbors Classification – Step 3 of 3** dialog box:

In the **Score Test Data** area, select the checkboxes for **Detailed Report, Summary Report**, and **Lift Charts;** leave all other checkboxes unchanged

Click **Finish**

This procedure runs the *k*-Nearest Neighbors method for values of *k* ranging from 1 to 20 on both the training set and validation set. The procedure generates a worksheet titled *KNNC_Output* that contains the overall error rate on the training set and the validation set for various values of *k*. As Figure 9.22 shows, $k = 1$ achieves the smallest

FIGURE 9.21 XLMiner Steps for k-Nearest Neighbors Classification

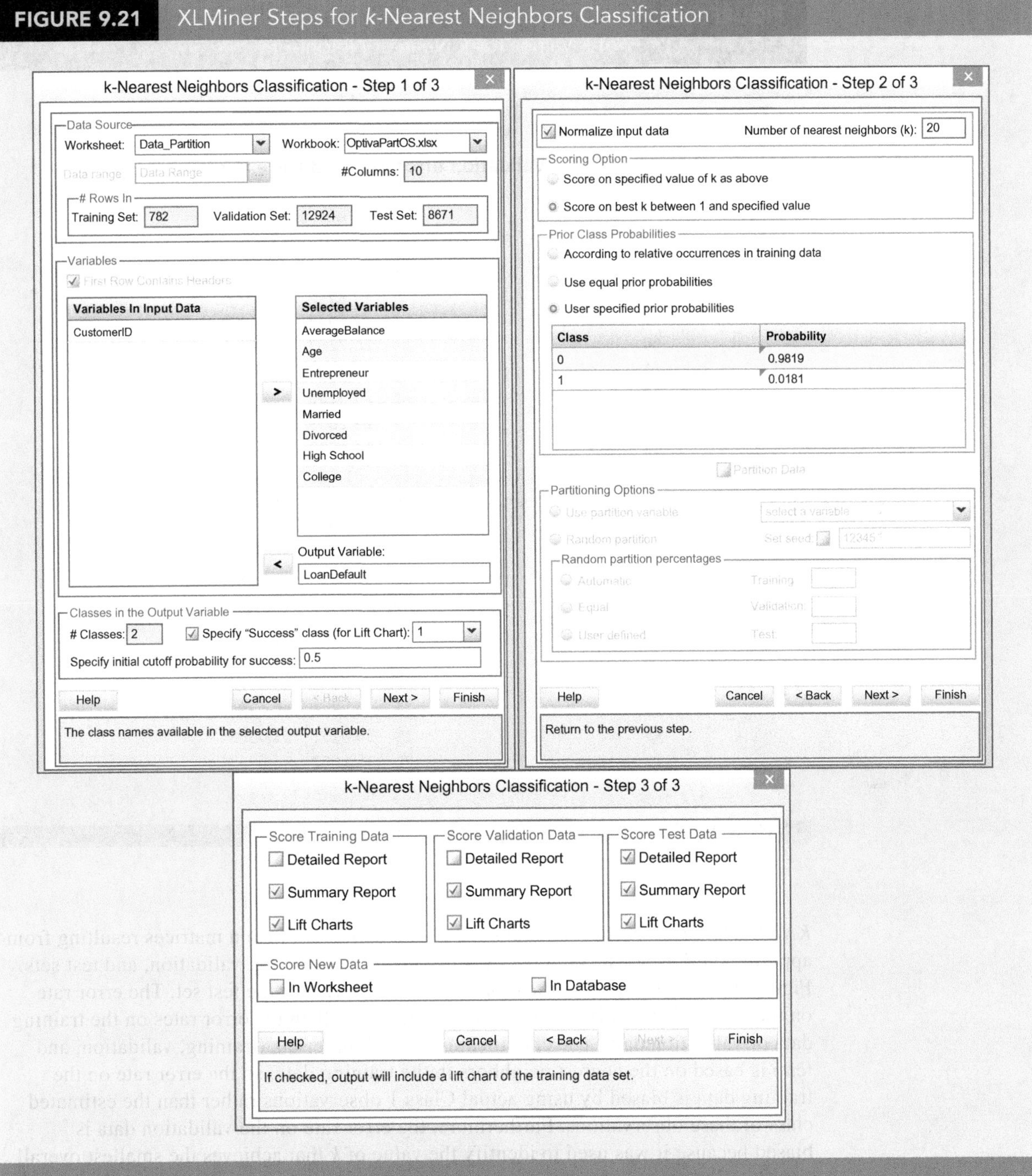

overall error rate on the validation set. This suggests that Optiva should classify a customer as "default or no default" based on the category of the most similar customer in the training set.

XLMiner applies k-Nearest Neighbors to the test set using the value of k that achieves the smallest overall error rate on the validation set ($k = 1$ in this case). The

FIGURE 9.22 *KNNC_Output* Worksheet: Classification Error Rates for Range of *k* Values for *k*-Nearest Neighbors

	A	B	C	D	E	F
54	Validation error log for different k					
55						
56			Value of k	% Error Training	% Error Validation	
57			1	0	43.2297	<- Best k
58			2	23.1458	62.9913	
59			3	21.4834	44.692	
60			4	26.7263	59.0994	
61			5	25.7033	46.9514	
62			6	29.9233	59.1535	
63			7	29.2839	48.8626	
64			8	31.4578	58.5809	
65			9	31.202	50.3637	
66			10	32.6087	58.5036	
67			11	32.9923	49.2572	
68			12	32.4808	55.0913	
69			13	32.8645	48.584	
70			14	32.6087	55.424	
71			15	31.9693	49.6828	
72			16	33.6317	55.4395	
73			17	32.8645	51.6326	
74			18	33.376	56.1281	
75			19	34.0153	51.0368	
76			20	35.1662	56.6852	

KNNC_Output worksheet contains the classification confusion matrices resulting from applying the *k*-Nearest Neighbors with $k = 1$ to the training, validation, and test sets. Figure 9.23 shows the classification confusion matrix for the test set. The error rate on the test set is more indicative of future accuracy than the error rates on the training data or validation data. The classification for all three sets (training, validation, and test) is based on the nearest neighbors in the training data, so the error rate on the training data is biased by using actual Class 1 observations rather than the estimated class of these observations. Furthermore, the error rate on the validation data is biased because it was used to identify the value of *k* that achieves the smallest overall error rate.

To demonstrate how to use *k*-Nearest Neighbors to estimate a continuous outcome, we consider a partitioned sample of data from *Optiva* and the task of predicting an observation's average balance. The following steps and Figure 9.24 demonstrate this process.

Step 1. In the *Data_Partition* worksheet, select any cell (such as cell B21) in the range of data listed below **Selected Variables**

FIGURE 9.23 Classification Confusion Matrix for *k*-Nearest Neighbors

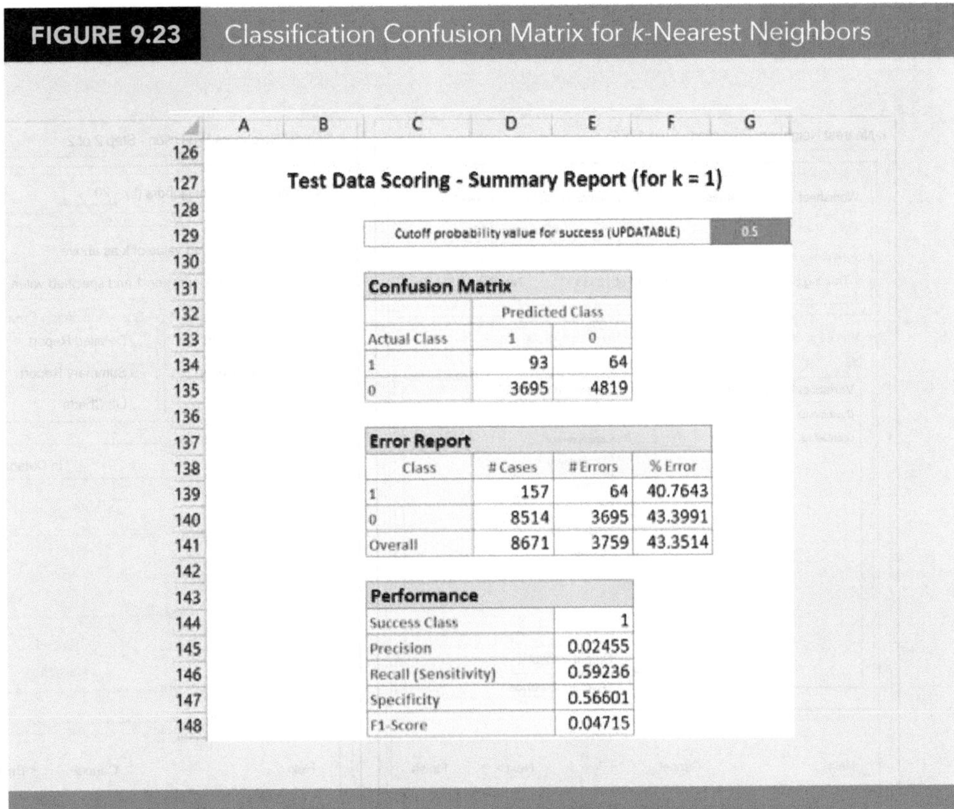
Test Data Scoring - Summary Report (for k = 1)

Cutoff probability value for success (UPDATABLE)	0.5

Confusion Matrix

	Predicted Class	
Actual Class	1	0
1	93	64
0	3695	4819

Error Report

Class	# Cases	# Errors	% Error
1	157	64	40.7643
0	8514	3695	43.3991
Overall	8671	3759	43.3514

Performance

Success Class	1
Precision	0.02455
Recall (Sensitivity)	0.59236
Specificity	0.56601
F1-Score	0.04715

Step 2. Click the **XLMiner Platform** tab on the Ribbon
Step 3. Click **Predict** from the **Data Mining** group
Step 4. Click ***k*-Nearest Neighbors**
Step 5. In the ***k*-Nearest Neighbors Prediction – Step 1 of 2** dialog box:
In the **Data Source** area, confirm that the **Worksheet:**, **Workbook:**, and **Data range:** entries correspond to the appropriate data
In the **Variables in Input Data** box of the **Variables** area, select **Age**, **Entrepreneur**, **Unemployed**, **Married**, **Divorced**, **High School**, and **College** variables and click the > button to the left of the **Selected Variables** box
Select **Average Balance** in the **Variables in input data** box of the **Variables** area and click the > button to the left of the **Output variable:** box
Click **Next**
Step 6. In the ***k*-Nearest Neighbors Prediction – Step 2 of 2** dialog box:
Enter *20* in the **Number of nearest neighbors (k)** box
Select the checkbox for **Normalize input data**
In the **Scoring Option** area, select **Score on best k between 1 and specified value**
In the **Score Test Data** area, select **Detailed Report**, **Summary Report**, and **Lift Charts**
Click **Finish**

The k-Nearest Neighbors procedure is computationally intense. Depending on your computer's capability, you may have to reduce the number of observations in the training set (by repartitioning the original data and reducing the percentage allocated to the training set) in order to successfully execute the k-Nearest Neighbors procedure.

FIGURE 9.24 XLMiner Steps for *k*-Nearest Neighbors Prediction

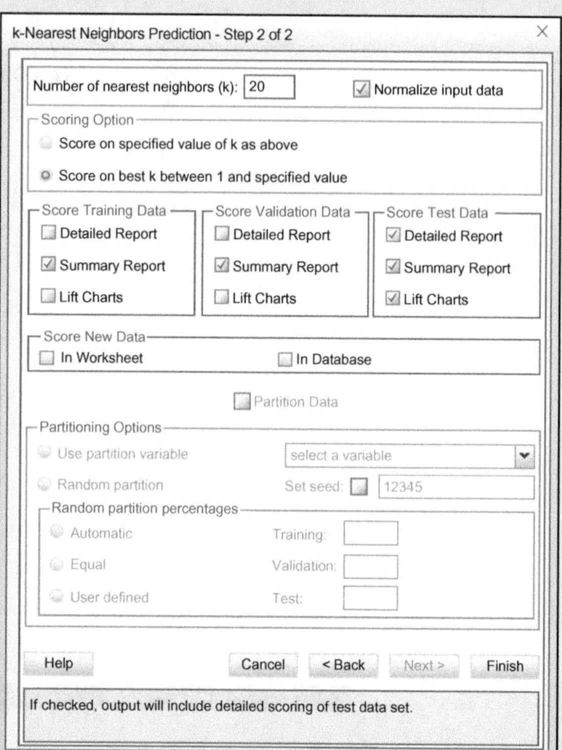

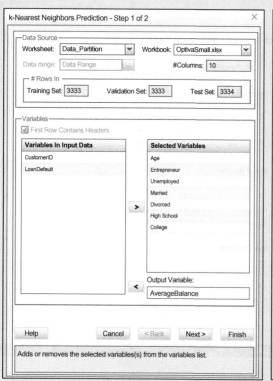

This procedure runs the *k*-Nearest Neighbors method for values of *k* ranging from 1 to 20 on both the training set and the validation set. The procedure generates a worksheet titled *KNNP_Output* that contains the RMSE on the training set and validation set for various values of *k*. As Figure 9.25 shows, $k = 20$ achieves the smallest RMSE on the validation set. This suggests that Optiva should estimate a customer's average balance with the average balance of the 20 most similar customers in the training set.

XLMiner applies *k*-Nearest Neighbors to the test set using the value of *k* that achieves the smallest RMSE on the validation set ($k = 20$ in this case). The *KNNP_Output* worksheet contains the RMSE and average error resulting from applying the *k*-Nearest Neighbors with $k = 20$ to the training, validation, and test sets. Figure 9.26 shows the RMSE for the training validation and test sets. The RMSE of $3,534.98 on the test set provides Optiva an estimate of how accurate the estimates will be on new data. The average error of −81.46 on the test set suggests a slight tendency to overestimate the average balance of observation in the test set.

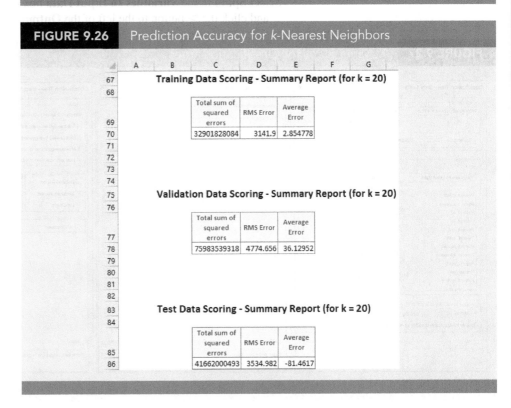

FIGURE 9.25 Prediction Error for Range of *k* Values for *k*-Nearest Neighbors

Validation error log for different k

Value of k	Training RMS Error	Validation RMS Error	
1	3141.9	4842.281	
2	3141.9	4809.831	
3	3141.9	4796.705	
4	3141.9	4792.274	
5	3141.9	4788.966	
6	3141.9	4787.244	
7	3141.9	4785.939	
8	3141.9	4784.502	
9	3141.9	4782.673	
10	3141.9	4780.596	
11	3141.9	4780.349	
12	3141.9	4779.681	
13	3141.9	4778.633	
14	3141.9	4777.672	
15	3141.9	4777.136	
16	3141.9	4776.57	
17	3141.9	4775.914	
18	3141.9	4774.993	
19	3141.9	4774.831	
20	3141.9	4774.656	<- Best k

FIGURE 9.26 Prediction Accuracy for *k*-Nearest Neighbors

Training Data Scoring - Summary Report (for k = 20)

Total sum of squared errors	RMS Error	Average Error
32901828084	3141.9	2.854778

Validation Data Scoring - Summary Report (for k = 20)

Total sum of squared errors	RMS Error	Average Error
75983539318	4774.656	36.12952

Test Data Scoring - Summary Report (for k = 20)

Total sum of squared errors	RMS Error	Average Error
41662000493	3534.982	-81.4617

Appendix 9.4 Single Classification and Regression Trees with XLMiner

XLMiner provides the capability to construct classification trees for classifying a 0–1 categorical outcome and to construct regression trees for estimating a continuous outcome. We begin by demonstrating how to use XLMiner to construct a single classification tree.

Using XLMiner's **Standard Partition** procedure, we randomly partition the 4,601 observations in the file *HawaiianHamStandard* so that 50% of the observations create a training set of 2,300 observations, 30% of the observations create a validation set of 1,380 observations, and 20% of the observations create a test set of 921 observations. We apply the following steps (illustrated in Figure 9.27) to conduct a classification tree analysis on these data partitions.

HawaiianHamStandard

Step 1. In the *Data_Partition* worksheet, select any cell (such as cell B21) in the range of data listed below **Selected Variables**

Step 2. Click the **XLMiner Platform** tab on the Ribbon

Step 3. Click **Classify** from the **Data Mining** group

Step 4. Click **Classification Tree**

Step 5. Click **Single Tree**

Step 6. In the **Classification Tree – Step 1 of 3** dialog box:

In the **Data source** area, confirm that the **Worksheet:** and **Workbook:** entries correspond to the appropriate data (see Figure 9.27)

In the **Variables In Input Data** box of the **Variables** area, select **Semicolon, LeftParen, LeftSquareParen, Exclamation, Dollar, PercentSign, AvgAllCap**, **LongAllCap**, and **TotalAllCap** and click the > button to the left of the **Selected Variables** box.

Select **Spam** in the **Variables In Input Data** box of the **Variables** area and click the > button to the left of the **Output variable:** box

FIGURE 9.27 XLMiner Steps for Classification Trees

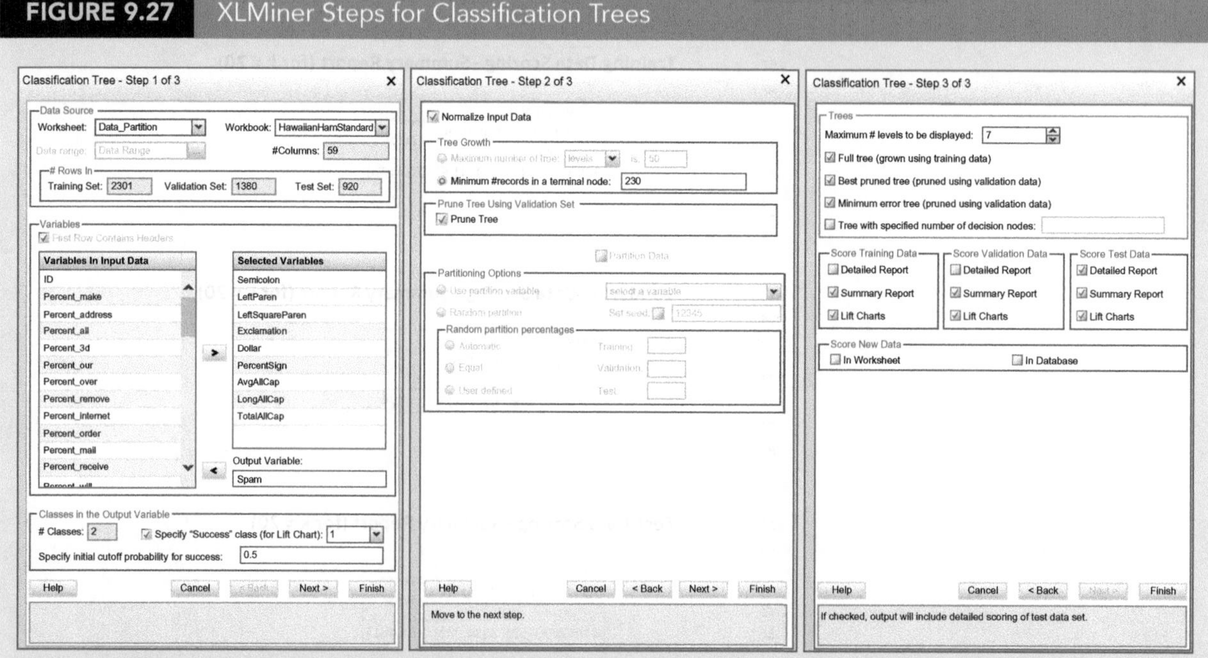

In the **Classes in the output variable** area, enter *2* for **# Classes:**, select **1** from dropdown box next to **Specify "Success" class (for Lift Chart)**, and enter *0.5* in the **Specify initial cutoff probability for success** box

Click **Next >**

Step 7. In the **Classification Tree – Step 2 of 3** dialog box:

Select the checkbox for **Normalize Input Data**

In the **Tree Growth** area, enter *230* in the box next to **Minimum # records in a terminal node:**

In the **Prune Tree Using Validation Set** area, select the checkbox for **Prune tree**

Click **Next**

Step 8. In the **Classification Tree – Step 3 of 3** dialog box:

In the **Trees** area, set the **Maximum # levels to be displayed:** box to **7**

In the **Trees** area, select the checkboxes for **Full tree (grown using training data)**, **Best pruned tree (pruned using validation data)**, and **Minimum error tree (pruned using validation data)**

In the **Score Test Data** area, select **Detailed Report**, **Summary Report**, and **Lift charts;** leave all other checkboxes unchanged

Click **Finish**

This procedure first constructs a "full" classification tree on the training data, that is, a tree that is successively partitioned by variable splitting rules until the resultant branches contain less than the minimum number of observations (230 observations in this example) or the number of displayed tree levels is reached (7 in this example). Figure 9.28 displays the first seven levels of the full tree, which XLMiner provides in a worksheet titled *CT_FullTree*. XLMiner sequentially prunes this full tree in varying degrees to investigate overfitting the

FIGURE 9.28 Full Classification Tree for Hawaiian Ham (*CT_Fulltree* Worksheet)

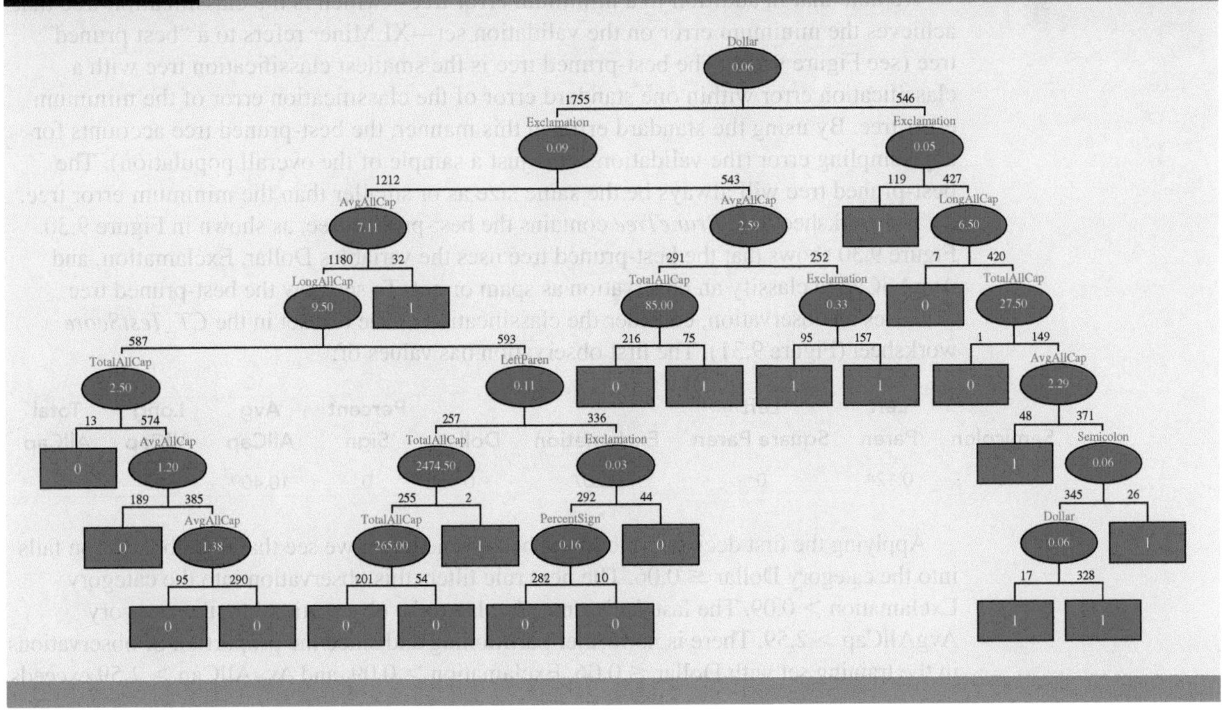

FIGURE 9.29 Prune Log for Classification Tree (*CT_PruneLog* Worksheet)

# Decision Nodes	% Error			
21	13.98551			
20	13.98551			
19	13.98551			
18	13.98551			
17	13.98551			
16	13.98551			
15	13.98551			
14	13.98551			
13	13.98551			
12	13.98551			
11	13.98551			
10	13.98551			
9	13.98551			
8	13.98551	<-- Min Error Tree	% Std. Error	0.933653
7	14.34783			
6	14.34783			
5	14.34783			
4	14.34783			
3	14.13043	<-- Best Pruned		
2	19.92754			
1	19.92754			
0	39.85507			

training data and records classification error on the validation set in *CT_PruneLog*. Figure 9.29 displays the content of the *CT_PruneLog* worksheet, which indicates that the minimum classification error on the validation set is achieved by an eight-decision-node tree.

We note that in addition to a minimum error tree—which is the classification tree that achieves the minimum error on the validation set—XLMiner refers to a "best pruned" tree (see Figure 9.29). The best-pruned tree is the smallest classification tree with a classification error within one standard error of the classification error of the minimum error tree. By using the standard error in this manner, the best-pruned tree accounts for any sampling error (the validation set is just a sample of the overall population). The best-pruned tree will always be the same size as or smaller than the minimum error tree.

The worksheet *CT_PruneTree* contains the best-pruned tree, as shown in Figure 9.30. Figure 9.30 shows that the best-pruned tree uses the variables Dollar, Exclamation, and AvgAllCap to classify an observation as spam or not. To see how the best-pruned tree classifies an observation, consider the classification of the test set in the *CT_TestScore* worksheet (Figure 9.31). The first observation has values of:

Semicolon	Left Paren	Left Square Paren	Exclamation	Dollar	Percent Sign	Avg AllCap	Long AllCap	Total AllCap
0	0.124	0	0.207	0	0	10.409	343	635

Applying the first decision rule in the best-pruned tree, we see that this observation falls into the category Dollar ≤ 0.06. The next rule filters this observation into the category Exclamation > 0.09. The last decision node places the observation into the category AvgAllCap > 2.59. There is no further partitioning and since the proportion of observations in the training set with Dollar ≤ 0.06, Exclamation > 0.09, and AvgAllCap > 2.59 exceeds

FIGURE 9.30 Best-Pruned Classification Tree for Hawaiian Ham (*CT_PruneTree* Worksheet)

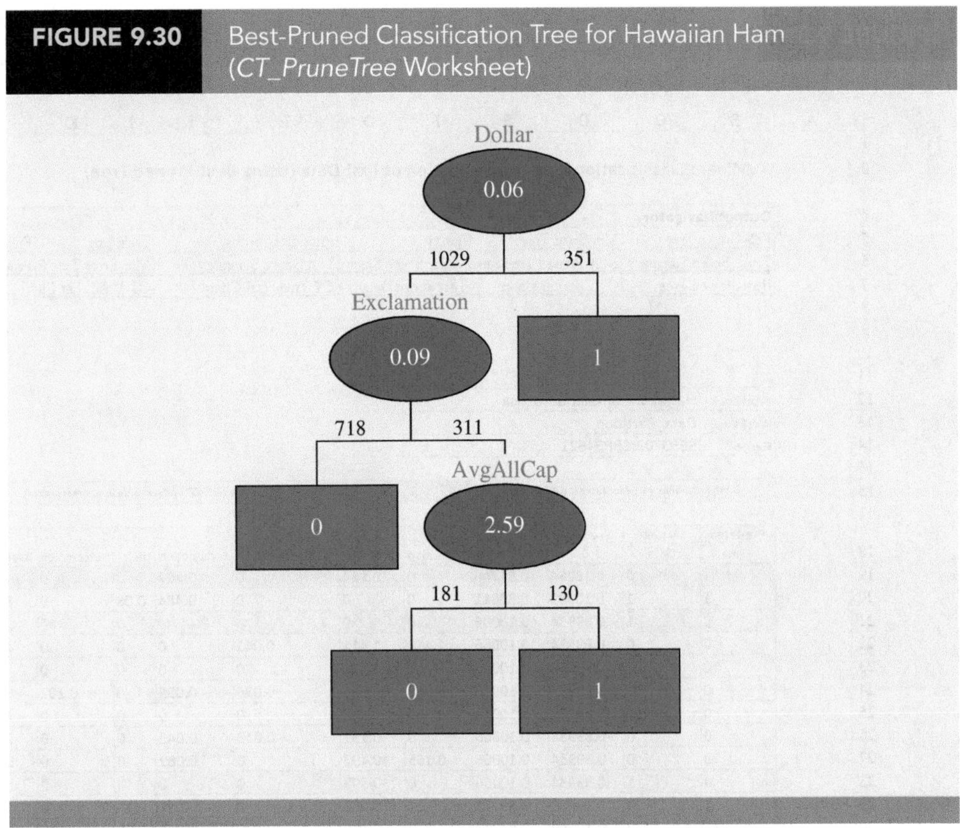

the cutoff value of 0.5, the best-pruned tree classifies this observation as Class 1 (spam). As Figure 9.31 shows, this is a misclassification, as the actual class for this observation is Class 0 (not spam). The overall classification accuracy for the best-pruned tree on the test set can be found in the *CT_Output* worksheet as shown in Figure 9.32.

To demonstrate how to construct a single regression tree with XLMiner for continuous estimation, we consider the partitioned data from the Optiva Credit Union problem to predict a customer's average checking account balance. The following steps and Figure 9.33 demonstrate this process.

Step 1. In the *Data_Partition* worksheet, select any cell (such as cell B21) in the range of data listed below **Selected Variables**
Step 2. Click the **XLMiner Platform** tab on the Ribbon
Step 3. Click **Predict** from the **Data Mining** group
Step 4. Click **Regression Tree**
Step 5. Click **Single Tree**
Step 6. In the **Regression Tree – Step 1 of 3** dialog box:
In the **Data Source** area, confirm that the **Worksheet:** and **Workbook:** entries correspond to the appropriate data (see Figure 9.33)
In the **Variables In Input Data** box of the **Variables** area, select **Age**, **Entrepreneur**, **Unemployed**, **Married**, **Divorced**, **High School**, and **College** variables and click the > to the left of the **Input Variables** box.
Select **AverageBalance** in the **Variables In Input Data** box of the **Variables** area, and click the > button to the left of the **Output variable:** box
Click **Next**

FIGURE 9.31 Best-Pruned Tree Classification of Test Set for Hawaiian Ham (*CT_TestScore* Worksheet)

XLMiner : Classification Tree - Classification of Test Data (Using Best Pruned Tree)

Output Navigator					
Full-Grown Tree	Min-Error Tree	Inputs	Prior class probs	Train Log	Full-Grown Tree Ru
Train. Score Summary	Best-Pruned Tree Rule	Valid. Score Summ	Test Score Summary	Min-Error Tree R	Prune Log
Best-Pruned Tree	CT Test Lift Chart	Test Score Detail	CT Train. Lift Chart	CT Valid. Lift Ch	

Workbook	HawaiianHamStandard.xlsx
Worksheet	Data_Partition
Range	$B$3702:$BH$4621

Cutoff probability value for success (UPDATABLE)	0.5	Updating the value here will NOT update value in summary report

Predicted Class	Actual Class	Prob. for 0	Prob. for 1(success)	Semicolon	LeftParen	LeftSquareParen	Exclamation	Dollar	PercentSign	AvgAllCap	LongAllCap	TotalAllCap
1	0	0.18254	0.81746	0	0.124	0	0.207	0	0	10.409	343	635
1	1	0.10989	0.89011	0	0	0	0.484	0.08	0	8.375	85	201
0	1	0.89934	0.10066	0	0	0	0	0	0	2.307	16	30
0	0	0.89934	0.10066	1.411	1.411	0.041	0	0	0	4.891	20	675
0	0	0.89934	0.10066	0	0	0	0	0	0	2.5	9	15
0	0	0.89934	0.10066	0.607	0.064	0.036	0.055	0	0.202	3.766	43	1789
0	0	0.89934	0.10066	0	0	0	0	0	0	4.333	11	13
0	0	0.89934	0.10066	0	0.131	0.043	0.043	0	0	2.468	15	195
0	0	0.89934	0.10066	0.165	0.497	0	0.082	0	0	3.525	20	208
0	1	0.89934	0.10066	0	0.307	0	0	0	0	3.39	45	139
1	1	0.10989	0.89011	0.01	0.052	0	0.01	0.17	0	1.818	13	462
1	0	0.10989	0.89011	0	0	0	0	0.07	0	2.216	44	215
0	0	0.89934	0.10066	0	0	0	0	0	0	4.117	47	70
0	1	0.89934	0.10066	0	0	0	0	0	0	3.642	8	51
1	1	0.18254	0.81746	0.094	0.189	0.284	0.662	0	0	10.068	131	292

Step 7. In the **Regression Tree – Step 2 of 3** dialog box:
Select the checkbox for **Normalize input data**
In the **Tree Growth** area, enter *999* in the box next to **Minimum # records in a terminal node:**
In the **Scoring option** area, select **Using Best Pruned Tree**
Click **Next**

Step 8. In the **Regression Tree – Step 3 of 3** dialog box:
Increase the **Maximum # levels to be displayed:** box to **7**
In the **Trees** area, select **Full tree (grown using training data)**, **Pruned tree (pruned using validation data)**, and **Minimum error tree (pruned using validation data)**
In the **Score Test Data** area, select **Detailed Report** and **Summary Report**
Click **Finish**

This procedure first constructs a "full" regression tree on the training data, that is, a tree that successively partitions the variable space via variable splitting rules until the resultant branches contain less than the specified minimum number of observations (999 observations in this example) or the number of displayed tree levels is reached (7 in this example). The worksheet *RT_FullTree* (shown in Figure 9.34) displays the full

FIGURE 9.32 Best-Pruned Tree Classification Confusion Matrix on Test Set (*CT_Output* Worksheet)

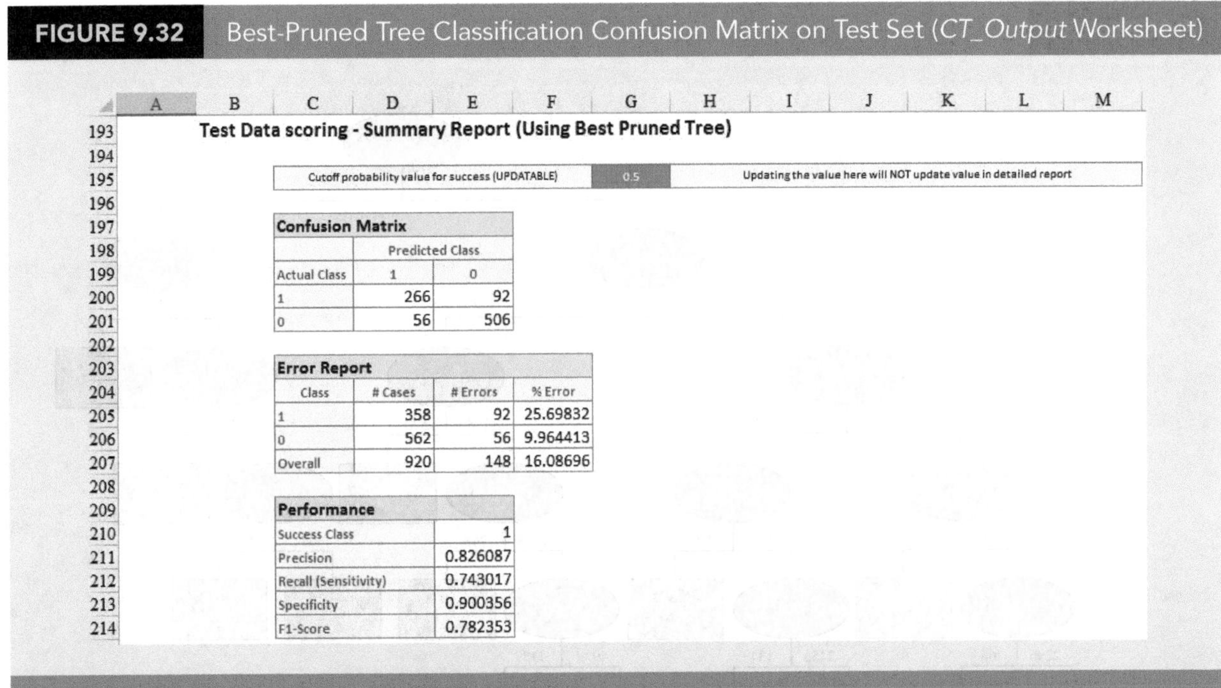

Test Data scoring - Summary Report (Using Best Pruned Tree)

Cutoff probability value for success (UPDATABLE)	0.5	Updating the value here will NOT update value in detailed report

Confusion Matrix

	Predicted Class	
Actual Class	1	0
1	266	92
0	56	506

Error Report

Class	# Cases	# Errors	% Error
1	358	92	25.69832
0	562	56	9.964413
Overall	920	148	16.08696

Performance

Success Class	1
Precision	0.826087
Recall (Sensitivity)	0.743017
Specificity	0.900356
F1-Score	0.782353

FIGURE 9.33 XLMiner Steps for Regression Trees

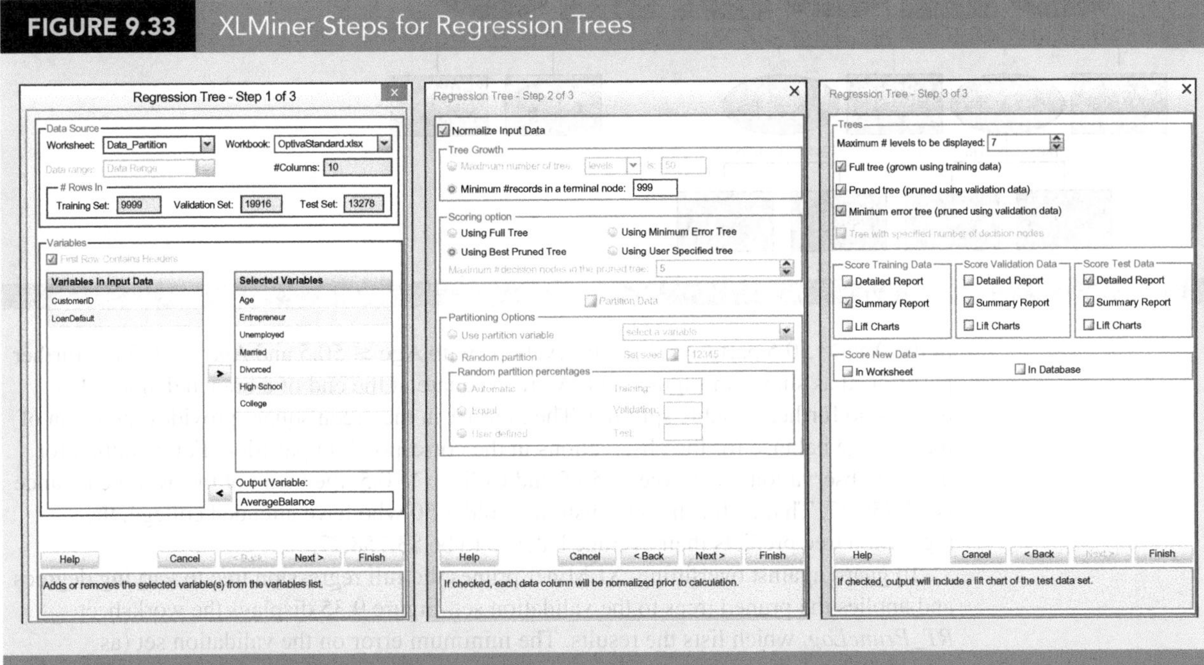

regression tree. In this tree, the number within the node represents the value on which the variable (whose name is listed above the node) is split. The first partition is formed by splitting observations into two groups, observations with Age ≤ 50.5 and observations with Age > 50.5. The numbers on the left and right arcs emanating from the blue oval node denote that there are 8,061 observations in the Age ≤ 50.5 partition and 1,938 observations

FIGURE 9.34 Full Regression Tree for Optiva Credit Union (*RT_FullTree* Worksheet)

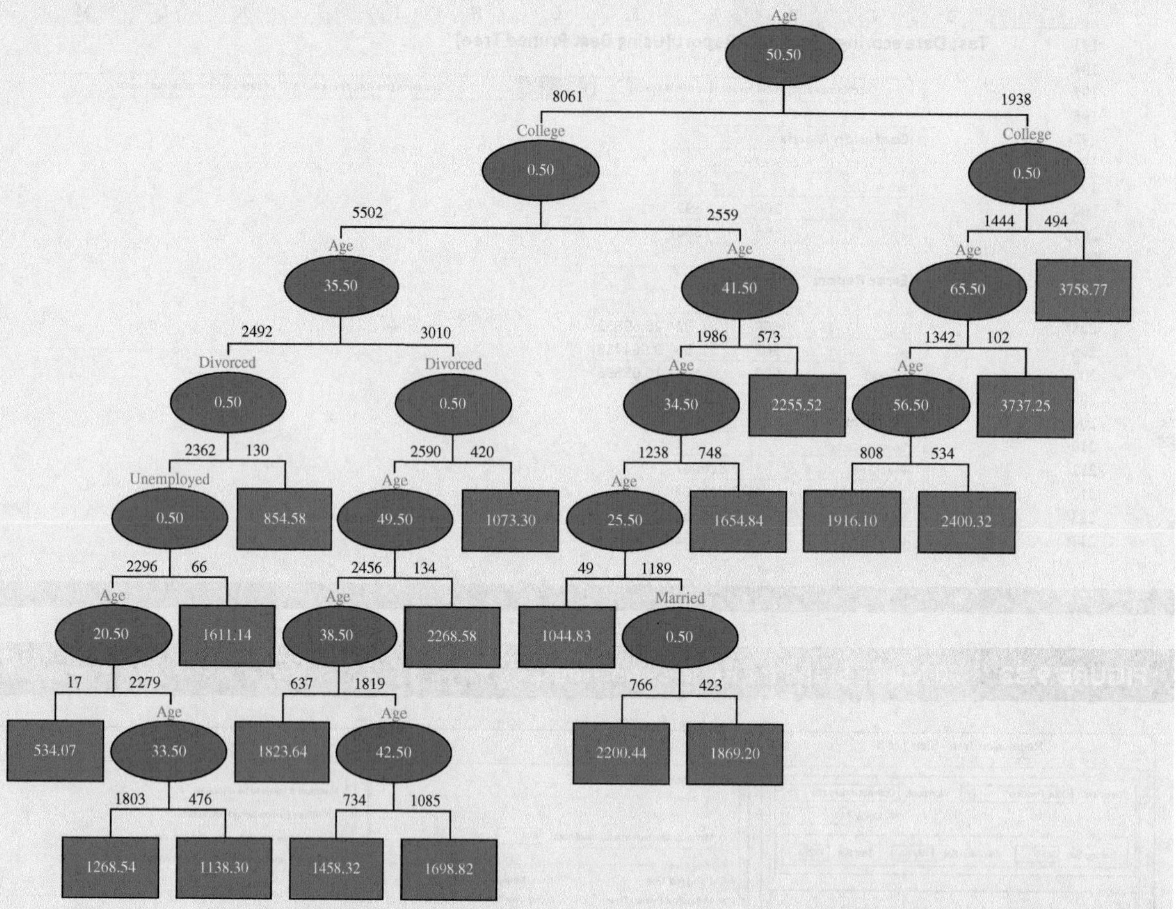

in the Age > 50.5 partition. The observations with Age ≤ 50.5 and Age > 50.5 are further partitioned as shown in Figure 9.34. A green square at the end of a branch denotes that there is no further variable splitting. The number in the green square provides the mean of the average balance for the observations in the corresponding partition. For example, for the 494 observations with Age > 50.5 and College > 0.5, the mean of the average balance is $3,758.77. That is, for the 494 customers older 50 who have attended college, the regression tree predicts their average balance to be $3,758.77.

To guard against overfitting, XLMiner prunes the full regression tree to varying degrees and applies the pruned trees to the validation set. Figure 9.35 displays the worksheet *RT_PruneLog,* which lists the results. The minimum error on the validation set (as measured by the sum of squared error between the regression tree predictions and actual observation values) is achieved by the seven-decision-node tree shown in Figure 9.36.

We note that in addition to a "minimum error tree"—which is the regression tree that achieves the minimum error on the validation set—XLMiner also refers to a "best pruned" tree (see Figure 9.35). The best-pruned tree is the smallest regression tree with a prediction error within one standard error of the prediction error of the minimum error tree. By using the standard error in this manner, the best-pruned tree accounts for any sampling error

FIGURE 9.35 Errors From the Validation Set (*RT_PruneLog* Worksheet)

# Decision Nodes	Cost Complexity	Train. MSE	Valid. MSE			
18	0	14,434,284	14,798,745			
17	11,500	14,436,817	14,796,021			
16	14,351	14,437,456	14,796,338			
15	14,439	14,440,446	14,795,740			
14	28,405	14,442,769	14,798,168			
13	31,559	14,443,613	14,790,154			
12	31,559	14,448,682	14,790,154			
11	35,883	14,453,399	14,789,452			
10	51,890	14,454,301	14,795,661			
9	50,688	14,461,841	14,801,872			
8	50,900	14,468,813	14,788,238			
7	50,900	14,482,597	14,788,238	<-- Best Pruned & Min Error Tree	Std. Error	3845.548
6	52,775	14,484,490	14,797,493			
5	82,700	14,509,632	14,799,763			
4	97,685	14,515,384	14,812,024			
3	100,566	14,534,921	14,851,006			
2	154,621	14,621,654	14,956,908			
1	173,465	14,673,194	14,949,313			
0	159,208	14,832,402	14,983,561			

FIGURE 9.36 Best-Pruned Regression Tree for Optiva Credit Union (*RT_PruneTree* Worksheet)

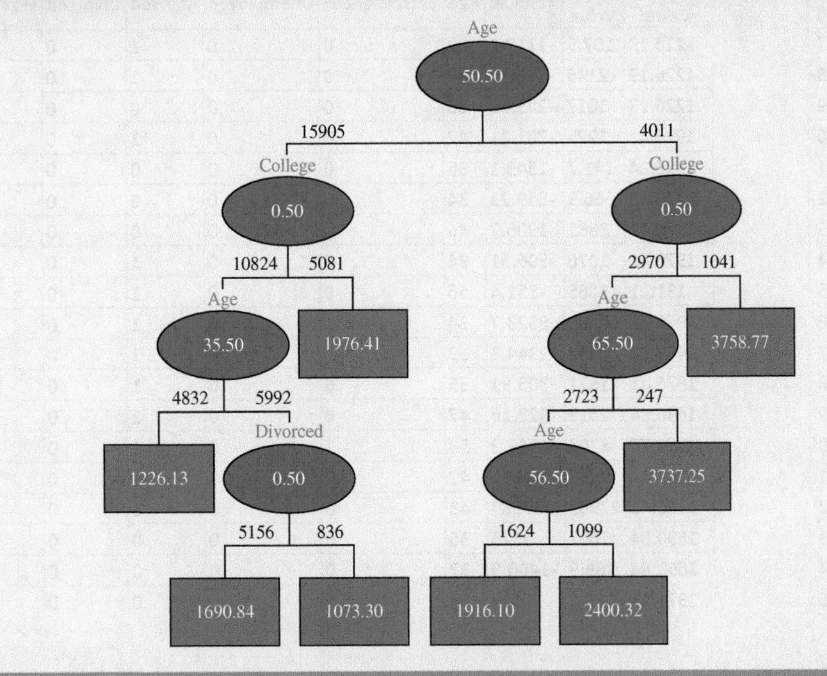

(the validation set is just a sample of the overall population). The best-pruned tree will always be the same size as or smaller than the minimum error tree.

To see how the best-pruned tree predicts an outcome for an observation, consider the classification of the test set in the *RT_TestScore* worksheet (Figure 9.37). The first observation in Figure 9.37 has values of Age = 22, Entrepreneur = 0, Unemployed = 0, Married = 1, Divorced = 0, High School = 1, and College = 0. Applying the first decision

FIGURE 9.37 Best-Pruned Tree Prediction of Test Set for Optiva Credit Union (*RT_TestScore* Worksheet)

XLMiner : Regression Tree - Prediction of Test Data (Using Best Pruned Tree)

Output Navigator				
Full-Grown Tree	Min-Error Tr	Inputs	Full-Grown Tree	Best Pruned Tree F
Min-Error Tree F	Train. Score	Valid. Score - Summary	Test Score - Sum	Prune Log
Best-Pruned Tre	RT Test Lift C	Test Score Detail		

Workbook	OptivaStandard.xlsx
Workshee	Data_Partition
Range	$B$29936:$K$43213

Predicted Value	Actual Value	Residual	Age	Entrepreneur	Unemployed	Married	Divorced	High School	College
1226.13	107.9	-1118.2	22	0	0	1	0	1	0
1226.13	2146	920.17	34	0	0	1	0	1	0
1226.13	1017	-209.53	30	0	0	0	0	1	0
1976.41	1275	-701.11	42	0	0	1	0	0	1
1690.84	141.7	-1549.1	36	0	0	0	0	0	0
1226.13	666.9	-559.23	34	0	0	0	0	1	0
1976.41	3883	1906.7	46	0	0	0	0	0	1
1976.41	1070	-906.51	34	0	0	1	0	0	1
1916.1	1065	-851.4	56	0	0	1	0	1	0
1976.41	10500	8523.7	34	0	0	1	0	0	1
2400.32	56	-2344.3	59	0	0	1	0	1	0
1976.41	1671	-305.91	35	0	0	1	0	0	1
1690.84	2613	922.16	47	0	0	1	0	1	0
3758.77	8108	4349.3	58	1	0	1	0	0	1
1690.84	202.8	-1488	42	0	0	0	0	0	0
1976.41	27963	25987	43	0	0	1	0	0	1
1690.84	7067	5376	36	0	0	0	0	1	0
1690.84	289.9	-1400.9	37	0	0	0	0	1	0
1976.41	49.4	-1927	38	0	0	0	0	0	1

FIGURE 9.38 Prediction Error of Regression Trees (*RT_Output* Worksheet)

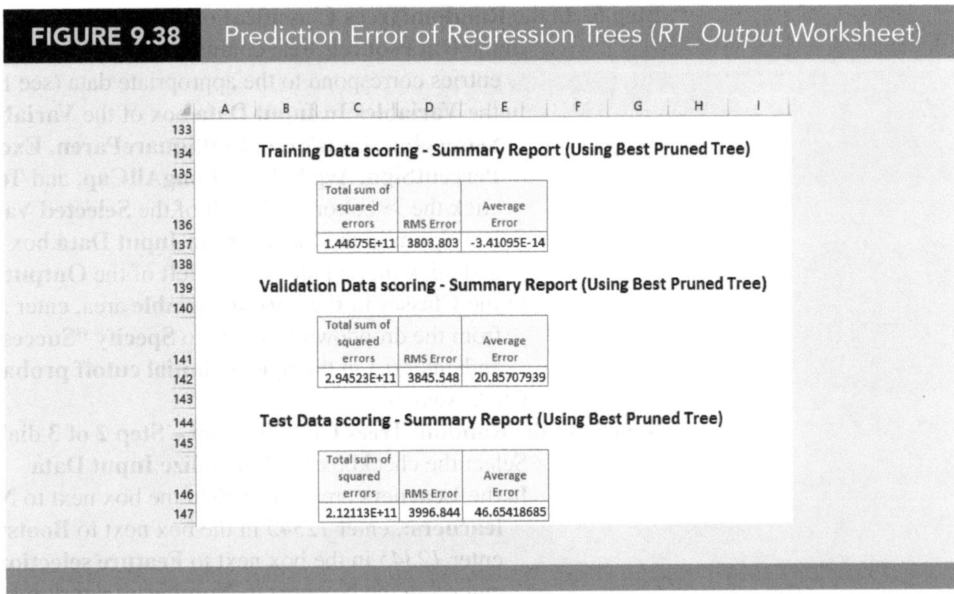

Training Data scoring - Summary Report (Using Best Pruned Tree)

Total sum of squared errors	RMS Error	Average Error
1.44675E+11	3803.803	-3.41095E-14

Validation Data scoring - Summary Report (Using Best Pruned Tree)

Total sum of squared errors	RMS Error	Average Error
2.94523E+11	3845.548	20.85707939

Test Data scoring - Summary Report (Using Best Pruned Tree)

Total sum of squared errors	RMS Error	Average Error
2.12113E+11	3996.844	46.65418685

rule in the best-pruned tree, we see that this observation falls into the Age ≤ 50.5 category. The next rule applies to the College variable, and we see that this observation falls into the College ≤ 0.5. The next rule places the observation in the Age ≤ 35.5 partition. There is no further partitioning, and the mean observation value of average balance for observations in the training set with Age ≤ 50.5, College ≤ 0.5, and Age ≤ 35.5 is $1,226. Therefore, the best-pruned regression tree predicts that the observation's average balance will be $1,226. As Figure 9.37 shows, the observation's actual average balance is $108, resulting in an error of −$1,118.

Reducing the minimum number of records required for a terminal node in XLMiner's regression tree procedure may result in more accurate predictions at the expense of increased time to construct the tree.

The *RT_Output* worksheet (Figure 9.38) provides the prediction error of the best-pruned tree on the training, validation, and test sets. Specifically, the RMSE of the best-pruned tree on the validation set and test set is $3,846 and $3,997, respectively. Using this best-pruned tree, which characterizes a customer based only on their age and whether they attended colleage, Optiva can expect that the RMSE will be approximately $3,997 when estimating the average balance of new customer data.

Appendix 9.5 Random Forests of Classification or Regression Trees with XLMiner

In this appendix, we demonstrate XLMiner's functionality for implementing the random forests (random trees) ensemble method for both classification and estimation problems. We begin by constructing a random forest of classification trees for classifying an observation as spam or not spam in the Hawaiian Ham example.

Step 1. In the *Data_Partition* worksheet, select any cell (such as cell B21) in the range of data listed below **Selected Variables**
Step 2. Click the **XLMiner Platform** tab on the Ribbon
Step 3. Click **Classify** from the **Data Mining** group
Step 4. Click **Classification Tree**
Step 5. Click **Random Trees**

Step 6. In the **Random Trees Classification – Step 1 of 3** dialog box:
In the **Data source** area, confirm that the **Worksheet:** and **Workbook:** entries correspond to the appropriate data (see Figure 9.39)
In the **Variables In Input Data** box of the **Variables** area, select **Semicolon, LeftParen, LeftSquareParen, Exclamation, Dollar, PercentSign, AvgAllCap**, **LongAllCap**, and **TotalAllCap** and click the > button to the left of the **Selected Variables** box.
Select **Spam** in the **Variables In Input Data** box of the **Variables** area and click the > button to the left of the **Output variable:** box
In the **Classes in the output variable** area, enter *2* for **# Classes:**, select **1** from the dropdown box next to **Specify "Success" class (for Lift Chart)**, and enter *0.5* in the **Specify initial cutoff probability for success** box
Click **Next** >

Step 7. In the **Random Trees Classification – Step 2 of 3** dialog box:
Select the checkbox for **Normalize Input Data**
In the **Learners** area, enter *20* in the box next to **Number of weak learners:**, enter *12345* in the box next to **Bootstrapping random seed:**, enter *12345* in the box next to **Feature selection random seed:**, and enter *3* in the box next to **Number of randomly selected features:**
In the **Tree Growth** area, enter 230 in the box next to **Minimum # records in a terminal node:**
Click **Next**

Step 8. In the **Random Trees Classification – Step 3 of 3** dialog box:
In the **Score Test Data** area, select **Detailed Report**, **Summary Report**, and **Lift charts;** leave all other checkboxes unchanged
Click **Finish**

FIGURE 9.39 XLMiner Steps for Random Trees Classification

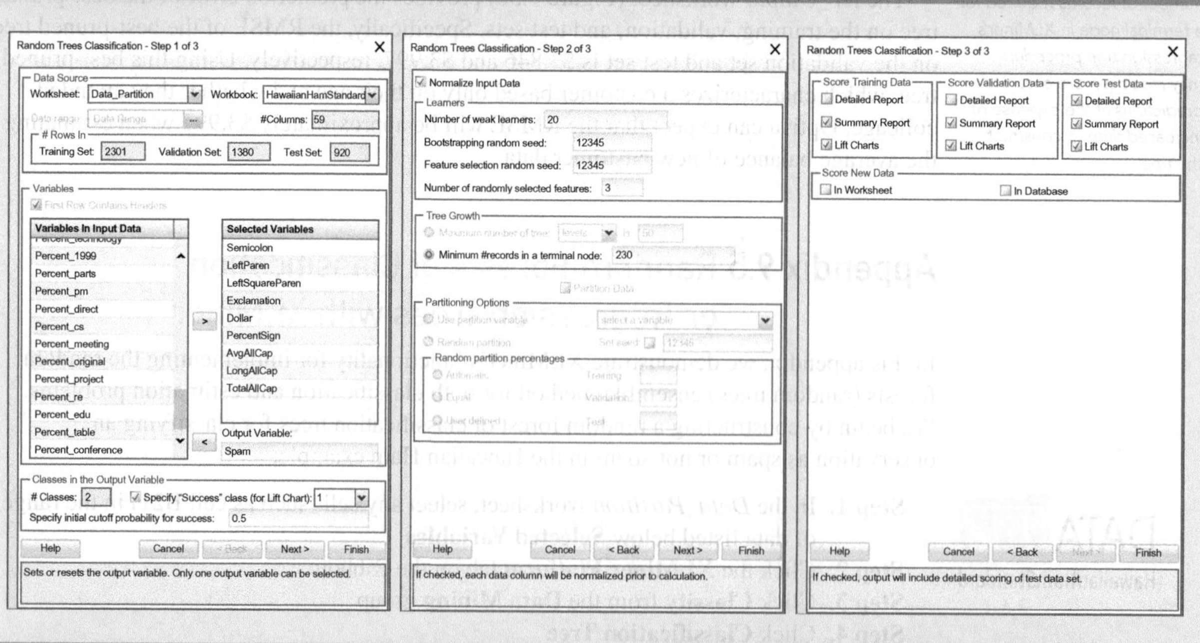

FIGURE 9.40 Variable Importance in Random Trees Ensemble

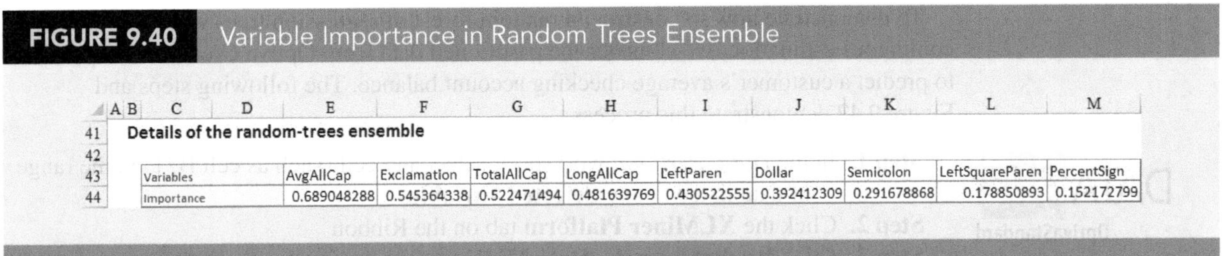

Details of the random-trees ensemble

Variables	AvgAllCap	Exclamation	TotalAllCap	LongAllCap	LeftParen	Dollar	Semicolon	LeftSquareParen	PercentSign
Importance	0.689048288	0.545364338	0.522471494	0.481639769	0.430522555	0.392412309	0.291678868	0.178850893	0.152172799

This procedure generates six worksheets of output. Figures 9.40 and 9.41 display two key pieces of information from the *CTRandTrees_Output* worksheet. Figure 9.40 lists each variable's importance, in decreasing order, a measure between 0 and 1 that describes a variable's contribution in reducing the total misclassification error of the ensemble's prediction. Figure 9.41 displays the classification accuracy measures of the 20 random trees. Comparing Figure 9.41 to Figure 9.32, we observe that the random trees ensemble approach outperforms the single classification tree constructed in Appendix 9.4.

The other five worksheets are analogous to the XLMiner output for the single classification tree method of Appendix 9.4. The *CTRandTrees_TestScore* worksheet lists the ensemble's classification of each observation in test set. The *CTRandTrees_TrainLiftChart*, *CTRandTrees_ValidLiftChart*, and *CTRandTrees_TestLiftChart* worksheets contain lift charts, decile-wise lift charts, and ROC curves for the random trees classifier on the training set, validation set, and test set, respectively. The *CTRandTrees_Stored* lists the variable-splitting rules for the 20 individual classification trees composing the random forest ensemble.

FIGURE 9.41 Random Trees Classification Confusion Matrix on Test Set

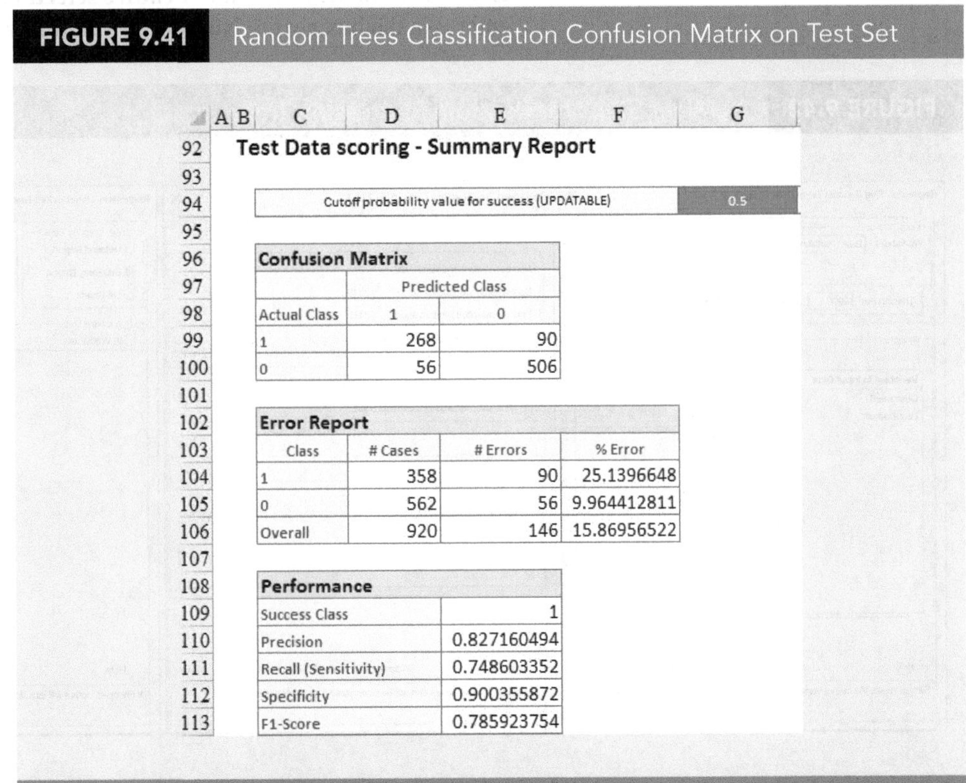

Test Data scoring - Summary Report

Cutoff probability value for success (UPDATABLE)	0.5

Confusion Matrix

	Predicted Class	
Actual Class	1	0
1	268	90
0	56	506

Error Report

Class	# Cases	# Errors	% Error
1	358	90	25.1396648
0	562	56	9.964412811
Overall	920	146	15.86956522

Performance

Success Class	1
Precision	0.827160494
Recall (Sensitivity)	0.748603352
Specificity	0.900355872
F1-Score	0.785923754

To demonstrate how to construct a random forest of regression trees with XLMiner for continuous estimation, we consider the partitioned data from Optiva Credit Union problem to predict a customer's average checking account balance. The following steps and Figure 9.42 demonstrate this process.

OptivaStandard

Step 1. In the *Data_Partition* worksheet, select any cell (such as cell B21) in the range of data listed below **Selected Variables**

Step 2. Click the **XLMiner Platform** tab on the Ribbon

Step 3. Click **Predict** from the **Data Mining** group

Step 4. Click **Regression Tree**

Step 5. Click **Single Tree**

Step 6. In the **Regression Tree Random Trees – Step 1 of 3** dialog box:
- In the **Data Source** area, confirm that the **Worksheet:** and **Workbook:** entries correspond to the appropriate data (see Figure 9.42)
- In the **Variables In Input Data** box of the **Variables** area, select **Age**, **Entrepreneur**, **Unemployed**, **Married**, **Divorced**, **High School**, and **College** variables and click the > to the left of the **Input Variables** box.
- Select **Average Balance** in the **Variables In Input Data** box of the **Variables** area, and click the > button to the left of the **Output variable:** box
- Click **Next**

Step 7. In the **Regression Tree Random Trees – Step 2 of 3** dialog box:
- Select the checkbox for **Normalize input data**
- In the **Learners** area, enter *20* in the box next to **Number of weak learners:**, enter *12345* in the box next to **Bootstrapping random seed:**, enter *12345* in the box next to **Feature selection random seed:**, and enter *2* in the box next to **Number of randomly selected features:**

FIGURE 9.42 XLMiner Steps for Random Regression Trees

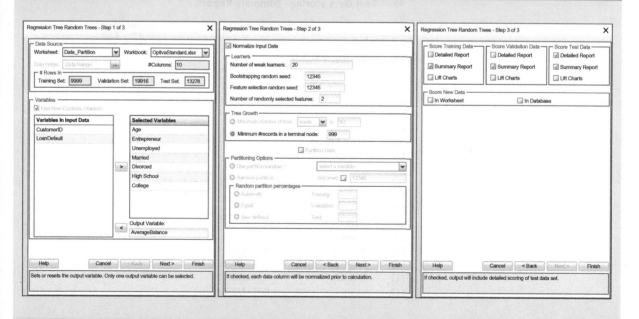

In the **Tree Growth** area, enter *999* in the box next to **Minimum # records in a terminal node:**
Click **Next**

Step 8. In the **Regression Tree Random Trees – Step 3 of 3** dialog box:
In the **Score Test Data** area, select **Detailed Report** and **Summary Report**
Click **Finish**

This procedure outputs three worksheets. As Figure 9.43 shows, the *RTRandTrees_Output* worksheet contains the estimation error on the training set, validation set, and test set for the predictions based on the 20 random regression trees. The *RTRandTrees_TestScore* worksheet compares the predicted value to the actual value for each observation in the test set. The *RTRandTrees_Stored* worksheet lists the variable-splitting rules for each of the 20 regression trees in the ensemble.

FIGURE 9.43 Random Regression Trees Prediction Error

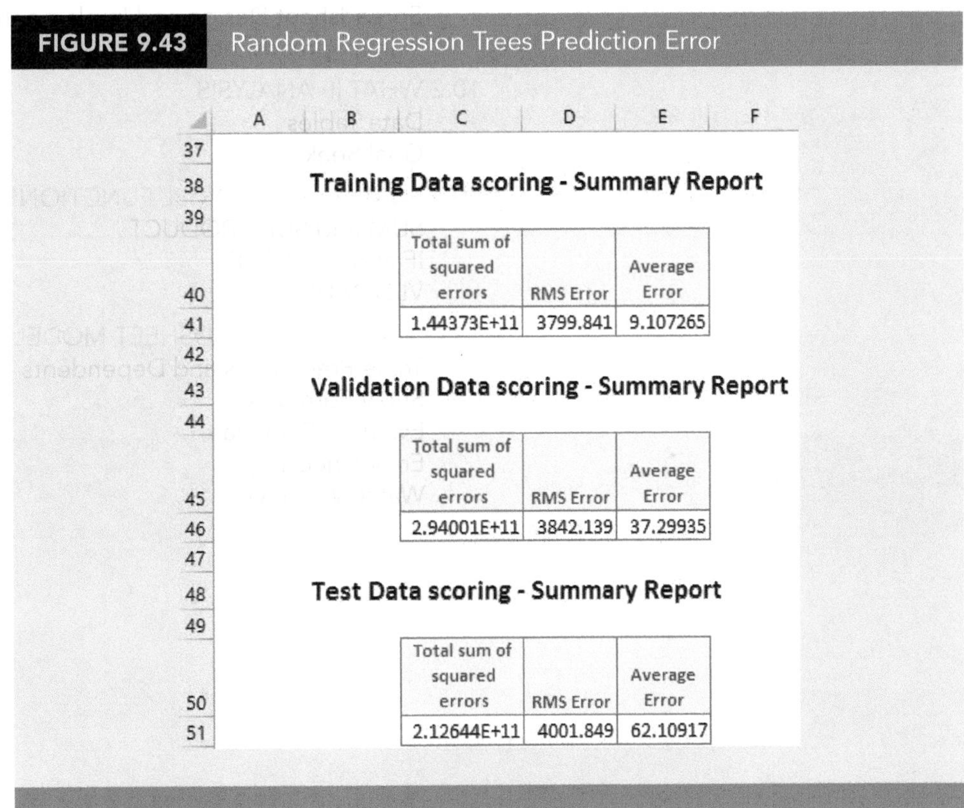

Training Data scoring - Summary Report

Total sum of squared errors	RMS Error	Average Error
1.44373E+11	3799.841	9.107265

Validation Data scoring - Summary Report

Total sum of squared errors	RMS Error	Average Error
2.94001E+11	3842.139	37.29935

Test Data scoring - Summary Report

Total sum of squared errors	RMS Error	Average Error
2.12644E+11	4001.849	62.10917

Chapter 10

Spreadsheet Models

CONTENTS

10.1 BUILDING GOOD SPREADSHEET MODELS
Influence Diagrams
Building a Mathematical Model
Spreadsheet Design and Implementing the Model in a Spreadsheet

10.2 WHAT-IF ANALYSIS
Data Tables
Goal Seek

10.3 SOME USEFUL EXCEL FUNCTIONS FOR MODELING
SUM and SUMPRODUCT
IF and COUNTIF
VLOOKUP

10.4 AUDITING SPREADSHEET MODELS
Trace Precedents and Dependents
Show Formulas
Evaluate Formulas
Error Checking
Watch Window

ANALYTICS IN ACTION

Procter & Gamble*

Procter & Gamble (P&G) is a Fortune 500 consumer goods company headquartered in Cincinnati, Ohio. P&G produces well-known brands such as Tide detergent, Gillette razors, Swiffer cleaning products, and many other consumer goods. P&G is a global company and has been recognized for its excellence in business analytics, including supply chain analytics and market research.

With operations around the world, P&G must do its best to maintain inventory at levels that meet its high customer service requirements. A lack of on-hand inventory can result in a stockout of a product and an inability to meet customer demand. This not only results in lost revenue for an immediate sale but can also cause customers to switch permanently to a competing brand. On the other hand, excessive inventory forces P&G to invest cash in inventory when that money could be invested in other opportunities, such as research and development.

To ensure that the inventory of its products around the world is set at appropriate levels, P&G analytics personnel developed and deployed a series of spreadsheet inventory models. These spreadsheets implement mathematical inventory models to tell business units when and how much to order to keep inventory levels where they need to be in order to maintain service and keep investment as low as possible.

The spreadsheet models were carefully designed to be easily understood by the users and easy to use and interpret. Their users can also customize the spreadsheets to their individual situations.

Over 70% of the P&G business units use these models, with a conservative estimate of a 10% reduction in inventory around the world. This equates to a cash savings of nearly $350 million.

*I. Farasyn, K. Perkoz, and W. Van de Velde, "Spreadsheet Model for Inventory Target Setting at Procter & Gamble, *Interfaces* 38, no. 4 (July–August 2008): 241–250.

Numerous specialized software packages are available for descriptive, predictive, and prescriptive business analytics. Because these software packages are specialized, they usually provide the user with numerous options and the capability to perform detailed analyses. However, they tend to be considerably more expensive than a spreadsheet package such as Excel. Also, specialized packages often require substantial user training. Because spreadsheets are less expensive, often come preloaded on computers, and are fairly easy to use, they are without question the most used business analytics tool. Every day, millions of people around the world use spreadsheet decision models to perform risk analysis, inventory tracking and control, investment planning, breakeven analysis, and many other essential business planning and decision tasks. A well-designed, well-documented, and accurate spreadsheet model can be a very valuable tool in decision making.

If you have never used a spreadsheet or have not done so recently, we suggest you first familiarize yourself with the material in Appendix A. It provides basic information that is fundamental to using Excel.

Spreadsheet models are mathematical and logic-based models. Their strength is that they provide easy-to-use, sophisticated mathematical and logical functions, allowing for easy instantaneous recalculation for a change in model inputs. This is why spreadsheet models are often referred to as **what-if models**. What-if models allow you to answer questions such as, "If the per unit cost is $4, what is the impact on profit?" Changing data in a given cell has an impact not only on that cell but also on any other cells containing a formula or function that uses that cell.

In this chapter we discuss principles for building reliable spreadsheet models. We begin with a discussion of how to build a conceptual model of a decision problem, how to convert the conceptual model to a mathematical model, and how to implement the model in a spreadsheet. We introduce two analysis tools available in Excel, Data Tables and Goal Seek, and we discuss some Excel functions that are useful for building spreadsheet models for decision making. Finally, we present how to audit a spreadsheet model to ensure its reliability.

10.1 Building Good Spreadsheet Models

Let us begin our discussion of spreadsheet models by considering the cost of producing a single product. The total cost of manufacturing a product can usually be defined as the sum of two costs: fixed cost and variable cost. *Fixed cost* is the portion of the total cost that does not depend on the production quantity; this cost remains the same no matter how much is produced. *Variable cost*, on the other hand, is the portion of the total cost that is dependent on and varies with the production quantity. To illustrate how cost models can be developed, we will consider a manufacturing problem faced by Nowlin Plastics.

Nowlin Plastics produces a line of cell phone covers. Nowlin's best-selling cover is its Viper model, a slim but very durable black and gray plastic cover. The annual fixed cost for the Viper cover is $234,000. This fixed cost includes management time and other costs that are incurred regardless of the number of units eventually produced. In addition, the total variable cost, including labor and material costs, is $2 for each unit produced.

Nowlin is considering outsourcing the production of some products for next year, including the Viper. Nowlin has a bid from an outside firm to produce the Viper for $3.50 per unit. Although it is more expensive per unit to outsource the Viper ($3.50 versus $2.00), the fixed cost can be avoided if Nowlin purchases rather than manufactures the product. Next year's exact demand for Viper is not yet known. Nowlin would like to compare the costs of manufacturing the Viper in-house to those of outsourcing its production to another firm, and management would like to do that for various production quantities. Many manufacturers face this type of decision, which is known as a **make-versus-buy decision**.

Influence Diagrams

It is often useful to begin the modeling process with a conceptual model that shows the relationships between the various parts of the problem being modeled. The conceptual model helps in organizing the data requirements and provides a road map for eventually constructing a mathematical model. A conceptual model also provides a clear way to communicate the model to others. An **influence diagram** is a visual representation of which entities influence others in a model. Parts of the model are represented by circular or oval symbols called *nodes*, and arrows connecting the nodes show influence.

Figure 10.1 shows an influence diagram for Nowlin's total cost of production for the Viper. Total manufacturing cost depends on fixed cost and variable cost, which in turn depends on the variable cost per unit and the quantity required.

An expanded influence diagram that includes an outsourcing option is shown in Figure 10.2. Note that the influence diagram in Figure 10.1 is a subset of the influence diagram in Figure 10.2. Our method here—namely, to build an influence diagram for a portion of the problem and then expand it until the total problem is conceptually modeled—is usually a good way to proceed. This modular approach simplifies the process and reduces the likelihood of error. This is true not just for influence diagrams but for the construction of the mathematical and spreadsheet models as well. Next we turn our attention to using the influence diagram in Figure 10.2 to guide us in the construction of the mathematical model.

Building a Mathematical Model

The task now is to use the influence diagram to build a mathematical model. Let us first consider the cost of manufacturing the required units of the Viper. As the influence diagram shows, this cost is a function of the fixed cost, the variable cost per unit, and the quantity required. In general, it is best to define notation for every node in the influence diagram. Let us define the following:

$$q = \text{quantity (number of units) required}$$
$$FC = \text{the fixed cost of manufacturing}$$

FIGURE 10.1 An Influence Diagram for Nowlin's Manufacturing Cost

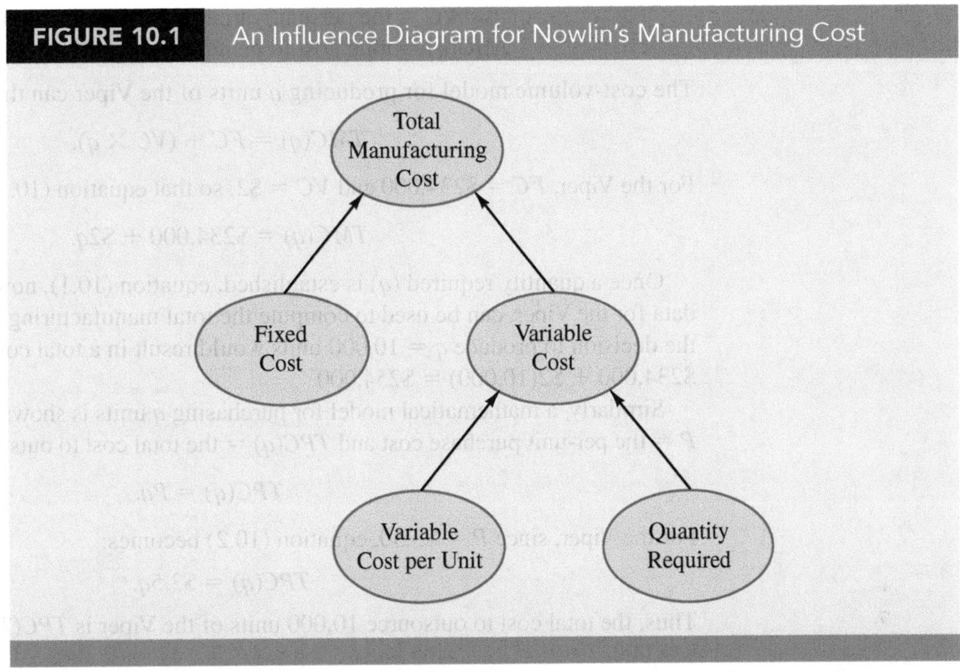

FIGURE 10.2 An Influence Diagram for Comparing Manufacturing Versus Outsourcing Cost for Nowlin Plastics

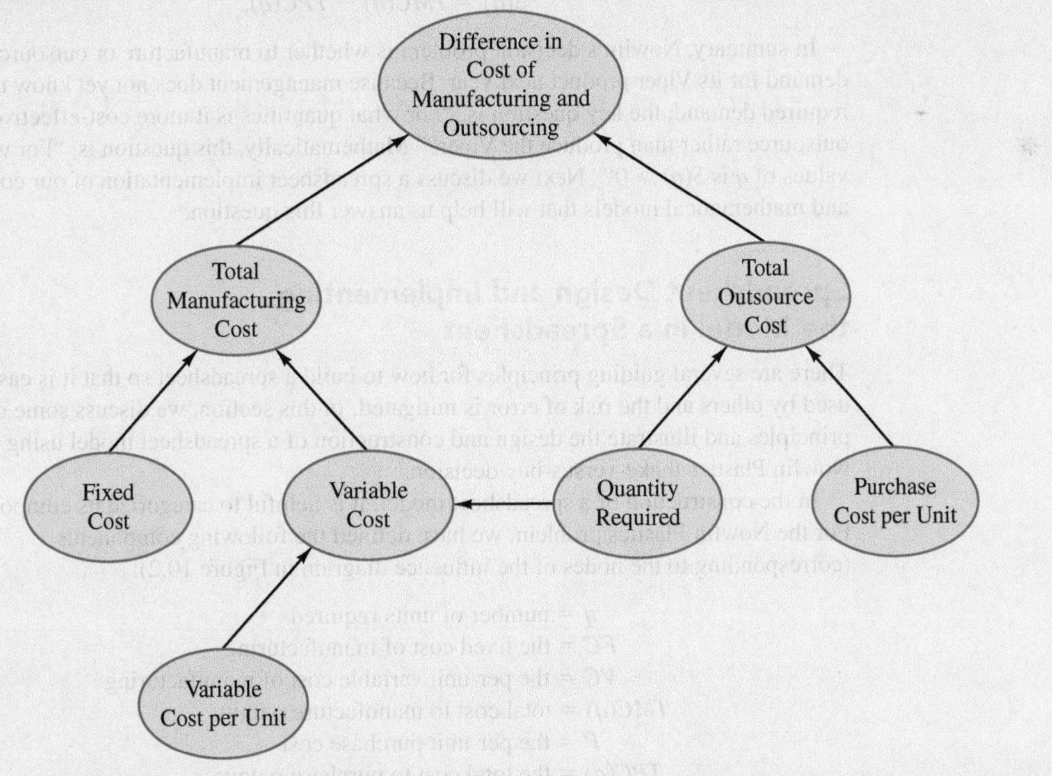

$$VC = \text{the per-unit variable cost of manufacturing}$$
$$TMC(q) = \text{total cost to manufacture } q \text{ units}$$

The cost-volume model for producing q units of the Viper can then be written as follows:

$$TMC(q) = FC + (VC \times q). \tag{10.1}$$

For the Viper, $FC = \$234{,}000$ and $VC = \$2$, so that equation (10.1) becomes:

$$TMC(q) = \$234{,}000 + \$2q.$$

Once a quantity required (q) is established, equation (10.1), now populated with the data for the Viper, can be used to compute the total manufacturing cost. For example, the decision to produce $q = 10{,}000$ units would result in a total cost of $TMC(10{,}000) = \$234{,}000 + \$2(10{,}000) = \$254{,}000$.

Similarly, a mathematical model for purchasing q units is shown in equation (10.2). Let P = the per-unit purchase cost and $TPC(q)$ = the total cost to outsource or purchase q units:

$$TPC(q) = Pq. \tag{10.2}$$

For the Viper, since $P = \$3.50$, equation (10.2) becomes:

$$TPC(q) = \$3.5q.$$

Thus, the total cost to outsource 10,000 units of the Viper is $TPC(10{,}000) = 3.5(10{,}000) = \$35{,}000$.

We can now state mathematically the savings associated with outsourcing. Let $S(q)$ = the savings due to outsourcing, that is, the difference between the total cost of manufacturing q units and the total cost of buying q units:

$$S(q) = TMC(q) - TPC(q). \tag{10.3}$$

In summary, Nowlin's decision problem is whether to manufacture or outsource the demand for its Viper product next year. Because management does not yet know the required demand, the key question is, "For what quantities is it more cost-effective to outsource rather than produce the Viper?" Mathematically, this question is, "For what values of q is $S(q) > 0$?" Next we discuss a spreadsheet implementation of our conceptual and mathematical models that will help us answer this question.

Spreadsheet Design and Implementing the Model in a Spreadsheet

There are several guiding principles for how to build a spreadsheet so that it is easily used by others and the risk of error is mitigated. In this section, we discuss some of those principles and illustrate the design and construction of a spreadsheet model using the Nowlin Plastics make-versus-buy decision.

In the construction of a spreadsheet model, it is helpful to categorize its components. For the Nowlin Plastics problem, we have defined the following components (corresponding to the nodes of the influence diagram in Figure 10.2):

$$q = \text{number of units required}$$
$$FC = \text{the fixed cost of manufacturing}$$
$$VC = \text{the per-unit variable cost of manufacturing}$$
$$TMC(q) = \text{total cost to manufacture } q \text{ units}$$
$$P = \text{the per-unit purchase cost}$$
$$TPC(q) = \text{the total cost to purchase } q \text{ units}$$
$$S(q) = \text{the savings from outsourcing } q \text{ units}$$

Note that q, FC, VC, and P each is the beginning of a path in the influence diagram in Figure 10.2. In other words, they have no inward-pointing arrows.

Several points are in order. Some of these components are a function of other components (TMC, TPC, and S), and some are not (q, FC, VC, and P). TMC, TPC, and S will be formulas involving other cells in the spreadsheet model, whereas q, FC, VC, and P will just be entries in the spreadsheet. Furthermore, the value we can control or choose is q. In our analysis, we seek the value of q, such that $S(q) > 0$; that is, the savings associated with outsourcing is positive. The number of Vipers to make or buy for next year is Nowlin's decision. So we will treat q somewhat differently than we will FC, VC, and P in the spreadsheet model, and we refer to the quantity q as a **decision variable**. FC, VC, and P are measurable factors that define characteristics of the process we are modeling and so are *uncontrollable inputs* to the model, which we refer to as **parameters** of the model.

Figure 10.3 shows a spreadsheet model for the Nowlin Plastics make-versus-buy decision.

Column A is reserved for labels, including cell A1, where we have named the model "Nowlin Plastics." The input parameters (FC, VC, and P) are placed in cells B4, B5, and B7, respectively. We offset P from FC and VC because it is for outsourcing. We have created a parameters section in the upper part of the sheet. Below the parameters section, we have created the Model section. The first entry in the Model section is the quantity q—the number of units of Viper produced or purchased in cell B11—and shaded it to signify that this is a decision variable. We have placed the formulas corresponding to equations (10.1) to (10.3) in cells B13, B15, and B17. Cell B13 corresponds to equation (10.1), cell B15 to (10.2), and cell B17 to (10.3).

As described in Appendix A, Excel formulas always begin with an equal sign.

In cell B11 of Figure 10.3, we have set the value of q to 10,000 units. The model shows that the cost to manufacture 10,000 units is \$254,000, the cost to purchase the 10,000 units is \$35,000, and the savings from outsourcing is \$219,000. At a quantity of 10,000 units, we see that it is better to incur the higher variable cost (\$3.50 versus \$2) than to manufacture and have to incur the additional fixed cost of \$234,000. It will take a value of q larger than 10,000 units to make up the fixed cost incurred when Nowlin manufactures the product. At this point, we could increase the value of q by placing a value higher than 10,000 in cell B11 and see how much the savings in cell B17 decreases, doing this until the savings are close to zero. This is called a *trial-and-error approach*. Fortunately, Excel has what-if analysis tools that will help us use our model to further analyze the problem. We will discuss these what-if analysis tools in Section 10.2. Before doing so, let us first review what we have learned in constructing the Nowlin spreadsheet model.

The general principles of spreadsheet model design and construction are:

- Separate the parameters from the model.
- Document the model, and use proper formatting and color as needed.
- Use simple formulas.

Let us discuss the general merits of each of these points.

Separate the parameters from the model Separating the parameters from the model enables the user to update the model parameters without the risk of mistakenly creating an error in a formula. For this reason, it is good practice to have a parameters section at the top of the spreadsheet. A separate model section should contain all calculations. For a what-if model or an optimization model, some cells in the model section might also correspond to controllable inputs or decision variables (values that are not parameters or calculations but are the values we choose). The Nowlin model in Figure 10.3 is an example of this. The parameters section is in the upper part of the spreadsheet, followed by the model section, below which are the calculations and a decision cell (B11 for q in our model). Cell B11 is shaded to signify that it is a decision cell.

FIGURE 10.3 Nowlin Plastics Make-Versus-Buy Spreadsheet Model

	A	B	C
1	**Nowlin Plastics**		
2			
3	**Parameters**		
4	Manufacturing Fixed Cost	234000	
5	Manufacturing Variable Cost per Unit	2	
6			
7	Outsourcing Cost per Unit	3.5	
8			
9			
10	**Model**		
11	Quantity	10000	
12			
13	Total Cost to Produce	=B4+B11*B5	
14			
15	Total Cost to Outsource	=B7*B11	
16			
17	Savings due to Outsourcing	=B13–B15	
18			
19			

	A	B
1	**Nowlin Plastics**	
2		
3	**Parameters**	
4	Manufacturing Fixed Cost	$234,000.00
5	Manufacturing Variable Cost per Unit	$2.00
6		
7	Outsourcing Cost per Unit	$3.50
8		
9		
10	**Model**	
11	Quantity	10,000
12		
13	Total Cost to Produce	$254,000.00
14		
15	Total Cost to Outsource	$35,000.00
16		
17	Savings due to Outsourcing	$219,000.00
18		
19		

Document the model and use proper formatting and color as needed A good spreadsheet model is well documented. Clear labels and proper formatting and alignment facilitate navigation and understanding. For example, if the values in a worksheet are cost, currency formatting should be used. Also, no cell with content should be unlabeled. A new user should be able to easily understand the model and its calculations. If color makes a model easier to understand and navigate, use it for cells and labels.

Use simple formulas Clear, simple formulas can reduce errors and make it easier to maintain the spreadsheet. Long and complex calculations should be divided into several cells. This makes the formula easier to understand and easier to edit. Avoid using numbers in a formula (separate the data from the model). Instead, put the number in a cell in the parameters section of your worksheet and refer to the cell location in the formula. Building the formula in this manner avoids having to edit the formula for a simple data change. For example, equation (10.3), the savings due to outsourcing, can be calculated as follows: $S(q) = TMC(q) - TPC(q) = FC + (VC)q - Pq = FC + (VC - P)q$. Since $VC - P = 3.50 - 2 = 1.50$, we could have just entered the following formula in a single cell: =234,000 −1.50 * B11. This is a very bad idea because if any of the input data change, the formula must be edited. Furthermore, the user would not know the values of *VC* and *P*, only that, for the current values, the difference is 1.50. The approach in Figure 10.3 is more transparent, is simpler, lends itself better to analysis of changes in the parameters, and is less likely to contain errors.

NOTES + COMMENTS

1. Some users of influence diagrams recommend using different symbols for the various types of model entities. For example, circles might denote known inputs, ovals might denote uncertain inputs, rectangles might denote decisions or controllable inputs, triangles might denote calculations, and so forth.
2. The use of color in a spreadsheet model is an effective way to draw attention to a cell or set of cells. For example, we shaded cell B11 in Figure 10.3 to draw attention to the fact that *q* is a controllable input. However, avoid using too much color. Overdoing it may overwhelm users and actually have a negative impact on their ability to understand the model.
3. Holding down the **Ctrl** key and pressing the ~ key (usually located above the Tab key) in Excel will toggle between displaying the formulas in a spreadsheet and the values.

10.2 What-If Analysis

Excel offers a number of tools to facilitate what-if analysis. In this section we introduce two such tools, Data Tables and Goal Seek. Both of these tools are designed to rid the user of the tedious manual trial-and-error approach to analysis. Let us see how these two tools can help us analyze Nowlin's make-versus-buy decision.

Data Tables

An Excel **Data Table** quantifies the impact of changing the value of a specific input on an output of interest. Excel can generate either a **one-way data table**, which summarizes a single input's impact on the output, or a **two-way data table**, which summarizes two inputs' impact on the output.

Let us consider how savings due to outsourcing changes as the quantity of Vipers changes. This should help us answer the question, "For which values of *q* is outsourcing more cost-effective?" A one-way data table changing the value of quantity and reporting savings due to outsourcing would be very useful. We will use the previously developed Nowlin spreadsheet for this analysis.

The first step in creating a one-way data table is to construct a sorted list of the values you would like to consider for the input. Let us investigate the quantity *q* over a range from 0 to 300,000 in increments of 25,000 units. Figure 10.4 shows the data entered in cells D5 through D17, with a column label in D4. This column of data is the set of values that Excel will use as inputs for *q*. Since the output of interest is savings due to outsourcing (located in cell B17), we have entered the formula =B17 in cell E4. In general, set the cell to the right of the label to the cell location of the output variable of interest. Once the basic structure is in place, we invoke the Data Table tool using the following steps:

FIGURE 10.4 The Input for Constructing a One-Way Data Table for Nowlin Plastics

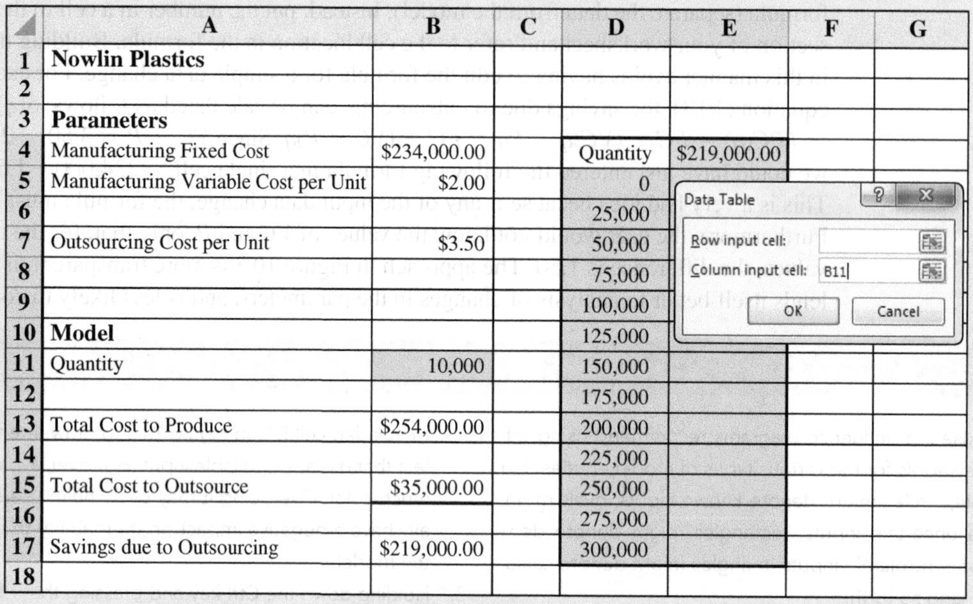

	A	B	C	D	E	F	G
1	**Nowlin Plastics**						
2							
3	**Parameters**						
4	Manufacturing Fixed Cost	$234,000.00		Quantity	$219,000.00		
5	Manufacturing Variable Cost per Unit	$2.00		0			
6				25,000			
7	Outsourcing Cost per Unit	$3.50		50,000			
8				75,000			
9				100,000			
10	**Model**			125,000			
11	Quantity	10,000		150,000			
12				175,000			
13	Total Cost to Produce	$254,000.00		200,000			
14				225,000			
15	Total Cost to Outsource	$35,000.00		250,000			
16				275,000			
17	Savings due to Outsourcing	$219,000.00		300,000			
18							

Data Table

Row input cell:

Column input cell: B11

OK Cancel

In versions of Excel prior to Excel 2016, the What-If Analysis tool can be found in the Data Tools group.

Step 1. Select cells D4:E17
Step 2. Click the **Data** tab in the Ribbon
Step 3. Click **What-If Analysis** in the **Forecast** group, and select **Data Table**
Step 4. When the **Data Table** dialog box appears, enter *B11* in the **Column input cell:** box
Click **OK**

Entering B11 in the Column input cell: box indicates that the column of data corresponds to different values of the input located in cell B11.

As shown in Figure 10.5, the table will be populated with the value of savings due to outsourcing for each value of quantity of Vipers in the table. For example, when $q = 25{,}000$ we see that $S(25{,}000) = \$196{,}500$, and when $q = 250{,}000$, $S(250{,}000) = -\$141{,}000$. A negative value for savings due to outsourcing means that manufacturing is cheaper than outsourcing for that quantity.

We have learned something very valuable from this table. Not only have we quantified the savings due to outsourcing for a number of quantities, we know too that, for quantities of 150,000 units or less, outsourcing is cheaper than manufacturing and that, for quantities of 175,000 units or more, manufacturing is cheaper than outsourcing. Depending on Nowlin's confidence in their demand forecast for the Viper product for next year, we have likely satisfactorily answered the make-versus-buy question. If, for example, management is highly confident that demand will be at least 200,000 units of Viper, then clearly they should manufacture the Viper rather than outsource. If management believes that Viper demand next year will be close to 150,000 units, they might still decide to manufacture rather than outsource. At 150,000 units, the savings due to outsourcing is only \$9,000. That might not justify outsourcing if, for example, the quality assurance standards at the outsource firm are not at an acceptable level. We have provided management with valuable information that they may use to decide whether to make or buy. Next we illustrate how to construct a two-way data table.

FIGURE 10.5 Results of One-Way Data Table for Nowlin Plastics

	A	B	C	D	E
1	**Nowlin Plastics**				
2					
3	**Parameters**				
4	Manufacturing Fixed Cost	$234,000.00		Quantity	$219,000.00
5	Manufacturing Variable Cost per Unit	$2.00		0	$234,000
6				25,000	$196,500
7	Outsourcing Cost per Unit	$3.50		50,000	$159,000
8				75,000	$121,500
9				100,000	$84,000
10	**Model**			125,000	$46,500
11	Quantity	10,000		150,000	$9,000
12				175,000	–$28,500
13	Total Cost to Produce	$254,000.00		200,000	–$66,000
14				225,000	–$103,500
15	Total Cost to Outsource	$35,000.00		250,000	–$141,000
16				275,000	–$178,500
17	Savings due to Outsourcing	$219,000.00		300,000	–$216,000
18					

Suppose that Nowlin has now received five different bids on the per-unit cost for outsourcing the production of the Viper. Clearly, the lowest bid provides the greatest savings. However, the selection of the outsource firm—if Nowlin decides to outsource—will depend on many factors, including reliability, quality, and on-time delivery. So it would be instructive to quantify the differences in savings for various quantities and bids. The five current bids are $2.89, $3.13, $3.50, $3.54, and $3.59. We may use the Excel Data Table to construct a two-way data table with quantity as a column and the five bids as a row, as shown in Figure 10.6.

In Figure 10.6, we have entered various quantities in cells D5 through D17, as in the one-way table. These correspond to cell B11 in our model. In cells E4 through I4, we have entered the bids. These correspond to B7, the outsourcing cost per unit. In cell D4, above the column input values and to the left of the row input values, we have entered the formula =B17, the location of the output of interest, in this case, savings due to outsourcing. Once the table inputs have been entered into the spreadsheet, we perform the following steps to construct the two-way Data Table.

In versions of Excel prior to Excel 2016, the **What-If Analysis** *tool can be found in the Data Tools group*

Step 1. Select cells D4:I17
Step 2. Click the **Data** tab in the Ribbon
Step 3. Click **What-If Analysis** in the **Forecast** group, and select **Data Table**
Step 4. When the **Data Table** dialog box appears:
Enter *B7* in the **Row input cell:** box
Enter *B11* in the **Column input cell:** box
Click **OK**

Figure 10.6 shows the selected cells and the **Data Table** dialog box. The results are shown in Figure 10.7.

We now have a table that shows the savings due to outsourcing for each combination of quantity and bid price. For example, for 75,000 Vipers at a cost of $3.13 per unit, the

FIGURE 10.6 The Input for Constructing a Two-Way Data Table for Nowlin Plastics

	A	B	C	D	E	F	G	H	I	J	K	L	M
1	**Nowlin Plastics**												
2													
3	**Parameters**												
4	Manufacturing Fixed Cost	$234,000.00		$219,000.00	$2.89	$3.13	$3.50	$3.54	$3.59				
5	Manufacturing Variable Cost per Unit	$2.00		0									
6				25,000									
7	Outsourcing Cost per Unit	$3.50		50,000									
8				75,000									
9				100,000									
10	**Model**			125,000									
11	Quantity	10,000		150,000									
12				175,000									
13	Total Cost to Produce	$254,000.00		200,000									
14				225,000									
15	Total Cost to Outsource	$35,000.00		250,000									
16				275,000									
17	Savings due to Outsourcing	$219,000.00		300,000									
18													
19													

Data Table

Row input cell: B7

Column input cell: B11

OK Cancel

FIGURE 10.7 Results of a Two-Way Data Table for Nowlin Plastics

	A	B	C	D	E	F	G	H	I
1	**Nowlin Plastics**								
2									
3	**Parameters**								
4	Manufacturing Fixed Cost	$234,000.00		$219,000.00	$2.89	$3.13	$3.50	$3.54	$3.59
5	Manufacturing Variable Cost per Unit	$2.00		0	$234,000	$234,000	$234,000	$234,000	$234,000
6				25,000	$211,750	$205,750	$196,500	$195,500	$194,250
7	Outsourcing Cost per Unit	$3.50		50,000	$189,500	$177,500	$159,000	$157,000	$154,500
8				75,000	$167,250	$149,250	$121,500	$118,500	$114,750
9				100,000	$145,000	$121,000	$84,000	$80,000	$75,000
10	**Model**			125,000	$122,750	$92,750	$46,500	$41,500	$35,250
11	Quantity	10,000		150,000	$100,500	$64,500	$9,000	$3,000	–$4,500
12				175,000	$78,250	$36,250	–$28,500	–$35,500	–$44,250
13	Total Cost to Produce	$254,000.00		200,000	$56,000	$8,000	–$66,000	–$74,000	–$84,000
14				225,000	$33,750	–$20,250	–$103,500	–$112,500	–$123,750
15	Total Cost to Outsource	$35,000.00		250,000	$11,500	–$48,500	–$141,000	–$151,000	–$163,500
16				275,000	–$10,750	–$76,750	–$178,500	–$189,500	–$203,250
17	Savings due to Outsourcing	$219,000.00		300,000	–$33,000	–$105,000	–$216,000	–$228,000	–$243,000
18									

savings from buying versus manufacturing the units is $149,250. We can also see the range for the quantity for each bid price that results in a negative savings. For these quantities and bid combinations, it is better to manufacture than to outsource.

Using the Data Table allows us to quantify the savings due to outsourcing for the quantities and bid prices specified. However, the table does not tell us the exact number at which the transition occurs from outsourcing being cheaper to manufacturing being cheaper. For example, although it is clear from the table that for a bid price of $3.50 the savings due to outsourcing goes from positive to negative at some quantity between 150,000 units and 175,000 units, we know only that this transition occurs somewhere in that range. As we illustrate next, the what-if analysis tool Goal Seek can tell us the precise number at which this transition occurs.

Goal Seek

Excel's **Goal Seek** tool allows the user to determine the value of an input cell that will cause the value of a related output cell to equal some specified value (the *goal*). In the case of Nowlin Plastics, suppose we want to know the value of the quantity of Vipers at which it becomes more cost-effective to manufacture rather than outsource. For example, we see from the table in Figure 10.7 that, for a bid price of $3.50 and some quantity between 150,000 units and 175,000 units, savings due to outsourcing goes from positive to negative. Somewhere in this range of quantity, the savings due to outsourcing is zero, and that is the point at which Nowlin would be indifferent to manufacturing and outsourcing. We may use Goal Seek to find the quantity of Vipers that satisfies the goal of zero savings due to outsourcing for a bid price of $3.50. The following steps describe how to use Goal Seek to find this point.

In versions of Excel prior to Excel 2016, the ***What-If Analysis*** *tool can be found in the* ***Data Tools*** *group*

Step 1. Click the **Data** tab in the Ribbon
Step 2. Click **What-If Analysis** in the **Forecast** group, and select **Goal Seek**
Step 3. When the **Goal Seek** dialog box appears (Figure 10.8):
Enter *B17* in the **Set cell:** box

FIGURE 10.8 Goal Seek Dialog Box for Nowlin Plastics

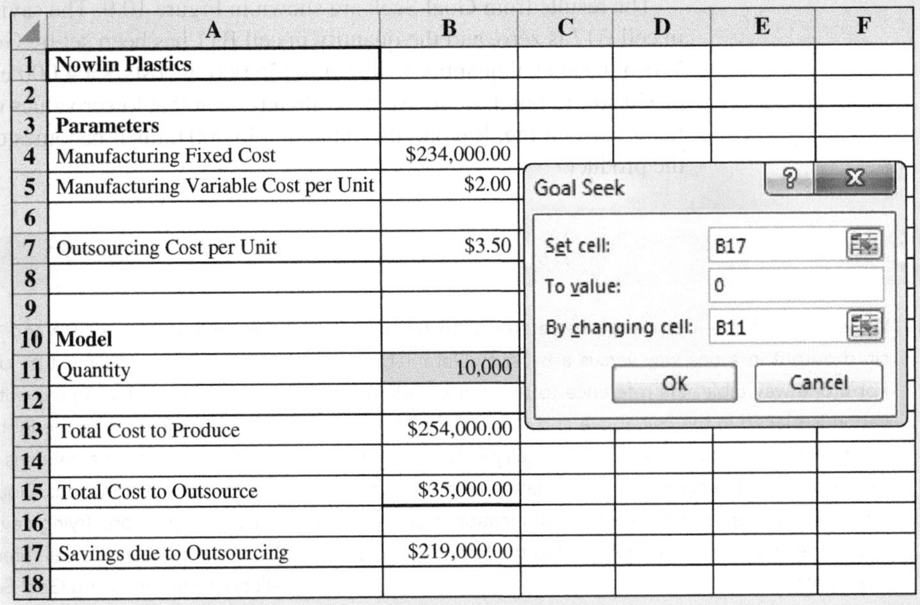

	A	B	C	D	E	F
1	**Nowlin Plastics**					
2						
3	**Parameters**					
4	Manufacturing Fixed Cost	$234,000.00				
5	Manufacturing Variable Cost per Unit	$2.00				
6						
7	Outsourcing Cost per Unit	$3.50				
8						
9						
10	**Model**					
11	Quantity	10,000				
12						
13	Total Cost to Produce	$254,000.00				
14						
15	Total Cost to Outsource	$35,000.00				
16						
17	Savings due to Outsourcing	$219,000.00				
18						

Goal Seek
Set cell: B17
To value: 0
By changing cell: B11
OK Cancel

FIGURE 10.9 Results from Goal Seek for Nowlin Plastics

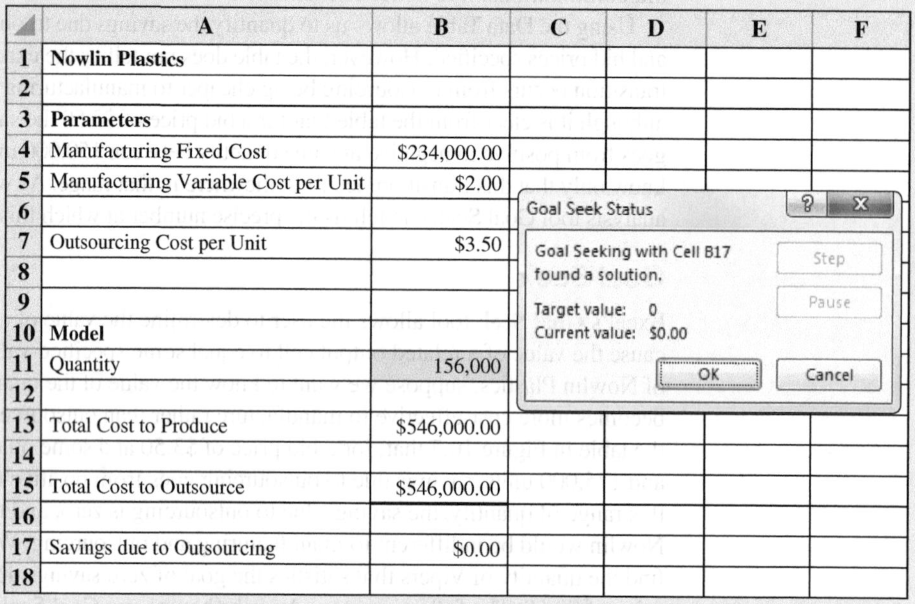

	A	B	C	D	E	F
1	**Nowlin Plastics**					
2						
3	**Parameters**					
4	Manufacturing Fixed Cost	$234,000.00				
5	Manufacturing Variable Cost per Unit	$2.00				
6						
7	Outsourcing Cost per Unit	$3.50				
8						
9						
10	**Model**					
11	Quantity	156,000				
12						
13	Total Cost to Produce	$546,000.00				
14						
15	Total Cost to Outsource	$546,000.00				
16						
17	Savings due to Outsourcing	$0.00				
18						

Goal Seek Status

Goal Seeking with Cell B17 found a solution.

Target value: 0
Current value: $0.00

Step | Pause | OK | Cancel

Enter *0* in the **To value:** box
Enter *B11* in the **By changing cell:** box
Click **OK**

Step 4. When the **Goal Seek Status** dialog box appears, click **OK**

The completed Goal Seek dialog box is shown in Figure 10.8.

The results from Goal Seek are shown in Figure 10.9. The savings due to outsourcing in cell B17 is zero, and the quantity in cell B11 has been set by Goal Seek to 156,000. When the annual quantity required is 156,000, it costs $564,000 either to manufacture the product or to purchase it. We have already seen that lower values of the quantity required favor outsourcing. Beyond the value of 156,000 units it becomes cheaper to manufacture the product.

NOTES + COMMENTS

1. We emphasize the location of the reference to the desired output in a one-way versus a two-way Data Table. For a one-way table, the reference to the output cell location is placed in the cell above and to the right of the column of input data so that it is in the cell just to the right of the label of the column of input data. For a two-way table, the reference to the output cell location is placed above the column of input data and to the left of the row input data.
2. Notice that in Figures 10.5 and 10.7, the tables are formatted as currency. This must be done manually after the table is constructed using the options in the **Number** group under the **Home** tab in the Ribbon. It also a good idea to label the rows and the columns of the table.
3. For very complex functions, Goal Seek might not converge to a stable solution. Trying several different initial values (the actual value in the cell referenced in the **By changing cell:** box) when invoking Goal Seek may help.

10.3 Some Useful Excel Functions for Modeling

In this section we use several examples to introduce additional Excel functions that have proven useful in modeling decision problems. Many of these functions will be used in the chapters on optimization, simulation, and decision analysis.

SUM and SUMPRODUCT

Two very useful functions are SUM and SUMPRODUCT. The SUM function adds up all of the numbers in a range of cells. The SUMPRODUCT function returns the sum of the products of elements in a set of arrays. As we shall see in Chapter 11, SUMPRODUCT is very useful for linear optimization models.

Let us illustrate the use of SUM and SUMPRODUCT by considering a transportation problem faced by Foster Generators. This problem involves the transportation of a product from three plants to four distribution centers. Foster Generators operates plants in Cleveland, Ohio; Bedford, Indiana; and York, Pennsylvania. Production capacities for the three plants over the next three-month planning period are known.

The firm distributes its generators through four regional distribution centers located in Boston, Massachusetts; Chicago, Illinois; St. Louis, Missouri; and Lexington, Kentucky. Foster has forecasted demand for the three-month period for each of the distribution centers. The per-unit shipping cost from each plant to each distribution center is also known. Management would like to determine how much of its products should be shipped from each plant to each distribution center.

A transportation analyst developed a what-if spreadsheet model to help Foster develop a plan for how to ship its generators from the plants to the distribution centers to minimize cost. Of course, capacity at the plants must not be exceeded, and forecasted demand must be satisfied at each of the four distribution centers. The what-if model is shown in Figure 10.10.

The parameters section is rows 2 through 10. Cells B5 through E7 contain the per-unit shipping cost from each origin (plant) to each destination (distribution center). For example, it costs $2.00 to ship one generator from Bedford to St. Louis. The plant capacities are given in cells F5 through F7, and the distribution center demands appear in cells B8 through E8.

The model is in rows 11 through 20. Trial values of shipment amounts from each plant to each distribution center appear in the shaded cells, B17 through E19. The total cost of shipping for this proposed plan is calculated in cell B13 using the SUMPRODUCT function. The general form of the SUMPRODUCT function is:

The arrays used as arguments in the SUMPRODUCT function must be of the same dimension. For example, in the Foster Generator model, B5:E7 is an array of three rows and four columns. B17:E19 is an array of the same dimensions.

=SUMPRODUCT(*array1*, *array2*).

The function pairs each element of the first array with its counterpart in the second array, multiplies the elements of the pairs together, and adds the results. In cell B13, =SUMPRODUCT(B5:E7,B17:E19) pairs the per-unit cost of shipping for each origin-destination pair with the proposed shipping plan for that and adds their products:

B5*B17 + C5*C17 + D5*D17 + E5*E17 + B6*B18 + · · · + E7*E19.

In cells F17 through F19, the SUM function is used to add up the amounts shipped for each plant. The general form of the SUM function is

=SUM(*range*),

where *range* is a range of cells. For example, the function in cell F17 is =SUM(B17:E17), which adds the values in B17, C17, D17, and E17: 5000 + 0 + 0 + 0 = 5000. The SUM function in cells B20 through E20 does the same for the amounts shipped to each distribution center.

FIGURE 10.10 What-If Model for Foster Generators

	A	B	C	D	E	F	G
1	**Foster Generators**						
2	**Parameters**						
3	Shipping Cost/Unit		**Destination**				
4	**Origin**	Boston	Chicago	St. Louis	Lexington	Supply	
5	Cleveland	3	2	7	6	5000	
6	Bedford	6	5	2	3	6000	
7	York	2	5	4	5	2500	
8	Demand	6000	4000	2000	1500		
9							
10							
11	**Model**						
12							
13	**Total Cost**	=SUMPRODUCT(B5:E7,B17:E19)					
14							
15			**Destination**				
16	**Origin**	Boston	Chicago	St. Louis	Lexington	**Total**	
17	Cleveland	5000	0	0	0	=SUM(B17:E17)	
18	Bedford	1000	4000	1000	0	=SUM(B18:E18)	
19	York	0	0	1000	1500	=SUM(B19:E19)	
20	**Total**	=SUM(B17:B19)	=SUM(C17:C19)	=SUM(D17:D19)	=SUM(E17:E19)		
21							

	A	B	C	D	E	F	G
1	**Foster Generators**						
2	**Parameters**						
3	Shipping Cost/Unit		**Destination**				
4	**Origin**	Boston	Chicago	St. Louis	Lexington	Supply	
5	Cleveland	$3.00	$2.00	$7.00	$6.00	5000	
6	Bedford	$6.00	$5.00	$2.00	$3.00	6000	
7	York	$2.00	$5.00	$4.00	$5.00	2500	
8	Demand	6000	4000	2000	1500		
9							
10							
11	**Model**						
12							
13	**Total Cost**	$54,500.00					
14							
15			**Destination**				
16	**Origin**	Boston	Chicago	St. Louis	Lexington	**Total**	
17	Cleveland	5000	0	0	0	5000	
18	Bedford	1000	4000	1000	0	6000	
19	York	0	0	1000	1500	2500	
20	**Total**	6000	4000	2000	1500		
21							

By comparing the amounts shipped from each plant to the capacity for that plant, we see that no plant violates its capacity. Likewise, by comparing the amounts shipped to each distribution center to the demand at that center, we see that all demands are met. The total shipping cost for the proposed plan is $54,500. Is this the lowest-cost plan? It is not clear. We will revisit the Foster Generators problem in Chapter 11, where we discuss linear optimization models.

IF and COUNTIF

Gambrell Manufacturing produces car stereos. Stereos are composed of a variety of components that the company must carry in inventory to keep production running smoothly. However, because inventory can be a costly investment, Gambrell generally likes to keep its components inventory to a minimum. To help monitor and control its inventory, Gambrell uses an inventory policy known as an *order-up-to policy*.

The order-up-to policy is as follows. Whenever the inventory on hand drops below a certain level, enough units are ordered to return the inventory to that predetermined level. If the current number of units in inventory, denoted by H, drops below M units, enough inventory is ordered to get the level back up to M units. M is called the *order-up-to point*. Stated mathematically, if Q is the amount we order, then:

$$Q = M - H.$$

An inventory model for Gambrell Manufacturing appears in Figure 10.11. In the upper half of the worksheet, the component ID number, inventory on hand (H), order-up-to point (M), and cost per unit are given for each of four components. Also given in this sheet is the fixed cost per order. The fixed cost is interpreted as follows: Each time a component is ordered, it costs Gambrell $120 to process the order. The fixed cost of $120 is incurred whenever an order is placed, regardless of how many units are ordered.

The model portion of the worksheet calculates the order quantity for each component. For example, for component 570, $M = 100$ and $H = 5$, so $Q = M - H = 100 - 5 = 95$. For component 741, $M = 70$ and $H = 70$ and no units are ordered because the on-hand inventory of 70 units is equal to the order-up-to point of 70. The calculations are similar for the other two components.

Depending on the number of units ordered, Gambrell receives a discount on the cost per unit. If 50 or more units are ordered, there is a quantity discount of 10% on every unit purchased. For example, for component 741, the cost per unit is $4.50, and 95 units are ordered. Because 95 exceeds the 50-unit requirement, there is a 10% discount, and the cost per unit is reduced to $4.50 – 0.1($4.50) = $4.50 – $0.45 = $4.05. Not including the fixed cost, the cost of goods purchased is then $4.05(95) = $384.75.

The Excel functions used to perform these calculations are shown in Figure 10.11 (for clarity, we show formulas for only the first three columns). The IF function is used to calculate the purchase cost of goods for each component in row 17. The general form of the IF function is:

=IF(*condition, result if condition is true, result if condition is false*).

For example, in cell B17 we have =IF(B16 >= $B$10, $B$11*B6, B6)*B16. This statement says that, if the order quantity (cell B16) is greater than or equal to minimum amount required for a discount (cell B10), then the cost per unit is B11*B6 (there is a 10% discount, so the cost is 90% of the original cost); otherwise, there is no discount, and the cost per unit is the amount given in cell B6. The cost per unit computed by the IF function is then multiplied by the order quantity (B16) to obtain the total purchase cost of component 570. The purchase cost of goods for the other components are computed in a like manner.

The total cost in cell B23 is the sum of the total fixed ordering costs (B21) and the total cost of goods (B22). Because we place three orders (one each for components 570, 578, and 755), the fixed cost of the orders is 3*120 = $360.

FIGURE 10.11 Gambrell Manufacturing Component Ordering Model

	A	B	C
1	**Gambrell Manufacturing**		
2	**Parameters**		
3	Component ID	**570**	**578**
4	Inventory On-Hand	5	30
5	Order-up-to Point	100	55
6	Cost per Unit	4.5	12.5
7			
8	Fixed Cost per Order	120	
9			
10	Minimum Order Size for Discount	50	
11	Discounted to	0.9	
12			
13	**Model**		
14			
15	Component ID	=B3	=C3
16	Order Quantity	=B5–B4	=C5–C4
17	Cost of Goods	=IF(B16 >= $B$10, $B$11*B6,B6)*B16	=IF(C16 >= $B$10, $B$11*C6,C6)*C16
18			
19	Total Number of Orders	=COUNTIF(B16:E16,">0")	
20			
21	Total Fixed Costs	=B19*B8	
22	Total Cost of Goods	=SUM(B17:E17)	
23	Total Cost	=SUM(B21:B22)	
24			

	A	B	C	D	E
1	**Gambrell Manufacturing**				
2	**Parameters**				
3	Component ID	**570**	**578**	**741**	**755**
4	Inventory On-Hand	5	30	70	17
5	Order-up-to Point	100	55	70	45
6	Cost per Unit	$4.50	$12.50	$3.26	$4.15
7					
8	Fixed Cost per Order	$120			
9					
10	Minimum Order Size for Discount	50			
11	Discounted to	90%			
12					
13	**Model**				
14					
15	Component ID	**570**	**578**	**741**	**755**
16	Order Quantity	95	25	0	28
17	Cost of Goods	$384.75	$312.50	$0.00	$116.20
18					
19	Total Number of Orders	3			
20					
21	Total Fixed Costs	$360.00			
22	Total Cost of Goods	$813.45			
23	Total Cost	$1,173.45			
24					

Notice the use of absolute references to B10 and B11 in row 17. As discussed in Appendix A, this facilitates copying cell B17 to cells C17, D17, and E17.

MODEL *file*
Gambrell

The COUNTIF function in cell B19 is used to count how many times we order. In particular, it counts the number of components having a positive order quantity. The general form of the COUNTIF function (which was discussed in Chapter 2 for creating frequency distributions) is:

=COUNTIF(*range, condition*).

The *range* is the range to search for the *condition*. The condition is the test to be counted when satisfied. In the Gambrell model in Figure 10.11, cell B19 counts the number of cells that are greater than zero in the range of cells B16:E16 via the syntax =COUNTIF(B16:E16, ">0"). Note that quotes are required for the condition with the COUNTIF function. In the model, because only cells B16, C16, and E16 are greater than zero, the COUNTIF function in cell B19 returns 3.

As we have seen, IF and COUNTIF are powerful functions that allow us to make calculations based on a condition holding (or not). There are other such conditional functions available in Excel. In a problem at the end of this chapter, we ask you to investigate one such function, the SUMIF function. Another conditional function that is extremely useful in modeling is the VLOOKUP function, which is illustrated with an example in the next section.

VLOOKUP

The director of sales at Granite Insurance needs to award bonuses to her sales force based on performance. There are 15 salespeople, each with his or her own territory. Based on the size and population of the territory, each salesperson has a sales target for the year.

The measure of performance for awarding bonuses is the percentage achieved above the sales target. Based on this metric, a salesperson is placed into one of five bonus bands and awarded bonus points. After all salespeople are placed in a band and awarded points, each is awarded a percentage of the bonus pool, based on the percentage of the total points awarded. The sales director has created a spreadsheet model to calculate the bonuses to be awarded. The spreadsheet model is shown in Figure 10.12 (note that we have hidden rows 19–28).

As shown in cell E3 in Figure 10.12, the bonus pool is $250,000 for this year. The bonus bands are in cells A7:C11. In this table, column A gives the lower limit of the bonus band, column B the upper limit, and column C the bonus points awarded to anyone in that bonus band. For example, salespeople who achieve 56% above their sales target would be awarded 15 bonus points.

As shown in Figure 10.12, the name and percentage above the target achieved for each salesperson appear below the bonus-band table in columns A and B. In column C, the VLOOKUP function is used to look in the bonus band table and automatically assign the number of bonus points to each salesperson.

The VLOOKUP function allows the user to pull a subset of data from a larger table of data based on some criterion. The general form of the VLOOKUP function is:

=VLOOKUP(*value, table, index, range*),

where

value = the value to search for in the first column of the table
table = the cell range containing the table
index = the column in the table containing the value to be returned
range = TRUE if looking for the first approximate match of *value* and FALSE if looking for an exact match of *value* (We will explain the difference between approximate and exact matches in a moment.)

VLOOKUP assumes that the first column of the table is sorted in ascending order.

If the range in the VLOOKUP function is FALSE, the only change is that Excel searches for an exact match of the first argument in the first column of the data.

The VLOOKUP function for salesperson Choi in cell C18 is as follows:

=VLOOKUP(B18,$A$7:$C$11,3,TRUE).

This function uses the percentage above target sales from cell B18 and searches the first column of the table defined by A7:C11. Because the *range* is set to TRUE, indicating

FIGURE 10.12 Granite Insurance Bonus Model

	A	B	C	D	E
1	**Granite Insurance Bonus Awards**				
2					
3	**Parameters**			Bonus Pool	250000
4					
5	Bonus Bands to be awarded for percentage above target sales.				
6	**Lower Limit**	**Upper Limit**	**Bonus Points**		
7	0	0.1	0		
8	0.11	0.5	10		
9	0.51	0.79	15		
10	0.8	0.99	25		
11	1	100	40		
12					
13	**Model**				
14	**Last Name**	**% Above Target Sales**	**Bonus Points**	**% of Pool**	**Bonus Amount**
15	Barth	0.83	=VLOOKUP(B15,$A$7:$C$11,3,TRUE)	=C15/$C$30	=D15*$E$3
16	Benson	0	=VLOOKUP(B16,$A$7:$C$11,3,TRUE)	=C16/$C$30	=D16*$E$3
17	Capel	1.18	=VLOOKUP(B17,$A$7:$C$11,3,TRUE)	=C17/$C$30	=D17*$E$3
18	Choi	0.44	=VLOOKUP(B18,$A$7:$C$11,3,TRUE)	=C18/$C$30	=D18*$E$3
29	Ruebush	0.85	=VLOOKUP(B29,$A$7:$C$11,3,TRUE)	=C29/$C$30	=D29*$E$3
30		Total	=SUM(C15:C29)	=SUM(D15:D29)	=SUM(E15:E29)

	A	B	C	D	E
1	**Granite Insurance Bonus Awards**				
2					
3	**Parameters**			Bonus Pool	$250,000
4					
5	Bonus Bands to be awarded for percentage above target sales.				
6	**Lower Limit**	**Upper Limit**	**Bonus Points**		
7	0%	10%	0		
8	11%	50%	10		
9	51%	79%	15		
10	80%	99%	25		
11	100%	10000%	40		
12					
13	**Model**				
14	**Last Name**	**% Above Target Sales**	**Bonus Points**	**% of Pool**	**Bonus Amount**
15	Barth	83%	25	8.5%	$21,186.44
16	Benson	0%	0	0.0%	$0.00
17	Capel	118%	40	13.6%	$33,898.31
18	Choi	44%	10	3.4%	$8,474.58
29	Ruebush	85%	25	8.5%	$21,186.44
30		Total	295	100%	$250,000.00

a search for the first approximate match, Excel searches in the first column of the table from the top until it finds a number strictly greater than the value of B18. B18 is 44%, and the first value in the table in column A larger than 44% is in cell A9 (51%). It then backs up one row (to row 8). In other words, it finds the last value in the first column less than or equal to 44%. Because a 3 is in the third argument of the VLOOKUP function, it takes the element in row 8 of the third column of the table, which is 10 bonus points. In summary, the VLOOKUP with *range* set to TRUE takes the first argument and searches the first column of the table for the last row that is less than or equal the first argument. It then selects from that row, the element in the column number of the third argument.

Once all salespeople are awarded bonus points based on VLOOKUP and the bonus-band table, the total number of bonus points awarded is given in cell C30 using the SUM function. Each person's bonus points as a percentage of the total awarded is calculated in column D, and in column E each person is awarded that percentage of the bonus pool. As a check, cells D30 and E30 give the total percentages and dollar amounts awarded.

Numerous mathematical, logical, and financial functions are available in Excel. In addition to those discussed here, we will introduce you to other functions, as needed, in examples and end-of-chapter problems. Having already discussed principles for building good spreadsheet models and after having seen a variety of spreadsheet models, we turn now to how to audit Excel models to ensure model integrity.

10.4 Auditing Spreadsheet Models

Excel contains a variety of tools to assist you in the development and debugging of spreadsheet models. These tools are found in the **Formula Auditing** group of the **Formulas** tab, as shown in Figure 10.13. Let us review each of the tools available in this group.

Trace Precedents and Dependents

After selecting cells, the Trace Precedents button creates arrows pointing to the selected cell from cells that are part of the formula in that cell. The Trace Dependents button, on the other hand, shows arrows pointing from the selected cell to cells that depend on the selected cell. Both of the tools are excellent for quickly ascertaining how parts of a model are linked.

An example of Trace Precedents is shown in Figure 10.14. Here we have opened the Foster Generators Excel file, selected cell B13, and clicked the **Trace Precedents** button in the **Formula Auditing** group. Recall that the cost in cell B13 is calculated as the SUMPRODUCT of the per-unit shipping cost and units shipped. In Figure 10.14, to show this relationship, arrows are drawn to these areas of the spreadsheet to cell B13. These arrows may be removed by clicking on the **Remove Arrows** button in the **Auditing Tools** group.

An example of Trace Dependents is shown in Figure 10.15. We have selected cell E18, the units shipped from Bedford to Lexington, and clicked on the **Trace Dependents** button

FIGURE 10.13 The Formula Auditing Group

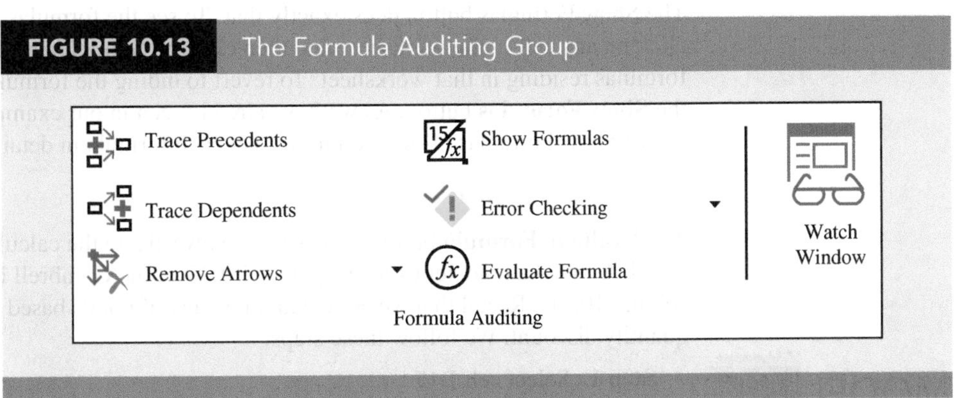

FIGURE 10.14 Trace Precedents for Foster Generator

	A	B	C	D	E	F	G
1	**Foster Generators**						
2	**Parameters**						
3	Shipping Cost/Unit		**Destination**				
4	**Origin**	Boston	Chicago	St. Louis	Lexington	Supply	
5	Cleveland	$3.00	$2.00	$7.00	$6.00	5000	
6	Bedford	$6.00	$5.00	$2.00	$3.00	6000	
7	York	$2.00	$5.00	$4.00	$5.00	2500	
8	Demand	6000	4000	2000	1500		
9							
10							
11	**Model**						
12							
13	**Total Cost**	$54,500.00					
14							
15			**Destination**				
16	**Origin**	Boston	Chicago	St. Louis	Lexington	**Total**	
17	Cleveland	5000	0	0	0	5000	
18	Bedford	1000	4000	1000	0	6000	
19	York	0	0	1000	1500	2500	
20	**Total**	6000	4000	2000	1500		
21							
22							

in the **Formula Auditing** group. As shown in Figure 10.15, units shipped from Bedford to Lexington impacts the cost function in cell B13, the total units shipped from Bedford given in cell F18, as well as the total units shipped to Lexington in cell E20. These arrows may be removed by clicking on the **Remove Arrows** button in the **Auditing Tools** group.

Trace Precedents and Trace Dependents can highlight errors in copying and formula construction by showing that incorrect sections of the worksheet are referenced.

Show Formulas

The Show Formulas button does exactly that. To see the formulas in a worksheet, simply click on any cell in the worksheet and then click on **Show Formulas**. You will see the formulas residing in that worksheet. To revert to hiding the formulas, click again on the **Show Formulas** button. As we have already seen in our examples in this chapter, the use of Show Formulas allows you to inspect each formula in detail in its cell location.

Evaluate Formulas

The **Evaluate Formula** button allows you to investigate the calculations of a cell in great detail. As an example, let us investigate cell B17 of the Gambrell Manufacturing model (Figure 10.11). Recall that we are calculating cost of goods based on whether there is a quantity discount. We follow these steps:

Step 1. Select cell B17
Step 2. Click the **Formulas** tab in the Ribbon
Step 3. Click the **Evaluate Formula** button in the **Formula Auditing** group

FIGURE 10.15 Trace Dependents for the Foster Generators Model

	A	B	C	D	E	F	G
1	**Foster Generators**						
2	**Parameters**						
3	Shipping Cost/Unit		**Destination**				
4	**Origin**	Boston	Chicago	St. Louis	Lexington	Supply	
5	Cleveland	$3.00	$2.00	$7.00	$6.00	5000	
6	Bedford	$6.00	$5.00	$2.00	$3.00	6000	
7	York	$2.00	$5.00	$4.00	$5.00	2500	
8	Demand	6000	4000	2000	1500		
9							
10							
11	**Model**						
12							
13	**Total Cost**	$54,500.00					
14							
15			**Destination**				
16	**Origin**	Boston	Chicago	St. Louis	Lexington	**Total**	
17	Cleveland	5000	0	0	0	5000	
18	Bedford	1000	4000	1000	0	6000	
19	York	0	0	1000	1500	2500	
20	**Total**	6000	4000	2000	1500		
21							
22							

Step 4. When the **Evaluate Formula** dialog box appears (Figure 10.16), click the **Evaluate** button

Step 5. Repeat Step 4 until the formula has been completely evaluated

Step 6. Click **Close**

Figure 10.17 shows the **Evaluate Formula** dialog box for cell B17 in the Gambrell Manufacturing spreadsheet model after four clicks of the **Evaluate** button.

The Evaluate Formula tool provides an excellent means of identifying the exact location of an error in a formula.

Error Checking

The **Error Checking** button provides an automatic means of checking for mathematical errors within formulas of a worksheet. Clicking on the **Error Checking** button causes Excel to check every formula in the sheet for calculation errors. If an error is found, the **Error Checking** dialog box appears. An example for a hypothetical division by zero error is shown in Figure 10.18. From this box, the formula can be edited, the calculation steps can be observed (as in the previous section on Evaluate Formulas), or help can be obtained through the Excel help function. The Error Checking procedure is particularly helpful for large models where not all cells of the model are visible.

Watch Window

The **Watch Window**, located in the Formula Auditing group, allows the user to observe the values of cells included in the Watch Window box list. This is useful for large models when

FIGURE 10.16 The Evaluate Formula Dialog Box for Gambrell Manufacturing

	A	B	C	D	E	F	G	H	I	J
1	**Gambrell Manufacturing**									
2	**Parameters**									
3	Component ID	**570**	**578**	**741**	**755**					
4	Inventory On-Hand	5	30	70	17					
5	Order Up to Point	100	55	70	45					
6	Cost per Unit	$4.50	$12.50	$3.26	$4.15					
7										
8	Fixed Cost per Order	$120								
9										
10	Minimum Order Size for Discount	50								
11	Discounted to	90%								
12										
13	**Model**									
14										
15	Component ID	**570**								
16	Order Quantity	95								
17	Cost of Goods	$384.75								
18										
19	Total Number of Orders	3								
20										
21	Total Fixed Costs	$360.00								
22	Total Cost of Goods	$813.45								
23	Total Cost	$1,173.45								
24										

Evaluate Formula

Reference: Model!$B$17

Evaluation: = IF(B16 >= $B$10, $B$11*B6,B6)*B16

To show the result of the underlined expression, click Evaluate. The most recent result appears italicized.

Evaluate | Step In | Step Out | Close

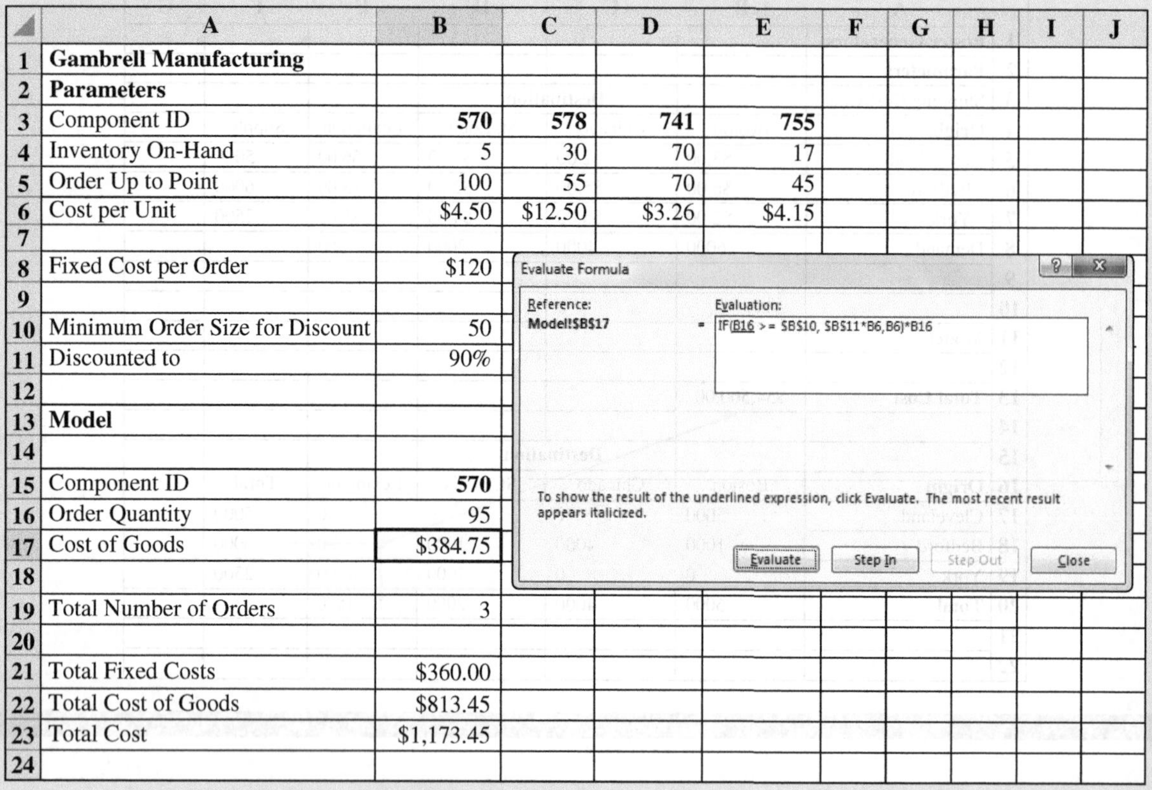

FIGURE 10.17 The Evaluate Formula Dialog Box for Gambrell Manufacturing Cell B17 after Four Clicks of the Evaluate Button

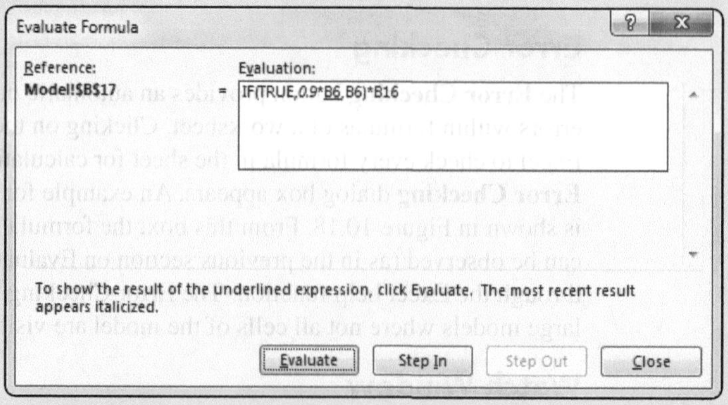

Evaluate Formula

Reference: Model!$B$17

Evaluation: = IF(TRUE,*0.9*B6*,B6)*B16

To show the result of the underlined expression, click Evaluate. The most recent result appears italicized.

Evaluate | Step In | Step Out | Close

FIGURE 10.18 The Error Checking Dialog Box for a Division by Zero Error

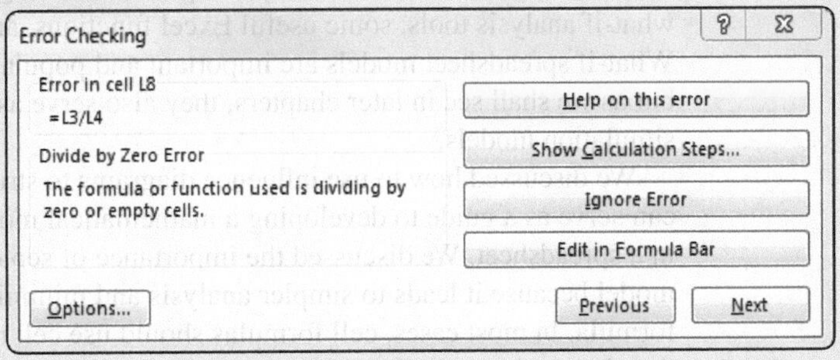

Error Checking

Error in cell L8
=L3/L4

Divide by Zero Error

The formula or function used is dividing by zero or empty cells.

Help on this error

Show Calculation Steps...

Ignore Error

Edit in Formula Bar

Options...

Previous

Next

not all of the model is observable on the screen or when multiple worksheets are used. The user can monitor how the listed cells change with a change in the model without searching through the worksheet or changing from one worksheet to another.

A Watch Window for the Gambrell Manufacturing model is shown in Figure 10.19. The following steps were used to add cell B17 to the watch list:

Step 1. Click the **Formulas** tab in the Ribbon
Step 2. Click **Watch Window** in the **Formula Auditing** group to display the **Watch Window**
Step 3. Click **Add Watch...**
Step 4. Select the cell you would like to add to the watch list (in this case B17)

As shown in Figure 10.19, the list gives the workbook name, worksheet name, cell name (if used), cell location, cell value, and cell formula. To delete a cell from the watch list, click on the entry from the list, and then click on the **Delete Watch** button that appears in the upper part of the **Watch Window**.

The Watch Window, as shown in Figure 10.19, allows us to monitor the value of B17 as we make changes elsewhere in the worksheet. Furthermore, if we had other worksheets in this workbook, we could monitor changes to B17 of the worksheet even from these other worksheets. The Watch Window is observable regardless of where we are in any worksheet of a workbook.

FIGURE 10.19 The Watch Window for Cell B17 of the Gambrell Manufacturing Model

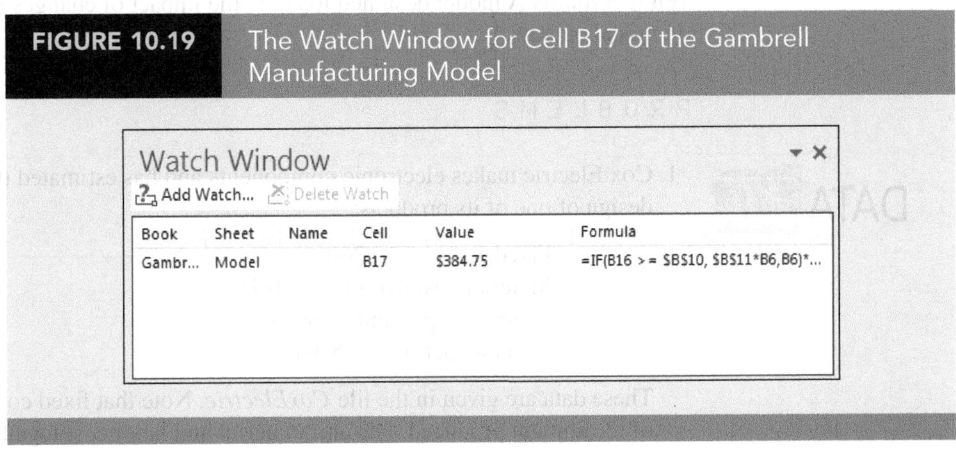

SUMMARY

In this chapter we discussed the principles of building good spreadsheet models, several what-if analysis tools, some useful Excel functions, and how to audit spreadsheet models. What-if spreadsheet models are important and popular analysis tools in and of themselves, but as we shall see in later chapters, they also serve as the basis for optimization and simulation models.

We discussed how to use influence diagrams to structure a problem. Influence diagrams can serve as a guide to developing a mathematical model and implementing the model in a spreadsheet. We discussed the importance of separating the parameters from the model because it leads to simpler analysis and minimizes the risk of creating an error in a formula. In most cases, cell formulas should use cell references in their arguments rather than being "hardwired" with values. We also discussed the use of proper formatting and color to enhance the ease of use and understanding of a spreadsheet model.

We used examples to illustrate how Excel What-If Analysis tools Data Tables and Goal Seek can be used to perform detailed and efficient what-if analysis. We also discussed a number of Excel functions that are useful for business analytics. Finally, we discussed Excel Formula Auditing tools that may be used to debug and monitor spreadsheet models to ensure that they are error-free and accurate.

GLOSSARY

Data Table An Excel tool that quantifies the impact of changing the value of a specific input on an output of interest.
Decision variable A model input the decision maker can control.
Goal Seek An Excel tool that allows the user to determine the value for an input cell that will cause the value of a related output cell to equal some specified value, called the *goal*.
Influence diagram A visual representation that shows which entities influence others in a model.
Make-versus-buy decision A decision often faced by companies that have to decide whether they should manufacture a product or outsource its production to another firm.
One-way data table An Excel Data Table that summarizes a single input's impact on the output of interest.
Parameter In a what-if model, the uncontrollable model input.
Two-way data table An Excel Data Table that summarizes two inputs' impact on the output of interest.
What-if model A model designed to study the impact of changes in model inputs on model outputs.

PROBLEMS

1. Cox Electric makes electronic components and has estimated the following for a new design of one of its products:

   Fixed cost = \$10,000
   Material cost per unit = \$0.15
   Labor cost per unit = \$0.10
   Revenue per unit = \$0.65

   These data are given in the file *CoxElectric*. Note that fixed cost is incurred regardless of the amount produced. Per-unit material and labor cost together make up the variable cost per unit. Assuming that Cox Electric sells all that it produces, profit is calculated by subtracting the fixed cost and total variable cost from total revenue.

a. Build an influence diagram that illustrates how to calculate profit.
b. Using mathematical notation similar to that used for Nowlin Plastics, give a mathematical model for calculating profit.
c. Implement your model from part (b) in Excel using the principles of good spreadsheet design.
d. If Cox Electric makes 12,000 units of the new product, what is the resulting profit?

2. Use the spreadsheet model constructed to answer Problem 1 to answer this problem.
   a. Construct a one-way data table with production volume as the column input and profit as the output. Breakeven occurs when profit goes from a negative to a positive value; that is, breakeven is when total revenue = total cost, yielding a profit of zero. Vary production volume from 0 to 100,000 in increments of 10,000. In which interval of production volume does breakeven occur?
   b. Use Goal Seek to find the exact breakeven point. Assign **Set cell:** equal to the location of profit, **To value:** = 0, and **By changing cell:** equal to the location of the production volume in your model.
3. Eastman Publishing Company is considering publishing an electronic textbook about spreadsheet applications for business. The fixed cost of manuscript preparation, textbook design, and web-site construction is estimated to be $160,000. Variable processing costs are estimated to be $6 per book. The publisher plans to sell single-user access to the book for $46.
   a. Build a spreadsheet model to calculate the profit/loss for a given demand. What profit can be anticipated with a demand of 3500 copies?
   b. Use a data table to vary demand from 1000 to 6000 in increments of 200 to assess the sensitivity of profit to demand.
   c. Use Goal Seek to determine the access price per copy that the publisher must charge to break even with a demand of 3500 copies.
4. The University of Cincinnati Center for Business Analytics is an outreach center that collaborates with industry partners on applied research and continuing education in business analytics. One of the programs offered by the center is a quarterly Business Intelligence Symposium. Each symposium features three speakers on the real-world use of analytics. Each corporate member of the center (there are currently 10) receives five free seats to each symposium. Nonmembers wishing to attend must pay $75 per person. Each attendee receives breakfast, lunch, and free parking. The following are the costs incurred for putting on this event:

Rental cost for the auditorium	$150
Registration processing	$8.50 per person
Speaker costs	3@$800 = $2400
Continental breakfast	$4.00 per person
Lunch	$7.00 per person
Parking	$5.00 per person

   a. Build a spreadsheet model that calculates a profit or loss based on the number of nonmember registrants.
   b. Use Goal Seek to find the number of nonmember registrants that will make the event break even.
5. Consider again the scenario described in Problem 4.
   a. The Center for Business Analytics is considering a refund policy for no-shows. No refund would be given for members who do not attend, but nonmembers who do not attend will be refunded 50% of the price. Extend the model you

developed in Problem 4 for the Business Intelligence Symposium to account for the fact that, historically, 25% of members who registered do not show and 10% of registered nonmembers do not attend. The center pays the caterer for breakfast and lunch based on the number of registrants (not the number of attendees). However, the center pays for parking only for those who attend. What is the profit if each corporate member registers their full allotment of tickets and 127 nonmembers register?

b. Use a two-way data table to show how profit changes as a function of number of registered nonmembers and the no-show percentage of nonmembers. Vary the number of nonmember registrants from 80 to 160 in increments of 5 and the percentage of nonmember no-shows from 10 to 30% in increments of 2%.

6. Consider again Problem 3. Through a series of web-based experiments, Eastman has created a predictive model that estimates demand as a function of price. The predictive model is demand $= 4{,}000 - 6p$, where p is the price of the e-book.
   a. Update your spreadsheet model constructed for Problem 3 to take into account this demand function.
   b. Use Goal Seek to calculate the price that results in breakeven.
   c. Use a data table that varies price from \$50 to \$400 in increments of \$25 to find the price that maximizes profit.
7. Lindsay is 25 years old and has a new job in web development. She wants to make sure that she is financially sound in 30 years, so she plans to invest the same amount into a retirement account at the end of every year for the next 30 years. Construct a data table that will show Lindsay the balance of her retirement account for various levels of annual investment and return. Develop the two-way table for annual investment amounts of \$5,000 to \$20,000 in increments of \$1,000 and for returns of 0 to 12% in increments of 1%. Note that because Lindsay invests at the end of the year, there is no interest earned on the contribution for the year in which she contributes.
8. Consider again Lindsay's investment in Problem 7. The real value of Lindsay's account after 30 years of investing will depend on inflation over that period. In the Excel function =NPV(*rate, value1, value2, ...*), *rate* is called the discount rate, and *value1, value 2*, etc. are incomes (positive) or expenditures (negative) over equal periods of time. Update your model from Problem 7 using the NPV function to get the net present value of Lindsay's retirement fund. Construct a data table that shows the net present value of Lindsay's retirement fund for various levels of return and inflation (discount rate). Use a data table to vary the return from 0 to 12% in increments of 1% and the discount rate from 0 to 4% in increments of 1% to show the impact on the net present value. (*Hint:* Calculate the total amount added to the account each year, and discount that stream of payments using the NPV function.)

9. Newton Manufacturing produces scientific calculators. The models are N350, N450, and the N900. Newton has planned its distribution of these products around eight customer zones: Brazil, China, France, Malaysia, U.S. Northeast, U.S. Southeast, U.S. Midwest, and U.S. West. Data for the current quarter (volume to be shipped in thousands of units) for each product and each customer zone are given in the file *Newton*. Newton would like to know the total number of units going to each customer zone and also the total units of each product shipped. There are several ways to get this information from the data set. One way is to use the SUMIF function.

   The SUMIF function extends the SUM function by allowing the user to add the values of cells meeting a logical condition. The general form of the function is:

   =SUMIF(*test range, condition, range to be summed*).

The *test range* is an area to search to test the *condition,* and the *range to be summed* is the position of the data to be summed. So, for example, using the file *Newton*, we use the following function to get the total units sent to Malaysia:

=SUMIF(A3:A26,A3,C3:C26).

Cell A3 contains the text "Malaysia"; A3:A26 is the range of customer zones; and C3:C26 are the volumes for each product for these customer zones. The SUMIF looks for matches of "Malaysia" in column A and, if a match is found, adds the volume to the total. Use the SUMIF function to get total volume by each zone and total volume by each product.

10. Consider the transportation model in the file *Williamson*, which is very similar to the Foster Generators model discussed in this chapter. Williamson produces a single product and has plants in Atlanta, Lexington, Chicago, and Salt Lake City and warehouses in Portland, St. Paul, Las Vegas, Tuscon, and Cleveland. Each plant has a capacity, and each warehouse has a demand. Williamson would like to find a low-cost shipping plan. Mr. Williamson has reviewed the results and notices right away that the total cost is way out of line. Use the **Formula Auditing** tool under the **Formulas** tab in Excel to find any errors in this model. Correct the errors. (*Hint:* The model contains two errors. Be sure to check every formula.)
11. Professor Rao would like to accurately calculate the grades for the 58 students in his Operations Planning and Scheduling class (OM 455). He has thus far constructed a spreadsheet, part of which follows:

	A	B	C	D	E
1	OM 455				
2	Section 001				
3	Course Grading Scale Based on Course Average:				
4		**Lower**	**Upper**	**Course**	
5		**Limit**	**Limit**	**Grade**	
6		0	59	F	
7		60	69	D	
8		70	79	C	
9		80	89	B	
10		90	100	A	
11					
12		Midterm	Final	Course	Course
13	Last Name	Score	Score	Average	Grade
14	Alt	70	56	63.0	
15	Amini	95	91	93.0	
16	Amoako	82	80	81.0	
17	Apland	45	78	61.5	
18	Bachman	68	45	56.5	
19	Corder	91	98	94.5	
20	Desi	87	74	80.5	
21	Dransman	60	80	70.0	
22	Duffuor	80	93	86.5	
23	Finkel	97	98	97.5	
24	Foster	90	91	90.5	

a. The Course Average is calculated by weighting the Midterm Score and Final Score 50% each. Use the VLOOKUP function with the table shown to generate the Course Grade for each student in cells E14 through E24.
b. Use the COUNTIF function to determine the number of students receiving each letter grade.

12. Richardson Ski Racing (RSR) sells equipment needed for downhill ski racing. One of RSR's products is fencing used on downhill courses. The fence product comes in 150-foot rolls and sells for $215 per roll. However, RSR offers quantity discounts. The following table shows the price per roll depending on order size:

Quantity Ordered		
From	**To**	**Price per Roll**
1	50	$215
51	100	$195
101	200	$175
201	and up	$155

The file *RSR* contains 172 orders that have arrived for the coming six weeks.
a. Use the VLOOKUP function with the preceding pricing table to determine the total revenue from these orders.
b. Use the COUNTIF function to determine the number of orders in each price bin.

13. A put option in finance allows you to sell a share of stock at a given price in the future. There are different types of put options. A European put option allows you to sell a share of stock at a given price, called the exercise price, at a particular point in time after the purchase of the option. For example, suppose you purchase a six-month European put option for a share of stock with an exercise price of $26. If six months later, the stock price per share is $26 or more, the option has no value. If in six months the stock price is lower than $26 per share, then you can purchase the stock and immediately sell it at the higher exercise price of $26. If the price per share in six months is $22.50, you can purchase a share of the stock for $22.50 and then use the put option to immediately sell the share for $26. Your profit would be the difference, $26 − $22.50 = $3.50 per share, less the cost of the option. If you paid $1.00 per put option, then your profit would be $3.50 − $1.00 = $2.50 per share.
a. Build a model to calculate the profit of this European put option.
b. Construct a data table that shows the profit per share for a share price in six months between $10 and $30 per share in increments of $1.00.

14. Consider again Problem 13. The point of purchasing a European option is to limit the risk of a decrease in the per-share price of the stock. Suppose you purchased 200 shares of the stock at $28 per share and 75 six-month European put options with an exercise price of $26. Each put option costs $1.
a. Using data tables, construct a model that shows the value of the portfolio with options and without options for a share price in six months between $15 and $35 per share in increments of $1.00.
b. Discuss the value of the portfolio with and without the European put options.

15. The Camera Shop sells two popular models of digital SLR cameras. The sales of these products are not independent; if the price of one increases, the sales of the other increases. In economics, these two camera models are called *substitutable products*. The store wishes to establish a pricing policy to maximize revenue from these products.

A study of price and sales data shows the following relationships between the quantity sold (N) and price (P) of each model:

$$N_A = 195 - 0.6P_A + 0.25P_B$$
$$N_B = 301 + 0.08P_A - 0.5P_B$$

a. Construct a model for the total revenue and implement it on a spreadsheet.
b. Develop a two-way data table to estimate the optimal prices for each product in order to maximize the total revenue. Vary each price from \$250 to \$500 in increments of \$10.

16. A few years back, Dave and Jana bought a new home. They borrowed \$230,415 at an annual fixed rate of 5.49% (15-year term) with monthly payments of \$1,881.46. They just made their 25th payment, and the current balance on the loan is \$208,555.87.

    Interest rates are at an all-time low, and Dave and Jana are thinking of refinancing to a new 15-year fixed loan. Their bank has made the following offer: 15-year term, 3.0%, plus out-of-pocket costs of \$2,937. The out-of-pocket costs must be paid in full at the time of refinancing.

    Build a spreadsheet model to evaluate this offer. The Excel function:

    =PMT(*rate*, *nper*, *pv*, *fv*, *type*)

    calculates the payment for a loan based on constant payments and a constant interest rate. The arguments of this function are:

    rate = the interest rate for the loan
    nper = the total number of payments
    pv = present value (the amount borrowed)
    fv = future value [the desired cash balance after the last payment (usually 0)]
    type = payment type (0 = end of period, 1 = beginning of the period)

    For example, for Dave and Jana's original loan, there will be 180 payments (12*15 = 180), so we would use =PMT(0.0549/12, 180, 230415,0,0) = \$1,881.46. Note that because payments are made monthly, the annual interest rate must be expressed as a monthly rate. Also, for payment calculations, we assume that the payment is made at the end of the month.

    The savings from refinancing occur over time, and therefore need to be discounted back to current dollars. The formula for converting K dollars saved t months from now to current dollars is:

    $$\frac{K}{(1 + r)^{t-1}}$$

    where r is the monthly inflation rate. Assume that $r = 0.002$ and that Dave and Jana make their payment at the end of each month.

    Use your model to calculate the savings in current dollars associated with the refinanced loan versus staying with the original loan.

17. Consider again the mortgage refinance problem in Problem 16. Assume that Dave and Jana have accepted the refinance offer of a 15-year loan at 3% interest rate with out-of-pocket expenses of \$2,937. Recall that they are borrowing \$208,555.87. Assume that there is no prepayment penalty, so that any amount over the required payment is applied to the principal. Construct a model so that you can use Goal Seek to determine the monthly payment that will allow Dave and Jana to pay off the loan in 12 years. Do the same for 10 and 11 years. Which option for prepayment, if any, would you choose and why? (*Hint:* Break each monthly payment up into interest and principal

[the amount that is deducted from the balance owed]. Recall that the monthly interest that is charged is the monthly loan rate multiplied by the remaining loan balance.)

18. Floyd's Bumpers has distribution centers in Lafayette, Indiana; Charlotte, North Carolina; Los Angeles, California; Dallas, Texas; and Pittsburgh, Pennsylvania. Each distribution center carries all products sold. Floyd's customers are auto repair shops and larger auto parts retail stores. You are asked to perform an analysis of the customer assignments to determine which of Floyd's customers should be assigned to each distribution center. The rule for assigning customers to distribution centers is simple: A customer should be assigned to the closest center. The file *Floyds* contains the distance from each of Floyd's 1,029 customers to each of the five distribution centers. Your task is to build a list that tells which distribution center should serve each customer. The following functions will be helpful:

=MIN(*array*).

The MIN function returns the smallest value in a set of numbers. For example, if the range A1:A3 contains the values 6, 25, and 38, then the formula =MIN(A1:A3) returns the number 6, because it is the smallest of the three numbers:

=MATCH(*lookup_value, lookup_array, match type*).

The MATCH function searches for a specified item in a range of cells and returns the relative position of that item in the range. The *lookup_value* is the value to match, the *lookup_array* is the range of search, and *match type* indicates the type of match (use 0 for an exact match).

For example, if the range A1:A3 contains the values 6, 25, and 38, then the formula =MATCH(25,A1:A3,0) returns the number 2, because 25 is the second item in the range.

=INDEX(*array, column_num*).

The INDEX function returns the value of an element in a position of an array. For example, if the range A1:A3 contains the values 6, 25, and 38, then the formula =INDEX(A1:A3, 2) = 25, because 25 is the value in the second position of the array A1:A3. (*Hint:* Create three new columns. In the first column, use the MIN function to calculate the minimum distance for the customer in that row. In the second column use the MATCH function to find the position of the minimum distance. In the third column, use the position in the previous column with the INDEX function referencing the row of distribution center names to find the name of the distribution center that should service that customer.)

19. Refer to Problem 18. Floyd's Bumpers pays a transportation company to ship its product in full truckloads to its customers. Therefore, the cost for shipping is a function of the distance traveled and a fuel surcharge (also on a per-mile basis). The cost per mile is $2.42, and the fuel surcharge is $0.56 per mile. The file *FloydsMay* contains data for shipments for the month of May (each record is simply the customer zip code for a given truckload shipment) as well as the distance table from the distribution centers to each customer. Use the MATCH and INDEX functions to retrieve the distance traveled for each shipment, and calculate the charge for each shipment. What is the total amount that Floyd's Bumpers spends on these May shipments? (*Hint:* The INDEX function may be used with a two-dimensional array: =INDEX(*array, row_num, column_num*), where *array* is a matrix, *row_num* is the row number, and *column_num* is the column position of the desired element of the matrix.)
20. An auto dealership is advertising that a new car with a sticker price of $35,208 is on sale for $25,995 if payment is made in full, or it can be financed at 0% interest

for 72 months with a monthly payment of $489. Note that 72 payments × $489 per payment = $35,208, which is the sticker price of the car. By allowing you to pay for the car in a series of payments (starting one month from now) rather than $25,995 now, the dealer is effectively loaning you $25,995. If you choose the 0% financing option, what is the effective interest rate that the auto dealership is earning on your loan? (*Hint:* Discount the payments back to current dollars [see Problem 16 for a discussion of discounting], and use Goal Seek to find the discount rate that makes the net present value of the payments = $25,995.)

CASE PROBLEM: RETIREMENT PLAN

Tim is 37 years old and would like to establish a retirement plan. Develop a spreadsheet model that could be used to assist Tim with retirement planning. Your model should include the following input parameters:

Tim's current age = 37 years
Tim's current total retirement savings = $259,000
Annual rate of return on retirement savings = 4%
Tim's current annual salary = $145,000
Tim's expected annual percentage increase in salary = 2%
Tim's percentage of annual salary contributed to retirement = 6%
Tim's expected age of retirement = 65
Tim's expected annual expenses after retirement (current dollars) = $90,000
Rate of return on retirement savings after retirement = 3%
Income tax rate postretirement = 15%

Assume that Tim's employer contributes 6% of Tim's salary to his retirement fund. Tim can make an additional annual contribution to his retirement fund before taxes (tax free) up to a contribution of $16,000. Assume that he contributes $6,000 per year. Also, assume an inflation rate of 2%.

Managerial Report

Your spreadsheet model should provide the accumulated savings at the onset of retirement as well as the age at which funds will be depleted (given assumptions on the input parameters).

As a feature of your spreadsheet model, build a data table to demonstrate the sensitivity of the age at which funds will be depleted to the retirement age and additional pre-tax contributions. Similarly, consider other factors you think might be important.

Develop a report for Tim outlining the factors that will have the greatest impact on his retirement.

Chapter 15

Decision Analysis

CONTENTS

15.1 PROBLEM FORMULATION
Payoff Tables
Decision Trees

15.2 DECISION ANALYSIS WITHOUT PROBABILITIES
Optimistic Approach
Conservative Approach
Minimax Regret Approach

15.3 DECISION ANALYSIS WITH PROBABILITIES
Expected Value Approach
Risk Analysis
Sensitivity Analysis

15.4 DECISION ANALYSIS WITH SAMPLE INFORMATION
Expected Value of Sample Information
Expected Value of Perfect Information

15.5 COMPUTING BRANCH PROBABILITIES WITH BAYES' THEOREM

15.6 UTILITY THEORY
Utility and Decision Analysis
Utility Functions
Exponential Utility Function

ANALYTICS IN ACTION

Phytopharm*

As a pharmaceutical development and functional food company, Phytopharm's primary revenue streams come from licensing agreements with larger companies. After Phytopharm establishes proof of principle for a new product by successfully completing early clinical trials, it seeks to reduce its risk by licensing the product to a large pharmaceutical or nutrition company that will further develop and market it.

There is substantial uncertainty regarding the future sales potential of early stage products; only 1 in 10 of such products makes it to market, and only 30% of these yield a healthy return. Phytopharm and its licensing partners would often initially propose very different terms for the licensing agreement. Therefore, Phytopharm employed a team of researchers to develop a flexible method for appraising a product's potential and subsequently supporting the negotiation of the lump-sum payments for development milestones and royalties on eventual sales that comprise the licensing agreement.

Using computer simulation, the resulting decision analysis model allows Phytopharm to perform sensitivity analysis on estimates of development cost, the probability of successful Food and Drug Administration clearance, launch date, market size, and patent expiry. In particular, a decision tree model allows Phytopharm and its licensing partner to mutually agree on the number of development milestones. Depending on the status of the project at a milestone, the licensing partner can opt to abandon the project or continue development. Laying out these sequential decisions in a decision tree allows Phytopharm to negotiate milestone payments and royalties that equitably split the project's value between Phytopharm and its potential licensee.

*Based on P. Crama, B. De Ryck, Z. Degraeve, and W. Chong, "Research and Development Project Valuation and Licensing Negotiations at Phytopharm plc," *Interfaces*, 37 no. 5 (September–October 2007): 472–487.

Ultimately, business analytics is about making better decisions. The tools and techniques we have introduced previously are designed to aid a decision maker in analyzing existing data, predicting future behavior, and recommending decisions. This chapter introduces a field known as decision analysis that can be used to develop an optimal strategy when a decision maker is faced with several decision alternatives and an uncertain or risk-filled pattern of future events. For example, by evaluating the different naming options and understanding the potential sources of uncertainty, Procter & Gamble used decision analysis techniques to help choose the best brand name when they introduced Crest White Strips.

Decision analysis techniques are used widely in many different settings. The Analytics in Action, Phytopharm, discusses the use of decision analysis to manage Phytopharm's pipeline of pharmaceutical products, which have long development times and relatively high levels of uncertainty. Federal agencies in the United States have used decision analysis to evaluate the potential risks from terrorist attacks and to recommend counterterrorism strategies. The State of North Carolina used decision analysis in evaluating whether to implement a medical screening test to detect metabolic disorders in newborns.

Even when a careful decision analysis has been conducted, uncertainty about future events means that the final outcome is not completely under the control of the decision maker. In some cases, the selected decision alternative may provide good or excellent results. In other cases, a relatively unlikely future event may occur, causing the selected decision alternative to provide only fair or even poor results. The risk associated with any decision alternative is a direct result of the uncertainty associated with the final outcome. A good decision analysis includes careful consideration of risk. Through risk analysis, the decision maker is provided with probability information about the favorable as well as the unfavorable outcomes that may occur.

We begin the study of decision analysis by considering problems that involve reasonably few decision alternatives and reasonably few possible future events. Payoff tables and decision trees are introduced to provide a structure for the decision problem and to illustrate the fundamentals of decision analysis. Decision trees are used to analyze more complex problems and to identify an optimal sequence of decisions, referred to as an *optimal decision strategy*. Sensitivity analysis shows how changes in various aspects of the problem affect the recommended decision alternative. We return to the use of Bayes' theorem (first seen in Chapter 5) for calculating the probabilities of future events and incorporating additional information about the decisions. We conclude this chapter with a discussion of utility and decision analysis that expands on different attitudes toward risk taken by decision makers.

15.1 Problem Formulation

The first step in the decision analysis process is problem formulation. We begin with a verbal statement of the problem. We then identify the **decision alternatives**; the uncertain future events, referred to as **chance events**; and the **outcomes** associated with each combination of decision alternative and chance event outcome. Let us begin by considering a construction project of the Pittsburgh Development Corporation.

Pittsburgh Development Corporation (PDC) purchased land that will be the site of a new luxury condominium complex. The location provides a spectacular view of downtown Pittsburgh and the Golden Triangle, where the Allegheny and Monongahela Rivers meet to form the Ohio River. PDC plans to price the individual condominium units between \$300,000 and \$1,400,000.

PDC commissioned preliminary architectural drawings for three different projects: one with 30 condominiums, one with 60 condominiums, and one with 90 condominiums. The financial success of the project depends on the size of the condominium complex and the chance event concerning the demand for the condominiums. The statement of the PDC decision problem is to select the size of the new luxury condominium project that will lead to the largest profit given the uncertainty concerning the demand for the condominiums.

Given the statement of the problem, it is clear that the decision is to select the best size for the condominium complex. PDC has the following three decision alternatives:

$$d_1 = \text{a small complex with 30 condominiums}$$
$$d_2 = \text{a medium complex with 60 condominiums}$$
$$d_3 = \text{a large complex with 90 condominiums}$$

A factor in selecting the best decision alternative is the uncertainty associated with the chance event concerning the demand for the condominiums. When asked about the possible demand for the condominiums, PDC's president acknowledged a wide range of possibilities but decided that it would be adequate to consider two possible chance event outcomes: a strong demand and a weak demand.

In decision analysis, the possible outcomes for a chance event are referred to as the **states of nature**. The states of nature are defined so that they are mutually exclusive (no more than one can occur) and collectively exhaustive (at least one must occur); thus, one and only one of the possible states of nature will occur. For the PDC problem, the chance event concerning the demand for the condominiums has two states of nature:

$$s_1 = \text{strong demand for the condominiums}$$
$$s_2 = \text{weak demand for the condominiums}$$

Management must first select a decision alternative (complex size); then a state of nature follows (demand for the condominiums), and finally an outcome will occur. In this case, the outcome is PDC's profit.

TABLE 15.1 Payoff Table for the PDC Condominium Project ($ Millions)

Decision Alternative	State of Nature: Strong Demand, s_1	Weak Demand, s_2
Small complex, d_1	8	7
Medium complex, d_2	14	5
Large complex, d_3	20	−9

Payoff Tables

Payoffs can be expressed in terms of profit, cost, time, distance, or any other measure appropriate for the decision problem being analyzed.

Given the three decision alternatives and the two states of nature, which complex size should PDC choose? To answer this question, PDC will need to know the outcome associated with each possible combination of decision alternative and state of nature. In decision analysis, we refer to the outcome resulting from a specific combination of a decision alternative and a state of nature as a **payoff**. A table showing payoffs for all combinations of decision alternatives and states of nature is a **payoff table**.

Because PDC wants to select the complex size that provides the largest profit, profit is used as the outcome. The payoff table with profits (in millions of dollars) is shown in Table 15.1. Note, for example, that if a medium complex is built and demand turns out to be strong, a profit of $14 million will be realized. We will use the notation V_{ij} to denote the payoff associated with decision alternative i and state of nature j. Using Table 15.1, $V_{31} = 20$ indicates that a payoff of $20 million occurs if the decision is to build a large complex (d_3) and the strong demand state of nature (s_1) occurs. Similarly, $V_{32} = -9$ indicates a loss of $9 million if the decision is to build a large complex (d_3) and the weak demand state of nature (s_2) occurs.

Decision Trees

A **decision tree** provides a graphical representation of the decision-making process. Figure 15.1 presents a decision tree for the PDC problem. Note that the decision tree shows the natural or logical progression that will occur over time. First, PDC must make a decision regarding the size of the condominium complex (d_1, d_2, or d_3). Then, after the decision is implemented, either state of nature s_1 or s_2 will occur. The number at each end point of the tree indicates that the payoff associated with a particular sequence. For example, the topmost payoff of 8 indicates that an $8 million profit is anticipated if PDC constructs a small condominium complex (d_1) and demand turns out to be strong (s_1). The next payoff of 7 indicates an anticipated profit of $7 million if PDC constructs a small condominium complex (d_1) and demand turns out to be weak (s_2). Thus, the decision tree provides a graphical depiction of the sequences of decision alternatives and states of nature that provide the six possible payoffs for PDC.

The decision tree in Figure 15.1 shows four nodes, numbered 1 to 4. **Nodes** are used to represent decisions and chance events. Squares are used to depict **decision nodes**, circles are used to depict **chance nodes**. Thus, node 1 is a decision node, and nodes 2, 3, and 4 are chance nodes. The **branches** connect the nodes; those leaving the decision node correspond to the decision alternatives. The branches leaving each chance node correspond to the states of nature. The outcomes (payoffs) are shown at the end of the states-of-nature branches. We now turn to the question: How can the decision maker use the information in the payoff table or the decision tree to select the best decision alternative? Several approaches may be used and are covered in the remaining sections of this chapter.

FIGURE 15.1 Decision Tree for the PDC Condominium Project ($ Millions)

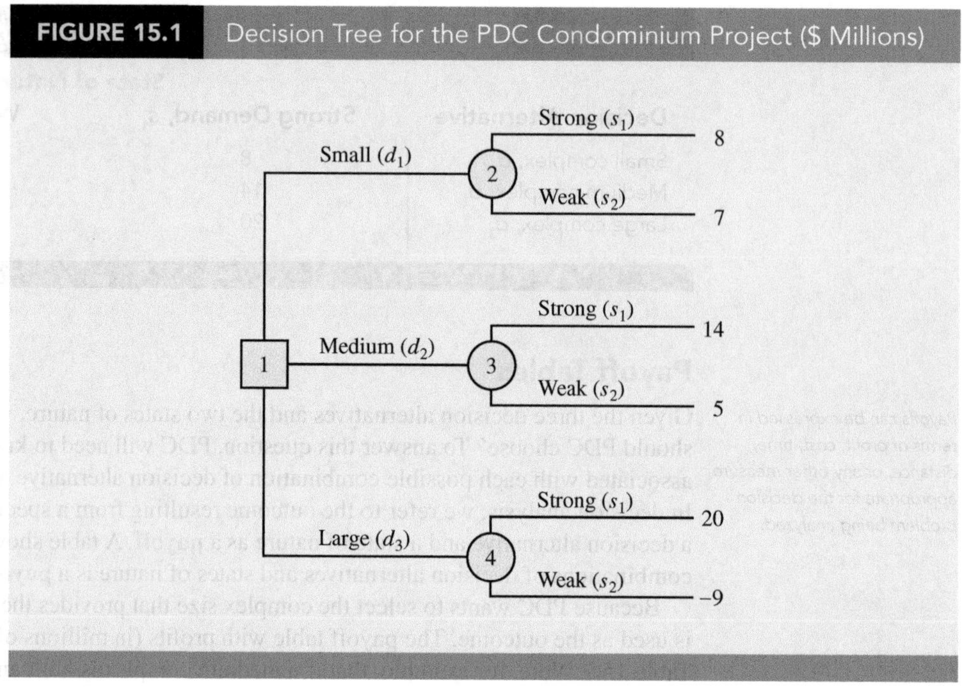

NOTES + COMMENTS

1. The first step in solving a complex problem is to decompose the problem into a series of smaller subproblems. Decision trees provide a useful way to decompose a problem and illustrate the sequential nature of the decision process.
2. People often view the same problem from different perspectives. Thus, the discussion regarding the development of a decision tree may provide additional insight into the problem.

15.2 Decision Analysis Without Probabilities

In this section we consider approaches to decision analysis that do not require knowledge of the probabilities of the states of nature. These approaches are appropriate in situations in which a simple best-case and worst-case analysis is sufficient and in which the decision maker has little confidence in his or her ability to assess the probabilities. Because different approaches sometimes lead to different decision recommendations, the decision maker must understand the approaches available and then select the specific approach that, according to the judgment of the decision maker, is the most appropriate.

Optimistic Approach

For a maximization problem, the optimistic approach often is referred to as the maximax approach; for a minimization problem, the corresponding terminology is minimin.

The **optimistic approach** evaluates each decision alternative in terms of the *best* payoff that can occur. The decision alternative that is recommended is the one that provides the best possible payoff. For a problem in which maximum profit is desired, as in the PDC problem, the optimistic approach would lead the decision maker to choose the alternative corresponding to the largest profit. For problems involving minimization, this approach leads to choosing the alternative with the smallest payoff.

TABLE 15.2 Maximum Payoff for Each PDC Decision Alternative

Decision Alternative	Maximum Payoff	
Small complex, d_1	8	
Medium complex, d_2	14	
Large complex, d_3	20 ←	Maximum of the maximum payoff values

To illustrate the optimistic approach, we use it to develop a recommendation for the PDC problem. First, we determine the maximum payoff for each decision alternative; then we select the decision alternative that provides the overall maximum payoff. These steps systematically identify the decision alternative that provides the largest possible profit. Table 15.2 illustrates these steps.

Because 20, corresponding to d_3, is the largest payoff, the decision to construct the large condominium complex is the recommended decision alternative using the optimistic approach.

Conservative Approach

For a maximization problem, the conservative approach often is referred to as the maximin approach; for a minimization problem the corresponding terminology is minimax.

The **conservative approach** evaluates each decision alternative in terms of the *worst* payoff that can occur. The decision alternative recommended is the one that provides the best of the worst possible payoffs. For a problem in which the output measure is profit, as in the PDC problem, the conservative approach would lead the decision maker to choose the alternative that maximizes the minimum possible profit that could be obtained. For problems involving minimization (for example, when the output measure is cost instead of profit), this approach identifies the alternative that will minimize the maximum payoff.

To illustrate the conservative approach, we use it to develop a recommendation for the PDC problem. First, we identify the minimum payoff for each of the decision alternatives; then we select the decision alternative that maximizes the minimum payoff. Table 15.3 illustrates these steps for the PDC problem.

Because 7, corresponding to d_1, yields the maximum of the minimum payoffs, the decision alternative of a small condominium complex is recommended. This decision approach is considered conservative because it identifies the worst possible payoffs and then recommends the decision alternative that avoids the possibility of extremely "bad" payoffs. In the conservative approach, PDC is guaranteed a profit of at least \$7 million. Although PDC may make more, it *cannot* make less than \$7 million.

Minimax Regret Approach

In decision analysis, **regret** is the difference between the payoff associated with a *particular* decision alternative and the payoff associated with the decision that would yield the most desirable payoff for a given state of nature. Thus, regret represents how much potential

TABLE 15.3 Minimum Payoff for Each PDC Decision Alternative

Decision Alternative	Minimum Payoff (\$ Millions)	
Small complex, d_1	7 ←	Maximum of the minimum payoff values
Medium complex, d_2	5	
Large complex, d_3	−9	

payoff one would forgo by selecting a *particular* decision alternative, given that a specific state of nature will occur. This is why regret is often referred to as **opportunity loss**.

As its name implies, under the **minimax regret approach** to decision analysis, one would choose the decision alternative that minimizes the maximum state of regret that could occur over all possible states of nature. This approach is neither purely optimistic nor purely conservative. Let us illustrate the minimax regret approach by showing how it can be used to select a decision alternative for the PDC problem.

Suppose that PDC constructs a small condominium complex (d_1) and demand turns out to be strong (s_1). Table 15.1 showed that the resulting profit for PDC would be \$8 million. However, given that the strong demand state of nature (s_1) has occurred, we realize that the decision to construct a large condominium complex (d_3), yielding a profit of \$20 million, would have been the best decision. The difference between the payoff for the best decision alternative (\$20 million) and the payoff for the decision to construct a small condominium complex (\$8 million) is the regret or opportunity loss associated with decision alternative d_1 when state of nature s_1 occurs; thus, for this case, the opportunity loss or regret is \$20 million − \$8 million = \$12 million. Similarly, if PDC makes the decision to construct a medium condominium complex (d_2) and the strong demand state of nature (s_1) occurs, the opportunity loss, or regret, associated with d_2 would be \$20 million − \$14 million = \$6 million. Of course, if PDC chooses to construct a large complex (d_3) and demand is strong, they would have no regret.

In general, the following expression represents the opportunity loss, or regret:

REGRET (OPPORTUNITY LOSS)

$$R_{ij} = |V_j^* - V_{ij}| \tag{15.1}$$

where

R_{ij} = the regret associated with decision alternative d_i and state of nature s_j
V_j^* = the payoff value corresponding to the best decision for the state of nature s_j
V_{ij} = the payoff corresponding to decision alternative d_i and state of nature s_j

Note the role of the absolute value in equation (15.1). For minimization problems, the best payoff, V_j^*, is the smallest entry in column j. Because this value always is less than or equal to V_{ij}, the absolute value of the difference between V_j^* and V_{ij} ensures that the regret is always the magnitude of the difference.

Using equation (15.1) and the payoffs in Table 15.1, we can compute the regret associated with each combination of decision alternative d_i and state of nature s_j. Because the PDC problem is a maximization problem, V_j^* will be the largest entry in column j of the payoff table. Thus, to compute the regret, we simply subtract each entry in a column from the largest entry in the column. Table 15.4 shows the opportunity loss, or regret, table for the PDC problem.

TABLE 15.4 Opportunity Loss, or Regret, Table for the PDC Condominium Project (\$ Millions)

	State of Nature	
Decision Alternative	**Strong Demand s_1**	**Weak Demand s_2**
Small complex, d_1	12	0
Medium complex, d_2	6	2
Large complex, d_3	0	16

TABLE 15.5 Maximum Regret for Each PDC Decision Alternative

Decision Alternative	Maximum Regret ($ millions)	
Small complex, d_1	12	
Medium complex, d_2	6	← Minimum of the maximum regret
Large complex, d_3	16	

The next step in applying the minimax regret approach is to list the maximum regret for each decision alternative; Table 15.5 shows the results for the PDC problem. Selecting the decision alternative with the *minimum* of the *maximum* regret values—hence, the name *minimax regret*—yields the minimax regret decision. For the PDC problem, the alternative to construct the medium condominium complex, with a corresponding maximum regret of $6 million, is the recommended minimax regret decision.

Note that the three approaches discussed in this section provide different recommendations, which in itself is not bad. It simply reflects the difference in decision-making philosophies that underlie the various approaches. Ultimately, the decision maker will have to choose the most appropriate approach and then make the final decision accordingly. The main criticism of the approaches discussed in this section is that they do not consider any information about the probabilities of the various states of nature. In the next section, we discuss an approach that utilizes probability information in selecting a decision alternative.

15.3 Decision Analysis with Probabilities

Expected Value Approach

In many decision-making situations, we can obtain probability assessments for the states of nature. When such probabilities are available, we can use the **expected value approach** to identify the best decision alternative. Let us first define the expected value of a decision alternative and then apply it to the PDC problem.

Let:

$$N = \text{the number of states of nature}$$
$$P(s_j) = \text{the probability of state of nature } s_j$$

Because one and only one of the N states of nature can occur, the probabilities must satisfy two conditions:

$$P(s_j) \geq 0 \qquad \text{for all states of nature}$$

$$\sum_{j=1}^{N} P(s_j) = P(s_1) + P(s_2) + \cdots + P(s_N) = 1$$

The **expected value (EV)** of decision alternative d_i is defined as follows:

EXPECTED VALUE OF DECISION ALTERNATIVE d_i

$$\text{EV}(d_i) = \sum_{j=1}^{N} P(s_j)V_{ij} \tag{15.2}$$

In words, the expected value of a decision alternative is the sum of weighted payoffs for the decision alternative. The weight for a payoff is the probability of the associated state of nature and therefore the probability that the payoff will occur. Let us return to the PDC problem to see how the expected value approach can be applied.

PDC is optimistic about the potential for the luxury high-rise condominium complex. Suppose that this optimism leads to an initial subjective probability assessment of 0.8 that demand will be strong (s_1) and a corresponding probability of 0.2 that demand will be weak (s_2). Thus, $P(s_1) = 0.8$ and $P(s_2) = 0.2$. Using the payoff values in Table 15.1 and equation (15.2), we compute the expected value for each of the three decision alternatives as follows:

$$\text{EV}(d_1) = 0.8\ (8) + 0.2\ (7) = 7.8$$
$$\text{EV}(d_2) = 0.8\ (14) + 0.2\ (5) = 12.2$$
$$\text{EV}(d_3) = 0.8\ (20) + 0.2\ (-9) = 14.2$$

Thus, using the expected value approach, we find that the large condominium complex, with an expected value of \$14.2 million, is the recommended decision.

Computer packages are available to help in constructing more complex decision trees. In the chapter appendix, we discuss the use of Analytic Solver Platform to create decision trees.

The calculations required to identify the decision alternative with the best expected value can be conveniently carried out on a decision tree. Figure 15.2 shows the decision tree for the PDC problem with state-of-nature branch probabilities. Working backward through the decision tree, we first compute the expected value at each chance node. In other words, at each chance node, we weight each possible payoff by its probability of occurrence. By doing so, we obtain the expected values for nodes 2, 3, and 4, as shown in Figure 15.3.

Because the decision maker controls the branch leaving decision node 1 and because we are trying to maximize the expected profit, the best decision alternative at node 1 is d_3. Thus, the decision tree analysis leads to a recommendation of d_3, with an expected value of \$14.2 million. Note that this recommendation is also obtained with the expected value approach in conjunction with the payoff table.

Other decision problems may be substantially more complex than the PDC problem, but if a reasonable number of decision alternatives and states of nature are present, you can use the decision tree approach outlined here. First, draw a decision tree consisting of decision nodes, chance nodes, and branches that describe the sequential nature of the problem. If

FIGURE 15.2 PDC Decision Tree with State-of-Nature Branch Probabilities

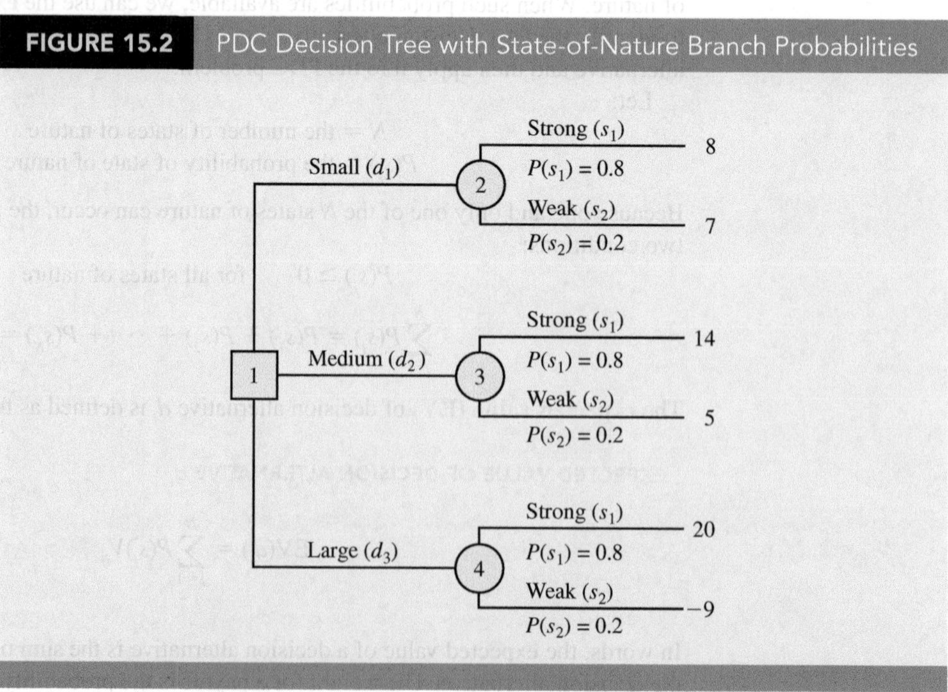

FIGURE 15.3 Applying the Expected Value Approach Using a Decision Tree for the PDC Condominium Project

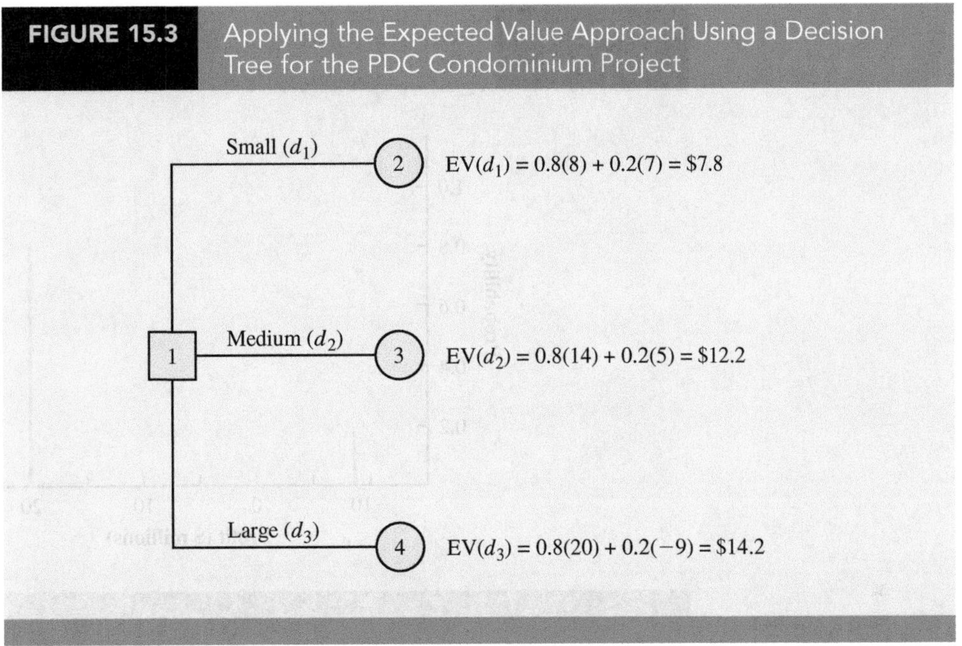

you use the expected value approach, the next step is to determine the probabilities for each of the states of nature and compute the expected value at each chance node. Then select the decision branch leading to the chance node with the best expected value. The decision alternative associated with this branch is the recommended decision.

In practice, obtaining precise estimates of the probabilities for each state of nature is often impossible. In some cases where similar decisions have been made many times in the past, one may use historical data to estimate the probabilities for the different states of nature. However, often there are little, or no, historical data to guide the estimates of these probabilities. In these cases, we may have to rely on subjective estimates to determine the probabilities for the states of nature. When relying on subjective estimates, we often want to get more than one estimate because many studies have shown that even knowledgeable experts are often overly optimistic in their estimates. It is also particularly important when dealing with subjective probability estimates to perform risk analysis and sensitivity analysis, as we will explain.

Risk Analysis

Risk analysis helps the decision maker recognize the difference between the expected value of a decision alternative and the payoff that may actually occur. A decision alternative and a state of nature combine to generate the payoff associated with a decision. The **risk profile** for a decision alternative shows the possible payoffs along with their associated probabilities.

Let us demonstrate risk analysis and the construction of a risk profile by returning to the PDC condominium construction project. Using the expected value approach, we identified the large condominium complex (d_3) as the best decision alternative. The expected value of $14.2 million for d_3 is based on a 0.8 probability of obtaining a $20 million profit and a 0.2 probability of obtaining a $9 million loss. The 0.8 probability for the $20 million payoff and the 0.2 probability for the −$9 million payoff provide the risk profile for the large complex decision alternative. This risk profile is shown graphically in Figure 15.4.

Sometimes a review of the risk profile associated with an optimal decision alternative may cause the decision maker to choose another decision alternative even though the expected value of the other decision alternative is not as good. For example, the risk profile

FIGURE 15.4 Risk Profile for the Large-Complex Decision Alternative for the PDC Condominium Project

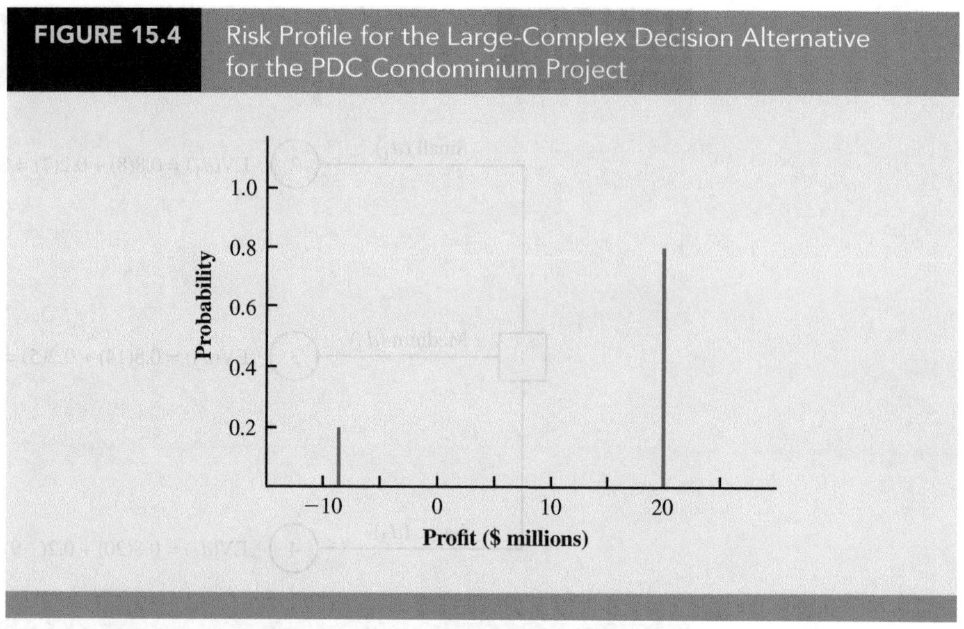

for the medium-complex decision alternative (d_2) shows a 0.8 probability for a $14 million payoff and a 0.2 probability for a $5 million payoff. Because no probability of a loss is associated with decision alternative d_2, the medium-complex decision alternative would be judged less risky than the large-complex decision alternative. As a result, a decision maker might prefer the less risky medium-complex decision alternative even though it has an expected value of $2 million less than the large-complex decision alternative.

Sensitivity Analysis

Sensitivity analysis can be used to determine how changes in the probabilities for the states of nature or changes in the payoffs affect the recommended decision alternative. In many cases, the probabilities for the states of nature and the payoffs are based on subjective assessments. Sensitivity analysis helps the decision maker understand which of these inputs are critical to the choice of the best decision alternative. If a small change in the value of one of the inputs causes a change in the recommended decision alternative, the solution to the decision analysis problem is sensitive to that particular input. Extra effort and care should be taken to make sure the input value is as accurate as possible. On the other hand, if a modest-to-large change in the value of one of the inputs does not cause a change in the recommended decision alternative, the solution to the decision analysis problem is not sensitive to that particular input. No extra time or effort would be needed to refine the estimated input value.

One approach to sensitivity analysis is to select different values for the probabilities of the states of nature and the payoffs and then resolve the decision analysis problem. If the recommended decision alternative changes, we know that the solution is sensitive to the changes made. For example, suppose that in the PDC problem the probability for a strong demand is revised to 0.2 and the probability for a weak demand is revised to 0.8. Would the recommended decision alternative change? Using $P(s_1) = 0.2$, $P(s_2) = 0.8$, and equation (15.2), the revised expected values for the three decision alternatives are:

$$\text{EV}(d_1) = 0.2\,(8) + 0.8\,(7) = 7.2$$
$$\text{EV}(d_2) = 0.2\,(14) + 0.8\,(5) = 6.8$$
$$\text{EV}(d_3) = 0.2\,(20) + 0.8\,(-9) = -3.2$$

With these probability assessments, the recommended decision alternative is to construct a small condominium complex (d_1), with an expected value of $7.2 million. The probability of strong demand is only 0.2, so constructing the large condominium complex (d_3) is the least preferred alternative, with an expected value of −$3.2 million (a loss).

Thus, when the probability of strong demand is large, PDC should build the large complex; when the probability of strong demand is small, PDC should build the small complex. Obviously, we could continue to modify the probabilities of the states of nature and learn even more about how changes in the probabilities affect the recommended decision alternative. Sensitivity analysis calculations can also be made for the values of the payoffs. We can easily change the payoff values and resolve the problem to see if the best decision changes.

NOTES + COMMENTS

1. The definition of expected value given in this chapter is consistent with that given in Chapter 5, but here we use the notation and terminology specific to decision analysis. In both cases, the expected value is defined as the weighted average of possible values.
2. The drawback to the sensitivity analysis approach described in this section is the numerous calculations required to evaluate the effect of several possible changes in the state-of-nature probabilities and/or payoff values. In the chapter appendix we demonstrate how to use Analytic Solver Platform and a Data Table in Excel to generate sensitivity analysis for decision problems.

15.4 Decision Analysis with Sample Information

Frequently, decision makers have the ability to collect additional information about the states of nature. It is worthwhile for the decision maker to consider the potential value of this additional information and how it can affect the decision analysis process. Most often, additional information is obtained through experiments designed to provide **sample information** about the states of nature. Raw material sampling, product testing, and market research studies are examples of experiments (or studies) that may enable management to revise or update the state-of-nature probabilities.

To analyze the potential benefit of additional information, we must first introduce a few additional terms related to decision analysis. The preliminary or **prior probability** assessments for the states of nature that are the best probability values available prior to obtaining additional information. These revised probabilities after obtaining additional information are called **posterior probabilities**.

Let us return to the PDC problem and assume that management is considering a 6-month market research study designed to learn more about potential market acceptance of the PDC condominium project. Management anticipates that the market research study will provide one of the following two results:

1. *Favorable report:* A substantial number of the individuals contacted express interest in purchasing a PDC condominium.
2. *Unfavorable report:* Very few of the individuals contacted express interest in purchasing a PDC condominium.

The decision tree for the PDC problem with sample information shows the logical sequence for the decisions and the chance events in Figure 15.5. By introducing the possibility of conducting a market research study, the PDC problem becomes more complex. First, PDC's management must decide whether the market research should be conducted. If it is conducted, PDC's management must be prepared to make a decision about the size of the condominium

FIGURE 15.5 The PDC Decision Tree Including the Market Research Study

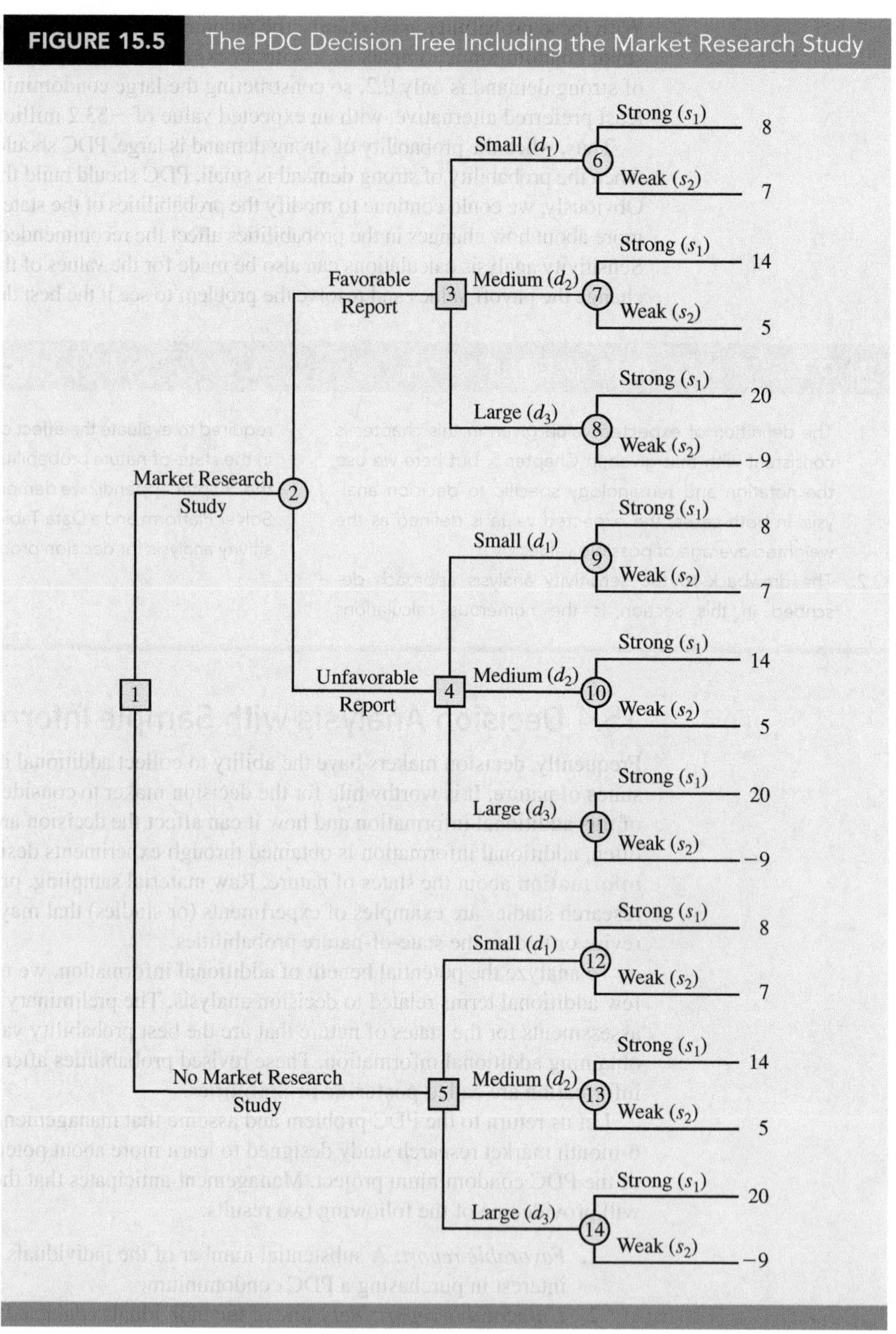

project if the market research report is favorable and, possibly, a different decision about the size of the condominium project if the market research report is unfavorable. In Figure 15.5, the squares are decision nodes and the circles are chance nodes. At each decision node, the branch of the tree that is taken is based on the decision made. At each chance node, the branch of the tree that is taken is based on probability or chance. For example, decision node 1 shows that PDC must first make the decision of whether to conduct the market research study. If the market research study is undertaken, chance node 2 indicates that both the favorable report branch and the unfavorable report branch are not under PDC's control and will be determined by chance. Node 3 is a decision node, indicating that PDC must make the decision to construct the small, medium, or large complex if the market research report is favorable. Node 4 is a decision node showing that PDC must make the decision to construct the small, medium, or large complex if the market research report is unfavorable. Node 5 is a decision node indicating that PDC must make the decision to construct the small, medium, or large complex if the market research is not undertaken. Nodes 6 to 14 are chance nodes indicating that the strong demand or weak demand state-of-nature branches will be determined by chance.

Analysis of the decision tree and the choice of an optimal strategy require that we know the branch probabilities corresponding to all chance nodes. PDC has developed the following branch probabilities:

The branch probabilities for P(favorable report) and P(unfavorable report) are calculated using Bayes' rule, first introduced in Chapter 5. We illustrate these calculations in Section 15.5.

If the market research study is undertaken:

$$P(\text{favorable report}) = 0.77$$
$$P(\text{unfavorable report}) = 0.23$$

If the market research report is favorable, the posterior probabilities are:

$$P(\text{strong demand given a favorable report}) = 0.94$$
$$P(\text{weak demand given a favorable report}) = 0.06$$

If the market research report is unfavorable, the posterior probabilities are:

$$P(\text{strong demand given an unfavorable report}) = 0.35$$
$$P(\text{weak demand given an unfavorable report}) = 0.65$$

If the market research report is not undertaken, the prior probabilities are applicable:

$$P(\text{strong demand}) = 0.80$$
$$P(\text{weak demand}) = 0.20$$

The branch probabilities are shown on the decision tree in Figure 15.6.

A **decision strategy** is a sequence of decisions and chance outcomes in which the decisions chosen depend on the yet-to-be-determined outcomes of chance events. The approach used to determine the optimal decision strategy is based on a rollback of the expected values in the decision tree using the following steps:

1. At chance nodes, compute the expected value by multiplying the payoff at the end of each branch by the corresponding branch probabilities.
2. At decision nodes, select the decision branch that leads to the best expected value. This expected value becomes the expected value at the decision node.

Starting the rollback calculations by computing the expected values at chance nodes 6 to 14 provides the following results:

$$\begin{aligned}
\text{EV(Node 6)} &= 0.94(8) + 0.06(7) &&= 7.94\\
\text{EV(Node 7)} &= 0.94(14) + 0.06(5) &&= 13.46\\
\text{EV(Node 8)} &= 0.94(20) + 0.06(-9) &&= 18.26\\
\text{EV(Node 9)} &= 0.35(8) + 0.65(7) &&= 7.35\\
\text{EV(Node 10)} &= 0.35(14) + 0.65(5) &&= 8.15\\
\text{EV(Node 11)} &= 0.35(20) + 0.65(-9) &&= 1.15\\
\text{EV(Node 12)} &= 0.80(8) + 0.20(7) &&= 7.80\\
\text{EV(Node 13)} &= 0.80(14) + 0.20(5) &&= 12.20\\
\text{EV(Node 14)} &= 0.80(20) + 0.20(-9) &&= 14.20
\end{aligned}$$

FIGURE 15.6 The PDC Decision Tree with Branch Probabilities

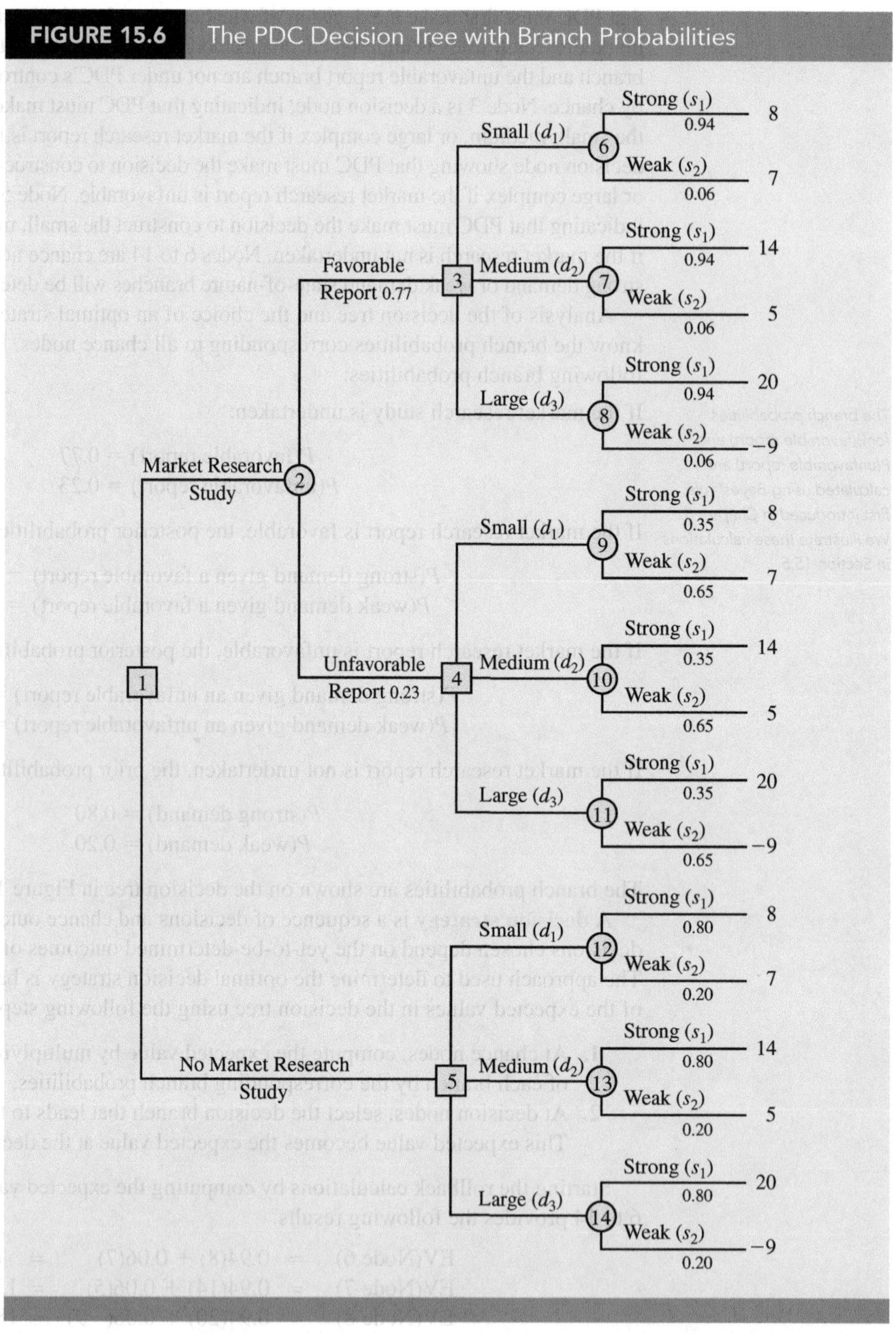

Figure 15.7 shows the reduced decision tree after computing expected values at these chance nodes.

Next, move to decision nodes 3, 4, and 5. For each of these nodes, we select the decision alternative branch that leads to the best expected value. For example, at node 3 we have the choice of the small complex branch with EV(Node 6) = 7.94, the medium complex branch

FIGURE 15.7 PDC Decision Tree after Computing Expected Values at Chance Nodes 6 to 14

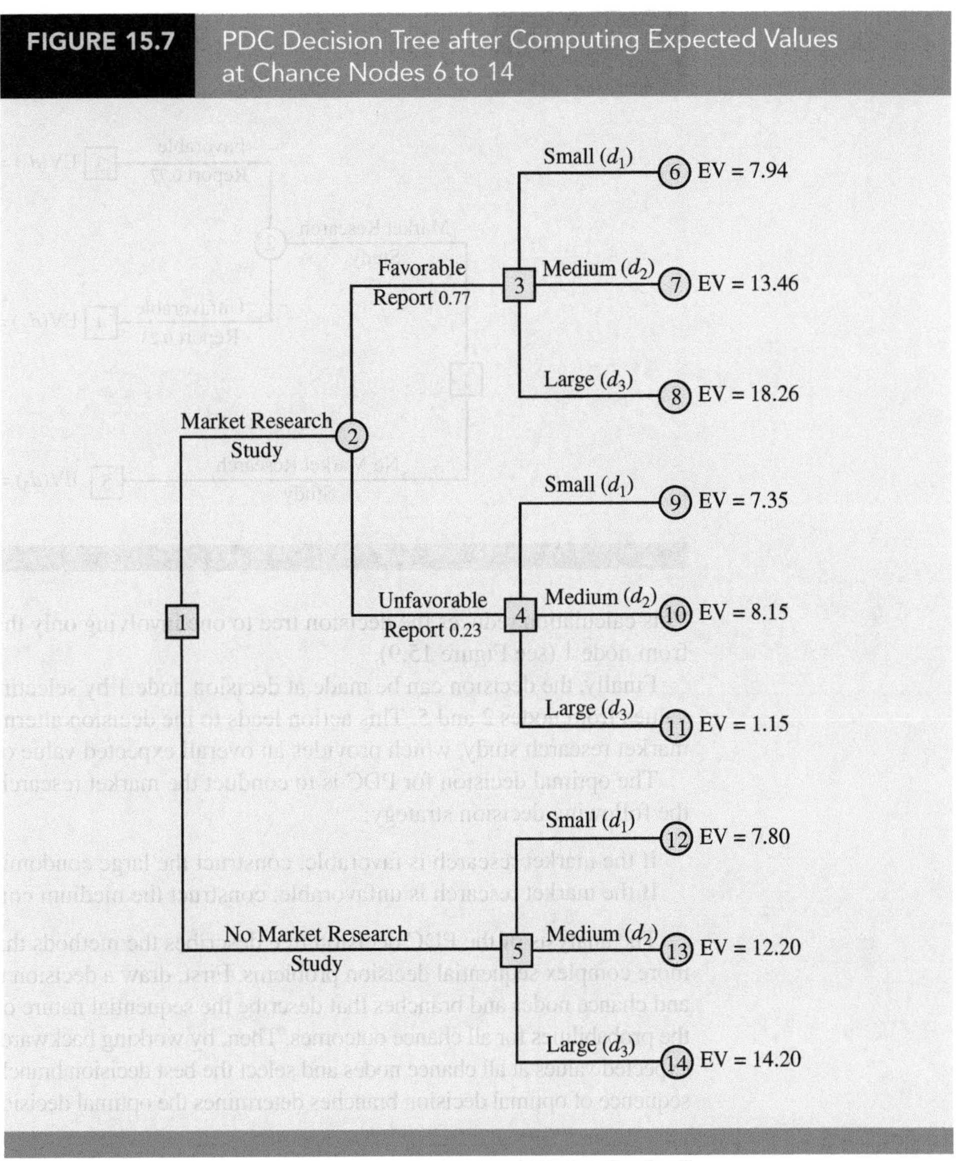

with EV(Node 7) = 13.46, and the large complex branch with EV(Node 8) = 18.26. Thus, we select the large complex decision alternative branch and the expected value at node 3 becomes EV(Node 3) = 18.26.

For node 4, we select the best expected value from nodes 9, 10, and 11. The best decision alternative is the medium complex branch that provides EV(Node 4) = 8.15. For node 5, we select the best expected value from nodes 12, 13, and 14. The best decision alternative is the large complex branch that provides EV(Node 5) = 14.20. Figure 15.8 shows the reduced decision tree after choosing the best decisions at nodes 3, 4, and 5 and rolling back the expected values to these nodes.

The expected value at chance node 2 can now be computed as follows:

$$\begin{aligned} \text{EV(Node 2)} &= 0.77\text{EV(Node 3)} + 0.23\text{EV(Node 4)} \\ &= 0.77(18.26) + 0.23(8.15) = 15.93 \end{aligned}$$

FIGURE 15.8 PDC Decision Tree after Choosing Best Decisions at Nodes 3, 4, and 5

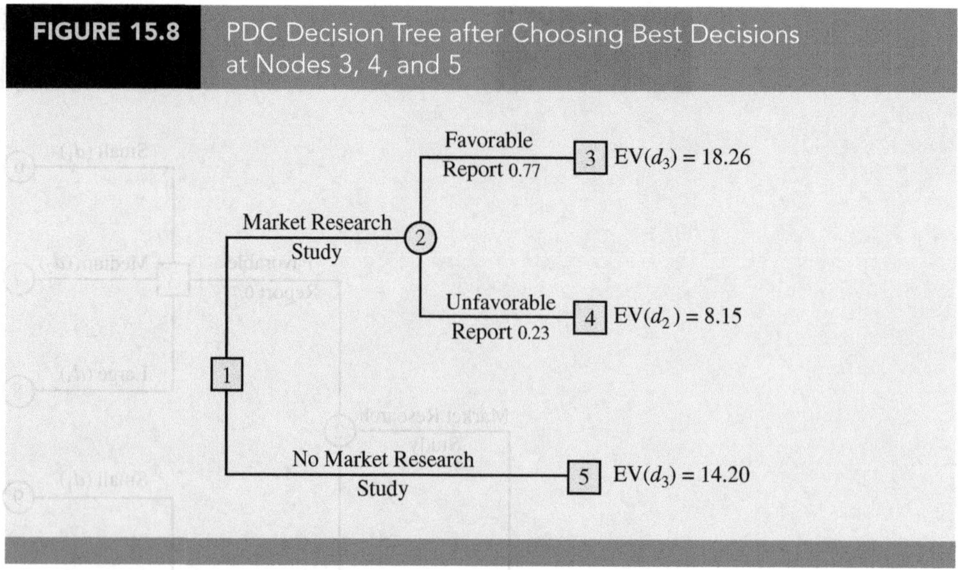

This calculation reduces the decision tree to one involving only the two decision branches from node 1 (see Figure 15.9).

Finally, the decision can be made at decision node 1 by selecting the best expected values from nodes 2 and 5. This action leads to the decision alternative to conduct the market research study, which provides an overall expected value of 15.93.

The optimal decision for PDC is to conduct the market research study and then carry out the following decision strategy:

If the market research is favorable, construct the large condominium complex.
If the market research is unfavorable, construct the medium condominium complex.

The analysis of the PDC decision tree describes the methods that can be used to analyze more complex sequential decision problems. First, draw a decision tree consisting of decision and chance nodes and branches that describe the sequential nature of the problem. Determine the probabilities for all chance outcomes. Then, by working backward through the tree, compute expected values at all chance nodes and select the best decision branch at all decision nodes. The sequence of optimal decision branches determines the optimal decision strategy for the problem.

FIGURE 15.9 PDC Decision Tree Reduced to Two Decision Branches

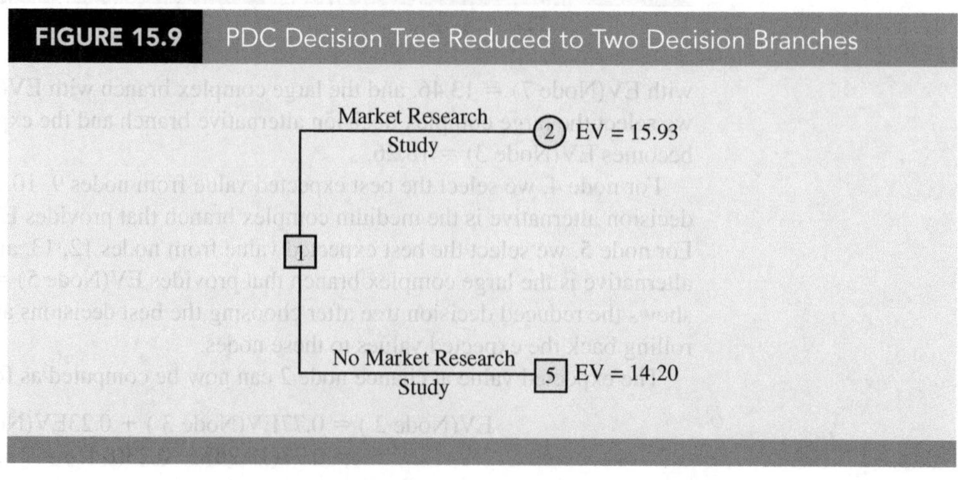

Expected Value of Sample Information

The EVSI = $1.73 million suggests PDC should be willing to pay up to $1.73 million to conduct the market research study.

In the PDC problem, the market research study is the sample information used to determine the optimal decision strategy. The expected value associated with the market research study is 15.93. Previously, we showed that the best expected value if the market research study is *not* undertaken is 14.20. Thus, we can conclude that the difference, 15.93 − 14.20 = 1.73, is the **expected value of sample information (EVSI)**. In other words, conducting the market research study adds $1.73 million to the PDC expected value. In general, the expected value of sample information is as follows:

EXPECTED VALUE OF SAMPLE INFORMATION (EVSI)

$$\text{EVSI} = |\text{EVwSI} - \text{EVwoSI}| \tag{15.3}$$

where

EVSI = expected value of sample information
EVwSI = expected value *with* sample information about the states of nature
EVwoSI = expected value *without* sample information about the states of nature

Expected Value of Perfect Information

A special case of gaining additional information related to a decision problem is when the sample information provides **perfect information** on the states of nature. In other words, consider a case in which the marketing study undertaken by PDC would determine exactly which state of nature will occur. Clearly, such a result is highly unlikely from a marketing study, but such an analysis provides a best-case analysis of the benefit provided by the marketing study. If the investment required for the additional information exceeds the expected value of perfect information, then we would not want to invest in procuring the additional information.

To illustrate the calculation of the expected value of perfect information, we return to the PDC decision. We assume for the moment that PDC could determine with certainty, prior to making a decision, which state of nature is going to occur. To make use of this perfect information, we will develop a decision strategy that PDC should follow once it knows which state of nature will occur.

To help determine the decision strategy for PDC, we reproduced PDC's payoff table as Table 15.6. If PDC knew for sure that state of nature s_1 would occur, the best decision alternative would be d_3, with a payoff of $20 million. Similarly, if PDC knew for sure that state of nature s_2 would occur, the best decision alternative would be d_1, with a payoff of $7 million. Thus, we can state PDC's optimal decision strategy when the perfect information becomes available as follows:

If s_1, select d_3 and receive a payoff of $20 million.
If s_2, select d_1 and receive a payoff of $7 million.

It would be worth $3.2 million for PDC to learn the level of market acceptance before selecting a decision alternative. This represents the maximum that PDC should invest in any market research to provide additional information on the states of nature because no market research study can be expected to provide perfect information.

TABLE 15.6 Payoff Table for the PDC Condominium Project ($ Millions)

	State of Nature	
Decision Alternative	**Strong Demand s_1**	**Weak Demand s_2**
Small complex, d_1	8	7
Medium complex, d_2	14	5
Large complex, d_3	20	−9

What is the expected value for this decision strategy? To compute the expected value with perfect information, we return to the original probabilities for the states of nature: $P(s_1) = 0.8$ and $P(s_2) = 0.2$. Thus, there is a 0.8 probability that the perfect information will indicate state of nature s_1, and the resulting decision alternative d_3 will provide a \$20 million profit. Similarly, with a 0.2 probability for state of nature s_2, the optimal decision alternative d_1 will provide a \$7 million profit. Thus, from equation (15.2) the expected value of the decision strategy that uses perfect information is $0.8(20) + 0.2(7) = 17.4$.

We refer to the expected value of \$17.4 million as the *expected value with perfect information* (EVwPI).

Earlier in this section we showed that the recommended decision using the expected value approach is decision alternative d_3, with an expected value of \$14.2 million. Because this decision recommendation and expected value computation were made without the benefit of perfect information, \$14.2 million is referred to as the *expected value without perfect information* (EVwoPI).

The expected value with perfect information is \$17.4 million, and the expected value without perfect information is \$14.2; therefore, the expected value of the perfect information (EVPI) is \$17.4 − \$14.2 = \$3.2 million. In other words, \$3.2 million represents the additional expected value that can be obtained if perfect information were available about the states of nature.

In general, the **expected value of perfect information (EVPI)** is computed as follows:

EXPECTED VALUE OF PERFECT INFORMATION (EVPI)

$$\text{EVPI} = |\text{EVwPI} - \text{EVwoPI}| \tag{15.4}$$

where

EVPI = expected value of perfect information
EVwPI = expected value *with* perfect information about the states of nature
EVwoPI = expected value *without* perfect information about the states of nature

15.5 Computing Branch Probabilities with Bayes' Theorem

In Section 15.4 the branch probabilities for the PDC decision tree chance nodes were provided in the problem description. No computations were required to determine these probabilities. In this section, we show how **Bayes' theorem** can be used to compute branch probabilities for decision trees.

We first introduced Bayes' theorem in Chapter 5 as a means of calculating posterior probabilities as updates of prior probabilities once additional information is obtained. For the PDC problem, the branch probabilities are the posterior probabilities for demand that have been updated based on the sample information of whether the market research report is favorable or unfavorable.

The PDC decision tree is shown again in Figure 15.10. Let:

F = favorable market research report
U = unfavorable market research report
s_1 = strong demand (state of nature 1)
s_2 = weak demand (state of nature 2)

At chance node 2, we need to know the branch probabilities $P(F)$ and $P(U)$. At chance nodes 6, 7, and 8, we need to know the branch probabilities $P(s_1|F)$, which is read as "the probability of state of nature 1 given a favorable market research report," and $P(s_2|F)$,

FIGURE 15.10 The PDC Decision Tree

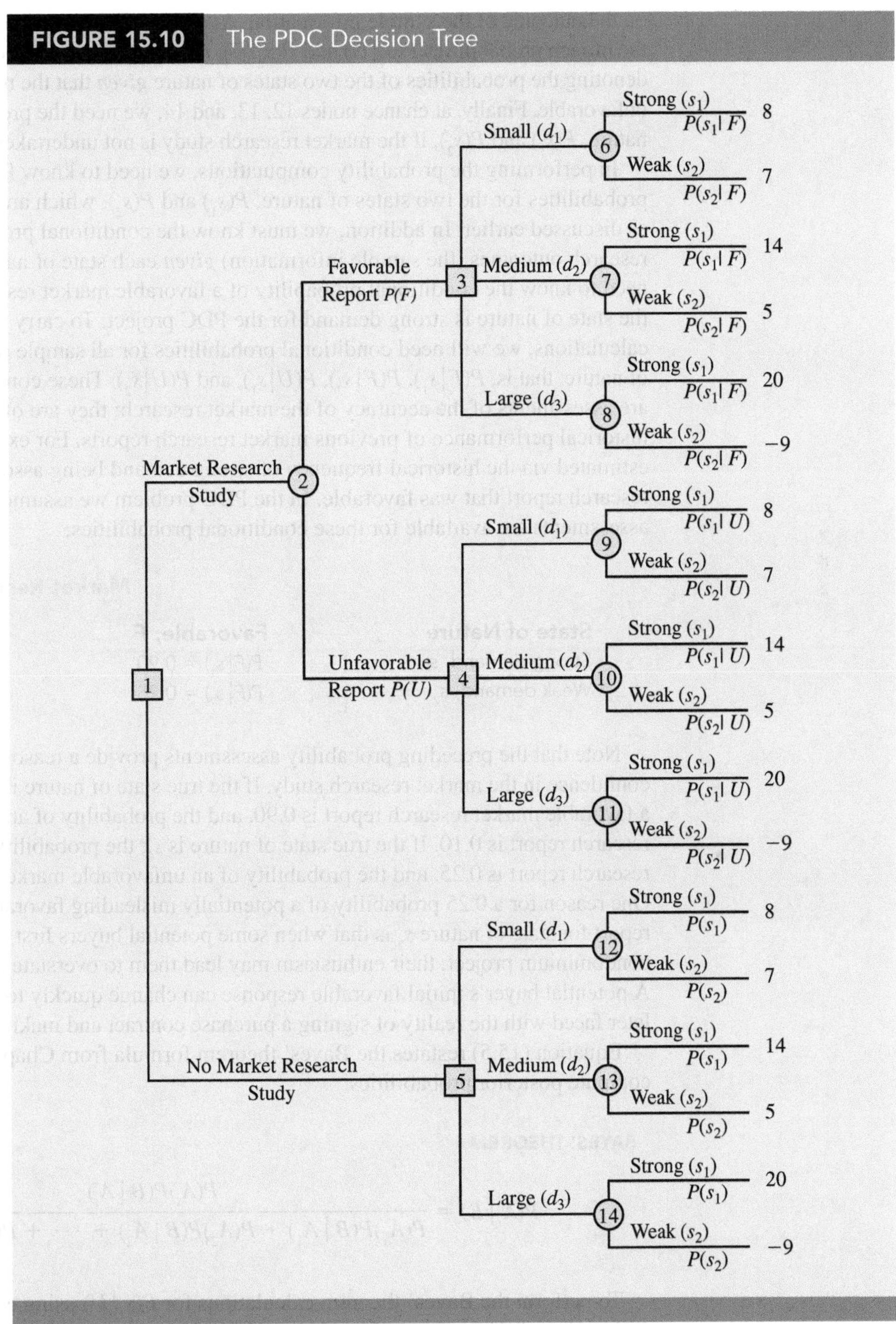

which is the probability of state of nature 2 given a favorable market research report. As described in Chapter 5, the notation | in $P(s_1|F)$ and $P(s_2|F)$ is read as "given" and indicates a **conditional probability** because we are interested in the probability of a particular state of nature "conditioned" on the fact that we receive a favorable market report. $P(s_1|F)$ and $P(s_2|F)$ are referred to as *posterior probabilities* because they are conditional probabilities based on the outcome of the sample information. At chance nodes 9, 10, and 11, we need to know the branch probabilities $P(s_1 | U)$ and $P(s_2 | U)$; note that these are also posterior probabilities, denoting the probabilities of the two states of nature *given* that the market research report is unfavorable. Finally, at chance nodes 12, 13, and 14, we need the probabilities for the states of nature, $P(s_1)$ and $P(s_2)$, if the market research study is not undertaken.

In performing the probability computations, we need to know PDC's assessment of the probabilities for the two states of nature, $P(s_1)$ and $P(s_2)$, which are the prior probabilities as discussed earlier. In addition, we must know the conditional probability of the market research outcomes (the sample information) *given* each state of nature. For example, we need to know the conditional probability of a favorable market research report given that the state of nature is strong demand for the PDC project. To carry out the probability calculations, we will need conditional probabilities for all sample outcomes given all states of nature, that is, $P(F|s_1)$, $P(F|s_2)$, $P(U|s_1)$, and $P(U|s_2)$. These conditional probabilities are assessments of the accuracy of the market research; they are often estimated using historical performance of previous market research reports. For example, $P(F|s_1)$ may be estimated via the historical frequency of strong demand being associated with a market research report that was favorable. In the PDC problem we assume that the following assessments are available for these conditional probabilities:

	Market Research	
State of Nature	**Favorable, *F***	**Unfavorable, *U***
Strong demand, s_1	$P(F\|s_1) = 0.90$	$P(U\|s_1) = 0.10$
Weak demand, s_2	$P(F\|s_2) = 0.25$	$P(U\|s_2) = 0.75$

Note that the preceding probability assessments provide a reasonable degree of confidence in the market research study. If the true state of nature is s_1, the probability of a favorable market research report is 0.90, and the probability of an unfavorable market research report is 0.10. If the true state of nature is s_2, the probability of a favorable market research report is 0.25, and the probability of an unfavorable market research report is 0.75. One reason for a 0.25 probability of a potentially misleading favorable market research report for state of nature s_2 is that when some potential buyers first hear about the new condominium project, their enthusiasm may lead them to overstate their real interest in it. A potential buyer's initial favorable response can change quickly to a "no-thank-you" when later faced with the reality of signing a purchase contract and making a down payment.

Equation (15.5) restates the Bayes' theorem formula from Chapter 5 that is used to compute posterior probabilities.

BAYES' THEOREM

$$P(A_i | B) = \frac{P(A_i)P(B | A_i)}{P(A_1)P(B | A_1) + P(A_2)P(B | A_2) + \cdots + P(A_n)P(B | A_n)} \tag{15.5}$$

To perform the Bayes' theorem calculations for $P(s_1 | U)$ using equation (15.5), we replace B with U (unfavorable report) and A_i with s_1 in equation (15.5) so that we have:

$$P(s_1|U) = \frac{P(U|s_1)P(s_1)}{P(U|s_1)P(s_1) + P(U|s_2)P(s_2)}$$

$$= \frac{0.10 \times 0.80}{(0.10 \times 0.80) + (0.20 \times 0.75)} = 0.35$$

which indicates that the probability of strong demand given an unfavorable market research report is 0.35. We can also calculate the probability of weak demand given an unfavorable market research report as shown below:

$$P(s_2|U) = \frac{P(U|s_2)P(s_2)}{P(U|s_1)P(s_1) + P(U|s_2)P(s_2)} = \frac{0.75 \times 0.20}{(0.10 \times 0.80) + (0.75 \times 0.20)} = 0.65.$$

Similarly, we can calculate the posterior probabilities for strong and weak demand given a favorable market research report using equation (15.5):

$$P(s_1|F) = \frac{P(F|s_1)P(s_1)}{P(F|s_1)P(s_1) + P(F|s_2)P(s_2)} = \frac{0.90 \times 0.80}{(0.90 \times 0.80) + (0.25 \times 0.20)} = 0.94$$

and

$$P(s_2|F) = \frac{P(F|s_2)P(s_2)}{P(F|s_1)P(s_1) + P(F|s_2)P(s_2)} = \frac{0.25 \times 0.20}{(0.90 \times 0.80) + (0.25 \times 0.20)} = 0.06.$$

This indicates that a favorable research report leads to a posterior probability of 0.94 that the demand will be strong and a posterior probability of only 0.06 that demand will be weak.

The discussion in this section shows an underlying relationship between the probabilities on the various branches in a decision tree. It would be inappropriate to assume different prior probabilities, $P(s_1)$ and $P(s_2)$, without determining how these changes would alter $P(F)$ and $P(U)$, as well as the posterior probabilities $P(s_1|F)$, $P(s_2|F)$, $P(s_1|U)$, and $P(s_2|U)$.

15.6 Utility Theory

The decision analysis situations presented so far in this chapter expressed outcomes (payoffs) in terms of monetary values. With probability information available about the outcomes of the chance events, we defined the optimal decision alternative as the one that provides the best expected value. However, in some situations the decision alternative with the best expected value may not be the preferred alternative. A decision maker may also wish to consider intangible factors such as risk, image, or other nonmonetary criteria in order to evaluate the decision alternatives. When monetary value does not necessarily lead to the most preferred decision, expressing the value (or worth) of a consequence in terms of its utility will permit the use of expected utility to identify the most desirable decision alternative. The discussion of utility and its application in decision analysis is presented in this section.

Utility is a measure of the total worth or relative desirability of a particular outcome; it reflects the decision maker's attitude toward a collection of factors such as profit, loss, and risk. Researchers have found that as long as the monetary value of payoffs stays within a range that the decision maker considers reasonable, selecting the decision alternative with the best expected value usually leads to selection of the most preferred decision. However, when the payoffs are extreme, decision makers are often unsatisfied or uneasy with the decision that simply provides the best expected value.

As an example of a situation in which utility can help in selecting the best decision alternative, let us consider the problem faced by Swofford, Inc., a relatively small real estate investment firm located in Atlanta, Georgia. Swofford currently has two investment opportunities that require approximately the same cash outlay. The cash requirements necessary prohibit Swofford from making more than one investment at this time. Consequently, three possible decision alternatives may be considered.

TABLE 15.7 Payoff Table for Swofford, Inc.

Decision Alternative	State of Nature Prices Go Up s_1	Prices Stable s_2	Prices Go Down s_3
Investment A, d_1	\$30,000	\$20,000	−\$50,000
Investment B, d_2	\$50,000	−\$20,000	−\$30,000
Do not invest, d_3	0	0	0

The three decision alternatives, denoted d_1, d_2, and d_3, are:

$$d_1 = \text{make investment A}$$
$$d_2 = \text{make investment B}$$
$$d_3 = \text{do not invest}$$

The monetary payoffs associated with the investment opportunities depend on the investment decision and on the direction of the real estate market during the next six months (the chance event). Real estate prices will go up, remain stable, or go down. Thus, the states of nature, denoted s_1, s_2, and s_3, are:

$$s_1 = \text{real estate prices go up}$$
$$s_2 = \text{real estate prices remain stable}$$
$$s_3 = \text{real estate prices go down}$$

Using the best information available, Swofford has estimated the profits, or payoffs, associated with each decision alternative and state-of-nature combination. The resulting payoff table is shown in Table 15.7.

The best estimate of the probability that real estate prices will go up is 0.3; the best estimate of the probability that prices will remain stable is 0.5; and the best estimate of the probability that prices will go down is 0.2. Thus, the expected values for the three decision alternatives are:

$$\begin{aligned}
\text{EV}(d_1) &= 0.3(30{,}000) + 0.5(20{,}000) + 0.2(-50{,}000) = 9000 \\
\text{EV}(d_2) &= 0.3(50{,}000) + 0.5(-20{,}000) + 0.2(-30{,}000) = -11{,}000 \\
\text{EV}(d_3) &= 0.3(0) + 0.5(0) + 0.2(0) = 0
\end{aligned}$$

Using the expected value approach, the optimal decision is to select investment A with an expected value of \$9,000. Is it really the best decision alternative? Let us consider some other relevant factors that relate to Swofford's capability for absorbing the loss of \$50,000 if investment A is made and prices actually go down.

Actually, Swofford's current financial position is weak. This condition is partly reflected in Swofford's ability to make only one investment. More important, however, the firm's president believes that, if the next investment results in a substantial loss, Swofford's future will be in jeopardy. Although the expected value approach leads to a recommendation for d_1, do you think the firm's president would prefer this decision? We suspect that the president would select d_2 or d_3 to avoid the possibility of incurring a \$50,000 loss. In fact, a reasonable conclusion is that, if a loss of even \$30,000 could drive Swofford out of business, the president would select d_3, believing that both investments A and B are too risky for Swofford's current financial position.

The way we resolve Swofford's dilemma is first to determine Swofford's utility for the various outcomes. Recall that the utility of any outcome is the total worth of that outcome, taking into account all risks and consequences involved. If the utilities for the various consequences are assessed correctly, the decision alternative with the highest expected utility is the most preferred, or best, alternative. We next show how to determine the utility of the outcomes so that the alternative with the highest expected utility can be identified.

Utility and Decision Analysis

The procedure we use to establish a utility for each of the payoffs in Swofford's situation requires that we first assign a utility to the best and worst possible payoffs. Any values will work as long as the utility assigned to the best payoff is greater than the utility assigned to the worst payoff. In this case, \$50,000 is the best payoff and −\$50,000 is the worst. Suppose, then, that we arbitrarily make assignments to these two payoffs as follows:

Utility values of 0 and 1 could have been selected here; we selected 0 and 10 to avoid any possible confusion between the utility value for a payoff and the probability p.

$$\text{Utility of } -\$50{,}000 = U(-50{,}000) = 0$$
$$\text{Utility of } \$50{,}000 = U(50{,}000) = 10$$

Let us now determine the utility associated with every other payoff.

Consider the process of establishing the utility of a payoff of \$30,000. First we ask Swofford's president to state a preference between a guaranteed \$30,000 payoff and an opportunity to engage in the following lottery, or bet, for some probability of p that we select:

p is often referred to as the indifference probability.

Lottery: Swofford obtains a payoff of \$50,000 with probability p and a payoff of −\$50,000 with probability $(1 - p)$.

Obviously, if p is very close to 1, Swofford's president would prefer the lottery to the guaranteed payoff of \$30,000 because the firm would virtually ensure itself a payoff of \$50,000. If p is very close to 0, Swofford's president would clearly prefer the guarantee of \$30,000. In any event, as p increases continuously from 0 to 1, the preference for the guaranteed payoff of \$30,000 decreases and at some point is equal to the preference for the lottery. At this value of p, Swofford's president would have equal preference for the guaranteed payoff of \$30,000 and the lottery; at greater values of p, Swofford's president would prefer the lottery to the guaranteed \$30,000 payoff. For example, let us assume that when $p = 0.95$, Swofford's president is indifferent between the guaranteed payoff of \$30,000 and the lottery. For this value of p, we can compute the utility of a \$30,000 payoff as follows:

$$\begin{aligned} U(30{,}000) &= pU(50{,}000) + (1 - p)U(-50{,}000) \\ &= 0.95(10) + (0.05)(0) \\ &= 9.5. \end{aligned}$$

Obviously, if we had started with a different assignment of utilities for a payoff of \$50,000 and −\$50,000, the result would have been a different utility for \$30,000. For example, if we had started with an assignment of 100 for \$50,000 and 10 for −\$50,000, the utility of a \$30,000 payoff would be:

$$\begin{aligned} U(30{,}000) &= 0.95(100) + 0.05(10) \\ &= 95.0 + 0.5 \\ &= 95.5. \end{aligned}$$

Hence, we must conclude that the utility assigned to each payoff is not unique but merely depends on the initial choice of utilities for the best and worst payoffs.

Before computing the utility for the other payoffs, let us consider the implication of Swofford's president assigning a utility of 9.5 to a payoff of \$30,000. Clearly, when $p = 0.95$, the expected value of the lottery is:

$$\begin{aligned} \text{EV(lottery)} &= 0.95(\$50{,}000) + 0.05(-\$50{,}000) \\ &= \$47{,}500 - \$2{,}500 \\ &= \$45{,}000. \end{aligned}$$

The difference between the expected value of the lottery and the guaranteed payoff can be viewed as the risk premium the decision maker is willing to pay.

Although the expected value of the lottery when $p = 0.95$ is \$45,000, Swofford's president is indifferent between the lottery (and its associated risk) and a guaranteed payoff of \$30,000. Thus, Swofford's president is taking a conservative, or risk-avoiding, viewpoint. A decision maker who would choose a guaranteed payoff over a lottery with a superior expected payoff is a **risk avoider** (or is said to be risk-averse). The president would rather have \$30,000 for certain than risk anything greater than a 5% chance of incurring a loss of \$50,000. In other words, the difference between the EV of \$45,000 and the guaranteed payoff of \$30,000 is the risk premium that Swofford's president would be willing to pay to avoid the 5% chance of losing \$50,000.

To compute the utility associated with a payoff of −\$20,000, we must ask Swofford's president to state a preference between a guaranteed −\$20,000 payoff and an opportunity to engage again in the following lottery:

Lottery: Swofford obtains a payoff of \$50,000 with probability p and a payoff of −\$50,000 with probability $(1 - p)$.

Note that this lottery is exactly the same as the one we used to establish the utility of a payoff of \$30,000 (in fact, we can use this lottery to establish the utility for any value in the Swofford payoff table). We need to determine the value of p that would make the president indifferent between a guaranteed payoff of −\$20,000 and the lottery. For example, we might begin by asking the president to choose between a certain loss of \$20,000 and the lottery with a payoff of \$50,000 with probability $p = 0.90$ and a payoff of −\$50,000 with probability $(1 - p) = 0.10$. What answer do you think we would get? Surely, with this high probability of obtaining a payoff of \$50,000, the president would elect the lottery. Next, we might ask whether $p = 0.85$ would result in indifference between the loss of \$20,000 for certain and the lottery. Again the president might prefer the lottery. Suppose that we continue until we get to $p = 0.55$, at which point the president is indifferent between the payoff of −\$20,000 and the lottery. In other words, for any value of p less than 0.55, the president would take a loss of \$20,000 for certain rather than risk the potential loss of \$50,000 with the lottery; and for any value of p above 0.55, the president would choose the lottery. Thus, the utility assigned to a payoff of −\$20,000 is:

$$\begin{aligned} U(-\$20{,}000) &= pU(50{,}000) + (1 - p)U(-\$50{,}000) \\ &= 0.55(10) + 0.45(0) \\ &= 5.5. \end{aligned}$$

Again let us assess the implication of this assignment by comparing it to the expected value approach. When $p = 0.55$, the expected value of the lottery is:

$$\begin{aligned} \text{EV(lottery)} &= 0.55(\$50{,}000) + 0.45(-\$50{,}000) \\ &= \$27{,}500 - \$22{,}500 \\ &= \$5{,}000. \end{aligned}$$

Thus, Swofford's president would just as soon absorb a certain loss of \$20,000 as take the lottery and its associated risk, even though the expected value of the lottery is \$5,000. Once again this preference demonstrates the conservative, or risk-avoiding, point of view of Swofford's president.

In these two examples, we computed the utility for the payoffs of \$30,000 and −\$20,000. We can determine the utility for any payoff M in a similar fashion. First, we must find the probability p for which the decision maker is indifferent between a guaranteed payoff of M and a lottery with a payoff of \$50,000 with probability p and −\$50,000 with probability $(1 - p)$. The utility of M is then computed as follows:

$$\begin{aligned} U(\text{M}) &= pU(\$50{,}000) + (1 - p)U(-\$50{,}000) \\ &= p(10) + (1 - p)0 \\ &= 10p. \end{aligned}$$

TABLE 15.8 Utility of Monetary Payoffs for Swofford, Inc.

Monetary Value	Indifference Value of p	Utility
$50,000	Does not apply	10.0
30,000	0.95	9.5
20,000	0.90	9.0
0	0.75	7.5
−20,000	0.55	5.5
−30,000	0.40	4.0
−50,000	Does not apply	0

Using this procedure we developed a utility for each of the remaining payoffs in Swofford's problem. The results are presented in Table 15.8.

Now that we have determined the utility of each of the possible monetary values, we can write the original payoff table in terms of utility. Table 15.9 shows the utility for the various outcomes in the Swofford problem. The notation we use for the entries in the utility table is U_{ij}, which denotes the utility associated with decision alternative d_i and state of nature s_j. Using this notation, we see that $U_{23} = 4.0$.

We can now compute the **expected utility (EU)** of the utilities in Table 15.9 in a similar fashion as we computed expected value in Section 15.3. In other words, to identify an optimal decision alternative for Swofford, Inc., the expected utility approach requires the analyst to compute the expected utility for each decision alternative and then select the alternative yielding the highest expected utility. With N possible states of nature, the expected utility of a decision alternative d_i is given by:

EXPECTED UTILITY (EU)

$$EU(d_i) = \sum_{j=1}^{N} P(s_j)U_{ij} \tag{15.6}$$

The expected utility for each of the decision alternatives in the Swofford problem is:

$$\text{EU}(d_1) = 0.3\,(9.5) + 0.5\,(9.0) + 0.2\,(0) = 7.35$$
$$\text{EU}(d_2) = 0.3\,(10) + 0.5\,(5.5) + 0.2\,(4.0) = 6.55$$
$$\text{EU}(d_3) = 0.3\,(7.5\,) + 0.5\,(7.5) + 0.2\,(7.5) = 7.50$$

TABLE 15.9 Utility Table for Swofford, Inc.

	State of Nature		
Decision Alternative	Prices Up s_1	Prices Stable s_2	Prices Down s_3
Investment A, d_1	9.5	9.0	0
Investment B, d_2	10.0	5.5	4.0
Do not invest, d_3	7.5	7.5	7.5

Note that the optimal decision using the expected utility approach is d_3, do not invest. The ranking of alternatives according to the president's utility assignments and the associated monetary values are as follows:

Ranking of Decision Alternatives	Expected Utility	Expected Value
Do not invest	7.50	0
Investment A	7.35	9,000
Investment B	6.55	−1,000

Note that, although investment A had the highest expected value of $9,000, the analysis indicates that Swofford should decline this investment. The rationale behind not selecting investment A is that the 0.20 probability of a $50,000 loss was considered by Swofford's president to involve a serious risk. The seriousness of this risk and its associated impact on the company were not adequately reflected by the expected value of investment A. We assessed the utility for each payoff to assess this risk adequately.

The following steps state in general terms the procedure used to solve the Swofford, Inc., investment problem:

Step 1. Develop a payoff table using monetary values

Step 2. Identify the best and worst payoff values in the table and assign each a utility, with $U(\text{best payoff}) > U(\text{worst payoff})$

Step 3. For every other monetary value M in the original payoff table, do the following to determine its utility:

a. Define the lottery such that there is a probability p of the best payoff and a probability $(1 - p)$ of the worst payoff

b. Determine the value of p such that the decision maker is indifferent between a guaranteed payoff of M and the lottery defined in step 3(a)

c. Calculate the utility of M as follows:

$$U(M) = pU(\text{best payoff}) + (1 - p)U(\text{worst payoff})$$

Step 4. Convert each monetary value in the payoff table to a utility

Step 5. Apply the expected utility approach to the utility table developed in step 4 and select the decision alternative with the highest expected utility

The procedure we described for determining the utility of monetary consequences can also be used to develop a utility measure for nonmonetary consequences. Assign the best consequence a utility of 10 and the worst a utility of 0. Then create a lottery with a probability of p for the best consequence and $(1 - p)$ for the worst consequence. For each of the other consequences, find the value of p that makes the decision maker indifferent between the lottery and the consequence. Then calculate the utility of the consequence in question as follows:

$$U(\text{consequence}) = pU(\text{best consequence}) + (1 - p)U(\text{worst consequence}).$$

Utility Functions

Next we describe how different decision makers may approach risk in terms of their assessment of utility. The financial position of Swofford, Inc., was such that the firm's president evaluated investment opportunities from a conservative, or risk-avoiding, point of view. However, if the firm had a surplus of cash and a stable future, Swofford's president might have been looking for investment alternatives that, although perhaps risky, contained a potential for substantial profit. That type of behavior would demonstrate that the president is a risk taker with respect to this decision.

TABLE 15.10 Revised Utilities for Swofford, Inc., Assuming a Risk Taker

Monetary Value	Indifference Value of p	Utility
\$50,000	Does not apply	10.0
30,000	0.50	5.0
20,000	0.40	4.0
0	0.25	2.5
−20,000	0.15	1.5
−30,000	0.10	1.0
−50,000	Does not apply	0

A **risk taker** is a decision maker who would choose a lottery over a guaranteed payoff when the expected value of the lottery is inferior to the guaranteed payoff. In this section, we analyze the decision problem faced by Swofford from the point of view of a decision maker who would be classified as a risk taker. We then compare the conservative point of view of Swofford's president (a risk avoider) with the behavior of a decision maker who is a risk taker.

For the decision problem facing Swofford, Inc., using the general procedure for developing utilities as discussed previously, a risk taker might express the utility for the various payoffs shown in Table 15.10. As before, $U(50{,}000) = 10$ and $U(-50{,}000) = 0$. Note the difference in behavior reflected in Table 15.10 and Table 15.8. In other words, in determining the value of p at which the decision maker is indifferent between a guaranteed payoff of M and a lottery in which \$50,000 is obtained with probability p and −\$50,000 with probability $(1 - p)$, the risk taker is willing to accept a greater risk of incurring a loss of \$50,000 in order to gain the opportunity to realize a profit of \$50,000.

To help develop the utility table for the risk taker, we have reproduced the Swofford, Inc. payoff table in Table 15.11. Using these payoffs and the risk taker's utilities given in Table 15.10, we can write the risk taker's utility table as shown in Table 15.12. Using the

TABLE 15.11 Payoff Table for Swofford, Inc.

		State of Nature	
Decision Alternative	**Prices Up s_1**	**Prices Stable s_2**	**Prices Down s_3**
Investment A, d_1	\$30,000	\$20,000	−\$50,000
Investment B, d_2	\$50,000	−\$20,000	−\$30,000
Do not invest, d_3	0	0	0

TABLE 15.12 Utility Table of a Risk Taker for Swofford, Inc.

		State of Nature	
Decision Alternative	**Prices Up s_1**	**Prices Stable s_2**	**Prices Down s_3**
Investment A, d_1	5.0	4.0	0
Investment B, d_2	10.0	1.5	1.0
Do not invest, d_3	2.5	2.5	2.5

state-of-nature probabilities $P(s_1) = 0.3$, $P(s_2) = 0.5$, and $P(s_3) = 0.2$, the expected utility for each decision alternative is:

$$\text{EU}(d_1) = 0.3\,(5.0) + 0.5\,(4.0) + 0.2\,(0) = 3.50$$
$$\text{EU}(d_2) = 0.3\,(10) + 0.5\,(1.5) + 0.2\,(1.0\,) = 3.95$$
$$\text{EU}(d_3) = 0.3\,(2.5) + 0.5\,(2.5) + 0.2\,(2.5) = 2.50$$

What is the recommended decision? Perhaps somewhat to your surprise, the analysis recommends investment B, with the highest expected utility of 3.95. Recall that this investment has a −$1,000 expected value. Why is it now the recommended decision? Remember that the decision maker in this revised problem is a risk taker. Thus, although the expected value of investment B is negative, utility analysis has shown that this decision maker is enough of a risk taker to prefer investment B and its potential for the $50,000 profit.

Ranking by the expected utilities generates the following order of preference of the decision alternatives for the risk taker and the associated expected values:

Ranking of Decision Alternatives	Expected Utility	Expected Value
Investment B	3.95	−$1,000
Investment A	3.50	$9,000
Do not invest	2.50	0

Comparing the utility analysis for a risk taker with the more conservative preferences of the president of Swofford, Inc., who is a risk avoider, we see that, even with the same decision problem, different attitudes toward risk can lead to different recommended decisions. The utilities established by Swofford's president indicated that the firm should not invest at this time, whereas the utilities established by the risk taker showed a preference for investment B. Note that both of these decisions differ from the best expected value decision, which was investment A.

We can obtain another perspective of the difference between behaviors of a risk avoider and a risk taker by developing a graph that depicts the relationship between monetary value and utility. We use the horizontal axis of the graph to represent monetary values and the vertical axis to represent the utility associated with each monetary value. Now, consider the data in Table 15.8, with a utility corresponding to each monetary value for the original Swofford, Inc., problem. These values can be plotted on a graph to produce the top curve in Figure 15.11. The resulting curve is the **utility function for money** for Swofford's president. Recall that these points reflected the conservative, or risk-avoiding, nature of Swofford's president. Hence, we refer to the top curve in Figure 15.11 as a utility function for a risk avoider. Using the data in Table 15.10 developed for a risk taker, we can plot these points to produce the bottom curve in Figure 15.11. The resulting curve depicts the utility function for a risk taker.

By looking at the utility functions in Figure 15.11, we can begin to generalize about the utility functions for risk avoiders and risk takers. Although the exact shape of the utility function will vary from one decision maker to another, we can see the general shape of these two types of utility functions. The utility function for a risk avoider shows a diminishing marginal return for money. For example, the increase in utility going from a monetary value of −$30,000 to $0 is 7.5 − 4.0 = 3.5, whereas the increase in utility in going from $0 to $30,000 is only 9.5 − 7.5 = 2.0.

However, the utility function for a risk taker shows an increasing marginal return for money. For example, in Figure 15.11, the increase in utility for the risk taker in going from −$30,000 to $0 is 2.5 − 1.0 = 1.5, whereas the increase in utility in going from $0 to $30,000 for the risk taker is 5.0 − 2.5 = 2.5. Note also that in either case the utility

FIGURE 15.11 Utility Function for Money for Risk-Avoider, Risk-Taker, and Risk-Neutral Decision Makers

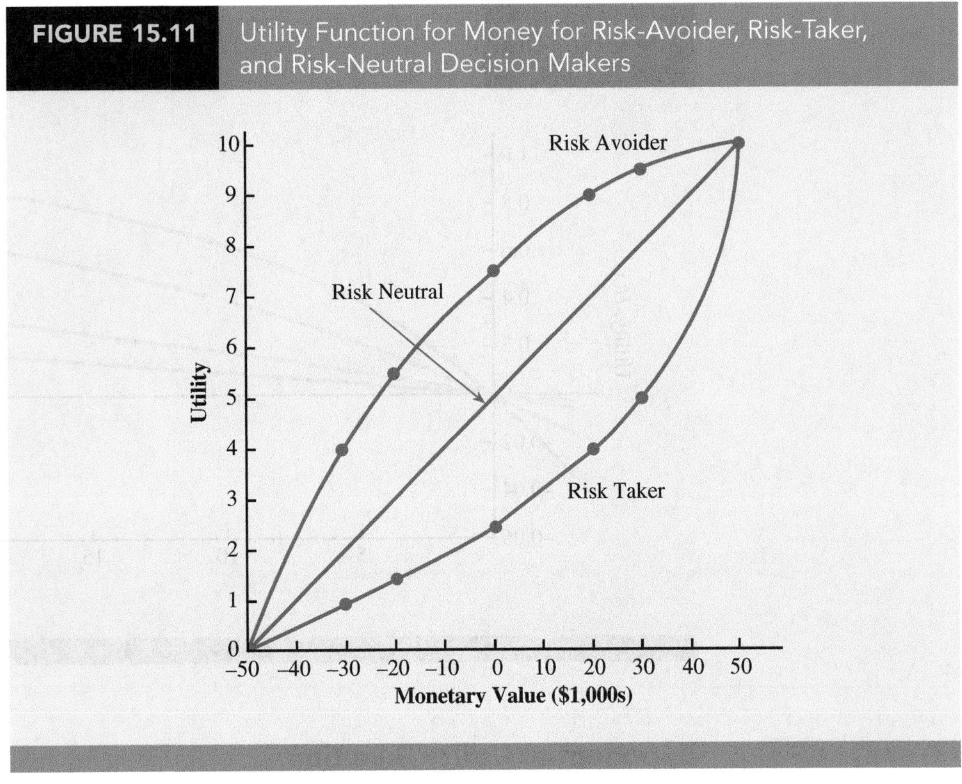

function is always increasing; that is, more money leads to more utility. All utility functions possess this property.

We concluded that the utility function for a risk avoider shows a diminishing marginal return for money and that the utility function for a risk taker shows an increasing marginal return. When the marginal return for money is neither decreasing nor increasing but remains constant, the corresponding utility function describes the behavior of a decision maker who is neutral to risk. The following characteristics are associated with a **risk-neutral** decision maker:

1. The utility function can be drawn as a straight line connecting the "best" and the "worst" points.
2. The expected utility approach and the expected value approach applied to monetary payoffs result in the same action.

The straight, diagonal line in Figure 15.11 depicts the utility function of a risk-neutral decision maker using the Swofford, Inc., problem data.

Generally, when the payoffs for a particular decision-making problem fall into a reasonable range—the best is not too good and the worst is not too bad—decision makers tend to express preferences in agreement with the expected value approach. Thus, we suggest asking the decision maker to consider the best and worst possible payoffs for a problem and assess their reasonableness. If the decision maker believes that they are in the reasonable range, the decision alternative with the best expected value can be used. However, if the payoffs appear unreasonably large or unreasonably small (e.g., a huge loss) and if the decision maker believes that monetary values do not adequately reflect her or his true preferences for the payoffs, a utility analysis of the problem should be considered.

FIGURE 15.12 Exponential Utility Functions with Different Risk Tolerance (R) Values

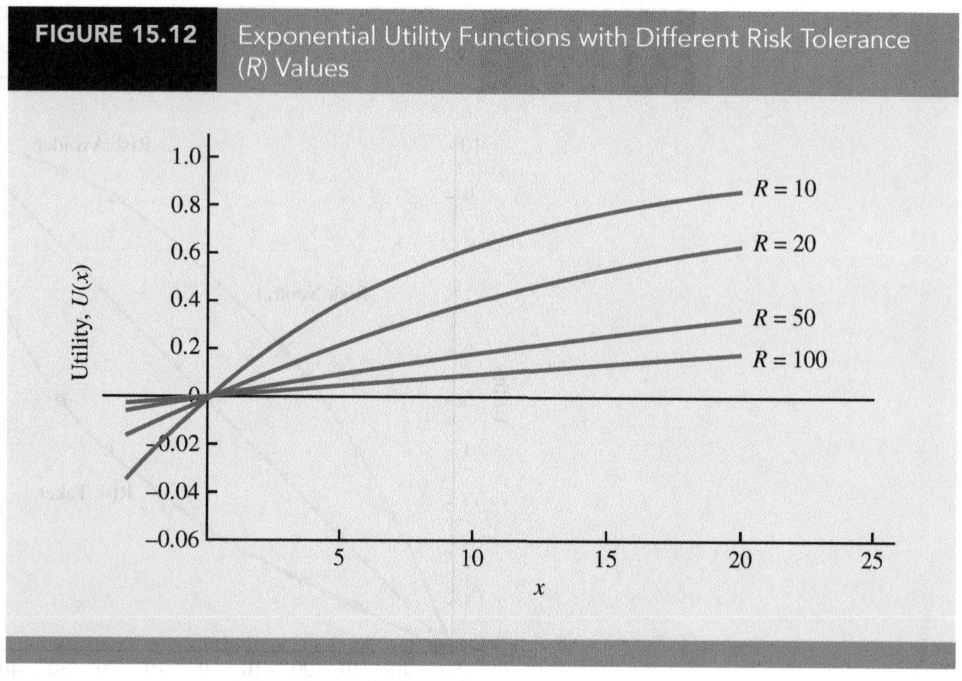

Exponential Utility Function

Having a decision maker provide enough indifference values to create a utility function can be time consuming. An alternative is to assume that the decision maker's utility is defined by an exponential function. Figure 15.12 shows examples of different exponential utility functions. Note that all the exponential utility functions indicate that the decision maker is risk averse. The form of the exponential utility function is as follows.

In equation (15.7), the number e ≈ 2.718282... is a mathematical constant corresponding to the base of the natural logarithm. In Excel, e^x can be evaluated for any power x using the function EXP(x).

EXPONENTIAL UTILITY FUNCTION

$$U(x) = 1 - e^{-x/R} \tag{15.7}$$

The R parameter in equation (15.7) represents the decision maker's risk tolerance; it controls the shape of the exponential utility function. Larger R values create flatter exponential functions, indicating that the decision maker is less risk averse (closer to risk neutral). Smaller R values indicate that the decision maker has less risk tolerance (is more risk averse). A common method to determine an approximate risk tolerance is to ask the decision maker to consider a scenario in which he or she could win \$$R$ with probability 0.5 and lose \$$R/2$ with probability 0.5. The R value to use in equation (15.7) is the largest \$$R$ for which the decision maker would accept this gamble. For instance, if the decision maker is comfortable accepting a gamble with a 50% chance of winning \$2,000 and a 50% chance of losing \$1,000, but not with a gamble with a 50% chance of winning \$3,000 and a 50% chance of losing \$1,500, then we would use R = \$2,000 in equation (15.7). Determining the maximum gamble that a decision maker is willing to take and then using this value in the exponential utility function can be much less time-consuming than generating a complete table of indifference probabilities. One should remember that using an exponential utility function assumes that the decision maker is risk averse; however, this is often true in practice for business decisions.

NOTES + COMMENTS

1. In the Swofford problem, we have been using a utility of 10 for the best payoff and 0 for the worst. We could have chosen any values as long as the utility associated with the best payoff exceeds the utility associated with the worst payoff. Alternatively, a utility of 1 can be associated with the best payoff and a utility of 0 associated with the worst payoff. Had we made this choice, the utility for any monetary value M would have been the value of p at which the decision maker was indifferent between a guaranteed payoff of M and a lottery in which the best payoff is obtained with probability p and the worst payoff is obtained with probability $(1 - p)$. Thus, the utility for any monetary value would have been equal to the probability of earning the best payoff. Often this choice is made because of the ease in computation. We chose not to do so to emphasize the distinction between the utilities and the indifference probabilities for the lottery.
2. Circumstances often dictate whether one acts as a risk avoider or a risk taker when making a decision. For example, you may think of yourself as a risk avoider when faced with financial decisions, but if you have ever purchased a lottery ticket, you have actually acted as a risk taker. For example, suppose you purchase a $1 lottery ticket for a simple lottery in which the object is to pick the six numbers that will be drawn from 50 potential numbers. Also suppose that the winner (who correctly choses all six numbers that are drawn) will receive $1,000,000. There are 15,890,700 possible winning combinations, so your probability of winning is 1/15890700 = 0.000000062929889809763 (i.e., *very low*) and the expected value of your ticket is:

$$\frac{1}{15{,}890{,}700}(\$1{,}000{,}000 - \$1) + \left(1 - \frac{1}{15{,}890{,}700}\right)(-\$1)$$
$$= -\$0.93707$$

or about −$0.94.

If a lottery ticket has a negative expected value, why does anyone play? The answer is in utility; most people who play lotteries associate great utility with the possiblity of winning the $1,000,000 prize and relatively little utility with the $1 cost for a ticket, and so the expected value of the utility of the lottery ticket is positive even though the expected value of the ticket is negative.

SUMMARY

Decision analysis can be used to determine a recommended decision alternative or an optimal decision strategy when a decision maker is faced with an uncertain and risk-filled pattern of future events. The goal of decision analysis is to identify the best decision alternative or the optimal decision strategy, given information about the uncertain events and the possible consequences or payoffs. The "best" decision should consider the risk preference of the decision maker in evaluating outcomes.

We showed how payoff tables and decision trees could be used to structure a decision problem and describe the relationships among the decisions, the chance events, and the consequences. We presented three approaches to decision making without probabilities: the optimistic approach, the conservative approach, and the minimax regret approach. When probability assessments are provided for the states of nature, the expected value approach can be used to identify the recommended decision alternative or decision strategy.

Even though the expected value approach can be used to obtain a recommended decision alternative or optimal decision strategy, the payoff that actually occurs will usually have a value different from the expected value. A risk profile provides a probability distribution for the possible payoffs and can assist the decision maker in assessing the risks associated with different decision alternatives. Sensitivity analysis can be conducted to determine the effect changes in the probabilities for the states of nature and changes in the values of the payoffs have on the recommended decision alternative.

In cases in which sample information about the chance events is available, a sequence of decisions has to be made. First we must decide whether to obtain the sample information. If the answer is yes, an optimal decision strategy based on the specific sample information must be developed. In this situation, decision trees and the expected value approach can be used to determine the optimal decision strategy.

Bayes' theorem can be used to compute branch probabilities for decision trees. Bayes' theorem updates a decision maker's prior probabilities regarding the states of nature using sample information to compute revised posterior probabilities.

We showed how utility could be used in decision-making situations in which monetary value did not provide an adequate measure of the payoffs. Utility is a measure of the total worth of an outcome. As such, utility takes into account the decision maker's assessment of all aspects of a consequence, including profit, loss, risk, and perhaps additional nonmonetary factors. The examples showed how the use of expected utility can lead to decision recommendations that differ from those based on expected value.

A decision maker's judgment must be used to establish the utility for each consequence. We presented a step-by-step procedure to determine a decision maker's utility for monetary payoffs. We also discussed how conservative, risk-avoiding decision makers assess utility differently from more aggressive, risk-taking decision makers.

GLOSSARY

Bayes' theorem A theorem that enables the use of sample information to revise prior probabilities.

Branch Lines showing the alternatives from decision nodes and the outcomes from chance nodes.

Chance event An uncertain future event affecting the consequence, or payoff, associated with a decision.

Chance nodes Nodes indicating points at which an uncertain event will occur.

Conditional probabilities The probability of one event, given the known outcome of a (possibly) related event.

Conservative approach An approach to choosing a decision alternative without using probabilities. For a maximization problem, it leads to choosing the decision alternative that maximizes the minimum payoff; for a minimization problem, it leads to choosing the decision alternative that minimizes the maximum payoff.

Decision alternatives Options available to the decision maker.

Decision nodes Nodes indicating points at which a decision is made.

Decision strategy A strategy involving a sequence of decisions and chance outcomes to provide the optimal solution to a decision problem.

Decision tree A graphical representation of the decision problem that shows the sequential nature of the decision-making process.

Expected utility (EU) The weighted average of the utilities associated with a decision alternative. The weights are the state-of-nature probabilities.

Expected value (EV) For a chance node, the weighted average of the payoffs. The weights are the state-of-nature probabilities.

Expected value approach An approach to choosing a decision alternative based on the expected value of each decision alternative. The recommended decision alternative is the one that provides the best expected value.

Expected value of perfect information (EVPI) The difference between the expected value of an optimal strategy based on perfect information and the "best" expected value without any sample information.

Expected value of sample information (EVSI) The difference between the expected value of an optimal strategy based on sample information and the "best" expected value without any sample information.

Minimax regret approach An approach to choosing a decision alternative without using probabilities. For each alternative, the maximum regret is computed, which leads to choosing the decision alternative that minimizes the maximum regret.

Node An intersection or junction point of a decision tree.

Optimistic approach An approach to choosing a decision alternative without using probabilities. For a maximization problem, it leads to choosing the decision alternative corresponding to the largest payoff; for a minimization problem, it leads to choosing the decision alternative corresponding to the smallest payoff.

Outcome The result obtained when a decision alternative is chosen and a chance event occurs.

Payoff A measure of the outcome of a decision such as profit, cost, or time. Each combination of a decision alternative and a state of nature has an associated payoff.

Payoff table A tabular representation of the payoffs for a decision problem.

Perfect information A special case of sample information in which the information tells the decision maker exactly which state of nature is going to occur.

Posterior (revised) probabilities The probabilities of the states of nature after revising the prior probabilities based on sample information.

Prior probabilities The probabilities of the states of nature prior to obtaining sample information.

Regret (opportunity loss) The amount of loss (lower profit or higher cost) from not making the best decision for each state of nature.

Risk analysis The study of the possible payoffs and probabilities associated with a decision alternative or a decision strategy in the face of uncertainty.

Risk avoider A decision maker who would choose a guaranteed payoff over a lottery with a better expected payoff.

Risk-neutral A decision maker who is neutral to risk. For this decision maker, the decision alternative with the best expected value is identical to the alternative with the highest expected utility.

Risk profile The probability distribution of the possible payoffs associated with a decision alternative or decision strategy.

Risk taker A decision maker who would choose a lottery over a better guaranteed payoff.

Sample information New information obtained through research or experimentation that enables updating or revising the state-of-nature probabilities.

Sensitivity analysis The study of how changes in the probability assessments for the states of nature or changes in the payoffs affect the recommended decision alternative.

States of nature The possible outcomes for chance events that affect the payoff associated with a decision alternative.

Utility A measure of the total worth of a consequence reflecting a decision maker's attitude toward considerations such as profit, loss, and risk.

Utility function for money A curve that depicts the relationship between monetary value and utility.

PROBLEMS

1. The following payoff table shows profit for a decision analysis problem with two decision alternatives and three states of nature:

Decision Alternative	State of Nature s_1	s_2	s_3
d_1	250	100	25
d_2	100	100	75

   a. Construct a decision tree for this problem.
   b. If the decision maker knows nothing about the probabilities of the three states of nature, what is the recommended decision using the optimistic, conservative, and minimax regret approaches?

2. Southland Corporation's decision to produce a new line of recreational products resulted in the need to construct either a small plant or a large plant. The best selection of plant size depends on how the marketplace reacts to the new product line. To conduct an analysis, marketing management has decided to view the possible long-run demand as low, medium, or high. The following payoff table shows the projected profit in millions of dollars:

Plan Size	Long-Run Demand Low	Medium	High
Small	150	200	200
Large	50	200	500

   a. What is the decision to be made, and what is the chance event for Southland's problem?
   b. Construct a decision tree.
   c. Recommend a decision based on the use of the optimistic, conservative, and minimax regret approaches.

3. Amy Lloyd is interested in leasing a new Honda and has contacted three automobile dealers for pricing information. Each dealer offered Amy a closed-end 36-month lease with no down payment due at the time of signing. Each lease includes a monthly charge and a mileage allowance. Additional miles receive a surcharge on a per-mile basis. The monthly lease cost, the mileage allowance, and the cost for additional miles follow:

Dealer	Monthly Cost	Mileage Allowance	Cost per Additional Mile
Hepburn Honda	$299	36,000	$0.15
Midtown Motors	$310	45,000	$0.20
Hopkins Automotive	$325	54,000	$0.15

   Amy decided to choose the lease option that will minimize her total 36-month cost. The difficulty is that Amy is not sure how many miles she will drive over the next three years. For purposes of this decision, she believes it is reasonable to assume that she will drive 12,000 miles per year, 15,000 miles per year, or 18,000 miles per year. With this assumption Amy estimated her total costs for the three lease options. For example, she figures that the Hepburn Honda lease will cost her 36($299) + $0.15(36,000 − 36,000) = $10,764 if she drives 12,000 miles per year, 36($299) + $0.15(45,000 − 36,000) = $12,114 if she drives 15,000 miles per year, or 36($299) + $0.15(54,000 − 36,000) = $13,464 if she drives 18,000 miles per year.

a. What is the decision, and what is the chance event?
b. Construct a payoff table for Amy's problem.
c. If Amy has no idea which of the three mileage assumptions is most appropriate, what is the recommended decision (leasing option) using the optimistic, conservative, and minimax regret approaches?
d. Suppose that the probabilities that Amy drives 12,000, 15,000, and 18,000 miles per year are 0.5, 0.4, and 0.1, respectively. What option should Amy choose using the expected value approach?
e. Develop a risk profile for the decision selected in part (d). What is the most likely cost, and what is its probability?
f. Suppose that, after further consideration, Amy concludes that the probabilities that she will drive 12,000, 15,000, and 18,000 miles per year are 0.3, 0.4, and 0.3, respectively. What decision should Amy make using the expected value approach?

4. Investment advisors estimated the stock market returns for four market segments: computers, financial, manufacturing, and pharmaceuticals. Annual return projections vary depending on whether the general economic conditions are improving, stable, or declining. The anticipated annual return percentages for each market segment under each economic condition are as follows:

	Economic Condition		
Market Segment	**Improving**	**Stable**	**Declining**
Computers	10	2	−4
Financial	8	5	−3
Manufacturing	6	4	−2
Pharmaceuticals	6	5	−1

a. Assume that an individual investor wants to select one market segment for a new investment. A forecast shows improving to declining economic conditions with the following probabilities: improving (0.2), stable (0.5), and declining (0.3). What is the preferred market segment for the investor, and what is the expected return percentage?
b. At a later date, a revised forecast shows a potential for an improvement in economic conditions. New probabilities are as follows: improving (0.4), stable (0.4), and declining (0.2). What is the preferred market segment for the investor based on these new probabilities? What is the expected return percentage?

5. Hudson Corporation is considering three options for managing its data warehouse: continuing with its own staff, hiring an outside vendor to do the managing, or using a combination of its own staff and an outside vendor. The cost of the operation depends on future demand. The annual cost of each option (in thousands of dollars) depends on demand as follows:

	Demand		
Staffing Options	**High**	**Medium**	**Low**
Own staff	650	650	600
Outside vendor	900	600	300
Combination	800	650	500

a. If the demand probabilities are 0.2, 0.5, and 0.3, which decision alternative will minimize the expected cost of the data warehouse? What is the expected annual cost associated with that recommendation?
b. Construct a risk profile for the optimal decision in part (a). What is the probability of the cost exceeding $700,000?

6. The following payoff table shows the profit for a decision problem with two states of nature and two decision alternatives:

	State of Nature	
Decision Alternative	s_1	s_2
d_1	10	1
d_2	4	3

a. Suppose $P(s_1) = 0.2$ and $P(s_2) = 0.8$. What is the best decision using the expected value approach?
b. Perform sensitivity analysis on the payoffs for decision alternative d_1. Assume the probabilities are as given in part (a), and find the range of payoffs under states of nature s_1 and s_2 that will keep the solution found in part (a) optimal. Is the solution more sensitive to the payoff under state of nature s_1 or s_2?

7. Myrtle Air Express decided to offer direct service from Cleveland to Myrtle Beach. Management must decide between a full-price service using the company's new fleet of jet aircraft and a discount service using smaller-capacity commuter planes. It is clear that the best choice depends on the market reaction to the service Myrtle Air offers. Management developed estimates of the contribution to profit for each type of service based on two possible levels of demand for service to Myrtle Beach: strong and weak. The following table shows the estimated quarterly profits (in thousands of dollars):

	Demand for Service	
Service	**Strong**	**Weak**
Full price	\$960	−\$490
Discount	\$670	\$320

a. What is the decision to be made, what is the chance event, and what is the consequence for this problem? How many decision alternatives are there? How many outcomes are there for the chance event?
b. If nothing is known about the probabilities of the chance outcomes, what is the recommended decision using the optimistic, conservative, and minimax regret approaches?
c. Suppose that management of Myrtle Air Express believes that the probability of strong demand is 0.7 and the probability of weak demand is 0.3. Use the expected value approach to determine an optimal decision.
d. Suppose that the probability of strong demand is 0.8 and the probability of weak demand is 0.2. What is the optimal decision using the expected value approach?
e. Use sensitivity analysis to determine the range of demand probabilities for which each of the decision alternatives has the largest expected value.

8. Video Tech is considering marketing one of two new video games for the coming holiday season: Battle Pacific or Space Pirates. Battle Pacific is a unique game and appears to have no competition. Estimated profits (in thousands of dollars) under high, medium, and low demand are as follows:

		Demand	
Battle Pacific	**High**	**Medium**	**Low**
Profit	\$1,000	\$700	\$300
Probability	0.2	0.5	0.3

Video Tech is optimistic about its Space Pirates game. However, the concern is that profitability will be affected by a competitor's introduction of a video game viewed as similar to Space Pirates. Estimated profits (in thousands of dollars) with and without competition are as follows:

Space Pirates With Competition	High	Demand Medium	Low
Profit	$800	$400	$200
Probability	0.3	0.4	0.3

Space Pirates Without Competition	High	Demand Medium	Low
Profit	$1,600	$800	$400
Probability	0.5	0.3	0.2

a. Develop a decision tree for the Video Tech problem.
b. For planning purposes, Video Tech believes there is a 0.6 probability that its competitor will produce a new game similar to Space Pirates. Given this probability of competition, the director of planning recommends marketing the Battle Pacific video game. Using expected value, what is your recommended decision?
c. Show a risk profile for your recommended decision.
d. Use sensitivity analysis to determine what the probability of competition for Space Pirates would have to be for you to change your recommended decision alternative.

9. Seneca Hill Winery recently purchased land for the purpose of establishing a new vineyard. Management is considering two varieties of white grapes for the new vineyard: Chardonnay and Riesling. The Chardonnay grapes would be used to produce a dry Chardonnay wine, and the Riesling grapes would be used to produce a semidry Riesling wine. It takes approximately four years from the time of planting before new grapes can be harvested. This length of time creates a great deal of uncertainty concerning future demand and makes the decision about the type of grapes to plant difficult. Three possibilities are being considered: Chardonnay grapes only; Riesling grapes only; and both Chardonnay and Riesling grapes. Seneca management decided that for planning purposes it would be adequate to consider only two demand possibilities for each type of wine: strong or weak. With two possibilities for each type of wine, it was necessary to assess four probabilities. With the help of some forecasts in industry publications, management made the following probability assessments:

	Riesling Demand	
Chardonnay Demand	**Weak**	**Strong**
Weak	0.05	0.50
Strong	0.25	0.20

Revenue projections show an annual contribution to profit of $20,000 if Seneca Hill plants only Chardonnay grapes and demand is weak for Chardonnay wine, and $70,000 if Seneca plants only Chardonnay grapes and demand is strong for Chardonnay wine. If Seneca plants only Riesling grapes, the annual profit projection is $25,000 if demand is weak for Riesling grapes and $45,000 if demand is strong for Riesling grapes. If Seneca plants both types of grapes, the annual profit projections are shown in the following table:

	Riesling Demand	
Chardonnay Demand	**Weak**	**Strong**
Weak	$22,000	$40,000
Strong	$26,000	$60,000

a. What is the decision to be made, what is the chance event, and what is the consequence? Identify the alternatives for the decisions and the possible outcomes for the chance events.
b. Develop a decision tree.
c. Use the expected value approach to recommend which alternative Seneca Hill Winery should follow in order to maximize expected annual profit.
d. Suppose management is concerned about the probability assessments when demand for Chardonnay wine is strong. Some believe it is likely for Riesling demand to also be strong in this case. Suppose that the probability of strong demand for Chardonnay and weak demand for Riesling is 0.05 and that the probability of strong demand for Chardonnay and strong demand for Riesling is 0.40. How does this change the recommended decision? Assume that the probabilities when Chardonnay demand is weak are still 0.05 and 0.50.
e. Other members of the management team expect the Chardonnay market to become saturated at some point in the future, causing a fall in prices. Suppose that the annual profit projections fall to $50,000 when demand for Chardonnay is strong and only Chardonnay grapes are planted. Using the original probability assessments, determine how this change would affect the optimal decision.

10. Hemmingway, Inc. is considering a $5 million research and development (R&D) project. Profit projections appear promising, but Hemmingway's president is concerned because the probability that the R&D project will be successful is only 0.50. Furthermore, the president knows that even if the project is successful, it will require that the company build a new production facility at a cost of $20 million in order to manufacture the product. If the facility is built, uncertainty remains about the demand and thus uncertainty about the profit that will be realized. Another option is that if the R&D project is successful, the company could sell the rights to the product for an estimated $25 million. Under this option, the company would not build the $20 million production facility.

    The decision tree follows. The profit projection for each outcome is shown at the end of the branches. For example, the revenue projection for the high demand outcome is $59 million. However, the cost of the R&D project ($5 million) and the cost of the production facility ($20 million) show the profit of this outcome to be $59 − $5 − $20 = $34 million. Branch probabilities are also shown for the chance events.

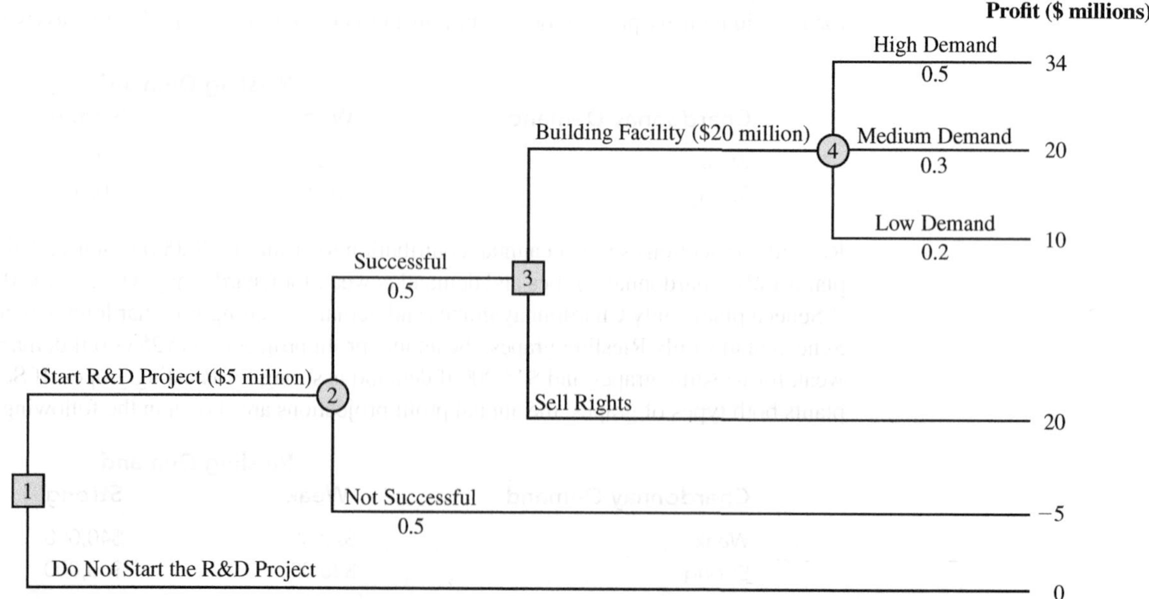

a. Analyze the decision tree to determine whether the company should undertake the R&D project. If it does, and if the R&D project is successful, what should the company do? What is the expected value of your strategy?
b. What must the selling price be for the company to consider selling the rights to the product?
c. Develop a risk profile for the optimal strategy.

11. Dante Development Corporation is considering bidding on a contract for a new office building complex. The following figure shows the decision tree prepared by one of Dante's analysts. At node 1, the company must decide whether to bid on the contract. The cost of preparing the bid is $200,000. The upper branch from node 2 shows that the company has a 0.8 probability of winning the contract if it submits a bid. If the company wins the bid, it will have to pay $2 million to become a partner in the project. Node 3 shows that the company will then consider doing a market research study to forecast demand for the office units prior to beginning construction. The cost of this study is $150,000. Node 4 is a chance node showing the possible outcomes of the market research study.

Nodes 5, 6, and 7 are similar in that they are the decision nodes for Dante to either build the office complex or sell the rights in the project to another developer. The decision to build the complex will result in an income of $5 million if demand is high and $3 million if demand is moderate. If Dante chooses to sell its rights in the project to another developer, income from the sale is estimated to be $3.5 million. The probabilities shown at nodes 4, 8, and 9 are based on the projected outcomes of the market research study.

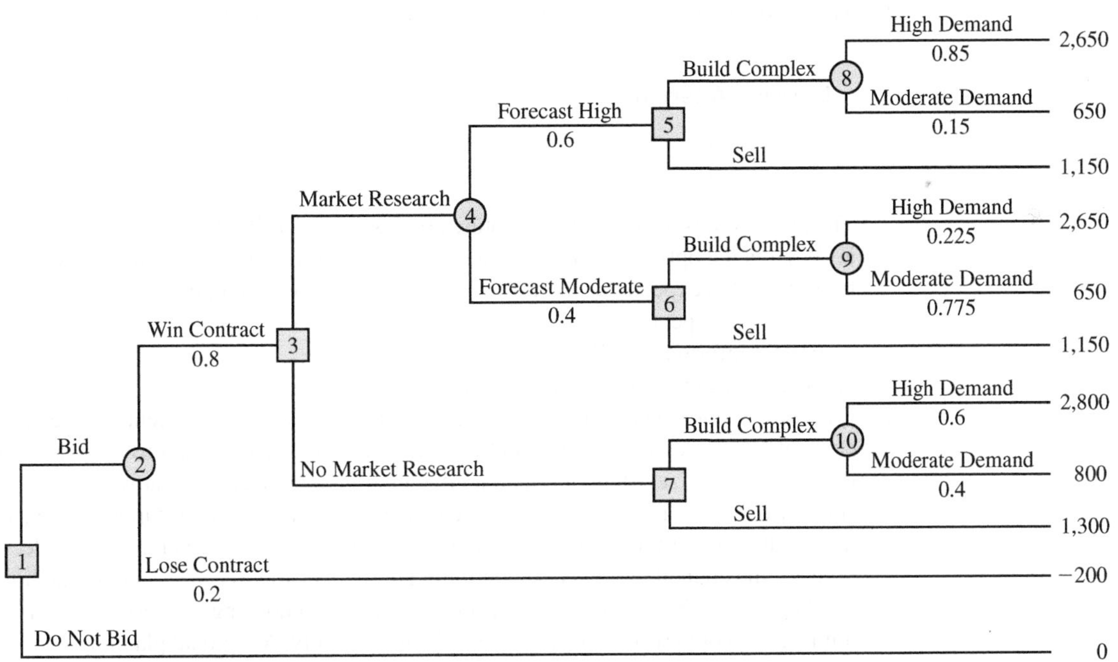

a. Verify Dante's profit projections shown at the ending branches of the decision tree by calculating the payoffs of $2,650,000 and $650,000 for first two outcomes.
b. What is the optimal decision strategy for Dante, and what is the expected profit for this project?
c. What would the cost of the market research study have to be before Dante would change its decision about the market research study?
d. Develop a risk profile for Dante.

12. Embassy Publishing Company received a six-chapter manuscript for a new college textbook. The editor of the college division is familiar with the manuscript and estimated a 0.65 probability that the textbook will be successful. If successful, a profit of \$750,000 will be realized. If the company decides to publish the textbook and it is unsuccessful, a loss of \$250,000 will occur.

    Before making the decision to accept or reject the manuscript, the editor is considering sending the manuscript out for review. A review process provides either a favorable (F) or unfavorable (U) evaluation of the manuscript. Past experience with the review process suggests that probabilities $P(F) = 0.7$ and $P(U) = 0.3$ apply. Let s_1 = the textbook is successful, and s_2 = the textbook is unsuccessful. The editor's initial probabilities of s_1 and s_2 will be revised based on whether the review is favorable or unfavorable. The revised probabilities are as follows:

$$P(s_1|F) = 0.75 \qquad P(s_1|U) = 0.417$$
$$P(s_2|F) = 0.25 \qquad P(s_2|U) = 0.583$$

    a. Construct a decision tree assuming that the company will first make the decision as to whether to send the manuscript out for review and then make the decision to accept or reject the manuscript.
    b. Analyze the decision tree to determine the optimal decision strategy for the publishing company.
    c. If the manuscript review costs \$5,000, what is your recommendation?
    d. What is the expected value of perfect information? What does this EVPI suggest for the company?

13. The following profit payoff table was presented in Problem 1:

Decision Alternative	State of Nature		
	s_1	s_2	s_3
d_1	250	100	25
d_2	100	100	75

    The probabilities for the states of nature are $P(s_1) = 0.65$, $P(s_2) = 0.15$, and $P(s_3) = 0.20$.
    a. What is the optimal decision strategy if perfect information were available?
    b. What is the expected value for the decision strategy developed in part (a)?
    c. Using the expected value approach, what is the recommended decision without perfect information? What is its expected value?
    d. What is the expected value of perfect information?

14. The Lake Placid Town Council decided to build a new community center to be used for conventions, concerts, and other public events, but considerable controversy surrounds the appropriate size. Many influential citizens want a large center that would be a showcase for the area. But the mayor feels that if demand does not support such a center, the community will lose a large amount of money. To provide structure for the decision process, the council narrowed the building alternatives to three sizes: small, medium, and large. Everybody agreed that the critical factor in choosing the best size is the number of people who will want to use the new facility. A regional planning consultant provided demand estimates under three scenarios: worst case, base case, and best case. The worst-case scenario corresponds to a situation in which tourism drops substantially; the base-case scenario corresponds to a situation in which Lake Placid continues to attract visitors at current levels; and the best-case scenario corresponds to a substantial increase in tourism. The consultant has provided probability assessments of 0.10, 0.60, and 0.30 for the worst-case, base-case, and best-case scenarios, respectively.

    The town council suggested using net cash flow over a five-year planning horizon as the criterion for deciding on the best size. The following projections of net cash flow (in thousands of dollars) for a five-year planning horizon have been developed. All costs, including the consultant's fee, have been included.

	Demand Scenario		
Center Size	**Worst Case**	**Base Case**	**Best Case**
Small	400	500	660
Medium	−250	650	800
Large	−400	580	990

a. What decision should Lake Placid make using the expected value approach?
b. Construct risk profiles for the medium and large alternatives. Given the mayor's concern over the possibility of losing money and the result of part (a), which alternative would you recommend?
c. Compute the expected value of perfect information. Do you think it would be worth trying to obtain additional information concerning which scenario is likely to occur?
d. Suppose the probability of the worst-case scenario increases to 0.2, the probability of the base-case scenario decreases to 0.5, and the probability of the best-case scenario remains at 0.3. What effect, if any, would these changes have on the decision recommendation?
e. The consultant has suggested that an expenditure of $150,000 on a promotional campaign over the planning horizon will effectively reduce the probability of the worst-case scenario to zero. If the campaign can be expected to also increase the probability of the best-case scenario to 0.4, is it a good investment?

15. A real estate investor has the opportunity to purchase land currently zoned as residential. If the county board approves a request to rezone the property as commercial within the next year, the investor will be able to lease the land to a large discount firm that wants to open a new store on the property. However, if the zoning change is not approved, the investor will have to sell the property at a loss. Profits (in thousands of dollars) are shown in the following payoff table:

	State of Nature	
	Rezoning Approved	**Rezoning Not Approved**
Decision Alternative	s_1	s_2
Purchase, d_1	600	−200
Do not purchase, d_2	0	0

a. If the probability that the rezoning will be approved is 0.5, what decision is recommended? What is the expected profit?
b. The investor can purchase an option to buy the land. Under the option, the investor maintains the rights to purchase the land anytime during the next three months while learning more about possible resistance to the rezoning proposal from area residents. Probabilities are as follows:

Let H = high resistance to rezoning
L = low resistance to rezoning

$$P(H) = 0.55 \qquad P(s_1|H) = 0.18 \qquad P(s_2|H) = 0.82$$
$$P(L) = 0.45 \qquad P(s_1|L) = 0.89 \qquad P(s_2|L) = 0.11$$

What is the optimal decision strategy if the investor uses the option period to learn more about the resistance from area residents before making the purchase decision?

c. If the option will cost the investor an additional $10,000, should the investor purchase the option? Why or why not? What is the maximum that the investor should be willing to pay for the option?

16. Suppose that you are given a decision situation with three possible states of nature: s_1, s_2, and s_3. The prior probabilities are $P(s_1) = 0.2$, $P(s_2) = 0.5$, and $P(s_3) = 0.3$. With sample information I, $P(I|s_1) = 0.1$, $P(I|s_2) = 0.05$, and $P(I|s_3) = 0.2$. Compute the revised (or posterior) probabilities: $P(s_1|I)$, $P(s_2|I)$, and $P(s_3|I)$.

17. To save on expenses, Rona and Jerry agreed to form a carpool for traveling to and from work. Rona prefers to use the somewhat longer but more consistent Queen City Avenue. Although Jerry prefers the quicker expressway, he agreed with Rona that they should take Queen City Avenue if the expressway has a traffic jam. The following payoff table provides the one-way time estimate in minutes for traveling to or from work:

	State of Nature	
	Expressway Open	**Expressway Jammed**
Decision Alternative	s_1	s_2
Queen City Avenue, d_1	30	30
Expressway, d_2	25	45

Based on their experience with traffic problems, Rona and Jerry agreed on a 0.15 probability that the expressway would be jammed.

In addition, they agreed that weather seemed to affect the traffic conditions on the expressway. Let

C = clear
O = overcast
R = rain

The following conditional probabilities apply:

$$P(C|s_1) = 0.8 \qquad P(O|s_1) = 0.2 \qquad P(R|s_1) = 0.0$$
$$P(C|s_2) = 0.1 \qquad P(O|s_2) = 0.3 \qquad P(R|s_2) = 0.6$$

a. Use Bayes' theorem for probability revision to compute the probability of each weather condition and the conditional probability of the expressway being open, s_1, or jammed, s_2, given each weather condition.
b. Show the decision tree for this problem.
c. What is the optimal decision strategy, and what is the expected travel time?

18. The Gorman Manufacturing Company must decide whether to manufacture a component part at its Milan, Michigan, plant or purchase the component part from a supplier. The resulting profit is dependent on the demand for the product. The following payoff table shows the projected profit (in thousands of dollars):

	State of Nature		
	Low Demand	**Medium Demand**	**High Demand**
Decision Alternative	s_1	s_2	s_3
Manufacture, d_1	−20	40	100
Purchase, d_2	10	45	70

The state-of-nature probabilities are $P(s_1) = 0.35$, $P(s_2) = 0.35$, and $P(s_3) = 0.30$.

a. Use a decision tree to recommend a decision.
b. Use EVPI to determine whether Gorman should attempt to obtain a better estimate of demand.

c. A test market study of the potential demand for the product is expected to report either a favorable (F) or unfavorable (U) condition. The relevant conditional probabilities are as follows:

$$P(F \mid s_1) = 0.10 \quad P(U \mid s_1) = 0.90$$
$$P(F \mid s_2) = 0.40 \quad P(U \mid s_2) = 0.60$$
$$P(F \mid s_3) = 0.60 \quad P(U \mid s_3) = 0.40$$

Joint probabilities are discussed in Chapter 5.

What is the probability that the market research report will be favorable? [*Hint:* We can find this value by summing the joint probability values as follows: $P(F) = P(F \cap s_1) + P(F \cap s_2) + P(F \cap s_3) = P(s_1)P(F \mid s_1) + P(s_2)P(F \mid s_2) + P(s_3)P(F \mid s_3)$.]

d. What is Gorman's optimal decision strategy?

e. What is the expected value of the market research information?

19. A firm has three investment alternatives. Payoffs are in thousands of dollars.

	Economic Conditions		
Decision Alternative	**Up** s_1	**Stable** s_2	**Down** s_3
Investment A, d_1	100	25	0
Investment B, d_2	75	50	25
Investment C, d_3	50	50	50
Probabilities	0.40	0.30	0.30

a. Using the expected value approach, which decision is preferred?

b. For the lottery having a payoff of \$100,000 with probability p and \$0 with probability $(1 - p)$, two decision makers expressed the following indifference probabilities. Find the most preferred decision for each decision maker using the expected utility approach.

	Indifference Probability (p)	
Profit	**Decision Maker A**	**Decision Maker B**
\$75,000	0.80	0.60
\$50,000	0.60	0.30
\$25,000	0.30	0.15

c. Why don't decision makers A and B select the same decision alternative?

20. Alexander Industries is considering purchasing an insurance policy for its new office building in St. Louis, Missouri. The policy has an annual cost of \$10,000. If Alexander Industries doesn't purchase the insurance and minor fire damage occurs, a cost of \$100,000 is anticipated; the cost if major or total destruction occurs is \$200,000. The costs, including the state-of-nature probabilities, are as follows:

		Damage	
Decision Alternative	**None** s_1	**Minor** s_2	**Major** s_3
Purchase insurance, d_1	10,000	10,000	10,000
Do not purchase insurance, d_2	0	100,000	200,000
Probabilities	0.96	0.03	0.01

a. Using the expected value approach, what decision do you recommend?

b. What lottery would you use to assess utilities? (*Note:* Because the data are costs, the best payoff is \$0.)

c. Assume that you found the following indifference probabilities for the lottery defined in part (b). What decision would you recommend?

Cost	Indifference Probability
10,000	$p = 0.99$
100,000	$p = 0.60$

d. Do you favor using expected value or expected utility for this decision problem? Why?

21. In a certain state lottery, a lottery ticket costs $2. In terms of the decision to purchase or not to purchase a lottery ticket, suppose that the following payoff table applies:

	State of Nature	
	Win	Lose
Decision Alternatives	s_1	s_2
Purchase lottery ticket, d_1	300,000	−2
Do not purchase lottery ticket, d_2	0	0

a. A realistic estimate of the chances of winning is 1 in 250,000. Use the expected value approach to recommend a decision.

b. If a particular decision maker assigns an indifference probability of 0.000001 to the $0 payoff, would this individual purchase a lottery ticket? Use expected utility to justify your answer.

22. Three decision makers have assessed utilities for the following decision problem (payoff in dollars):

	State of Nature		
Decision Alternative	s_1	s_2	s_3
d_1	20	50	−20
d_2	80	100	−100

The indifference probabilities are as follows:

	Indifference Probability (p)		
Payoff	**Decision Maker A**	**Decision Maker B**	**Decision Maker C**
100	1.00	1.00	1.00
80	0.95	0.70	0.90
50	0.90	0.60	0.75
20	0.70	0.45	0.60
−20	0.50	0.25	0.40
−100	0.00	0.00	0.00

a. Plot the utility function for money for each decision maker.

b. Classify each decision maker as a risk avoider, a risk taker, or risk-neutral.

c. For the payoff of 20, what is the premium that the risk avoider will pay to avoid risk? What is the premium that the risk taker will pay to have the opportunity of the high payoff?

23. In Problem 22, if $P(s_1) = 0.25$, $P(s_2) = 0.50$, and $P(s_3) = 0.25$, find a recommended decision for each of the three decision makers. (*Note:* For the same decision problem, different utilities can lead to different decisions.)

24. Translate the following monetary payoffs into utilities for a decision maker whose utility function is described by an exponential function with $R = 250$: −$200, −$100, $0, $100, $200, $300, $400, $500.

25. Consider a decision maker who is comfortable with an investment decision that has a 50% chance of earning \$25,000 and a 50% chance of losing \$12,500, but not with any larger investments that have the same relative payoffs.
   a. Write the equation for the exponential function that approximates this decision maker's utility function.
   b. Plot the exponential utility function for this decision maker for x values between −20,000 and 35,000. Is this decision maker risk-seeking, risk-neutral, or risk-averse?
   c. Suppose the decision maker decides that she would actually be willing to make an investment that has a 50% chance of earning \$30,000 and a 50% chance of losing \$15,000. Plot the exponential function that approximates this utility function and compare it to the utility function from part (b). Is the decision maker becoming more risk-seeking or more risk-averse?

CASE PROBLEM: PROPERTY PURCHASE STRATEGY

Glenn Foreman, president of Oceanview Development Corporation, is considering submitting a bid to purchase property that will be sold by sealed-bid auction at a county tax foreclosure. Glenn's initial judgment is to submit a bid of \$5 million. Based on his experience, Glenn estimates that a bid of \$5 million will have a 0.2 probability of being the highest bid and securing the property for Oceanview. The current date is June 1. Sealed bids for the property must be submitted by August 15. The winning bid will be announced on September 1.

If Oceanview submits the highest bid and obtains the property, the firm plans to build and sell a complex of luxury condominiums. However, a complicating factor is that the property is currently zoned for single-family residences only. Glenn believes that a referendum could be placed on the voting ballot in time for the November election. Passage of the referendum would change the zoning of the property and permit construction of the condominiums.

The sealed-bid procedure requires the bid to be submitted with a certified check for 10% of the amount bid. If the bid is rejected, the deposit is refunded. If the bid is accepted, the deposit is the down payment for the property. However, if the bid is accepted and the bidder does not follow through with the purchase and meet the remainder of the financial obligation within six months, the deposit will be forfeited. In this case, the county will offer the property to the next highest bidder.

To determine whether Oceanview should submit the \$5 million bid, Glenn conducted some preliminary analysis. This preliminary work provided an assessment of 0.3 for the probability that the referendum for a zoning change will be approved and resulted in the following estimates of the costs and revenues that will be incurred if the condominiums are built:

Costs and Revenue Estimates	
Revenue from condominium sales	\$15,000,000
Costs	
Property	\$5,000,000
Construction expenses	\$8,000,000

If Oceanview obtains the property and the zoning change is rejected in November, Glenn believes that the best option would be for the firm not to complete the purchase of the property. In this case, Oceanview would forfeit the 10% deposit that accompanied the bid.

Because the likelihood that the zoning referendum will be approved is such an important factor in the decision process, Glenn suggested that the firm hire a market research service to conduct a survey of voters. The survey would provide a better estimate of the likelihood that the referendum for a zoning change would be approved. The market research firm that Oceanview Development has worked with in the past has agreed to do the study for $15,000. The results of the study will be available August 1, so that Oceanview will have this information before the August 15 bid deadline. The results of the survey will be a prediction either that the zoning change will be approved or that the zoning change will be rejected. After considering the record of the market research service in previous studies conducted for Oceanview, Glenn developed the following probability estimates concerning the accuracy of the market research information:

$$P(A|s_1) = 0.9 \quad P(N|s_1) = 0.1$$
$$P(A|s_2) = 0.2 \quad P(N|s_2) = 0.8$$

where

A = prediction of zoning change approval
N = prediction that zoning change will not be approved
s_1 = the zoning change is approved by the voters
s_2 = the zoning change is rejected by the voters

Managerial Report

Perform an analysis of the problem facing the Oceanview Development Corporation, and prepare a report that summarizes your findings and recommendations. Include the following items in your report:

1. A decision tree that shows the logical sequence of the decision problem
2. A recommendation regarding what Oceanview should do if the market research information is not available
3. A decision strategy that Oceanview should follow if the market research is conducted
4. A recommendation as to whether Oceanview should employ the market research firm, along with the value of the information provided by the market research firm

Include the details of your analysis as an appendix to your report.

Appendix A—Basics of Excel

CONTENTS

A.1 USING MICROSOFT EXCEL
- Basic Spreadsheet Workbook Operations
- Creating, Saving, and Opening Files in Excel

A.2 SPREADSHEET BASICS
- Cells, References, and Formulas in Excel
- Finding the Right Excel Function
- Colon Notation
- Inserting a Function into a Worksheet Cell
- Using Relative Versus Absolute Cell References

A.1 Using Microsoft Excel

Depending on the settings for your particular installation of Excel, you may see additional worksheets labeled Sheet2, Sheet3, and so on.

When using Excel for modeling, the data and the model are displayed in a **workbook**, each of which contains a series of **worksheets**. Figure A.1 shows the layout of a blank workbook created in Excel 2016. The workbook is named Book1 and by default contains a worksheet named Sheet1.

The wide bar located across the top of the workbook is referred to as the Ribbon. Tabs, located at the top of the Ribbon, contain groups of related commands. By default, nine tabs are included on the Ribbon in Excel: File, Home, Insert, Page Layout, Formulas, Data, Review, and View. Loading additional packages (such as Analytic Solver Platform or Acrobat)

FIGURE A.1 Blank Workbook in Excel

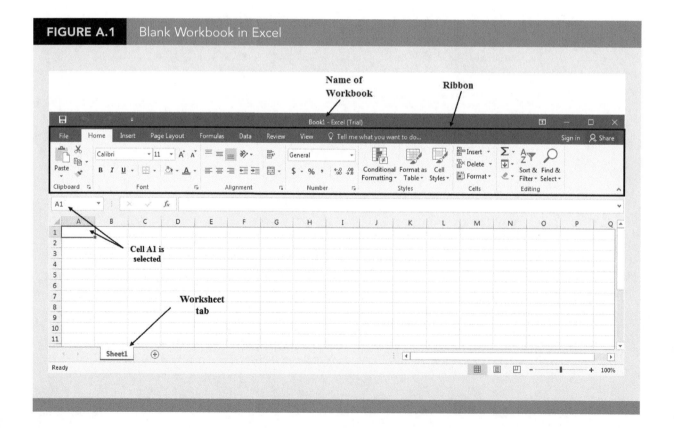

FIGURE A.2 Groups on the Home tab in the Ribbon of an Excel Workbook

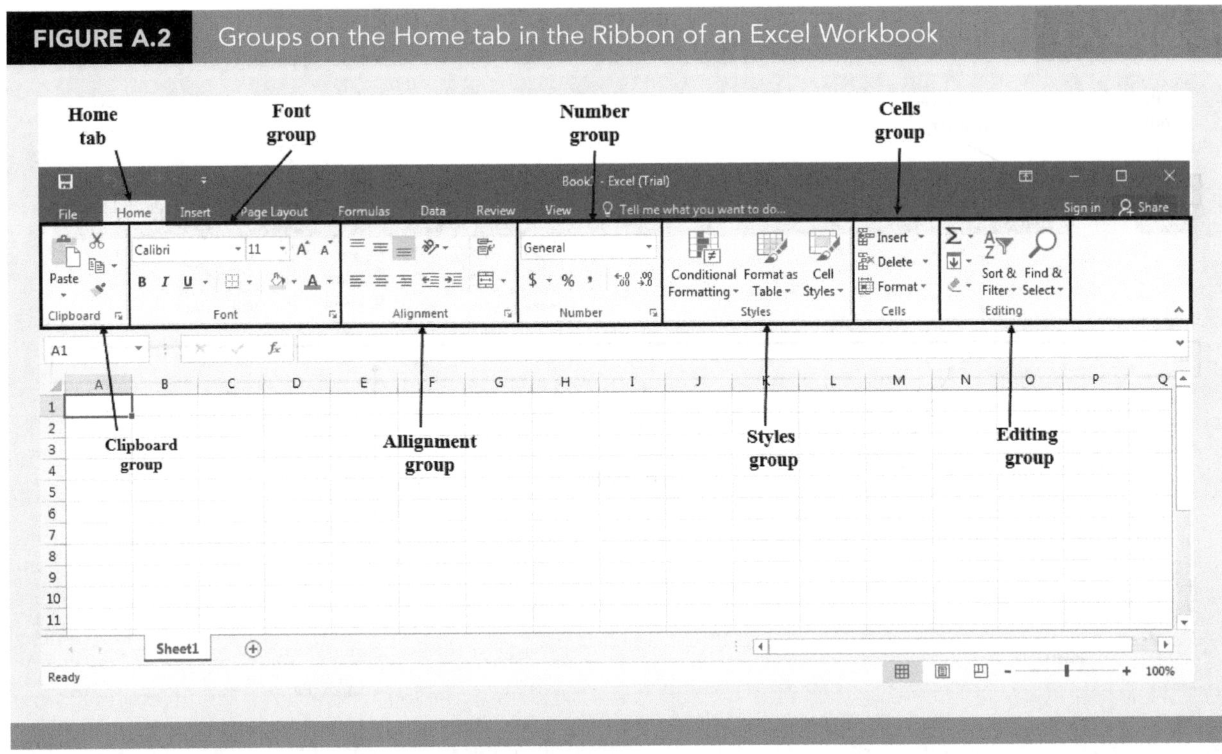

may create additional tabs. Each tab contains several groups of related commands. The File tab is used to Open, Save, and Print files as well as to change the Options being used by Excel and to load Add-ins. Note that the Home tab is selected when a workbook is opened. Figure A.2 displays the seven groups located in the Home tab: Clipboard, Font, Alignment, Number, Styles, Cells, and Editing. Commands are arranged within each group.

Keyboard shortcut: pressing Ctrl-B will change the font of the text in the selected cell to bold. We include a full list of keyboard shortcuts for Excel at the end of this appendix.

For example, to change selected text to boldface, click the **Home** tab and click the **Bold** button **B** in the **Font** group. The other tabs in the Ribbon are used to modify data in your spreadsheet or to perform analysis.

Figure A.3 illustrates the location of the File tab, the Quick Access Toolbar, and the Formula Bar. The Quick Access Toolbar allows you to quickly access commonly used workbook functions.

For instance, the Quick Access Toolbar shown in Figure A.3 includes a **Save** button that can be used to save files without having to first click the **File** tab. To add or remove features on the Quick Access Toolbar, click the **Customize Quick Access Toolbar** button on the Quick Access Toolbar.

The Formula Bar contains a Name box, the Insert Function button *fx*, and a Formula box. In Figure A.3, “A1” appears in the Name box because cell A1 is selected. You can select any other cell in the worksheet by using the mouse to move the cursor to another cell and clicking or by typing the new cell location in the name box and pressing the Enter key. The Formula box is used to display the formula in the currently selected cell. For instance, if you had entered *=A1+A2* into cell A3, whenever you select cell A3, the formula =A1+A2 will be shown in the Formula box. This feature makes it very easy to see and edit a formula in a cell. The Insert Function button allows you to quickly access all of the functions available in Excel. Later, we show how to find and use a particular function with the Insert Function button.

FIGURE A.3 File Tab, Quick Access Toolbar, and Formula Bar of an Excel Workbook

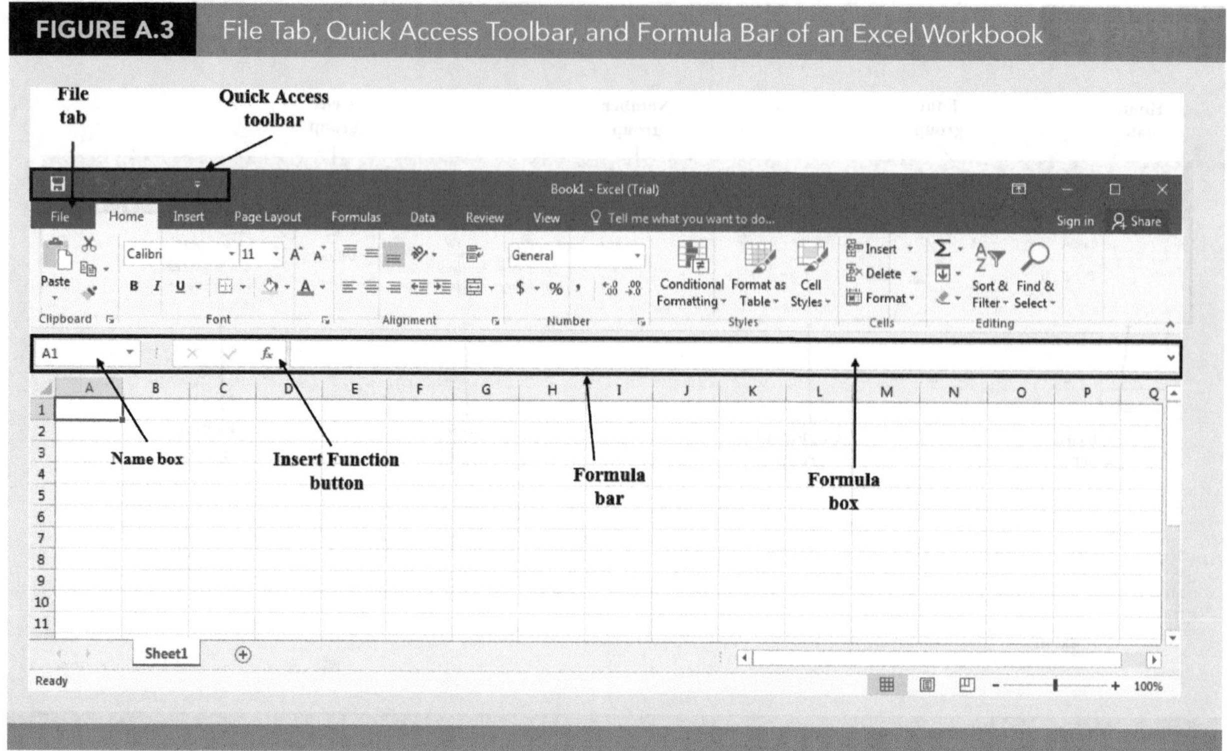

Basic Spreadsheet Workbook Operations

To change the name of the current worksheet, we take the following steps:

Step 1. Right-click on the worksheet tab named **Sheet1**
Step 2. Select the **Rename** option
Step 3. Enter *Nowlin* to rename the worksheet and press **Enter**

You can create a copy of the newly renamed Nowlin worksheet by following these steps:

Step 1. Right-click the worksheet tab named **Nowlin**
Step 2. Select the **Move or Copy…** option
Step 3. When the **Move or Copy** dialog box appears, select the checkbox for **Create a Copy**, and click **OK**

The name of the copied worksheet will appear as "Nowlin (2)." You can then rename it, if desired, by following the steps outlined previously. Worksheets can also be moved to other workbooks or to a different position in the current workbook by using the Move or Copy option.

To create additional worksheets follow these steps:

New worksheets can also be created using the insert worksheet button ⊕ at the bottom of the screen.

Step 1. Right-click on the tab of any existing worksheet
Step 2. Select **Insert…**
Step 3. When the **Insert** dialog box appears, select **Worksheet** from the **General** area, and click **OK**

Worksheets can be deleted by right-clicking the worksheet tab and choosing **Delete**. After clicking Delete, a window may appear, warning you that any data appearing in the worksheet will be lost. Click **Delete** to confirm that you do want to delete the worksheet.

Creating, Saving, and Opening Files in Excel

To illustrate manually entering, saving, and opening a file, we will use the Nowlin Plastics make-versus-buy model from Chapter 10. The objective is to determine whether Nowlin should manufacture or outsource production for its Viper product next year. Nowlin must pay a fixed cost of $234,000 and a variable cost per unit of $2 to manufacture the product. Nowlin can outsource production for $3.50 per unit.

We begin by assuming that Excel is open and a blank worksheet is displayed. The Nowlin data can now be entered manually by simply typing the manufacturing fixed cost of $234,000, the variable cost of $2, and the outsourcing cost of $3.50 into the worksheet.

We will place the data for the Nowlin example in the top portion of Sheet1 of the new workbook. First, we enter the label *Nowlin Plastics* in cell A1 and click the Bold button in the font group. Next we enter the label Parameters and click on the Bold button in the Font group. To identify each of the three data values, we enter the label *Manufacturing Fixed Cost* in cell A4, the label *Manufacturing Variable Cost per Unit* in cell A5, and the label *Outsourcing Cost per Unit* in cell A7. Next, we enter the actual data into the corresponding cells in column B: the value of *$234,000* in cell B4; the value of *$2* in cell B5; and the value of *$3.50* in cell B7. Figure A.4 shows a portion of the worksheet we have just developed.

Before we begin the development of the model portion of the worksheet, we recommend that you first save the current file; this will prevent you from having to reenter the data in case something happens that causes Excel to close. To save the workbook using the filename *Nowlin*, we perform the following steps:

Step 1. Click the **File** tab on the Ribbon
Step 2. Click **Save** in the list of options
Step 3. Select **This PC** under **Save As**, and click **Browse**
Step 4. When the **Save As** dialog box appears
Select the location where you want to save the file
Enter the file name *Nowlin* in the **File name:** box
Click **Save**

Keyboard shortcut: To save the file, press Ctrl-S.

Excel's Save command is designed to save the file as an Excel workbook. As you work with and build models in Excel, you should follow the practice of periodically saving the file so that you will not lose any work. After you have saved your file for the first time,

FIGURE A.4 Nowlin Plastics Data

	A	B	C
1	**Nowlin Plastics**		
2			
3	**Parameters**		
4	Manufacturing Fixed Cost	$234,000.00	
5	Manufacturing Variable Cost per Unit	$2.00	
6			
7	Outsourcing Cost per Unit	$3.50	
8			

the Save command will overwrite the existing version of the file, and you will not have to perform Steps 3 and 4.

Sometimes you may want to create a copy of an existing file. For instance, suppose you change one or more of the data values and would like to save the modified file using the filename *NowlinMod*. The following steps show how to save the modified workbook using filename *NowlinMod*:

Step 1. Click the **File** tab in the Ribbon
Step 2. Click **Save As** in the list of options
Step 3. Select **This PC** under **Save As**, and click **Browse**
Step 4. When the **Save As** dialog box appears:
Select the location where you want to save the file
Type the file name *NowlinMod* in the **File name:** box
Click **Save**

Once the *NowlinMod* workbook has been saved, you can continue to work with the file to perform whatever type of analysis is appropriate. When you are finished working with the file, simply click the close-window button ✕ located at the top right-hand corner of the Ribbon.

Later, you can easily access a previously saved file. For example, the following steps show how to open the previously saved Nowlin workbook:

Step 1. Click the **File** tab in the Ribbon
Step 2. Click **Open** in the list of options
Step 3. Select **This PC** under **Open** and click **Browse**
Step 4. When the **Open** dialog box appears:
Find the location where you previously saved the *Nowlin* file
Click on the filename **Nowlin** so that it appears in the **File name:** box
Click **Open**

A.2 Spreadsheet Basics

Cells, References, and Formulas in Excel

We begin by assuming that the Nowlin workbook is open again and that we would like to develop a model that can be used to compute the manufacturing and outsourcing cost given a certain required volume. We will use the bottom portion of the worksheet shown in Figure A.4 to develop the model. The model will contain formulas that refer to the location of the data cells in the upper section of the worksheet. By putting the location of the data cells in the formula, we will build a model that can be easily updated with new data.

To display all formulas in the cells of a worksheet, hold down the Ctrl key and then press the ~ key (usually located above the Tab key).

We enter the label *Model* into cell A10 and press the **Bold** button in the **Font** group. To provide a visual reminder that the bottom portion of this worksheet will contain the model. In cell A11, we enter the label *Quantity*. Next, we enter the labels *Total Cost to Produce* in cell A13, *Total Cost to Outsource* in cell A15, and *Savings due to Outsourcing* in cell A17.

In cell B11 we enter *10000* to represent the quantity produced/outsourced by Nowlin Plastics. We will now enter formulas in cells B13, B15, and B17 that use the quantity in cell B11 to compute the values for production cost, outsourcing cost, and savings from outsourcing. The total cost to produce is the sum of the manufacturing fixed cost (cell B4) and the manufacturing variable cost. The manufacturing variable cost is the product of the production volume (cell B11) and the variable cost per unit (cell B5). Thus, the formula for total variable cost is B11*B5; to compute the value of total cost, we enter the formula =B4+B11*B5 in cell B13. Next, total cost to outsource is the product of the outsourcing cost per unit (cell B7) and the quantity (cell B11); this is computed by entering the formula =B7*B11 in cell B15. Finally, the savings due to outsourcing is computed by subtracting the cost of outsourcing (cell B15) from the production cost (cell B13). Thus, in cell B17 we enter the formula =B13-B15. Figure A.5 shows the Excel worksheet values and formulas used for these calculations.

We can now compute the savings due to outsourcing by entering a value for the quantity to be manufactured or outsourced in cell B11. Figure A.5 shows the results after entering a value of 10,000 in cell B11. We see that a quantity of 10,000 units results in a production cost of $254,000 and outsourcing cost of 35,000. Thus, the savings due to outsourcing is $219,000.

FIGURE A.5 Nowlin Plastics Data and Model

	A	B	C
1	**Nowlin Plastics**		
2			
3	**Parameters**		
4	Manufacturing Fixed Cost	234000	
5	Manufacturing Variable Cost per Unit	2	
6			
7	Outsourcing Cost per Unit	3.5	
8			
9			
10	**Model**		
11	Quantity	10000	
12			
13	Total Cost to Produce	=B4+B11*B5	
14			
15	Total Cost to Outsource	=B7*B11	
16			
17	Savings due to Outsourcing	=B13-B15	
18			

MODEL *file*

Nowlin

	A	B	C
1	**Nowlin Plastics**		
2			
3	**Parameters**		
4	Manufacturing Fixed Cost	$234,000.00	
5	Manufacturing Variable Cost per Unit	$2.00	
6			
7	Outsourcing Cost per Unit	$3.50	
8			
9			
10	**Model**		
11	Quantity	10,000	
12			
13	Total Cost to Produce	$254,000.00	
14			
15	Total Cost to Outsource	$35,000.00	
16			
17	Savings due to Outsourcing	$219,000.00	
18			

Finding the Right Excel Function

Excel provides a variety of built-in formulas or functions for developing mathematical models. If we know which function is needed and how to use it, we can simply enter the function into the appropriate worksheet cell. However, if we are not sure which functions are available to accomplish a task or are not sure how to use a particular function, Excel can provide assistance.

To identify the functions available in Excel click the **Insert Function** button *fx* on the formula bar; this opens the **Insert Function** dialog box shown in Figure A.6. The **Search for a function:** box at the top of the dialog box enables us to type a brief description for what we want to do. After doing so and clicking **Go**, Excel will search for and display, in the **Select a function** box, the functions that may accomplish our task. In many situations, however, we may want to browse through an entire category of functions to see what is available. For this task, the **Or select a category:** box is helpful. It contains a drop-down list of several categories of functions provided by Excel. Figure A.6 shows that we selected the **Math & Trig** category. As a result, Excel's Math & Trig functions appear in alphabetical order in the **Select a function:** area. We see the ABS function listed first, followed by the ACOS function, and so on.

The ABS function calculates the absolute value of a number. The ACOS function calculates the arccosine of a number.

Colon Notation

Although many functions, such as the ABS function, have a single argument, some Excel functions depend on arrays. **Colon notation** provides an efficient way to convey arrays and matrices of cells to functions. The colon notation may be described as follows:

FIGURE A.6 Insert Function Dialog Box

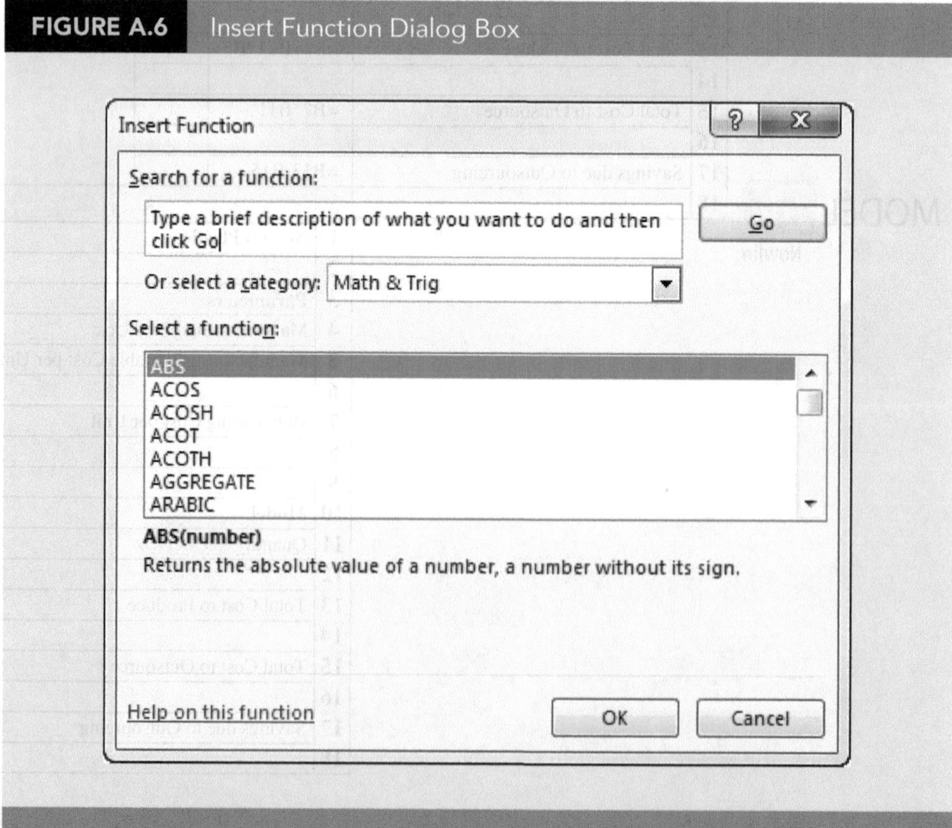

B1:B5 means cell B1 "through" cell B5, namely the array of values stored in the locations (B1,B2,B3,B4,B5). Consider, for example, the following function =SUM(B1:B5). The sum function adds up the elements contained in the function's argument. Hence, =SUM(B1:B5) evaluates the following formula:

=B1+B2+B3+B4+B5.

NowlinFinancial

To illustrate the use of colon notation, we will consider the financial data for Nowlin Plastics contained in the DATAfile *NowlinFinancial* and shown in Figure A.7. Column A contains the name of each month, column B the revenue for each month, and column C

FIGURE A.7 Nowlin Plastics Monthly Revenues and Costs

	A	B	C
1	**Month**	**Revenue**	**Cost**
2	January	3459000	3250000
3	February	2873000	2640000
4	March	3195000	3021000
5	April	2925000	3015000
6	May	3682000	3150000
7	June	3436000	3240000
8	July	3410000	3185000
9	August	3782000	3237000
10	September	3548000	3196000
11	October	3136000	2997000
12	November	3028000	2815000
13	December	2845000	2803000
14			
15	**Total:**	=SUM(B2:B13)	=SUM(C2:C13)
16			
17	**Average:**	=AVERAGE(B2:B13)	=AVERAGE(C2:C13)

NowlinFinancial

	A	B	C
1	**Month**	**Revenue**	**Cost**
2	January	$ 3,459,000	$ 3,250,000
3	February	$ 2,873,000	$ 2,640,000
4	March	$ 3,195,000	$ 3,021,000
5	April	$ 2,925,000	$ 3,015,000
6	May	$ 3,682,000	$ 3,150,000
7	June	$ 3,436,000	$ 3,240,000
8	July	$ 3,410,000	$ 3,185,000
9	August	$ 3,782,000	$ 3,237,000
10	September	$ 3,548,000	$ 3,196,000
11	October	$ 3,136,000	$ 2,997,000
12	November	$ 3,028,000	$ 2,815,000
13	December	$ 2,845,000	$ 2,803,000
14			
15	**Total:**	$39,319,000	$36,549,000
16			
17	**Average:**	$ 3,276,583	$ 3,045,750

the cost data. In row 15, we compute the total revenues and costs for the year. To do this we first enter *Total:* in cell A15. Next, we enter the formula =SUM(B2:B13) in cell B15 and =SUM(C2:C13) in cell C15. This shows that the total revenues for the company are $39,319,000 and the total costs are $36,549,000.

Inserting a Function into a Worksheet Cell

Continuing with the Nowlin financial data, we will now show how to use the Insert Function and Function Arguments dialog boxes to select a function, develop its arguments, and insert the function into a worksheet cell. We wish to calculate the average monthly revenue and cost at Nowlin. To do so, we take the following steps.

The Function Arguments *dialog box contains a link* Help on this function *in case you need additional guidance on the use of a particular function in Excel.*

Step 1. Select cell B17 in the DATAfile *NowlinFinancial*
Step 2. Click the Insert Function button *fx*.
Select **Statistical** in the **Or select a category:** box
Select **AVERAGE** from the **Select a function:** options
Step 3. When the **Function Arguments** dialog box appears:
Enter *B2:B13* in the **Number1** box
Click **OK**
Step 4. Repeat Steps 1 through 3 for the cost data in column C

Figure A.7 shows that the average monthly revenue is $3,276,583 and the average monthly cost is $3,045,750.

Using Relative Versus Absolute Cell References

NowlinFinancial

One of the most powerful abilities of spreadsheet software such as Excel is the ability to use relative references in formulas. Use of a **relative reference** allows the user to enter a formula once into Excel and then copy and paste that formula to other places so that the formula will update with the correct data without having to retype the formula. We will demonstrate the use of relative references in Excel by calculating the monthly profit at Nowlin Plastics using the following steps:

Step 1. Enter the label *Profit* in cell D1 and press the **Bold** button in the **Font** group of the Home tab
Step 2. Enter the formula =B2-C2 in cell D2
Step 3. Copy the formula from cell D2 by selecting cell D2 and clicking **Copy** from the **Clipboard** group of the **Home** tab
Step 4. Select cells D3:D13
Step 5. Paste the formula from cell D2 by clicking **Paste** from the **Clipboard** group of the **Home** tab

After completing Step 2, a shortcut to copying the formula to the range D3:D13 is to place the pointer in the bottom-right corner of cell D2 and then double-click.

Keyboard shortcut: You can copy in Excel by pressing Ctrl-C. You can paste in Excel by pressing Ctrl-V.

The result of these steps is shown in Figure A.8, where we have calculated the profit for each month. Note that even though the only formula we entered was =B2-C2 in cell D2, the formulas in cells D3 through D13 have been updated correctly to calculate the profit of each month using that month's revenue and cost.

In some situations, however, we do not want to use relative referencing in formulas. The alternative is to use an absolute reference, which we indicate to Excel by putting "$" before the row and/or column locations of the cell location. An **absolute reference** does *not* update to a new cell reference when the formula is copied to another location. We illustrate the use of an absolute reference by continuing to use the Nowlin financial data. Nowlin calculates an after-tax profit each month by multiplying its actual monthly profit by one minus its tax rate, which is currently estimated to be 30%. Cell B19 in

FIGURE A.8 Nowlin Plastics Profit Calculation

	A	B	C	D
1	**Month**	**Revenue**	**Cost**	**Profit**
2	January	3459000	3250000	=B2-C2
3	February	2873000	2640000	=B3-C3
4	March	3195000	3021000	=B4-C4
5	April	2925000	3015000	=B5-C5
6	May	3682000	3150000	=B6-C6
7	June	3436000	3240000	=B7-C7
8	July	3410000	3185000	=B8-C8
9	August	3782000	3237000	=B9-C9
10	September	3548000	3196000	=B10-C10
11	October	3136000	2997000	=B11-C11
12	November	3028000	2815000	=B12-C12
13	December	2845000	2803000	=B13-C13
14				
15	**Total:**	=SUM(B2:B13)	=SUM(C2:C13)	
16				
17	**Average:**	=AVERAGE(B2:B13)	=AVERAGE(C2:C13)	

	A	B	C	D
1	**Month**	**Revenue**	**Cost**	**Profit**
2	January	$ 3,459,000	$ 3,250,000	$ 209,000
3	February	$ 2,873,000	$ 2,640,000	$ 233,000
4	March	$ 3,195,000	$ 3,021,000	$ 174,000
5	April	$ 2,925,000	$ 3,015,000	$ (90,000)
6	May	$ 3,682,000	$ 3,150,000	$ 532,000
7	June	$ 3,436,000	$ 3,240,000	$ 196,000
8	July	$ 3,410,000	$ 3,185,000	$ 225,000
9	August	$ 3,782,000	$ 3,237,000	$ 545,000
10	September	$ 3,548,000	$ 3,196,000	$ 352,000
11	October	$ 3,136,000	$ 2,997,000	$ 139,000
12	November	$ 3,028,000	$ 2,815,000	$ 213,000
13	December	$ 2,845,000	$ 2,803,000	$ 42,000
14				
15	**Total:**	$39,319,000	$36,549,000	
16				
17	**Average:**	$ 3,276,583	$ 3,045,750	

In some cases, you may want Excel to use relative referencing for either the column or row location and absolute referencing for the other. For instance, to force Excel to always refer to column A but use relative referencing for the row, you would enter =$A1 into, say, cell B1. If this formula is copied into cell C3, the updated formula would be =$A3 (whereas it would be updated to =B3 if relative referencing was used for both the column and row location).

Figure A.9 contains this tax rate. In column E, we calculate the after-tax profit for Nowlin in each month by using the following steps:

Step 1. Enter the label *After-Tax Profit* in cell E1 and press the **Bold** Button in the **Font** group of the **Home** tab.
Step 2. Enter the formula =D2*(1-$B$19) in cell E2
Step 3. Copy the formula from cell E2 by selecting cell E2 and clicking **Copy** from the **Clipboard** group of the **Home** tab
Step 4. Select cells E3:E13
Step 5. Paste the formula from cell E2 by clicking **Paste** from the **Clipboard** group of the **Home** tab

Figure A.9 shows the after-tax profit in each month. Using $B$19 in the formula in cell E2 forces Excel to always refer to cell $B$19, even if we copy and paste this formula

FIGURE A.9 Nowlin Plastics After-Tax Profit Calculation Illustrating Relative Versus Absolute References

	A	B	C	D	E
1	**Month**	**Revenue**	**Cost**	**Profit**	**After-Tax Profit**
2	January	3459000	3250000	=B2-C2	=D2*(1-$B$19)
3	February	2873000	2640000	=B3-C3	=D3*(1-$B$19)
4	March	3195000	3021000	=B4-C4	=D4*(1-$B$19)
5	April	2925000	3015000	=B5-C5	=D5*(1-$B$19)
6	May	3682000	3150000	=B6-C6	=D6*(1-$B$19)
7	June	3436000	3240000	=B7-C7	=D7*(1-$B$19)
8	July	3410000	3185000	=B8-C8	=D8*(1-$B$19)
9	August	3782000	3237000	=B9-C9	=D9*(1-$B$19)
10	September	3548000	3196000	=B10-C10	=D10*(1-$B$19)
11	October	3136000	2997000	=B11-C11	=D11*(1-$B$19)
12	November	3028000	2815000	=B12-C12	=D12*(1-$B$19)
13	December	2845000	2803000	=B13-C13	=D13*(1-$B$19)
14					
15	**Total:**	=SUM(B2:B13)	=SUM(C2:C13)		
16					
17	**Average:**	=AVERAGE(B2:B13)	=AVERAGE(C2:C13)		
18					
19	**Tax Rate:**	0.3			

	A	B	C	D	E
1	**Month**	**Revenue**	**Cost**	**Profit**	**After-Tax Profit**
2	January	$ 3,459,000	$ 3,250,000	$ 209,000	$ 146,300
3	February	$ 2,873,000	$ 2,640,000	$ 233,000	$ 163,100
4	March	$ 3,195,000	$ 3,021,000	$ 174,000	$ 121,800
5	April	$ 2,925,000	$ 3,015,000	$ (90,000)	$ (63,000)
6	May	$ 3,682,000	$ 3,150,000	$ 532,000	$ 372,400
7	June	$ 3,436,000	$ 3,240,000	$ 196,000	$ 137,200
8	July	$ 3,410,000	$ 3,185,000	$ 225,000	$ 157,500
9	August	$ 3,782,000	$ 3,237,000	$ 545,000	$ 381,500
10	September	$ 3,548,000	$ 3,196,000	$ 352,000	$ 246,400
11	October	$ 3,136,000	$ 2,997,000	$ 139,000	$ 97,300
12	November	$ 3,028,000	$ 2,815,000	$ 213,000	$ 149,100
13	December	$ 2,845,000	$ 2,803,000	$ 42,000	$ 29,400
14					
15	**Total:**	$39,319,000	$36,549,000		
16					
17	**Average:**	$ 3,276,583	$ 3,045,750		
18					
19	**Tax Rate:**	30%			

NowlinFinancialComplete

somewhere else in our worksheet. Notice that D2 continues to be a relative reference and is updated to D3, D4, and so on when we copy this formula to cells E3, E4, etc., respectively.

SUMMARY

In this appendix we have reviewed the basics of using Microsoft Excel. We have discussed the basic layout of Excel, file creation, saving, and editing as well as how to reference cells, use formulas, and use the copy and paste functions in an Excel worksheet. We have illustrated how to find and enter Excel functions and described the difference between relative and absolute cell references. In Chapter 10, we give a detailed treatment of how to create more advanced business analytics models in Excel. We conclude this appendix with Table A.1, which shows commonly used keyboard shortcut keys in Excel. Keyboard shortcut keys can save considerable time when entering data into Excel.

GLOSSARY

Absolute reference The reference to a cell location in an Excel worksheet formula or function. This reference does not update according to its relative position when copied.

Colon notation Notation used in an Excel worksheet to denote "through." For example, =SUM(B1:B4) implies sum cells B1 through B4, or equivalently, B1+B2+B3+B4.

Relative reference The reference to a cell location in an Excel worksheet formula or function. This reference updates according to its relative position when copied.

Workbook An Excel file that contains a series of worksheets.

Worksheet A single page in Excel containing a matrix of cells defined by their column and row locations in an Excel workbook.

A data region refers to all adjacent cells that contain data in an Excel worksheet.

*Holding down the **Ctrl** key and clicking on multiple cells allows you to select multiple nonadjacent cells. Holding down the **Shift** key and clicking on two nonadjacent cells selects all cells between the two cells.*

TABLE A.1 Keyboard Shortcut Keys in Excel

Keyboard Shortcut Key	Task Description
Ctrl-S	Save
Ctrl-C	Copy
Ctrl-V	Paste
Ctrl-F	Find (can be used to find text both within a cell and within a formula in Excel)
Ctrl-P	Print
Ctrl-A	Selects all cells in the current data region
Ctrl-B	Changes the selected text to/from bold font
Ctrl-I	Changes the selected text to/from italic font
Ctrl-~ (usually located above the Tab key)	Toggles between displaying values and formulas in the Worksheet.
Ctrl-↓ (down arrow key)	Moves to the bottom-most cell of the current data region
Ctrl-↑ (up arrow key)	Moves to the top-most cell of the current data region
Ctrl-→ (right arrow key)	Moves to the right-most cell of the current data region
Ctrl-← (left arrow key)	Moves to the left-most cell of the current data region
Ctrl-Home	Moves to the top-left-most cell of the current data region
Ctrl-End	Moves to the bottom-left-most cell of the current data region
Shift-↓	Selects the current cell and the cell below
Shift-↑	Selects the current cell and the cell above
Shift-→	Selects the current cell and the cell to the right
Shift-←	Selects the current cell and the cell to the left
Ctrl-Shift-↓	Selects all cells from the current cell to the bottom-most cell of the data region
Ctrl-Shift-↑	Selects all cells from the current cell to the top-most cell of the data region
Ctrl-Shift-→	Selects all cells from the current cell to the right-most cell in the data region
Ctrl-Shift-←	Selects all cells from the current cell to the left-most cell in the data region
Ctrl-Shift-Home	Selects all cells from the current cell to the top-left-most cell in the data region
Ctrl-Shift-End	Selects all cells from the current cell to the bottom-right-most cell in the data region
Ctrl-Spacebar	Selects the entire current column
Shift-Spacebar	Selects the entire current row

Appendix B: Tables

TABLE 1 CUMULATIVE PROBABILITIES FOR THE STANDARD NORMAL DISTRIBUTION

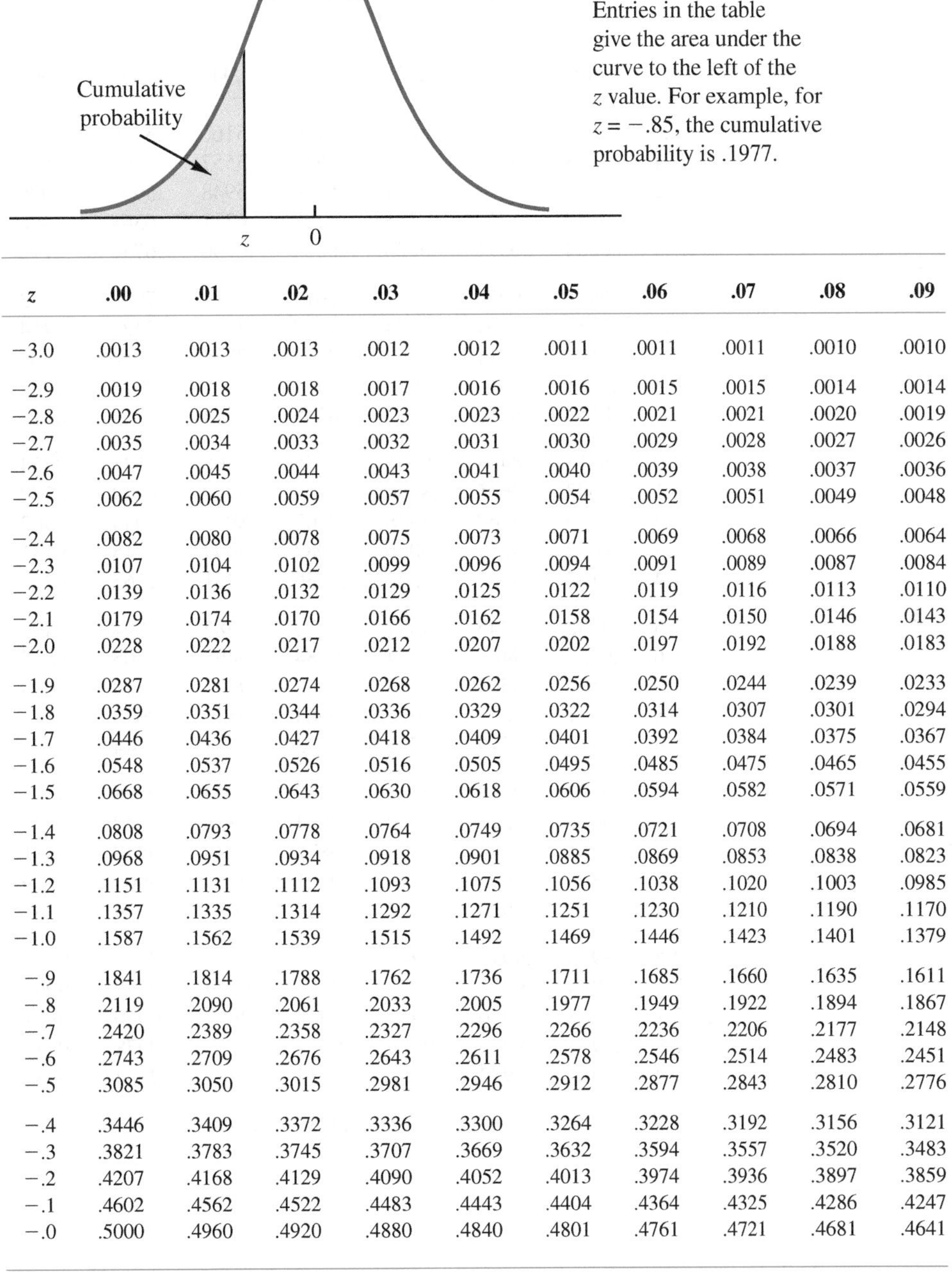
Cumulative
probability
z
0
Entries in the table give the area under the curve to the left of the z value. For example, for z = −.85, the cumulative probability is .1977.

z	.00	.01	.02	.03	.04	.05	.06	.07	.08	.09
−3.0	.0013	.0013	.0013	.0012	.0012	.0011	.0011	.0011	.0010	.0010
−2.9	.0019	.0018	.0018	.0017	.0016	.0016	.0015	.0015	.0014	.0014
−2.8	.0026	.0025	.0024	.0023	.0023	.0022	.0021	.0021	.0020	.0019
−2.7	.0035	.0034	.0033	.0032	.0031	.0030	.0029	.0028	.0027	.0026
−2.6	.0047	.0045	.0044	.0043	.0041	.0040	.0039	.0038	.0037	.0036
−2.5	.0062	.0060	.0059	.0057	.0055	.0054	.0052	.0051	.0049	.0048
−2.4	.0082	.0080	.0078	.0075	.0073	.0071	.0069	.0068	.0066	.0064
−2.3	.0107	.0104	.0102	.0099	.0096	.0094	.0091	.0089	.0087	.0084
−2.2	.0139	.0136	.0132	.0129	.0125	.0122	.0119	.0116	.0113	.0110
−2.1	.0179	.0174	.0170	.0166	.0162	.0158	.0154	.0150	.0146	.0143
−2.0	.0228	.0222	.0217	.0212	.0207	.0202	.0197	.0192	.0188	.0183
−1.9	.0287	.0281	.0274	.0268	.0262	.0256	.0250	.0244	.0239	.0233
−1.8	.0359	.0351	.0344	.0336	.0329	.0322	.0314	.0307	.0301	.0294
−1.7	.0446	.0436	.0427	.0418	.0409	.0401	.0392	.0384	.0375	.0367
−1.6	.0548	.0537	.0526	.0516	.0505	.0495	.0485	.0475	.0465	.0455
−1.5	.0668	.0655	.0643	.0630	.0618	.0606	.0594	.0582	.0571	.0559
−1.4	.0808	.0793	.0778	.0764	.0749	.0735	.0721	.0708	.0694	.0681
−1.3	.0968	.0951	.0934	.0918	.0901	.0885	.0869	.0853	.0838	.0823
−1.2	.1151	.1131	.1112	.1093	.1075	.1056	.1038	.1020	.1003	.0985
−1.1	.1357	.1335	.1314	.1292	.1271	.1251	.1230	.1210	.1190	.1170
−1.0	.1587	.1562	.1539	.1515	.1492	.1469	.1446	.1423	.1401	.1379
−.9	.1841	.1814	.1788	.1762	.1736	.1711	.1685	.1660	.1635	.1611
−.8	.2119	.2090	.2061	.2033	.2005	.1977	.1949	.1922	.1894	.1867
−.7	.2420	.2389	.2358	.2327	.2296	.2266	.2236	.2206	.2177	.2148
−.6	.2743	.2709	.2676	.2643	.2611	.2578	.2546	.2514	.2483	.2451
−.5	.3085	.3050	.3015	.2981	.2946	.2912	.2877	.2843	.2810	.2776
−.4	.3446	.3409	.3372	.3336	.3300	.3264	.3228	.3192	.3156	.3121
−.3	.3821	.3783	.3745	.3707	.3669	.3632	.3594	.3557	.3520	.3483
−.2	.4207	.4168	.4129	.4090	.4052	.4013	.3974	.3936	.3897	.3859
−.1	.4602	.4562	.4522	.4483	.4443	.4404	.4364	.4325	.4286	.4247
−.0	.5000	.4960	.4920	.4880	.4840	.4801	.4761	.4721	.4681	.4641

TABLE 1 CUMULATIVE PROBABILITIES FOR THE STANDARD NORMAL DISTRIBUTION (*Continued*)

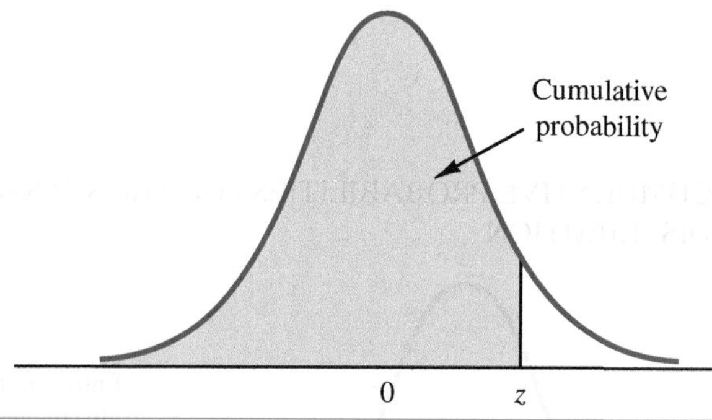

Entries in the table give the area under the curve to the left of the z value. For example, for $z = 1.25$, the cumulative probability is .8944.

z	.00	.01	.02	.03	.04	.05	.06	.07	.08	.09
.0	.5000	.5040	.5080	.5120	.5160	.5199	.5239	.5279	.5319	.5359
.1	.5398	.5438	.5478	.5517	.5557	.5596	.5636	.5675	.5714	.5753
.2	.5793	.5832	.5871	.5910	.5948	.5987	.6026	.6064	.6103	.6141
.3	.6179	.6217	.6255	.6293	.6331	.6368	.6406	.6443	.6480	.6517
.4	.6554	.6591	.6628	.6664	.6700	.6736	.6772	.6808	.6844	.6879
.5	.6915	.6950	.6985	.7019	.7054	.7088	.7123	.7157	.7190	.7224
.6	.7257	.7291	.7324	.7357	.7389	.7422	.7454	.7486	.7517	.7549
.7	.7580	.7611	.7642	.7673	.7704	.7734	.7764	.7794	.7823	.7852
.8	.7881	.7910	.7939	.7967	.7995	.8023	.8051	.8078	.8106	.8133
.9	.8159	.8186	.8212	.8238	.8264	.8289	.8315	.8340	.8365	.8389
1.0	.8413	.8438	.8461	.8485	.8508	.8531	.8554	.8577	.8599	.8621
1.1	.8643	.8665	.8686	.8708	.8729	.8749	.8770	.8790	.8810	.8830
1.2	.8849	.8869	.8888	.8907	.8925	.8944	.8962	.8980	.8997	.9015
1.3	.9032	.9049	.9066	.9082	.9099	.9115	.9131	.9147	.9162	.9177
1.4	.9192	.9207	.9222	.9236	.9251	.9265	.9279	.9292	.9306	.9319
1.5	.9332	.9345	.9357	.9370	.9382	.9394	.9406	.9418	.9429	.9441
1.6	.9452	.9463	.9474	.9484	.9495	.9505	.9515	.9525	.9535	.9545
1.7	.9554	.9564	.9573	.9582	.9591	.9599	.9608	.9616	.9625	.9633
1.8	.9641	.9649	.9656	.9664	.9671	.9678	.9686	.9693	.9699	.9706
1.9	.9713	.9719	.9726	.9732	.9738	.9744	.9750	.9756	.9761	.9767
2.0	.9772	.9778	.9783	.9788	.9793	.9798	.9803	.9808	.9812	.9817
2.1	.9821	.9826	.9830	.9834	.9838	.9842	.9846	.9850	.9854	.9857
2.2	.9861	.9864	.9868	.9871	.9875	.9878	.9881	.9884	.9887	.9890
2.3	.9893	.9896	.9898	.9901	.9904	.9906	.9909	.9911	.9913	.9916
2.4	.9918	.9920	.9922	.9925	.9927	.9929	.9931	.9932	.9934	.9936
2.5	.9938	.9940	.9941	.9943	.9945	.9946	.9948	.9949	.9951	.9952
2.6	.9953	.9955	.9956	.9957	.9959	.9960	.9961	.9962	.9963	.9964
2.7	.9965	.9966	.9967	.9968	.9969	.9970	.9971	.9972	.9973	.9974
2.8	.9974	.9975	.9976	.9977	.9977	.9978	.9979	.9979	.9980	.9981
2.9	.9981	.9982	.9982	.9983	.9984	.9984	.9985	.9985	.9986	.9986
3.0	.9987	.9987	.9987	.9988	.9988	.9989	.9989	.9989	.9990	.9990

TABLE 2 *t* DISTRIBUTION

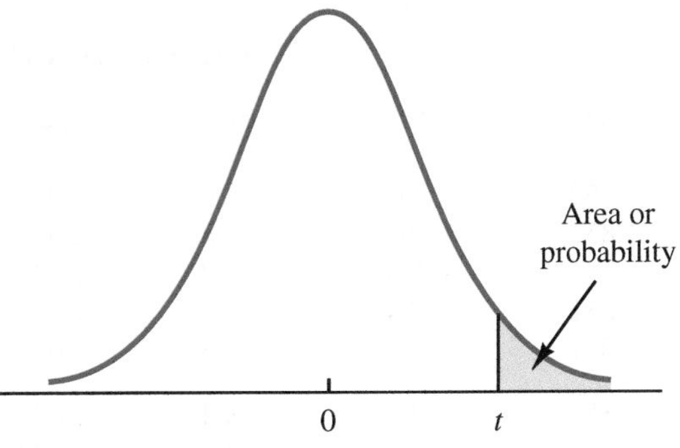

Entries in the table give t values for an area or probability in the upper tail of the t distribution. For example, with 10 degrees of freedom and a .05 area in the upper tail, $t_{.05} = 1.812$.

Degrees of Freedom	Area in Upper Tail .20	.10	.05	.025	.01	.005
1	1.376	3.078	6.314	12.706	31.821	63.656
2	1.061	1.886	2.920	4.303	6.965	9.925
3	.978	1.638	2.353	3.182	4.541	5.841
4	.941	1.533	2.132	2.776	3.747	4.604
5	.920	1.476	2.015	2.571	3.365	4.032
6	.906	1.440	1.943	2.447	3.143	3.707
7	.896	1.415	1.895	2.365	2.998	3.499
8	.889	1.397	1.860	2.306	2.896	3.355
9	.883	1.383	1.833	2.262	2.821	3.250
10	.879	1.372	1.812	2.228	2.764	3.169
11	.876	1.363	1.796	2.201	2.718	3.106
12	.873	1.356	1.782	2.179	2.681	3.055
13	.870	1.350	1.771	2.160	2.650	3.012
14	.868	1.345	1.761	2.145	2.624	2.977
15	.866	1.341	1.753	2.131	2.602	2.947
16	.865	1.337	1.746	2.120	2.583	2.921
17	.863	1.333	1.740	2.110	2.567	2.898
18	.862	1.330	1.734	2.101	2.552	2.878
19	.861	1.328	1.729	2.093	2.539	2.861
20	.860	1.325	1.725	2.086	2.528	2.845
21	.859	1.323	1.721	2.080	2.518	2.831
22	.858	1.321	1.717	2.074	2.508	2.819
23	.858	1.319	1.714	2.069	2.500	2.807
24	.857	1.318	1.711	2.064	2.492	2.797
25	.856	1.316	1.708	2.060	2.485	2.787
26	.856	1.315	1.706	2.056	2.479	2.779
27	.855	1.314	1.703	2.052	2.473	2.771
28	.855	1.313	1.701	2.048	2.467	2.763
29	.854	1.311	1.699	2.045	2.462	2.756
30	.854	1.310	1.697	2.042	2.457	2.750
31	.853	1.309	1.696	2.040	2.453	2.744
32	.853	1.309	1.694	2.037	2.449	2.738
33	.853	1.308	1.692	2.035	2.445	2.733
34	.852	1.307	1.691	2.032	2.441	2.728

TABLE 2 *t* DISTRIBUTION (*Continued*)

Degrees of Freedom	Area in Upper Tail					
	.20	.10	.05	.025	.01	.005
35	.852	1.306	1.690	2.030	2.438	2.724
36	.852	1.306	1.688	2.028	2.434	2.719
37	.851	1.305	1.687	2.026	2.431	2.715
38	.851	1.304	1.686	2.024	2.429	2.712
39	.851	1.304	1.685	2.023	2.426	2.708
40	.851	1.303	1.684	2.021	2.423	2.704
41	.850	1.303	1.683	2.020	2.421	2.701
42	.850	1.302	1.682	2.018	2.418	2.698
43	.850	1.302	1.681	2.017	2.416	2.695
44	.850	1.301	1.680	2.015	2.414	2.692
45	.850	1.301	1.679	2.014	2.412	2.690
46	.850	1.300	1.679	2.013	2.410	2.687
47	.849	1.300	1.678	2.012	2.408	2.685
48	.849	1.299	1.677	2.011	2.407	2.682
49	.849	1.299	1.677	2.010	2.405	2.680
50	.849	1.299	1.676	2.009	2.403	2.678
51	.849	1.298	1.675	2.008	2.402	2.676
52	.849	1.298	1.675	2.007	2.400	2.674
53	.848	1.298	1.674	2.006	2.399	2.672
54	.848	1.297	1.674	2.005	2.397	2.670
55	.848	1.297	1.673	2.004	2.396	2.668
56	.848	1.297	1.673	2.003	2.395	2.667
57	.848	1.297	1.672	2.002	2.394	2.665
58	.848	1.296	1.672	2.002	2.392	2.663
59	.848	1.296	1.671	2.001	2.391	2.662
60	.848	1.296	1.671	2.000	2.390	2.660
61	.848	1.296	1.670	2.000	2.389	2.659
62	.847	1.295	1.670	1.999	2.388	2.657
63	.847	1.295	1.669	1.998	2.387	2.656
64	.847	1.295	1.669	1.998	2.386	2.655
65	.847	1.295	1.669	1.997	2.385	2.654
66	.847	1.295	1.668	1.997	2.384	2.652
67	.847	1.294	1.668	1.996	2.383	2.651
68	.847	1.294	1.668	1.995	2.382	2.650
69	.847	1.294	1.667	1.995	2.382	2.649
70	.847	1.294	1.667	1.994	2.381	2.648
71	.847	1.294	1.667	1.994	2.380	2.647
72	.847	1.293	1.666	1.993	2.379	2.646
73	.847	1.293	1.666	1.993	2.379	2.645
74	.847	1.293	1.666	1.993	2.378	2.644
75	.846	1.293	1.665	1.992	2.377	2.643
76	.846	1.293	1.665	1.992	2.376	2.642
77	.846	1.293	1.665	1.991	2.376	2.641
78	.846	1.292	1.665	1.991	2.375	2.640
79	.846	1.292	1.664	1.990	2.374	2.639

TABLE 2 *t* DISTRIBUTION (*Continued*)

Degrees of Freedom	Area in Upper Tail					
	.20	**.10**	**.05**	**.025**	**.01**	**.005**
80	.846	1.292	1.664	1.990	2.374	2.639
81	.846	1.292	1.664	1.990	2.373	2.638
82	.846	1.292	1.664	1.989	2.373	2.637
83	.846	1.292	1.663	1.989	2.372	2.636
84	.846	1.292	1.663	1.989	2.372	2.636
85	.846	1.292	1.663	1.988	2.371	2.635
86	.846	1.291	1.663	1.988	2.370	2.634
87	.846	1.291	1.663	1.988	2.370	2.634
88	.846	1.291	1.662	1.987	2.369	2.633
89	.846	1.291	1.662	1.987	2.369	2.632
90	.846	1.291	1.662	1.987	2.368	2.632
91	.846	1.291	1.662	1.986	2.368	2.631
92	.846	1.291	1.662	1.986	2.368	2.630
93	.846	1.291	1.661	1.986	2.367	2.630
94	.845	1.291	1.661	1.986	2.367	2.629
95	.845	1.291	1.661	1.985	2.366	2.629
96	.845	1.290	1.661	1.985	2.366	2.628
97	.845	1.290	1.661	1.985	2.365	2.627
98	.845	1.290	1.661	1.984	2.365	2.627
99	.845	1.290	1.660	1.984	2.364	2.626
100	.845	1.290	1.660	1.984	2.364	2.626
∞	.842	1.282	1.645	1.960	2.326	2.576

TABLE 3 CHI-SQUARE DISTRIBUTION

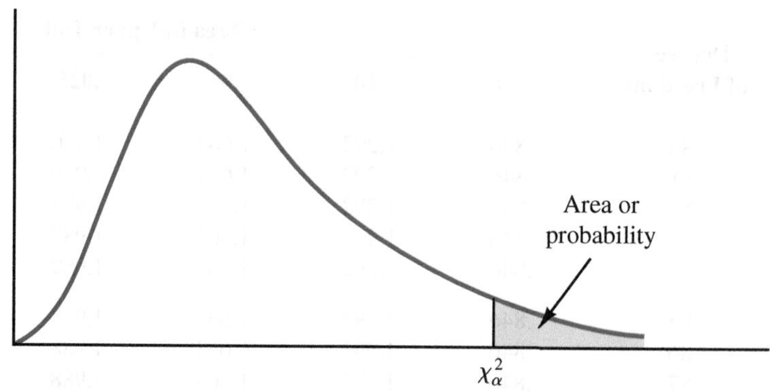

Entries in the table give χ^2_α values, where α is the area or probability in the upper tail of the chi-square distribution. For example, with 10 degrees of freedom and a .01 area in the upper tail, $\chi^2_{.01} = 23.209$.

Degrees of Freedom	Area in Upper Tail									
	.995	.99	.975	.95	.90	.10	.05	.025	.01	.005
1	.000	.000	.001	.004	.016	2.706	3.841	5.024	6.635	7.879
2	.010	.020	.051	.103	.211	4.605	5.991	7.378	9.210	10.597
3	.072	.115	.216	.352	.584	6.251	7.815	9.348	11.345	12.838
4	.207	.297	.484	.711	1.064	7.779	9.488	11.143	13.277	14.860
5	.412	.554	.831	1.145	1.610	9.236	11.070	12.832	15.086	16.750
6	.676	.872	1.237	1.635	2.204	10.645	12.592	14.449	16.812	18.548
7	.989	1.239	1.690	2.167	2.833	12.017	14.067	16.013	18.475	20.278
8	1.344	1.647	2.180	2.733	3.490	13.362	15.507	17.535	20.090	21.955
9	1.735	2.088	2.700	3.325	4.168	14.684	16.919	19.023	21.666	23.589
10	2.156	2.558	3.247	3.940	4.865	15.987	18.307	20.483	23.209	25.188
11	2.603	3.053	3.816	4.575	5.578	17.275	19.675	21.920	24.725	26.757
12	3.074	3.571	4.404	5.226	6.304	18.549	21.026	23.337	26.217	28.300
13	3.565	4.107	5.009	5.892	7.041	19.812	22.362	24.736	27.688	29.819
14	4.075	4.660	5.629	6.571	7.790	21.064	23.685	26.119	29.141	31.319
15	4.601	5.229	6.262	7.261	8.547	22.307	24.996	27.488	30.578	32.801
16	5.142	5.812	6.908	7.962	9.312	23.542	26.296	28.845	32.000	34.267
17	5.697	6.408	7.564	8.672	10.085	24.769	27.587	30.191	33.409	35.718
18	6.265	7.015	8.231	9.390	10.865	25.989	28.869	31.526	34.805	37.156
19	6.844	7.633	8.907	10.117	11.651	27.204	30.144	32.852	36.191	38.582
20	7.434	8.260	9.591	10.851	12.443	28.412	31.410	34.170	37.566	39.997
21	8.034	8.897	10.283	11.591	13.240	29.615	32.671	35.479	38.932	41.401
22	8.643	9.542	10.982	12.338	14.041	30.813	33.924	36.781	40.289	42.796
23	9.260	10.196	11.689	13.091	14.848	32.007	35.172	38.076	41.638	44.181
24	9.886	10.856	12.401	13.848	15.659	33.196	36.415	39.364	42.980	45.558
25	10.520	11.524	13.120	14.611	16.473	34.382	37.652	40.646	44.314	46.928
26	11.160	12.198	13.844	15.379	17.292	35.563	38.885	41.923	45.642	48.290
27	11.808	12.878	14.573	16.151	18.114	36.741	40.113	43.195	46.963	49.645
28	12.461	13.565	15.308	16.928	18.939	37.916	41.337	44.461	48.278	50.994
29	13.121	14.256	16.047	17.708	19.768	39.087	42.557	45.722	49.588	52.335

TABLE 3 CHI-SQUARE DISTRIBUTION (*Continued*)

Degrees of Freedom	Area in Upper Tail									
	.995	.99	.975	.95	.90	.10	.05	.025	.01	.005
30	13.787	14.953	16.791	18.493	20.599	40.256	43.773	46.979	50.892	53.672
35	17.192	18.509	20.569	22.465	24.797	46.059	49.802	53.203	57.342	60.275
40	20.707	22.164	24.433	26.509	29.051	51.805	55.758	59.342	63.691	66.766
45	24.311	25.901	28.366	30.612	33.350	57.505	61.656	65.410	69.957	73.166
50	27.991	29.707	32.357	34.764	37.689	63.167	67.505	71.420	76.154	79.490
55	31.735	33.571	36.398	38.958	42.060	68.796	73.311	77.380	82.292	85.749
60	35.534	37.485	40.482	43.188	46.459	74.397	79.082	83.298	88.379	91.952
65	39.383	41.444	44.603	47.450	50.883	79.973	84.821	89.177	94.422	98.105
70	43.275	45.442	48.758	51.739	55.329	85.527	90.531	95.023	100.425	104.215
75	47.206	49.475	52.942	56.054	59.795	91.061	96.217	100.839	106.393	110.285
80	51.172	53.540	57.153	60.391	64.278	96.578	101.879	106.629	112.329	116.321
85	55.170	57.634	61.389	64.749	68.777	102.079	107.522	112.393	118.236	122.324
90	59.196	61.754	65.647	69.126	73.291	107.565	113.145	118.136	124.116	128.299
95	63.250	65.898	69.925	73.520	77.818	113.038	118.752	123.858	129.973	134.247
100	67.328	70.065	74.222	77.929	82.358	118.498	124.342	129.561	135.807	140.170

TABLE 4 *F* DISTRIBUTION

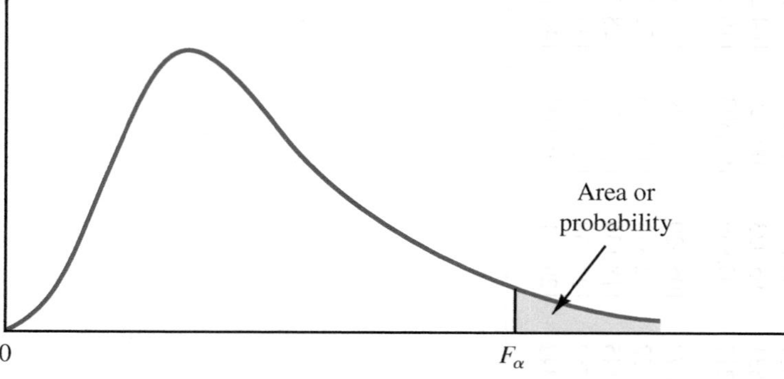

Entries in the table give F_α values, where α is the area or probability in the upper tail of the F distribution. For example, with 4 numerator degrees of freedom, 8 denominator degrees of freedom, and a .05 area in the upper tail, $F_{.05} = 3.84$.

Denominattor Degrees of Freedom	Area in Upper Tail	Numerator Degrees of Freedom																	
		1	2	3	4	5	6	7	8	9	10	15	20	25	30	40	60	100	100
1	.10	39.86	49.50	53.59	55.83	57.24	58.20	58.91	59.44	59.86	60.19	61.22	61.74	62.05	62.26	62.53	62.79	63.01	63.30
	.05	161.45	199.50	215.71	224.58	230.16	233.99	236.77	238.88	240.54	241.88	245.95	248.02	249.26	250.10	251.14	252.20	253.04	254.19
	.025	647.79	799.48	864.15	899.60	921.83	937.11	948.20	956.64	963.28	968.63	984.87	993.08	998.09	1001.40	1005.60	1009.79	1013.16	1017.76
	.01	4052.18	4999.34	5403.53	5624.26	5763.96	5858.95	5928.33	5980.95	6022.40	6055.93	6156.97	6208.66	6239.86	6260.35	6286.43	6312.97	6333.92	6362.80
2	.10	8.53	9.00	9.16	9.24	9.29	9.33	9.35	9.37	9.38	9.39	9.42	9.44	9.45	9.46	9.47	9.47	9.48	9.49
	.05	18.51	19.00	19.16	19.25	19.30	19.33	19.35	19.37	19.38	19.40	19.43	19.45	19.46	19.46	19.47	19.48	19.49	19.49
	.025	38.51	39.00	39.17	39.25	39.30	39.33	39.36	39.37	39.39	39.40	39.43	39.45	39.46	39.46	39.47	39.48	39.49	39.50
	.01	98.50	99.00	99.16	99.25	99.30	99.33	99.36	99.38	99.39	99.40	99.43	99.45	99.46	99.47	99.48	99.48	99.49	99.50
3	.10	5.54	5.46	5.39	5.34	5.31	5.28	5.27	5.25	5.24	5.23	5.20	5.18	5.17	5.17	5.16	5.15	5.14	5.13
	.05	10.13	9.55	9.28	9.12	9.01	8.94	8.89	8.85	8.81	8.79	8.70	8.66	8.63	8.62	8.59	8.57	8.55	8.53
	.025	17.44	16.04	15.44	15.10	14.88	14.73	14.62	14.54	14.47	14.42	14.25	14.17	14.12	14.08	14.04	13.99	13.96	13.91
	.01	34.12	30.82	29.46	28.71	28.24	27.91	27.67	27.49	27.34	27.23	26.87	26.69	26.58	26.50	26.41	26.32	26.24	26.14
4	.10	4.54	4.32	4.19	4.11	4.05	4.01	3.98	3.95	3.94	3.92	3.87	3.84	3.83	3.82	3.80	3.79	3.78	3.76
	.05	7.71	6.94	6.59	6.39	6.26	6.16	6.09	6.04	6.00	5.96	5.86	5.80	5.77	5.75	5.72	5.69	5.66	5.63
	.025	12.22	10.65	9.98	9.60	9.36	9.20	9.07	8.98	8.90	8.84	8.66	8.56	8.50	8.46	8.41	8.36	8.32	8.26
	.01	21.20	18.00	16.69	15.98	15.52	15.21	14.98	14.80	14.66	14.55	14.20	14.02	13.91	13.84	13.75	13.65	13.58	13.47
5	.10	4.06	3.78	3.62	3.52	3.45	3.40	3.37	3.34	3.32	3.30	3.324	3.21	3.19	3.17	3.16	3.14	3.13	3.11
	.05	6.61.	5.79	5.41	5.19	5.05	4.95	4.88	4.82	4.77	4.74	4.62	4.56	4.52	4.50	4.46	4.43	4.41	4.37
	.025	10.01	8.43	7.76	7.39	7.15	6.98	6.85	6.76	6.68	6.62	6.43	6.33	6.27	6.23	6.18	6.12	6.08	6.02
	.01	16.26	13.27	12.06	11.39	10.97	10.67	10.46	10.29	10.16	10.05	9.72	9.55	9.45	9.38	9.29	9.20	9.13	9.03

Denominator Degrees of Freedom	Area in Upper Tail	Numerator Degrees of Freedom																	
		1	2	3	4	5	6	7	8	9	10	15	20	25	30	40	60	100	1000
6	.10	3.78	3.46	3.29	3.18	3.11	3.05	3.01	2.98	2.96	2.94	2.87	2.84	2.81	2.80	2.78	2.76	2.75	2.72
	.05	5.99	5.14	4.76	4.53	4.39	4.28	4.21	4.15	4.10	4.06	3.94	3.87	3.83	3.81	3.77	3.74	3.71	3.67
	.025	8.81	7.26	6.60	6.23	5.99	5.82	5.70	5.60	5.52	5.46	5.27	5.17	5.11	5.07	5.01	4.96	4.92	4.86
	.01	13.75	10.92	9.78	9.15	8.75	8.47	8.26	8.10	7.98	7.87	7.56	7.40	7.30	7.23	7.14	7.06	6.99	6.89
7	.10	3.59	3.26	3.07	2.96	2.88	2.83	2.78	2.75	2.72	2.70	2.63	2.59	2.57	2.56	2.54	2.51	2.50	2.47
	.05	5.59	4.74	4.35	4.12	3.97	3.87	3.79	3.73	3.68	3.64	3.51	3.44	3.40	3.38	3.34	3.30	3.27	3.23
	.025	8.07	6.54	5.89	5.52	5.29	5.12	4.99	4.90	4.82	4.76	4.57	4.47	4.40	4.36	4.31	4.25	4.21	4.15
	.01	12.25	9.55	8.45	7.85	7.46	7.19	6.99	6.84	6.72	6.62	6.31	6.16	6.06	5.99	5.91	5.82	5.75	5.66
8	.10	3.46	3.11	2.92	2.81	2.73	2.67	2.62	2.59	2.56	2.54	2.46	2.42	2.40	2.38	2.36	2.34	2.32	2.30
	.05	5.32	4.46	4.07	3.84	3.69	3.58	3.50	3.44	3.39	3.35	3.22	3.15	3.11	3.08	3.04	3.01	2.97	2.93
	.025	7.57	6.06	5.42	5.05	4.82	4.65	4.53	4.43	4.36	4.30	4.10	4.00	3.94	3.89	3.84	3.78	3.74	3.68
	.01	11.26	8.65	7.59	7.01	6.63	6.37	6.18	6.03	5.91	5.81	5.52	5.36	5.26	5.20	5.12	5.03	4.96	4.87
9	.10	3.36	3.01	2.81	2.69	2.61	2.55	2.51	2.47	2.44	2.42	2.34	2.30	2.27	2.25	2.23	2.21	2.19	2.16
	.05	5.12	4.26	3.86	3.63	3.48	3.37	3.29	3.23	3.18	3.14	3.01	2.94	2.89	2.86	2.83	2.79	2.76	2.71
	.025	7.21	5.71	5.08	4.72	4.48	4.32	4.20	4.10	4.03	3.96	3.77	3.67	3.60	3.56	3.51	3.45	3.40	3.34
	.01	10.56	8.02	6.99	6.42	6.06	5.80	5.61	5.47	5.35	5.26	4.96	4.81	4.71	4.65	4.57	4.48	4.41	4.32
10	.10	3.29	2.92	2.73	2.61	2.52	2.46	2.41	2.38	2.35	2.32	2.24	2.20	2.17	2.16	2.13	2.11	2.09	2.06
	.05	4.96	4.10	3.71	3.48	3.33	3.22	3.14	3.07	3.02	2.98	2.85	2.77	2.73	2.70	2.66	2.62	2.59	2.54
	.025	6.94	5.46	4.83	4.47	4.24	4.07	3.95	3.85	3.78	3.72	3.52	3.42	3.35	3.31	3.26	3.20	3.15	3.09
	.01	10.04	7.56	6.55	5.99	5.64	5.39	5.20	5.06	4.94	4.85	4.56	4.41	4.31	4.25	4.17	4.08	4.01	3.92
11	.10	3.23	2.86	2.66	2.54	2.45	2.39	2.34	2.30	2.27	2.25	2.17	2.12	2.10	2.08	2.05	2.03	2.01	1.98
	.05	4.84	3.98	3.59	3.36	3.20	3.09	3.01	2.95	2.90	2.85	2.72	2.65	2.60	2.57	2.53	2.49	2.46	2.41
	.025	6.72	5.26	4.63	4.28	4.04	3.88	3.76	3.66	3.59	3.53	3.33	3.23	3.16	3.12	3.06	3.00	2.96	2.89
	.01	9.65	7.21	6.22	5.67	5.32	5.07	4.89	4.74	4.63	4.54	4.25	4.10	4.01	3.94	3.86	3.78	3.71	3.61
12	.10	3.18	2.81	2.61	2.48	2.39	2.33	2.28	2.24	2.21	2.19	2.10	2.06	2.03	2.01	1.99	1.96	1.94	1.91
	.05	4.75	3.89	3.49	3.26	3.11	3.00	2.91	2.85	2.80	2.75	2.62	2.54	2.50	2.47	2.43	2.38	2.35	2.30
	.025	6.55	5.10	4.47	4.12	3.89	3.73	3.61	3.51	3.44	3.37	3.18	3.07	3.01	2.96	2.91	2.85	2.80	2.73
	.01	9.33	6.93	5.95	5.41	5.06	4.82	4.64	4.50	4.39	4.30	4.01	3.86	3.76	3.70	3.62	3.54	3.47	3.37
13	.10	3.14	2.76	2.56	2.43	2.35	2.28	2.23	2.20	2.16	2.14	2.05	2.01	1.98	1.96	1.93	1.90	1.88	1.85
	.05	4.67	3.81	3.41	3.18	3.03	2.92	2.83	2.77	2.71	2.67	2.53	2.46	2.41	2.38	2.34	2.30	2.26	2.21
	.025	6.41	4.97	4.35	4.00	3.77	3.60	3.48	3.39	3.31	3.25	3.05	2.95	2.88	2.84	2.78	2.72	2.67	2.60
	.01	9.07	6.70	5.74	5.21	4.86	4.62	4.44	4.30	4.19	4.10	3.82	3.66	3.57	3.51	3.43	3.34	3.27	3.18
14	.10	3.10	2.73	2.52	2.39	2.31	2.24	2.19	2.15	2.12	2.10	2.01	1.96	1.93	1.99	1.89	1.86	1.83	1.80
	.05	4.60	3.74	3.34	3.11	2.96	2.85	2.76	2.70	2.65	2.60	2.46	2.39	2.34	2.31	2.27	2.22	2.19	2.14
	.025	6.30	4.86	4.24	3.89	3.66	3.50	3.38	3.29	3.21	3.15	2.95	2.84	2.78	2.73	2.67	2.61	2.56	2.50
	.01	8.86	6.51	5.56	5.04	4.69	4.46	4.28	4.14	4.03	3.94	3.66	3.51	3.41	3.35	3.27	3.18	3.11	3.02
15	.10	3.07	2.70	2.49	2.36	2.27	2.21	2.16	2.12	2.09	2.06	1.97	1.92	1.89	1.87	1.85	1.82	1.79	1.76
	.05	4.54	3.68	3.29	3.06	2.90	2.79	2.71	2.64	2.59	2.54	2.40	2.33	2.28	2.25	2.20	2.16	2.12	2.07
	.025	6.20	4.77	4.15	3.80	3.58	3.41	3.29	3.20	3.12	3.06	2.86	2.76	2.69	2.64	2.59	2.52	2.47	2.40
	.01	8.68	6.36	5.42	4.89	4.56	4.32	4.14	4.00	3.89	3.80	3.52	3.37	3.28	3.21	3.13	3.05	2.98	2.88

TABLE 4 *F* DISTRIBUTION (*Continued*)

Denominator Degrees of Freedom	Area in Upper Tail	Numerator Degrees of Freedom																	
		1	2	3	4	5	6	7	8	9	10	15	20	25	30	40	60	100	1000
16	.10	3.05	2.67	2.46	2.33	2.24	2.18	2.13	2.09	2.06	2.03	1.94	1.89	1.86	1.84	1.81	1.78	1.76	1.72
	.05	4.49	3.63	3.24	3.01	2.85	2.74	2.66	2.59	2.54	2.49	2.35	2.28	2.23	2.19	2.15	2.11	2.07	2.02
	.025	6.12	4.69	4.08	3.73	3.50	3.34	3.22	3.12	3.05	2.99	2.79	2.68	2.61	2.57	2.51	2.45	2.40	2.32
	.01	8.53	6.23	5.29	4.77	4.44	4.20	4.03	3.89	3.78	3.69	3.41	3.26	3.16	3.10	3.02	2.93	2.86	2.76
17	.10	3.03	2.64	2.44	2.31	2.22	2.15	2.10	2.06	2.03	2.00	1.91	1.86	1.83	1.81	1.78	1.75	1.73	1.69
	.05	4.45	3.59	3.20	2.96	2.81	2.70	2.61	2.55	2.49	2.45	2.31	2.23	2.18	2.15	2.10	2.06	2.02	1.97
	.025	6.04	4.62	4.01	3.66	3.44	3.28	3.16	3.06	2.98	2.92	2.72	2.62	2.55	2.50	2.44	2.38	2.33	2.26
	.01	8.40	6.11	5.19	4.67	4.34	4.10	3.93	3.79	3.68	3.59	3.31	3.16	3.07	3.00	2.92	2.83	2.76	2.66
18	.10	3.01	2.62	2.42	2.29	2.20	2.13	2.08	2.04	2.00	1.98	1.89	1.84	1.80	1.78	1.75	1.72	1.70	1.66
	.05	4.41	3.55	3.16	2.93	2.77	2.66	2.58	2.51	2.46	2.41	2.27	2.19	2.14	2.11	2.06	2.02	1.98	1.92
	.025	5.98	4.56	3.95	3.61	3.38	3.22	3.10	3.01	2.93	2.87	2.67	2.56	2.49	2.44	2.38	2.32	2.27	2.20
	.01	8.29	6.01	5.09	4.58	4.25	4.01	3.84	3.71	3.60	3.51	3.23	3.08	2.98	2.92	2.84	2.75	2.68	2.58
19	.10	2.99	2.61	2.40	2.27	2.18	2.11	2.06	2.02	1.98	1.96	1.86	1.81	1.78	1.76	1.73	1.70	1.67	1.64
	.05	4.38	3.52	3.13	2.90	2.74	2.63	2.54	2.48	2.42	2.38	2.23	2.16	2.11	2.07	2.03	1.98	1.94	1.88
	.025	5.92	4.51	3.90	3.56	3.33	3.17	3.05	2.96	2.88	2.82	2.62	2.51	2.44	2.39	2.33	2.27	2.22	2.14
	.01	8.18	5.93	5.01	4.50	4.17	3.94	3.77	3.63	3.52	3.43	3.15	3.00	2.91	2.84	2.76	2.67	2.60	2.50
20	.10	2.97	2.59	2.38	2.25	2.16	2.09	2.04	2.00	1.96	1.94	1.84	1.79	1.76	1.74	1.71	1.68	1.65	1.61
	.05	4.35	3.49	3.10	2.87	2.71	2.60	2.51	2.45	2.39	2.35	2.20	2.12	2.07	2.04	1.99	1.95	1.91	1.85
	.025	5.87	4.46	3.86	3.51	3.29	3.13	3.01	2.91	2.84	2.77	2.57	2.46	2.40	2.35	2.29	2.22	2.17	2.09
	.01	8.10	5.85	4.94	4.43	4.10	3.87	3.70	3.56	3.46	3.37	3.09	2.94	2.84	2.78	2.69	2.61	2.54	2.43
21	.10	2.96	2.57	2.36	2.23	2.14	2.08	2.02	1.98	1.95	1.92	1.83	1.78	1.74	1.72	1.69	1.66	1.63	1.59
	.05	4.32	3.47	3.07	2.84	2.68	2.57	2.49	2.42	2.37	2.32	2.18	2.10	2.05	2.01	1.96	1.92	1.88	1.82
	.025	5.83	4.42	3.82	3.48	3.25	3.09	2.97	2.87	2.80	2.73	2.53	2.42	2.36	2.31	2.25	2.18	2.13	2.05
	.01	8.02	5.78	4.87	4.37	4.04	3.81	3.64	3.51	3.40	3.31	3.03	2.88	2.79	2.72	2.64	2.55	2.48	2.37
22	.10	2.95	2.56	2.35	2.22	2.13	2.06	2.01	1.97	1.93	1.90	1.81	1.76	1.73	1.70	1.67	1.64	1.61	1.57
	.05	4.30	3.44	3.05	2.82	2.66	2.55	2.46	2.40	2.34	2.30	2.15	2.07	2.02	1.98	1.94	1.89	1.85	1.79
	.025	5.79	4.38	3.78	3.44	3.22	3.05	2.93	2.84	2.76	2.70	2.50	2.39	2.32	2.27	2.21	2.14	2.09	2.01
	.01	7.95	5.72	4.82	4.31	3.99	3.76	3.59	3.45	3.35	3.26	2.98	2.83	2.73	2.67	2.58	2.50	2.42	2.32
23	.10	2.94	2.55	2.34	2.21	2.11	2.05	1.99	1.95	1.92	1.89	1.80	1.74	1.71	1.69	1.66	1.62	1.59	1.55
	.05	4.28	3.42	3.03	2.80	2.64	2.53	2.44	2.37	2.32	2.27	2.13	2.05	2.00	1.96	1.91	1.86	1.82	1.76
	.025	5.75	4.35	3.75	3.41	3.18	3.02	2.90	2.81	2.73	2.67	2.47	2.36	2.29	2.24	2.18	2.11	2.06	1.98
	.01	7.88	5.66	4.76	4.26	3.94	3.71	3.54	3.41	3.30	3.21	2.93	2.78	2.69	2.62	2.54	2.45	2.37	2.27
24	.10	2.93	2.54	2.33	2.19	2.10	2.04	1.98	1.94	1.91	1.88	1.78	1.73	1.70	1.67	1.64	1.61	1.58	1.54
	.05	4.26	3.40	3.01	2.78	2.62	2.51	2.42	2.36	2.30	2.25	2.11	2.03	1.97	1.94	1.89	1.84	1.80	1.74
	.025	5.72	4.32	3.72	3.38	3.15	2.99	2.87	2.78	2.70	2.64	2.44	2.33	2.26	2.21	2.15	2.08	2.02	1.94
	.01	7.82	5.61	4.72	4.22	3.90	3.67	3.50	3.36	3.26	3.17	2.89	2.74	2.64	2.58	2.49	2.40	2.33	2.22

Denominator Degrees of Freedom	Area in Upper Tail	Numerator Degrees of Freedom																	
		1	2	3	4	5	6	7	8	9	10	15	20	25	30	40	60	100	1000
25	.10	2.92	2.53	2.32	2.18	2.09	2.02	1.97	1.93	1.89	1.87	1.77	1.72	1.68	1.66	1.63	1.59	1.56	1.52
	.05	4.24	3.39	2.99	2.76	2.60	2.49	2.40	2.34	2.28	2.24	2.09	2.01	1.96	1.92	1.87	1.82	1.78	1.72
	.025	5.69	4.29	3.69	3.35	3.13	2.97	2.85	2.75	2.68	2.61	2.41	2.30	2.23	2.18	2.12	2.05	2.00	1.91
	.01	7.77	5.57	4.68	4.18	3.85	3.63	3.46	3.32	3.22	3.13	2.85	2.70	2.60	2.54	2.45	2.36	2.29	2.18
26	.10	2.91	2.52	2.31	2.17	2.08	2.01	1.96	1.92	1.88	1.86	1.76	1.71	1.67	1.65	1.61	1.58	1.55	1.51
	.05	4.23	3.37	2.98	2.74	2.59	2.47	2.39	2.32	2.27	2.22	2.07	1.99	1.94	1.90	1.85	1.80	1.76	1.70
	.025	5.66	4.27	3.67	3.33	3.10	2.94	2.82	2.73	2.65	2.59	2.39	2.28	2.21	2.16	2.09	2.03	1.97	1.89
	.01	7.72	5.53	4.64	4.14	3.82	3.59	3.42	3.29	3.18	3.09	2.81	2.66	2.57	2.50	2.42	2.33	2.25	2.14
27	.10	2.90	2.51	2.30	2.17	2.07	2.00	1.95	1.91	1.87	1.85	1.75	1.70	1.66	1.64	1.60	1.57	1.54	1.50
	.05	4.21	3.35	2.96	2.73	2.57	2.46	2.37	2.31	2.25	2.20	2.06	1.97	1.92	1.88	1.84	1.79	1.74	1.68
	.025	5.63	4.24	3.65	3.31	3.08	2.92	2.80	2.71	2.63	2.57	2.36	2.25	2.18	2.13	2.07	2.00	1.94	1.86
	.01	7.68	5.49	4.60	4.11	3.78	3.56	3.39	3.26	3.15	3.06	2.78	2.63	2.54	2.47	2.38	2.29	2.22	2.11
28	.10	2.89	2.50	2.29	2.16	2.06	2.00	1.94	1.90	1.87	1.84	1.74	1.69	1.65	1.63	1.59	1.56	1.53	1.48
	.05	4.20	3.34	2.95	2.71	2.56	2.45	2.36	2.29	2.24	2.19	2.04	1.96	1.91	1.87	1.82	1.77	1.73	1.66
	.025	5.61	4.22	3.63	3.29	3.06	2.90	2.78	2.69	2.61	2.55	2.34	2.23	2.16	2.11	2.05	1.98	1.92	1.84
	.01	7.64	5.45	4.57	4.07	3.75	3.53	3.36	3.23	3.12	3.03	2.75	2.60	2.51	2.44	2.35	2.26	2.19	2.08
29	.10	2.89	2.50	2.28	2.15	2.06	1.99	1.93	1.89	1.86	1.83	1.73	1.68	1.64	1.62	1.58	1.55	1.52	1.47
	.05	4.18	3.33	2.93	2.70	2.55	2.43	2.35	2.28	2.22	2.18	2.03	1.94	1.89	1.85	1.81	1.75	1.71	1.65
	.025	5.59	4.20	3.61	3.27	3.04	2.88	2.76	2.67	2.59	2.53	2.32	2.21	2.14	2.09	2.03	1.96	1.90	1.82
	.01	7.60	5.42	4.54	4.04	3.73	3.50	3.33	3.20	3.09	3.00	2.73	2.57	2.48	2.41	2.33	2.23	2.16	2.05
30	.10	2.88	2.49	2.28	2.14	2.05	1.98	1.93	1.88	1.85	1.82	1.72	1.67	1.63	1.61	1.57	1.54	1.51	1.46
	.05	4.17	3.32	2.92	2.69	2.53	2.42	2.33	2.27	2.21	2.16	2.01	1.93	1.88	1.84	1.79	1.74	1.70	1.63
	.025	5.57	4.18	3.59	3.25	3.03	2.87	2.75	2.65	2.57	2.51	2.31	2.20	2.12	2.07	2.01	1.94	1.88	1.80
	.01	7.56	5.39	4.51	4.02	3.70	3.47	3.30	3.17	3.07	2.98	2.70	2.55	2.45	2.39	2.30	2.21	2.13	2.02
40	.10	2.84	2.44	2.23	2.09	2.00	1.93	1.87	1.83	1.79	1.76	1.66	1.61	1.57	1.54	1.51	1.47	1.43	1.38
	.05	4.08	3.23	2.84	2.61	2.45	2.34	2.25	2.18	2.12	2.08	1.92	1.84	1.78	1.74	1.69	1.64	1.59	1.52
	.025	5.42	4.05	3.46	3.13	2.90	2.74	2.62	2.53	2.45	2.39	2.18	2.07	1.99	1.94	1.88	1.80	1.74	1.65
	.01	7.31	5.18	4.31	3.83	3.51	3.29	3.12	2.99	2.89	2.80	2.52	2.37	2.27	2.20	2.11	2.02	1.94	1.82
60	.10	2.79	2.39	2.18	2.04	1.95	1.87	1.82	1.77	1.74	1.71	1.60	1.54	1.50	1.48	1.44	1.40	1.36	1.30
	.05	4.00	3.15	2.76	2.53	2.37	2.25	2.17	2.10	2.04	1.99	1.84	1.75	1.69	1.65	1.59	1.53	1.48	1.40
	.025	5.29	3.93	3.34	3.01	2.79	2.63	2.51	2.41	2.33	2.27	2.06	1.94	1.87	1.82	1.74	1.67	1.60	1.49
	.01	7.08	4.98	4.13	3.65	3.34	3.12	2.95	2.82	2.72	2.63	2.35	2.20	2.10	2.03	1.94	1.84	1.75	1.62
100	.10	2.76	2.36	2.14	2.00	1.91	1.83	1.78	1.73	1.69	1.66	1.56	1.49	1.45	1.42	1.38	1.34	1.29	1.22
	.05	3.94	3.09	2.70	2.46	2.31	2.19	2.10	2.03	1.97	1.93	1.77	1.68	1.62	1.57	1.52	1.45	1.39	1.30
	.025	5.18	3.83	3.25	2.92	2.70	2.54	2.42	2.32	2.24	2.18	1.97	1.85	1.77	1.71	1.64	1.56	1.48	1.36
	.01	6.90	4.82	3.98	3.51	3.21	2.99	2.82	2.69	2.59	2.50	2.22	2.07	1.97	1.89	1.80	1.69	1.60	1.45
1000	.10	2.71	2.31	2.09	1.95	1.85	1.78	1.72	1.68	1.64	1.61	1.49	1.43	1.38	1.35	1.30	1.25	1.20	1.08
	.05	3.85	3.00	2.61	2.38	2.22	2.11	2.02	1.95	1.89	1.84	1.68	1.58	1.52	1.47	1.41	1.33	1.26	1.11
	.025	5.04	3.70	3.13	2.80	2.58	2.42	2.30	2.20	2.13	2.06	1.85	1.72	1.64	1.58	1.50	1.41	1.32	1.13
	.01	6.66	4.63	3.80	3.34	3.04	2.82	2.66	2.53	2.43	2.34	2.06	1.90	1.79	1.72	1.61	1.50	1.38	1.16

TABLE 5 BINOMIAL PROBABILITIES

Entries in the table give the probability of x successes in n trials of a binomial experiment, where p is the probability of a success on one trial. For example, with six trials and $p = .05$, the probability of two successes is .0305.

		p								
n	*x*	**.01**	**.02**	**.03**	**.04**	**.05**	**.06**	**.07**	**.08**	**.09**
2	0	.9801	.9604	.9409	.9216	.9025	.8836	.8649	.8464	.8281
	1	.0198	.0392	.0582	.0768	.0950	.1128	.1302	.1472	.1638
	2	.0001	.0004	.0009	.0016	.0025	.0036	.0049	.0064	.0081
3	0	.9703	.9412	.9127	.8847	.8574	.8306	.8044	.7787	.7536
	1	.0294	.0576	.0847	.1106	.1354	.1590	.1816	.2031	.2236
	2	.0003	.0012	.0026	.0046	.0071	.0102	.0137	.0177	.0221
	3	.0000	.0000	.0000	.0001	.0001	.0002	.0003	.0005	.0007
4	0	.9606	.9224	.8853	.8493	.8145	.7807	.7481	.7164	.6857
	1	.0388	.0753	.1095	.1416	.1715	.1993	.2252	.2492	.2713
	2	.0006	.0023	.0051	.0088	.0135	.0191	.0254	.0325	.0402
	3	.0000	.0000	.0001	.0002	.0005	.0008	.0013	.0019	.0027
	4	.0000	.0000	.0000	.0000	.0000	.0000	.0000	.0000	.0001
5	0	.9510	.9039	.8587	.8154	.7738	.7339	.6957	.6591	.6240
	1	.0480	.0922	.1328	.1699	.2036	.2342	.2618	.2866	.3086
	2	.0010	.0038	.0082	.0142	.0214	.0299	.0394	.0498	.0610
	3	.0000	.0001	.0003	.0006	.0011	.0019	.0030	.0043	.0060
	4	.0000	.0000	.0000	.0000	.0000	.0001	.0001	.0002	.0003
	5	.0000	.0000	.0000	.0000	.0000	.0000	.0000	.0000	.0000
6	0	.9415	.8858	.8330	.7828	.7351	.6899	.6470	.6064	.5679
	1	.0571	.1085	.1546	.1957	.2321	.2642	.2922	.3164	.3370
	2	.0014	.0055	.0120	.0204	.0305	.0422	.0550	.0688	.0833
	3	.0000	.0002	.0005	.0011	.0021	.0036	.0055	.0080	.0110
	4	.0000	.0000	.0000	.0000	.0001	.0002	.0003	.0005	.0008
	5	.0000	.0000	.0000	.0000	.0000	.0000	.0000	.0000	.0000
	6	.0000	.0000	.0000	.0000	.0000	.0000	.0000	.0000	.0000
7	0	.9321	.8681	.8080	.7514	.6983	.6485	.6017	.5578	.5168
	1	.0659	.1240	.1749	.2192	.2573	.2897	.3170	.3396	.3578
	2	.0020	.0076	.0162	.0274	.0406	.0555	.0716	.0886	.1061
	3	.0000	.0003	.0008	.0019	.0036	.0059	.0090	.0128	.0175
	4	.0000	.0000	.0000	.0001	.0002	.0004	.0007	.0011	.0017
	5	.0000	.0000	.0000	.0000	.0000	.0000	.0000	.0001	.0001
	6	.0000	.0000	.0000	.0000	.0000	.0000	.0000	.0000	.0000
	7	.0000	.0000	.0000	.0000	.0000	.0000	.0000	.0000	.0000
8	0	.9227	.8508	.7837	.7214	.6634	.6096	.5596	.5132	.4703
	1	.0746	.1389	.1939	.2405	.2793	.3113	.3370	.3570	.3721
	2	.0026	.0099	.0210	.0351	.0515	.0695	.0888	.1087	.1288
	3	.0001	.0004	.0013	.0029	.0054	.0089	.0134	.0189	.0255
	4	.0000	.0000	.0001	.0002	.0004	.0007	.0013	.0021	.0031
	5	.0000	.0000	.0000	.0000	.0000	.0000	.0001	.0001	.0002
	6	.0000	.0000	.0000	.0000	.0000	.0000	.0000	.0000	.0000
	7	.0000	.0000	.0000	.0000	.0000	.0000	.0000	.0000	.0000
	8	.0000	.0000	.0000	.0000	.0000	.0000	.0000	.0000	.0000

TABLE 5 BINOMIAL PROBABILITIES (*Continued*)

		p								
n	*x*	.01	.02	.03	.04	.05	.06	.07	.08	.09
9	0	.9135	.8337	.7602	.6925	.6302	.5730	.5204	.4722	.4279
	1	.0830	.1531	.2116	.2597	.2985	.3292	.3525	.3695	.3809
	2	.0034	.0125	.0262	.0433	.0629	.0840	.1061	.1285	.1507
	3	.0001	.0006	.0019	.0042	.0077	.0125	.0186	.0261	.0348
	4	.0000	.0000	.0001	.0003	.0006	.0012	.0021	.0034	.0052
	5	.0000	.0000	.0000	.0000	.0000	.0001	.0002	.0003	.0005
	6	.0000	.0000	.0000	.0000	.0000	.0000	.0000	.0000	.0000
	7	.0000	.0000	.0000	.0000	.0000	.0000	.0000	.0000	.0000
	8	.0000	.0000	.0000	.0000	.0000	.0000	.0000	.0000	.0000
	9	.0000	.0000	.0000	.0000	.0000	.0000	.0000	.0000	.0000
10	0	.9044	.8171	.7374	.6648	.5987	.5386	.4840	.4344	.3894
	1	.0914	.1667	.2281	.2770	.3151	.3438	.3643	.3777	.3851
	2	.0042	.0153	.0317	.0519	.0746	.0988	.1234	.1478	.1714
	3	.0001	.0008	.0026	.0058	.0105	.0168	.0248	.0343	.0452
	4	.0000	.0000	.0001	.0004	.0010	.0019	.0033	.0052	.0078
	5	.0000	.0000	.0000	.0000	.0001	.0001	.0003	.0005	.0009
	6	.0000	.0000	.0000	.0000	.0000	.0000	.0000	.0000	.0001
	7	.0000	.0000	.0000	.0000	.0000	.0000	.0000	.0000	.0000
	8	.0000	.0000	.0000	.0000	.0000	.0000	.0000	.0000	.0000
	9	.0000	.0000	.0000	.0000	.0000	.0000	.0000	.0000	.0000
	10	.0000	.0000	.0000	.0000	.0000	.0000	.0000	.0000	.0000
12	0	.8864	.7847	.6938	.6127	.5404	.4759	.4186	.3677	.3225
	1	.1074	.1922	.2575	.3064	.3413	.3645	.3781	.3837	.3827
	2	.0060	.0216	.0438	.0702	.0988	.1280	.1565	.1835	.2082
	3	.0002	.0015	.0045	.0098	.0173	.0272	.0393	.0532	.0686
	4	.0000	.0001	.0003	.0009	.0021	.0039	.0067	.0104	.0153
	5	.0000	.0000	.0000	.0001	.0002	.0004	.0008	.0014	.0024
	6	.0000	.0000	.0000	.0000	.0000	.0000	.0001	.0001	.0003
	7	.0000	.0000	.0000	.0000	.0000	.0000	.0000	.0000	.0000
	8	.0000	.0000	.0000	.0000	.0000	.0000	.0000	.0000	.0000
	9	.0000	.0000	.0000	.0000	.0000	.0000	.0000	.0000	.0000
	10	.0000	.0000	.0000	.0000	.0000	.0000	.0000	.0000	.0000
	11	.0000	.0000	.0000	.0000	.0000	.0000	.0000	.0000	.0000
	12	.0000	.0000	.0000	.0000	.0000	.0000	.0000	.0000	.0000
15	0	.8601	.7386	.6333	.5421	.4633	.3953	.3367	.2863	.2430
	1	.1303	.2261	.2938	.3388	.3658	.3785	.3801	.3734	.3605
	2	.0092	.0323	.0636	.0988	.1348	.1691	.2003	.2273	.2496
	3	.0004	.0029	.0085	.0178	.0307	.0468	.0653	.0857	.1070
	4	.0000	.0002	.0008	.0022	.0049	.0090	.0148	.0223	.0317
	5	.0000	.0000	.0001	.0002	.0006	.0013	.0024	.0043	.0069
	6	.0000	.0000	.0000	.0000	.0000	.0001	.0003	.0006	.0011
	7	.0000	.0000	.0000	.0000	.0000	.0000	.0000	.0001	.0001
	8	.0000	.0000	.0000	.0000	.0000	.0000	.0000	.0000	.0000
	9	.0000	.0000	.0000	.0000	.0000	.0000	.0000	.0000	.0000
	10	.0000	.0000	.0000	.0000	.0000	.0000	.0000	.0000	.0000
	11	.0000	.0000	.0000	.0000	.0000	.0000	.0000	.0000	.0000
	12	.0000	.0000	.0000	.0000	.0000	.0000	.0000	.0000	.0000
	13	.0000	.0000	.0000	.0000	.0000	.0000	.0000	.0000	.0000
	14	.0000	.0000	.0000	.0000	.0000	.0000	.0000	.0000	.0000
	15	.0000	.0000	.0000	.0000	.0000	.0000	.0000	.0000	.0000

TABLE 5 BINOMIAL PROBABILITIES (*Continued*)

		p								
n	*x*	.01	.02	.03	.04	.05	.06	.07	.08	.09
18	0	.8345	.6951	.5780	.4796	.3972	.3283	.2708	.2229	.1831
	1	.1517	.2554	.3217	.3597	.3763	.3772	.3669	.3489	.3260
	2	.0130	.0443	.0846	.1274	.1683	.2047	.2348	.2579	.2741
	3	.0007	.0048	.0140	.0283	.0473	.0697	.0942	.1196	.1446
	4	.0000	.0004	.0016	.0044	.0093	.0167	.0266	.0390	.0536
	5	.0000	.0000	.0001	.0005	.0014	.0030	.0056	.0095	.0148
	6	.0000	.0000	.0000	.0000	.0002	.0004	.0009	.0018	.0032
	7	.0000	.0000	.0000	.0000	.0000	.0000	.0001	.0003	.0005
	8	.0000	.0000	.0000	.0000	.0000	.0000	.0000	.0000	.0001
	9	.0000	.0000	.0000	.0000	.0000	.0000	.0000	.0000	.0000
	10	.0000	.0000	.0000	.0000	.0000	.0000	.0000	.0000	.0000
	11	.0000	.0000	.0000	.0000	.0000	.0000	.0000	.0000	.0000
	12	.0000	.0000	.0000	.0000	.0000	.0000	.0000	.0000	.0000
	13	.0000	.0000	.0000	.0000	.0000	.0000	.0000	.0000	.0000
	14	.0000	.0000	.0000	.0000	.0000	.0000	.0000	.0000	.0000
	15	.0000	.0000	.0000	.0000	.0000	.0000	.0000	.0000	.0000
	16	.0000	.0000	.0000	.0000	.0000	.0000	.0000	.0000	.0000
	17	.0000	.0000	.0000	.0000	.0000	.0000	.0000	.0000	.0000
	18	.0000	.0000	.0000	.0000	.0000	.0000	.0000	.0000	.0000
20	0	.8179	.6676	.5438	.4420	.3585	.2901	.2342	.1887	.1516
	1	.1652	.2725	.3364	.3683	.3774	.3703	.3526	.3282	.3000
	2	.0159	.0528	.0988	.1458	.1887	.2246	.2521	.2711	.2818
	3	.0010	.0065	.0183	.0364	.0596	.0860	.1139	.1414	.1672
	4	.0000	.0006	.0024	.0065	.0133	.0233	.0364	.0523	.0703
	5	.0000	.0000	.0002	.0009	.0022	.0048	.0088	.0145	.0222
	6	.0000	.0000	.0000	.0001	.0003	.0008	.0017	.0032	.0055
	7	.0000	.0000	.0000	.0000	.0000	.0001	.0002	.0005	.0011
	8	.0000	.0000	.0000	.0000	.0000	.0000	.0000	.0001	.0002
	9	.0000	.0000	.0000	.0000	.0000	.0000	.0000	.0000	.0000
	10	.0000	.0000	.0000	.0000	.0000	.0000	.0000	.0000	.0000
	11	.0000	.0000	.0000	.0000	.0000	.0000	.0000	.0000	.0000
	12	.0000	.0000	.0000	.0000	.0000	.0000	.0000	.0000	.0000
	13	.0000	.0000	.0000	.0000	.0000	.0000	.0000	.0000	.0000
	14	.0000	.0000	.0000	.0000	.0000	.0000	.0000	.0000	.0000
	15	.0000	.0000	.0000	.0000	.0000	.0000	.0000	.0000	.0000
	16	.0000	.0000	.0000	.0000	.0000	.0000	.0000	.0000	.0000
	17	.0000	.0000	.0000	.0000	.0000	.0000	.0000	.0000	.0000
	18	.0000	.0000	.0000	.0000	.0000	.0000	.0000	.0000	.0000
	19	.0000	.0000	.0000	.0000	.0000	.0000	.0000	.0000	.0000
	20	.0000	.0000	.0000	.0000	.0000	.0000	.0000	.0000	.0000

TABLE 5 BINOMIAL PROBABILITIES (*Continued*)

		p								
n	*x*	.10	.15	.20	.25	.30	.35	.40	.45	.50
2	0	.8100	.7225	.6400	.5625	.4900	.4225	.3600	.3025	.2500
	1	.1800	.2550	.3200	.3750	.4200	.4550	.4800	.4950	.5000
	2	.0100	.0225	.0400	.0625	.0900	.1225	.1600	.2025	.2500
3	0	.7290	.6141	.5120	.4219	.3430	.2746	.2160	.1664	.1250
	1	.2430	.3251	.3840	.4219	.4410	.4436	.4320	.4084	.3750
	2	.0270	.0574	.0960	.1406	.1890	.2389	.2880	.3341	.3750
	3	.0010	.0034	.0080	.0156	.0270	.0429	.0640	.0911	.1250
4	0	.6561	.5220	.4096	.3164	.2401	.1785	.1296	.0915	.0625
	1	.2916	.3685	.4096	.4219	.4116	.3845	.3456	.2995	.2500
	2	.0486	.0975	.1536	.2109	.2646	.3105	.3456	.3675	.3750
	3	.0036	.0115	.0256	.0469	.0756	.1115	.1536	.2005	.2500
	4	.0001	.0005	.0016	.0039	.0081	.0150	.0256	.0410	.0625
5	0	.5905	.4437	.3277	.2373	.1681	.1160	.0778	.0503	.0312
	1	.3280	.3915	.4096	.3955	.3602	.3124	.2592	.2059	.1562
	2	.0729	.1382	.2048	.2637	.3087	.3364	.3456	.3369	.3125
	3	.0081	.0244	.0512	.0879	.1323	.1811	.2304	.2757	.3125
	4	.0004	.0022	.0064	.0146	.0284	.0488	.0768	.1128	.1562
	5	.0000	.0001	.0003	.0010	.0024	.0053	.0102	.0185	.0312
6	0	.5314	.3771	.2621	.1780	.1176	.0754	.0467	.0277	.0156
	1	.3543	.3993	.3932	.3560	.3025	.2437	.1866	.1359	.0938
	2	.0984	.1762	.2458	.2966	.3241	.3280	.3110	.2780	.2344
	3	.0146	.0415	.0819	.1318	.1852	.2355	.2765	.3032	.3125
	4	.0012	.0055	.0154	.0330	.0595	.0951	.1382	.1861	.2344
	5	.0001	.0004	.0015	.0044	.0102	.0205	.0369	.0609	.0938
	6	.0000	.0000	.0001	.0002	.0007	.0018	.0041	.0083	.0156
7	0	.4783	.3206	.2097	.1335	.0824	.0490	.0280	.0152	.0078
	1	.3720	.3960	.3670	.3115	.2471	.1848	.1306	.0872	.0547
	2	.1240	.2097	.2753	.3115	.3177	.2985	.2613	.2140	.1641
	3	.0230	.0617	.1147	.1730	.2269	.2679	.2903	.2918	.2734
	4	.0026	.0109	.0287	.0577	.0972	.1442	.1935	.2388	.2734
	5	.0002	.0012	.0043	.0115	.0250	.0466	.0774	.1172	.1641
	6	.0000	.0001	.0004	.0013	.0036	.0084	.0172	.0320	.0547
	7	.0000	.0000	.0000	.0001	.0002	.0006	.0016	.0037	.0078
8	0	.4305	.2725	.1678	.1001	.0576	.0319	.0168	.0084	.0039
	1	.3826	.3847	.3355	.2670	.1977	.1373	.0896	.0548	.0312
	2	.1488	.2376	.2936	.3115	.2965	.2587	.2090	.1569	.1094
	3	.0331	.0839	.1468	.2076	.2541	.2786	.2787	.2568	.2188
	4	.0046	.0185	.0459	.0865	.1361	.1875	.2322	.2627	.2734
	5	.0004	.0026	.0092	.0231	.0467	.0808	.1239	.1719	.2188
	6	.0000	.0002	.0011	.0038	.0100	.0217	.0413	.0703	.1094
	7	.0000	.0000	.0001	.0004	.0012	.0033	.0079	.0164	.0313
	8	.0000	.0000	.0000	.0000	.0001	.0002	.0007	.0017	.0039

TABLE 5 BINOMIAL PROBABILITIES (*Continued*)

		p								
n	x	.10	.15	.20	.25	.30	.35	.40	.45	.50
9	0	.3874	.2316	.1342	.0751	.0404	.0207	.0101	.0046	.0020
	1	.3874	.3679	.3020	.2253	.1556	.1004	.0605	.0339	.0176
	2	.1722	.2597	.3020	.3003	.2668	.2162	.1612	.1110	.0703
	3	.0446	.1069	.1762	.2336	.2668	.2716	.2508	.2119	.1641
	4	.0074	.0283	.0661	.1168	.1715	.2194	.2508	.2600	.2461
	5	.0008	.0050	.0165	.0389	.0735	.1181	.1672	.2128	.2461
	6	.0001	.0006	.0028	.0087	.0210	.0424	.0743	.1160	.1641
	7	.0000	.0000	.0003	.0012	.0039	.0098	.0212	.0407	.0703
	8	.0000	.0000	.0000	.0001	.0004	.0013	.0035	.0083	.0176
	9	.0000	.0000	.0000	.0000	.0000	.0001	.0003	.0008	.0020
10	0	.3487	.1969	.1074	.0563	.0282	.0135	.0060	.0025	.0010
	1	.3874	.3474	.2684	.1877	.1211	.0725	.0403	.0207	.0098
	2	.1937	.2759	.3020	.2816	.2335	.1757	.1209	.0763	.0439
	3	.0574	.1298	.2013	.2503	.2668	.2522	.2150	.1665	.1172
	4	.0112	.0401	.0881	.1460	.2001	.2377	.2508	.2384	.2051
	5	.0015	.0085	.0264	.0584	.1029	.1536	.2007	.2340	.2461
	6	.0001	.0012	.0055	.0162	.0368	.0689	.1115	.1596	.2051
	7	.0000	.0001	.0008	.0031	.0090	.0212	.0425	.0746	.1172
	8	.0000	.0000	.0001	.0004	.0014	.0043	.0106	.0229	.0439
	9	.0000	.0000	.0000	.0000	.0001	.0005	.0016	.0042	.0098
	10	.0000	.0000	.0000	.0000	.0000	.0000	.0001	.0003	.0010
12	0	.2824	.1422	.0687	.0317	.0138	.0057	.0022	.0008	.0002
	1	.3766	.3012	.2062	.1267	.0712	.0368	.0174	.0075	.0029
	2	.2301	.2924	.2835	.2323	.1678	.1088	.0639	.0339	.0161
	3	.0853	.1720	.2362	.2581	.2397	.1954	.1419	.0923	.0537
	4	.0213	.0683	.1329	.1936	.2311	.2367	.2128	.1700	.1208
	5	.0038	.0193	.0532	.1032	.1585	.2039	.2270	.2225	.1934
	6	.0005	.0040	.0155	.0401	.0792	.1281	.1766	.2124	.2256
	7	.0000	.0006	.0033	.0115	.0291	.0591	.1009	.1489	.1934
	8	.0000	.0001	.0005	.0024	.0078	.0199	.0420	.0762	.1208
	9	.0000	.0000	.0001	.0004	.0015	.0048	.0125	.0277	.0537
	10	.0000	.0000	.0000	.0000	.0002	.0008	.0025	.0068	.0161
	11	.0000	.0000	.0000	.0000	.0000	.0001	.0003	.0010	.0029
	12	.0000	.0000	.0000	.0000	.0000	.0000	.0000	.0001	.0002
15	0	.2059	.0874	.0352	.0134	.0047	.0016	.0005	.0001	.0000
	1	.3432	.2312	.1319	.0668	.0305	.0126	.0047	.0016	.0005
	2	.2669	.2856	.2309	.1559	.0916	.0476	.0219	.0090	.0032
	3	.1285	.2184	.2501	.2252	.1700	.1110	.0634	.0318	.0139
	4	.0428	.1156	.1876	.2252	.2186	.1792	.1268	.0780	.0417
	5	.0105	.0449	.1032	.1651	.2061	.2123	.1859	.1404	.0916
	6	.0019	.0132	.0430	.0917	.1472	.1906	.2066	.1914	.1527
	7	.0003	.0030	.0138	.0393	.0811	.1319	.1771	.2013	.1964
	8	.0000	.0005	.0035	.0131	.0348	.0710	.1181	.1647	.1964
	9	.0000	.0001	.0007	.0034	.0016	.0298	.0612	.1048	.1527
	10	.0000	.0000	.0001	.0007	.0030	.0096	.0245	.0515	.0916
	11	.0000	.0000	.0000	.0001	.0006	.0024	.0074	.0191	.0417
	12	.0000	.0000	.0000	.0000	.0001	.0004	.0016	.0052	.0139
	13	.0000	.0000	.0000	.0000	.0000	.0001	.0003	.0010	.0032
	14	.0000	.0000	.0000	.0000	.0000	.0000	.0000	.0001	.0005
	15	.0000	.0000	.0000	.0000	.0000	.0000	.0000	.0000	.0000

TABLE 5 BINOMIAL PROBABILITIES (*Continued*)

		p								
n	*x*	.10	.15	.20	.25	.30	.35	.40	.45	.50
18	0	.1501	.0536	.0180	.0056	.0016	.0004	.0001	.0000	.0000
	1	.3002	.1704	.0811	.0338	.0126	.0042	.0012	.0003	.0001
	2	.2835	.2556	.1723	.0958	.0458	.0190	.0069	.0022	.0006
	3	.1680	.2406	.2297	.1704	.1046	.0547	.0246	.0095	.0031
	4	.0700	.1592	.2153	.2130	.1681	.1104	.0614	.0291	.0117
	5	.0218	.0787	.1507	.1988	.2017	.1664	.1146	.0666	.0327
	6	.0052	.0301	.0816	.1436	.1873	.1941	.1655	.1181	.0708
	7	.0010	.0091	.0350	.0820	.1376	.1792	.1892	.1657	.1214
	8	.0002	.0022	.0120	.0376	.0811	.1327	.1734	.1864	.1669
	9	.0000	.0004	.0033	.0139	.0386	.0794	.1284	.1694	.1855
	10	.0000	.0001	.0008	.0042	.0149	.0385	.0771	.1248	.1669
	11	.0000	.0000	.0001	.0010	.0046	.0151	.0374	.0742	.1214
	12	.0000	.0000	.0000	.0002	.0012	.0047	.0145	.0354	.0708
	13	.0000	.0000	.0000	.0000	.0002	.0012	.0045	.0134	.0327
	14	.0000	.0000	.0000	.0000	.0000	.0002	.0011	.0039	.0117
	15	.0000	.0000	.0000	.0000	.0000	.0000	.0002	.0009	.0031
	16	.0000	.0000	.0000	.0000	.0000	.0000	.0000	.0001	.0006
	17	.0000	.0000	.0000	.0000	.0000	.0000	.0000	.0000	.0001
	18	.0000	.0000	.0000	.0000	.0000	.0000	.0000	.0000	.0000
20	0	.1216	.0388	.0115	.0032	.0008	.0002	.0000	.0000	.0000
	1	.2702	.1368	.0576	.0211	.0068	.0020	.0005	.0001	.0000
	2	.2852	.2293	.1369	.0669	.0278	.0100	.0031	.0008	.0002
	3	.1901	.2428	.2054	.1339	.0716	.0323	.0123	.0040	.0011
	4	.0898	.1821	.2182	.1897	.1304	.0738	.0350	.0139	.0046
	5	.0319	.1028	.1746	.2023	.1789	.1272	.0746	.0365	.0148
	6	.0089	.0454	.1091	.1686	.1916	.1712	.1244	.0746	.0370
	7	.0020	.0160	.0545	.1124	.1643	.1844	.1659	.1221	.0739
	8	.0004	.0046	.0222	.0609	.1144	.1614	.1797	.1623	.1201
	9	.0001	.0011	.0074	.0271	.0654	.1158	.1597	.1771	.1602
	10	.0000	.0002	.0020	.0099	.0308	.0686	.1171	.1593	.1762
	11	.0000	.0000	.0005	.0030	.0120	.0336	.0710	.1185	.1602
	12	.0000	.0000	.0001	.0008	.0039	.0136	.0355	.0727	.1201
	13	.0000	.0000	.0000	.0002	.0010	.0045	.0146	.0366	.0739
	14	.0000	.0000	.0000	.0000	.0002	.0012	.0049	.0150	.0370
	15	.0000	.0000	.0000	.0000	.0000	.0003	.0013	.0049	.0148
	16	.0000	.0000	.0000	.0000	.0000	.0000	.0003	.0013	.0046
	17	.0000	.0000	.0000	.0000	.0000	.0000	.0000	.0002	.0011
	18	.0000	.0000	.0000	.0000	.0000	.0000	.0000	.0000	.0002
	19	.0000	.0000	.0000	.0000	.0000	.0000	.0000	.0000	.0000
	20	.0000	.0000	.0000	.0000	.0000	.0000	.0000	.0000	.0000

TABLE 5 BINOMIAL PROBABILITIES (*Continued*)

		p								
n	*x*	**.55**	**.60**	**.65**	**.70**	**.75**	**.80**	**.85**	**.90**	**.95**
2	0	.2025	.1600	.1225	.0900	.0625	.0400	.0225	.0100	.0025
	1	.4950	.4800	.4550	.4200	.3750	.3200	.2550	.1800	.0950
	2	.3025	.3600	.4225	.4900	.5625	.6400	.7225	.8100	.9025
3	0	.0911	.0640	.0429	.0270	.0156	.0080	.0034	.0010	.0001
	1	.3341	.2880	.2389	.1890	.1406	.0960	.0574	.0270	.0071
	2	.4084	.4320	.4436	.4410	.4219	.3840	.3251	.2430	.1354
	3	.1664	.2160	.2746	.3430	.4219	.5120	.6141	.7290	.8574
4	0	.0410	.0256	.0150	.0081	.0039	.0016	.0005	.0001	.0000
	1	.2005	.1536	.1115	.0756	.0469	.0256	.0115	.0036	.0005
	2	.3675	.3456	.3105	.2646	.2109	.1536	.0975	.0486	.0135
	3	.2995	.3456	.3845	.4116	.4219	.4096	.3685	.2916	.1715
	4	.0915	.1296	.1785	.2401	.3164	.4096	.5220	.6561	.8145
5	0	.0185	.0102	.0053	.0024	.0010	.0003	.0001	.0000	.0000
	1	.1128	.0768	.0488	.0284	.0146	.0064	.0022	.0005	.0000
	2	.2757	.2304	.1811	.1323	.0879	.0512	.0244	.0081	.0011
	3	.3369	.3456	.3364	.3087	.2637	.2048	.1382	.0729	.0214
	4	.2059	.2592	.3124	.3601	.3955	.4096	.3915	.3281	.2036
	5	.0503	.0778	.1160	.1681	.2373	.3277	.4437	.5905	.7738
6	0	.0083	.0041	.0018	.0007	.0002	.0001	.0000	.0000	.0000
	1	.0609	.0369	.0205	.0102	.0044	.0015	.0004	.0001	.0000
	2	.1861	.1382	.0951	.0595	.0330	.0154	.0055	.0012	.0001
	3	.3032	.2765	.2355	.1852	.1318	.0819	.0415	.0146	.0021
	4	.2780	.3110	.3280	.3241	.2966	.2458	.1762	.0984	.0305
	5	.1359	.1866	.2437	.3025	.3560	.3932	.3993	.3543	.2321
	6	.0277	.0467	.0754	.1176	.1780	.2621	.3771	.5314	.7351
7	0	.0037	.0016	.0006	.0002	.0001	.0000	.0000	.0000	.0000
	1	.0320	.0172	.0084	.0036	.0013	.0004	.0001	.0000	.0000
	2	.1172	.0774	.0466	.0250	.0115	.0043	.0012	.0002	.0000
	3	.2388	.1935	.1442	.0972	.0577	.0287	.0109	.0026	.0002
	4	.2918	.2903	.2679	.2269	.1730	.1147	.0617	.0230	.0036
	5	.2140	.2613	.2985	.3177	.3115	.2753	.2097	.1240	.0406
	6	.0872	.1306	.1848	.2471	.3115	.3670	.3960	.3720	.2573
	7	.0152	.0280	.0490	.0824	.1335	.2097	.3206	.4783	.6983
8	0	.0017	.0007	.0002	.0001	.0000	.0000	.0000	.0000	.0000
	1	.0164	.0079	.0033	.0012	.0004	.0001	.0000	.0000	.0000
	2	.0703	.0413	.0217	.0100	.0038	.0011	.0002	.0000	.0000
	3	.1719	.1239	.0808	.0467	.0231	.0092	.0026	.0004	.0000
	4	.2627	.2322	.1875	.1361	.0865	.0459	.0185	.0046	.0004
	5	.2568	.2787	.2786	.2541	.2076	.1468	.0839	.0331	.0054
	6	.1569	.2090	.2587	.2965	.3115	.2936	.2376	.1488	.0515
	7	.0548	.0896	.1373	.1977	.2670	.3355	.3847	.3826	.2793
	8	.0084	.0168	.0319	.0576	.1001	.1678	.2725	.4305	.6634

TABLE 5 BINOMIAL PROBABILITIES (*Continued*)

		p								
n	*x*	**.55**	**.60**	**.65**	**.70**	**.75**	**.80**	**.85**	**.90**	**.95**
9	0	.0008	.0003	.0001	.0000	.0000	.0000	.0000	.0000	.0000
	1	.0083	.0035	.0013	.0004	.0001	.0000	.0000	.0000	.0000
	2	.0407	.0212	.0098	.0039	.0012	.0003	.0000	.0000	.0000
	3	.1160	.0743	.0424	.0210	.0087	.0028	.0006	.0001	.0000
	4	.2128	.1672	.1181	.0735	.0389	.0165	.0050	.0008	.0000
	5	.2600	.2508	.2194	.1715	.1168	.0661	.0283	.0074	.0006
	6	.2119	.2508	.2716	.2668	.2336	.1762	.1069	.0446	.0077
	7	.1110	.1612	.2162	.2668	.3003	.3020	.2597	.1722	.0629
	8	.0339	.0605	.1004	.1556	.2253	.3020	.3679	.3874	.2985
	9	.0046	.0101	.0207	.0404	.0751	.1342	.2316	.3874	.6302
10	0	.0003	.0001	.0000	.0000	.0000	.0000	.0000	.0000	.0000
	1	.0042	.0016	.0005	.0001	.0000	.0000	.0000	.0000	.0000
	2	.0229	.0106	.0043	.0014	.0004	.0001	.0000	.0000	.0000
	3	.0746	.0425	.0212	.0090	.0031	.0008	.0001	.0000	.0000
	4	.1596	.1115	.0689	.0368	.0162	.0055	.0012	.0001	.0000
	5	.2340	.2007	.1536	.1029	.0584	.0264	.0085	.0015	.0001
	6	.2384	.2508	.2377	.2001	.1460	.0881	.0401	.0112	.0010
	7	.1665	.2150	.2522	.2668	.2503	.2013	.1298	.0574	.0105
	8	.0763	.1209	.1757	.2335	.2816	.3020	.2759	.1937	.0746
	9	.0207	.0403	.0725	.1211	.1877	.2684	.3474	.3874	.3151
	10	.0025	.0060	.0135	.0282	.0563	.1074	.1969	.3487	.5987
12	0	.0001	.0000	.0000	.0000	.0000	.0000	.0000	.0000	.0000
	1	.0010	.0003	.0001	.0000	.0000	.0000	.0000	.0000	.0000
	2	.0068	.0025	.0008	.0002	.0000	.0000	.0000	.0000	.0000
	3	.0277	.0125	.0048	.0015	.0004	.0001	.0000	.0000	.0000
	4	.0762	.0420	.0199	.0078	.0024	.0005	.0001	.0000	.0000
	5	.1489	.1009	.0591	.0291	.0115	.0033	.0006	.0000	.0000
	6	.2124	.1766	.1281	.0792	.0401	.0155	.0040	.0005	.0000
	7	.2225	.2270	.2039	.1585	.1032	.0532	.0193	.0038	.0002
	8	.1700	.2128	.2367	.2311	.1936	.1329	.0683	.0213	.0021
	9	.0923	.1419	.1954	.2397	.2581	.2362	.1720	.0852	.0173
	10	.0339	.0639	.1088	.1678	.2323	.2835	.2924	.2301	.0988
	11	.0075	.0174	.0368	.0712	.1267	.2062	.3012	.3766	.3413
	12	.0008	.0022	.0057	.0138	.0317	.0687	.1422	.2824	.5404
15	0	.0000	.0000	.0000	.0000	.0000	.0000	.0000	.0000	.0000
	1	.0001	.0000	.0000	.0000	.0000	.0000	.0000	.0000	.0000
	2	.0010	.0003	.0001	.0000	.0000	.0000	.0000	.0000	.0000
	3	.0052	.0016	.0004	.0001	.0000	.0000	.0000	.0000	.0000
	4	.0191	.0074	.0024	.0006	.0001	.0000	.0000	.0000	.0000
	5	.0515	.0245	.0096	.0030	.0007	.0001	.0000	.0000	.0000
	6	.1048	.0612	.0298	.0116	.0034	.0007	.0001	.0000	.0000
	7	.1647	.1181	.0710	.0348	.0131	.0035	.0005	.0000	.0000
	8	.2013	.1771	.1319	.0811	.0393	.0138	.0030	.0003	.0000
	9	.1914	.2066	.1906	.1472	.0917	.0430	.0132	.0019	.0000
	10	.1404	.1859	.2123	.2061	.1651	.1032	.0449	.0105	.0006
	11	.0780	.1268	.1792	.2186	.2252	.1876	.1156	.0428	.0049

TABLE 5 BINOMIAL PROBABILITIES (*Continued*)

		p								
n	*x*	.55	.60	.65	.70	.75	.80	.85	.90	.95
	12	.0318	.0634	.1110	.1700	.2252	.2501	.2184	.1285	.0307
	13	.0090	.0219	.0476	.0916	.1559	.2309	.2856	.2669	.1348
	14	.0016	.0047	.0126	.0305	.0668	.1319	.2312	.3432	.3658
	15	.0001	.0005	.0016	.0047	.0134	.0352	.0874	.2059	.4633
18	0	.0000	.0000	.0000	.0000	.0000	.0000	.0000	.0000	.0000
	1	.0000	.0000	.0000	.0000	.0000	.0000	.0000	.0000	.0000
	2	.0001	.0000	.0000	.0000	.0000	.0000	.0000	.0000	.0000
	3	.0009	.0002	.0000	.0000	.0000	.0000	.0000	.0000	.0000
	4	.0039	.0011	.0002	.0000	.0000	.0000	.0000	.0000	.0000
	5	.0134	.0045	.0012	.0002	.0000	.0000	.0000	.0000	.0000
	6	.0354	.0145	.0047	.0012	.0002	.0000	.0000	.0000	.0000
	7	.0742	.0374	.0151	.0046	.0010	.0001	.0000	.0000	.0000
	8	.1248	.0771	.0385	.0149	.0042	.0008	.0001	.0000	.0000
	9	.1694	.1284	.0794	.0386	.0139	.0033	.0004	.0000	.0000
	10	.1864	.1734	.1327	.0811	.0376	.0120	.0022	.0002	.0000
	11	.1657	.1892	.1792	.1376	.0820	.0350	.0091	.0010	.0000
	12	.1181	.1655	.1941	.1873	.1436	.0816	.0301	.0052	.0002
	13	.0666	.1146	.1664	.2017	.1988	.1507	.0787	.0218	.0014
	14	.0291	.0614	.1104	.1681	.2130	.2153	.1592	.0700	.0093
	15	.0095	.0246	.0547	.1046	.1704	.2297	.2406	.1680	.0473
	16	.0022	.0069	.0190	.0458	.0958	.1723	.2556	.2835	.1683
	17	.0003	.0012	.0042	.0126	.0338	.0811	.1704	.3002	.3763
	18	.0000	.0001	.0004	.0016	.0056	.0180	.0536	.1501	.3972
20	0	.0000	.0000	.0000	.0000	.0000	.0000	.0000	.0000	.0000
	1	.0000	.0000	.0000	.0000	.0000	.0000	.0000	.0000	.0000
	2	.0000	.0000	.0000	.0000	.0000	.0000	.0000	.0000	.0000
	3	.0002	.0000	.0000	.0000	.0000	.0000	.0000	.0000	.0000
	4	.0013	.0003	.0000	.0000	.0000	.0000	.0000	.0000	.0000
	5	.0049	.0013	.0003	.0000	.0000	.0000	.0000	.0000	.0000
	6	.0150	.0049	.0012	.0002	.0000	.0000	.0000	.0000	.0000
	7	.0366	.0146	.0045	.0010	.0002	.0000	.0000	.0000	.0000
	8	.0727	.0355	.0136	.0039	.0008	.0001	.0000	.0000	.0000
	9	.1185	.0710	.0336	.0120	.0030	.0005	.0000	.0000	.0000
	10	.1593	.1171	.0686	.0308	.0099	.0020	.0002	.0000	.0000
	11	.1771	.1597	.1158	.0654	.0271	.0074	.0011	.0001	.0000
	12	.1623	.1797	.1614	.1144	.0609	.0222	.0046	.0004	.0000
	13	.1221	.1659	.1844	.1643	.1124	.0545	.0160	.0020	.0000
	14	.0746	.1244	.1712	.1916	.1686	.1091	.0454	.0089	.0003
	15	.0365	.0746	.1272	.1789	.2023	.1746	.1028	.0319	.0022
	16	.0139	.0350	.0738	.1304	.1897	.2182	.1821	.0898	.0133
	17	.0040	.0123	.0323	.0716	.1339	.2054	.2428	.1901	.0596
	18	.0008	.0031	.0100	.0278	.0669	.1369	.2293	.2852	.1887
	19	.0001	.0005	.0020	.0068	.0211	.0576	.1368	.2702	.3774
	20	.0000	.0000	.0002	.0008	.0032	.0115	.0388	.1216	.3585

Chapter 4: Descriptive Data Mining

Solutions

2. a.

Row Labels	Count of Cluster ID	Average of StadiumCapacity	Average of Latitude	Average of Longitude	Average of Endowment ($000)	Average of Enrollment
1	15	37,212	35	-90	406,181	10,121
2	21	28,846	40	-81	331,399	24,199
3	15	87,616	32	-93	1,116,701	38,993
4	11	48,549	32	-114	268,646	27,591
5	30	64,044	37	-86	1,088,388	25,718
6	14	43,701	43	-115	759,956	25,970
7	4	50,946	39	-85	5,651,059	15,059
8	7	31,164	29	-85	195,311	38,524
9	9	78,518	41	-86	2,394,620	46,104
10	1	50,000	37	-122	16,502,606	19,945
Grand Total	**127**	**52,945**	**37**	**-93**	**1,087,199**	**27,157**

b. Cluster 3 has the largest average football stadium capacity (87,616). This cluster is a collection of 15 southern schools characterized by a cluster center indicating largest average football stadium capacity, an average endowment over $1 billion, and the second-largest average enrollment.

c. Cluster 10 is a single school (Stanford), which is extreme because of its $16 billion endowment.

d. Between 8 and 17 clusters seem to be reasonable. There are relatively small increases in distance until going from 17 to 16 clusters, which results in an increase of 0.913 distance unit. After that, the next relatively large increases in distance occur when going from 11 to 10 clusters (1.838 units) and going from 8 to 7 clusters (2.735 units). On the dendrogram below, the distance between the two black horizontal lines depicts the marginal increase of 2.735 units when going from 8 to 7 clusters. There is a jump of 0.10 (=8.743 − 8.643) distance units when going from 10 to 9 clusters.

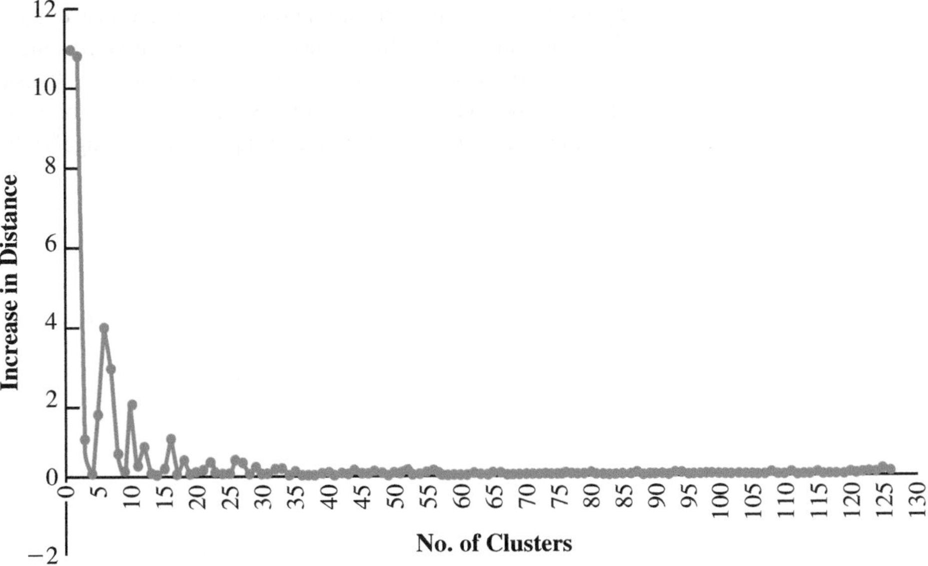

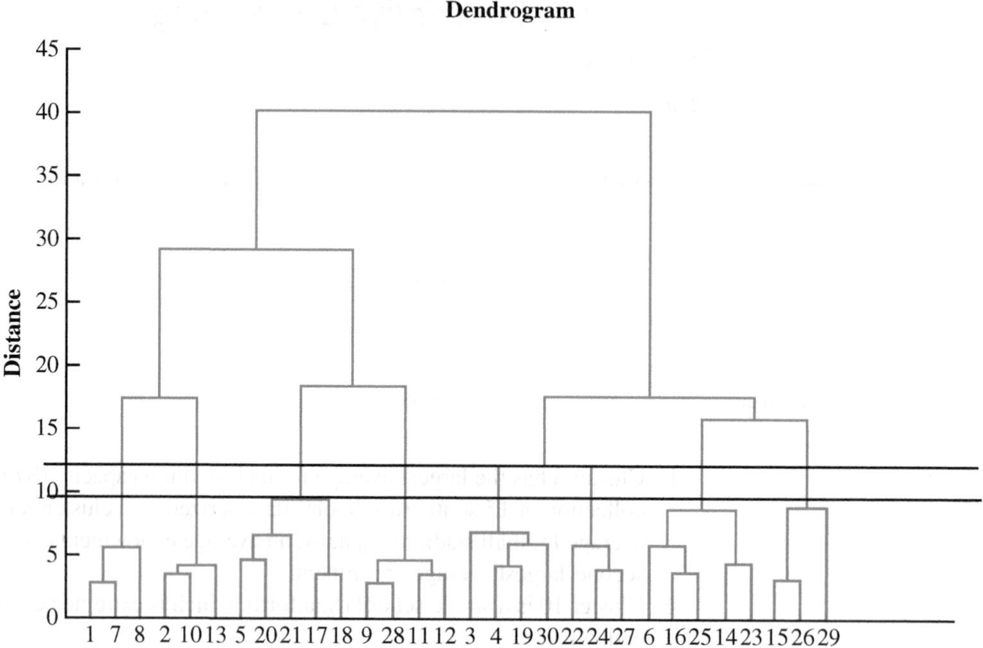

4. Ward's method results in clusters similar to the group average linkage clusters. It results in only one cluster with a single school (Hawaii). There are four clusters different from the group average linkage. Cluster 2 from Ward's method is the Cluster 2 from the group average linkage with the 11 westernmost schools removed. Cluster 7 from Ward's method consists of the 11 westernmost schools from the group average linkage's Cluster 2 plus the four northernmost schools from the group average linkage's Cluster 5 and the singleton Cluster 10 (Minnesota). Cluster 3 from Ward's method consists of the four southernmost schools from the group average linkage's Cluster 5 plus 18 schools from the group average linkage's Cluster 3. Cluster 8 from the Ward's method consists of eight of the northeastern schools in the group average linkage's Cluster 3.

Row Labels	Count of Cluster ID	Min of Latitude	Max of Latitude	Min of Longitude	Max of Longitude
1	7	38.86	41.74	-111.93	-104.76
2	28	38.04	43.04	-88.26	-71.02
3	22	31.81	36.97	-97.51	-80.83
4	14	31.85	39.44	-122.30	-106.44
5	18	29.46	33.21	-98.51	-88.09
6	6	43.61	47.62	-123.11	-116.23
7	16	38.95	44.96	-96.69	-83.62
8	8	35.60	38.04	-80.43	-76.24
9	7	25.78	30.46	-84.28	-80.11
10	1	19.70	19.70	-155.09	-155.09
Grand Total	**127**	**19.70**	**47.62**	**-155.09**	**-71.02**

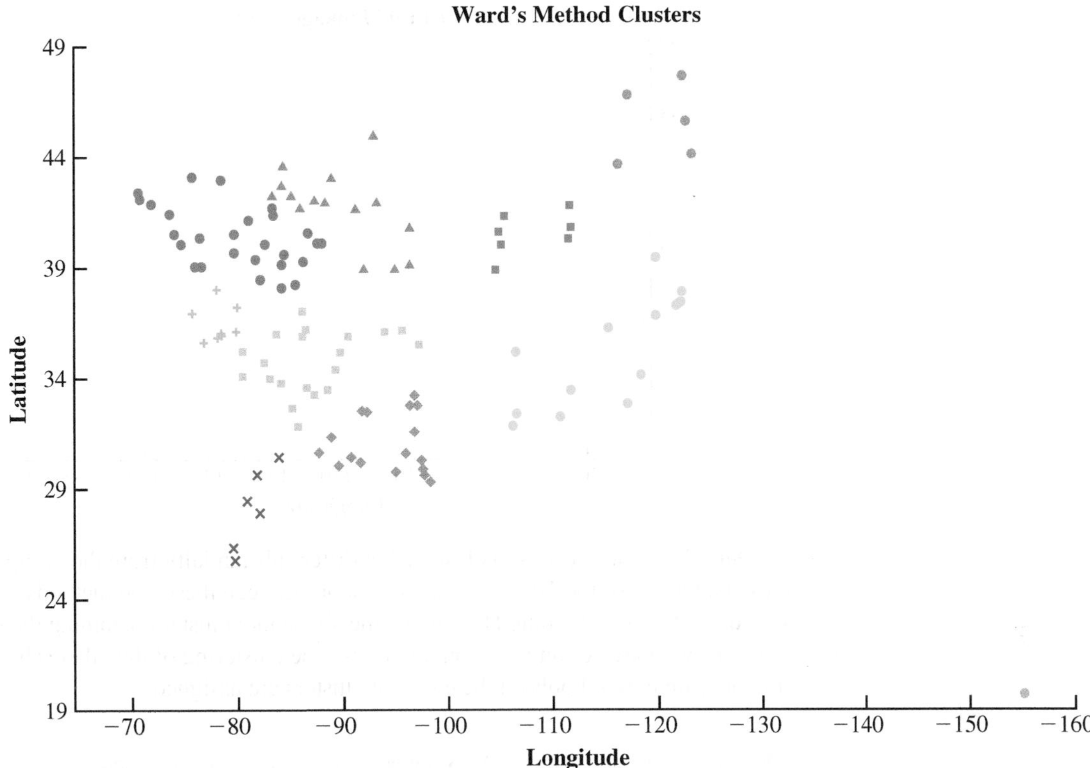

6. Centroid linkage results in clusters similar to group average linkage, sharing six clusters in common. Centroid linkage's Cluster 2 is the group average linkage's Cluster 2 plus the four northernmost schools from the group average linkage's Cluster 5. Centroid linkage's Cluster 3 is the group average linkage's Cluster 3 plus the four southernmost schools from the group average linkage's Cluster 5. Centroid linkage's Cluster 4 is the eight easternmost schools from the group average linkage's Cluster 4. Centroid linkage's Cluster 7 is the six westernmost schools from the group average linkage's Cluster 4.

Row Labels	Count of Cluster ID	Min of Latitude	Max of Latitude	Min of Longitude	Max of Longitude
1	7	38.86	41.74	-111.93	-104.76
2	43	38.04	43.60	-96.69	-71.02
3	30	31.81	38.04	-97.51	-76.24
4	8	31.85	35.11	-118.41	-106.44
5	18	29.46	33.21	-98.51	-88.09
6	6	43.61	47.62	-123.11	-116.23
7	6	36.21	39.44	-122.30	-115.33
8	7	25.78	30.46	-84.28	-80.11
9	1	19.70	19.70	-155.09	-155.09
10	1	44.96	44.96	-93.27	-93.27
Grand Total	**127**	**19.70**	**47.62**	**-155.09**	**-71.02**

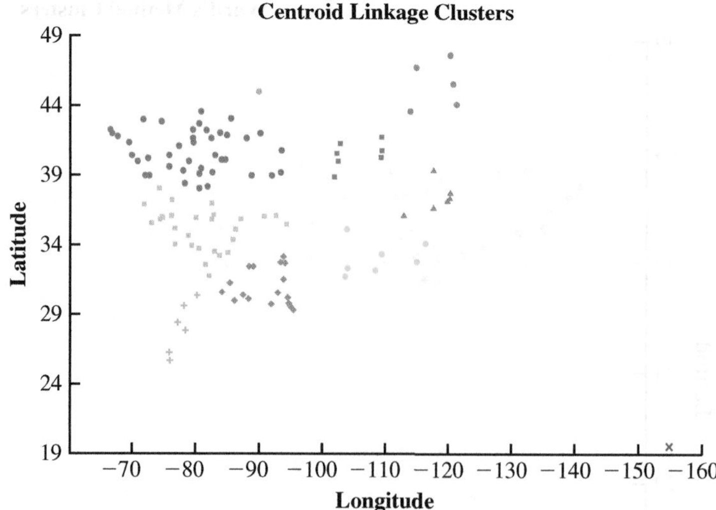

8. McQuitty's method results in clusters that differ substantially from the group average clusters. Only 2 of the 10 clusters are the same between these two methods—the singleton cluster containing Hawaii and the six-school cluster containing the schools in the Northwest are common to both methods. The clustering of the other schools differs primarily on how schools on the edges of clusters are assigned.

Row Labels	Count of Cluster ID	Min of Latitude	Max of Latitude	Min of Longitude	Max of Longitude
1	13	36.21	41.74	-122.30	-104.76
2	35	38.04	43.04	-88.75	-71.02
3	24	33.24	38.04	-90.69	-76.24
4	8	31.85	35.11	-118.41	-106.44
5	4	35.47	36.13	-97.51	-94.16
6	24	27.96	33.21	-98.51	-81.37
7	6	43.61	47.62	-123.11	-116.23
8	9	38.95	44.96	-96.69	-84.78
9	3	25.78	26.37	-80.21	-80.11
10	1	19.70	19.70	-155.09	-155.09
Grand Total	**127**	**19.70**	**47.62**	**-155.09**	**-71.02**

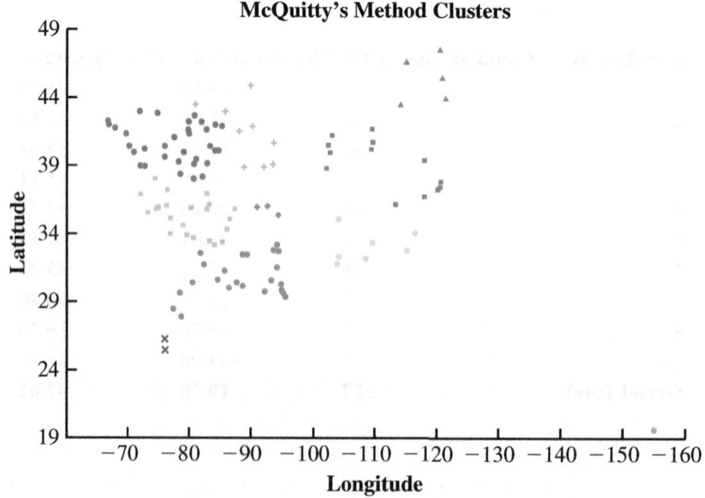

10. The 3-means clustering of the original data set of 127 schools results in Cluster 1 of 46 schools (geographically in the southern United States), Cluster 2 of 55 schools (geographically in the eastern United States), and Cluster 3 of 26 schools (geographically in the western United States). We will call these Regions 1, 2, and 3, respectively.

Cluster Centers

Original coordinates		
Cluster	Latitude	Longitude
Cluster-1	31.9698	-90.442
Cluster-2	39.9859	-83.094
Cluster-3	38.6253	-116.7

Normalized coordinates		
Cluster	Latitude	Longitude
Cluster-1	-0.9573	0.14971
Cluster-2	0.63017	0.65106
Cluster-3	0.36071	-1.6421

Original coordinates			
Distance Between Centers	Cluster-1	Cluster-2	Cluster-3
Cluster-1	0	10.874	27.0901
Cluster-2	10.874	0	33.6348
Cluster-3	27.0901	33.6348	0

Normalized coordinates			
Distance Between Centers	Cluster-1	Cluster-2	Cluster-3
Cluster-1	0	1.66479	2.22438
Cluster-2	1.66479	0	2.30894
Cluster-3	2.22438	2.30894	0

Data Summary

Original coordinates		
Cluster	#Obs	Avg. Dist
Cluster-1	46	6.54151
Cluster-2	55	5.66704
Cluster-3	26	8.58514
Overall	127	6.58119

Normalized coordinates		
Cluster	#Obs	Avg. Dist
Cluster-1	46	0.64086
Cluster-2	55	0.56441
Cluster-3	26	1.04462
Overall	127	0.69041

a. Region 1 consists of southern schools. Separating southern schools into four clusters results in disparate clusters. There is a two-school cluster with large stadium capacities, large endowments and relatively low enrollments; a 25-school cluster with above-average stadium capacities, moderate endowments, and above-average enrollments; an 11-school cluster distinguished by small stadiums and small enrollments; an 8-school cluster with small stadiums, small endowments, and relatively large enrollments; and a 24-school cluster with moderate stadium capacities and moderate endowments.

Row Labels	Count of Cluster ID	Average of StadiumCapacity	Average of Endowment ($000)	Average of Enrollment
1	25	72,896	606,596	29,458
2	11	35,684	447,074	12,264
3	8	27,394	180,691	32,937
4	2	85,812	3,652,206	22,331
Grand Total	**46**	**56,646**	**626,797**	**25,642**

b. Region 2 consists of eastern schools. We split these eastern schools into two clusters: Cluster 1 is characterized by small stadium capacity, small endowments, and moderate enrollments; Cluster 2 contains 29 schools with large stadium capacity, moderate endowments, and large enrollments; and Cluster 3 contains 4 schools with moderate stadium capacity, large endowments, and small enrollments.

Row Labels	Count of Cluster ID	Average of StadiumCapacity	Average of Endowment ($000)	Average of Enrollment
1	22	29,705	465,794	20,596
2	29	66,797	1,352,315	34,649
3	4	56,373	5,987,559	18,082
Grand Total	**55**	**51,202**	**1,334,815**	**27,823**

c. Region 3 consists of western schools. The two clusters of western schools can be characterized as "small" and "big" schools with respect to stadium capacity, endowment, and enrollment.

Row Labels	Count of Cluster ID	Average of StadiumCapacity	Average of Endowment ($000)	Average of Enrollment
1	17	39,043	311,581	23,210
2	9	70,934	3,392,219	38,293
Grand Total	**26**	**50,082**	**1,377,956**	**28,431**

d. The sizes of the clusters vary substantially and do not correspond to feasible conferences. Developing clusters with size constraints is a very difficult optimization problem. As a method to address this, for each region, clusters could be aggregated until reaching a maximum size limit. Upon reaching the maximum size, a cluster would be removed from the data and then the rest of the data would be considered, repeating the aggregation of clusters until a cluster met the maximum size limit again (prompting its removal and repetition of the process).

12. a. Matching coefficient results in three clusters with distinguishing characteristics. Cluster 1 is a mix of males and females, 15 of 17 are married, none have car loans, and 5 of 18 have mortgages. Cluster 2 is all males with car loans, 5 of 6 are married, and 2 of 6 have mortgages. Cluster 3 is all females with car loans, 4 of 7 are married, and 5 of 7 have mortgages.

Row Labels	Count of Cluster ID	Sum of Female	Sum of Married	Sum of Car Loan	Sum of Mortgage
1	17	10	15	0	5
2	6	0	5	6	2
3	7	7	4	7	5
Grand Total	**30**	**17**	**24**	**13**	**12**

b. Jaccard's coefficient results in unbalanced clusters. Cluster 1 has 28 observations and is a mix of males and females, 24 of 28 are married, 12 of 28 have car loans, and 12 of 28 have mortgages. Cluster 2 consists of an unmarried male with no car loan or mortgage. Cluster 3 consists of an unmarried male with a car loan, but no mortgage.

Row Labels	Count of Cluster ID	Sum of Female	Sum of Married	Sum of Car Loan	Sum of Mortgage
1	28	17	24	12	12
2	1	0	0	0	0
3	1	0	0	1	0
Grand Total	**30**	**17**	**24**	**13**	**12**

c. Because Jaccard's coefficient only measures similarity based on "1" values of a binary variable, it is biased toward clustering the attributes coded as "1." In this case, being female, married, and having a car loan or mortgage are attributes it seeks in order to cluster observations. In this case, the matching coefficient is a better choice, as the attributes corresponding to a nonzero value (male, single, and no car loan or mortgage) are equally as helpful in characterizing individuals.

14. Cluster 1 is characterized by low-rated movies that generated little revenue at the box office. This cluster represents half of the movies in the data. Cluster 2 represents moderate-rated movies that generated large box office revenue and contains 15 of the 48 observations. Cluster 3 contains highly rated movies that still generated relatively low box office revenue.

Cluster Centers

Original coordinates		
Cluster	Rating	Box Office (2015 Dollars)
Cluster-1	17.08333333	36.78625
Cluster-2	29.2	162.2546667
Cluster-3	63	50.37222222

Normalized coordinates		
Cluster	Rating	Box Office (2015 Dollars)
Cluster-1	-0.59356616	-0.647117648
Cluster-2	-0.013367708	1.297829632
Cluster-3	1.605122609	-0.436568991

Original coordinates			
Distance Between Centers	Cluster-1	Cluster-2	Cluster-3
Cluster-1	0	126.0521209	47.88443295
Cluster-2	126.0521209	0	116.8765219
Cluster-3	47.88443295	116.8765219	0

Normalized coordinates			
Distance Between Centers	Cluster-1	Cluster-2	Cluster-3
Cluster-1	0	2.029163736	2.208746939
Cluster-2	2.029163736	0	2.371901208
Cluster-3	2.208746939	2.371901208	0

Data Summary

Original coordinates		
Cluster	#Obs	Avg. Dist
Cluster-1	24	23.05251209
Cluster-2	15	32.08746692
Cluster-3	9	25.68957845
Overall	48	26.37038542

Normalized coordinates		
Cluster	#Obs	Avg. Dist
Cluster-1	24	0.572324172
Cluster-2	15	0.744118115
Cluster-3	9	0.71100553
Overall	48	0.652012534

16.

Inputs

Data	
# Transactions in Input Data	2000
# Columns in Input Data	12
# Items in Input Data	12
# Association Rules	15
Minimum Support	200
Minimum Confidence	50.00%

List of Rules

Rule: If all Antecedent items are purchased, then with Confidence percentage Consequent items will also be purchased.

Row ID	Confidence %	Antecedent (A)	Consequent (C)	Support for A	Support for C	Support for A & C	Lift Ratio
1	62.76923077	RetinaDisplay & Stand	Speakers	325	552	204	2.274247492
2	52.30769231	RetinaDisplay & Speakers	Stand	390	482	204	2.170443664
3	57.73480663	RetinaDisplay & 32GB	Speakers	362	552	209	2.09184082
4	52.90456432	Stand	Speakers	482	552	255	1.91683204
5	80	Stand & Speakers	RetinaDisplay	255	846	204	1.891252955
6	51.51515152	Case	Speakers	429	552	221	1.866490097
7	74.11347518	32GB & Speakers	RetinaDisplay	282	846	209	1.752091612
8	70.65217391	Speakers	RetinaDisplay	552	846	390	1.670264159
9	70.62937063	Case	RetinaDisplay	429	846	303	1.669725074
10	67.42738589	Stand	RetinaDisplay	482	846	325	1.594028035
11	66.66666667	Cellular	RetinaDisplay	495	846	330	1.576044129
12	53.58974359	RetinaDisplay & Speakers	32GB	390	689	209	1.555580065
13	51.08695652	Speakers	32GB	552	689	282	1.482950523
14	62.32686981	64GB	RetinaDisplay	361	846	225	1.473448459
15	52.53991292	32GB	RetinaDisplay	689	846	362	1.24207852

a. Antecedent: RetinaDisplay, Stand; Consequent: Speakers. If an iPad with retina display is purchased with a stand, then speakers are also purchased.
b. The support count of this item set is 204, which means that these three items were purchased together 204 times.
c. The confidence of this rule 62.77%, which means of the 325 times that the retina display and a stand were purchased together, speakers were also purchased 204 times.
d. The lift ratio = 2.27, which means that a customer who has purchased a retina display and a stand is 127% more likely than a randomly selected customer to buy speakers.
e. The top 15 rules have many features in common that allow Apple to focus on these collections. For instance, an iPad with retina display is often purchased along with other accessories, including a stand, speakers, cellular service, and a case. An iPad with retina display often is paired with a memory upgrade. A memory upgrade to 32 GB is commonly associated with speakers and/or retina display. Commonly associated accessories include stand and speakers or case and speakers.

18. a. 581 rules have a support count of at least 100 and 50% confidence. A partial list is shown below.

Inputs

Data	
# Transactions in Input Data	1002
# Columns in Input Data	7
# Items in Input Data	21
# Association Rules	581
Minimum Support	100
Minimum Confidence	50.00%

List of Rules

Rule: If all Antecedent items are purchased, then with Confidence percentage Consequent items will also be purchased.

Row ID	Confidence %	Antecedent (A)	Consequent (C)	Support for A	Support for C	Support for A & C	Lift Ratio
1	96.66666667	coke & peroni & pretzels	chicken & gelato	120	140	116	6.918571429
2	82.85714286	chicken & gelato	coke & peroni & pretzels	140	120	116	6.918571429
3	94.30894309	gelato & peroni & pretzels	chicken & coke	123	139	116	6.798385682
4	83.45323741	chicken & coke	gelato & peroni & pretzels	139	123	116	6.798385682
5	97.4789916	chicken & gelato & peroni	coke & pretzels	119	147	116	6.644486566
6	78.91156463	coke & pretzels	chicken & gelato & peroni	147	119	116	6.644486566
7	98.30508475	chicken & coke & peroni	gelato & pretzels	118	151	116	6.523291054
8	76.82119205	gelato & pretzels	chicken & coke & peroni	151	118	116	6.523291054
9	84.29752066	ham & olives & tuna	prosciutto & turkey	121	134	102	6.30344147
10	76.11940299	prosciutto & turkey	ham & olives & tuna	134	121	102	6.30344147
11	85.92592593	chicken & pretzels	coke & gelato & peroni	135	139	116	6.194084732
12	83.45323741	coke & gelato & peroni	chicken & pretzels	139	135	116	6.194084732
13	100	chicken & gelato & pretzels	coke & peroni	116	174	116	5.75862069
14	66.66666667	coke & peroni	chicken & gelato & pretzels	174	116	116	5.75862069
15	90.26548673	prosciutto & tuna & turkey	ham & olives	113	158	102	5.7244315
16	64.55696203	ham & olives	prosciutto & tuna & turkey	158	113	102	5.7244315
17	82.85714286	chicken & gelato	coke & pretzels	140	147	116	5.647813411
18	78.91156463	coke & pretzels	chicken & gelato	147	140	116	5.647813411
19	82.92682927	ham & olives & prosciutto	tuna & turkey	123	150	102	5.539512195
20	68	tuna & turkey	ham & olives & prosciutto	150	123	102	5.539512195
21	83.45323741	chicken & coke	gelato & pretzels	139	151	116	5.537757873
22	76.82119205	gelato & pretzels	chicken & coke	151	139	116	5.537757873
23	99.14529915	chicken & coke & pretzels	gelato & peroni	117	184	116	5.399108138
24	63.04347826	gelato & peroni	chicken & coke & pretzels	184	117	116	5.399108138

b. 10 rules have a support count of at least 250 and 50% confidence. Increasing the minimum support required removes spurious rules resulting from coincidence. The risk of raising the minimum support required is that we cull out meaningful rules that involve uncommon items.

Inputs

Data	
# Transactions in Input Data	1002
# Columns in Input Data	7
# Items in Input Data	21
# Association Rules	10
Minimum Support	250
Minimum Confidence	50.00%

List of Rules

Rule: If all Antecedent items are purchased, then with Confidence percentage Consequent items will also be purchased.

Row ID	Confidence %	Antecedent (A)	Consequent (C)	Support for A	Support for C	Support for A & C	Lift Ratio
1	78.93081761	soda	crackers	318	488	251	1.620669657
2	51.43442623	crackers	soda	488	318	251	1.620669657
3	82.62295082	hummus	peroni	305	600	252	1.379803279
4	80.81761006	soda	peroni	318	600	257	1.349654088
5	75	crackers	peroni	488	600	366	1.2525
6	61	peroni	crackers	600	488	366	1.2525
7	52.67489712	tuna	olives	486	473	256	1.115861457
8	54.12262156	olives	tuna	473	486	256	1.115861457
9	66.58163265	risotto	peroni	392	600	261	1.111913265
10	59.25925926	tuna	peroni	486	600	288	0.98962963

c. Antecedent: hummus; Consequent: peroni. If hummus is purchased, then peroni is also purchased.

d. The support of this rule is 252, meaning that hummus and peroni have been purchased together 252 times.

e. The confidence of this rule is 82.62%, which means that of the 305 times that hummus was purchased, peroni was also purchased 252 times.

f. The lift ratio of this rule is 1.38, which means that a customer purchasing hummus is 38% more likely than a randomly selected customer to purchase hummus.

g. Customers who enjoy snacking on hummus apparently also drink more peroni than do other customers. Perhaps the two products could be displayed near each other or tied together in a promotion or couponing campaign.

Chapter 7: Regression Analysis

Solutions

2. a. The scatter chart with line speed as the independent variable follows:

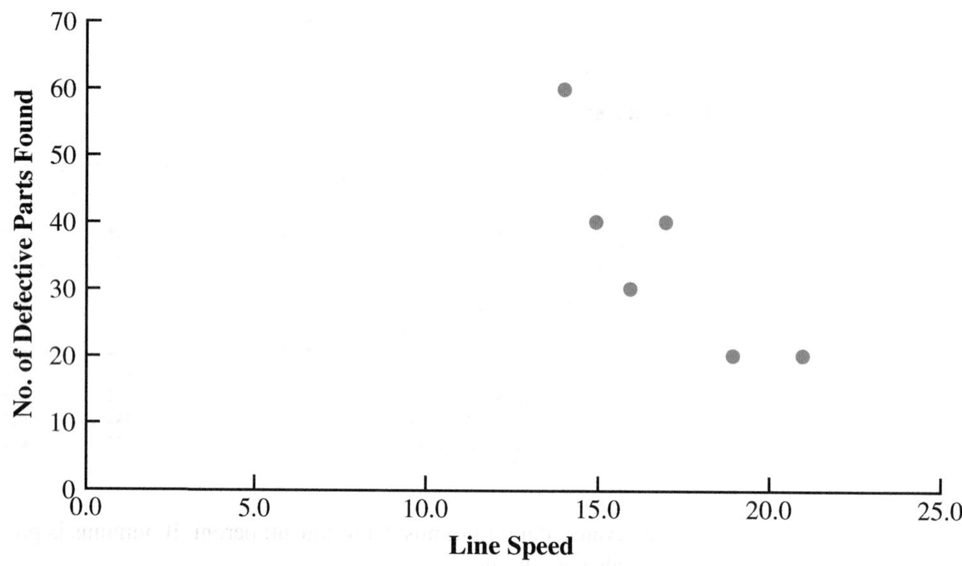

This scatter chart indicates that there may be a negative linear relationship between line speed and number of defective parts found. The number of defective parts found is expected to decrease as the line speed increases, so this scatter chart is consistent with what would be expected.

b. The following Excel output provides the estimated regression equation that could be used to predict the number of defective parts found (y) given the line speed (x):

	A	B	C	D	E	F	G	H	I
1	SUMMARY OUTPUT								
2									
3	*Regression Statistics*								
4	Multiple R	0.859726954							
5	R Square	0.739130435							
6	Adjusted R Square	0.673913043							
7	Standard Error	1.489090764							
8	Observations	6							
9									
10	ANOVA								
11		*df*	*SS*	*MS*	*F*	*Significance F*			
12	Regression	1	25.13043478	25.13043478	11.33333333	0.028134748			
13	Residual	4	8.869565217	2.217391304					
14	Total	5	34						
15									
16		*Coefficients*	*Standard Error*	*t Stat*	*P-value*	*Lower 95%*	*Upper 95%*	*Lower 99.0%*	*Upper 99.0%*
17	Intercept	22.17391304	1.652745896	13.41640786	0.000178521	17.58515479	26.7626713	14.56451414	29.78331195
18	Line Speed	-0.147826087	0.043910891	-3.366501646	0.028134748	-0.269742265	-0.025909908	-0.349995995	0.054343821

The estimated simple linear regression equation is $\hat{y} = 22.1739 - 0.1478x$.

c. First, we check the conditions necessary for valid inference in regression. The Excel plot of the residuals and line speed is as follows:

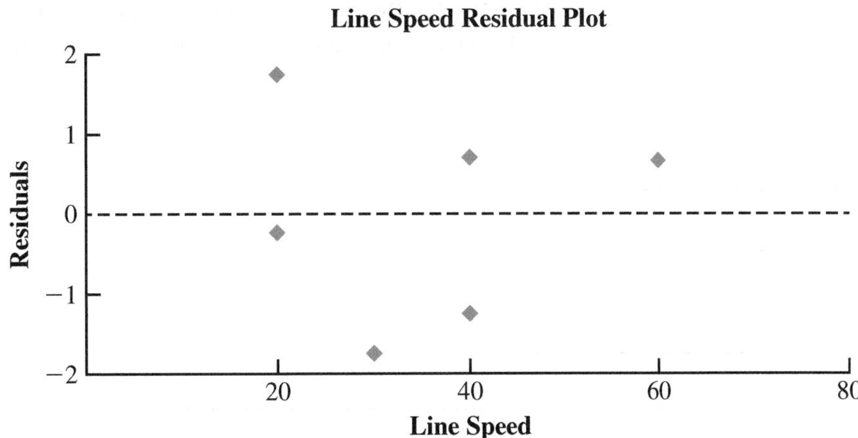

Because we are working with only 6 observations, assessing the conditions necessary for inference to be valid in regression is extremely difficult. However, this scatter chart does not provide strong evidence of a violation of the conditions, so we will proceed with our inference.

The p value associated with the estimated regression parameter b_1 is 0.02813. Because this p value is greater than the 0.01 level of significance, we do not reject the hypothesis that $\beta_1 = 0$. We conclude that there is no relationship between line speed and number of defective parts found.

The estimated regression parameter b_0 suggests that when the line speed is zero, the number of defect parts found is 22.1739. This result is obviously not realistic, but this parameter estimate and the test of the hypothesis that $\beta_0 = 0$ are meaningless because the y-intercept has been estimated through extrapolation (there is no observation in the sample data with a line speed near zero).

d. The coefficient of determination r^2 is 0.7391, so the regression model estimated in part b explains approximately 74% of the variation in the number of defective parts found in the sample.

4. a. The scatter chart with distance to work as the independent variable is as follows:

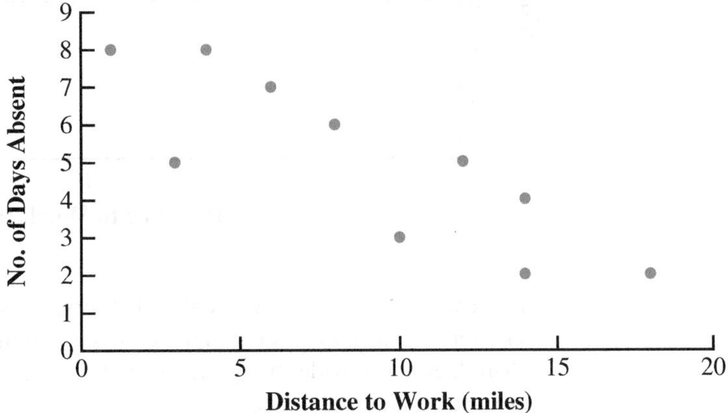

This scatter chart indicates there may be a negative linear relationship between distance to work and number of days absent. This is not what would be expected—an employee who lives farther from her or his job is expected to be absent more frequently than an employee who lives closer to her/his job.

b. The following Excel output provides the estimated regression equation that could be used to predict the number of days absent (y) given the distance to work (x).

	A	B	C	D	E	F	G	H	I
1	SUMMARY OUTPUT								
2									
3	*Regression Statistics*								
4	Multiple R	0.843121469							
5	R Square	0.710853812							
6	Adjusted R Square	0.674710539							
7	Standard Error	1.289414821							
8	Observations	10							
9									
10	ANOVA								
11		*df*	*SS*	*MS*	*F*	*Significance F*			
12	Regression	1	32.69927536	32.69927536	19.66766549	0.002182936			
13	Residual	8	13.30072464	1.66259058					
14	Total	9	46						
15									
16		*Coefficients*	*Standard Error*	*t Stat*	*P-value*	*Lower 95%*	*Upper 95%*	*Lower 99.0%*	*Upper 99.0%*
17	Intercept	8.097826087	0.808822137	10.01187494	8.4133E-06	6.232678894	9.96297328	5.383914534	10.81173764
18	Distance to Work (miles)	-0.344202899	0.077613652	-4.434824178	0.002182936	-0.5231803	-0.165225497	-0.604626762	-0.083779035

The estimated simple linear regression equation is $\hat{y} = 8.0978 - 0.3442x$.

c. First we check the conditions necessary for valid inference in regression. The Excel plot of the residuals and weight is as follows:

Distance to Work (miles) Residual Plot

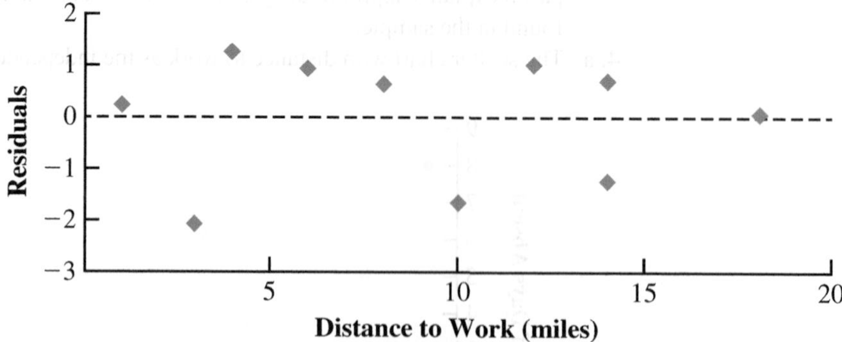

Distance to Work (miles)

Because we are working with only 10 observations, assessing the conditions necessary for inference to be valid in regression is extremely difficult. However, this scatter chart does not provide strong evidence of a violation of the conditions, so we will proceed with our inference.

The 99% confidence interval for the regression parameter β_1 provided in the Excel output is (−0.6046, −0.0838). Because this interval does not include zero, we reject the hypothesis that $\beta_1 = 0$. We conclude that there is a relationship between distance to work and number of absences. Our best estimate is that a one mile increase in the distance to work corresponds to a decrease of 0.3442 day absent.

d. The 99% confidence interval for the regression parameter β_0 provided in the Excel output is (5.3839, 10.8117). However, this confidence interval and the test of the hypothesis that $\beta_0 = 0$ are meaningless because the *y*-intercept has been estimated through extrapolation (there is no observation in the sample data with a distance to work near zero).

e. The coefficient of determination r^2 is 0.7109, so the regression model estimated in part b explains approximately 71% of the variation in the values of number of days absent in the sample.

6. a. The scatter chart with hours spent studying as the independent variable is as follows:

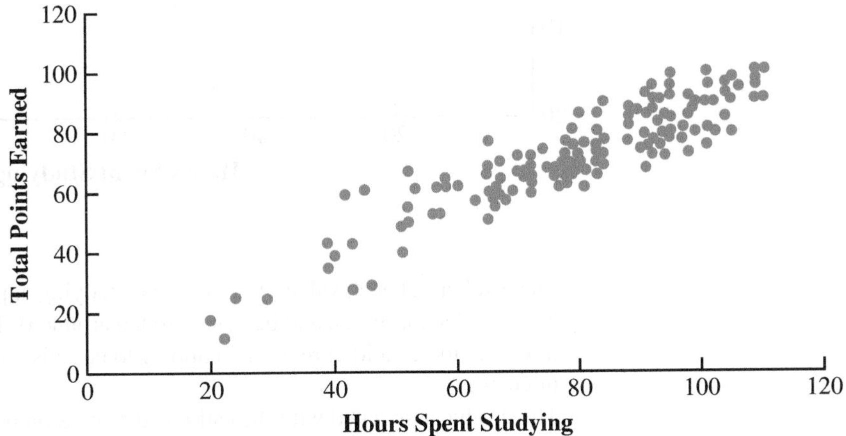

This scatter chart indicates that there may be a positive linear relationship between hours spent studying and total points earned. Students who spend more time studying generally earn more points, and this scatter chart is consistent with what is expected.

b. The following Excel output provides the estimated regression equation showing how total points earned (*y*) is related to hours spent studying (*x*).

	A	B	C	D	E	F	G	H	I
1	SUMMARY OUTPUT								
2									
3	*Regression Statistics*								
4	Multiple R	0.909785963							
5	R Square	0.827710499							
6	Adjusted R Square	0.826591736							
7	Standard Error	7.177298036							
8	Observations	156							
9									
10	ANOVA								
11		*df*	*SS*	*MS*	*F*	*Significance F*			
12	Regression	1	38112.05194	38112.05194	739.8443652	1.09619E-60			
13	Residual	154	7933.095493	51.5136071					
14	Total	155	46045.14744						
15									
16		*Coefficients*	*Standard Error*	*t Stat*	*P-value*	*Lower 95%*	*Upper 95%*	*Lower 99.0%*	*Upper 99.0%*
17	Intercept	8.67422449	2.447697434	3.543830365	0.000522385	3.838827439	13.50962154	2.290309406	15.05813957
18	Hours Spent Studying	0.801382837	0.029462517	27.20008024	1.09619E-60	0.743179986	0.859585688	0.724540738	0.878224936

The estimated simple linear regression equation is $\hat{y} = 8.6742 + 0.8014x$.

c. First, we check the conditions necessary for valid inference in regression. The Excel plot of the residuals and hours spent studying is as follows:

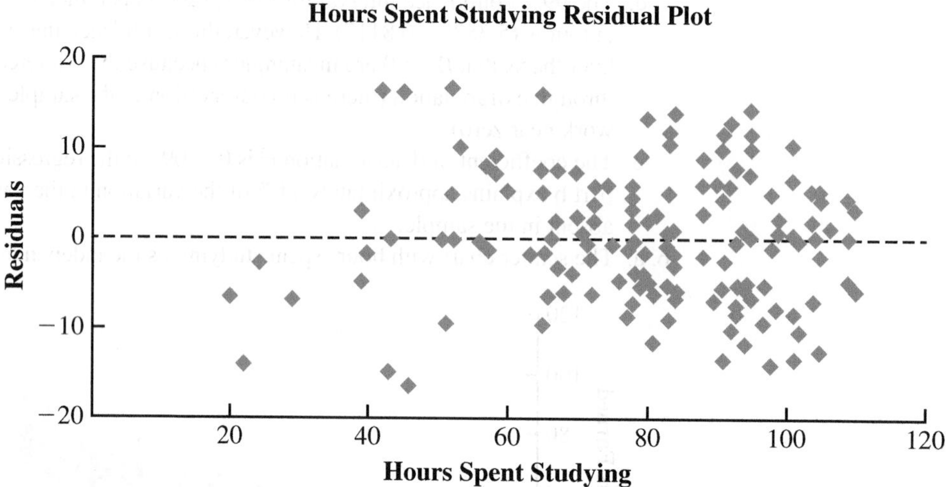

The residuals at each value of hours spent studying appear to have a mean of 0, have similar variances, and be concentrated around 0. The conditions necessary for inference to be valid in regression appear to be satisfied, so we will proceed with our inference.

The p value associated with the estimated regression parameter b_1 is 1.09619E-60. Because this p value is less than the 0.01 level of significance, we reject the hypothesis that $\beta_1 = 0$. We conclude that there is a relationship between hours spent studying and total points earned, and our best estimate is that a one-hour increase in hours spent studying corresponds to an increase of 0.8014 in total points earned. This result is consistent with what would be expected.

The estimated regression parameter b_0 suggests that when a student spends zero hours studying, the total points earned by the student is 8.6742. This parameter estimate and the test of the hypothesis that $\beta_0 = 0$ are meaningless because the y-intercept has been estimated through extrapolation (there is no observation in the sample data with hours of studying near zero).

d. The coefficient of determination r^2 is 0.8277, so the regression model estimated in part b explains approximately 83% of the variation in the values of total points earned in the sample.

e. Using this regression model, the predicted total points earned by Mark (who spent 95 hours studying) is:

$$\hat{y} = 8.6742 + 0.8014(95) = 84.8056,$$

or approximately 85 points.

8. a. The scatter chart with miles as the independent variable is as follows:

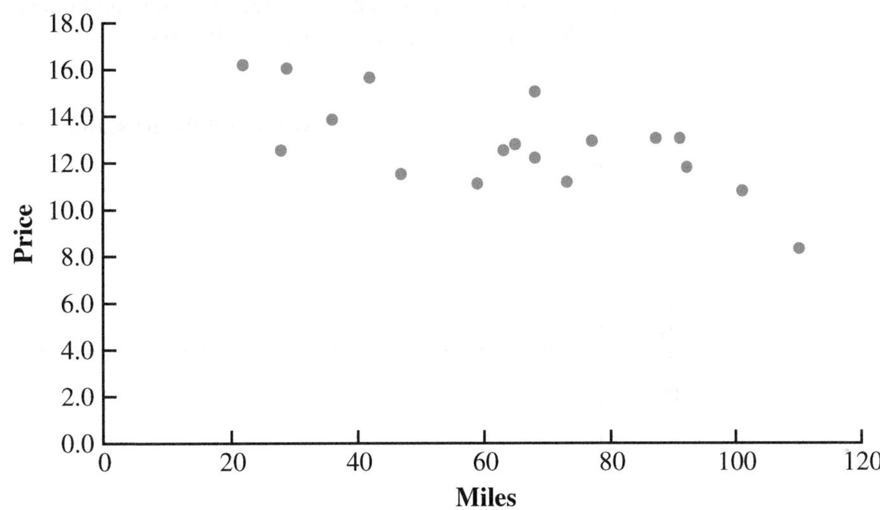

This scatter chart indicates that there may be a negative linear relationship between miles and price. Since a Camry with higher mileage will generally sell for a lower price, a positive relationship is expected between these two variables. This scatter chart is consistent with what is expected.

b. The following Excel output provides the estimated regression equation showing how price (y) is related to miles (x).

	A	B	C	D	E	F	G	H	I
1	SUMMARY OUTPUT								
2									
3	*Regression Statistics*								
4	Multiple R	0.733932829							
5	R Square	0.538657397							
6	Adjusted R Square	0.511519597							
7	Standard Error	1.541376979							
8	Observations	19							
9									
10	ANOVA								
11		*df*	*SS*	*MS*	*F*	*Significance F*			
12	Regression	1	47.15803759	47.15803759	19.84897057	0.000347511			
13	Residual	17	40.38933083	2.37584299					
14	Total	18	87.54736842						
15									
16		*Coefficients*	*Standard Error*	*t Stat*	*P-value*	*Lower 95%*	*Upper 95%*	*Lower 99.0%*	*Upper 99.0%*
17	Intercept	16.46975503	0.948764153	17.35916663	2.98677E-12	14.46803764	18.47147242	13.72001781	19.21949226
18	Miles (1000s)	-0.058773932	0.013192155	-4.455218353	0.000347511	-0.086606946	-0.030940917	-0.097007839	-0.020540025

The estimated simple linear regression equation is $\hat{y} = 16.4698 - 0.0588x$.

c. First, we check the conditions necessary for valid inference in regression. The Excel plot of the residuals and miles is as follows:

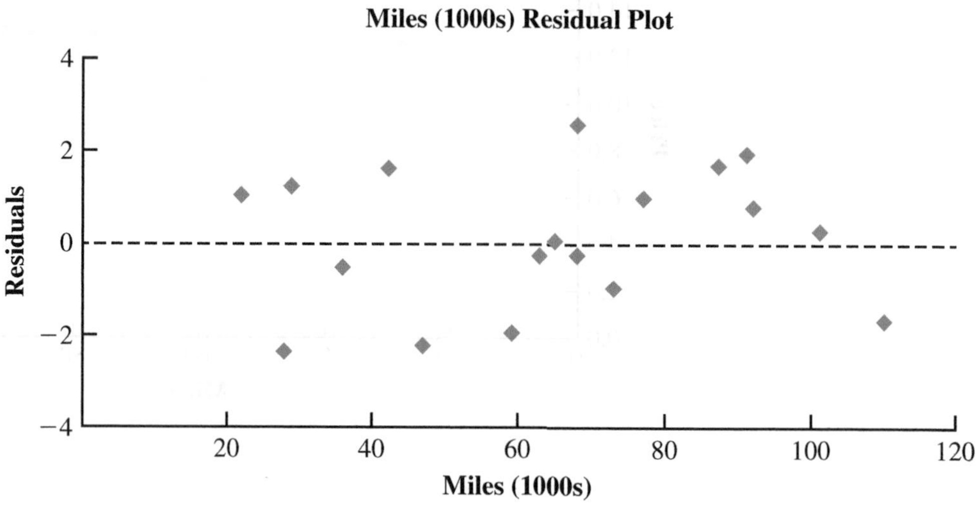

Because we are working with only 19 observations, assessing the conditions necessary for inference to be valid in regression is extremely difficult. However, this scatter chart does not provide strong evidence of a violation of the conditions, so we will proceed with our inference.

The p value associated with the estimated regression parameter b_1 is 0.0003. Because this p value is less than the 0.01 level of significance, we reject the hypothesis that $\beta_1 = 0$. We conclude that there is a relationship between miles and price, and our best estimate is that a 1,000-mile increase corresponds to a decrease of \$58.77. This result appears to be reasonable.

The estimated regression parameter b_0 suggests that if a Camry has zero miles, the predicted price is \$16,469.76. This result is obviously not realistic, but this parameter estimate and the test of the hypothesis that $\beta_0 = 0$ are meaningless because the y-intercept has been estimated through extrapolation (there is no observation in the sample data with miles near zero).

d. The coefficient of determination r^2 is 0.5387, so the regression model estimated in part b explains approximately 54% of the variation in the values of price in the sample.

e. Excel output for the predicted prices and residuals for the model estimated in part b is as follows:

A bargain is a Camry for which the predicted price given its miles exceeds the actual price (the price of the automobile is less than the value of the automobile given its mileage). The residuals $e_i = y_i - \hat{y}_i$ for this simple linear regression model are the differences between the actual prices and the predicted prices, so the Camry with the largest negative residual is the best bargain. The 12th automobile in the sample sold for \$12,500, and with 28,000 miles its predicted price is \$14,824. Thus, this automobile sold for \$2,324 less than the predicted price for a Camry with 28,000 miles. The fourth automobile in the data, which has 47,000 miles, was almost as big a bargain, selling for \$2,207 less than the predicted price for a Camry with 47,000 miles.

	A	B	C
22	RESIDUAL OUTPUT		
23			
24	*Observation*	*Predicted Price ($1000s)*	*Residuals*
25	1	15.17672853	1.023271468
26	2	14.76531101	1.234688992
27	3	14.35389349	-0.553893485
28	4	13.70738023	-2.207380235
29	5	12.76699732	-0.266997324
30	6	11.94416228	0.955837722
31	7	12.17925801	-0.979258006
32	8	11.35642296	1.643577041
33	9	11.06255533	0.7374467
34	10	10.53358791	0.266412087
35	11	10.00462253	-1.704622526
36	12	14.82408494	-2.32408494
37	13	13.00209305	1.902093052
38	14	12.47312766	2.526872335
39	15	12.47312766	-0.273127665
40	16	11.12132723	1.878672768
41	17	14.00124989	1.598750106
42	18	12.64944946	0.050550539
43	19	10.00462253	-1.704622526

f. Using the estimated regression equation developed in part b, the predicted mean price for a previously owned 2007 Camry that has been driven 60,000 miles is:

$$\hat{y} = 16.4698 - 0.0588(60) = 12.9433,$$

or $12,943. Depending on other factors not considered in the model (various options, the physical condition of the body and interior, etc.), this is a reasonable price to expect to pay for a Camry that has been driven 60,000 miles.

10. a. The following Excel output provides the estimated multiple linear regression equation with comfort (x_1), amenities (x_2), and in-house dining (x_3) as the independent variables.

	A	B	C	D	E	F	G	H	I
1	SUMMARY OUTPUT								
2									
3	*Regression Statistics*								
4	Multiple R	0.865895539							
5	R Square	0.749775085							
6	Adjusted R Square	0.702857913							
7	Standard Error	1.387873302							
8	Observations	20							
9									
10	ANOVA								
11		*df*	*SS*	*MS*	*F*	*Significance F*			
12	Regression	3	92.34642318	30.78214106	15.98082447	4.52386E-05			
13	Residual	16	30.81907682	1.926192301					
14	Total	19	123.1655						
15									
16		*Coefficients*	*Standard Error*	*t Stat*	*P-value*	*Lower 95%*	*Upper 95%*	*Lower 99.0%*	*Upper 99.0%*
17	Intercept	35.69673648	13.21538296	2.701150363	0.015734886	7.681376109	63.71209686	-2.902511208	74.29598417
18	Comfort	0.109348527	0.129718771	0.842966109	0.411672372	-0.165642982	0.384340037	-0.269531674	0.488228729
19	Amenities	0.244268002	0.043315458	5.639280131	3.69454E-05	0.152443333	0.336092671	0.117753008	0.370782996
20	In-House Dining	0.247431197	0.06212369	3.982879927	0.001069855	0.115734858	0.379127536	0.065981466	0.428880929

The estimated multiple linear regression equation is
$\hat{y} = 35.6967 + 0.1093x_1 + 0.2443x_2 + 0.2474x_3$.

b. Before performing any hypothesis tests on the results, we check the conditions necessary for valid inference in regression. The Excel plots of the residuals and comfort, amenities, and in-house dining are as follows:

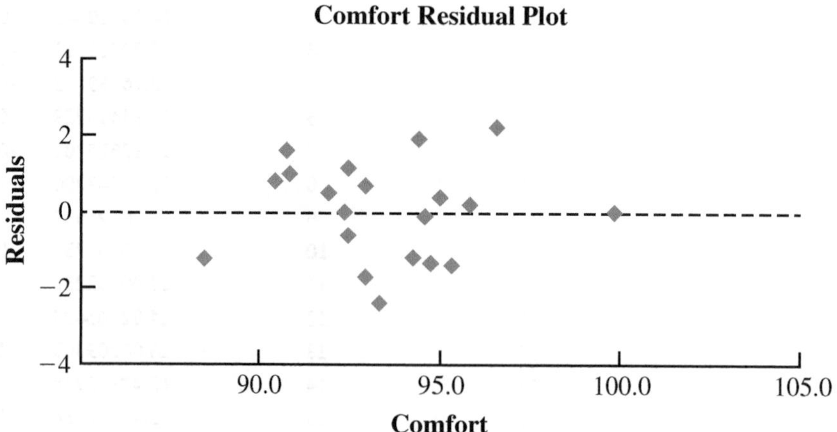

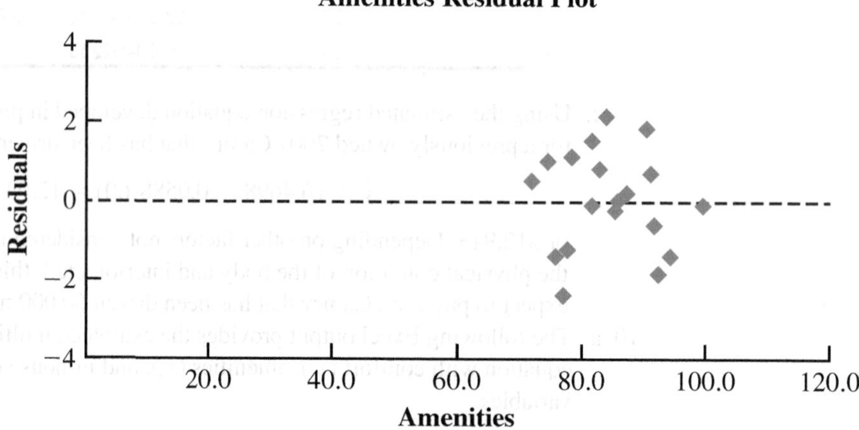

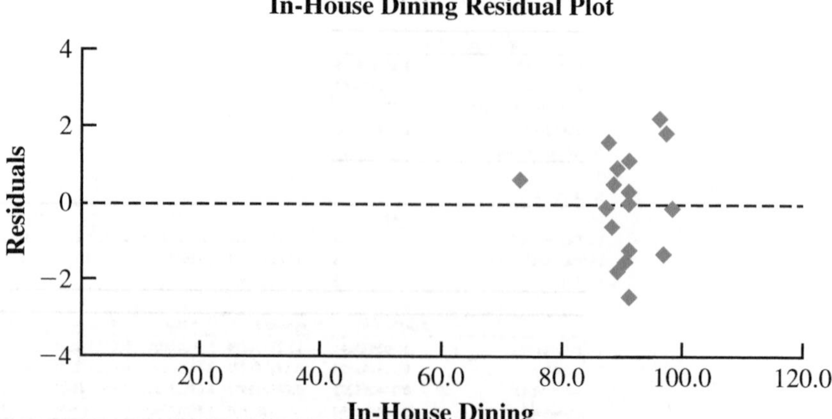

None of these scatter charts provides strong evidence of a violation of the conditions necessary for valid inference in regression, so we will proceed with our inference. The p value associated with the estimated regression parameter b_1 is 0.4117. Because this p value is greater than the 0.01 level of significance, we do not reject the hypothesis that $\beta_1 = 0$. We conclude that there is not a relationship between the score on comfort and the overall score at the 0.01 level of significance when controlling for amenities and in-house dining.

The p-value associated with the estimated regression parameter b_2 is 3.69454E-05. Because this p value is less than the 0.01 level of significance, we reject the hypothesis that $\beta_2 = 0$. We conclude that there is a relationship between the score on amenities and the overall score at the 0.01 level of significance, and our best estimate is that if we hold the scores on comfort and in-house dining constant, a one-point increase in the score on amenities corresponds to an increase of 0.2443 in overall score.

The p value associated with the estimated regression parameter b_3 is 0.0011. Because this p value is less than the 0.01 level of significance, we reject the hypothesis that $\beta_3 = 0$. We conclude that there is a relationship between the score on in-house dining and the overall score at the 0.01 level of significance, and our best estimate is that if we hold the scores on comfort and amenities constant, a one-point increase in the score on in-house dining corresponds to an increase of 0.2443 in overall score.

If ratings for comfort, amenities, and in-house dining are related to overall score, the relationships are expected to be positive. The results are consistent with expectations for all three relationships.

c. The following Excel output provides the estimated multiple linear regression equation with amenities (x_1) and in-house dining (x_2) as the independent variables.

	A	B	C	D	E	F	G	H	I
1	SUMMARY OUTPUT								
2									
3	*Regression Statistics*								
4	Multiple R	0.859454535							
5	R Square	0.738662098							
6	Adjusted R Square	0.707916462							
7	Standard Error	1.376009007							
8	Observations	20							
9									
10	ANOVA								
11		*df*	*SS*	*MS*	*F*	*Significance F*			
12	Regression	2	90.97768661	45.4888433	24.02494157	1.1123E-05			
13	Residual	17	32.18781339	1.893400788					
14	Total	19	123.1655						
15									
16		*Coefficients*	*Standard Error*	*t Stat*	*P-value*	*Lower 95%*	*Upper 95%*	*Lower 99.0%*	*Upper 99.0%*
17	Intercept	45.14614888	6.939350597	6.505817547	5.38421E-06	30.50539889	59.78689887	25.03431119	65.25798656
18	Amenities	0.252580552	0.041817492	6.04006936	1.32524E-05	0.164353356	0.340807749	0.131383821	0.373777284
19	In-House Dining	0.248265677	0.061584802	4.031281543	0.000866459	0.118333102	0.378198253	0.069778723	0.426752632
20									

The estimated multiple linear regression equation is $\hat{y} = 45.1461 + 0.2526x_1 + 0.2483x_2$. A review of the Excel plots of the residuals and the two independent variables that follow show no dramatic departures from the conditions necessary for valid inference in regression. We can proceed with inference.

Amenities Residual Plot

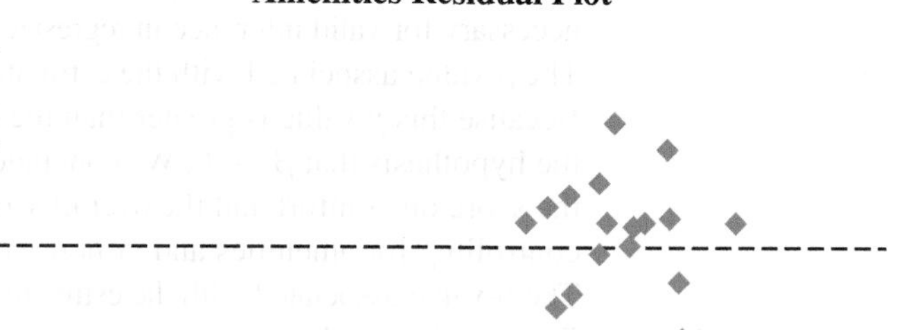

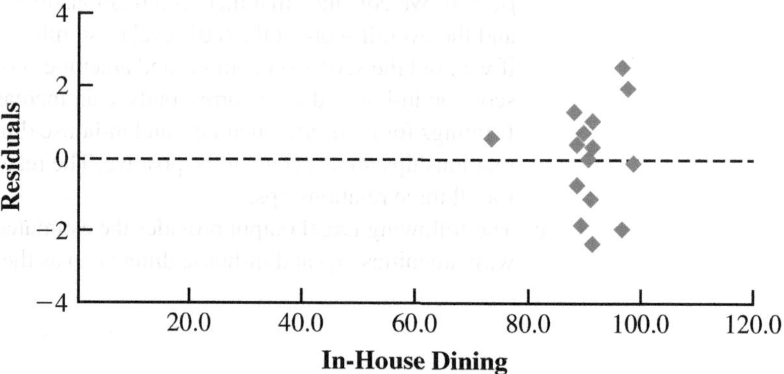

The p value associated with the estimated regression parameter b_1 (which now corresponds to amenities) is 1.32524E-05. Because this p value is less than the 0.01 level of significance, we reject the hypothesis that $\beta_1 = 0$. We conclude that there is a relationship between the score on amenities and the overall score at the 0.01 level of significance, and our best estimate is that if we hold the scores on in-house dining constant, a one-point increase in the score on amenities corresponds to an increase of 0.2526 on overall score. The p value associated with the estimated regression parameter b_2 (which now corresponds to in-house dining) is 0.0009. Because this p value is less than the 0.01 level of significance, we reject the hypothesis that $\beta_2 = 0$. We conclude that there is a relationship between the score on in-house dining and the overall score at the 0.01 level of significance, and our best estimate is that if we hold the scores on amenities constant, a one-point increase in the score on in-house dining corresponds to an increase of 0.2483 in overall score.

For this multiple linear regression model, the overall regression relationship is significant, and the estimated regression coefficients b_1 and b_2 are significant and consistent with what would be expected. Furthermore, this model has a coefficient of determination of $R^2 = 0.7387$. The model with all three independent variables (comfort, amenities, and in-house dining) from part a has a multiple coefficient of determination of $R^2 = 0.7498$, so this model explains little more than 1% more of the variation in overall ratings in the sample than does the model that includes only the independent variables amenities and in-house dining (i.e., removing comfort as an independent variable resulted in a loss of little more that 1% of the explained variation in overall score). Thus, the simpler multiple regression model developed in part d is preferred.

12. a. The following Excel output provides the estimated simple linear regression equation that could be used to predict the percentage of games won (y) given the average number of passing yards per attempt (x).

	A	B	C	D	E	F	G	H	I
1	SUMMARY OUTPUT								
2									
3	*Regression Statistics*								
4	Multiple R	0.759692807							
5	R Square	0.577133161							
6	Adjusted R Square	0.546928387							
7	Standard Error	15.87319309							
8	Observations	16							
9									
10	ANOVA								
11		*df*	*SS*	*MS*	*F*	*Significance F*			
12	Regression	1	4814.254375	4814.254375	19.10734895	0.000639317			
13	Residual	14	3527.415625	251.9582589					
14	Total	15	8341.67						
15									
16		*Coefficients*	*Standard Error*	*t Stat*	*P-value*	*Lower 95%*	*Upper 95%*	*Lower 99.0%*	*Upper 99.0%*
17	Intercept	-58.7703125	26.17541056	-2.245248928	0.041423237	-114.9109846	-2.629640373	-136.6903933	19.14976826
18	Yds/Att	16.390625	3.749689414	4.371195369	0.000639317	8.348341062	24.43290894	5.228389313	27.55286069

The estimated simple linear regression equation is $\hat{y} = -58.7703 + 16.3906x$, and the coefficient of determination r_2 is 0.5771, so this regression model explains approximately 58% of the variation in the sample values of percentage of games won.

b. The following Excel output provides the estimated simple linear regression equation that could be used to predict the percentage of games won (y) given the number of interceptions thrown per attempt (x).

	A	B	C	D	E	F	G	H	I
1	SUMMARY OUTPUT								
2									
3	*Regression Statistics*								
4	Multiple R	0.661738595							
5	R Square	0.437897968							
6	Adjusted R Square	0.397747823							
7	Standard Error	18.30079947							
8	Observations	16							
9									
10	ANOVA								
11		*df*	*SS*	*MS*	*F*	*Significance F*			
12	Regression	1	3652.800344	3652.800344	10.90651022	0.005236168			
13	Residual	14	4688.869656	334.9192612					
14	Total	15	8341.67						
15									
16		*Coefficients*	*Standard Error*	*t Stat*	*P-value*	*Lower 95%*	*Upper 95%*	*Lower 99.0%*	*Upper 99.0%*
17	Intercept	97.53825386	13.86181605	7.036470076	5.89808E-06	67.80761532	127.2688924	56.27380746	138.8027003
18	Int/Att	-1600.490884	484.6300053	-3.302500601	0.005236168	-2639.918868	-561.0628996	-3043.158194	-157.8235734

The estimated simple linear regression equation is $\hat{y} = 97.5383 - 1600.4909x$, and the coefficient of determination r^2 is 0.4379, so this regression model explains approximately 44% of the variation in the sample values of percentage of games won.

c. The following Excel output provides the estimated multiple linear regression equation that could be used to predict the percentage of games won (y) given the average number of passing yards per attempt (x_1) and the number of interceptions thrown per attempt (x_2).

	A	B	C	D	E	F	G	H	I
1	SUMMARY OUTPUT								
2									
3	*Regression Statistics*								
4	Multiple R	0.867461188							
5	R Square	0.752488913							
6	Adjusted R Square	0.714410284							
7	Standard Error	12.60236794							
8	Observations	16							
9									
10	ANOVA								
11		*df*	*SS*	*MS*	*F*	*Significance F*			
12	Regression	2	6277.014191	3138.507096	19.76144986	0.000114384			
13	Residual	13	2064.655809	158.8196776					
14	Total	15	8341.67						
15									
16		*Coefficients*	*Standard Error*	*t Stat*	*P-value*	*Lower 95%*	*Upper 95%*	*Lower 99.0%*	*Upper 99.0%*
17	Intercept	-5.763283816	27.1467994	-0.212300674	0.835165005	-64.41037837	52.88381074	-87.53693176	76.01036413
18	Yds/Att	12.94935632	3.185669555	4.064877446	0.001338458	6.067135667	19.83157698	3.353240893	22.54547175
19	Int/Att	-1083.787956	357.1165398	-3.034829909	0.009575422	-1855.291335	-312.2845768	-2159.52148	-8.054431663

The estimated multiple linear regression equation is $\hat{y} = -5.7633 + 12.9494x_i - 1083.7880x_2$, and the coefficient of determination R^2 is 0.7525, so this regression model explains approximately 75% of the variation in the sample values of percentage of games won.

d. Using the estimated regression equation developed in part c, the predicted percentage of games won by the Kansas City Chiefs for the 2011 season (during which the Kansas City Chiefs' average number of passing yards per attempt was 6.2 and the number of interceptions thrown per attempt was 0.036) is:

$$\hat{y} = -5.7633 + 12.9494(6.2) - 1083.7880(0.036) = 35.5064,$$

or 35.51%. During the 2011 season, the Kansas City Chiefs won 43.75% of its games (recall that the team's record for the 2011 season was 7 wins and 9 losses, so the team performed better than what we would predict for a team with an average number of passing yards per attempt of 6.2 and number of interceptions thrown per attempt of 0.036.

e. The estimated simple linear regression equation that uses only the average number of passing yards per attempt as the independent variable to predict the percentage of games won has a coefficient of determination of $r^2 = 0.5771$, and the estimated multiple linear regression equation that uses both the average number of passing yards per attempt and the number of interceptions thrown per attempt as the independent variables to predict the percentage of games won has a coefficient of determination of $R^2 = 0.7525$. The multiple linear regression model fits the data better, as it explains over 17% more variation the percentage of games won than did the simple linear regression.

14. a. The following Excel output provides the estimated multiple linear regression equation that could be used to predict delay given the industry dummy variable (x_1), the public dummy variable (x_2), quality (x_3), and finished (x_4).

	A	B	C	D	E	F	G	H	I
3	*Regression Statistics*								
4	Multiple R	0.618518551							
5	R Square	0.382565198							
6	Adjusted R Square	0.312001221							
7	Standard Error	10.92351796							
8	Observations	40							
9									
10	ANOVA								
11		*df*	*SS*	*MS*	*F*	*Significance F*			
12	Regression	4	2587.661436	646.915359	5.421536774	0.001665508			
13	Residual	35	4176.313564	119.3232447					
14	Total	39	6763.975						
15									
16		*Coefficients*	*Standard Error*	*t Stat*	*P-value*	*Lower 95%*	*Upper 95%*	*Lower 99.0%*	*Upper 99.0%*
17	Intercept	80.42857175	5.91586135	13.59541189	1.57309E-15	68.41873472	92.43840878	64.31491554	96.54222796
18	Industry	11.94418923	3.797800763	3.145027865	0.003379559	4.234243788	19.65413466	1.599718282	22.28866017
19	Public	-4.816257126	4.229181312	-1.138815475	0.262515036	-13.40195164	3.769437385	-16.33572482	6.703210569
20	Quality	-2.623635035	1.183593557	-2.216668907	0.033238643	-5.026457698	-0.220812372	-5.64751378	0.60024371
21	Finished	-4.072510795	1.851430781	-2.199655982	0.034527054	-7.831115103	-0.313906486	-9.115448305	0.970426716

The estimated multiple linear regression equation is:

$$\hat{y} = 80.4286 + 11.9442x_1 - 4.8163x_2 - 2.6236x_3 - 4.0725x_4.$$

b. The coefficient of determination is $R^2 = 0.3826$, so the regression model explains approximately 38% of the variation in the values of repair time in the sample. Other independent variables that you could include in this regression model to improve the fit comprise the amount of taxes reported by the company that is being audited and what type of audit (Taxpayer Compliance Measurement Program Audit, IRS Correspondence, IRS Office Audit, or IRS Field Audit) is being conducted.

c. Before testing any hypotheses about this regression model, we check the conditions necessary for valid inference in regression. Excel plots of the residuals and each of the independent variables are as follows:

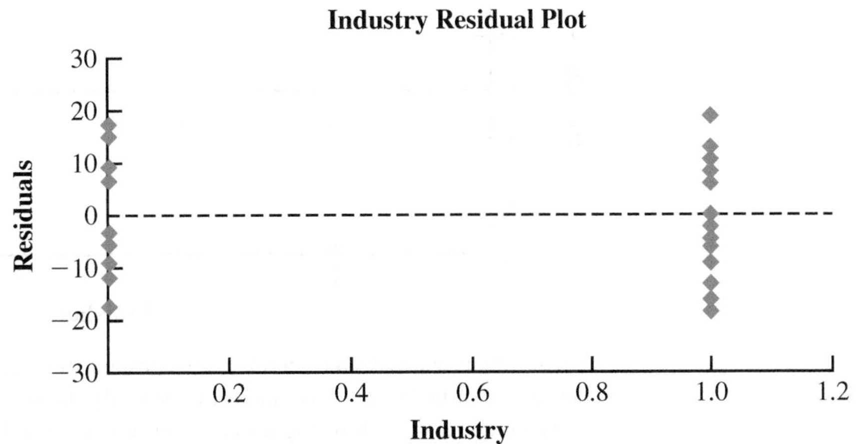

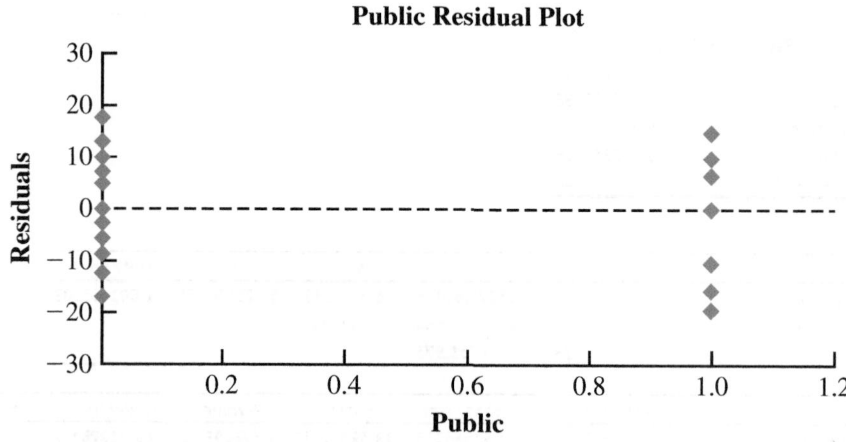

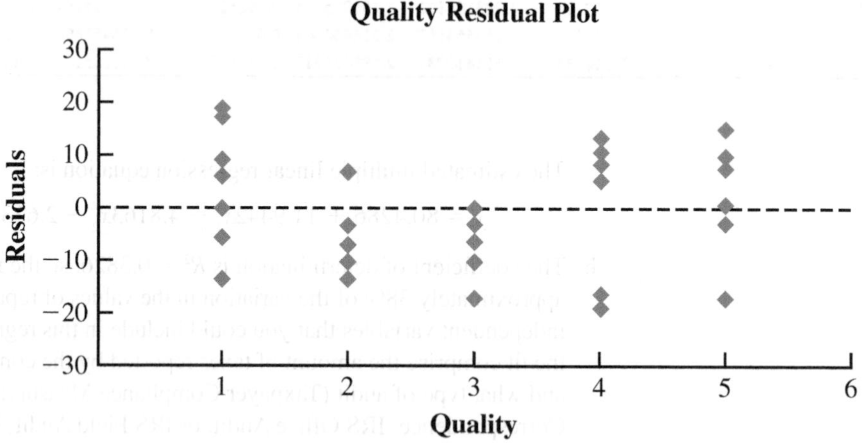

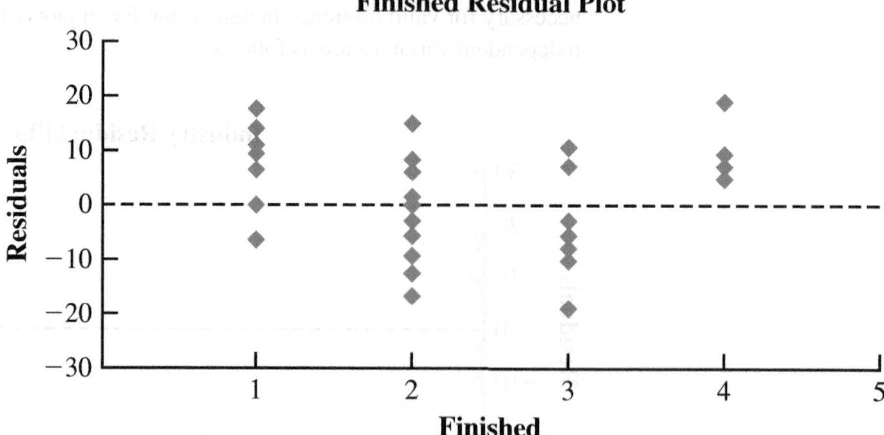

The residuals appear to have a relatively constant variance across the values of each independent variable and do not appear to be badly skewed for any variable. However, the mean of the residuals possibly differs from zero at several values of each of the quantitative independent variables (quality and finished). A closer look at these scatter charts suggests that both quality and finished may have a nonlinear relationship with delay. We will keep these findings in mind as we proceed.

In checking for multicollinearity, we first calculate the correlation coefficient r for the quantitative independent variables (quality and finished) to determine whether our quantitative variables are strongly correlated. We note that the correlation between quality and finished is 0.0356, which indicates that multicollinearity between the quantitative variables is not a concern.

Next, we rerun the regression after removing the industry dummy variable (x_1) from the original model and compare the parameter estimates and associated p values for each of the remaining independent variables to the parameter estimates and associated p values for the original model.

	A	B	C	D	E	F	G	H	I
1	SUMMARY OUTPUT								
2									
3	*Regression Statistics*								
4	Multiple R	0.456151937							
5	R Square	0.20807459							
6	Adjusted R Square	0.142080806							
7	Standard Error	12.19809147							
8	Observations	40							
9									
10	ANOVA								
11		*df*	*SS*	*MS*	*F*	*Significance F*			
12	Regression	3	1407.411325	469.1371085	3.152942247	0.036544153			
13	Residual	36	5356.563675	148.7934354					
14	Total	39	6763.975						
15									
16		*Coefficients*	*Standard Error*	*t Stat*	*P-value*	*Lower 95%*	*Upper 95%*	*Lower 95.0%*	*Upper 95.0%*
17	Intercept	86.78606274	6.20850748	13.97857102	4.07662E-16	74.19462596	99.37749952	74.19462596	99.37749952
18	Public	-6.972450006	4.660181876	-1.496175512	0.143324158	-16.42373691	2.478836901	-16.42373691	2.478836901
19	Quality	-1.888027661	1.295633003	-1.457224119	0.153722801	-4.515693183	0.73963786	-4.515693183	0.73963786
20	Finished	-4.080080226	2.067456932	-1.973477737	0.056155259	-8.273077227	0.112916774	-8.273077227	0.112916774

When making these comparisons, we observe that these values do not change substantially when the dummy variable for industry is introduced into or removed from the model and conclude that the industry dummy variable does not create a problem with multicollinearity.

Finally, we rerun the regression after removing the public dummy variable (x_2) from the original model and compare the parameter estimates and associated p values for each of the remaining independent variables to the parameter estimates and associated p values for the original model.

	A	B	C	D	E	F	G	H	I
1	SUMMARY OUTPUT								
2									
3	*Regression Statistics*								
4	Multiple R	0.59973876							
5	R Square	0.35968658							
6	Adjusted R Square	0.306327129							
7	Standard Error	10.96846991							
8	Observations	40							
9									
10	ANOVA								
11		*df*	*SS*	*MS*	*F*	*Significance F*			
12	Regression	3	2432.911038	810.970346	6.740822281	0.001002568			
13	Residual	36	4331.063962	120.3073323					
14	Total	39	6763.975						
15									
16		*Coefficients*	*Standard Error*	*t Stat*	*P-value*	*Lower 95%*	*Upper 95%*	*Lower 99.0%*	*Upper 99.0%*
17	Intercept	79.73238793	5.908405031	13.4947397	1.18869E-15	67.74958714	91.71518873	63.66457126	95.8002046
18	Industry	12.64530921	3.762988597	3.360443137	0.001853058	5.013614605	20.27700381	2.41191955	22.87869886
19	Quality	-2.82042791	1.175729311	-2.398875221	0.021748939	-5.204917473	-0.435938348	-6.017805701	0.37694988
20	Finished	-4.19401704	1.855960137	-2.259755992	0.029984566	-7.958078659	-0.429955421	-9.241272107	0.853238026

When making these comparisons, we observe that these values do not change substantially when the dummy variable for whether the company is publicly traded is introduced into or removed from the model and conclude that the public dummy variable does not create a problem with multicollinearity.

Our results suggest that multicollinearity is not an issue for this regression model. We will therefore proceed with our inferences.

The p value for the test of the hypothesis that $\beta_1 = 0$ is 0.0034. Because this p value is less than the 0.05 level of significance, we reject the hypothesis that $\beta_1 = 0$ and conclude that there is a difference in delay between the industries at the 0.05 level of significance. We estimate that, holding the values of public, quality, and finished constant, the delay experienced by an industrial company is 11.9442 days longer than the delay experienced by a bank, savings and loan, or insurance company.

The p value for the test of the hypothesis that $\beta_2 = 0$ is 0.2625. Because this p value is greater than the 0.05 level of significance, we do not reject the hypothesis that $\beta_2 =$ 0, and we conclude that there is no difference in the delays whether the company was traded on an organized exchange or over the counter when controlling for industry, quality, and finished.

The p value for the test of the hypothesis that $\beta_3 = 0$ is 0.0332. Because this p value is less than the 0.05 level of significance, we reject the hypothesis that $\beta_3 = 0$ and conclude that there is a relationship between delay and quality at the 0.05 level of significance. We estimate that, holding the values of industry, public, and finished constant, when the overall quality of internal controls (as judged by the auditor) increases by one point, the delay decreases by 2.6236 days.

The p value for the test of the hypothesis that $\beta_4 = 0$ is 0.0345. Because this p value is less than the 0.05 level of significance, we reject the hypothesis that $\beta_4 = 0$, and conclude that there is a relationship between delay and overall quality of internal controls (as judged by the auditor) at the 0.05 level of significance. We estimate that, holding the values of industry, public, and quality constant, when finished (as judged by the auditor) increases by one point, the delay decreases by 4.0725 days.

d. Since we did not reject the hypothesis $\beta_2 = 0$ in the previous model, we will remove x_2 (the public dummy) from our multiple linear regression model. The following Excel output provides the estimated multiple linear regression equation that could be used to predict delay given the industry dummy variable (x_1), quality (x_2), and finished (x_3).

	A	B	C	D	E	F	G	H	I
1	SUMMARY OUTPUT								
2									
3	*Regression Statistics*								
4	Multiple R	0.59973876							
5	R Square	0.35968658							
6	Adjusted R Square	0.306327129							
7	Standard Error	10.96846991							
8	Observations	40							
9									
10	ANOVA								
11		*df*	*SS*	*MS*	*F*	*Significance F*			
12	Regression	3	2432.911038	810.970346	6.740822281	0.001002568			
13	Residual	36	4331.063962	120.3073323					
14	Total	39	6763.975						
15									
16		*Coefficients*	*Standard Error*	*t Stat*	*P-value*	*Lower 95%*	*Upper 95%*	*Lower 99.0%*	*Upper 99.0%*
17	Intercept	79.71238793	5.908405031	13.4947397	1.18869E-15	67.74958714	91.71518873	63.66457126	95.8002046
18	Industry	12.64530921	3.762988597	3.360443137	0.001833058	5.013614605	20.27700381	2.41191935	22.87869886
19	Quality	-2.82042791	1.175729311	-2.398875221	0.021748939	-5.204917473	-0.435938348	-6.017805701	0.37694988
20	Finished	-4.19401704	1.855960137	-2.259755992	0.029984566	-7.958078659	-0.429955421	-9.241272107	0.853238026

The estimated multiple linear regression equation is $\hat{y} = 79.7324 + 12.6453x_1 - 2.8204x_2 - 4.1940x_3$ and the coefficient of determination for this model is $R^2 = 0.3597$, so the regression model explains almost as much variation in the values of repair time in the sample as did the model that included all four independent variables.

Before testing any hypotheses about this regression model, we again check the conditions necessary for valid inference in regression.

The Excel plots of the residuals and each of the independent variables follow.

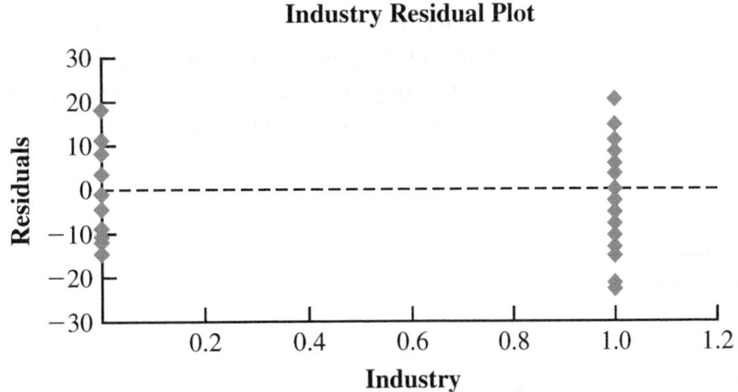

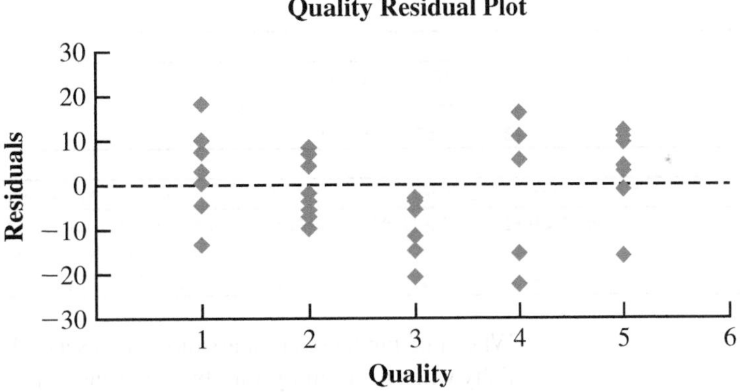

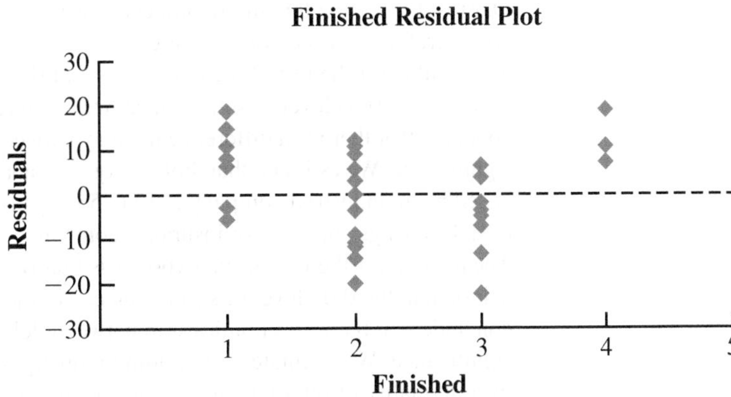

The residuals appear to have a relatively constant variance across the values of each independent variable and do not appear to be badly skewed at any value of any independent variable. However, the mean of the residuals possibly differs from zero at several values of each of the quantitative independent variables (quality and finished). A closer look at these scatter charts again suggests that quality and finished may each have a nonlinear relationship with delay. We will proceed with our inference but will keep our findings in mind as we proceed.

We have already determined that the correlation coefficient r for quality and finished is 0.0356, which indicates that multicollinearity between the quantitative variables is not a concern.

Next, we rerun this regression after removing the industry dummy variable (x_1) from our model and compare the parameter estimates and associated p values for each of the remaining independent variables to the parameter estimates and associated p values for the original model.

	A	B	C	D	E	F	G	H	I
1	SUMMARY OUTPUT								
2									
3	*Regression Statistics*								
4	Multiple R	0.398536476							
5	R Square	0.158831323							
6	Adjusted R Square	0.113362745							
7	Standard Error	12.40057094							
8	Observations	40							
9									
10	ANOVA								
11		*df*	*SS*	*MS*	*F*	*Significance F*			
12	Regression	2	1074.331095	537.1655477	3.493210753	0.040769671			
13	Residual	37	5689.643905	153.7741596					
14	Total	39	6763.975						
15									
16		*Coefficients*	*Standard Error*	*t Stat*	*P-value*	*Lower 95%*	*Upper 95%*	*Lower 95.0%*	*Upper 95.0%*
17	Intercept	86.30583698	6.303124077	13.69254927	4.64063E-16	73.53449448	99.07717948	73.53449448	99.07717948
18	Quality	-2.116413519	1.307966261	-1.618094887	0.114136747	-4.766604899	0.533777861	-4.766604899	0.533777861
19	Finished	-4.26139165	2.098161601	-2.031012124	0.049485002	-8.512670872	-0.010112428	-8.512670872	-0.010112428

When making these comparisons, we observe that these values do not change substantially when the dummy variable for industry is introduced into or removed from the model and conclude that the industry dummy variable does not create a problem with multicollinearity.

Our results suggest that multicollinearity is not an issue for this regression model. We will therefore proceed with our inferences.

The p value for the test of the hypothesis that $\beta_1 = 0$ is 0.0019. Because this p value is less than the 0.05 level of significance, we again reject the hypothesis that $\beta_1 = 0$ and conclude that there is a difference in delay between the industries at the 0.05 level of significance. We estimate that, holding quality and finished constant, the delay experienced by an industrial company is 12.6453 days longer than the delay experienced by a bank, savings and loan, or insurance company.

The p value for the test of the hypothesis that $\beta_2 = 0$ is 0.0217. Because this p value is less than the 0.05 level of significance, we reject the hypothesis that $\beta_2 = 0$ and conclude that there is a relationship between delay and quality at the 0.05 level of significance. We estimate that, holding industry and finished constant, when the overall quality of internal controls (as judged by the auditor) increases by one point the delay decreases by 2.8204 days.

The p value for the test of the hypothesis that $\beta_3 = 0$ is 0.0300. Because this p value is less than the 0.05 level of significance, we reject the hypothesis that $\beta 3 = 0$ and conclude that there is a relationship between delay and overall quality of internal controls (as judged by the auditor) at the 0.05 level of significance. We estimate that, holding industry and quality constant, when finished (as judged by the auditor) increases by one point, the delay decreases by 4.1940 days.

We have noted that the residuals plotted over each of the quantitative variables suggested possible nonlinear relationships between the dependent variable delay and the two quantitative variables (quality and finished). If we can think of plausible reasons why these two relationships could be nonlinear, we may wish to consider this quadratic model next:

$$\hat{y} = \beta_0 + \beta_1 x_1 + \beta_2 x_2 + \beta_3 x_2^2 + \beta_4 x_3 + \beta_5 x_3^2,$$

where x_1 is industry, x_2 is quality, and x_3 is finished.

16. a. The scatter chart with vehicle speed as the independent variable is as follows:

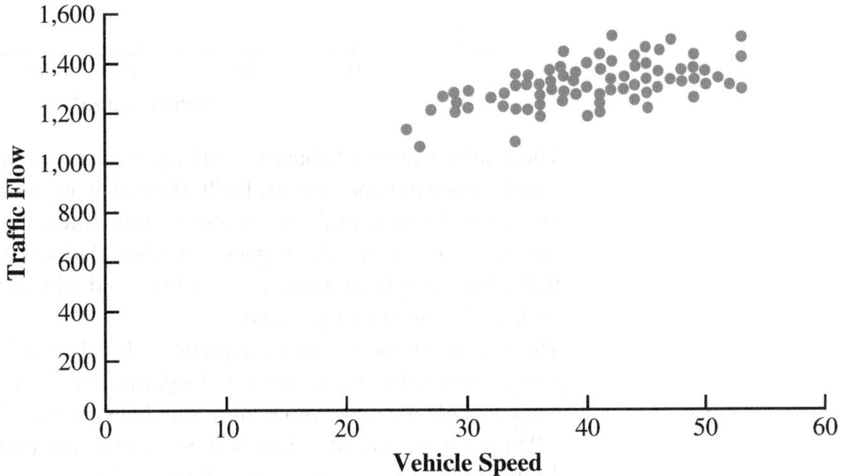

The scatter chart suggests that vehicle speed and traffic flow are positively related.

b. The following Excel output provides the estimated simple linear regression equation that could be used to predict traffic flow (y) given the vehicle speed (x).

	A	B	C	D	E	F	G	H	I
1	SUMMARY OUTPUT								
2									
3	*Regression Statistics*								
4	Multiple R	0.559690486							
5	R Square	0.31325344							
6	Adjusted R Square	0.306245822							
7	Standard Error	67.37376387							
8	Observations	100							
9									
10	ANOVA								
11		*df*	*SS*	*MS*	*F*	*Significance F*			
12	Regression	1	202911.6823	202911.6823	44.70184324	1.41658E-09			
13	Residual	98	444843.9577	4539.224058					
14	Total	99	647755.64						
15									
16		*Coefficients*	*Standard Error*	*t Stat*	*P-value*	*Lower 95%*	*Upper 95%*	*Lower 99.0%*	*Upper 99.0%*
17	Intercept	1039.575736	41.16037814	25.25671004	1.07523E-44	957.8943049	1121.257167	931.4502585	1147.701213
18	Vehicle Speed	6.600638566	0.987241122	6.685943706	1.41658E-09	4.64149069	8.559786442	4.007224164	9.194052968

The estimated multiple linear regression equation is $\hat{y} = 1039.5757 + 6.6006x$, and the coefficient of determination for this model is $r^2 = 0.3133$, so the regression model explains approximately 31% of the variation in the sample values of traffic flow. Before testing any hypotheses about this regression model, we check the conditions necessary for valid inference in regression. The scatter plot of the residuals and vehicle speed is as follows:

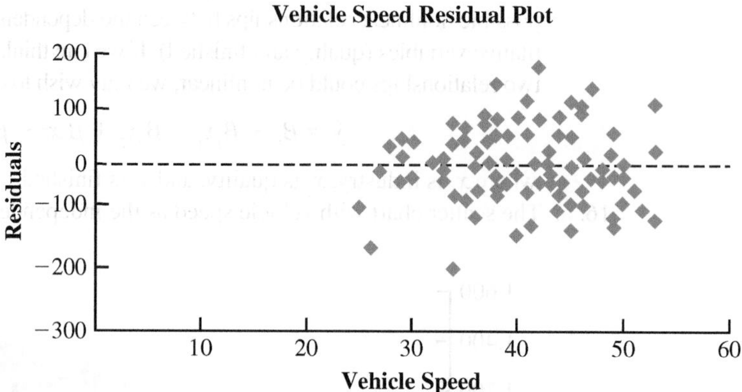

The residuals appear to have a relatively constant variance across the values of vehicle speed and do not appear to be badly skewed at any value of the independent variable. However, the mean of the residuals possibly differs from zero at several values of the independent variable; this suggests that the relationship between vehicle speed and traffic flow may be nonlinear. We will proceed with our inference but will keep our findings in mind as we proceed.

The p value for the test of the hypothesis that $\beta_1 = 0$ is 1.41658E-09. Because this p value is less than the 0.05 level of significance, we reject the hypothesis that $\beta_1 = 0$ and conclude that there is a relationship between vehicle speed and traffic flow at the 0.05 level of significance. Our best estimate is that when vehicle speed increases by 1 mph, traffic flow increases by 6.6006 vehicles.

c. The following Excel output provides the estimated second order quadratic regression equation that could be used to predict traffic flow (y) given the vehicle speed (x).

	A	B	C	D	E	F	G	H	I
1	SUMMARY OUTPUT								
2									
3	*Regression Statistics*								
4	Multiple R	0.585751157							
5	R Square	0.343104418							
6	Adjusted R Square	0.32956018							
7	Standard Error	66.23200536							
8	Observations	100							
9									
10	ANOVA								
11		*df*	*SS*	*MS*	*F*	*Significance F*			
12	Regression	2	222247.8222	111123.9111	25.33213004	1.4079E-09			
13	Residual	97	425507.8178	4386.678534					
14	Total	99	647755.64						
15									
16		*Coefficients*	*Standard Error*	*t Stat*	*P-value*	*Lower 95%*	*Upper 95%*	*Lower 99.0%*	*Upper 99.0%*
17	Intercept	621.2138072	203.3335703	3.055146311	0.002904915	217.6529558	1024.774659	86.96140391	1155.46621
18	Vehicle Speed	28.03721253	10.25631824	2.733652746	0.00744558	7.681259911	48.39316516	1.089066867	54.9853582
19	Vehicle Speed Sq	-0.266546445	0.126956783	-2.099505346	0.038368222	-0.518520517	-0.014572374	-0.600121302	0.067028412

The estimated second-order quadratic regression equation is $\hat{y} = 621.2138 + 28.0372x - 0.2665x^2$, and the coefficient of determination for this model is $R^2 = 0.3431$, so the quadratic regression model explains approximately 3% more of the variation in the sample values of traffic flow than did the linear regression model in part b.
Before testing any hypotheses about this regression model, we again check the conditions necessary for valid inference in regression. The scatter plot of the residuals and vehicle speed is as follows:

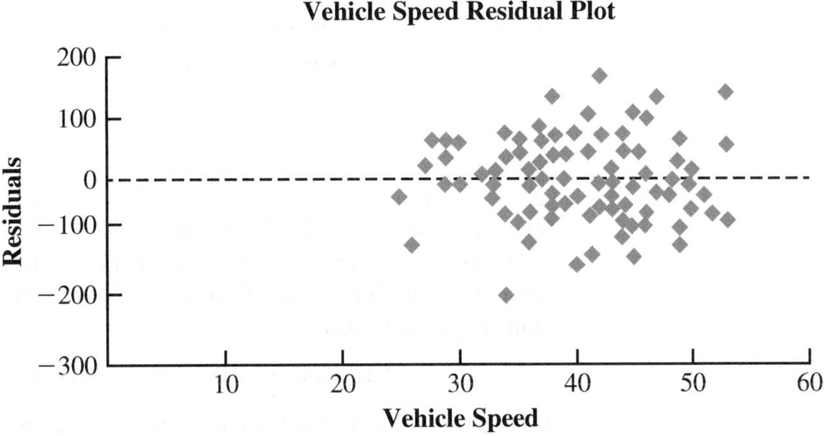

This scatter chart is very similar to the scatter chart of the residuals from the simple linear regression model estimated in part b. When we plot the residuals from the quadratic model against squared values of vehicle speed, the scatter chart does not provide strong evidence of a violation of the conditions, so we will proceed with our inference.

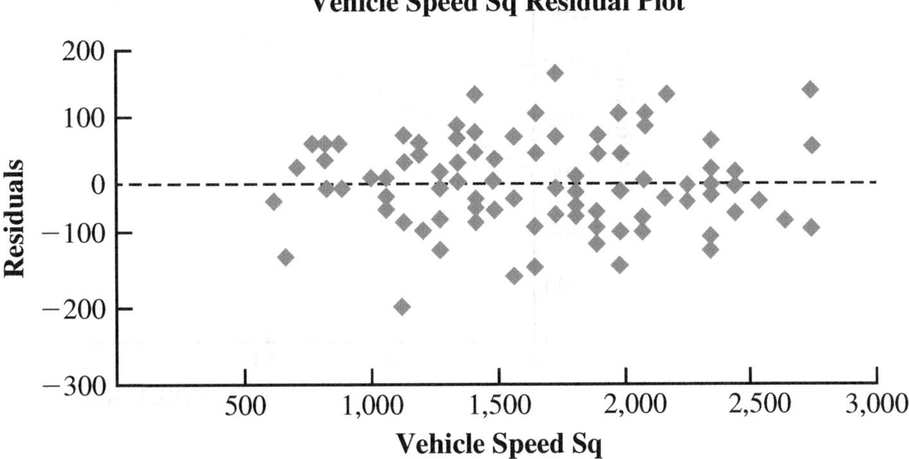

The p value for the test of the hypothesis that $\beta_1 = 0$ is 0.0074. Because this p value is less than the 0.05 level of significance, we again reject the hypothesis that $\beta_1 = 0$. Similarly, the p value for the test of the hypothesis that $\beta_2 = 0$ is 0.0384. Because this p value is less than the 0.05 level of significance, we reject the hypothesis that $\beta_2 = 0$. We therefore conclude that there is a nonlinear relationship between vehicle speed and traffic flow. We estimate that when vehicle speed increases from some value x to $x + 1$, the traffic flow changes by:

$$28.0372\,[(x + 1) - x] - 0.2665\,[(x + 1)^2 - x^2]$$
$$= 28.0372\,(x - x + 1) - 0.2665\,(x^2 + 2x + 1 - x^2)$$
$$= 28.0372 - 0.2665\,(2x + 1)$$
$$= 27.7707 - 0.5331x$$

That is, estimated traffic flow initially increases as vehicle speed increases when the traffic is traveling at a relatively low speed, and then eventually decreases as vehicle speed increases. Solving this result for x:

$$27.7707 - 0.5331x = 0$$
$$-0.5331x = -27.7707$$
$$x = -27.7707/-0.5330 = 52.0935.$$

tells us that estimated maximum traffic flow occurs at a vehicle speed of 52 miles per hour; at speeds below 52 miles per hour. the traffic flow increases as vehicle speed increases, and at speeds above 52 miles per hour. the traffic flow decreases as vehicle speed increases. Substituting 52 miles per hour into the estimated second order quadratic regression equation:

$$\hat{y} = 621.2138 + 28.0372(52) - 0.2665(52^2) = 1358.41$$

yields the estimated maximum traffic flow of approximately 1,358 vehicles.

A plot of the linear and quadratic regression lines helps us better understand the difference in how these two models fit the sample data.

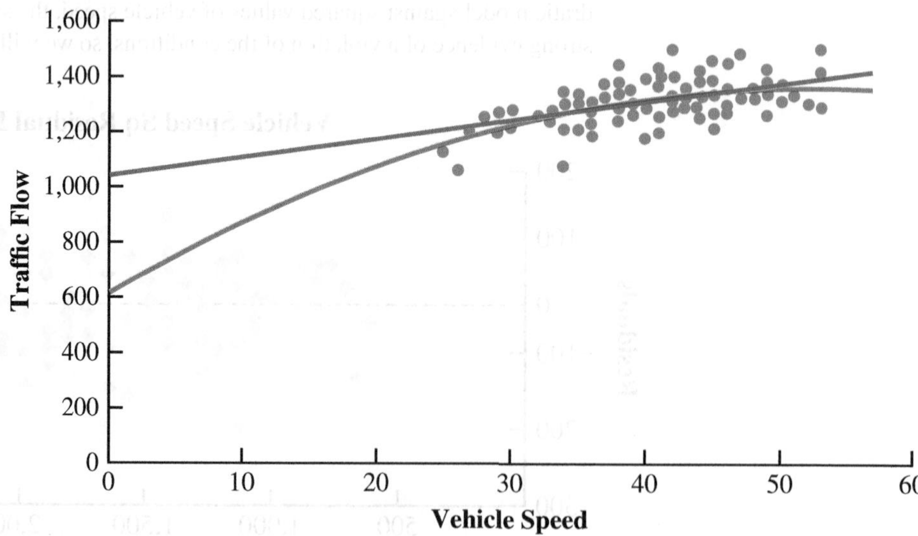

This display shows that there is little difference in how the simple linear regression line (in green) and the quadratic regression line (in red) fit the sample data. Comparison of the coefficients of determination for these two models shows that the estimated second-order quadratic regression equation explains only slightly more than 3% of the variation in the sample values of traffic flow than did the less complex simple linear regression model, Since the simple linear regression model has almost the same explanatory power as the quadratic regression model and is far simpler, the simple linear regression model is superior.

d. By reducing the range of the axes for the scatter chart we developed in part a, we can see more clearly where (if at all) the relationship between vehicle speed and traffic flow changes:

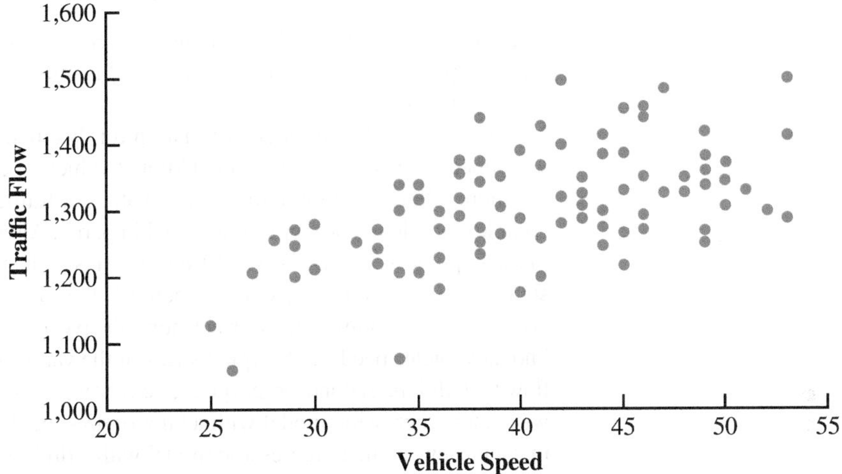

If there is a change in the relationship between vehicle speed and traffic flow, it is not prominent. We will use 45 as the knot (you could select a different value to use as the knot—this is subjective—and the results of part c could be used to estimate the value to use for the knot).

First, we create a dummy variable that is equal to 1 if vehicle speed exceeds the knot value of 45 and 0 otherwise, then we multiply this dummy variable by the difference between vehicle speed and the knot value of 45. We then estimate a regression model with this new variable (the product of the knot dummy variable and the difference between vehicle speed and the knot value of 45) and vehicle speed as the independent variables. The following Excel output provides the estimated piecewise linear regression equation with a knot at vehicle speed = 45 that could be used to predict traffic flow (y) given the vehicle speed (x).

	A	B	C	D	E	F	G	H	I
1	SUMMARY OUTPUT								
2									
3	*Regression Statistics*								
4	Multiple R	0.572827027							
5	R Square	0.328130803							
6	Adjusted R Square	0.314277829							
7	Standard Error	66.98261522							
8	Observations	100							
9									
10	ANOVA								
11		*df*	*SS*	*MS*	*F*	*Significance F*			
12	Regression	2	212548.6	106274.289	23.68666995	4.20058E-09			
13	Residual	97	435207.1	4486.670742					
14	Total	99	647755.6						
15									
16		*Coefficients*	*andard Err*	*t Stat*	*P-value*	*Lower 95%*	*Upper 95%*	*Lower 99.0%*	*Upper 99.0%*
17	Intercept	984.5875335	55.51859	17.73437523	3.35386E-32	874.3984978	1094.776569	838.7142236	1130.460843
18	Vehicle Speed	8.128695783	1.43194	5.676700851	1.42825E-07	5.286690746	10.97070082	4.366318892	11.89107267
19	Knot Interaction	-6.550659202	4.469702	-1.465569711	0.145999635	-15.42177949	2.320461089	-18.29465597	5.193337567

If vehicle speed does not exceed 45 miles per hour, the estimated regression equation is:

$$\hat{y} = 984.5875 + 8.1287x$$

and if vehicle speed exceeds 45 miles per hour, the estimated regression equation is

$$\begin{aligned}\hat{y} &= 984.5875 + 8.1287x - 6.5507(x - 45)\\ &= 1279.3672 + 1.5780x\end{aligned}$$

According to this model, the estimated increase in traffic flow that corresponds with a 1-mile-per-hour increase in vehicle speed is much smaller if the traffic speed is over 45 miles per hour.

Note that the coefficient of determination for this model is $R^2 = 0.3281$, so the piecewise linear regression model with a knot at vehicle speed = 45 explains approximately 1% more of the variation in the sample values of traffic flow than did the much less complex simple linear regression model in part b. Also note that the p value for the test of the hypothesis that $\beta_2 = 0$ is 0.1460. Because this p value exceeds the 0.05 level of significance, we do not reject the hypothesis that $\beta_2 = 0$ (i.e., the knot interaction is not statistically significant). Furthermore, the piecewise linear regression model with a knot at vehicle speed = 45 explains less of the variation in the sample values of traffic flow than did the second-order quadratic regression model in part c. Thus, the piecewise linear regression model with a knot of 45 should not be considered further. Note that a piecewise linear regression model with a different knot (perhaps a knot of 52) may perform much better than our piecewise linear regression model with a knot of 45.

e. We split the data set so that the first data set contains 65 observations with values of vehicle speed less than 45 and the second data set contains 35 observations with values of vehicle speed greater than or equal to 45.

The following Excel output provides the estimated simple linear regression equation that could be used to predict traffic flow (y) given vehicle speed (x) below 45.

	A	B	C	D	E	F	G	H	I
1	SUMMARY OUTPUT								
2									
3	*Regression Statistics*								
4	Multiple R	0.545746678							
5	R Square	0.297839436							
6	Adjusted R Square	0.286694031							
7	Standard Error	67.66095307							
8	Observations	65							
9									
10	ANOVA								
11		*df*	*SS*	*MS*	*F*	*Significance F*			
12	Regression	1	122338.3274	122338.3274	26.72306799	2.58072E-06			
13	Residual	63	288414.288	4578.004571					
14	Total	64	410752.6154						
15									
16		*Coefficients*	*Standard Error*	*t Stat*	*P-value*	*Lower 95%*	*Upper 95%*	*Lower 95.0%*	*Upper 95.0%*
17	Intercept	961.5736286	63.90721366	15.04640202	1.56428E-22	833.8652526	1089.282005	833.8652526	1089.282005
18	Vehicle Speed	8.803852002	1.703058534	5.169435945	2.58072E-06	5.400561088	12.20714292	5.400561088	12.20714292

The estimated multiple linear regression equation is $\hat{y} = 961.5736 + 8.8039x$, and the coefficient of determination for this model is $r^2 = 0.2978$, so the regression model explains approximately 30% of the variation in the sample values of traffic flow corresponding to vehicle speeds less than 45.

The following Excel output provides the estimated simple linear regression equation that could be used to predict traffic flow (y) given vehicle speed (x) greater than or equal to 45.

	A	B	C	D	E	F	G	H	I
1	SUMMARY OUTPUT								
2									
3	*Regression Statistics*								
4	Multiple R	0.143794419							
5	R Square	0.020676835							
6	Adjusted R Square	-0.008999625							
7	Standard Error	66.10615071							
8	Observations	35							
9									
10	ANOVA								
11		*df*	*SS*	*MS*	*F*	*Significance F*			
12	Regression	1	3044.778542	3044.778542	0.696741969	0.409882918			
13	Residual	33	144210.7643	4370.023161					
14	Total	34	147255.5429						
15									
16		*Coefficients*	*Standard Error*	*t Stat*	*P-value*	*Lower 95%*	*Upper 95%*	*Lower 95.0%*	*Upper 95.0%*
17	Intercept	1167.732293	220.9022439	5.2861948	7.92887E-06	718.3032986	1617.161288	718.3032986	1617.161288
18	Vehicle Speed	3.802578019	4.555563951	0.83471071	0.409882918	-5.465786527	13.07094257	-5.465786527	13.07094257

The estimated multiple linear regression equation is $\hat{y} = 1167.7323 + 3.8026x$, and the coefficient of determination for this model is $r^2 = 0.0207$, so the regression model explains approximately 2% of the variation in the sample values of traffic flow corresponding to vehicle speeds ≥ 45.

Separating the data into two sets and fitting separate simple linear regression equations to each set results in an even worse fit than the piecewise linear regression with a single knot at vehicle speed = 45.

Comparing predicted values of traffic flow for vehicle speeds of 44 and 46 (slightly below and above the knot value of 45) will allow us to see the difference between the piecewise linear regression with a single knot and two separate simple regression equations.

For vehicle speed = 44 the piecewise linear regression with a single knot produces:

$$\hat{y} = 984.5875 + 8.1287(44) = 1342.25$$

For vehicle speed = 46, the piecewise linear regression with a single knot produces:

$$\hat{y} = 984.5875 + 8.1287(46) - 6.5507(46 - 45) = 1351.96$$

Alternatively, for vehicle speed = 44 the simple linear regression fit on observations with vehicle speeds <45 produces:

$$\hat{y} = 961.5736 + 8.8039(44) = 1348.94.$$

For vehicle speed = 46, the simple linear regression fit on observations with vehicle speeds ≥ 45:

$$\hat{y} = 1167.7323 + 3.8026(46) = 1342.65.$$

That is, fitting two separate simple linear regression equations results in predicted traffic flow being considerably less at vehicle speed = 46 than at vehicle speed = 44. This is opposite the behavior predicted by the piecewise linear regression with a single knot at vehicle speed = 45.

To visualize how this happens, note from the charts below how the piecewise linear regression "connects" two regression lines at the knot value of 45 while the two linear regression equations fit separately result in a disjointed fit.

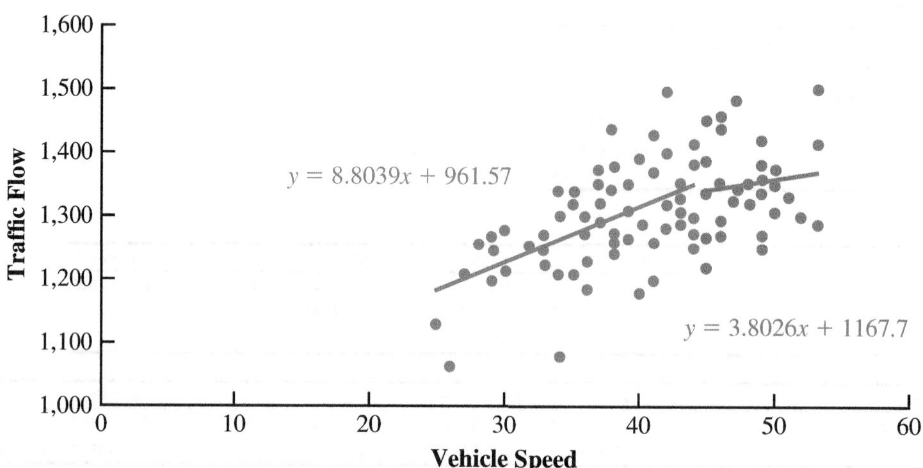

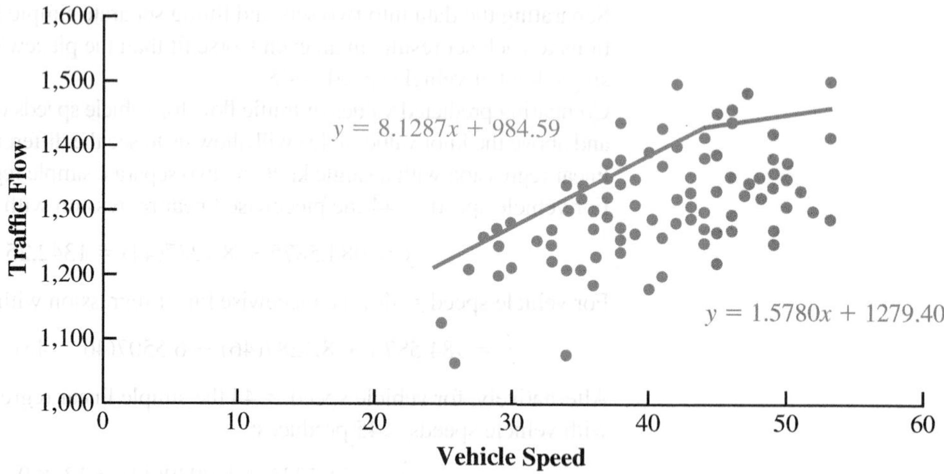

f. Other independent variables that you could add to your regression model to explain more variation in traffic flow include number of accidents and weather conditions (i.e., rainy or snowy).

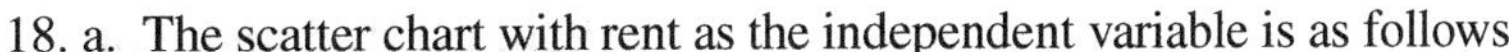

18. a. The scatter chart with rent as the independent variable is as follows:

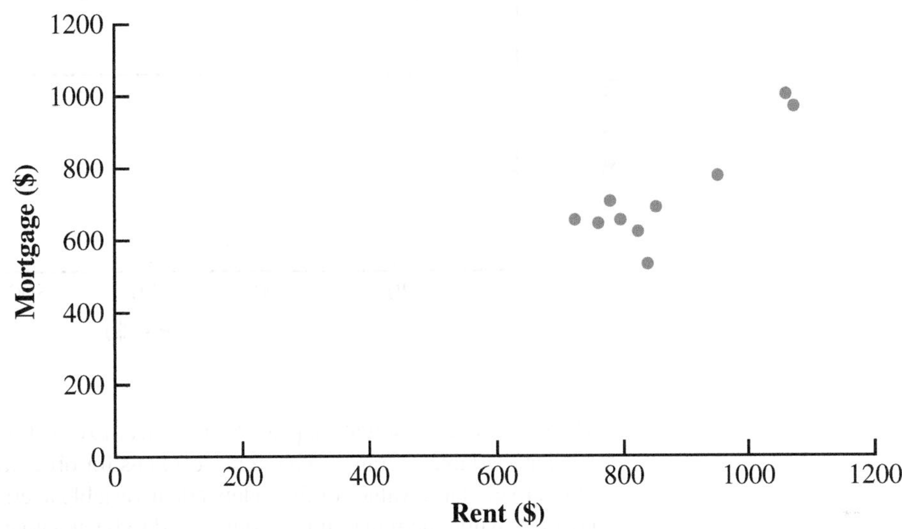

The scatter chart suggests that rent is positively related to mortgage. However, it is not clear that the relationship is linear, so a simple linear regression model may not be appropriate.

b. The following Excel output provides the estimated simple linear regression equation that could be used to predict the monthly mortgage on the median-priced home (y) given the average asking rent (x).

	A	B	C	D	E	F	G	H	I
1	SUMMARY OUTPUT								
2									
3	*Regression Statistics*								
4	Multiple R	0.869565051							
5	R Square	0.756143377							
6	Adjusted R Square	0.725661299							
7	Standard Error	78.7819141							
8	Observations	10							
9									
10	ANOVA								
11		*df*	*SS*	*MS*	*F*	*Significance F*			
12	Regression	1	153961.6801	153961.6801	24.80616254	0.001078711			
13	Residual	8	49652.71992	6206.58999					
14	Total	9	203614.4						
15									
16		*Coefficients*	*Standard Error*	*t Stat*	*P-value*	*Lower 95%*	*Upper 95%*	*Lower 99.0%*	*Upper 99.0%*
17	Intercept	-197.9583149	187.6949928	-1.054680852	0.322379429	-630.7837445	234.8671148	-827.747716	431.8310862
18	Rent ($)	1.06992877	0.214820179	4.980578534	0.001078711	0.57455255	1.56530499	0.349123864	1.790733676

The estimated multiple linear regression equation is $\hat{y} = -197.9583 + 1.0699x$. The plot of the residuals for this model against the independent variable average asking rent is as follows:

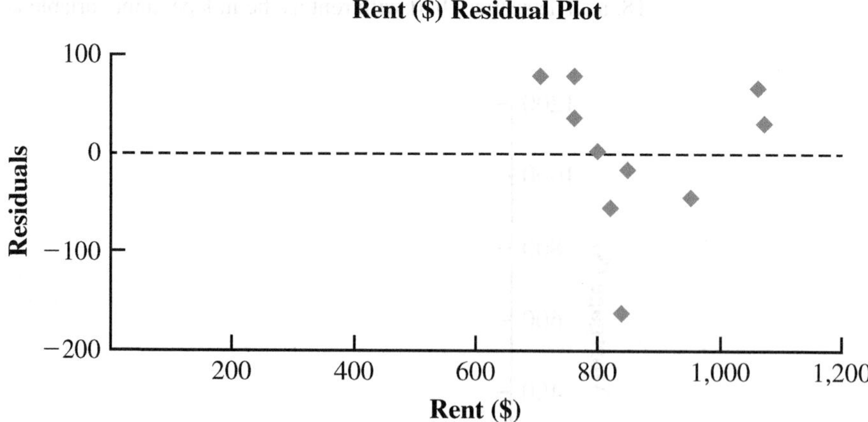

The mean of the residuals appears to differ from zero at several values of the independent variable average asking rent; residuals for observations with relatively small or relatively large values of the independent variable average asking rent tend to be positive, while the remaining residuals tend to be negative. This suggests that the relationship between the independent variable average asking rent and the dependent variable monthly mortgage on the median-priced home may be nonlinear, so a simple linear regression model may not be appropriate.

c. The following Excel output provides the estimated second-order quadratic regression equation that could be used to predict the monthly mortgage on the median-priced home (y) given the average asking rent (x).

	A	B	C	D	E	F	G	H	I
1	SUMMARY OUTPUT								
2									
3	*Regression Statistics*								
4	Multiple R	0.947891902							
5	R Square	0.898499058							
6	Adjusted R Square	0.869498789							
7	Standard Error	54.33632482							
8	Observations	10							
9									
10	ANOVA								
11		*df*	*SS*	*MS*	*F*	*Significance F*			
12	Regression	2	182947.3466	91473.67332	30.98243867	0.000333154			
13	Residual	7	20667.05336	2952.436194					
14	Total	9	203614.4						
15									
16		*Coefficients*	*Standard Error*	*t Stat*	*P-value*	*Lower 95%*	*Upper 95%*	*Lower 99.0%*	*Upper 99.0%*
17	Intercept	3965.633075	1335.112564	2.970261221	0.020800039	808.5935275	7122.672622	-706.5710428	8637.837193
18	Rent ($)	-8.260622772	2.981554951	-2.77057539	0.027671164	-15.31087992	-1.210365627	-18.69452452	2.173278979
19	Rent Squared	0.005130519	0.001637419	3.133295721	0.016533359	0.001258638	0.009002401	-0.000599603	0.010860642

The estimated second-order quadratic regression equation is:

$$\hat{y} = 3965.6331 - 8.2606x + 0.0051x^2.$$

d. Excel plots of the residuals for the estimated second-order quadratic regression model against the independent variables average asking rent and average asking rent squared are as follows:

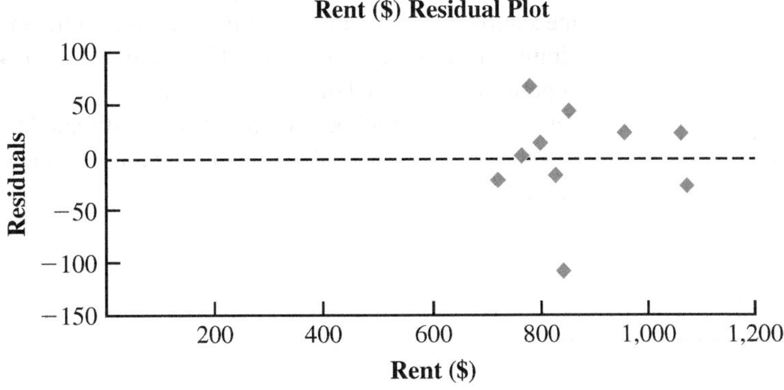

These scatter charts suggest that the estimated second-order quadratic regression model fits the sample data much better than the simple linear regression model. A plot of the linear and quadratic regression lines overlaid on the scatter chart of the monthly mortgage on the median-priced home and the average asking rent will also help us better understand the difference in how the quadratic regression model and a simple linear regression model fit the sample data.

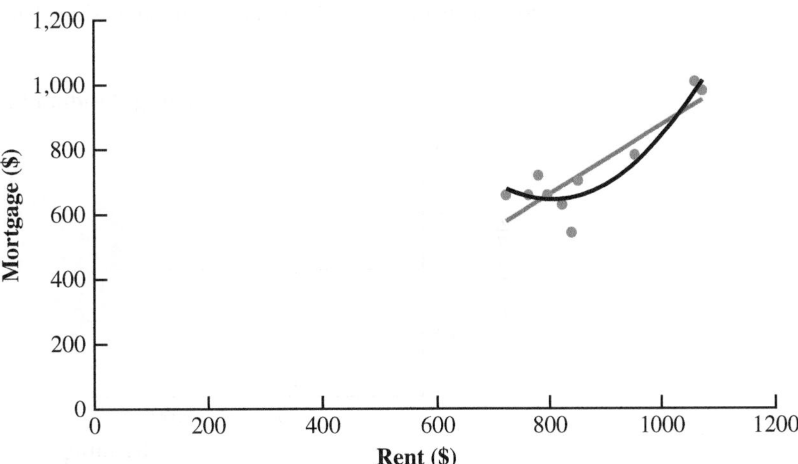

This display shows that there is a substantial difference in how the simple linear regression line (in green) and the quadratic regression line (in red) fit the sample data. Note that the coefficient of determination for the second-order quadratic regression model is $R^2 = 0.8985$, so the regression model explains almost 13% more variation in the sample values of the monthly mortgage on the median-priced home than does the simple linear regression model. The estimated regression model developed in part c is superior to the model developed in part a.

20. a. The following Excel output provides the estimated multiple linear regression equation that that includes critical reading (x_1) and mathematics (x_2) SAT scores as independent variables.

	A	B	C	D	E	F	G	H	I
1	SUMMARY OUTPUT								
2									
3	*Regression Statistics*								
4	Multiple R	0.878764528							
5	R Square	0.772227096							
6	Adjusted R Square	0.769914681							
7	Standard Error	0.318207048							
8	Observations	200							
9									
10	ANOVA								
11		*df*	*SS*	*MS*	*F*	*Significance F*			
12	Regression	2	67.62835012	33.81417506	333.9482776	5.17551E-64			
13	Residual	197	19.94737788	0.101255725					
14	Total	199	87.575728						
15									
16		*Coefficients*	*Standard Error*	*t Stat*	*P-value*	*Lower 95%*	*Upper 95%*	*Lower 99.0%*	*Upper 99.0%*
17	Intercept	-2.671709674	0.21944785	-12.17469059	8.64934E-26	-3.104478178	-2.23894117	-3.242496964	-2.100922384
18	Reading	0.004343448	0.000239975	18.09959107	9.06411E-44	0.003870198	0.004816697	0.003719269	0.004967626
19	Math	0.004534844	0.000242036	18.73627058	1.20495E-45	0.004057531	0.005012157	0.003905306	0.005164382

The estimated multiple linear regression equation is $\hat{y} = -2.6717 + 0.0043x_i + 0.0045x_2$, and the coefficient of determination for this multiple regression model is $R^2 = 0.7722$, so the regression model explains approximately 77% of the variation in the sample values of the freshman GPA.

Before testing any hypotheses about this regression model, we check the conditions necessary for valid inference in regression. The correlation between the two

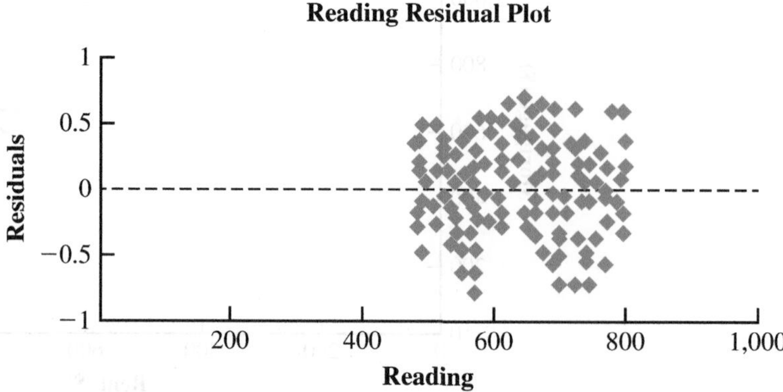

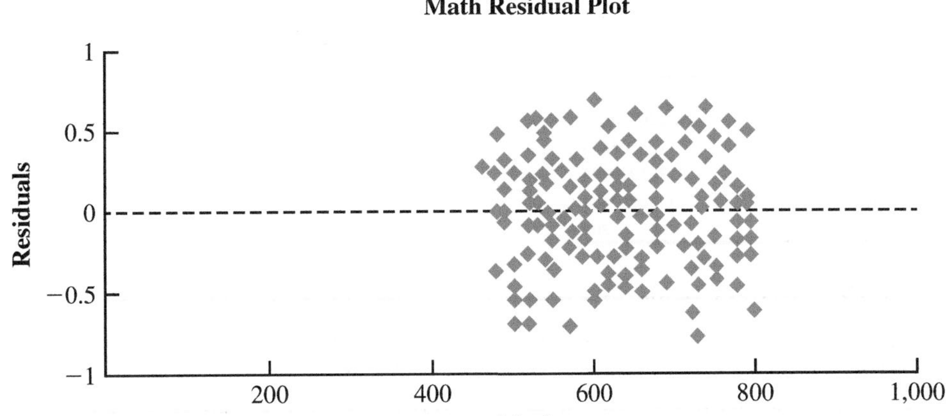

independent variables (critical reading and mathematics SAT scores) is −0.0161, so there is no need for concern about autocorrelation. Furthermore, the Excel plots of the residuals and each of the quantitative independent variables (critical reading and mathematics SAT scores) are as follows:

The residuals appear to have a relatively constant variance across the values of each independent variable and do not appear to be badly skewed at any value of either variable. However, the mean of the residuals possibly differs from zero at several values of each independent variable. Although these violations do not appear to be dramatic, we will proceed with our inference but will keep our findings in mind as we proceed.

The p value for the test of the hypothesis that $\beta_1 = 0$ is 9.06411E-44. Because this p value is less than the 0.05 level of significance, we again reject the hypothesis that $\beta_1 = 0$ and conclude that there is a relationship between SAT scores on critical reading and freshman GPA. We estimate that holding the SAT score on mathematics constant, a one-point increase in the SAT score on critical reading corresponds to an increase in freshman GPA of 0.0043. We expect freshman GPA to increase as the SAT score on critical reading increases, so this result appears to be reasonable.

The p value for the test of the hypothesis that $\beta_2 = 0$ is 1.20495E-45. Because this p value is less than the 0.05 level of significance, we again reject the hypothesis that $\beta_2 = 0$ and conclude that there is a relationship between SAT scores on mathematics and freshman GPA. We estimate that holding the SAT score on critical reading constant, a one-point increase in the SAT score on mathematics corresponds to an increase in freshman GPA of 0.0045. We expect freshman GPA to increase as the SAT score on mathematics increases, so this result appears to be reasonable.

b. Using the multiple linear regression model developed in part a, the predicted freshman GPA of Bobby Engle (a student who has been admitted to Ruggles College with a 660 SAT score on critical reading and at a 630 SAT score on mathematics) is:

$$\hat{y} = -2.6717 + 0.0043(660) + 0.0045(630) = 3.0519,$$

or approximately 3.05.

c. The following Excel output provides the estimated multiple linear regression equation that that includes critical reading (x_1) and mathematics (x_2) SAT scores and their interaction (x_1x_2) as independent variables.

	A	B	C	D	E	F	G	H	I
1	SUMMARY OUTPUT								
2									
3	*Regression Statistics*								
4	Multiple R	0.886287861							
5	R Square	0.785506173							
6	Adjusted R Square	0.782223104							
7	Standard Error	0.30957882							
8	Observations	200							
9									
10	ANOVA								
11		*df*	*SS*	*MS*	*F*	*Significance F*			
12	Regression	3	68.79127497	22.93042499	239.2597374	2.99604E-65			
13	Residual	196	18.78445303	0.095839046					
14	Total	199	87.575728						
15									
16		*Coefficients*	*Standard Error*	*t Stat*	*P-value*	*Lower 95%*	*Upper 95%*	*Lower 99.0%*	*Upper 99.0%*
17	Intercept	0.797737205	1.018616886	0.783157255	0.434480039	-1.211119146	2.806593555	-1.851833349	3.447307758
18	Reading	-0.001119552	0.001585573	-0.70608628	0.480972921	-0.004246526	0.002007423	-0.005243858	0.003004755
19	Math	-0.00096018	0.001594962	-0.602008133	0.547864481	-0.00410567	0.00218531	-0.005108908	0.003188548
20	ReadMath	8.65563E-06	2.48482E-06	3.483409928	0.000610558	3.75522E-06	1.3556E-05	2.19227E-06	1.5119E-05

The estimated multiple linear regression equation is

$$\hat{y} = 0.7977 - 0.0011x_1 - 0.0010x_2 + 0.000009x_1x_2$$

and the coefficient of determination for this multiple regression model is $R^2 = 0.7855$, so the regression model explains approximately 79% of the variation in the sample values of the freshman GPA.

Before testing any hypotheses about this regression model, we again check the conditions necessary for valid inference in regression. As noted before, the correlation between the two independent variables (critical reading and mathematics SAT scores) is −0.0161, so there is no need for concern about autocorrelation. Scatter plots of the residuals and each of the independent variables follow.

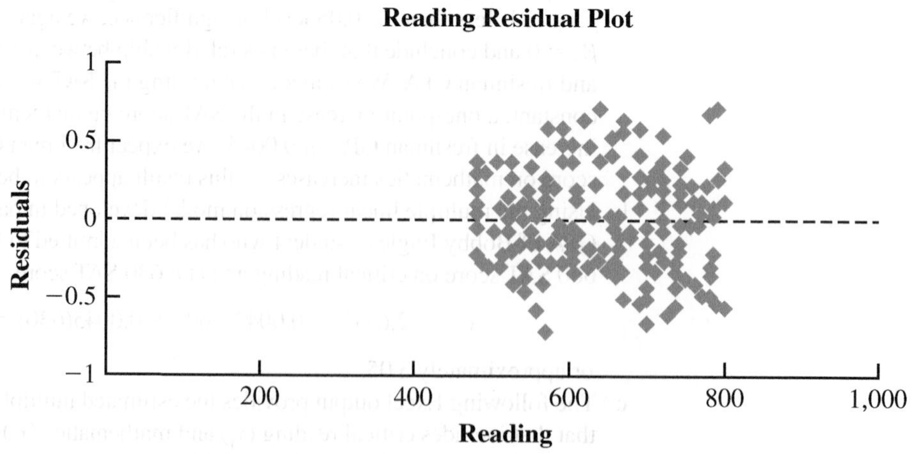

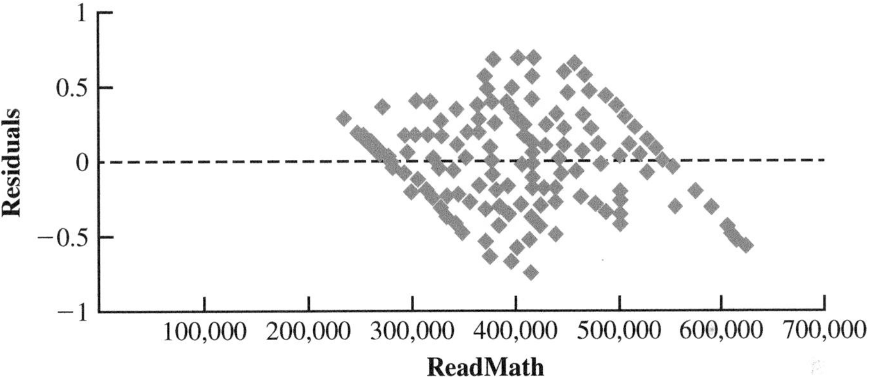

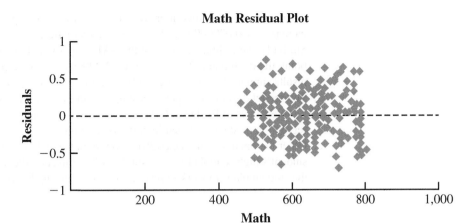

The addition of the readmath interation appears to have had relatively little impact on the residuals. However, we did not believe that these violations were extreme in the multiple regression model that did not include the interaction, so we will proceed with our inference.

The p value for the test of the hypothesis that $\beta_1 = 0$ is 0.4810. Because this p value is greater than the 0.05 level of significance, we do not reject the hypothesis that $\beta_1 = 0$ and we conclude that there is not a linear relationship between SAT scores on critical reading and freshman GPA when controlling for SAT scores on mathematics and the interaction between SAT scores on critical reading and SAT scores on mathematics.

The p value for the test of the hypothesis that $\beta_2 = 0$ is 0.5479. Because this p value is greater than the 0.05 level of significance, we do not reject the hypothesis that $\beta_2 = 0$ and we conclude that there is not a linear relationship between SAT scores on mathematics and freshman GPA when controlling for SAT scores on reading and the interaction between SAT scores on critical reading and SAT scores on mathematics.

The p value for the test of the hypothesis that $\beta_3 = 0$ is 0.0006. Because this p value is less than the 0.05 level of significance, we reject the hypothesis that $\beta_3 = 0$ and we conclude that there is a relationship between the interaction of SAT scores on critical reading and mathematics and the dependent variable freshman GPA. We estimate that when the SAT score on critical reading increases by one point, the freshman GPA increases by 0.000009 * SAT score on mathematics.

Similarly, we estimate that when the SAT score on mathematics increases by one point, the freshman GPA increases by 0.000009 * SAT score on critical reading. These results support the conjecture made by the Ruggles College Director of Admissions.

d. The model developed in part a is simpler and explains almost as much variation in the sample values of freshman GPA as the regression model developed in part c, so the regression model developed in part a is superior.

e. Other factors that could be added to the model as independent variables include the student's high school GPA, the number of credits, and the number of hours per week the student plans to work in paid employment during her/his freshman year.

Chapter 8: Time Series Analysis and Forecasting

Solutions

2. The following table shows the calculations for parts a, b, and c.

Week	Time Series Value	Forecast	Forecast Error	Absolute Value of Forecast Error	Squared Forecast Error	Percentage Error	Absolute Value of Percentage Error
1	18						
2	13	18.00	−5.00	5.00	25.00	−38.46	38.46
3	16	15.50	0.50	0.50	0.25	3.13	3.13
4	11	15.67	−4.67	4.67	21.81	−42.45	42.45
5	17	14.50	2.50	2.50	6.25	14.71	14.71
6	14	15.00	−1.00	1.00	1.00	−7.14	7.14
			Totals	13.67	54.31	−70.21	105.86

a. MAE = 13.67/5 = 2.73
b. MSE = 54.31/5 = 10.86
c. MAPE = 105.89/5 = 21.18
d. The forecast for week 7 is $\hat{y}_7 = (y_1 + y_2 + y_3 + y_4 + y_5 + y_6) / 6 = (18 + 13 + 16 + 11 + 17 + 14) / 6 = 14.83$.

4. a.

Month	Time Series Value	Forecast	Forecast Error	Squared Forecast Error
1	24			
2	13	24	−11	121
3	20	13	7	49
4	12	20	−8	64
5	19	12	7	49
6	23	19	4	16
7	15	23	−8	64
			Total	363

MSE = 363/6 = 60.5
The forecast for month 8 is $\hat{y}_8 = y_7 = 15$.

b.

Week	Time Series Value	Forecast	Forecast Error	Squared Forecast Error
1	24			
2	13	24.00	−11.00	121.00
3	20	18.50	1.50	2.25
4	12	19.00	−7.00	49.00
5	19	17.25	1.75	3.06
6	23	17.60	5.40	29.16
7	15	18.50	−3.50	12.25
			Total	216.72

MSE = 216.72/6 = 36.12

The forecast for month 8 is $\hat{y}_8 = (y_1 + y_2 + y_3 + y_4 + y_5 + y_6 + y_7) / 7 = (24 + 13 + 20 + 12 + 19 + 23 + 15) / 7 = 18.$

c. The average of all the previous values is better because MSE is smaller.

6. a.

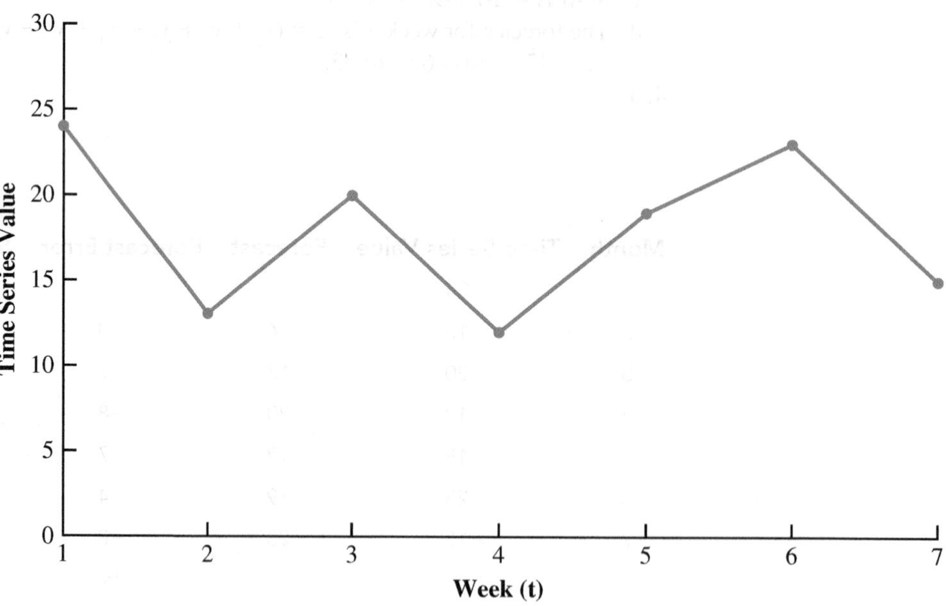

The data appear to follow a horizontal pattern.

b. Three-week moving average.

Week	Time Series Value	Forecast	Forecast Error	Squared Forecast Error
1	24			
2	13			
3	20			
4	12	19.00	−7.00	49.00
5	19	15.00	4.00	16.00
6	23	17.00	6.00	36.00
7	15	18.00	−3.00	9.00
			Total	110.00

MSE = 110/4 = 27.5.

The forecast for week 8 is $\hat{y}_8 = (y_5 + y_6 + y_7) / 3 = (19 + 23 + 15) / 3 = 19$.

c. Smoothing constant $\alpha = 0.2$

Week	Time Series Value	Forecast	Forecast Error	Squared Forecast Error
1	24			
2	13	24.00	−11.00	121.00
3	20	21.80	−1.80	3.24
4	12	21.44	−9.44	89.11
5	19	19.55	−0.55	0.30
6	23	19.44	3.56	12.66
7	15	20.15	−5.15	26.56
			Total	252.87

MSE = 252.87/6 = 42.15

The forecast for week 8 is $\hat{y}_8 = \alpha y_7 + (1 - \alpha)\,\hat{y}_7 = 0.2(15) + (1 - 0.2)20.15 = 19.12$.

d. The three-week moving average provides a better forecast since it has a smaller MSE.

e. Several values of α will yield an MSE smaller than the MSE associated with $\alpha = 0.2$. The table below shows the resulting MSE for several different α values.

α	MSE
0.1	48.86
0.2	42.15
0.3	39.85
0.4	39.79
0.5	41.02
0.6	43.18
0.7	46.15

The value of α that yields the minimum MSE is $\alpha = 0.351$, which yields an MSE of 39.61.

$\alpha = 0.351$

Month	Time Series Value	Forecast	Forecast Error	Squared Forecast Error
1	24			
2	13	24	−11.00	121.00
3	20	20.13	−0.13	0.02
4	12	20.09	−8.09	65.40
5	19	17.25	1.75	3.08
6	23	17.86	5.14	26.40
7	15	19.67	−4.67	21.79
			Total	237.69

MSE = 237.69/6 = 39.61428577

8. a. Exponential smoothing forecasts using $\alpha = 0.1$:

Week	Time Series Value	Forecast	Forecast Error	Squared Forecast Error
1	17	17.00		
2	21	17.00	4.00	16.00
3	19	17.40	1.60	2.56
4	23	17.56	5.44	29.59
5	18	18.10	−0.10	0.01
6	16	18.09	−2.09	4.38
7	20	17.88	2.12	4.48
8	18	18.10	−0.10	0.01
9	22	18.09	3.91	15.32
10	20	18.48	1.52	2.32
11	15	18.63	−3.63	13.18
12	22	18.27	3.73	13.94
			Total	101.78

MSE = 101.78/11 = 9.253

For a smoothing constant of $\alpha = 0.2$:

Week	Time Series Value	Forecast	Forecast Error	Squared Forecast Error
1	17	17.00		
2	21	17.00	4.00	16.00
3	19	17.80	1.20	1.44
4	23	18.04	4.96	24.60
5	18	19.03	−1.03	1.07
6	16	18.83	−2.83	7.98
7	20	18.26	1.74	3.03
8	18	18.61	−0.61	0.37
9	22	18.49	3.51	12.34
10	20	19.19	0.81	0.66
11	15	19.35	−4.35	18.94
12	22	18.48	3.52	12.38
			Total	98.80

MSE = 98.80 / 11 = 8.982

Applying the MSE measure of forecast accuracy, a smoothing constant of $\alpha = 0.2$ produces a smaller MSE and so is preferred.

b. For a smoothing constant of $\alpha = 0.1$:

Week	Time Series Value	Forecast	Forecast Error	Absolute Forecast Error
1	17	17.00		
2	21	17.00	4.00	4.00
3	19	17.40	1.60	1.60
4	23	17.56	5.44	5.44
5	18	18.10	−0.10	0.10
6	16	18.09	−2.09	2.09
7	20	17.88	2.12	2.12
8	18	18.10	−0.10	0.10
9	22	18.09	3.91	3.91
10	20	18.48	1.52	1.52
11	15	18.63	−3.63	3.63
12	22	18.27	3.73	3.73
			Total	28.25

MAE = 28.25 / 11 = 2.568

For a smoothing constant of $\alpha = 0.2$:

Week	Time Series Value	Forecast	Forecast Error	Absolute Forecast Error
1	17	17.00		
2	21	17.00	4.00	4.00
3	19	17.80	1.20	1.20
4	23	18.04	4.96	4.96
5	18	19.03	−1.03	1.03
6	16	18.83	−2.83	2.83
7	20	18.26	1.74	1.74
8	18	18.61	−0.61	0.61
9	22	18.49	3.51	3.51
10	20	19.19	0.81	0.81
11	15	19.35	−4.35	4.35
12	22	18.48	3.52	3.52
			Total	28.56

MAE = 28.56 / 11 = 2.596

Applying the MAE measure of forecast accuracy, a smoothing constant of $\alpha = 0.1$ produces a slightly smaller MAE and so is preferred.

c. For a smoothing constant of $\alpha = 0.1$:

Week	Time Series Value	Forecast	Forecast Error	100 * (Forecast Error / Time Series Value)	Absolute Value of 100*(Forecast Error / Time Series Value)
1	17	17.00			
2	21	17.00	4.00	19.05	19.05
3	19	17.40	1.60	8.42	8.42
4	23	17.56	5.44	23.65	23.65
5	18	18.10	−0.10	−0.58	0.58
6	16	18.09	−2.09	−13.09	13.09
7	20	17.88	2.12	10.58	10.58
8	18	18.10	−0.10	−0.53	0.53
9	22	18.09	3.91	17.79	17.79
10	20	18.48	1.52	7.61	7.61
11	15	18.63	−3.63	−24.20	24.20
12	22	18.27	3.73	16.97	16.97
				Total	142.46

MAPE = 142.46 / 11 = 12.95

For a smoothing constant of $\alpha = 0.2$:

Week	Time Series Value	Forecast	Forecast Error	100 * (Forecast Error / Time Series Value)	Absolute Value of 100 * (Forecast Error / Time Series Value)
1	17	17.00			
2	21	17.00	4.00	19.05	19.05
3	19	17.80	1.20	6.32	6.32
4	23	18.04	4.96	21.57	21.57
5	18	19.03	−1.03	−5.73	5.73
6	16	18.83	−2.83	−17.66	17.66
7	20	18.26	1.74	8.70	8.70
8	18	18.61	−0.61	−3.38	3.38
9	22	18.49	3.51	15.97	15.97
10	20	19.19	0.81	4.05	4.05
11	15	19.35	−4.35	−29.01	29.01
12	22	18.48	3.52	15.99	15.99
				Total	147.43

MAPE = 147.43 / 11 = 13.40

Applying the MAPE measure of forecast accuracy, a smoothing constant of $\alpha = 0.1$ produces a smaller MAPE and so is preferred.

10. a.

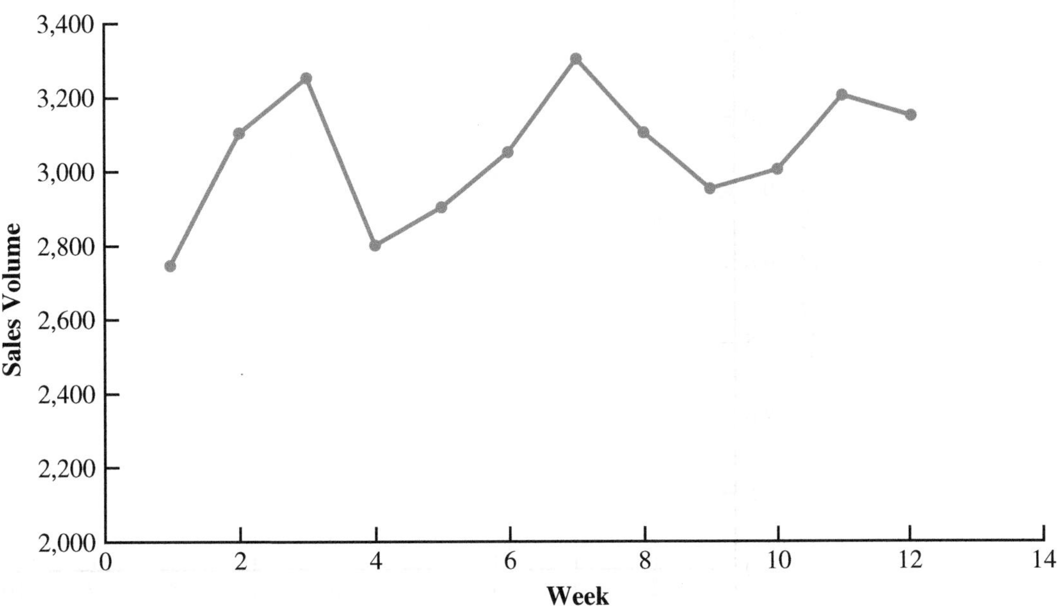

The time series plot indicates a horizontal pattern.

b.

Week	Sales Volume	Forecast	Forecast Error	Squared Value of Forecast Error
1	2,750			
2	3,100	2,750.00	350.000	122,500.00
3	3,250	2,890.00	360.000	129,600.00
4	2,800	3,034.00	−234.000	54,756.00
5	2,900	2,940.40	−40.400	1,632.16
6	3,050	2,924.24	125.760	15,815.58
7	3,300	2,974.54	325.456	105,921.61
8	3,100	3,104.73	−4.726	22.34
9	2,950	3,102.84	−152.836	23,358.79
10	3,000	3,041.70	−41.702	1,739.02
11	3,200	3,025.02	174.979	30,617.68
12	3,150	3,095.01	54.987	3,023.62
			Total	488,986.80

Note: MSE = 488,986.80/11 = 44,453

Forecast for week 13 is $\hat{y}_{13} = \alpha y_{12} + (1 - \alpha)\, \hat{y}_{12} = 0.4(3150) + 0.6(3095.01) =$ 3117.01, or 3117 half-gallons of milk.

12. a.

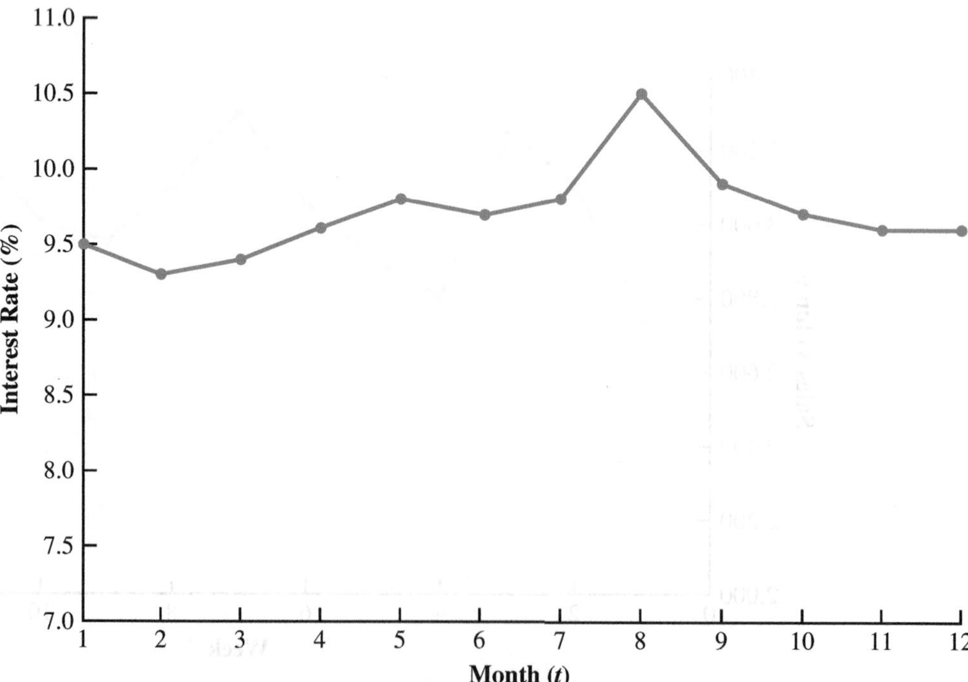

The data appear to follow a horizontal pattern.

b.

Month	Time-Series Value	3-Month Moving Average Forecast	(Error)^2	4-Month Moving Average Forecast	(Error)^2
1	9.5				
2	9.3				
3	9.4				
4	9.6	9.40	0.04		
5	9.8	9.43	0.14	9.45	0.12
6	9.7	9.60	0.01	9.53	0.03
7	9.8	9.70	0.01	9.63	0.03
8	10.5	9.77	0.53	9.73	0.59
9	9.9	10.00	0.01	9.95	0.00
10	9.7	10.07	0.14	9.98	0.08
11	9.6	10.03	0.18	9.97	0.14
12	9.6	9.73	0.02	9.92	0.10
			1.08		1.09

MSE(3-Month) = 1.08/9 = 0.12
MSE(4-Month) = 1.09/8 = 0.14
The MSE for the 3-month moving average is smaller, so use the 3-month moving average.

c. The forecast for month 13 is $\hat{y}_{13} = (y_{10} + y_{11} + y_{12}) / 3 = (9.7 + 9.6 + 9.6) / 3 = 9.63$.

14. a.

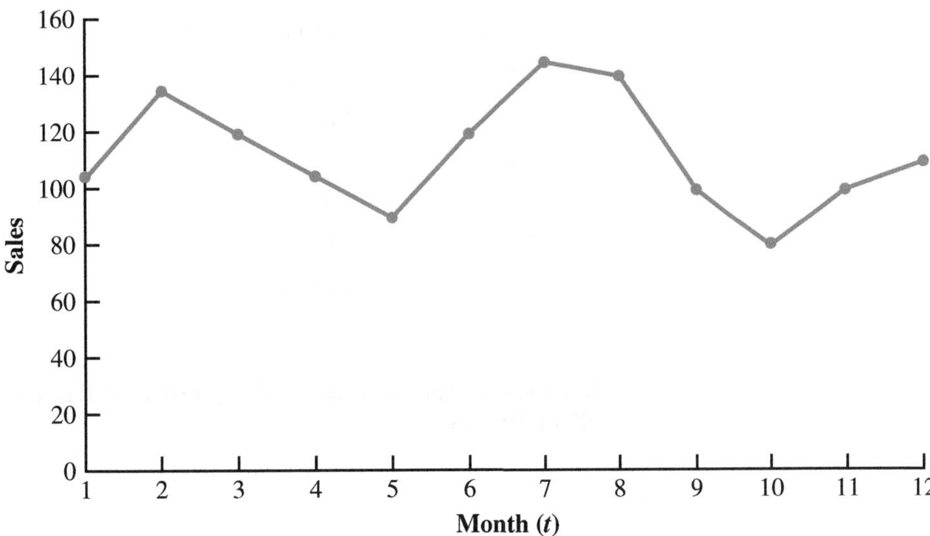

The data appear to follow a horizontal pattern.

b. Smoothing constant $\alpha = 0.3$.

Month t	Time-Series Value y_t	Forecast $\hat{y}_t$	Forecast Error $y_t - \hat{y}_t$	Squared Error $(y_t - \hat{y}_t)^2$
1	105			
2	135	105.00	30.00	900.00
3	120	114.00	6.00	36.00
4	105	115.80	−10.80	116.64
5	90	112.56	−22.56	508.95
6	120	105.79	14.21	201.92
7	145	110.05	34.95	1221.50
8	140	120.54	19.46	378.69
9	100	126.38	−26.38	695.90
10	80	118.46	−38.46	1479.17
11	100	106.92	−6.92	47.89
12	110	104.85	5.15	26.52
			Total	5613.18

MSE = 5613.18 / 11 = 510.29

The forecast for month 13 is $\hat{y}_{13} = \alpha y_{12} + (1 - \alpha)\,\hat{y}_{12} = 0.3(110) + 0.7(104.85) = 106.4$.

c. The MSE values for exponential smoothing forecasts with several different values of α appear below.

α	MSE
0.01	461.45
0.05	460.48
0.1	468.11
0.2	489.82
0.3	510.28
0.4	527.61
0.5	540.57
0.6	547.63
0.7	547.73

The value of α that yields the smallest possible MSE is $\alpha = 0.033$, which yields an MSE of 459.693.

$\alpha = 0.033$

Month	Time Series Value	Forecast	Forecast Error	Squared Forecast Error
1	105			
2	135	105.00	30.00	900.00
3	120	105.98	14.02	196.65
4	105	106.43	−1.43	2.06
5	90	106.39	−16.39	268.53
6	120	105.85	14.15	200.13
7	145	106.31	38.69	1496.61
8	140	107.57	32.43	1051.46
9	100	108.63	−8.63	74.47
10	80	108.35	−28.35	803.65
11	100	107.43	−7.43	55.14
12	110	107.18	2.82	7.93
			Total	5056.62

MSE = 5056.62 / 11 = 459.693

16. a.

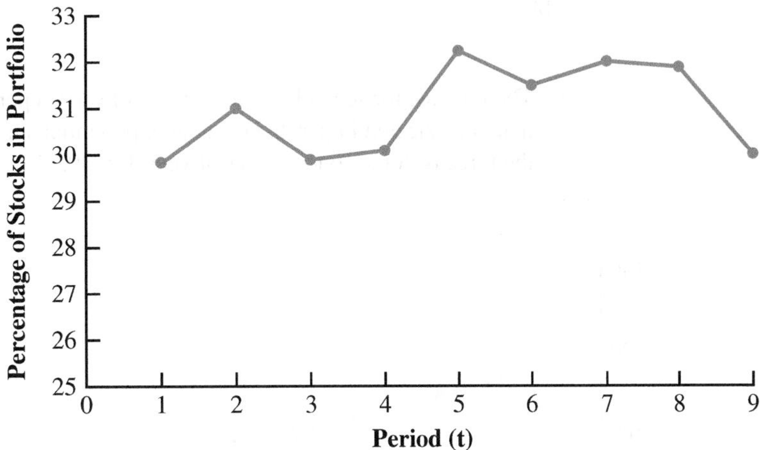

b. The value of the MSE will vary depending on the ultimate value of α that you select. The resulting MSE values for several different α values appear below.

α	MSE
0.1	1.71
0.2	1.40
0.3	1.27
0.4	1.23
0.5	1.22
0.6	1.24
0.7	1.27

The value of α that yields the smallest possible MSE is $\alpha = 0.467$, which yields an MSE of 1.22.

$$\alpha = 0.467$$

Period	Stock %	Forecast	Forecast Error	Squared Forecast Error
1st quarter of 2011	29.8			
2nd quarter of 2011	31.0	29.8.0	1.20	1.44
3rd quarter of 2011	29.9	30.36	−0.46	0.21
4th quarter of 2011	30.1	30.15	−0.05	0.00
1st quarter of 2012	32.2	30.12	2.08	4.31
2nd quarter of 2012	31.5	31.09	0.41	0.16
3rd quarter of 2012	32.0	31.28	0.72	0.51
4th quarter of 2012	31.9	31.62	0.28	0.08
1st quarter of 2013	30.0	31.75	−1.75	3.06
2nd quarter of 2013		30.93	Total	9.78

MSE = 1.22

c. The forecast for second quarter 2013 will vary depending on the ultimate value of α that you selected in part b. Using an exponential smoothing model with $\alpha = 0.467$, the forecast for second quarter of year 3 = 30.93.

18. a.

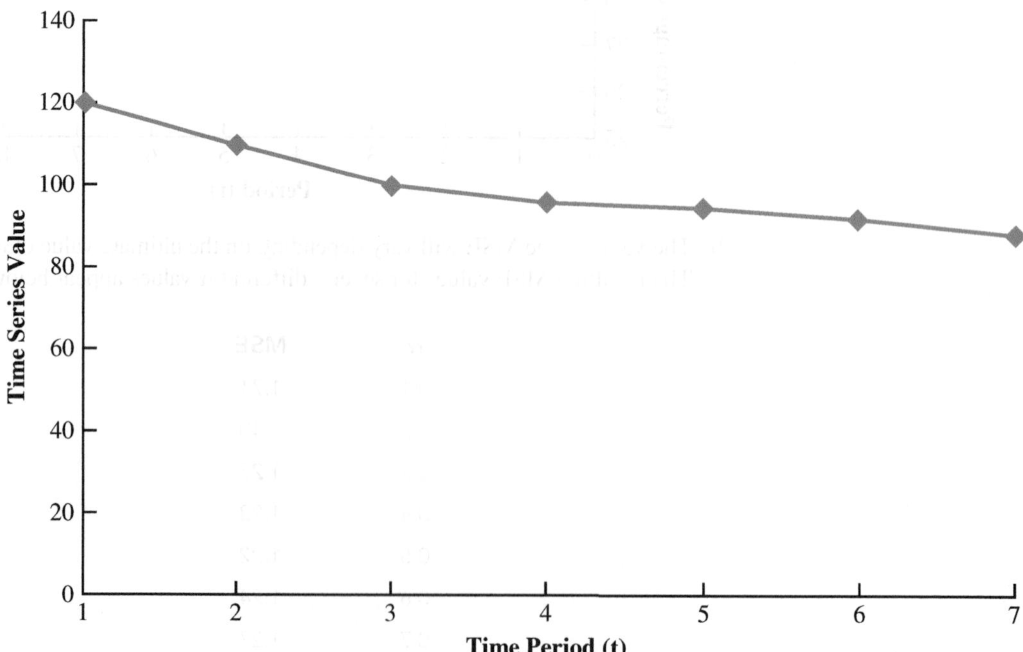

The data are following a downward trend.

b. From the Excel output shown here:

	A	B	C	D	E	F	G	H	I
1	SUMMARY OUTPUT								
2									
3	*Regression Statistics*								
4	Multiple R	0.946004658							
5	R Square	0.894924812							
6	Adjusted R Square	0.873909774							
7	Standard Error	3.996426976							
8	Observations	7							
9									
10	ANOVA								
11		*df*	*SS*	*MS*	*F*	*Significance F*			
12	Regression	1	680.1428571	680.1428571	42.58497317	0.001263761			
13	Residual	5	79.85714286	15.97142857					
14	Total	6	760						
15									
16		*Coefficients*	*Standard Error*	*t Stat*	*P-value*	*Lower 95%*	*Upper 95%*	*Lower 99.0%*	*Upper 99.0%*
17	Intercept	119.7142857	3.377597262	35.44362351	3.36447E-07	111.0318955	128.3966759	106.0953306	133.3332408
18	t	-4.928571429	0.755253708	-6.525716295	0.001263761	-6.870012891	-2.987129966	-7.973862368	-1.88328049

the regression estimates for the slope and *y*-intercept that minimize MSE for this time series are are $b_0 = 119.714$ and $b_1 = -4.929$, which results in the following forecasts, errors, and MSE:

Period	Time Series Value	Forecast	Forecast Error	Squared Forecast Error
1	120	114.7857	5.2143	27.1888
2	110	109.8571	0.1429	0.0204
3	100	104.9286	−4.9286	24.2908
4	96	100.0000	−4.0000	16.0000
5	94	95.0714	−1.0714	1.1480
6	92	90.1429	1.8571	3.4490
7	88	85.2143	2.7857	7.7602
			Total	79.8571

MSE = 79.8571 / 7 = 11.4082.

c. $\hat{y}_8 = b_0 + b_1 t = 119.714 - 4.929(8) = 80.282$

20. a.

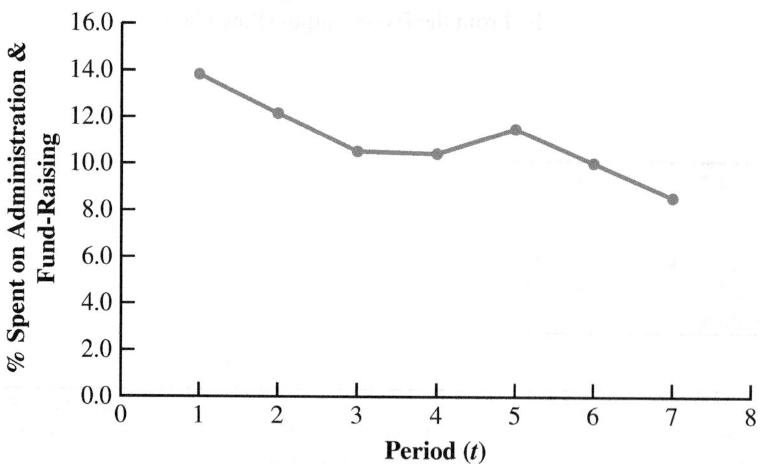

The data appear to follow a downward trend.

b. From the Excel output shown here:

	A	B	C	D	E	F	G	H	I
1	SUMMARY OUTPUT								
2									
3	*Regression Statistics*								
4	Multiple R	0.874025069							
5	R Square	0.763919822							
6	Adjusted R Square	0.716703786							
7	Standard Error	0.920869155							
8	Observations	7							
9									
10	ANOVA								
11		*df*	*SS*	*MS*	*F*	*Significance F*			
12	Regression	1	13.72	13.72	16.17924528	0.01009735			
13	Residual	5	4.24	0.848					
14	Total	6	17.96						
15									
16		*Coefficients*	*Standard Error*	*t Stat*	*P-value*	*Lower 95%*	*Upper 95%*	*Lower 99.0%*	*Upper 99.0%*
17	Intercept	13.8	0.778276484	17.73146782	1.04687E-05	11.79937661	15.80062339	10.66187794	16.93812206
18	Period (t)	-0.7	0.174027912	-4.022343258	0.01009735	-1.14735299	-0.25264701	-1.401705426	0.001705426

the regression estimates for the slope and *y*-intercept that minimize MSE for this time series are are $b_0 = 13.8$ and $b_1 = -0.7$, which results in the following forecasts, errors, and MSE:

t	Time Series Value	Forecast	Forecast Error	Squared Forecast Error
1	13.9	13.10	0.80	0.64
2	12.2	12.40	−0.20	0.04
3	10.5	11.70	−1.20	1.44
4	10.4	11.00	−0.60	0.36
5	11.5	10.30	1.20	1.44
6	10.0	9.60	0.40	0.16
7	8.5	8.90	−0.40	0.16
			Total	4.24

MSE = 4.24 / 7 = 0.606.

c. $\hat{y}_8 = b_0 + b_1 t = 13.8 - 0.7(8) = 8.20$

d. Using the forecast model $\hat{y}_t = b_0 + b_1 t$ for $t = 9, 10, \ldots, 15$ gives us the following:

t	$\hat{y}_t$
9	7.5
10	6.8
11	6.1
12	5.4
13	4.7
14	4.0
15	3.3

Thus, we predict that SCC will achieve a level less than 5% in year 13 (6 years from now) at 4.7%.

22. a.

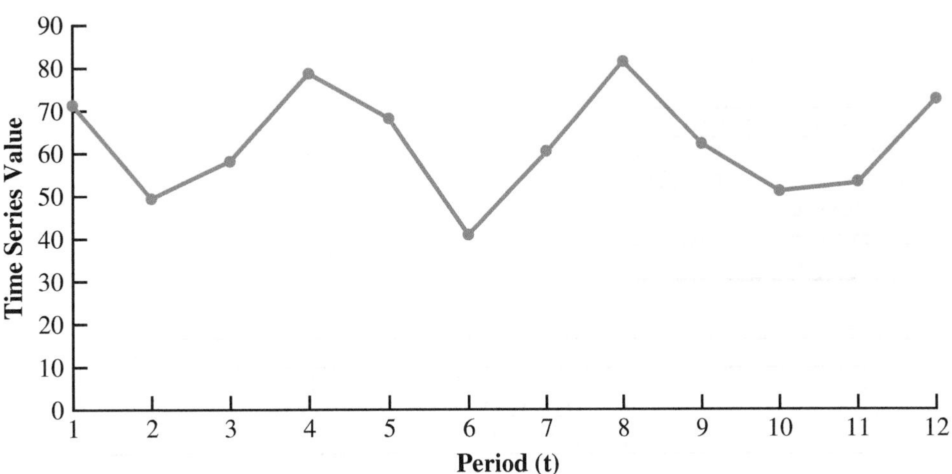

The time series plot shows a horizontal pattern. But there is a seasonal pattern in the data. For instance, in each year, the lowest value occurs in quarter 2 and the highest value occurs in quarter 4.

b. After putting the data into the following format:

		Dummy Variables			
Year	Quarter	Qtr1	Qtr2	Qtr3	y_t
1	1	1	0	0	71
1	2	0	1	0	48
1	3	0	0	1	58
1	4	0	0	0	78
2	1	1	0	0	68
2	2	0	1	0	41
2	3	0	0	1	60
2	4	0	0	0	81
3	1	1	0	0	62
3	2	0	1	0	51
3	3	0	0	1	53
3	4	0	0	0	72

we can use the Excel Regression tool to find the regression model that accounts for seasonal effects in the data. From the Excel output:

	A	B	C	D	E	F	G	H	I
1	SUMMARY OUTPUT								
2									
3	*Regression Statistics*								
4	Multiple R	0.950743585							
5	R Square	0.903913365							
6	Adjusted R Square	0.867880876							
7	Standard Error	4.509249753							
8	Observations	12							
9									
10	ANOVA								
11		*df*	*SS*	*MS*	*F*	*Significance F*			
12	Regression	3	1530.25	510.0833333	25.08606557	0.000201543			
13	Residual	8	162.6666667	20.33333333					
14	Total	11	1692.916667						
15									
16		*Coefficients*	*Standard Error*	*t Stat*	*P-value*	*Lower 95%*	*Upper 95%*	*Lower 99.0%*	*Upper 99.0%*
17	Intercept	77	2.603416559	29.57651926	1.851E-09	70.99651065	83.00348935	68.26452906	85.73547094
18	Qtr1	-10	3.681787006	-2.716072381	0.026408733	-18.49021606	-1.50978394	-22.35382148	2.353821476
19	Qtr2	-30.33333333	3.681787006	-8.23875289	3.53157E-05	-38.82354939	-21.84311727	-42.68715481	-17.97951186
20	Qtr3	-20	3.681787006	-5.432144763	0.000621751	-28.49021606	-11.50978394	-32.35382148	-7.646178524

the regression model that minimizes MSE for this time series is:
Value = 77 − 10 Qtr1 − 30.333 Qtr2 − 20 Qtr3

c. The quarterly forecasts for next year are as follows:
Quarter 1 forecast = 77 – 10(1) − 30.333(0) − 20(0) = 67
Quarter 2 forecast = 77 – 10(0) − 30.333(1) − 20(0) = 46.667
Quarter 3 forecast = 77 – 10(0) − 30.333(0) − 20(1) = 57
Quarter 4 forecast = 77 – 10(0) − 30.333(0) − 20(0) = 77

24. a.

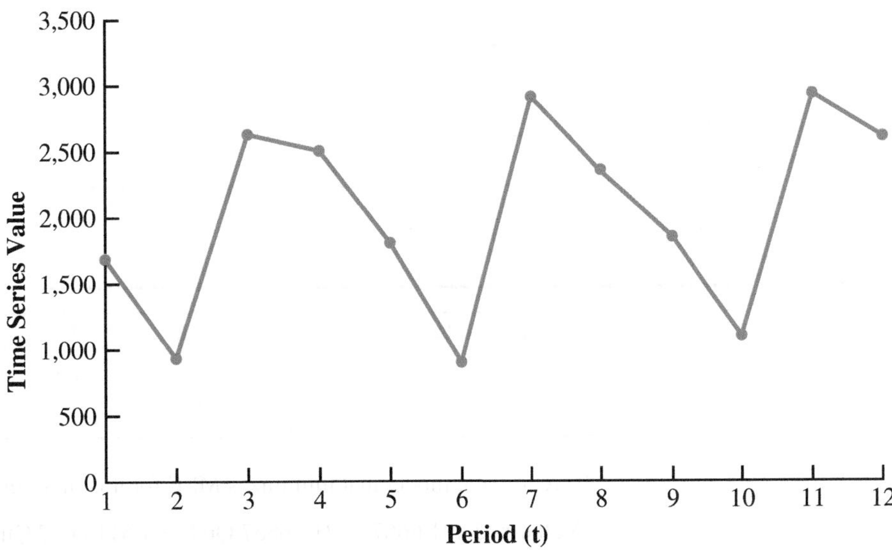

There appears to be a seasonal pattern in the data and perhaps a moderate upward linear trend.

b. After putting the data into the following format:

		Dummy Variables			
Year	Quarter	Qtr1	Qtr2	Qtr3	y_t
	1	1	0	0	1,690
1	2	0	1	0	940
1	3	0	0	1	2,625
1	4	0	0	0	2,500
2	1	1	0	0	1,800
2	2	0	1	0	900
2	3	0	0	1	2,900
2	4	0	0	0	2,360
3	1	1	0	0	1,850
3	2	0	1	0	1,100
3	3	0	0	1	2,930
3	4	0	0	0	2,615

we can use the Excel Regression tool to find the regression model that accounts for seasonal effects in the data. From the Excel output shown here:

SUMMARY OUTPUT								
Regression Statistics								
Multiple R	0.989743557							
R Square	0.979592309							
Adjusted R Square	0.971939425							
Standard Error	124.9666622							
Observations	12							
ANOVA								
	df	*SS*	*MS*	*F*	*Significance F*			
Regression	3	5996941.667	1998980.556	128.0030238	4.23351E-07			
Residual	8	124933.3333	15616.66667					
Total	11	6121875						
	Coefficients	*Standard Error*	*t Stat*	*P-value*	*Lower 95%*	*Upper 95%*	*Lower 99.0%*	*Upper 99.0%*
Intercept	2491.666667	72.14953607	34.53475659	5.40398E-10	2325.289538	2658.043795	2249.577027	2733.756306
Qtr1	-711.6666667	102.0348524	-6.97474098	0.000115518	-946.9594583	-476.373875	-1054.033118	-369.3002155
Qtr2	-1511.666667	102.0348524	-14.81519922	4.24199E-07	-1746.959458	-1276.373875	-1854.033118	-1169.300215
Qtr3	326.6666667	102.0348524	3.20152045	0.012583566	91.37387502	561.9594583	-15.69978454	669.0331179

the regression model that minimizes MSE for this time series is:

Value = 2,491.6667 − 711.6667 Qtr1 − 1,511.6667 Qtr2 + 326.6667 Qtr3

c. Based on the model in part b, the quarterly forecasts for next year are as follows:
Quarter 1 forecast = 2,491.6667 − 711.6667(1) − 1,511.6667(0) + 326.6667(0) = 1,780.00
Quarter 2 forecast = 2,491.6667 − 711.6667(0) − 1,511.6667(1) + 326.6667(0) = 980.00
Quarter 3 forecast = 2,491.6667 − 711.6667(0) − 1,511.6667(0) + 326.6667(1) = 2,818.3333
Quarter 4 forecast = 2,491.6667 − 711.6667(0) − 1,511.6667(0) + 326.6667(0) = 2,491.6667

d. After putting the data into the following format:

		Dummy Variables				
Year	**Quarter**	**Qtr1**	**Qtr2**	**Qtr3**	**t**	y_t
1	1	1	0	0	1	1690
1	2	0	1	0	2	940
1	3	0	0	1	3	2625
1	4	0	0	0	4	2500
2	1	1	0	0	5	1800
2	2	0	1	0	6	900
2	3	0	0	1	7	2900
2	4	0	0	0	8	2360
3	1	1	0	0	9	1850
3	2	0	1	0	10	1100
3	3	0	0	1	11	2930
3	4	0	0	0	12	2615

we can use the Excel Regression tool to find the regression model that accounts for seasonal effects in the data. From the following Excel output:

SUMMARY OUTPUT

Regression Statistics	
Multiple R	0.995376072
R Square	0.990773524
Adjusted R Square	0.985501252
Standard Error	89.82787774
Observations	12

ANOVA

	df	*SS*	*MS*	*F*	*Significance F*
Regression	4	6065391.667	1516347.917	187.9215477	3.37062E-07
Residual	7	56483.33333	8069.047619		
Total	11	6121875			

	Coefficients	*Standard Error*	*t Stat*	*P-value*	*Lower 95%*	*Upper 95%*	*Lower 99.0%*	*Upper 99.0%*
Intercept	2306.666667	82.00123822	28.12964968	1.84384E-08	2112.764503	2500.568831	2019.704633	2593.6287
Qtr1	-642.2916667	77.11497903	-8.32901305	7.04053E-05	-824.6396162	-459.9437171	-912.1542477	-372.4290856
Qtr2	-1465.416667	75.04347285	-19.52756997	2.30492E-07	-1642.866282	-1287.967051	-1728.030046	-1202.803287
Qtr3	349.7916667	73.77265424	4.741481383	0.002104246	175.3470593	524.236274	91.62549535	607.957838
t	23.125	7.939737686	2.912564736	0.022577878	4.350503716	41.89949628	-4.659979418	50.90997942

the regression model that minimizes MSE for this time series is:

$$\text{Value} = 2306.6667 - 642.2917\ \text{Qtr1} - 1465.417\ \text{Qtr2} + 349.7917\ \text{Qtr3} + 23.125t$$

e. Based on the model in part c, the quarterly forecasts for next year are as follows:
   Quarter 1 forecast = 2,306.6667 − 642.2917(1) − 1,465.417(0) + 349.7917(0) + 23.125(13) = 1,965.00
   Quarter 2 forecast = 2,306.6667 − 642.2917(0) − 1,465.417(1) + 349.7917(0) + 23.125(14) = 1,165.00
   Quarter 3 forecast = 2,306.6667 − 642.2917(0) − 1,465.417(0) + 349.7917(1) + 23.125(15) = 2,011.3333
   Quarter 4 forecast = 2,306.6667 − 642.2917(0) − 1,465.417(0) + 349.7917(0) + 23.125(16) = 2,676.6667

f. For the model from part b that only includes seasonal effects, as shown here:

Year	Quarter	y_t	Forecast	Forecast Error	Squared Forecast Error
1	1	1690	1,780.0000	−90.0000	8,100.0000
1	2	940	980.0000	−40.0000	1,600.0000
1	3	2625	2,818.3333	−193.3333	37,377.7778
1	4	2500	2,491.6667	8.3333	69.4444
2	1	1800	1,780.0000	20.0000	400.0000
2	2	900	980.0000	−80.0000	6,400.0000
2	3	2900	2,818.3333	81.6667	6,669.4444
2	4	2360	2,491.6667	−131.6667	17,336.1111
3	1	1850	1,780.0000	70.0000	4,900.0000
3	2	1100	980.0000	120.0000	14,400.0000
3	3	2930	2,818.3333	111.6667	12,469.4444
3	4	2615	2,491.6667	123.3333	15,211.1111
				Total	124,933.3333

$$\text{MSE} = 124{,}933.3333 / 12 = 10{,}411.1111.$$

For the model from part d that includes both trend and seasonal effects:

Year	Quarter	t	y_t	Forecast	Forecast Error	Squared Forecast Error
1	1	1	1,690	1,687.5000	2.5000	6.2500
1	2	2	940	887.5000	52.5000	2,756.2500
1	3	3	2,625	2,725.8333	−100.8333	10,167.3611
1	4	4	2,500	2,399.1667	100.8333	10,167.3611
2	1	5	1,800	1,780.0000	20.0000	400.0000
2	2	6	900	980.0000	−80.0000	6,400.0000
2	3	7	2,900	2,818.3333	81.6667	6,669.4444
2	4	8	2,360	2,491.6667	−131.6667	17,336.1111
3	1	9	1,850	1,872.5000	−22.5000	506.2500
3	2	10	1,100	1,072.5000	27.5000	756.2500
3	3	11	2,930	2,910.8333	19.1667	367.3611
3	4	12	2,615	2,584.1667	30.8333	950.6944
					Total	56,483.3333

$$\text{MSE} = 56{,}483.3333 / 12 = 4{,}706.9444.$$

The mean squared error for the model from part d that includes both trend and seasonal effects is much smaller than the mean squared error for the model from part b that includes only seasonal effects. This supports our preliminary conclusions reached in review of the time series plot constructed in part a—these data show a linear trend with seasonality.

26. a.

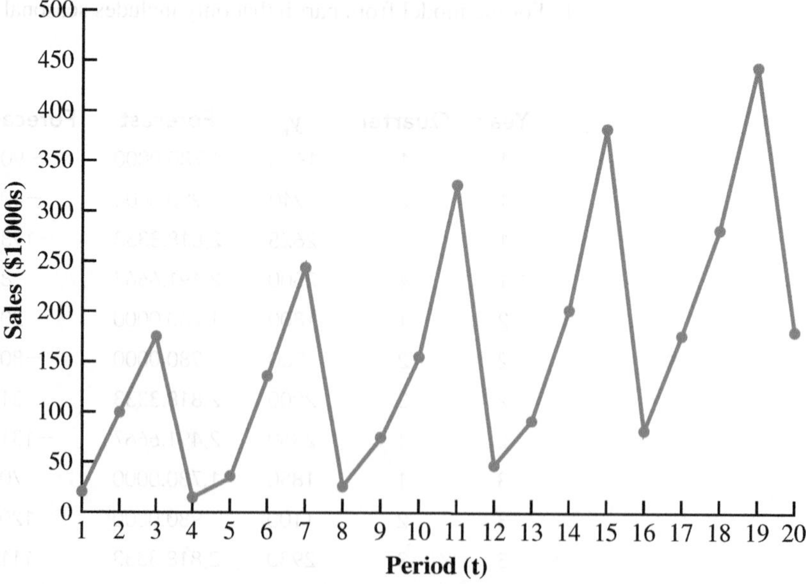

The time series plot shows both a linear trend and seasonal effects.

b. After putting the data into the following format:

		Quarterly Dummy Variables			
Year	**Quarter**	**Qtr1**	**Qtr 2**	**Qtr3**	y_t
1	1	1	0	0	20
1	2	0	1	0	100
1	3	0	0	1	175
1	4	0	0	0	13
2	1	1	0	0	37
2	2	0	1	0	136
2	3	0	0	1	245
2	4	0	0	0	26
3	1	1	0	0	75
3	2	0	1	0	155
3	3	0	0	1	326
3	4	0	0	0	48
4	1	1	0	0	92
4	2	0	1	0	202
4	3	0	0	1	384
4	4	0	0	0	82
5	1	1	0	0	176
5	2	0	1	0	282
5	3	0	0	1	445
5	4	0	0	0	181

we can use the Excel Regression tool to find the regression model that accounts for the seasonal effects in the data. From the Excel output shown here:

	A	B	C	D	E	F	G	H	I
1	SUMMARY OUTPUT								
2									
3	*Regression Statistics*								
4	Multiple R	0.813563938							
5	R Square	0.661886282							
6	Adjusted R Square	0.59848996							
7	Standard Error	78.65033376							
8	Observations	20							
9									
10	ANOVA								
11		*df*	*SS*	*MS*	*F*	*Significance F*			
12	Regression	3	193750	64583.33333	10.44045237	0.000476769			
13	Residual	16	98974	6185.875					
14	Total	19	292724						
15									
16		*Coefficients*	*Standard Error*	*t Stat*	*P-value*	*Lower 95%*	*Upper 95%*	*Lower 99.0%*	*Upper 99.0%*
17	Intercept	70	35.17349855	1.990134701	0.063944637	-4.564485961	144.564486	-32.73410815	172.7341082
18	Qtr1	10	49.74283868	0.201033963	0.843205394	-95.45010732	115.4501073	-135.2879691	155.2879691
19	Qtr2	105	49.74283868	2.110856613	0.050873764	-0.450107317	210.4501073	-40.28796907	250.2879691
20	Qtr3	245	49.74283868	4.925332098	0.000152185	139.5498927	350.4501073	99.71203093	390.2879691

the regression model that minimizes MSE for this time series is:

$$\text{Revenue} = 70.0 + 10.0\,\text{Qtr1} + 105\,\text{Qtr2} + 245\,\text{Qtr3}$$

c. Based on the model in part b, the quarterly forecasts for next year are as follows:
Quarter 1 forecast = 70.0 + 10.0(1) + 105(0) + 245(0) = 80
Quarter 2 forecast = 70.0 + 10.0(0) + 105(1) + 245(0) = 175
Quarter 3 forecast = 70.0 + 10.0(0) + 105(0) + 245(1) = 315
Quarter 4 forecast = 70.0 + 10.0(0) + 105(0) + 245(0) = 70

d. After putting the data into the following format:

		Quarterly Dummy Variables				
Year	**Quarter**	**Qtr1**	**Qtr2**	**Qtr3**	**t**	**y_t**
1	1	1	0	0	1	20
1	2	0	1	0	2	100
1	3	0	0	1	3	175
1	4	0	0	0	4	13
2	1	1	0	0	5	37
2	2	0	1	0	6	136
2	3	0	0	1	7	245
2	4	0	0	0	8	26
3	1	1	0	0	9	75
3	2	0	1	0	10	155
3	3	0	0	1	11	326
3	4	0	0	0	12	48
4	1	1	0	0	13	92
4	2	0	1	0	14	202
4	3	0	0	1	15	384
4	4	0	0	0	16	82
5	1	1	0	0	17	176
5	2	0	1	0	18	282
5	3	0	0	1	19	445
5	4	0	0	0	20	181

we can use the Excel Regression tool to find the regression model that accounts for the seasonal effects in the data. From the Excel output shown here:

	A	B	C	D	E	F	G	H	I
1	SUMMARY OUTPUT								
2									
3	*Regression Statistics*								
4	Multiple R	0.979744573							
5	R Square	0.959899427							
6	Adjusted R Square	0.949205941							
7	Standard Error	27.9742739							
8	Observations	20							
9									
10	ANOVA								
11		*df*	*SS*	*MS*	*F*	*Significance F*			
12	Regression	4	280985.6	70246.4	89.76487426	2.73781E-10			
13	Residual	15	11738.4	782.56					
14	Total	19	292724						
15									
16		*Coefficients*	*Standard Error*	*t Stat*	*P-value*	*Lower 95%*	*Upper 95%*	*Lower 99.0%*	*Upper 99.0%*
17	Intercept	-70.1	18.23699537	-3.843834941	0.001593865	-108.9712355	-31.22876451	-123.8391892	-16.3608108
18	Qtr1	45.025	18.00079859	2.501277916	0.024444066	6.657206018	83.39279398	-8.018185128	98.06818513
19	Qtr2	128.35	17.83017106	7.198472722	3.08116E-06	90.34589	166.35411	75.80960523	180.8903948
20	Qtr3	256.675	17.72700623	14.47932023	3.19324E-10	218.8907806	294.4592194	204.4386023	308.9113977
21	t	11.675	1.105780268	10.55815549	2.43419E-08	9.318085151	14.03191485	8.416583039	14.93341696

the regression model that minimizes MSE for this time series is:

Revenue = –70.1 + 45.025 Qtr1 + 128.35 Qtr2 + 256.675 Qtr3 + 11.675 t

e. Based on the model in part b, the quarterly forecasts for next year are as follows:
Quarter 1 forecast = −70.1 + 45.025(1) + 128.35(0) + 256.675(0) + 11.675(21) = 220.1
Quarter 2 forecast = −70.1 + 45.025(0) + 128.35(1) + 256.675(0) + 11.675(22) = 315.1
Quarter 3 forecast = −70.1 + 45.025(0) + 128.35(0) + 256.675(1) + 11.675(23) = 455.1
Quarter 4 forecast = −70.1 + 45.025(0) + 128.35(0) + 256.675(0) + 11.675(24) = 210.1

f. For the model from part b that includes only seasonal effects:

Year	Quarter	y_t	Forecast	Forecast Error	Squared Forecast Error
1	1	20	80	−60	3,600
1	2	100	175	−75	5,625
1	3	175	315	−140	19,600
1	4	13	70	−57	3,249
2	1	37	80	−43	1,849
2	2	136	175	−39	1,521
2	3	245	315	−70	4,900
2	4	26	70	−44	1,936

3	1	75	80	−5	25
3	2	155	175	−20	400
3	3	326	315	11	121
3	4	48	70	−22	484
		92	80	12	144
		202	175	27	729
		384	315	69	4,761
		82	70	12	144
		176	80	96	9,216
		282	175	107	11,449
		445	315	130	16,900
		181	70	111	12,321
				Total	98,974

MSE = 98,974 / 20 = 4,948.7.

For the model from part d that includes both trend and seasonal effects:

Year	Quarter	t	y_t	Forecast	Forecast Error	Squared Forecast Error
1	1	1	20	−13.40	33.40	1,115.56
1	2	2	100	81.60	18.40	338.56
1	3	3	175	221.60	−46.60	2,171.56
1	4	4	13	−23.40	36.40	1,324.96
2	1	5	37	33.30	3.70	13.69
2	2	6	136	128.30	7.70	59.29
2	3	7	245	268.30	−23.30	542.89
2	4	8	26	23.30	2.70	7.29
3	1	9	75	80.00	−5.00	25.00
3	2	10	155	175.00	−20.00	400.00
3	3	11	326	315.00	11.00	121.00
3	4	12	48	70.00	−22.00	484.00
		13	92	126.70	−34.70	1,204.09
		14	202	221.70	−19.70	388.09
		15	384	361.70	22.30	497.29
		16	82	116.70	−34.70	1,204.09
		17	176	173.40	2.60	6.76
		18	282	268.40	13.60	184.96
		19	445	408.40	36.60	1,339.56
		20	181	163.40	17.60	309.76
				Total	11,738.40	

$$\text{MSE} = 11{,}738.4 / 20 = 586.92.$$

The mean squared error for the model from part d that includes both trend and seasonal effects is much smaller than the mean squared error for the model from part b that includes only seasonal effects. This supports our preliminary conclusions reached in review of the time series plot constructed in part a—these data show a linear trend with seasonality.

28. a.

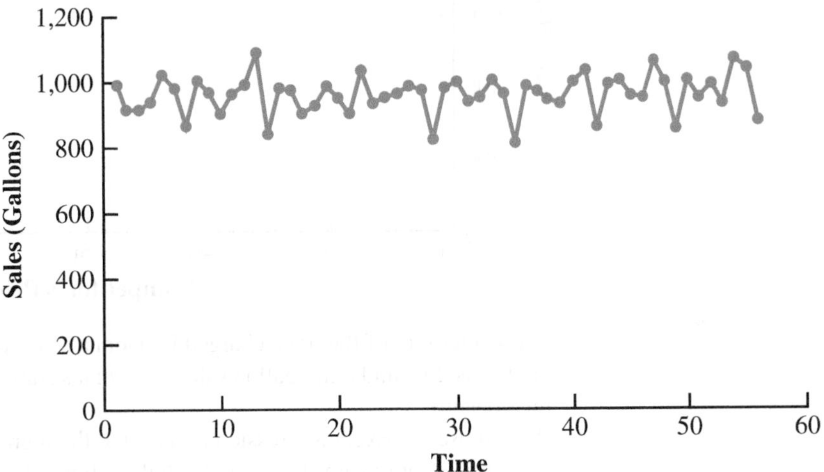

A plot of these data over time reveals little or no trend and a possible seasonal effect for daily gallon sales.

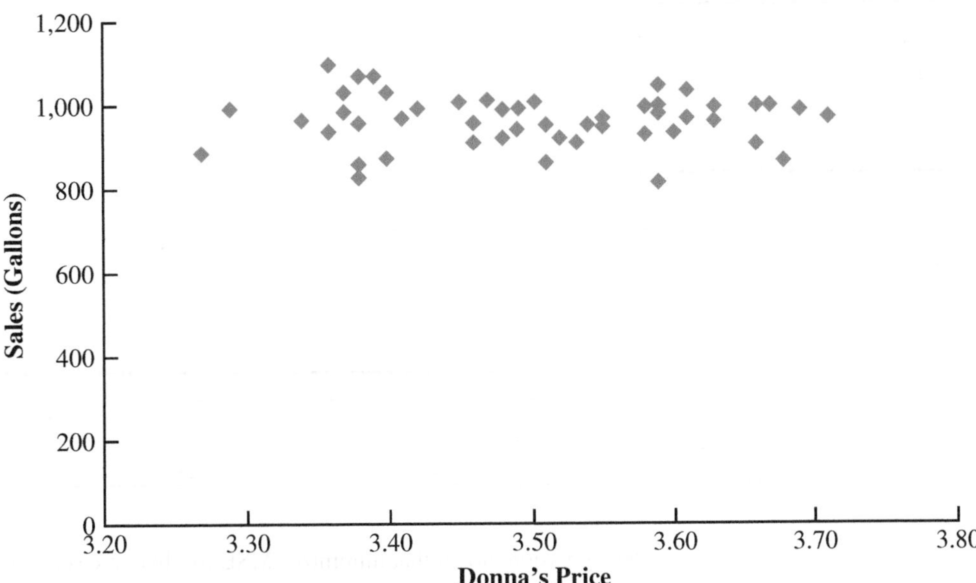

The scatter chart of the price charged by Donna for a gallon of regular-grade gasoline and daily gallon sales at Donna's station provides little evidence of a relationship.

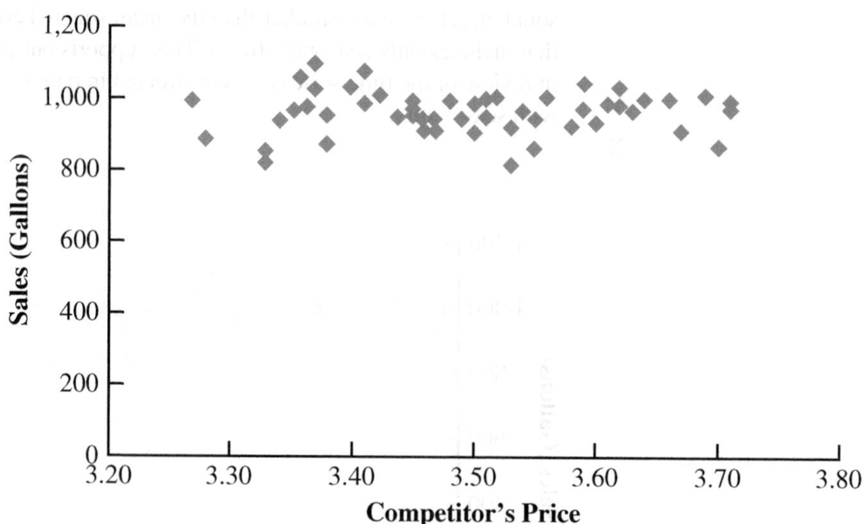

The scatter plot of the price charged by Donna's competitor for a gallon of regular-grade gasoline and daily gallon sales at Donna's station provides little evidence of a relationship.

b. We can use the Excel Regression tool to find the regression model that accounts for the causal relationships between the daily gallon sales of regular gasoline by Donna's station and the prices that she and her competitor charge for a gallon of regular gasoline. From the Excel output shown here:

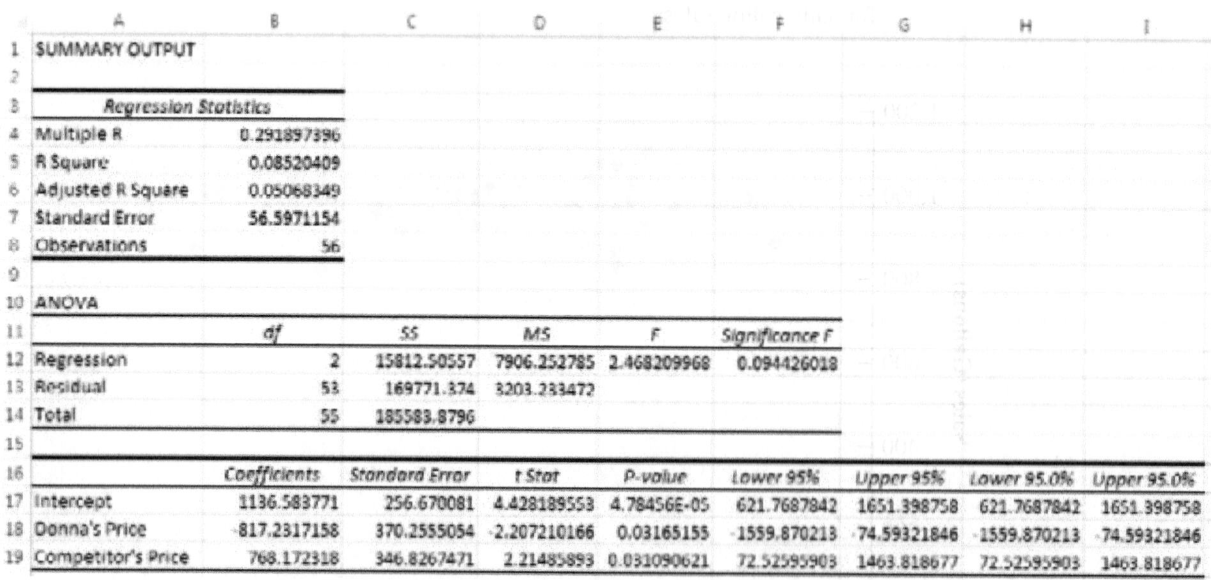

SUMMARY OUTPUT

Regression Statistics	
Multiple R	0.291897396
R Square	0.08520409
Adjusted R Square	0.05068349
Standard Error	56.5971154
Observations	56

ANOVA

	df	*SS*	*MS*	*F*	*Significance F*
Regression	2	15812.50557	7906.252785	2.468209968	0.094426018
Residual	53	169771.374	3203.233472		
Total	55	185583.8796			

	Coefficients	*Standard Error*	*t Stat*	*P-value*	*Lower 95%*	*Upper 95%*	*Lower 95.0%*	*Upper 95.0%*
Intercept	1136.583771	256.670081	4.428189553	4.78456E-05	621.7687842	1651.398758	621.7687842	1651.398758
Donna's Price	-817.2317158	370.2555054	-2.207210166	0.03165155	-1559.870213	-74.59321846	-1559.870213	-74.59321846
Competitor's Price	768.172318	346.8267471	2.21485893	0.031090621	72.52595903	1463.818677	72.52595903	1463.818677

the regression model that minimizes MSE for this time series is:

Sales = 1136.5838 – 817.2317 (Donna's Price) + 768.1723 (Competitor's Price)

Given these results, we estimate that Donna's daily sales of regular gasoline decrease by approximately 817 gallons when Donna increases her price for a gallon of regular gasoline by \$1.00 (i.e., we estimate that Donna's daily sales of regular gasoline decrease by approximately 8.17 gallons when Donna increases her price for a gallon of regular gasoline by one cent). We also estimate that Donna's daily sales of regular gasoline increase by approximately 768 gallons when Donna's competitor increases its price for a gallon of regular gasoline by \$1.00 (i.e., we estimate that Donna's daily sales of regular gasoline increase by approximately 7.68 gallons when Donna's competitor increases its price for a gallon of regular gasoline by one cent).
Based on this model, estimated sales for a day on which Donna is charging \$3.50 for a gallon for regular gasoline and her competitor is charging \$3.45 for a gallon of regular gasoline are:

$$\text{Sales} = 1136.5838 - 817.2317\,(3.50) + 768.1723\,(3.45) = 926.4673 \text{ gallons.}$$

c. After putting the data into the following format:

				Dummy Variables							
Week	Day	Donna's Price	Competitor's Price	Mon	Tues	Wed	Thurs	Fri	Sat	t	Sales
1	Monday	3.48	3.48	1	0	0	0	0	0	1	994.33
1	Tuesday	3.52	3.53	0	1	0	0	0	0	2	917.53
1	Wednesday	3.48	3.46	0	0	1	0	0	0	3	920.26
1	Thursday	3.49	3.47	0	0	0	1	0	0	4	940.49
1	Friday	3.37	3.37	0	0	0	0	1	0	5	1,026.05
1	Saturday	3.48	3.45	0	0	0	0	0	1	6	982.85
1	Sunday	3.40	3.38	0	0	0	0	0	0	7	868.82
2	Monday	3.59	3.56	1	0	0	0	0	0	8	1,001.85
2	Tuesday	3.71	3.71	0	1	0	0	0	0	9	969.33
2	Wednesday	3.53	3.50	0	0	1	0	0	0	10	907.81
2	Thursday	3.41	3.45	0	0	0	1	0	0	11	965.42
2	Friday	3.58	3.61	0	0	0	0	1	0	12	988.87
2	Saturday	3.36	3.37	0	0	0	0	0	1	13	1,092.33
2	Sunday	3.38	3.33	0	0	0	0	0	0	14	844.32
3	Monday	3.49	3.50	1	0	0	0	0	0	15	983.25
3	Tuesday	3.59	3.62	0	1	0	0	0	0	16	978.40
3	Wednesday	3.66	3.67	0	0	1	0	0	0	17	905.00
3	Thursday	3.58	3.58	0	0	0	1	0	0	18	926.72
3	Friday	3.29	3.27	0	0	0	0	1	0	19	990.25
3	Saturday	3.38	3.38	0	0	0	0	0	1	20	954.78
3	Sunday	3.46	3.47	0	0	0	0	0	0	21	905.12
4	Monday	3.40	3.40	1	0	0	0	0	0	22	1,032.73
4	Tuesday	3.49	3.46	0	1	0	0	0	0	23	937.92

4	Wednesday	3.54	3.54	0	0	1	0	0	0	24	954.31
4	Thursday	3.61	3.59	0	0	0	1	0	0	25	967.57
4	Friday	3.69	3.71	0	0	0	0	1	0	26	987.20
4	Saturday	3.37	3.36	0	0	0	0	0	1	27	976.94
4	Sunday	3.38	3.33	0	0	0	0	0	0	28	824.32
5	Monday	3.59	3.62	1	0	0	0	0	0	29	985.53
5	Tuesday	3.50	3.45	0	1	0	0	0	0	30	1,004.14
5	Wednesday	3.49	3.49	0	0	1	0	0	0	31	939.62
5	Thursday	3.46	3.44	0	0	0	1	0	0	32	952.71
5	Friday	3.67	3.69	0	0	0	0	1	0	33	1,006.75
5	Saturday	3.34	3.35	0	0	0	0	0	1	34	967.02
5	Sunday	3.59	3.53	0	0	0	0	0	0	35	817.03
6	Monday	3.42	3.41	1	0	0	0	0	0	36	986.83
6	Tuesday	3.63	3.63	0	1	0	0	0	0	37	970.02
6	Wednesday	3.55	3.55	0	0	1	0	0	0	38	945.04
6	Thursday	3.60	3.60	0	0	0	1	0	0	39	934.36
6	Friday	3.63	3.64	0	0	0	0	1	0	40	998.38
6	Saturday	3.61	3.62	0	0	0	0	0	1	41	1,031.23
6	Sunday	3.68	3.70	0	0	0	0	0	0	42	867.18
7	Monday	3.49	3.51	1	0	0	0	0	0	43	994.00
7	Tuesday	3.47	3.45	0	1	0	0	0	0	44	1,005.76
7	Wednesday	3.55	3.54	0	0	1	0	0	0	45	959.69
7	Thursday	3.51	3.51	0	0	0	1	0	0	46	950.12
7	Friday	3.38	3.36	0	0	0	0	1	0	47	1,063.42
7	Saturday	3.50	3.52	0	0	0	0	0	1	48	1,003.03
7	Sunday	3.51	3.55	0	0	0	0	0	0	49	861.59
8	Monday	3.45	3.42	1	0	0	0	0	0	50	1,004.04
8	Tuesday	3.51	3.51	0	1	0	0	0	0	51	953.20
8	Wednesday	3.66	3.66	0	0	1	0	0	0	52	996.66
8	Thursday	3.36	3.34	0	0	0	1	0	0	53	938.04
8	Friday	3.39	3.41	0	0	0	0	1	0	54	1,072.94
8	Saturday	3.59	3.59	0	0	0	0	0	1	55	1,042.82
8	Sunday	3.27	3.28	0	0	0	0	0	0	56	885.81

we can use the Excel Regression tool to find the regression model that accounts for the trend and seasonal effects in the data. From the Excel output shown here:

	A	B	C	D	E	F	G	H	I
1	SUMMARY OUTPUT								
2									
3	*Regression Statistics*								
4	Multiple R	0.882210698							
5	R Square	0.778295716							
6	Adjusted R Square	0.745963842							
7	Standard Error	29.27767248							
8	Observations	56							
9									
10	ANOVA								
11		*df*	*SS*	*MS*	*F*	*Significance F*			
12	Regression	7	144439.1385	20634.16264	24.07208748	1.10623E-13			
13	Residual	48	41144.74109	857.182106					
14	Total	55	185583.8796						
15									
16		*Coefficients*	*Standard Error*	*t Stat*	*P-value*	*Lower 95%*	*Upper 95%*	*Lower 95.0%*	*Upper 95.0%*
17	Intercept	841.6613004	12.89140673	65.28855368	1.52155E-48	815.7413899	867.5812108	815.7413899	867.5812108
18	Mon	141.9016938	14.71181801	9.645422047	8.14757E-13	112.3216012	171.4817865	112.3216012	171.4817865
19	Tues	110.5604486	14.6895565	7.526466071	1.1522E-09	81.02511571	140.0957814	81.02511571	140.0957814
20	Wed	84.01255008	14.6713174	5.726312625	6.54725E-07	54.51388936	113.5112108	54.51388936	113.5112108
21	Thurs	89.33254757	14.65711575	6.094824458	1.79605E-07	59.86244119	118.8026539	59.86244119	118.8026539
22	Fri	158.5784951	14.64696329	10.82671486	1.76412E-14	129.1288016	188.0281885	129.1288016	188.0281885
23	Sat	147.6606647	14.64086843	10.08551272	1.91527E-13	118.2232257	177.0981036	118.2232257	177.0981036
24	t	0.559082671	0.243929791	2.291981923	0.026334701	0.068628955	1.049536386	0.068628955	1.049536386

the regression model that minimizes MSE for this time series is:

Sales = 841.6613 + 141.9016938 Mon + 110.56045 Tues + 84.0126 Wed + 89.3325 Thurs + 158.5785 Fri + 147.6607 Sat + 0.5591 t.

Given these results, we estimate that Donna's daily sales of regular gasoline are increasing by approximately 0.56 gallons per day and her station's peak sales days are Friday, Saturday, and Monday.
Based on this model, estimated sales for Tuesday of the first week after Donna collected her data (note that this is the second day of week nine, so $t = 58$) is:

$$\text{Sales} = 841.6613 + 110.56045 + 0.5591\ (58) = 984.6485 \text{ gallons.}$$

d. We can use the Excel Regression tool to find the regression model that accounts for the trend and seasonal effects as well as the causal relationships between the daily gallon sales of regular gasoline by Donna's station and the prices that she and her competitor charge for a gallon of regular gasoline. From the Excel output shown here:

	A	B	C	D	E	F	G	H	I
1	SUMMARY OUTPUT								
2									
3	*Regression Statistics*								
4	Multiple R	0.8866154							
5	R Square	0.786086867							
6	Adjusted R Square	0.744234297							
7	Standard Error	29.37716844							
8	Observations	56							
9									
10	ANOVA								
11		*df*	*SS*	*MS*	*F*	*Significance F*			
12	Regression	9	145885.0504	16209.45005	18.78228446	1.22495E-12			
13	Residual	46	39698.82917	863.0180254					
14	Total	55	185583.8796						
15									
16		*Coefficients*	*Standard Error*	*t Stat*	*P-value*	*Lower 95%*	*Upper 95%*	*Lower 95.0%*	*Upper 95.0%*
17	Intercept	991.5094567	143.2680249	6.920661168	1.19856E-08	703.1258799	1279.893034	703.1258799	1279.893034
18	Donna's Price	-237.3570474	204.9832235	-1.157934017	0.252867864	-649.9668759	175.2527811	-649.9668759	175.2527811
19	Competitor's Price	194.9032918	190.3244278	1.024058205	0.311163183	-188.1999112	578.0064949	-188.1999112	578.0064949
20	Mon	140.8731324	14.95011567	9.422879094	2.60334E-12	110.7801104	170.9661545	110.7801104	170.9661545
21	Tues	113.4747117	15.21963536	7.455810143	1.89616E-09	82.83917466	144.1102487	82.83917466	144.1102487
22	Wed	86.91370486	15.25051539	5.69906673	8.16232E-07	56.21600955	117.6114002	56.21600955	117.6114002
23	Thurs	89.67336868	14.85078009	6.038293487	2.53718E-07	59.7802988	119.5664386	59.7802988	119.5664386
24	Fri	156.3951426	15.1809679	10.30205344	1.56633E-13	125.8374392	186.9528461	125.8374392	186.9528461
25	Sat	144.7502236	14.93777703	9.690211826	1.09662E-12	114.682038	174.8184093	114.682038	174.8184093
26	t	0.540830668	0.246880495	2.190657741	0.033581786	0.043886006	1.037775331	0.043886006	1.037775331

the regression model that minimizes MSE for this time series is:

Sales = 991.5095 − 237.3570 Donna's Price + 194.9033 Competitor's Price + 140.8731 Mon + 113.4747 Tues + 86.9137 Wed + 89.6734 Thurs + 156.3951 Fri + 144.7502 Sat + 0.5408 *t*.

Given these results, we estimate that Donna's daily sales of regular gasoline decrease by approximately 237 gallons when Donna increases her price for a gallon of regular gasoline by $1.00 (i.e., we estimate that Donna's daily sales of regular gasoline decrease by approximately 2.37 gallons when Donna increases her price for a gallon of regular gasoline by one cent). We also estimate that Donna's daily sales of regular gasoline increase by approximately 195 gallons when Donna's competitor increases its price for a gallon of regular grade gasoline by $1.00 (i.e., we estimate that Donna's daily sales of regular gasoline increase by approximately 1.95 gallons when Donna's competitor increases its price for a gallon of regular gasoline by one cent). We also estimate that Donna's daily sales of regular gasoline are increasing by approximately 0.54 gallons per day and her station's peak sales days are Friday, Saturday, and Monday.

Based on this model, estimated sales for Tuesday of the first week after Donna collected her data (note that this is the second day of week nine, so $t = 58$), if Donna is charging $3.50 for a gallon for regular gasoline and her competitor is charging $3.45 for a gallon of regular gasoline are:

Sales = 991.5095 − 237.3570 (3.50) + 194.9033 (3.45) + 113.4747 + 0.5408 (58) = 978.0190 gallons.

e. For the model from part b that only includes the causal variables the price Donna charges for a gallon of regular gasoline and the price Donna's competitor charges for a gallon of regular gasoline, MSE = 169,771.374 / 56 = 3031.6317.
For the model from part c that only includes the trend and seasonal effects (day of operation), MSE = 41,144.7411 / 56 = 734.7275.
For the model from part d that includes the trend, seasonal effects (day of operation), and the price Donna charges for a gallon of regular gasoline and the price Donna's competitor charges for a gallon of regular gasoline as causalsvariables, MSE = 39,698.82917 / 56 = 708.9077.
The mean squared errors for the models from part c and part d are much smaller than the mean squared error for the model from part b. Furthermore, the mean squared error for the models from parts c and d are essentially equal and the model in part c is simpler than the model in part d. When two models are approximately equal in effectiveness, we select and use the simpler model, which in this case is the model from part c that includes only the causal relationship between outside temperature and hourly sales.

Chapter 9: Predictive Data Mining

Solutions

2. a. Classification error is minimized at 9.5% for a value of $k = 17$.

Validation Error Log for Different *k*

Value of k	% Error Training	% Error Validation	
1	2.166667	14.25	
2	5.5	14.25	
3	5.5	11.25	
4	7	12	
5	7.333333	11	
6	7.833333	11.25	
7	7.333333	10.75	
8	7.333333	11	
9	7.5	11	
10	8.166667	12	
11	8.333333	12	
12	8.5	12	
13	9	11	
14	9.5	11.25	
15	8.333333	9.75	
16	8.833333	9.75	
17	8.333333	9.5	<- Best k
18	8.833333	9.5	
19	8.5	9.5	
20	8.666667	9.5	

b. The area under the ROC curve is 0.9607. By hovering the cursor over the ROC curve, we see that to achieve sensitivity of at least 0.80, 1 − Specificity = 0.0683 = Class 0 error rate.

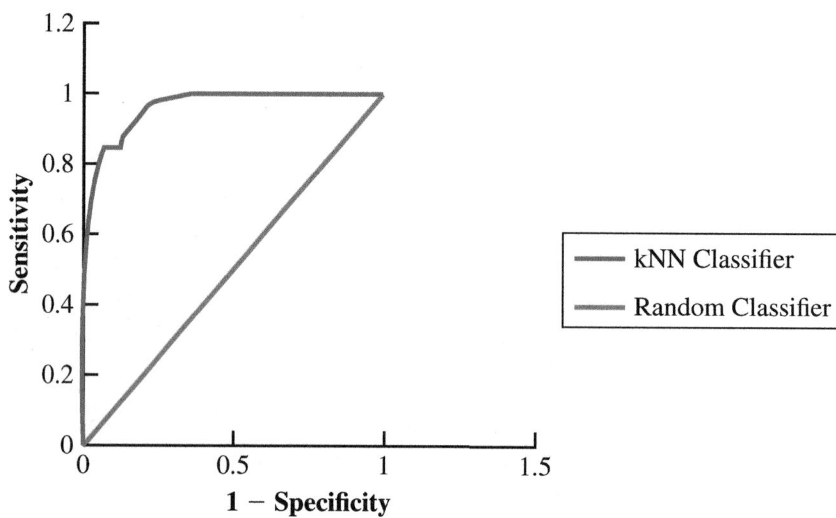

c. From the *KNNC_NewScore* worksheet, we see that the 17-nearest neighbors classifier predicts that 98 of the 200 customers in the Customer worksheet will use the promotional coupon.

4. a. For $k = 1$, the overall error rates on the training and validation sets are 0% and 6.87%, respectively. The overall error rate for the training set is computed by comparing the actual classification of each observation in the training set to the classification of the majority of the k most similar observations from the training set. Thus, for an observation (from the training set) and $k = 1$, the most similar observation in the training set is the observation itself. Therefore, if there are no observations with identical values of the input variables, $k = 1$ will lead to a 100% correct classification. However, if a training set has observations that have identical values of the input variables but different values of the output variable (Undecided), the training error will be nonzero (but typically small).
The overall error rate for the validation set is computed by comparing the true classification of each observation in the validation set to the classification of the majority of the k most similar observations from the training set. Thus, for $k = 1$, an observation (from the validation set) may not have the same classification as the most similar observation in the training, thereby leading to a misclassification.

Validation Error Log for Different *k*

Value of k	% Error Training	% Error Validation	
1	0	6.866667	
2	2.92	8.266667	
3	2.78	5.433333	
4	3.74	5.9	
5	3.28	5.166667	<- Best k
6	4.16	6.166667	
7	3.56	5.2	
8	3.86	5.633333	
9	3.7	5.3	
10	3.82	5.766667	
11	3.94	5.8	
12	4.28	6.166667	
13	4.36	6	
14	4.46	6.266667	
15	4.74	6	
16	5.02	6.2	
17	5.2	5.933333	
18	5.34	6.366667	
19	5.24	6.4	
20	5.42	6.633333	

b. The overall error rate is minimized at $k = 5$. The overall error rate is the lowest on the training data (3.28%), since a training set observation's set of k nearest neighbors will always include itself, artificially lowering the error rate.
For $k = 5$, the overall error rate on the validation data is biased since this overall error rate is the lowest error rate over all values of k. Thus, applying $k = 5$ on the test data will typically result in a more representative overall error rate, since we are not using the test data to find the best value of k. For this particular data partition, we observe that the overall error rate on the test set is 5%, which is slightly smaller than the overall error rate for the validation set (5.17%). Therefore, we can be confident that the overall error rate for the 5-nearest neighbor classifier is robust and is conservatively about 5%.

Training Data Scoring – Summary Report (for *k* = 5)

Cutoff probability value for success (UPDATABLE)	0.5

Confusion Matrix

	Predicted Class	
Actual Class	1	0
1	1907	107
0	57	2929

Error Report

Class	# Cases	# Errors	% Error
1	2014	107	5.31281
0	2986	57	1.908908
Overall	5000	164	3.28

Performance

Success Class	1
Precision	0.970978
Recall (Sensitivity)	0.946872
Specificity	0.980911
F1-Score	0.958773

Validation Data Scoring – Summary Report (for *k* = 5)

Cutoff probability value for success (UPDATABLE)	0.5

Confusion Matrix

	Predicted Class	
Actual Class	1	0
1	1117	92
0	63	1728

Error Report

Class	# Cases	# Errors	% Error
1	1209	92	7.609595
0	1791	63	3.517588
Overall	3000	155	5.166667

Performance

Success Class	1
Precision	0.94661
Recall (Sensitivity)	0.923904
Specificity	0.964824
F1-Score	0.935119

Test Data Scoring – Summary Report (for k = 5)

Cutoff probability value for success (UPDATABLE)	0.5

Confusion Matrix

	Predicted Class	
Actual Class	1	0
1	735	56
0	44	1165

Error Report

Class	# Cases	# Errors	% Error
1	791	56	7.079646
0	1209	44	3.639371
Overall	2000	100	5

Performance

Success Class	1
Precision	0.943517
Recall (Sensitivity)	0.929204
Specificity	0.963606
F1-Score	0.936306

c. The first decile lift is 2.50 (found by hovering the cursor over first decile in decile-wise lift chart). For this test set of 2,000 observations and 791 actual undecided voters, if we randomly selected 200 voters, on average 79.1 of them would be undecided. However, if we use k-NN with k = 5 to identify the top 200 voters most likely to be undecided, then (79.1)(2.50) = 198 of them would be undecided.

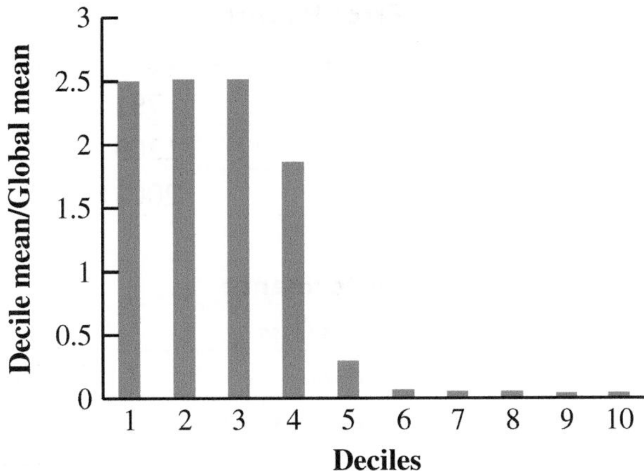

d. A cutoff value of 0.3 appears to provide a good tradeoff between the Class 1 and Class 0 error rates.

Cutoff	Class 1 Error Rate	Class 0 Error Rate
0.5	7.61%	3.52%
0.4	5.29%	8.65%
0.3	5.29%	8.65%
0.2	3.31%	23.95%

6. a. Age is the most important variable in reducing classification error of the ensemble.

Variables	Age	Education	Income	HouseholdSize	Church	HomeOwner	Female	Married
Importance	0.82906215	0.780809109	0.710666521	0.58064882	0.417534482	0.352785161	0.348484054	0.167516656

b. The overall classification error of the random trees ensemble is 8.4%, the Class 1 error rate is 19.60%, and the Class 0 error rate is 1.08%. Compared to the single (best-pruned) tree constructed in Problem 5 (which had an overall error rate of 2.05%, a Class 1 error rate of 3.54%, and a Class 0 error rate of 1.08%), we observe that the random forests approach does *worse*.

Test Data Scoring – Summary Report

Cutoff probability value for success (UPDATABLE)	0.5

Confusion Matrix

	Predicted Class	
Actual Class	1	0
1	636	155
0	13	1196

Error Report

Class	# Cases	# Errors	% Error
1	791	155	19.5954488
0	1209	13	1.075268817
Overall	2000	168	8.4

Performance

Success Class	1
Precision	0.97996918
Recall (Sensitivity)	0.80404551
Specificity	0.98924731
F1-Score	0.88333333

8. a. Churn observations make up only 14.49% of the data set. By oversampling the churn observations in the training set, a data-mining algorithm can better learn how to classify them.

b. A value of $k = 19$ minimizes the overall error rate on the validation set.

Validation Error Log for Different k

Value of k	% Error Training	% Error Validation	
1	0	26.1	
2	12.24066	37.5	
3	10.58091	19.6	
4	13.90041	26	
5	14.52282	16.8	
6	14.52282	19.5	
7	14.93776	15.1	
8	15.3527	17.1	
9	17.01245	15	
10	16.39004	17.5	
11	17.63485	14.6	
12	16.39004	16.1	
13	17.63485	14.6	
14	17.21992	15.8	
15	17.01245	14.3	
16	16.80498	15.5	
17	18.04979	14.3	
18	17.42739	14.9	
19	19.08714	14.2	<- Best k
20	17.84232	15.1	

c. The overall error rate on the test set for $k = 19$ is 12.11%.

Test Data Scoring – Summary Report (for k = 19)

Cutoff probability value for success (UPDATABLE)	0.5

Confusion Matrix

	Predicted Class	
Actual Class	1	0
1	77	20
0	61	511

Error Report

Class	# Cases	# Errors	% Error
1	97	20	20.61856
0	572	61	10.66434
Overall	669	81	12.10762

Performance

Success Class	1
Precision	0.557971
Recall (Sensitivity)	0.793814
Specificity	0.893357
F1-Score	0.655319

d. The class 1 error rate is 20.62% and the Class 0 error rate is 10.66% for $k = 19$ on the test set.

e. Sensitivity = 1 − Class 1 error rate = 79.38%. This means that the model can correctly identify 79.38% of the churners in the test set. Specificity = 1 − Class 0 error rate = 89.34%. This means that the model can correctly identify 89.34% of the non-churners in the test set.

f. There were 61 false positives (non-churners classified as churners). There were 20 false negatives (churners classified as non-churners). Of the observations predicted to be churners, 61 / (61 + 77) = 44.20% were false positives. Of the observations predicted to be non-churners, 20 / (20 + 511) = 3.77% were false negatives.

g. The first decile lift is 4.08. For this set of 669 customers, there are 97 actual churners. Thus, if we randomly selected 67 customers, on average 9.7 of them would be churners. However, if we use k-NN with $k = 19$ to identify the top 67 customers most likely to be churners, then (9.7)(4.08) = 40 of them would be churners.

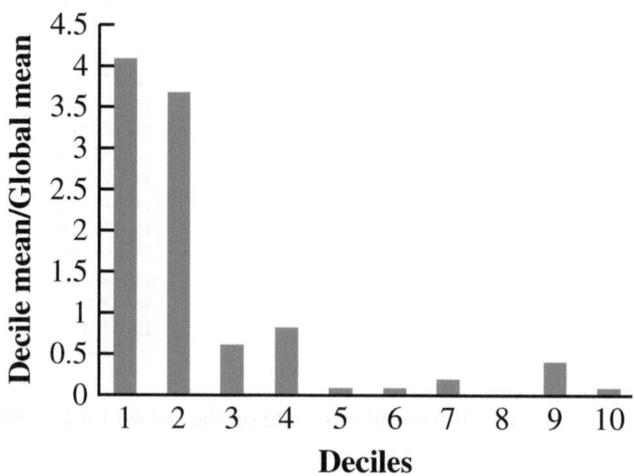

10. a The most important variable in reducing classification error of the ensemble is the number of weeks the customer's account has been active.

Variables	AccountWeeks	DayMins	MonthlyCharge	RoamMins	DayCalls	CustServCalls	OverageFee	ContractRenewal	DataUsage	DataPlan
Importance	0.613755752	0.488371563	0.467607885	0.427797107	0.401824428	0.349977617	0.335974696	0.280397088	0.248453857	0.123462288

g. The overall classification error of the random trees ensemble is 15.10%, the Class 1 error rate is 12.37%, and the Class 0 error rate is 15.56%. Each of these error rates is smaller than the corresponding error rates for the single (best-pruned) tree constructed in Problem 9 (which had an overall error rate of 15.84%, a Class 1 error rate of 15.46%, and a Class 0 error rate of 15.91%.

Test Data Scoring – Summary Report

Cutoff probability value for success (UPDATABLE)	0.5

Confusion Matrix

	Predicted Class	
Actual Class	1	0
1	85	12
0	89	483

Error Report			
Class	# Cases	# Errors	% Error
1	97	12	12.37113402
0	572	89	15.55944056
Overall	669	101	15.09715994

Performance	
Success Class	1
Precision	0.488505747
Recall (Sensitivity)	0.87628866
Specificity	0.844405594
F1-Score	0.627306273

12. a. The value of $k = 17$ minimizes the RMSE on the validation data.

Validation Error Log for Different *k*

Value of k	Training RMS Error	Validation RMS Error	
1	5.697933	66.8109289	
2	5.697933	61.86547462	
3	5.697933	59.02955387	
4	5.697933	57.90640801	
5	5.697933	57.13012016	
6	5.697933	56.88778375	
7	5.697933	56.54099439	
8	5.697933	56.2557058	
9	5.697933	56.15093959	
10	5.697933	56.12061932	
11	5.697933	55.99690391	
12	5.697933	55.99276283	
13	5.697933	56.047191	
14	5.697933	56.08216336	
15	5.697933	55.95927151	
16	5.697933	55.96689038	
17	5.697933	55.94879866	<- Best k
18	5.697933	56.00945598	
19	5.697933	55.99859864	
20	5.697933	56.04361266	

b. The RMSE = 55.95 on the validation set and RMSE = 51.52 on the test set. This is an encouraging sign that the RMSE of $k = 17$ on new data should be relatively stable and in the range of 51 to 56.

Validation Data Scoring – Summary Report (for k = 17)

Total sum of squared errors	RMS Error	Average Error
4598364	55.9488	-5.99384273

Test Data Scoring – Summary Report (for k = 17)

Total sum of squared errors	RMS Error	Average Error
2600915	51.51693	0.043670645

h. The average error on the test set is 0.04, suggesting that there is essentially no bias in the prediction. That is, the predicted credit scores are equally likely to be overestimated as they are to be underestimated. A histogram of the residuals shows that the prediction error is roughly symmetric around zero (slightly skewed to the left).

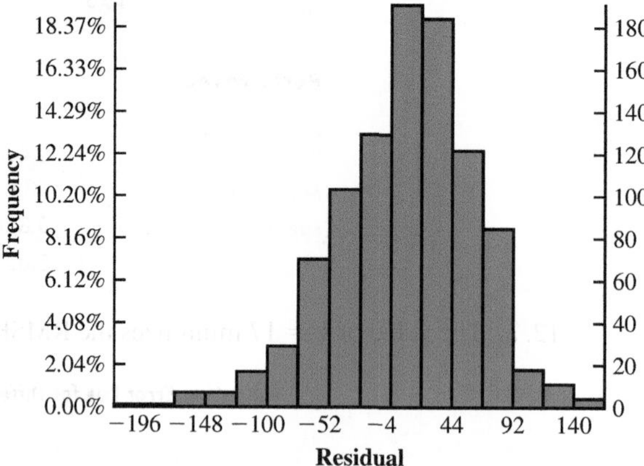

14. The root mean squared error of the random forest of regression trees is 55.71, which is slightly smaller than the root mean squared error of 55.75 for the single best-pruned tree in part a of Problem 13.

Test Data scoring - Summary Report

Total sum of squared errors	RMS Error	Average Error
3041763	55.71211	3.456719

16. a. i. A value of $k = 7$ minimizes the RMSE on the precrisis validation data.

Validation Error Log for Different *k*

Value of k	Training RMS Error	Validation RMS Error	
1	0	29651.4278	
2	797.1594	25869.9914	
3	956.5913	24556.43032	
4	1024.919	23922.79711	
5	1062.879	23429.85569	
6	1087.036	23495.3136	
7	1103.759	23389.26841	<- Best k
8	1116.023	23498.25568	
9	1125.402	23748.6476	
10	1132.805	23764.50319	
11	1138.799	23755.51613	
12	1143.75	23742.36843	
13	1147.91	23814.53491	
14	1151.452	23880.17824	
15	1154.507	24108.23952	
16	1157.167	24265.92884	
17	1159.505	24426.3947	
18	1161.575	24505.82421	
19	1163.422	24583.29765	
20	1165.079	24614.02538	

ii. The RMSE on the validation set is $23,389 and the RMSE on the test data is $27,268.

Validation Data Scoring – Summary Report (for k = 7)

Total sum of squared errors	RMS Error	Average Error
3.24405E+11	23389.27	3119.372779

Test Data Scoring – Summary Report (for k = 7)

Total sum of squared errors	RMS Error	Average Error
2.94445E+11	27268.06	3987.932319

iii. The average error on the validation set is $3,119 and the average error on the test data is $3,988. This suggests that the k-NN model tends to underestimate the price of a home. This is likely due to the fact that there are very few expensive homes in the precrisis data set, so the predicted prices of these homes are vastly underestimated.

b. i. A value of $k = 4$ minimizes the RMSE on the postcrisis validation data.

Validation Error Log for Different k

Value of k	Training RMS Error	Validation RMS Error	
1	0	27337.81	
2	0	24855.29	
3	5.33417E-12	24683.41	
4	0	24152.33	<- Best k
5	5.66651E-12	24327.6	
6	8.72974E-12	24322.26	
7	1.2957E-11	24372.03	
8	1.16756E-11	24291.14	
9	1.16455E-11	24452.16	
10	1.57187E-11	24438	
11	1.90624E-11	24469.41	
12	2.02959E-11	24452.92	
13	2.32951E-11	24547.27	
14	2.36947E-11	24768.16	
15	2.68866E-11	24935.11	
16	2.67867E-11	25141.27	
17	2.63995E-11	25031.27	
18	2.82552E-11	25130.46	
19	3.03715E-11	25298.9	
20	2.99181E-11	25321.25	

ii. The RMSE on the validation set is \$24,152 and the RMSE on the test set is \$24,396.

Validation Data Scoring – Summary Report (for *k* = 4)

Total sum of squared errors	RMS Error	Average Error
2.89918E+11	24152.32942	1289.55

Test Data Scoring – Summary Report (for *k* = 4)

Total sum of squared errors	RMS Error	Average Error
1.96996E+11	24395.75254	2831.026

iii. The average error on the validation set is \$1,290 and the average error on the test data is \$2,831. This suggests that the *k*-NN model tends to underestimate the price of a home. This is likely due to the fact that there are very few expensive homes in the postcrisis data set, so the predicted prices of these homes are vastly underestimated.

c. The average percentage change = −2.42%. Predicted sales price based on postcrisis data is on average 2.42% lower than predicted sales price based on precrisis data.

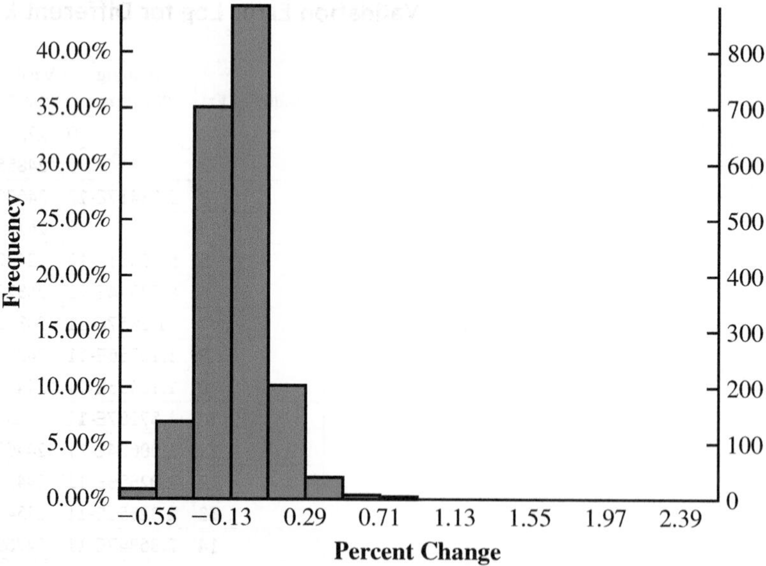

18. a. Using goodness-of-fit measures such as Mallow's C_p statistic and adjusted R^2, we see that there are several viable models for consideration. After comparing several of the candidate models based on prediction error on the validation set, we suggest the one that includes 8 independent variables is a strong candidate.

i.

Regression Model

Input Variables	Coefficient	Std. Error	t-Statistic	P-Value	CI Lower	CI Upper	RSS Reduction
Intercept	1100.425	1892.754227	0.581388276	0.561112	-2613.89	4814.743	1.28337E+13
LandValue	1.277029	0.076668634	16.65647257	4.84E-55	1.126575	1.427483	1.50786E+12
BuildingValue	0.754726	0.026038266	28.98525944	6.6E-134	0.703629	0.805823	7.81582E+11
Acres	-8796.527	2716.764721	-3.23786848	0.001245	-14127.9	-3465.18	2540777078
AboveSpace	10.75424	1.965529804	5.47142208	5.67E-08	6.897112	14.61137	2124495923
Basement	5.986766	2.47531594	2.418586733	0.015762	1.129237	10.8443	894267990.3
AC	3359.778	1376.431854	2.440932804	0.014826	658.6848	6060.87	5713777784
PoorCondition	-14534.5	2357.512784	-6.1651826	1.03E-09	-19160.9	-9908.14	16150471081
GoodCondition	5442.207	1135.962693	4.790832625	1.92E-06	3213.008	7671.406	5730125066

Residual DF	980
R^2	0.904698579
Adjusted R^2	0.903920608
Std. Error Estim	15800.50807
RSS	2.44663E+11

ii. The RMSE on the validation set is $16,863 and the RMSE on the test data is $16,709.

Validation Data Scoring – Summary Report

Total sum of squared errors	RMS Error	Average Error
1.68619E+11	16862.65	622.0128697

Test Data Scoring – Summary Report

Total sum of squared errors	RMS Error	Average Error
1.10564E+11	16709.33	172.925614

iii. The average error on the validation set is $622 and the average error on the test data is $173. There is very slight evidence of systematic underestimation of home price.

b. Using goodness-of-fit measures such as Mallow's C_p statistic and adjusted R^2, we see that there are several viable models to consider. After comparing several of the candidate models based on prediction error on the validation set, we suggest the one that includes 9 independent variables is a strong candidate.

i.

Regression Model

Input Variables	Coefficient	Std. Error	t-Statistic	P-Value	CI Lower	CI Upper	RSS Reduction
Intercept	-7471.893	2962.412377	-2.52223251	0.01184975	-13286.7	-1657.08	1.07216E+13
LandValue	1.231007	0.08239607	14.94011191	8.2315E-45	1.069274	1.392739	1.38567E+12
BuildingValue	0.787454	0.023111488	34.07198106	3.759E-159	0.742089	0.832819	8.03672E+11
Acres	-10597.16	3451.010132	-3.07074151	0.00220581	-17371	-3823.29	2690860840
Baths	3444.247	1432.515455	2.404335126	0.01642302	632.4131	6256.081	900052710.8
Fireplaces	5044.389	1370.157277	3.681613156	0.00024695	2354.956	7733.822	2967506546
Beds	3282.083	944.8395825	3.473693781	0.00054029	1427.491	5136.676	2844029519
AC	4647.542	1717.679814	2.705708868	0.00695757	1275.968	8019.115	5636911875
PoorCondition	-9083.007	2460.20367	-3.69197369	0.00023726	-13912.1	-4253.96	7524928450
GoodCondition	4352.854	1351.292945	3.221251089	0.00132671	1700.449	7005.259	3000590252

Residual DF	819
R^2	0.903402401
Adjusted R^2	0.902340889
Std. Error Estim	17005.0835
RSS	2.36833E+11

ii. The RMSE on the validation set is \$18,403 and the RMSE on the test data is \$17,321.

Validation Data Scoring – Summary Report

Total sum of squared errors	RMS Error	Average Error
1.68324E+11	18403.27	-692.0220872

Test Data Scoring – Summary Report

Total sum of squared errors	RMS Error	Average Error
99306710466	17321.09	-70.4377605

iii. The average error on the validation set is −\$692 and the average error on the test data is −\$70. Estimates of home price using the postcrisis data appear to have a very slight bias toward overestimation.

c. The average percentage change = −5.43%. Predicted sales price based on postcrisis data is on average 5.43% lower than predicted sales price based on precrisis data.

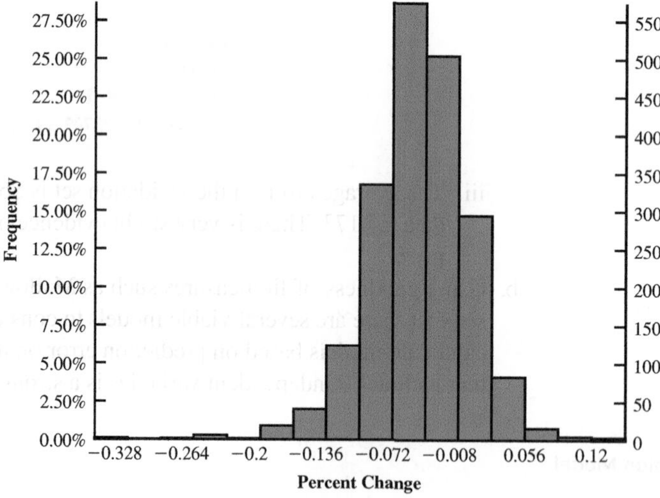

Chapter 10: Spreadsheet Models

Solutions

2. a.

	A	B	C	D	E
1	**Cox Electric Breakeven Analysis**				
2	**Parameters**				
3	Revenue per Unit	$0.65			
4				-$5,200.00	
5	Fixed Costs	$10,000.00	0	0	
6			10000	-$6,000.00	
7	Material Cost per Unit	$0.15	20000	-$2,000.00	
8			30000	$2,000.00	
9	Labor Cost per Unit	$0.10	40000	$6,000.00	
10			50000	$10,000.00	
11			60000	$14,000.00	
12	**Model**		70000	$18,000.00	
13			80000	$22,000.00	
14	Production Volume	12,000	90000	$26,000.00	
15			100000	$30,000.00	
16	Total Revenue	$7,800.00			
17					
18	Material Cost	$1,800.00			
19	Labor Cost	$1,200.00			
20	Fixed Cost	$10,000.00			
21	Total Cost	$13,000.00			
22					
23	Profit	-$5,200.00			
24					

Data Table
Row input cell:
Column input cell: $B$14
OK Cancel

Breakeven appears in the interval of 20,000 to 30,000 units.

b.

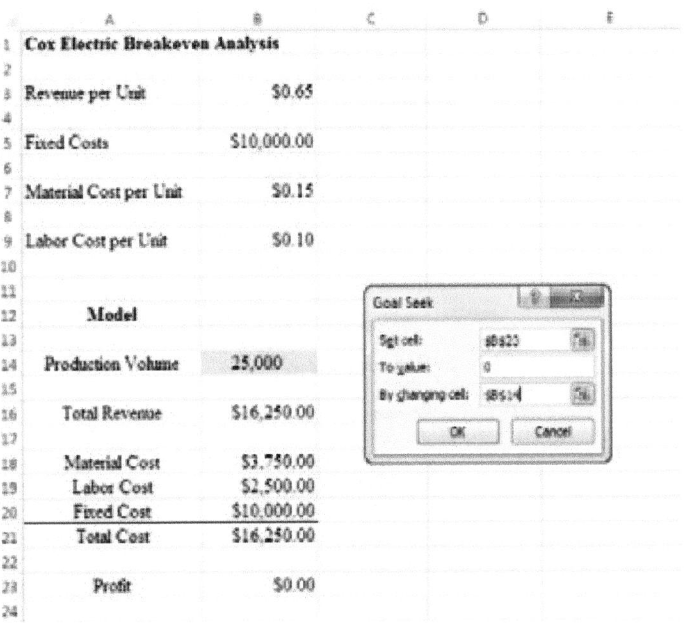

	A	B
1	**Cox Electric Breakeven Analysis**	
2		
3	Revenue per Unit	$0.65
4		
5	Fixed Costs	$10,000.00
6		
7	Material Cost per Unit	$0.15
8		
9	Labor Cost per Unit	$0.10
10		
11		
12	**Model**	
13		
14	Production Volume	25,000
15		
16	Total Revenue	$16,250.00
17		
18	Material Cost	$3,750.00
19	Labor Cost	$2,500.00
20	Fixed Cost	$10,000.00
21	Total Cost	$16,250.00
22		
23	Profit	$0.00
24		

Goal Seek
Set cell: $B$23
To value: 0
By changing cell: $B$14
OK Cancel

4. a.

	A	B
1	**BI Symposium Breakeven Analysis**	
2		
3	**Parameters**	
4		
5	Auditorium Cost	$150.00
6	Registration Processing/ Person	$8.50
7	Breakfast Cost/Person	$4.00
8	Lunch Cost/ Person	$7.00
9	Parking Cost/Person	$5.00
10	Cost of Speakers (3 speakers @ $800 each)	$2,400.00
11	Number of Corporate Members	10
12	Free Seats per Corporate Member	5
13	Nonmember Fee per Person	$75.00
14		
15		
16	**Model**	
17		
18	Number of Nonmember Registrants	100.000
19		
20	Number of Attendees	150.000
21		
22	Revenue	$7,500.00
23		
24	Registration Cost	$1,275.00
25	Breakfast Cost	$600.00
26	Lunch Cost	$1,050.00
27	Parking Cost	$750.00
28	Speaker Cost	$2,400.00
29	Auditorium Cost	$150.00
30	Total Cost	$6,225.00
31		
32	Profit	$1,275.00

	A	B
1	**BI Symposium Breakeven Analysis**	
2		
3	**Parameters**	
4		
5	Auditorium Cost	150
6	Registration Processing/ Person	8.5
7	Breakfast Cost/Person	4
8	Lunch Cost/ Person	7
9	Parking Cost/Person	5
10	Cost of Speakers (3 speakers @ $800 each)	2400
11	Number of Corporate Members	10
12	Free Seats per Corporate Member	5
13	Nonmember Fee per Person	75
14		
15		
16	**Model**	
17		
18	Number of Nonmember Registrants	100
19		
20	Number of Attendees	=B18+B11*B12
21		
22	Revenue	=B13*B18
23		
24	Registration Cost	=B20*B6
25	Breakfast Cost	=B20*B7
26	Lunch Cost	=B20*B8
27	Parking Cost	=B20*B9
28	Speaker Cost	=B10
29	Auditorium Cost	=B5
30	Total Cost	=SUM(B24:B29)
31		
32	Profit	=B22-B30

b.

	A	B
1	**BI Symposium Breakeven Analysis**	
2		
3	**Parameters**	
4		
5	Auditorium Cost	$150.00
6	Registration Processing/ Person	$8.50
7	Breakfast Cost/Person	$4.00
8	Lunch Cost/ Person	$7.00
9	Parking Cost/Person	$5.00
10	Cost of Speakers (3 speakers @ $800 each)	$2,400.00
11	Number of Corporate Members	10
12	Free Seats per Corporate Member	5
13	Nonmember Fee per Person	$75.00
14		
15		
16	**Model**	
17		
18	Number of Nonmember Registrants	74.752
19		
20	Number of Attendees	124.752
21		
22	Revenue	$5,606.44
23		
24	Registration Cost	$1,060.40
25	Breakfast Cost	$499.01
26	Lunch Cost	$873.27
27	Parking Cost	$623.76
28	Speaker Cost	$2,400.00
29	Auditorium Cost	$150.00
30	Total Cost	$5,606.44
31		
32	Profit	$0.00

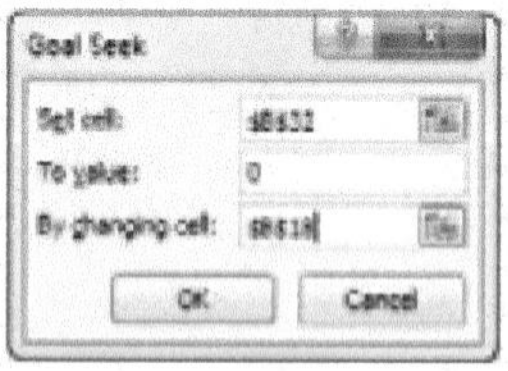

Goal Seek

Set cell:	$B$32
To value:	0
By changing cell:	$B$18

OK Cancel

Breakeven is 74.752 (or 75) Nonmembers.

6. a.

	A	B
1	**Eastman Publishing**	
2		
3	**Parameters**	
4		
5	Fixed Cost	$160,000.00
6	Variable Cost/Book	$6.00
7	Acecess Price	$46.00
8		
9		
10	**Model**	
11		
12	Demand	3,724
13		
14	Revenue	$171,304.00
15		
16	Fixed Cost	$160,000.00
17	Variable Cost	$22,344.00
18	Total Cost	$182,344.00
19		
20	Profit	-$11,040.00

	A	B
1	**Eastman Publishing**	
2		
3	**Parameters**	
4		
5	Fixed Cost	160000
6	Variable Cost/Book	6
7	Acecess Price	46
8		
9		
10	**Model**	
11		
12	Demand	=4000-6*B7
13		
14	Revenue	=B7*B12
15		
16	Fixed Cost	=B5
17	Variable Cost	=B12*B6
18	Total Cost	=SUM(B16:B17)
19		
20	Profit	=B14-B18

b.

	A	B	C	D	E	F
1	**Eastman Publishing**					
2						
3	**Parameters**					
4						
5	Fixed Cost	$160,000.00				
6	Variable Cost/Book	$6.00				
7	Acecess Price	$49.19				
8						
9						
10	**Model**					
11						
12	Demand	3,705				
13						
14	Revenue	$182,229.29				
15						
16	Fixed Cost	$160,000.00				
17	Variable Cost	$22,229.29				
18	Total Cost	$182,229.29				
19						
20	Profit	$0.00				

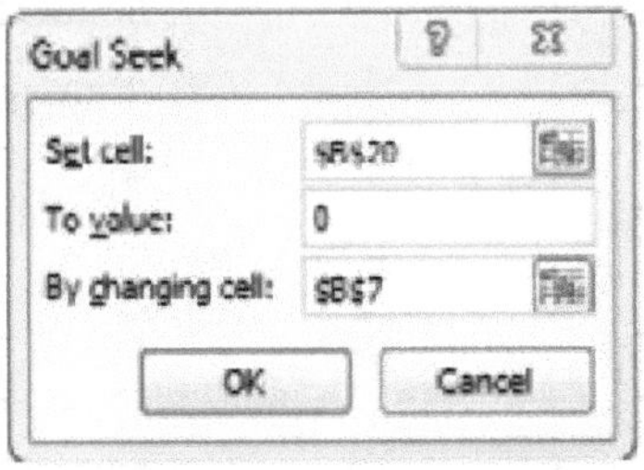

Goal Seek

Set cell: $B$20

To value: 0

By changing cell: $B$7

OK Cancel

c.

	A	B	C	D	E
1	**Eastman Publishing**				
2					
3	**Parameters**				-$11,040.00
4				$50	$2,800
5	Fixed Cost	$160,000.00		$75	$84,950
6	Variable Cost/Book	$6.00		$100	$159,600
7	Aceress Price	$46.00		$125	$226,750
8				$150	$286,400
9				$175	$338,550
10	**Model**			$200	$383,200
11				$225	$420,350
12	Demand	3,724		$250	$450,000
13				$275	$472,150
14	Revenue	$171,304.00		$300	$486,800
15				$325	$493,950
16	Fixed Cost	$160,000.00		$350	$493,600
17	Variable Cost	$22,344.00		$375	$485,750
18	Total Cost	$182,344.00		$400	$470,400
19					
20	Profit	-$11,040.00			

The access price of $325 maximizes profit.

8. Part of the spreadsheet mode appears below:

	A	B	C	D	E
1	**Lindsay's Retirement Account**				
2					
3	**Parameters**				
4					
5	Annual Investment	$10,000.00			
6	Annual Return	6.0%			
7	Discount Rate	3.0%			
8					
9	**Model**				
10			Discounted Flow	$455,414.11	
11					
12	Year	Return on Investment	Contribution	Inflow	Ending Balance
13	1	0	$10,000.00	$10,000.00	$10,000.00
14	2	$600.00	$10,000.00	$10,600.00	$20,600.00
15	3	$1,236.00	$10,000.00	$11,236.00	$31,836.00
16	4	$1,910.16	$10,000.00	$11,910.16	$43,746.16
17	5	$2,624.77	$10,000.00	$12,624.77	$56,370.93
18	6	$3,382.26	$10,000.00	$13,382.26	$69,753.19
19	7	$4,185.19	$10,000.00	$14,185.19	$83,938.38
20	8	$5,036.30	$10,000.00	$15,036.30	$98,974.68
21	9	$5,938.48	$10,000.00	$15,938.48	$114,913.16
22	10	$6,894.79	$10,000.00	$16,894.79	$131,807.95
23	11	$7,908.48	$10,000.00	$17,908.48	$149,716.43
24	12	$8,982.99	$10,000.00	$18,982.99	$168,699.41
25	13	$10,121.96	$10,000.00	$20,121.96	$188,821.38

	A	B	C	D	E
1	**Lindsay's Retirement Account**				
2					
3	**Parameters**				
4					
5	Annual Investment	10000			
6	Annual Return	0.06			
7	Discount Rate	0.03			
8					
9	**Model**				
10			Discounted Flow	=NPV(B7,D13:D42)	
11					
12	Year	Return on Investment	Contribution	Inflow	Ending Balance
13	1	0	=$B$5	=B13+C13	=D13
14	2	=E13*$B$6	=$B$5	=B14+C14	=E13+D14
15	3	=E14*$B$6	=$B$5	=B15+C15	=E14+D15
16	4	=E15*$B$6	=$B$5	=B16+C16	=E15+D16
17	5	=E16*$B$6	=$B$5	=B17+C17	=E16+D17
18	6	=E17*$B$6	=$B$5	=B18+C18	=E17+D18
19	7	=E18*$B$6	=$B$5	=B19+C19	=E18+D19

A portion of the data table appears below:

	G	H	I	J	K	L
8	$455,414.11	0.0%	1.0%	2.0%	3.0%	4.0%
9	0.0%	$300,000	$258,077	$223,965	$196,004	$172,920
10	1.0%	$347,849	$297,030	$255,892	$222,352	$194,811
11	2.0%	$405,681	$343,891	$294,118	$253,743	$220,762
12	3.0%	$475,754	$400,421	$340,021	$291,262	$251,630
13	4.0%	$560,849	$468,784	$395,293	$336,237	$288,462
14	5.0%	$664,388	$551,637	$462,006	$390,292	$332,536
15	6.0%	$790,582	$652,246	$542,704	$455,414	$385,413
16	7.0%	$944,608	$774,618	$640,501	$534,037	$449,000
17	8.0%	$1,132,832	$923,674	$759,217	$629,136	$525,626
18	9.0%	$1,363,075	$1,105,449	$903,528	$744,351	$618,135
19	10.0%	$1,644,940	$1,327,346	$1,079,163	$884,132	$729,996
20	11.0%	$1,990,209	$1,598,432	$1,293,130	$1,053,915	$865,446
21	12.0%	$2,413,327	$1,929,814	$1,554,000	$1,260,343	$1,029,650

10. Error #1: The formula in cell C17 is:

=SUMPRODUCT(C8:G11,B22:F25),

but should be

=SUMPRODUCT(C8:F11,B22:F25).

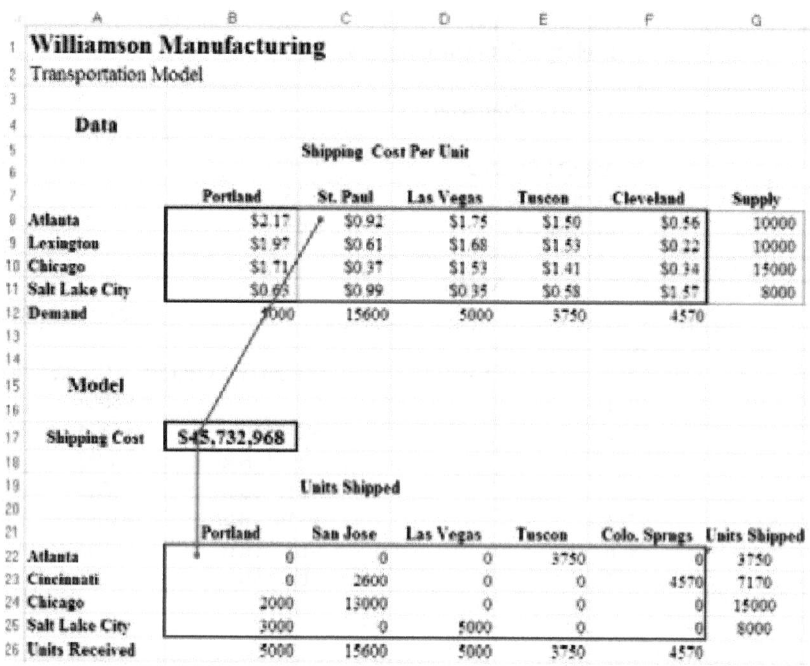

Williamson Manufacturing
Transportation Model

Data

Shipping Cost Per Unit

	Portland	St. Paul	Las Vegas	Tuscon	Cleveland	Supply
Atlanta	$2.17	$0.92	$1.75	$1.50	$0.56	10000
Lexington	$1.97	$0.61	$1.68	$1.53	$0.22	10000
Chicago	$1.71	$0.37	$1.53	$1.41	$0.34	15000
Salt Lake City	$0.63	$0.99	$0.35	$0.58	$1.57	8000
Demand	5000	15600	5000	3750	4570	

Model

Shipping Cost $45,732,968

Units Shipped

	Portland	San Jose	Las Vegas	Tuscon	Colo. Sprngs	Units Shipped
Atlanta	0	0	0	3750	0	3750
Cincinnati	0	2600	0	0	4570	7170
Chicago	2000	13000	0	0	0	15000
Salt Lake City	3000	0	5000	0	0	8000
Units Received	5000	15600	5000	3750	4570	

Error #2: The formula in cell G22 is:

=SUM(B22:E22),

but should be

=SUM(B22:F22).

Williamson Manufacturing
Transportation Model

Data

Shipping Cost Per Unit

	Portland	St. Paul	Las Vegas	Tuscon	Cleveland	Supply
Atlanta	$2.17	$0.92	$1.75	$1.50	$0.56	10000
Lexington	$1.97	$0.61	$1.68	$1.53	$0.22	10000
Chicago	$1.71	$0.37	$1.53	$1.41	$0.34	15000
Salt Lake City	$0.63	$0.99	$0.35	$0.58	$1.57	8000
Demand	5000	15600	5000	3750	4570	

Model

Shipping Cost $45,732,968

Units Shipped

	Portland	San Jose	Las Vegas	Tuscon	Colo. Sprngs	Units Shipped
Atlanta	0	0	0	3750	0	3750
Cincinnati	0	2600	0	0	4570	7170
Chicago	2000	13000	0	0	0	15000
Salt Lake City	3000	0	5000	0	0	8000
Units Received	5000	15600	5000	3750	4570	

12. a. A portion of the spreadsheet is shown below.
    b. See column I below.

	A	B	C	D	E	F	G	H	I	J
1	Order	Quantity	Price per Roll	Revenue						
2	1	86	$195	$16,770		Quantity Ordered				
3	2	452	$155	$70,060		From	To	Price per Roll		
4	3	492	$155	$76,260		1	50	$215		
5	4	191	$175	$33,425		51	100	$195		
6	5	356	$155	$55,180		101	200	$175		
7	6	148	$175	$25,900		201	and up	$155		
8	7	342	$155	$53,010						
9	8	382	$155	$59,210						
10	9	276	$155	$42,780						
11	10	118	$175	$20,650		Total Revenue	$7,107,505			
12	11	464	$155	$71,920						
13	12	188	$175	$32,900						
14	13	25	$215	$5,375		From	To	Price per Roll	Number Orders	% of Orders
15	14	427	$155	$66,185		1	50	$215	13	7.6%
16	15	30	$215	$6,450		51	100	$195	15	8.7%
17	16	111	$175	$19,425		101	200	$175	37	21.5%
18	17	161	$175	$28,175		201	and up	$155	107	62.2%
19	18	314	$155	$48,670				Total	172	100.0%
20	19	442	$155	$68,510						

	A	B	C	D	E	F	G	H	I	J
1	Order	Quantity	Price per Roll	Revenue						
2	1	86	=VLOOKUP(B2,$F$4:$H$7,3)	=B2*C2		Quantity Ordered				
3	2	452	=VLOOKUP(B3,$F$4:$H$7,3)	=B3*C3		From	To	Price per Roll		
4	3	492	=VLOOKUP(B4,$F$4:$H$7,3)	=B4*C4		1	50	215		
5	4	191	=VLOOKUP(B5,$F$4:$H$7,3)	=B5*C5		51	100	195		
6	5	356	=VLOOKUP(B6,$F$4:$H$7,3)	=B6*C6		101	200	175		
7	6	148	=VLOOKUP(B7,$F$4:$H$7,3)	=B7*C7		201	and up	155		
8	7	342	=VLOOKUP(B8,$F$4:$H$7,3)	=B8*C8						
9	8	382	=VLOOKUP(B9,$F$4:$H$7,3)	=B9*C9						
10	9	276	=VLOOKUP(B10,$F$4:$H$7,3)	=B10*C10						
11	10	118	=VLOOKUP(B11,$F$4:$H$7,3)	=B11*C11		Total Revenue	=SUM(D2:D173)			
12	11	464	=VLOOKUP(B12,$F$4:$H$7,3)	=B12*C12						
13	12	188	=VLOOKUP(B13,$F$4:$H$7,3)	=B13*C13						
14	13	25	=VLOOKUP(B14,$F$4:$H$7,3)	=B14*C14		=F3	=G3	=H3	Number Orders	% of Orders
15	14	427	=VLOOKUP(B15,$F$4:$H$7,3)	=B15*C15		=F4	=G4	=H4	=COUNTIF($C$2:$C$173,H15)	=I15/$I$19
16	15	30	=VLOOKUP(B16,$F$4:$H$7,3)	=B16*C16		=F5	=G5	=H5	=COUNTIF($C$2:$C$173,H16)	=I16/$I$19
17	16	111	=VLOOKUP(B17,$F$4:$H$7,3)	=B17*C17		=F6	=G6	=H6	=COUNTIF($C$2:$C$173,H17)	=I17/$I$19
18	17	161	=VLOOKUP(B18,$F$4:$H$7,3)	=B18*C18		=F7	=G7	=H7	=COUNTIF($C$2:$C$173,H18)	=I18/$I$19
19	18	314	=VLOOKUP(B19,$F$4:$H$7,3)	=B19*C19				Total	=SUM(I15:I18)	=SUM(J15:J18)
20	19	442	=VLOOKUP(B20,$F$4:$H$7,3)	=B20*C20						

14. a.

	A	B
1	**European Put Option**	
2		
3	**Parameters**	
4	Cost of Put Option	$1.00
5	Exercise Price	$26.00
6	Horizon (months)	6
7	Price per Share	$28.00
8	Price - end of horizon	$23.00
9		
10		
11	**Model**	
12		
13	Number of Shares Purchased	200
14	Number of Puts Purchased	75
15		
16	Value of the Option	$3.00
17		
18	Portfolio Value with Options	$4,825.00
19	Cost of the Portfolio with Options	$5,675.00
20	Profit with Options	-$850.00
21		
22	Portfolio Value without Options	$4,600.00
23	Cost of the Portfolio without Options	$5,600.00
24	Profit without Options	-$1,000.00

	A	B
1	**European Put Option**	
2		
3	**Parameters**	
4	Cost of Put Option	1
5	Exercise Price	26
6	Horizon (months)	6
7	Price per Share	28
8	Price - end of horizon	23
9		
10		
11	**Model**	
12		
13	Number of Shares Purchased	200
14	Number of Puts Purchased	75
15		
16	Value of the Option	=IF(B5>B8,B5-B8, 0)
17		
18	Portfolio Value with Options	=B8*B13+B16*B14
19	Cost of the Portfolio with Options	=B13*B7+B14*B4
20	Profit with Options	=B18-B19
21		
22	Portfolio Value without Options	=B8*B13
23	Cost of the Portfolio without Options	=B13*B7
24	Profit without Options	=B22-B23

Portfolio Value with Options		Portfolio Value without Options		
	-$850.00		-$1,000.00	Benefit of Options
$15.00	-$1,850.00	$15.00	-$2,600.00	$750.00
$16.00	-$1,725.00	$16.00	-$2,400.00	$675.00
$17.00	-$1,600.00	$17.00	-$2,200.00	$600.00
$18.00	-$1,475.00	$18.00	-$2,000.00	$525.00
$19.00	-$1,350.00	$19.00	-$1,800.00	$450.00
$20.00	-$1,225.00	$20.00	-$1,600.00	$375.00
$21.00	-$1,100.00	$21.00	-$1,400.00	$300.00
$22.00	-$975.00	$22.00	-$1,200.00	$225.00
$23.00	-$850.00	$23.00	-$1,000.00	$150.00
$24.00	-$725.00	$24.00	-$800.00	$75.00
$25.00	-$600.00	$25.00	-$600.00	$0.00
$26.00	-$475.00	$26.00	-$400.00	-$75.00
$27.00	-$275.00	$27.00	-$200.00	-$75.00
$28.00	-$75.00	$28.00	$0.00	-$75.00
$29.00	$125.00	$29.00	$200.00	-$75.00
$30.00	$325.00	$30.00	$400.00	-$75.00
$31.00	$525.00	$31.00	$600.00	-$75.00
$32.00	$725.00	$32.00	$800.00	-$75.00
$33.00	$925.00	$33.00	$1,000.00	-$75.00
$34.00	$1,125.00	$34.00	$1,200.00	-$75.00
$35.00	$1,325.00	$35.00	$1,400.00	-$75.00

b. The lower the stock price, the more beneficial the put options. The options are worth nothing at a stock price of $26 or above. There is a benefit from the put options to the overall portfolio for stock prices of $24 or lower.

16.

Dave and Jana's Refinance Analysis

Parameters

Original Loan			Proposed refinance			Monthly Inflation Rate
Amount Borrowed	$230,415.00		Amount Borrowed	$208,555.87		0.002
Annual Interest Rate	5.49%		Annual Interest Rate	3.00%		
Number of Years	15		Number of Years	15		
Monthly Payment	[illegible]		Monthly Payment	($1,440.29)		
			Out-of-Pocket	$2,937		

Model

Old Payment #	New Payment #	Savings	Discounted Savings
26	1	$441.21	$441.21
27	2	$441.21	$440.33
28	3	$441.21	$439.45
29	4	$441.21	$438.58
30	5	$441.21	$437.70
31	6	$441.21	$436.83
32	7	$441.21	$435.95
33	8	$441.21	$435.08
34	9	$441.21	$434.22
35	10	$441.21	$433.35
36	11	$441.21	$432.48
37	12	$441.21	$431.62

Total Discounted Savings	$33,076.92
Out-of-Pocket	$2,937.00
Savings in Today's Dollars	$30,139.92

Note: Negative savings starting with New Payment # 156. See row 164

Key cell formulas:

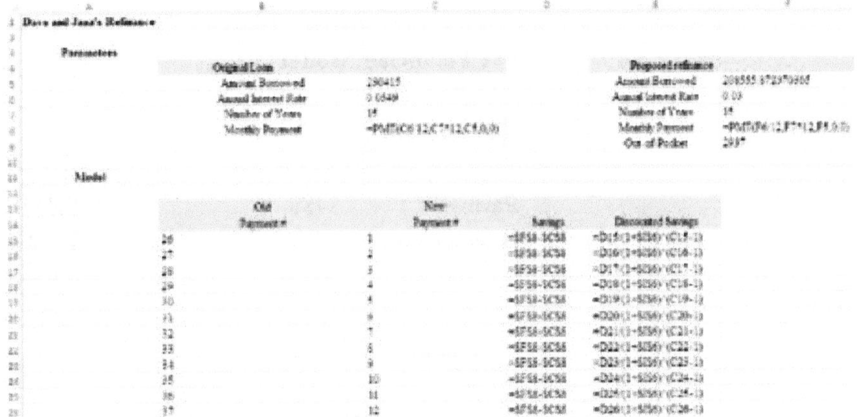

Dave and Jana's Refinance

Parameters

Original Loan		Proposed refinance	
Amount Borrowed	230415	Amount Borrowed	[illegible]
Annual Interest Rate	0.0549	Annual Interest Rate	0.03
Number of Years	15	Number of Years	15
Monthly Payment	=PMT(C6/12,C7*12,C5,0,0)	Monthly Payment	=PMT(F6/12,F7*12,F5,0,0)
		Out-of-Pocket	2937

Model

Old Payment #	New Payment #	Savings	Discounted Savings
26	1	=$F$8-$C$8	=D15/(1+$I$6)^(C15-1)
27	2	=$F$8-$C$8	=D16/(1+$I$6)^(C16-1)
28	3	=$F$8-$C$8	=D17/(1+$I$6)^(C17-1)
29	4	=$F$8-$C$8	=D18/(1+$I$6)^(C18-1)
30	5	=$F$8-$C$8	=D19/(1+$I$6)^(C19-1)
31	6	=$F$8-$C$8	=D20/(1+$I$6)^(C20-1)
32	7	=$F$8-$C$8	=D21/(1+$I$6)^(C21-1)
33	8	=$F$8-$C$8	=D22/(1+$I$6)^(C22-1)
34	9	=$F$8-$C$8	=D23/(1+$I$6)^(C23-1)
35	10	=$F$8-$C$8	=D24/(1+$I$6)^(C24-1)
36	11	=$F$8-$C$8	=D25/(1+$I$6)^(C25-1)
37	12	=$F$8-$C$8	=D26/(1+$I$6)^(C26-1)

18. A portion of the spreadsheet is shown below:

	A	B	C	D	E	F	G	H	I
1			Distribution Center						
2		Charlotte, NC	Dallas, TX	Lafayette, IN	Los Angeles, CA	Pittsburgh, PA			
3	Customer Zipcode	28202	75201	47905	90058	15122	Min Distance	Position	DC Location
4	00738	731	1312	1262	2735	1178	731	1	Charlotte, NC
5	00739	731	1312	1262	2735	1178	731	1	Charlotte, NC
6	00757	731	1312	1262	2735	1178	731	1	Charlotte, NC
7	00926	731	1312	1262	2735	1178	731	1	Charlotte, NC
8	01013	790	1696	927	2902	525	525	5	Pittsburgh, PA
9	01060	804	1710	936	2911	533	533	5	Pittsburgh, PA
10	01238	792	1693	889	2864	486	486	5	Pittsburgh, PA

	G	H	I
3	Min Distance	Position	DC Location
4	=MIN(B4:F4)	=MATCH(G4,B4:F4,0)	=INDEX($B$2:$F$2,H4)
5	-MIN(B5:F5)	-MATCH(G5,B5:F5,0)	-INDEX($B$2:$F$2,H5)
6	=MIN(B6:F6)	=MATCH(G6,B6:F6,0)	=INDEX($B$2:$F$2,H6)
7	=MIN(B7:F7)	=MATCH(G7,B7:F7,0)	=INDEX($B$2:$F$2,H7)
8	=MIN(B8:F8)	=MATCH(G8,B8:F8,0)	=INDEX($B$2:$F$2,H8)
9	=MIN(B9:F9)	=MATCH(G9,B9:F9,0)	=INDEX($B$2:$F$2,H9)
10	=MIN(B10:F10)	=MATCH(G10,B10:F10,0)	=INDEX($B$2:$F$2,H10)

20. A portion of the spreadsheet is shown below:

	A	B	C	D	E
1	**0% Financing Model**				
2					
3	**Parameters**				
4					
5	Payment	$489		Sale Price	$25,995
6	Discount rate	0.10899		Total Payments	$35,208
7				NPV of Payments	$25,995
8					
9	**Model**				
10					
11		Payment	Discounted		
12	1	$489	$489.00		
13	2	$489	$484.60		
14	3	$489	$480.24		
15	4	$489	$475.91		
16	5	$489	$471.63		

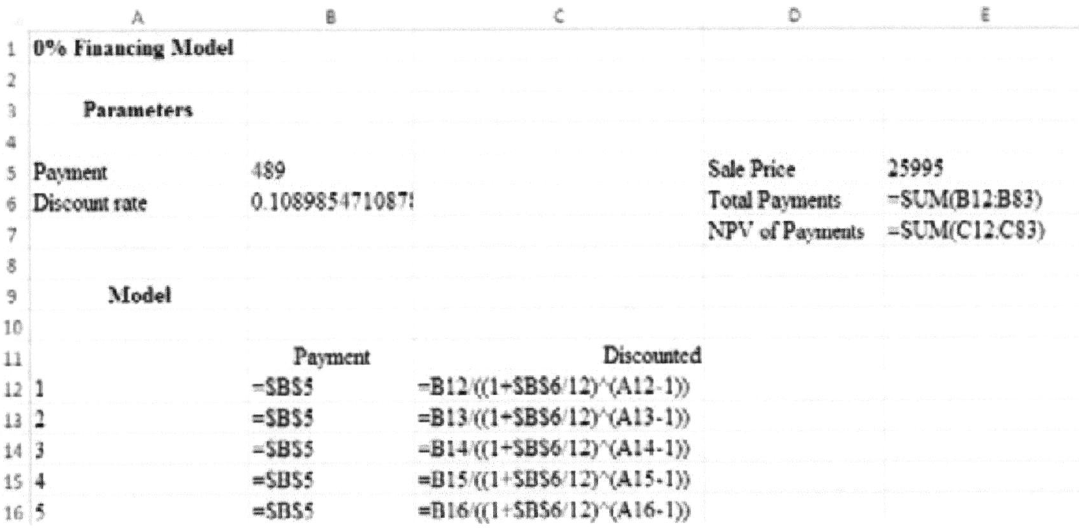

	A	B	C	D	E
1	**0% Financing Model**				
2					
3	**Parameters**				
4					
5	Payment	489		Sale Price	25995
6	Discount rate	0.108985471087		Total Payments	=SUM(B12:B83)
7				NPV of Payments	=SUM(C12:C83)
8					
9	**Model**				
10					
11		Payment	Discounted		
12	1	=$B$5	=B12/((1+$B$6/12)^(A12-1))		
13	2	=$B$5	=B13/((1+$B$6/12)^(A13-1))		
14	3	=$B$5	=B14/((1+$B$6/12)^(A14-1))		
15	4	=$B$5	=B15/((1+$B$6/12)^(A15-1))		
16	5	=$B$5	=B16/((1+$B$6/12)^(A16-1))		

We use goal seek to find the discount rate that results in an NPV of $25,995:

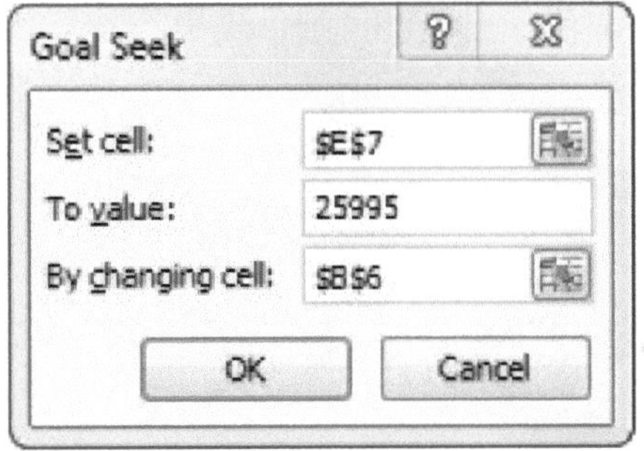

The result is 10.9%. So effectively, the dealer is making 10.9% interest on the loan of $25,995.

Chapter 15: Decision Analysis

Solutions

2. a. The decision to be made is to choose the best plant size. The two alternatives from which to choose are a small plant and a large plant.
   The chance event is the market demand for the new product line. It is viewed as having three possible outcomes (states of nature): low, medium, and high.

   b. Decision Tree:

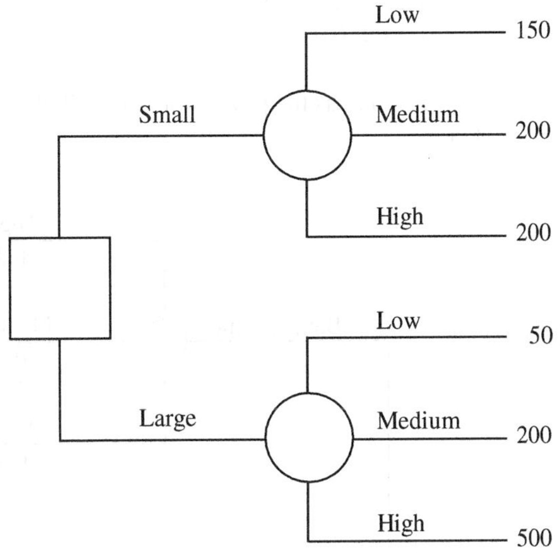

   c.

Decision	Maximum Profit	Minimum Profit	Maximum Regret
Small	200	150	300
Large	500	50	100

   Optimistic approach: select Large plant which has the largest maximum profit.
   Conservative approach: select Small plant which has the largest minimum profit.
   Minimax regret approach: select Large plant which minimizes the maximum regret.

4. a.
   EV(Computers) = 0.2(10) + 0.5(2) + 0.3(−4) = 1.8
   EV(Financial) = 0.2(8) + 0.5(5) + 0.3(−3) = 3.2
   EV(Manufacturing) = 0.2(6) + 0.5(4) + 0.3(−2) = 2.6
   EV(Pharmaceuticals) = 0.2(6) + 0.5(5) + 0.3(−1) = 3.4
   Pharmaceuticals has the highest expected return percentage, at 3.4%

   b. Using probabilities 0.4, 0.4, and 0.2:
   EV(Computers) = 4.0
   EV(Financial) = 4.6
   EV(Manufacturing) = 3.6
   EV(Pharmaceuticals) = 4.2
   Financial now has the highest expected return percentage, at 4.6%

6. a. $EV(d_1) = 0.2(10) + 0.8(1) = 2.8$
$EV(d_2) = 0.2(4) + 0.8(3) = 3.2$
Therefore, the best decision is d_2.

b. The best decision in part b is d_2, with $EV(d_2) = 3.2$. Decision d_2 will remain optimal as long as its expected value is higher than that for d_1 [$EV(d_1) = 2.8$].
Decision d_2 will remain optimal as long as the expected value of choosing d_2 is greater than the expected value of choosing d_1. Let s = payoff for d_2 under state of nature s_1.
$EV(d_2) = 0.2(s) + 0.8(3) \geq 2.8$
$0.2s \geq 2.8 - 2.4$
$0.2s \geq 0.4$
$s \geq 2$
As long as the payoff for s_1 is ≥ 2, then d_2 will be optimal.

8. a.

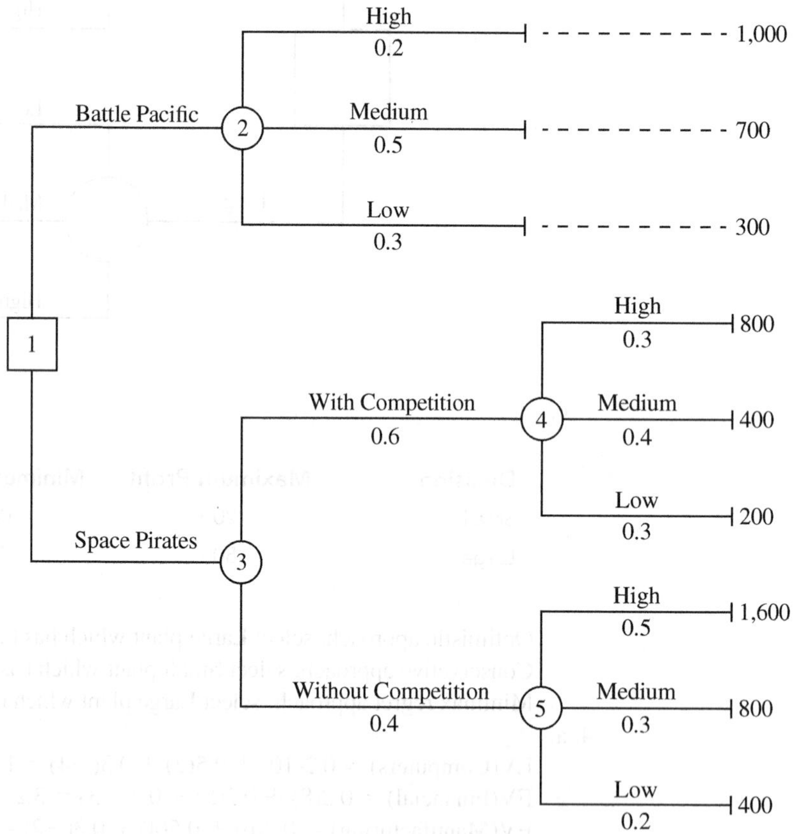

b. EV(node 2) = 0.2(1000) + 0.5(700) + 0.3(300) = 640
EV(node 4) = 0.3(800) + 0.4(400) + 0.3(200) = 460
EV(node 5) = 0.5(1600) + 0.3(800) + 0.2(400) = 1120
EV(node 3) = 0.6EV(node 4) + 0.4EV(node 5) = 0.6(460) + 0.4(1120) = 724
Space Pirates is recommended. Expected value of $724,000 is $84,000 better than Battle Pacific.

c. Risk Profile for Space Pirates
Outcome:
1,600 (0.4)(0.5) = 0.20
800 (0.6)(0.3) + (0.4)(0.3) = 0.30
400 (0.6)(0.4) + (0.4)(0.2) = 0.32
200 (0.6)(0.3) = 0.18

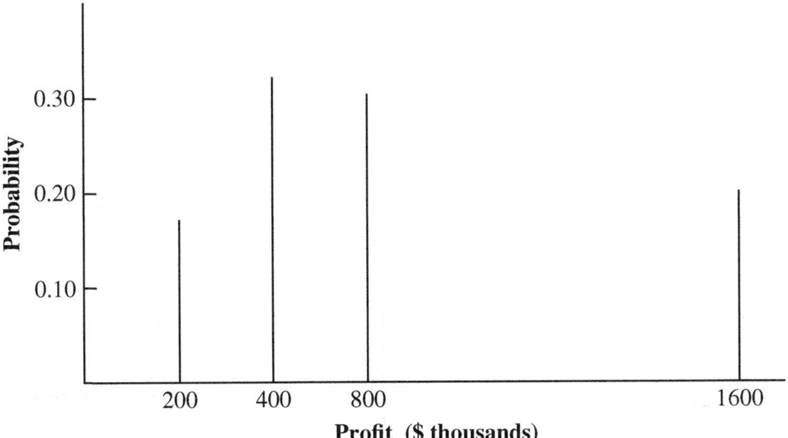

d. Let:
p = probability of competition
$p = 0$ EV(node 5) = 1,120
$p = 1$ EV(node 4) = 460
Setting the Expected Value of both decisions equal to each other gives us:

$$\text{EV(Space Pirates)} = \text{EV(Battle Pacific)}$$

$1{,}120 - p(1{,}120 - 460) = 640$
$660p = 480$
$p = 480 / 660 = 0.7273$
For $p > 0.7273$, the EV of Space Pirates is greater; for $p < 0.7273$, the EV of Battle Pacific is greater. Therefore, the probability of competition would have to be greater than 0.7273 before we would change to the Battle Pacific video game.

10. a. EV(node 4) = 0.5(34) + 0.3(20) + 0.2(10) = 25
EV(node 3) = Max(25,20) = 25 Decision: Build
EV(node 2) = 0.5(25) + 0.5(−5) = 10
EV(node 1) = Max(10,0) = 10 Decision: Start R&D
Optimal Strategy:
Start the R&D project
If it is successful, build the facility.
Expected value = $10M

b. At node 3, payoff for sell rights would have to be $25M or more. In order to recover the $5M R&D cost, the selling price would have to be $30M or more.

c.

Possible Profit		
$34M	(0.5)(0.5) =	0.25
$20M	(0.5)(0.3) =	0.15
$10M	(0.5)(0.2) =	0.10
−$5M		0.50
		1.00

12. a.

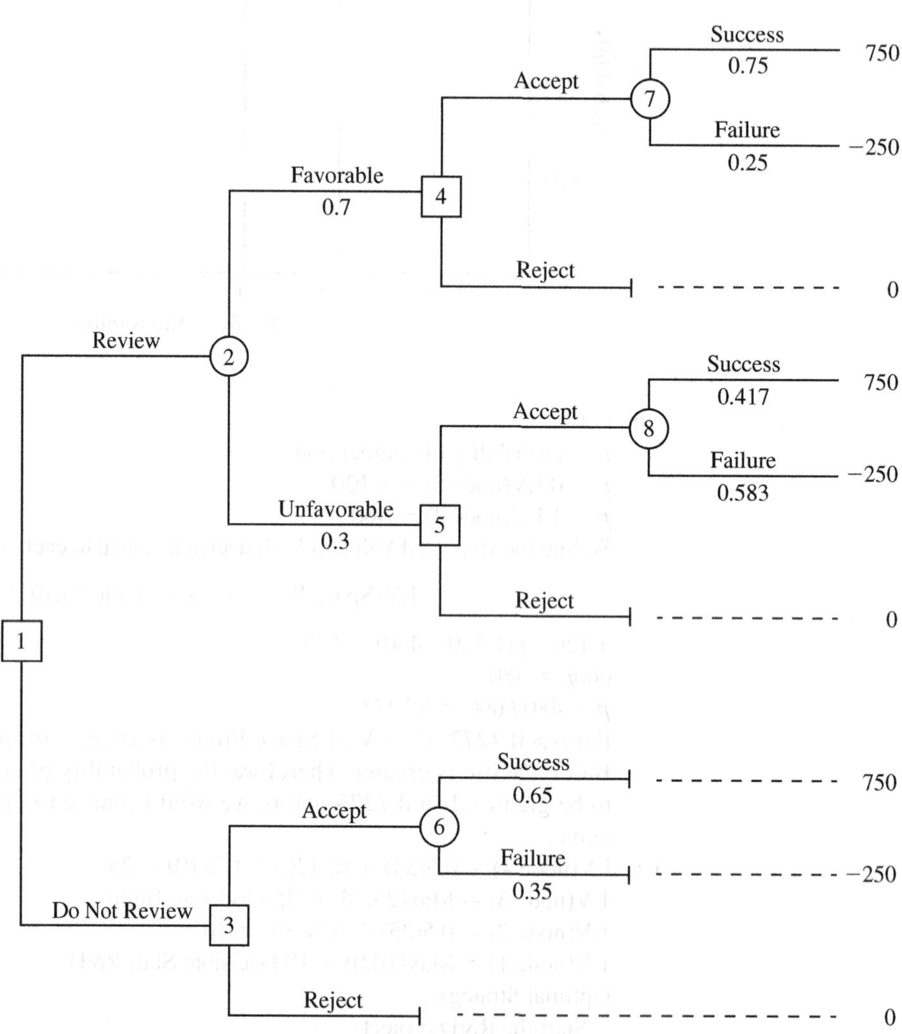

b. EV(node 7) = 0.75(750) + 0.25(−250) = 500
EV(node 8) = 0.417(750) + 0.583(−250) = 167
Decision (node 4) → Accept EV = 500
Decision (node 5) → Accept EV = 167
EV(node 2) = 0.7(500) + 0.3(167) = $400
(*Note:* Regardless of the review outcome *F* or *U*, the recommended decision alternative is to accept the manuscript.)
EV(node 3) = .65(750) + .35(−250) = $400

The expected value is \$400,000 regardless of review process. The company should accept the manuscript.

c. The manuscript review cannot alter the decision to accept the manuscript. Do not do the manuscript review.

d. Perfect Information.

If s_1, accept manuscript \$750

If s_2, reject manuscript −\$250

EVwPI = 0.65(750) + 0.35(0) = 487.5

EVwoPI = 400

EVPI = 487.5 − 400 = 87.5, or \$87,500.

Using a better procedure for assessing the market potential for the textbook may be worthwhile.

14. a. EV(Small) = 0.1(400) + 0.6(500) + 0.3(660) = 538

EV(Medium) = 0.1(250) + 0.6(650) + 0.3(800) = 605

EV(Large) = 0.1(400) + 0.6(580) + 0.3(990) = 605

Best decision: Build a medium or large community center.

(*Note:* Using the expected value approach, the Town Council would be undecided between building a medium community center and a large center.

b. Risk profile for medium community center:

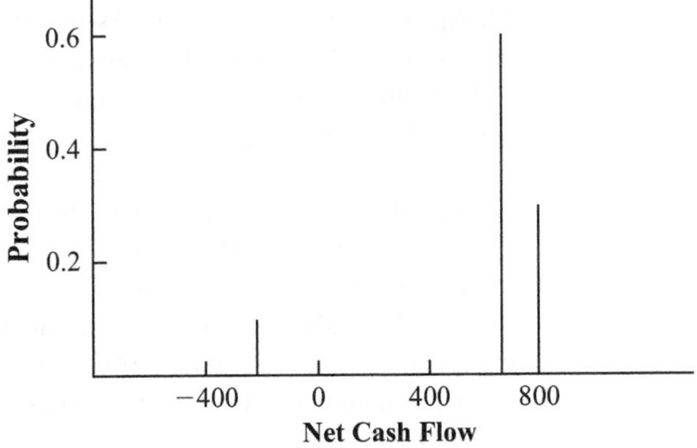

Risk profile for large community center:

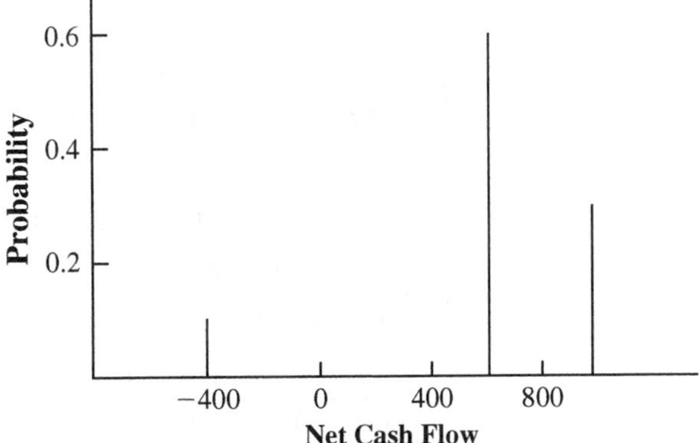

Given the mayor's concern about the sizable loss that would be incurred if demand is not enough to support a large center, we would recommend the medium center. The large center has a probability of 0.1 of losing $400,000. With the medium center, the most the town can lose is $250,000.

c. The town's optimal decision strategy based on perfect information is as follows:
If the worst-case scenario, build a small center.
If the base-case scenario, build a medium center.
If the best-case scenario, build a large center.
Using the consultant's original probability assessments for each scenario—0.10, 0.60, and 0.30—the expected value of a decision strategy that uses perfect information is:

$$\text{EVwPI} = 0.1(400) + 0.6(650) + 0.3(990) = 727$$

In part a, the expected value approach showed that EV(Medium) = EV(Large) = 605. Therefore, EVwoPI = 605 and EVPI = 727 − 605 = 122.
The town should seriously consider additional information about the likelihood of the three scenarios. Since perfect information would be worth $122,000, a good market research study could possibly make a significant contribution.

d. EV(Small) = 0.2(400) + 0.5(500) + 0.3(660) = 528
EV(Medium) = 0.2(−250) + 0.5(650) + 0.3(800) = 515
EV(Small) = 0.2(−400) + 0.5(580) + 0.3(990) = 507
Best decision: Build a small community center.

e. If the promotional campaign is conducted, the probabilities will change to 0.0, 0.6, and 0.4 for the worst-case, base-case, and best-case scenarios, respectively.
EV(Small) = 0.0(400) + 0.6(500) + 0.4(660) = 564
EV(Medium) = 0.0(−250) + 0.6(650) + 0.4(800) = 710
EV(Small) = 0.0(−400) + 0.6(580) + 0.4(990) = 744
In this case, the recommended decision is to build a large community center. Compared to the analysis in part a, the promotional campaign has increased the best expected value by $744,000 − 605,000 = $139,000. Compared to the analysis in part d, the promotional campaign has increased the best expected value by $744,000 − 528,000 = $216,000.
Even though the promotional campaign does not increase the expected value by more than its cost ($150,000), when compared to the analysis in part a, it appears to be a good investment. That is, it eliminates the risk of a loss, which appears to be a significant factor in the mayor's decision-making process.

16.

$$P(s_1|I) = \frac{P(I|s_1)P(s_1)}{P(I|s_1) + P(I|s_2) + P(I|s_3)}$$

$$= \frac{0.1 \times 0.2}{0.1 \times 0.2 + 0.05 \times 0.5 + 0.2 \times 0.3} = \frac{0.02}{0.105} = 0.190$$

$$P(s_2|I) = \frac{P(I|s_2)P(s_2)}{P(I|s_1) + P(I|s_2) + P(I|s_3)}$$

$$= \frac{0.05 \times 0.5}{0.1 \times 0.2 + 0.05 \times 0.5 + 0.2 \times 0.3} = \frac{0.025}{0.105} = 0.238$$

$$P(s_3|I) = \frac{P(I|s_3)P(s_3)}{P(I|s_1) + P(I|s_2) + P(I|s_3)}$$

$$= \frac{0.2 \times 0.3}{0.1 \times 0.2 + 0.05 \times 0.5 + 0.2 \times 0.3} = \frac{0.06}{0.105} = 0.571$$

18. a. d_1 = Manufacture component s_1 = Low demand
d_2 = Purchase component s_2 = Medium demand
s_3 = High demand

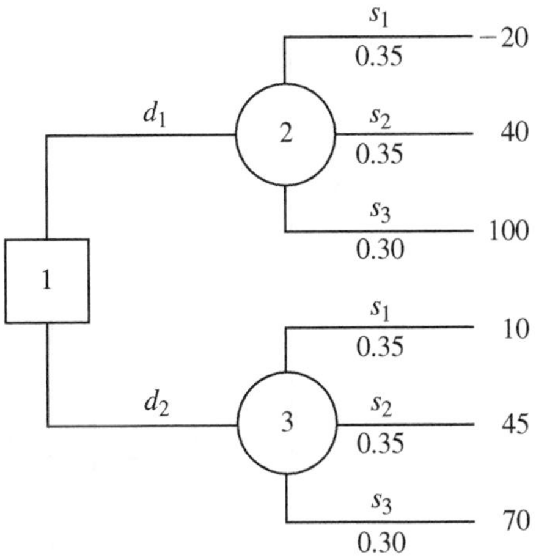

1
d_1
2
s_1 0.35 −20
s_2 0.35 40
s_3 0.30 100
d_2
3
s_1 0.35 10
s_2 0.35 45
s_3 0.30 70

EV(node 2) = (0.35)(−20) + (0.35)(40) + (0.30)(100) = 37
EV(node 3) = (0.35)(10) + (0.35)(45) + (0.30)(70) = 40.25
Recommended decision: d_2 (purchase component)

b. Optimal decision strategy with perfect information:
If s_1 then d_2
If s_2 then d_2
If s_3 then d_1
The expected value of this strategy is 0.35(10) + 0.35(45) + 0.30(100) = 49.25. The EVPI = 49.25 − 40.25 = 9, or $9,000. Therefore, additional information could be worth up to $9,000 for Gorman in this problem.

c.

$$P(F) = P(F \cap s_1) + P(F \cap s_2) + P(F \cap s_3)$$
$$= P(s_1)P(F|s_1) + P(s_2)P(F|s_2) + P(s_3)P(F|s_3)$$
$$= 0.35 \times 0.10 + 0.35 \times 0.40 + 0.30 \times 0.60$$
$$= 0.355$$

d. Assuming that the test market study is used, a portion of the decision tree is as follows:

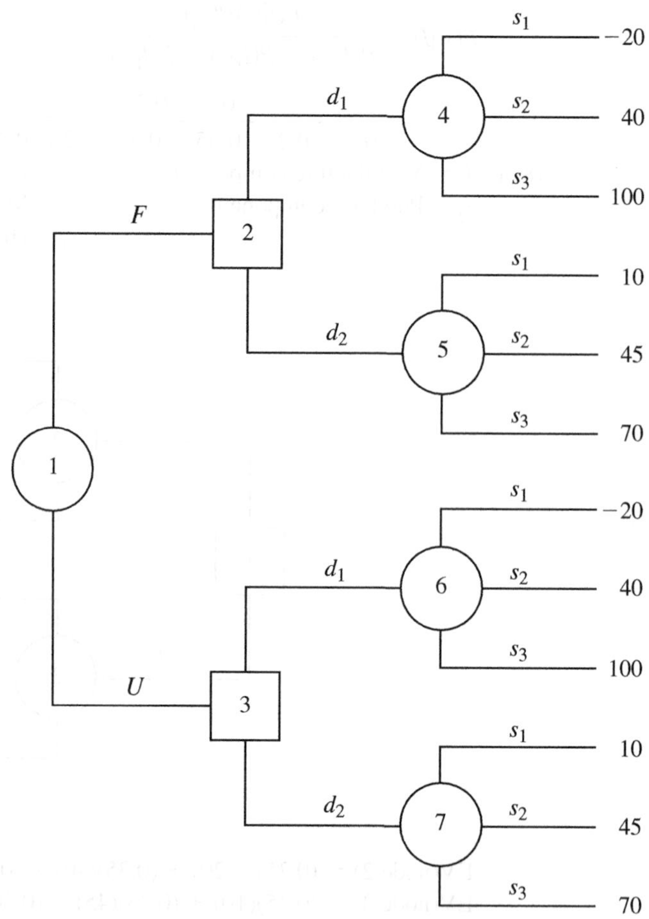

Summary of Calculations

Node	Expected Value
4	64.51
5	54.23
6	21.86
7	32.56

Decision strategy:
If F then d_1 since EV(node 4) > EV(node 5)
If U then d_2 since EV(node 7) > EV(node 6)
EV(node 1) = 0.355(64.51) + 0.645(32.56) = 43.90

e. With no information, from part a:
$EV(d_1) = 0.35(-20) + 0.35(40) + 0.30(100) = 37$
$EV(d_2) = 0.35(10) + 0.35(45) + 0.30(70) = 40.25$
So the recommended decision is d_2 and the expected value is 40.25. With the market research report, the expected value found in part d is 43.9. Thus, the expected value of the market research report is 43.9 − 40.25 = 3.65 or $3,650.

20. a. $EV(d_1) = 10{,}000$
$EV(d_2) = 0.96(0) + 0.03(100{,}000) + 0.01(200{,}000) = 5{,}000$
Using the EV approach, we should choose No Insurance (d_2).
b. Lottery:
p = probability of a \$0 Cost
$1 - p$ = probability of a \$200,000 Cost
c.

		s_1 None	s_2 Minor	s_3 Major
Insurance	d_1	9.9	9.9	9.9
No Insurance	d_2	10.0	6.0	0.0

$EU(d_1) = 9.9$
$EU(d_2) = 0.96(10.0) + 0.03(6.0) + 0.01(0.0) = 9.78$
Therefore using the EU approach → Insurance (d_1)
d. Use the expected utility approach. The EV approach results in a decision that can be very risky since it means that the decision maker could lose up to \$200,000. Most decision makers (particularly those considering insurance) are risk averse.

22. a.

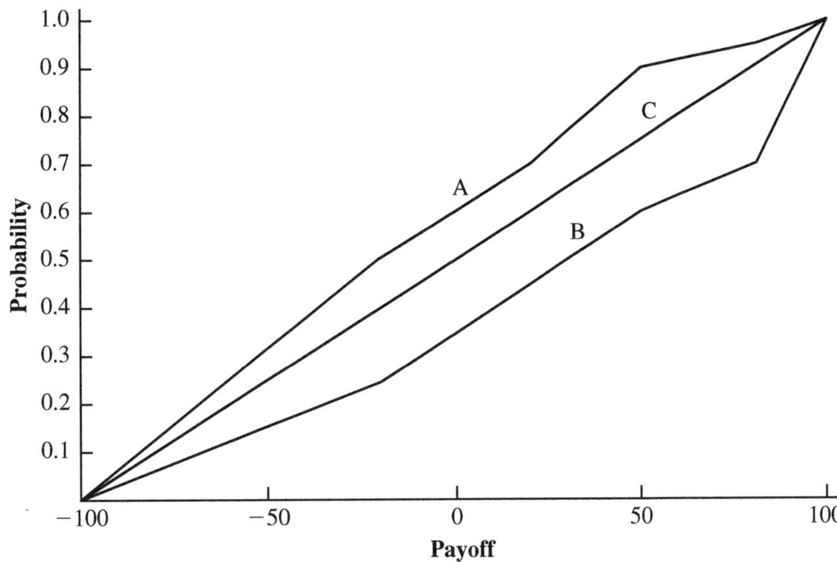

b. A = Risk avoider
B = Risk taker
C = Risk neutral

c.

Risk avoider A, at \$20 payoff $p = 0.70$
Thus, EV(Lottery) = 0.70(100) + 0.30(−100) = \$40
Therefore, will pay 40 − 20 = \$20
Risk taker B, at \$20 payoff $p = 0.45$
Thus, EV(Lottery) = 0.45(100) + 0.55(−100) = −\$10
Therefore, will pay 20 − (−10) = \$30

24.

Monetary Payoff, x	**Utility, *U*(*x*)**
−200	−1.226
−100	−0.492
0	0.000
100	0.330
200	0.551
300	0.699
400	0.798
500	0.865

Appendix D: Self-Test Solutions and Answers to Even-Numbered Exercises

Chapter 1

2. a. The 10 elements are the 10 tablet computers
b. Five variables: Cost ($), Operating System, Display Size (inches), Battery Life (hours), CPU Manufacturer
c. Categorical variables: Operating System and CPU Manufacturer
Quantitative variables: Cost ($), Display Size (inches), and Battery Life (hours)
d.

Variable	Measurement Scale
Cost($)	Ratio
Operating System	Nominal
Display Size (inches)	Ratio
Battery Life (hours)	Ratio
CPU Manufacturer	Nominal

3. a. Average cost = 5829/10 = $582.90
b. Average cost with a Windows operating system = 3616/5 = $723.20
Average cost with an Android operating system = 1714/4 = $428.5
The average cost with Windows is much higher
c. 2 of 10 or 20% use a CPU manufactured by TI OMAP
d. 4 of 10 or 40% use an Android operating system

4. a. There are eight elements in this data set; each element corresponds to one of the eight models of cordless telephones
b. Categorical variables: Voice Quality and Handset on Base
Quantitative variables: Price, Overall Score, and Talk Time
c. Price – ratio measurement
Overall Score – interval measurement
Voice Quality – ordinal measurement
Handset on Base – nominal measurement
Talk Time – ratio measurement

6. a. Categorical
b. Quantitative
c. Categorical
d. Quantitative
e. Quantitative

8. a. 762
b. Categorical
c. Percentages
d. .67(762) = 510.54; 510 or 511 respondents

10. a. Categorical
b. Percentages
c. 15%
d. Support against

12. a. All visitors to Hawaii
b. Yes
c. First and fourth questions provide quantitative data
Second and third questions provide categorical data

13. a. Federal spending ($ trillions)
b. Quantitative
c. Time series
d. Federal spending has increased over time

14. a. Graph with time series line for each company
b. Hertz leader in 2007–2008; Avis increasing and now similar to Hertz; Dollar declining
c. A bar chart of cross-sectional data
Bar heights: Hertz 290, Dollar 108, Avis 270

18. a. 67%
b. 612
c. Categorical

20. a. 43% of managers were bullish or very bullish, and 21% of managers expected health care to be the leading industry over the next 12 months
b. The average 12-month return estimate is 11.2% for the population of investment managers
c. The sample average of 2.5 years is an estimate of how long the population of investment managers think it will take to resume sustainable growth

22. a. The population consists of all clients that currently have a home listed for sale with the agency or have hired the agency to help them locate a new home
b. Some of the ways that could be used to collect the data are as follows:
- A questionnaire could be mailed to each of the agency's clients
- Each client could be sent an email with a questionnaire attached
- The next time one of the firm's agents meets with a client, the agent could conduct a personal interview to obtain the data

24. a. Correct
b. Incorrect
c. Correct
d. Incorrect
e. Incorrect

Chapter 2

2. a. .20
b. 40

c/d.

Class	Frequency	Percent Frequency
A	44	22
B	36	18
C	80	40
D	40	20
Total	200	100

3. a. $360° \times 58/120 = 174°$

b. $360° \times 42/120 = 126°$

c.

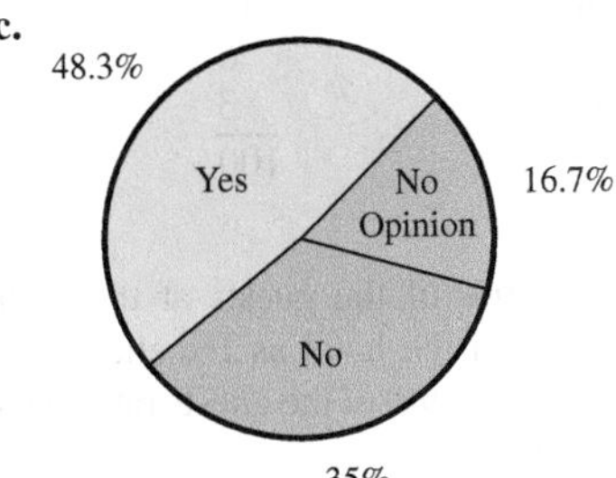

d.

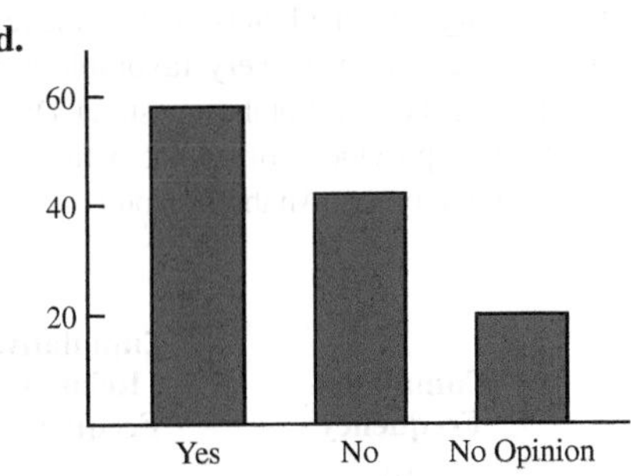

4. a. These data are categorical

b.

Show	Relative Frequency	Percent Frequency
Jep	10	20
JJ	8	16
OWS	7	14
THM	12	24
WoF	13	26
Total	50	100

c.

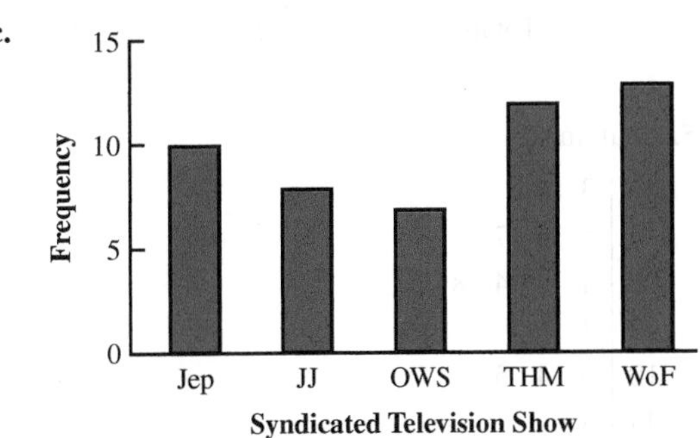

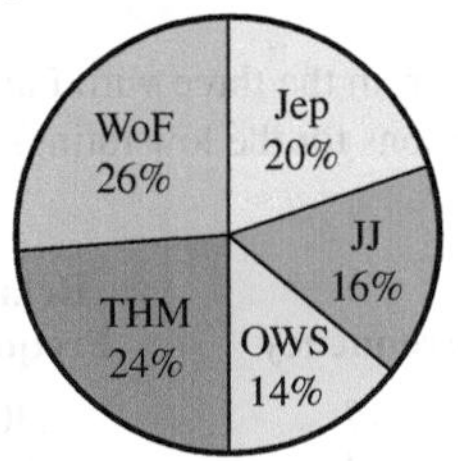

d. The largest viewing audience is for *Wheel of Fortune* and the second largest is for *Two and a Half Men*

6. a.

Network	Relative Frequency	Percent Frequency
ABC	6	24
CBS	9	36
FOX	1	4
NBC	9	36
Total	25	100

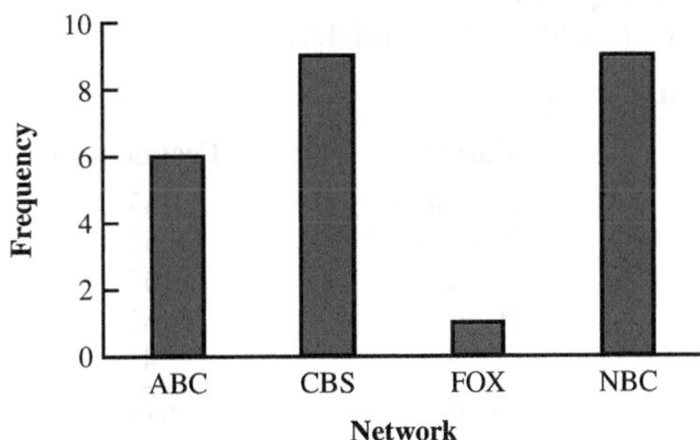

b. For these data, NBC and CBS tie for the number of top-rated shows; each has 9 (36%) of the top 25; ABC is third with 6 (24%) and the much younger FOX network has 1 (4%)

7. a.

Rating	Frequency	Percent Frequency
Excellent	20	40
Very Good	23	46
Good	4	8
Fair	1	2
Poor	2	4
Total	50	100

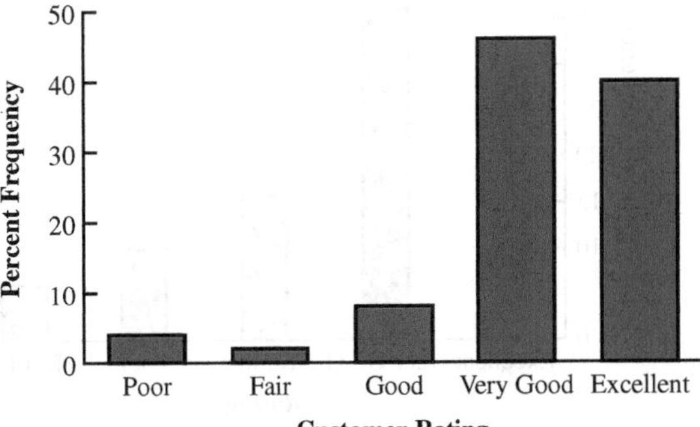

Management should be very pleased; 86% of the ratings are very good or excellent

b. Review explanations from the three with Fair or Poor ratings to identify reasons for the low ratings

8. a.

Position	Frequency	Relative Frequency
P	17	.309
H	4	.073
1	5	.091
2	4	.073
3	2	.036
S	5	.091
L	6	.109
C	5	.091
R	7	.127
Totals	55	1.000

b. Pitcher

c. 3rd base

d. Right field

e. Infielders 16 to outfielders 18

10. a.

Rating	Frequency
Excellent	187
Very Good	252
Average	107
Poor	62
Terrible	41
Total	649

b.

Rating	Percent Frequency
Excellent	29
Very Good	39
Average	16
Poor	10
Terrible	6
Total	100

c.

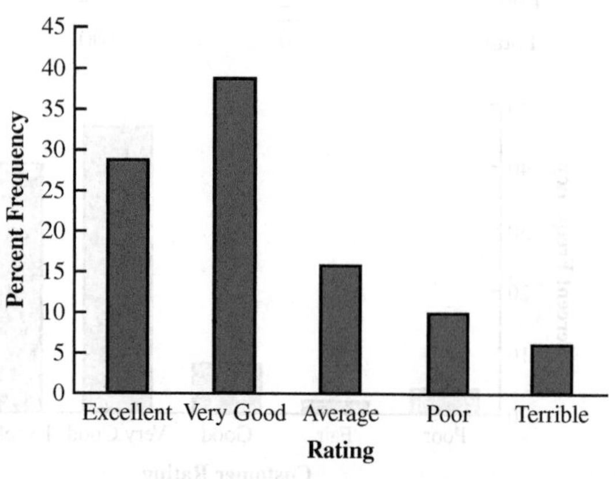

d. 29% + 39% = 68% of the guests at the Sheraton Anaheim Hotel rated the hotel as Excellent or Very Good, but 10% + 6% = 16% of the guests rated the hotel as poor or terrible

e. The percent frequency distribution for Disney's Grand Californian follows:

Rating	Percent Frequency
Excellent	48
Very Good	31
Average	12
Poor	6
Terrible	3
Total	100

48% + 31% = 79% of the guests at the Sheraton Anaheim Hotel rated the hotel as Excellent or Very Good, and 6% + 3% = 9% of the guests rated the hotel as poor or terrible

Compared to ratings of other hotels in the same region, both of these hotels received very favorable ratings; but, in comparing the two hotels, guests at Disney's Grand Californian provided somewhat better ratings than guests at the Sheraton Anaheim Hotel

12.

Class	Cumulative Frequency	Cumulative Relative Frequency
≤19	10	.20
≤29	24	.48
≤39	41	.82
≤49	48	.96
≤59	50	1.00

14. b/c.

Class	Frequency	Percent Frequency
6.0–7.9	4	20
8.0–9.9	2	10
10.0–11.9	8	40
12.0–13.9	3	15
14.0–15.9	3	15
Totals	20	100

15. Leaf unit = .1

6	3
7	5 5 7
8	1 3 4 8
9	3 6
10	0 4 5
11	3

16. Leaf unit = 10

11	6
12	0 2
13	0 6 7
14	2 2 7
15	5
16	0 2 8
17	0 2 3

17. a/b.

Waiting Time	Frequency	Relative Frequency
0–4	4	.20
5–9	8	.40
10–14	5	.25
15–19	2	.10
20–24	1	.05
Totals	20	1.00

c/d.

Waiting Time	Cumulative Frequency	Cumulative Relative Frequency
≤4	4	.20
≤9	12	.60
≤14	17	.85
≤19	19	.95
≤24	20	1.00

e. 12/20 = .60

18. a.

PPG	Frequency
10–12	1
12–14	3
14–16	7
16–18	19
18–20	9
22–22	4
22–24	2
24–26	0
26–28	3
28–30	2
Total	50

b.

PPG	Relative Frequency
10–12	0.02
12–14	0.06
14–16	0.14
16–18	0.38
18–20	0.18
22–22	0.08
22–24	0.04
24–26	0.00
26–28	0.06
28–30	0.04
Total	1.00

c.

PPG	Cumulative Percent Frequency
less than 12	2
less than 14	8
less than 16	22
less than 18	60
less than 20	78
less than 22	86
less than 24	90
less than 26	90
less than 28	96
less than 30	100

d.

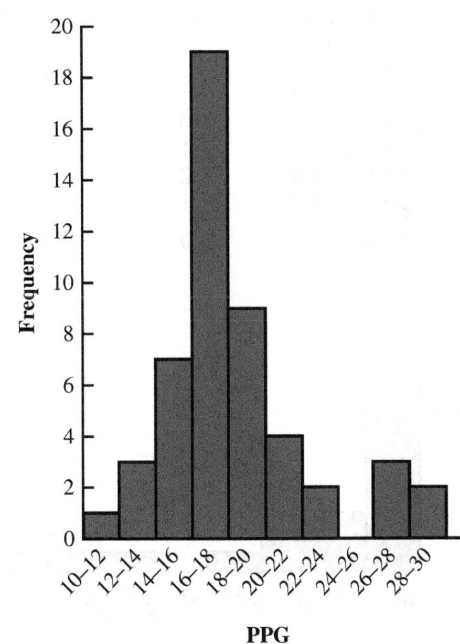

e. There is skewness to the right

f. (11/50)(100) = 22%

20. a. Lowest = 12, Highest = 23

b.

Hours in Meetings per Week	Frequency	Percent Frequency
11–12	1	4
13–14	2	8
15–16	6	24
17–18	3	12
19–20	5	20
21–22	4	16
23–24	4	16
	25	100

c.

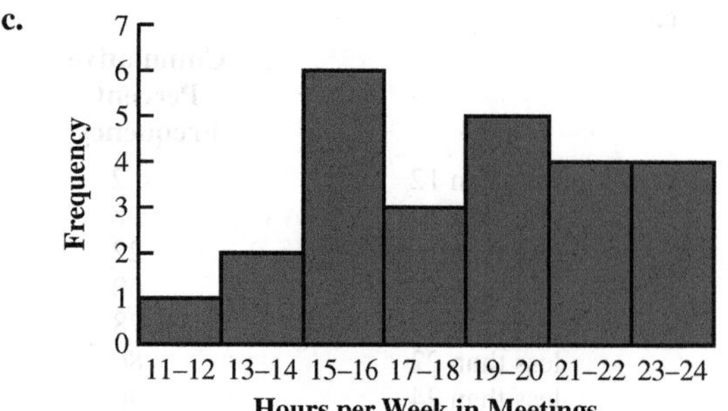

d. The distribution is slightly skewed to the left

22. a.

# U.S. Locations	Frequency	Percent Frequency
0–4999	10	50
5000–9999	3	15
10000–14999	2	10
15000–19999	1	5
20000–24999	0	0
25000–29999	1	5
30000–34999	2	10
35000–39999	1	5
Total:	20	100

b.

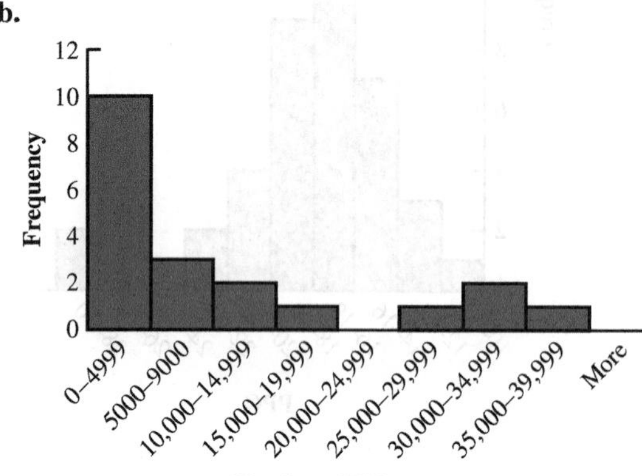

c. The distribution is skewed to the right; the majority of the franchises in this list have fewer than 20,000 locations (50% + 15% + 15% = 80%); McDonald's, Subway, and 7-Eleven have the highest number of locations

24. Median Pay

6 | 6 7 7
4 | 2 4 6 7 7 8 9
8 | 0 0 1 3 7
9 | 9
10 | 0 6
11 | 0
12 | 1

Top Pay

10 | 0 6 9
11 | 1 6 9
12 | 2 5 6
13 | 0 5 8 8
14 | 0 6
15 | 2 5 7
16 |
17 |
18 |
19 |
20 |
21 | 4
22 | 1

The median pay for these careers is generally in the $70 and $80 thousands; the top pay is rather evenly distributed between $100 and $160 thousand

26. a.

2 | 14
2 | 67
3 | 011123
3 | 5677
4 | 003333344
4 | 6679
5 | 00022
5 | 5679
6 | 14
6 | 6
7 | 2

b. 40–44 with 9

c. 43 with 5

27. a.

		y		
		1	**2**	**Total**
x	**A**	5	0	5
	B	11	2	13
	C	2	10	12
	Total	18	12	30

b.

		y		
		1	**2**	**Total**
x	**A**	100.0	0.0	100.0
	B	84.6	15.4	100.0
	C	16.7	83.3	100.0

c.

		y	
		1	**2**
x	**A**	27.8	0.0
	B	61.1	16.7
	C	11.1	83.3
	Total	100.0	100.0

d. *A* values are always in $y = 1$
B values are most often in $y = 1$
C values are most often in $y = 2$

28. a.

		y				
		20–39	**40–59**	**60–79**	**80–100**	**Grand Total**
x	**10–29**			1	4	5
	30–49	2		4		6
	50–69	1	3	1		5
	70–90	4				4
	Grand Total	7	3	6	4	20

b.

		y				
		20–39	**40–59**	**60–79**	**80–100**	**Grand Total**
	10–29			20.0	80.0	100
x	**30–49**	33.3		66.7		100
	50–69	20.0	60.0	20.0		100
	70–90	100.0				100

c.

		y			
		20–39	**40–59**	**60–79**	**80–100**
	10–29	0.0	0.0	16.7	100.0
x	**30–49**	28.6	0.0	66.7	0.0
	50–69	14.3	100.0	16.7	0.0
	70–90	57.1	0.0	0.0	0.0
	Grand Total	100	100	100	100

d. Higher values of x are associated with lower values of y and vice versa

30. a.

	Year					
Average Speed	**1988–1992**	**1993–1997**	**1998–2002**	**2003–2007**	**2008–2012**	**Total**
130–139.9	16.7	0.0	0.0	33.3	50.0	100
140–149.9	25.0	25.0	12.5	25.0	12.5	100
150–159.9	0.0	50.0	16.7	16.7	16.7	100
160–169.9	50.0	0.0	50.0	0.0	0.0	100
170–179.9	0.0	0.0	100.0	0.0	0.0	100

b. It appears that most of the faster average winning times occur before 2003; this could be due to new regulations that take into account driver safety, fan safety, the environmental impact, and fuel consumption during races

32. a. Row percentages are shown below.

Region	**Under $15,000**	**$15,000 to $24,999**	**$25,000 to $34,999**	**$35,000 to $49,999**	**$50,000 to $74,999**	**$75,000 to $99,999**	**$100,000 and over**	**Total**
Northeast	12.72	10.45	10.54	13.07	17.22	11.57	24.42	100.00
Midwest	12.40	12.60	11.58	14.27	19.11	12.06	17.97	100.00
South	14.30	12.97	11.55	14.85	17.73	11.04	17.57	100.00
West	11.84	10.73	10.15	13.65	18.44	11.77	23.43	100.00
Total	13.04	11.93	11.06	14.13	18.10	11.53	20.21	100.00

The percent frequency distributions for each region now appear in each row of the table

b. West: 18.44 + 11.77 + 23.43 = 53.64%

South: 17.73 + 11.04 + 17.57 = 46.34%

c. The largest difference appears to be a higher percentage of household incomes of $100,000 and over for the Northeast and West regions

d. Column percentages are shown below.

Region	**Under $15,000**	**$15,000 to $24,999**	**$25,000 to $34,999**	**$35,000 to $49,999**	**$50,000 to $74,999**	**$75,000 to $99,999**	**$100,000 and over**
Northeast	17.83	16.00	17.41	16.90	17.38	18.35	22.09
Midwest	21.35	23.72	23.50	22.68	23.71	23.49	19.96
South	40.68	40.34	38.75	39.00	36.33	35.53	32.25
West	20.13	19.94	20.34	21.42	22.58	22.63	25.70
Total	100.00	100.00	100.00	100.00	100.00	100.00	100.00

Each column is a percent frequency distribution of the region variable for one of the household income categories.

e. 32.25% of the households with a household income of $100,000 and over are from the South region. The cross-tabulation of row percentage shows that 17.57 of the households in the South region had a household income of $100,000 and over

34. a.

	Brand Value ($ billions)						
Industry	**0–25**	**25–50**	**50–75**	**75–100**	**100–125**	**125–150**	**Total**
Automotive & Luxury	10	1	1		1	2	15
Consumer Packaged Goods	12						12
Financial Services	2	4	2	2	2	2	14
Other	13	5	3	2	2	1	26
Technology	4	4	4	1	2		15
Total	41	14	10	5	7	5	82

b.

Brand Value ($ billions)	Frequency
0–25	41
25–50	14
50–75	10
75–100	5
100–125	7
125–150	5
Total	82

c. Consumer packaged goods have the lowest brand values; each of the 12 brands in the sample data had a brand value of less than $25 billion. Approximately 57% of the financial services brands (8 out of 15) had a brand value of $50 billion or greater, and 50% of the technology brands had a brand value of at least $50 billion

d.

	1-Yr Value Change (%)						
Industry	**−60–41**	**−40–21**	**−20–1**	**0–19**	**20–29**	**40–60**	**Total**
Automotive & Luxury				11	4		15
Consumer Packaged Goods			2	10			12
Financial Services		1	6	7			14
Other			2	20	4		26
Technology	1	3	4	4	2	1	15
Total	1	4	14	52	10	1	82

e.

1-Yr Value Change (%)	Frequency
−60–41	1
−40–21	4
−20–1	14
0–19	52
20–29	10
40–60	1
Total	82

f. The automotive & luxury brands all had a positive 1-year value change (%). The technology brands had the greatest variability

36. a.

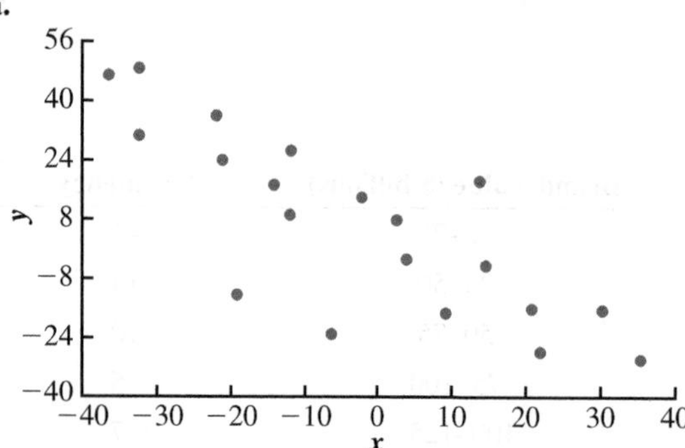

b. A negative relationship between x and y; y decreases as x increases

38. a.

		y		
		Yes	**No**	
x	**Low**	66.667	33.333	100
	Medium	30.000	70.000	100
	High	80.000	20.000	100

b.

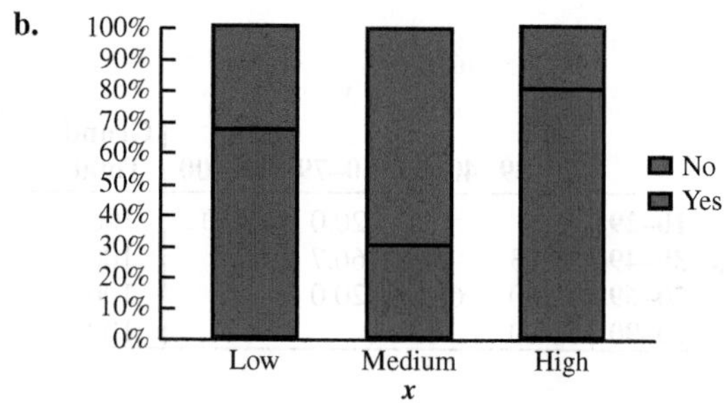

40. a.

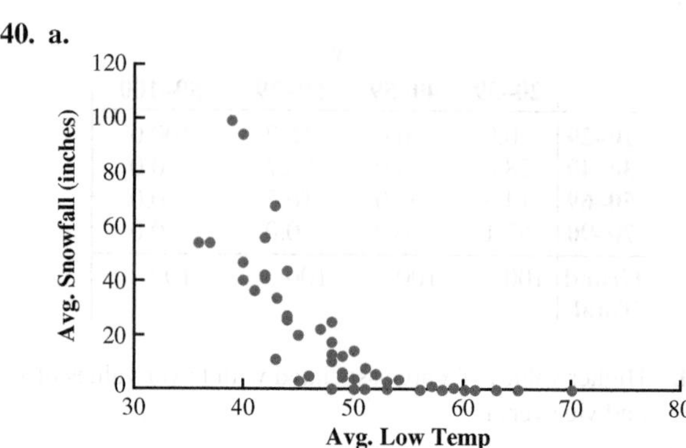

b. Colder average low temperature seems to lead to higher amounts of snowfall

c. Two cities have an average snowfall of nearly 100 inches of snowfall: Buffalo, New York, and Rochester, New York; both are located near large lakes in New York

42. a.

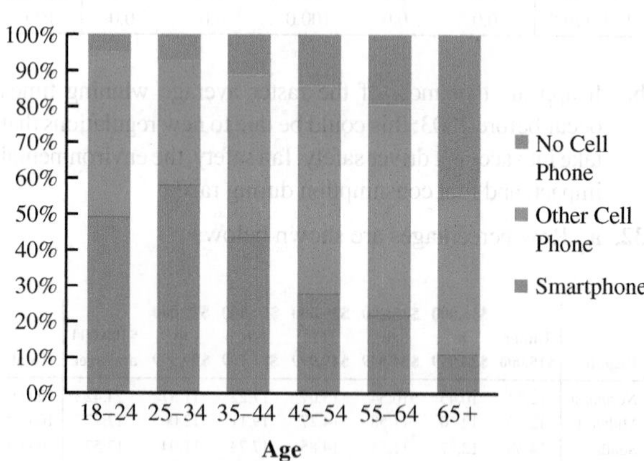

b. After an increase in age 25–34, smartphone ownership decreases as age increases; the percentage of people with no cell phone increases with age; there is less variation across age groups in the percentage who own other cell phones

c. Unless a newer device replaces the smartphone, we would expect smartphone ownership would become less sensitive to age; this would be true because current users will become older and because the device will become to be seen more as a necessity than a luxury

44. a.

SAT Score	Frequency
800–999	1
1000–1199	3
1200–1399	6
1400–1599	10
1600–1799	7
1800–1999	2
2000–2199	1
Total	30

b. Nearly symmetrical

c. 33% of the scores fall between 1400 and 1599
A score below 800 or above 2200 is unusual
The average is near or slightly above 1500

46. a.

Population in Millions	Frequency	Percent Frequency
0.0–2.4	15	30.0
2.5–4.9	13	26.0
5.0–7.4	10	20.0
7.5–9.9	5	10.0
10.0–12.4	1	2.0
12.5–14.9	2	4.0
15.0–17.4	0	0.0
17.5–19.9	2	4.0
20.0–22.4	0	0.0
22.5–24.9	0	0.0
25.0–27.4	1	2.0
27.5–29.9	0	0.0
30.0–32.4	0	0.0
32.5–34.9	0	0.0
35.0–37.4	1	2.0
37.5–39.9	0	0.0
More	0	0.0

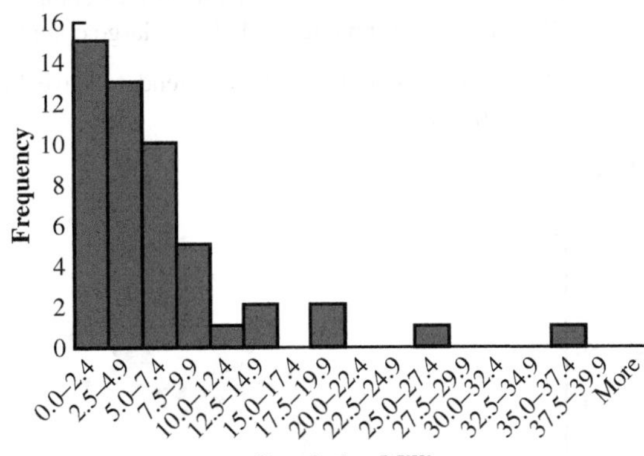

b. The distribution is skewed to the right

c. Fifteen states (30%) have a population less than 2.5 million; over half the states have population less than 5 million (28 states—56%); only seven states have a population greater than 10 million (California, Florida, Illinois, New York, Ohio, Pennsylvania, and Texas); the largest state is California (37.3 million) and the smallest states are Vermont and Wyoming (600 thousand)

48. a.

Industry	Frequency	Percent Frequency
Bank	26	13
Cable	44	22
Car	42	21
Cell	60	30
Collection	28	14
Total	200	100

b.

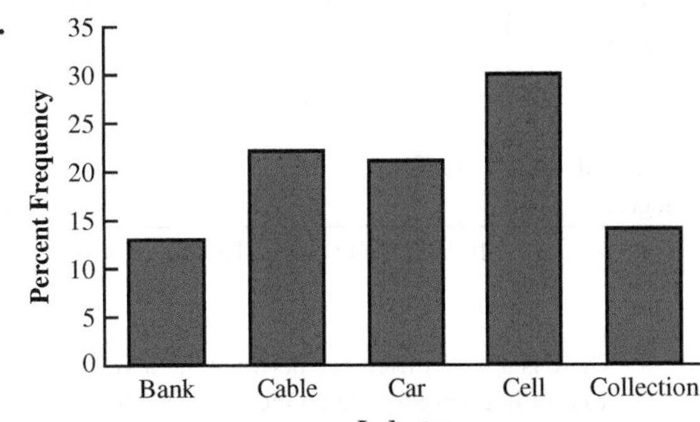

c. The cellular phone providers had the highest number of complaints

d. The percentage frequency distribution shows that the two financial industries (banks and collection agencies) had about the same number of complaints; new car dealers and cable and satellite television companies also had about the same number of complaints

50. a.

Level of Education	Percent Frequency
High school graduate	49.93
Bachelor's degree	33.71
Master's degree	13.71
Doctoral degree	2.65
Total	100.00

13.71 + 2.65 = 16.36% of heads of households have a master's or doctoral degree

b.

Household Income	Percent Frequency
Under $25,000	20.00
$25,000 to $49,999	23.61
$50,000 to $99,999	31.30
$100,000 and over	25.09
Total	100.00

31.30 + 25.09 = 56.39% of households have an income of $50,000 or more

c.

	Household Income			
Level of Education	**Under $25,000**	**$25,000 to $49,999**	**$50,000 to $99,999**	**$100,000 and over**
High School graduate	75.26	64.33	45.95	21.14
Bachelor's degree	18.92	26.87	37.31	47.46
Master's degree	5.22	7.77	14.69	24.86
Doctoral degree	0.60	1.03	2.05	6.53
Total	100.00	100.00	100.00	100.00

There is a large difference between the level of education for households with an income of under $25,000 and households with an income of $100,000 or more

52. a.

	Size of Company			
Job Growth (%)	**Small**	**Midsized**	**Large**	**Total**
−10–0	4	6	2	12
0–10	18	13	29	60
10–20	7	2	4	13
20–30	3	3	2	8
30–40	0	3	1	4
60–70	0	1	0	1
Total	32	28	38	98

b. Frequency distribution for growth rate:

Job Growth (%)	**Total**
−10–0	12
0–10	60
10–20	13
20–30	8
30–40	4
60–70	1
Total	98

Frequency distribution for size of company:

Size	**Total**
Small	32
Medium	28
Large	38
Total	98

c. Crosstabulation showing column percentages:

	Size of Company		
Job Growth (%)	**Small**	**Midsized**	**Large**
−10–0	13	21	5
0–10	56	46	76
10–20	22	7	11
20–30	9	11	5
30–40	0	11	3
60–70	0	4	0
Total	100	100	100

d. Crosstabulation showing row percentages:

	Size of Company			
Job Growth (%)	**Small**	**Midsized**	**Large**	**Total**
−10–0	33	50	17	100
0–10	30	22	48	100
10–20	54	15	31	100
20–30	38	38	25	100
30–40	0	75	25	100
60–70	0	4	0	100

e. Twelve companies had a negative job growth: 13% were small companies; 21% were midsized companies; and 5% were large companies; so, in terms of avoiding negative job growth, large companies were better off than small and midsized companies; but, although 95% of the large companies had a positive job growth, the growth rate was below 10% for 76% of these companies; in terms of better job growth rates, midsized companies performed better than either small or large companies; for instance, 26% of the midsized companies had a job growth of at least 20% as compared to 9% for small companies and 8% for large companies

54. c. Older colleges and universities tend to have higher graduation rates

56. a.

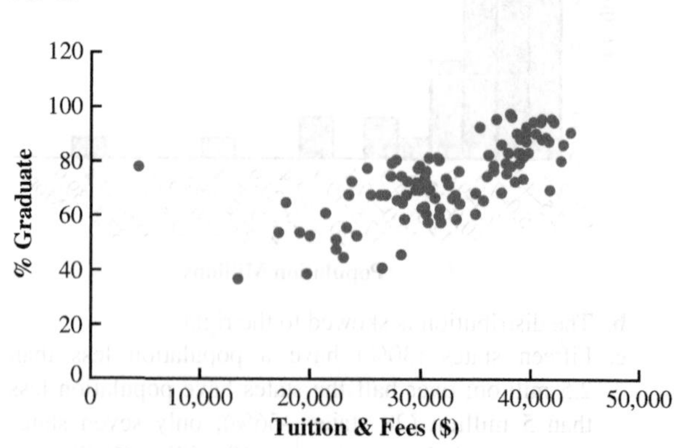

b. There appears to be a strong positive relationship between Tuition & Fees and % Graduation.

58. a.

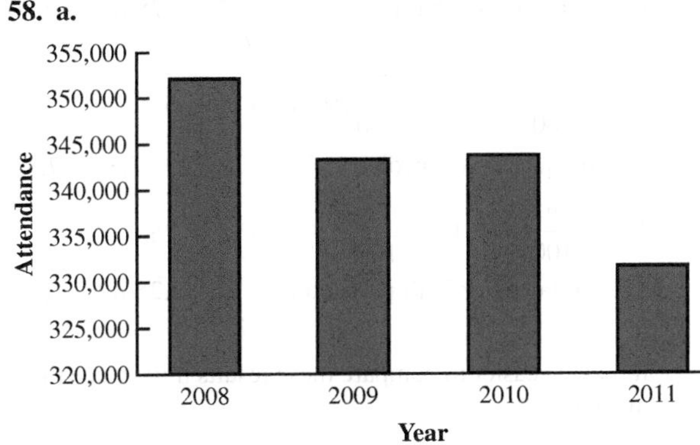

Zoo attendance appears to be dropping over time

b.

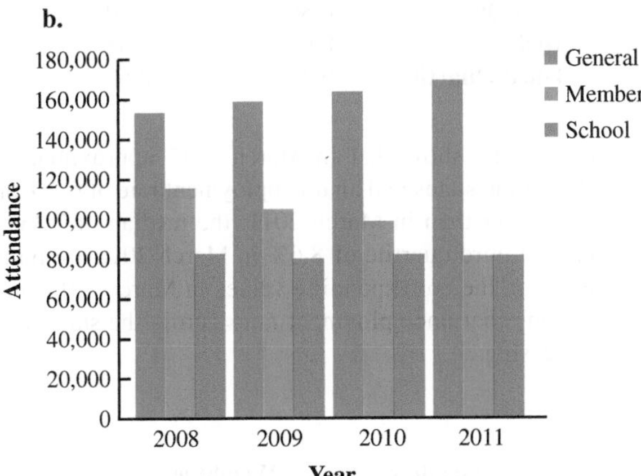

c. General attendance is increasing, but not enough to offset the decrease in member attendance; school membership appears fairly stable

Chapter 3

2. 16, 16.5

4.

Period	Return (%)
1	−0.060
2	−0.080
3	−0.040
4	0.020
5	0.054

The mean growth factor over the five periods is

$$\bar{x}_g = \sqrt[n]{(x_1)(x_2)\cdots(x_5)}$$
$$= \sqrt[5]{(0.940)(0.920)(0.960)(1.020)(1.054)}$$
$$= \sqrt[5]{(0.8925)} = 0.9775$$

So the mean growth rate $(0.9775 - 1)100\% = -2.25\%$

5. Arrange data in order: 15, 20, 25, 25, 27, 28, 30, 34

$i = \frac{20}{100}(8) = 1.6$; round up to position 2

20th percentile = 20

$i = \frac{25}{100}(8) = 2$; use positions 2 and 3

25th percentile $= \frac{20 + 25}{2} = 22.5$

$i = \frac{65}{100}(8) = 5.2$; round up to position 6

65th percentile = 28

$i = \frac{75}{100}(8) = 6$; use positions 6 and 7

75th percentile $= \frac{28 + 30}{2} = 29$

6. 59.73, 57, 53

8. a. Median = 80 or $80,000. The median salary for the sample of 15 middle managers working at firms in Atlanta is slightly lower than the median salary reported by the *Wall Street Journal*

b. Mean salary is $84,000. The sample mean salary is greater than the median salary. This indicates that the distribution of salaries for middle managers working at firms in Atlanta is positively skewed

c. First quartile or 25th percentile is 67

Third quartile or 75th percentile is 106

10. a. $\bar{x} = \frac{\Sigma x_i}{n} = \frac{1318}{20} = 65.9$

Order the data from the lowest rating (42) to the highest rating (83)

Position	Rating	Position	Rating
1	42	11	67
2	53	12	67
3	54	13	68
4	61	14	69
5	61	15	71
6	61	16	71
7	62	17	76
8	63	18	78
9	64	19	81
10	66	20	83

$L_{50} = \frac{p}{100}(n + 1) = \frac{50}{100}(20 + 1) = 10.5$

Median or 50th percentile $= 66 + .5(67 - 66) = 66.5$

Mode is 61

b. $L_{25} = \frac{p}{100}(n + 1) = \frac{25}{100}(20 + 1) = 5.25$

First quartile or 25th percentile = 61

$L_{75} = \frac{p}{100}(n + 1) = \frac{75}{100}(20 + 1) = 15.75$

Third quartile or 75th percentile = 71

c. $L_{90} = \frac{p}{100}(n + 1) = \frac{90}{100}(20 + 1) = 18.9$

90th percentile $= 78 + .9(81 - 78) = 80.7$

90% of the ratings are 80.7 or less; 10% of the ratings are 80.7 or greater

12. a. The minimum number of viewers who watched a new episode is 13.3 million, and the maximum number is 16.5 million

b. The mean number of viewers who watched a new episode is 15.04 million or approximately 15.0 million; the median is also 15.0 million; the data are multimodal (13.6, 14.0, 16.1, and 16.2 million); in such cases the mode is usually not reported

c. The data are first arranged in ascending order:

$$L_{25} = \frac{p}{100}(n + 1) = \frac{25}{100}(21 + 1) = 5.50$$

First quartile or 25th percentile $= 14 + .50(14.1 - 14)$
$= 14.05$

$$L_{75} = \frac{p}{100}(n + 1) = \frac{75}{100}(21 + 1) = 16.5$$

Third quartile or 75th percentile $= 16 + .5(16.1 - 16)$
$= 16.05$

d. A graph showing the viewership data over the air dates follows; period 1 corresponds to the first episode of the season, period 2 corresponds to the second episode, and so on

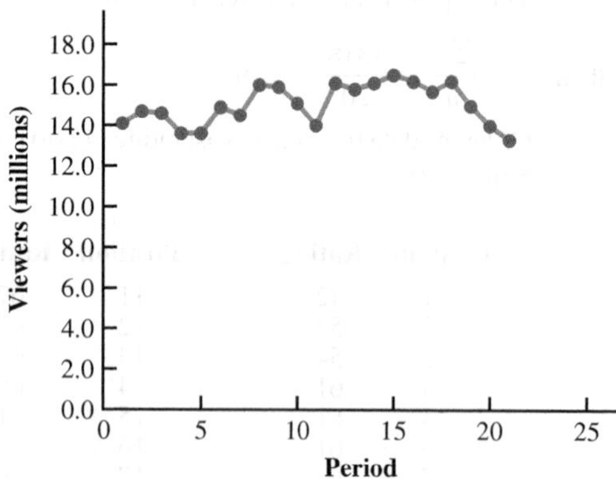

This graph shows that viewership of *The Big Bang Theory* has been relatively stable over the 2011–2012 television season

14. For March 2011:

$$L_{25} = \frac{p}{100}(n + 1) = \frac{25}{100}(50 + 1) = 12.75$$

First quartile or 25th percentile $= 6.8 + .75(6.8 - 6.8)$
$= 6.8$

$$L_{50} = \frac{p}{100}(n + 1) = \frac{50}{100}(50 + 1) = 25.5$$

Second quartile or median $= 8 + .5(8 - 8) = 8$

$$L_{75} = \frac{p}{100}(n + 1) = \frac{75}{100}(50 + 1) = 38.25$$

Third quartile or 75th percentile $= 9.4 + .25(9.6 - 9.4)$
$= 9.45$

For March 2012:

$$L_{25} = \frac{p}{100}(n + 1) = \frac{25}{100}(50 + 1) = 12.75$$

First quartile or 25th percentile $= 6.2 + .75(6.2 - 6.2)$
$= 6.2$

$$L_{50} = \frac{p}{100}(n + 1) = \frac{50}{100}(50 + 1) = 25.5$$

Second quartile or median $= 7.3 + .5(7.4 - 7.3) = 7.35$

$$L_{75} = \frac{p}{100}(n + 1) = \frac{75}{100}(50 + 1) = 38.25$$

Third quartile or 75th percentile $= 8.6 + .25(8.6 - 8.6)$
$= 8.6$

It may be easier to compare these results if we place them in a table.

	March 2011	March 2012
First Quartile	6.80	6.20
Median	8.00	7.35
Third Quartile	9.45	8.60

The results show that in March 2012 approximately 25% of the states had an unemployment rate of 6.2% or less, lower than in March 2011; the median of 7.35% and the third quartile of 8.6% in March 2012 are both less than the corresponding values in March 2011, indicating that unemployment rates across the states are decreasing

16. a.

Grade x_i	Weight w_i
4 (A)	9
3 (B)	15
2 (C)	33
1 (D)	3
0 (F)	0
	60 credit hours

$$\bar{x} = \frac{\Sigma w_i x_i}{\Sigma w_i} = \frac{9(4) + 15(3) + 33(2) + 3(1)}{9 + 15 + 33 + 3}$$

$$= \frac{150}{60} = 2.5$$

b. Yes

18. 3.8, 3.7

20.

	Stivers		Trippi	
Year	**End of Year Value ($)**	**Growth Factor**	**End of Year Value ($)**	**Growth Factor**
2004	11,000	1.100	5600	1.120
2005	12,000	1.091	6300	1.125
2006	13,000	1.083	6900	1.095
2007	14,000	1.077	7600	1.101
2008	15,000	1.071	8500	1.118
2009	16,000	1.067	9200	1.082
2010	17,000	1.063	9900	1.076
2011	18,000	1.059	10,600	1.071

For the Stivers mutual fund we have

$18000 = 10000[(x_1)(x_2)\cdots(x_8)]$, so $[(x_1)(x_2)\cdots(x_8)] = 1.8$ and

$$\bar{x}_g = \sqrt[n]{(x_1)(x_2)\cdots(x_8)} = \sqrt[8]{1.80} = 1.07624$$

So the mean annual return for the Stivers mutual fund is $(1.07624 - 1)100 = 7.624\%$

For the Trippi mutual fund we have

$10600 = 5000\,[(x_1)(x_2)\cdots(x_8)]$, so $[(x_1)(x_2)\cdots(x_8)] = 2.12$ and

$$\bar{x}_g = \sqrt[n]{(x_1)(x_2)\cdots(x_8)} = \sqrt[8]{2.12} = 1.09848$$

So the mean annual return for the Trippi mutual fund is $(1.09848 - 1)100 = 9.848\%$

While the Stivers mutual fund has generated a nice annual return of 7.6%, the annual return of 9.8% earned by the Trippi mutual fund is far superior

22. $25{,}000{,}000 = 10{,}000{,}000[(x_1)(x_2)\cdots(x_6)]$,

so $[(x_1)(x_2)\cdots(x_6)] = 2.50$

so $\bar{x}_g = \sqrt[n]{(x_1)(x_2)\cdots(x_6)} = \sqrt[6]{2.50} = 1.165$

So the mean annual growth rate is $(1.165 - 1)100 = 16.5\%$

24. 16, 4

25. Range $= 34 - 15 = 19$

Arrange data in order: 15, 20, 25, 25, 27, 28, 30, 34

$$L_{25} = \frac{p}{100}(n + 1) = \frac{25}{100}(8 + 1) = 2.25$$

First quartile or 25th percentile $= 20 + .25(20 - 15) = 21.25$

$$L_{75} = \frac{p}{100}(n + 1) = \frac{75}{100}(8 + 1) = 6.75$$

Third quartile or 75th percentile $= 28 + .75(30 - 28) = 29.5$

$\text{IQR} = Q_3 - Q_1 = 29.5 - 21.25 = 8.25$

x_i	$(x_i - \bar{x})$	$(x_i - \bar{x})^2$
27	1.5	2.25
25	−.5	.25
20	−5.5	30.25
15	−10.5	110.25
30	4.5	20.25
34	8.5	72.25
28	2.5	6.25
25	−.5	.25
		242.00

$$s^2 = \frac{\Sigma(x_i - \bar{x})^2}{n - 1} = \frac{242}{8 - 1} = 34.57$$

$$s = \sqrt{34.57} = 5.88$$

26. Excel's Descriptive Statistics tool provides the following values:

Mean	3.72
Standard Error	0.0659
Median	3.605
Mode	3.59
Standard Deviation	0.2948
Sample Variance	0.0869
Kurtosis	9.4208
Skewness	2.9402
Range	1.24
Minimum	3.55
Maximum	4.79
Sum	74.4
Count	20

a. $\bar{x} = 3.72$

b. $s = .2948$

c. The z-score corresponding to observation 3 (4.79) is

$$z = \frac{x - \bar{x}}{s} = \frac{4.79 - 3.72}{.2948} = -3.63$$

This observation is an outlier

d. The average price for a gallon of unleaded gasoline in San Francisco is much higher than the national average. This suggests that the cost of living in San Francisco may be higher than it would be for cities that have an average gasoline price close to the national average

28. a. The mean serve speed is 180.95, the variance is 21.42, and the standard deviation is 4.63

b. Although the mean serve speed for the 20 Women's Singles serve speed leaders for the 2011 Wimbledon tournament is slightly higher, the difference is very small; furthermore, given the variation in the 20 Women's Singles serve speed leaders from the 2012 Australian Open and the 20 Women's Singles serve speed leaders from the 2011 Wimbledon tournament, the difference in the mean serve speeds is most likely due to random variation in the players' performances

30. *Dawson:* range $= 2$, $s = .67$

Clark: range $= 8$, $s = 2.58$

32. a. 1960.05, 692.85

b. 481.65, 155.06

c. 2303, 563

d. Auto: IQR $= 2228 - 1717 = 511$

Dept Store: IQR $= 803 - 593 = 210$

e. Automotive spends more, has a larger standard deviation, larger max and min, and larger range than Department Store. Automotive spends more on advertising.

34. *Quarter-milers:* $s = .0564$, Coef. of Var. $= 5.8\%$

Milers: $s = .1295$, Coef. of Var. $= 2.9\%$

36. .20, 1.50, 0, −.50, −2.20

37. a. $z = \dfrac{20 - 30}{5} = -2,\ z = \dfrac{40 - 30}{5} = 2 \quad 1 - \dfrac{1}{2^2} = .75$

At least 75%

b. $z = \dfrac{15 - 30}{5} = -3,\ z = \dfrac{45 - 30}{5} = 3 \quad 1 - \dfrac{1}{3^2} = .89$

At least 89%

c. $z = \dfrac{22 - 30}{5} = -1.6,\ z = \dfrac{38 - 30}{5} = 1.6 \quad 1 - \dfrac{1}{1.6^2} = .61$

At least 61%

d. $z = \dfrac{18 - 30}{5} = -2.4,\ z = \dfrac{42 - 30}{5} = 2.4 \quad 1 - \dfrac{1}{2.4^2} = .83$

At least 83%

e. $z = \dfrac{12 - 30}{5} = -3.6,\ z = \dfrac{48 - 30}{5} = 3.6 \quad 1 - \dfrac{1}{3.6^2} = .92$

At least 92%

38. a. 95%
b. Almost all
c. 68%

39. a. $z = 2$ standard deviations

$1 - \dfrac{1}{z^2} = 1 - \dfrac{1}{2^2} = \dfrac{3}{4}$; at least 75%

b. $z = 2.5$ standard deviations

$1 - \dfrac{1}{z^2} = 1 - \dfrac{1}{2.5^2} = .84$; at least 84%

c. $z = 2$ standard deviations
Empirical rule: 95%

40. a. 68%
b. 81.5%
c. 2.5%

42. a. −.67
b. 1.50
c. Neither is an outlier
d. Yes; $z = 8.25$

44. a. 76.5, 7
b. 16%, 2.5%
c. 12.2, 7.89; no outliers

46. 15, 21.25, 26, 29.5, 34

48. 5, 6, 8, 10, 10, 12, 15, 16, 18

Smallest = 5

$L_{25} = \dfrac{p}{100}(n + 1) = \dfrac{25}{100}(9 + 1) = 2.5$

First quartile or 25th percentile = 6 + .5(8 − 6) = 7

$L_{50} = \dfrac{p}{100}(n + 1) = \dfrac{50}{100}(9 + 1) = 5.0$

Second quartile or median = 10

$L_{75} = \dfrac{p}{100}(n + 1) = \dfrac{75}{100}(9 + 1) = 7.5$

Third quartile or 75th percentile = 15 + .5(16 − 15) = 15.5

Largest = 18

A box plot created using StatTools follows:

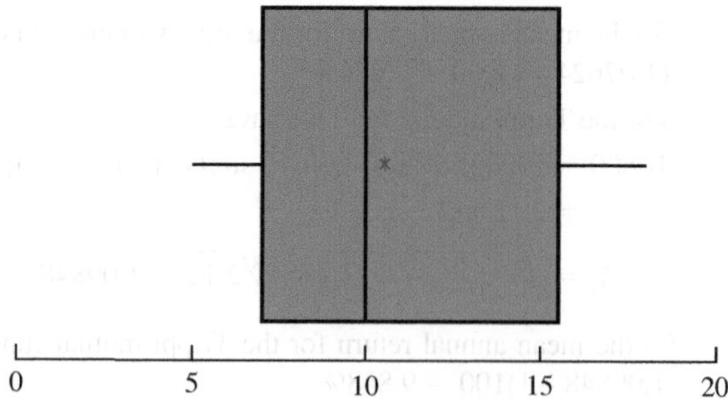

50. a. Men's 1st place 43.73 minutes faster
b. Medians: 109.64, 131.67
Men's median time 22.03 minutes faster
c. 65.30, 83.1025, 109.64, 129.025, 148.70
109.03, 122.08, 131.67, 147.18, 189.28
d. Men's Limits: 14.22 to 197.91; no outliers
Women's Limits: 84.43 to 184.83; 2 outliers
e. Women runners show less variation

51. a. Arrange data in order low to high

$i = \dfrac{25}{100}(21) = 5.25$; round up to 6th position

$Q_1 = 1872$
Median (11th position) = 4019

$i = \dfrac{75}{100}(21) = 15.75$; round up to 16th position

$Q_3 = 8305$
5-number summary: 608, 1872, 4019, 8305, 14,138

b. IQR = $Q_3 - Q_1$ = 8305 − 1872 = 6433
Lower limit: 1872 − 1.5(6433) = −7777.5
Upper limit: 8305 + 1.5(6433) = 17,955
c. No; data are within limits
d. 41,138 > 27,604; 41,138 would be an outlier; data value would be reviewed and corrected

e.

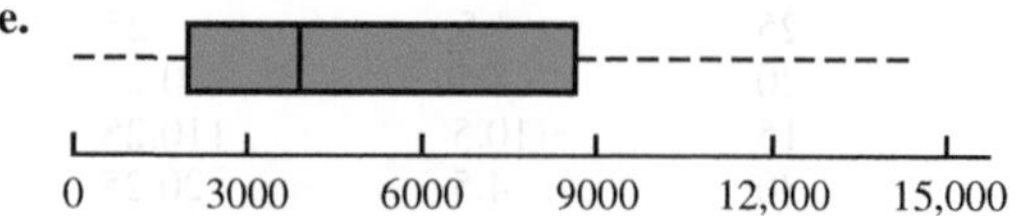

52. a. 73.5
b. 68, 71.25, 73.5, 74.75, 77
c. Limits: 66 and 80; no outliers
d. 66, 68, 71, 73, 75; 60.5 and 80.5
63, 65, 66, 67.75, 69; 60.875 and 71.875
75, 77, 78.5, 79.75, 81; 72.875 and 83.875
No outliers for any of the services
e. Verizon is highest rated
Sprint is lowest rated

54. **a.** Mean = 173.24 and median (second quartile) = 89.5
b. First quartile = 38.5 and the third quartile = 232
c. 21, 38.5, 89.5, 232, 995
d. A box plot created using StatTools follows:

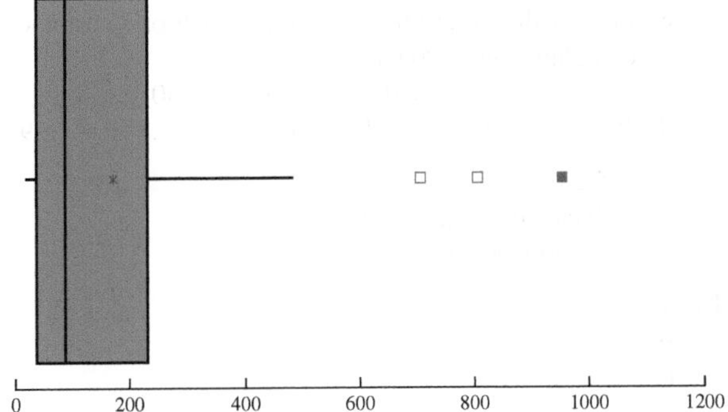

Three ports of entry are considered outliers:

NY: Buffalo-Niagara Falls	707
TX: El Paso	807
CA: San Ysidro	995

55. **b.** There appears to be a negative linear relationship between x and y
c.

x_i	y_i	$x_i-\bar{x}$	$y_i-\bar{y}$	$(x_i-\bar{x})(y_i-\bar{y})$
4	50	−4	4	−16
6	50	−2	4	−8
11	40	3	−6	−18
3	60	−5	14	−70
16	30	8	−16	−128
40	230	0	0	−240

$\bar{x} = 8; \bar{y} = 46$

$$s_{xy} = \frac{\Sigma(x_i - \bar{x})(y_i - \bar{y})}{n - 1} = \frac{-240}{4} = -60$$

The sample covariance indicates a negative linear association between x and y

d. $r_{xy} = \frac{s_{xy}}{s_x s_y} = \frac{-60}{(5.43)(11.40)} = -.969$

The sample correlation coefficient of −.969 is indicative of a strong negative linear relationship

56. **b.** There appears to be a positive linear relationship between x and y
c. $s_{xy} = 26.5$
d. $r_{xy} = .693$

58. −.91; negative relationship

60. **b.** DJIA: $\bar{x} = 9.10$ $s = 15.37$
Russell 1000: $\bar{x} = 9.09$ $s = 17.89$
c. $r_{xy} = .959$
d. The two indexes are very similar.

62. **a.** The mean is 2.95 and the median is 3.0
b. $L_{25} = 5.25$; first quartile = 1
$L_{75} = 15.75$; third quartile = 4 + .75(1) = 4.75
c. The range is 7 and the interquartile range is 4.75 – 1 = 3.75
d. The variance is 4.37 and standard deviation is 2.09
e. Because most people dine out relatively few times per week and a few families dine out very frequently, we would expect the data to be positively skewed; the skewness measure of 0.34 indicates the data are somewhat skewed to the right
f. The lower limit is −4.625 and the upper limit is 10.375; no values in the data are less than the lower limit or greater than the upper limit, so there are no outliers

64. **a.** The mean and median patient wait times for offices with a wait-tracking system are 17.2 and 13.5, respectively; the mean and median patient wait times for offices without a wait-tracking system are 29.1 and 23.5, respectively
b. The variance and standard deviation of patient wait times for offices with a wait-tracking system are 86.2 and 9.3, respectively; the variance and standard deviation of patient wait times for offices without a wait-tracking system are 275.7 and 16.6, respectively
c. Offices with a wait-tracking system have substantially shorter patient wait times than offices without a wait-tracking system
d. $z = \frac{37 - 29.1}{16.6} = 0.48$
e. $z = \frac{37 - 17.2}{9.3} = 2.13$

As indicated by the positive z-scores, both patients had wait times that exceeded the means of their respective samples; even though the patients had the same wait time, the z-score for the sixth patient in the sample who visited an office with a wait-tracking system is much larger because that patient is part of a sample with a smaller mean and a smaller standard deviation
f. The z-scores for all patients follow:

Without Wait-Tracking System	With Wait-Tracking System
−0.31	1.49
2.28	−0.67
−0.73	−0.34
−0.55	0.09
0.11	−0.56
0.90	2.13
−1.03	−0.88
−0.37	−0.45
−0.79	−0.56
0.48	−0.24

The z-scores do not indicate the existence of any outliers in either sample

66. a. $\bar{x} = 413.3$ This is slightly higher than the mean for the study

b. $s = 37.64$

c. LL = 292.5
UL = 536.5
There are no outliers

68. a. Median or 50th percentile = 52.1 + .5(52.1 − 52.1) = 52.1

b. Percentage change $= \left(\dfrac{52.1 - 55.5}{55.5}\right)100 = -6.1\%$

c. 75th percentile = 52.6

d. 46.5 50.75 52.1 52.6 64.5

e. The last household income (64.5) has a z-score = 3.07 > 3 and is an outlier
Lower Limit = 47.98
Upper Limit = 55.38
Using this approach, the first observation (46.5) and the last observation (54.5) would be consider outliers

70. a. 364 rooms

b. $457

c. −.293; slight negative correlation
Higher cost per night tends to be associated with smaller hotels

72. a. .286, low or weak positive correlation

b. Very poor predictor; spring training is practice and does not count toward standings or playoffs

74. a. 60.68

b. $s^2 = 31.23$; $s = 5.59$

Chapter 4

2. $\binom{6}{3} = \dfrac{6!}{3!3!} = \dfrac{6 \cdot 5 \cdot 4 \cdot 3 \cdot 2 \cdot 1}{(3 \cdot 2 \cdot 1)(3 \cdot 2 \cdot 1)} = 20$

ABC	ACE	BCD	BEF
ABD	ACF	BCE	CDE
ABE	ADE	BCF	CDF
ABF	ADF	BDE	CEF
ACD	AEF	BDF	DEF

4. b. (H,H,H), (H,H,T), (H,T,H), (H,T,T), (T,H,H), (T,H,T), (T,T,H), (T,T,T)

c. ⅛

6. $P(E_1) = .40$, $P(E_2) = .26$, $P(E_3) = .34$
The relative frequency method was used

8. a. 4: Commission Positive—Council Approves
Commission Positive—Council Disapproves
Commission Negative—Council Approves
Commission Negative—Council Disapproves

9. $\binom{50}{4} = \dfrac{50!}{4!46!} = \dfrac{50 \cdot 49 \cdot 48 \cdot 47}{4 \cdot 3 \cdot 2 \cdot 1} = 230{,}300$

10. a. Using the table provided, 86.5% of Delta flights arrive on time
$P(\text{on-time arrival}) = .865$

b. Three of the 10 airlines have less than two mishandled baggage reports per 1000 passengers
$P(\text{less than } 2) = 3/10 = .30$

c. Five of the 10 airlines have more than one customer complaint per 1000 passengers
$P(\text{more than } 1) = 5/10 = .50$

d. $P(\text{not on time}) = 1 - P(\text{on time}) = 1 - .871 = .129$

12. a. 175,223,510

b. 1 chance in 175,223,510
= .000000005707

14. a. ¼

b. ½

c. ¾

15. a. S = {ace of clubs, ace of diamonds, ace of hearts, ace of spades}

b. S = {2 of clubs, 3 of clubs, . . . , 10 of clubs, J of clubs, Q of clubs, K of clubs, A of clubs}

c. There are 12; jack, queen, or king in each of the four suits

d. For (a): 4/52 = 1/13 = .08
For (b): 13/52 = 1/4 = .25
For (c): 12/52 = .23

16. a. 36

c. ⅙

d. 5/18

e. No; $P(\text{odd}) = P(\text{even}) = \frac{1}{2}$

f. Classical

17. a. (4, 6), (4, 7), (4, 8)

b. .05 + .10 + .15 = .30

c. (2, 8), (3, 8), (4, 8)

d. .05 + .05 + .15 = .25

e. .15

18. a. .106

b. .31

c. .566

20. a. .2023, .4947, .2585, .0445

b. .6970

c. .3030

d. Probability of being financially independent before age 25 appears unrealistically high

22. a. .40, .40, .60

b. .80, yes

c. $A^c = \{E_3, E_4, E_5\}$; $C^c = \{E_1, E_4\}$;
$P(A^c) = .60$; $P(C^c) = .40$

d. (E_1, E_2, E_5); .60

e. .80

23. a. $P(A) = P(E_1) + P(E_4) + P(E_6)$
$= .05 + .25 + .10 = .40$

$P(B) = P(E_2) + P(E_4) + P(E_7)$
$= .20 + .25 + .05 = .50$
$P(C) = P(E_2) + P(E_3) + P(E_5) + P(E_7)$
$= .20 + .20 + .15 + .05 = .60$

b. $A \cup B = \{E_1, E_2, E_4, E_6, E_7\}$;
$P(A \cup B) = P(E_1) + P(E_2) + P(E_4) + P(E_6) + P(E_7)$
$= .05 + .20 + .25 + .10 + .05$
$= .65$

c. $A \cap B = \{E_4\}$; $P(A \cap B) = P(E_4) = .25$

d. Yes, they are mutually exclusive

e. $B^c = \{E_1, E_3, E_5, E_6\}$;
$P(B^c) = P(E_1) + P(E_3) + P(E_5) + P(E_6)$
$= .05 + .20 + .15 + .10$
$= .50$

24. a. .05
b. .70

26. a. .64
b. .48
c. .36
d. .76

28. Let B = rented a car for business reasons
P = rented a car for personal reasons

a. $P(B \cup P) = P(B) + P(P) - P(B \cap P)$
$= .540 + .458 - .300$
$= .698$

b. $P(\text{Neither}) = 1 - .698 = .302$

30. a. $P(A \mid B) = \dfrac{P(A \cap B)}{P(B)} = \dfrac{.40}{.60} = .6667$

b. $P(B \mid A) = \dfrac{P(A \cap B)}{P(A)} = \dfrac{.40}{.50} = .80$

c. No, because $P(A \mid B) \neq P(A)$

32. a.

	Car	Light Truck	Total
U.S	.1330	.2939	.4269
Non-U.S	.3478	.2253	.5731
Total	.4808	.5192	1.0000

b. .4269, .5731 Non-U.S. higher
.4808, .5192 Light Truck slightly higher

c. .3115, .6885 Light Truck higher

d. .6909, .3931 Car higher

e. .5661, U.S. higher for Light Trucks

33. a.

	Undergraduate Major			
	Business	Engineering	Other	Totals
Full-Time	.2697	.1510	.1923	.6130
Part-Time	.1149	.1234	.1487	.3870
Totals	.3847	.2743	.3410	1.0000

b. $P(B) = .3847$, $P(E) = .2743$, and $P(O) = .3410$, so business has most

c. $P(E \mid F) = \dfrac{P(E \cap F)}{P(F)} = \dfrac{.1510}{.6130} = .2463$

d. $P(F \mid B) = \dfrac{P(F \cap B)}{P(B)} = \dfrac{.2697}{.3847} = .7012$

e. Independent if $P(F)P(B) = P(F \cap B)$
$P(F)P(B) = (.6130)(.3847) = .4299$
But $P(F \cap B) = .2697$ in the joint probability table $P(F)P(B) \neq P(F \cap B)$; events F and B are not independent

34. a.

	On Time	Late	Total
JetBlue	.2304	.0696	.30
United	.2288	.0912	.32
US Airways	.3124	.0676	.38
Total	.7716	.2284	1.00

b. .7716
c. US Airways .38
d. United .3992

36. a. .8649
b. .9951
c. .0049
d. .3346, .8236, .1764
Foul the center is best strategy

38. a. .42
b. .58
c. .3810
d. .5862
e. No degree leads to greater financial problems

39. a. Yes, because $P(A_1 \cap A_2) = 0$

b. $P(A_1 \cap B) = P(A_1)P(B \mid A_1) = .40(.20) = .08$
$P(A_2 \cap B) = P(A_2)P(B \mid A_2) = .60(.05) = .03$

c. $P(B) = P(A_1 \cap B) + P(A_2 \cap B) = .08 + .03 = .11$

d. $P(A_1 \mid B) = \dfrac{.08}{.11} = .7273$

$P(A_2 \mid B) = \dfrac{.03}{.11} = .2727$

40. a. .10, .20, .09
b. .51
c. .26, .51, .23

42. M = missed payment
D_1 = customer defaults
D_2 = customer does not default
$P(D_1) = .05$, $P(D_2) = .95$, $P(M \mid D_2) = .2$, $P(M \mid D_1) = 1$

a. $P(D_1 \mid M) = \dfrac{P(D_1)P(M \mid D_1)}{P(D_1)P(M \mid D_1) + P(D_2)P(M \mid D_2)}$

$= \dfrac{(.05)(1)}{(.05)(1) + (.95)(.2)}$

$= \dfrac{.05}{.24} = .21$

b. Yes, the probability of default is greater than .20

44. a. .40
b. .6667; offer to female

46. a. 1005
b. A day or less; .4199
c. .20
d. 382/1005 = .3801

48. a.

	A	B	Total
Female	.2896	.2133	.5029
Male	.2368	.2603	.4971
Total	.5264	.4736	1.0000

b. .5029
c. .5758
d. Events are not independent

50. a. .76
b. .24

52. b. .2022
c. .4618
d. .4005

54. a. .7768
b. .2852
c. .5161
d. Not independent
e. Probability of not okay is higher for 50 + age category; .8472 to .7109

56. a. .25
b. .125
c. .0125
d. .10
e. No

58. a. .1139
b. .0761
c. .5005, .4995

60. a. .7907, .2093, spam
b. .6944, .6320, *today!* more likely
c. .2750, .5858, *fingertips!* more likely
d. These words occur more often in spam

Chapter 5

1. a. Head, Head (H, H)
Head, Tail (H, T)
Tail, Head (T, H)
Tail, Tail (T, T)
b. x = number of heads on two coin tosses
c.

Outcome	Values of x
(H, H)	2
(H, T)	1
(T, H)	1
(T, T)	0

d. Discrete; 0, 1, and 2

2. a. x = time in minutes to assemble product
b. Any positive value: $x > 0$
c. Continuous

3. Let Y = position is offered
N = position is not offered
a. $S = \{(Y, Y, Y), (Y, Y, N), (Y, N, Y), (Y, N, N), (N, Y, Y), (N, Y, N), (N, N, Y), (N, N, N)\}$
b. Let N = number of offers made; N is a discrete random variable
c.

Experimental Outcome	(Y, Y, Y)	(Y, Y, N)	(Y, N, Y)	(Y, N, N)	(N, Y, Y)	(N, Y, N)	(N, N, Y)	(N, N, N)
Value of N	3	2	2	1	2	1	1	0

4. $x = 0, 1, 2, \ldots, 9$

6. a. 0, 1, 2, . . . , 20; discrete
b. 0, 1, 2, . . . ; discrete
c. 0, 1, 2, . . . , 50; discrete
d. $0 \le x \le 8$; continuous
e. $x > 0$; continuous

7. a. $f(x) \ge 0$ for all values of x
$\Sigma f(x) = 1$; therefore, it is a valid probability distribution
b. Probability $x = 30$ is $f(30) = .25$
c. Probability $x \le 25$ is $f(20) + f(25) = .20 + .15 = .35$
d. Probability $x > 30$ is $f(35) = .40$

8. a.

x	$f(x)$
1	3/20 = .15
2	5/20 = .25
3	8/20 = .40
4	4/20 = .20
	Total 1.00

b.

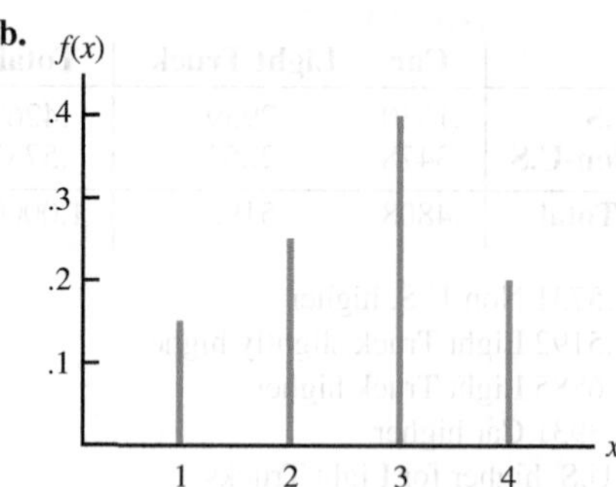

c. $f(x) \ge 0$ for $x = 1, 2, 3, 4$
$\Sigma f(x) = 1$

10. a.

x	1	2	3	4	5
$f(x)$	.05	.09	.03	.42	.41

b.

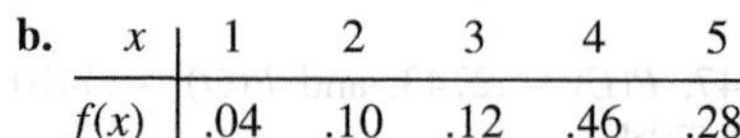

x	1	2	3	4	5
$f(x)$	.04	.10	.12	.46	.28

c. .83

d. .28
e. Senior executives are more satisfied

12. a. Yes
b. .15
c. .10

14. a. .05
b. .70
c. .40

16. a.

y	$f(y)$	$yf(y)$
2	.20	.4
4	.30	1.2
7	.40	2.8
8	.10	.8
Totals	1.00	5.2

$E(y) = \mu = 5.2$

b.

y	$y-\mu$	$(y-\mu)^2$	$f(y)$	$(y-\mu)^2 f(y)$
2	−3.20	10.24	.20	2.048
4	−1.20	1.44	.30	.432
7	1.80	3.24	.40	1.296
8	2.80	7.84	.10	.784
			Total	4.560

$Var(y) = 4.56$

$\sigma = \sqrt{4.56} = 2.14$

18. a/b.

x	$f(x)$	$xf(x)$	$x-\mu$	$(x-\mu)^2$	$(x-\mu)^2 f(x)$
0	.2188	.0000	−1.1825	1.3982	.3060
1	.5484	.5484	−.1825	.0333	.0183
2	.1241	.2483	.8175	.6684	.0830
3	.0489	.1466	1.8175	3.3035	.1614
4	.0598	.2393	2.8175	7.9386	.4749
Total	1.0000	1.1825			1.0435
		↑ $E(x)$			↑ $Var(x)$

c/d.

y	$f(y)$	$yf(y)$	$y-\mu$	$(y-\mu)^2$	$(y-\mu)^2 f(y)$
0	.2497	.0000	−1.2180	1.4835	.3704
1	.4816	.4816	−.2180	.0475	.0229
2	.1401	.2801	−.7820	.6115	.0856
3	.0583	.1749	1.7820	3.1755	.1851
4	.0703	.2814	2.7820	7.7395	.5444
Total	1.0000	1.2180			1.2085
		↑ $E(y)$			↑ $Var(y)$

e. The expected number of times that owner-occupied units have a water supply stoppage lasting 6 or more hours in the past 3 months is 1.1825, slightly less than the expected value of 1.2180 for renter-occupied units; and the variability is somewhat less for owner-occupied units (1.0435) as compared to renter-occupied units (1.2085)

20. a. 430
b. −90; concern is to protect against the expense of a large loss

22. a. 445
b. $1250 loss

24. a. Medium: 145; large: 140
b. Medium: 2725; large: 12,400

25. a.

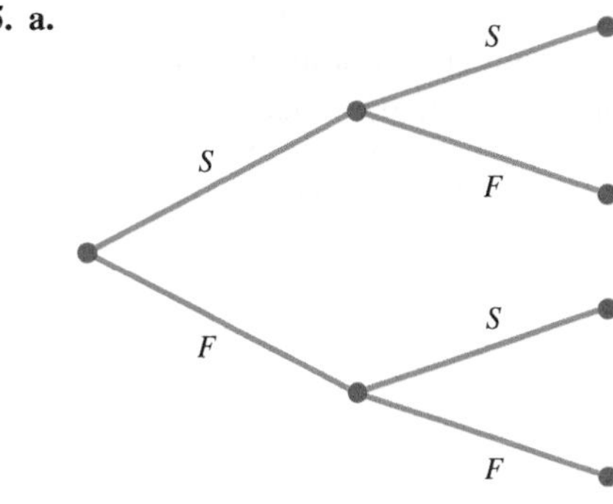

b. $f(1) = \binom{2}{1}(.4)^1(.6)^1 = \frac{2!}{1!1!}(.4)(.6) = .48$

c. $f(0) = \binom{2}{0}(.4)^0(.6)^2 = \frac{2!}{0!2!}(1)(.36) = .36$

d. $f(2) = \binom{2}{2}(.4)^2(.6)^0 = \frac{2!}{2!0!}(.16)(.1) = .16$

e. $P(x \geq 1) = f(1) + f(2) = .48 + .16 = .64$
f. $E(x) = np = 2(.4) = .8$
$Var(x) = np(1-p) = 2(.4)(.6) = .48$
$\sigma = \sqrt{.48} = .6928$

26. a. .3487
b. .1937
c. .9298
d. .6513
e. 1
f. .9, .95

28. a. Yes
b. .0135
c. .2377
d. .9140

30. a. Probability of a defective part being produced must be .03 for each part selected; parts must be selected independently
b. Let D = defective
G = not defective

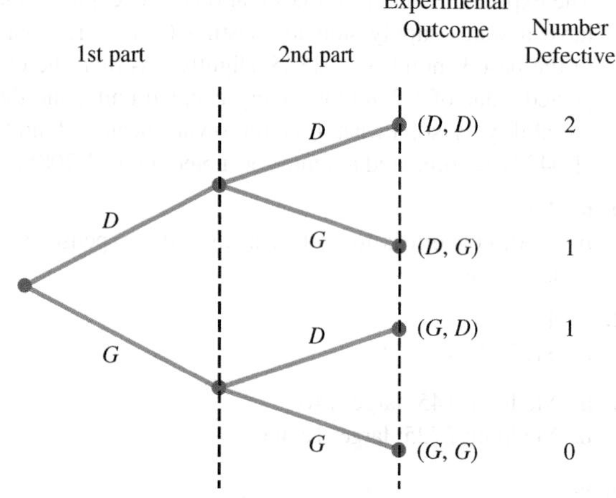

c. Two outcomes result in exactly one defect

d. $P(\text{no defects}) = (.97)(.97) = .9409$
$P(1 \text{ defect}) = 2(.03)(.97) = .0582$
$P(2 \text{ defects}) = (.03)(.03) = .0009$

32. a. .90
b. .99
c. .999
d. Yes

34. a. Yes
b. .0000
c. .8516

36. a. .1304
b. .9924
c. 6
d. 4.2; 2.0499

38. a. $f(x) = \dfrac{3^x e^{-3}}{x!}$
b. .2241
c. .1494
d. .8008

39. a. $f(x) = \dfrac{2^x e^{-2}}{x!}$
b. $\mu = 6$ for 3 time periods
c. $f(x) = \dfrac{6^x e^{-6}}{x!}$
d. $f(2) = \dfrac{2^2 e^{-2}}{2!} = \dfrac{4(.1353)}{2} = .2706$
e. $f(6) = \dfrac{6^6 e^{-6}}{6!} = .1606$
f. $f(5) = \dfrac{4^5 e^{-4}}{5!} = .1563$

40. a. .1952
b. .1048
c. .0183
d. .0907

42. a. .0273
b. .9727
c. .4847

44. a. $\mu = .6$
b. .5488
c. .3293
d. .1219

46. a. $f(1) = \dfrac{\binom{3}{1}\binom{10-3}{4-1}}{\binom{10}{4}} = \dfrac{\left(\frac{3!}{1!2!}\right)\left(\frac{7!}{3!4!}\right)}{\frac{10!}{4!6!}}$

$= \dfrac{(3)(35)}{210} = .50$

b. $f(2) = \dfrac{\binom{3}{2}\binom{10-3}{2-2}}{\binom{10}{2}} = \dfrac{(3)(1)}{45} = .067$

c. $f(0) = \dfrac{\binom{3}{0}\binom{10-3}{2-0}}{\binom{10}{2}} = \dfrac{(1)(21)}{45} = .4667$

d. $f(2) = \dfrac{\binom{3}{2}\binom{10-3}{4-2}}{\binom{10}{4}} = \dfrac{(3)(21)}{210} = .30$

e. $x = 4$ is *greater than* $r = 3$; thus, $f(4) = 0$

48. a. .5250
b. .8167

50. $N = 60$, $n = 10$
a. $r = 20$, $x = 0$

$$f(0) = \frac{\binom{20}{0}\binom{40}{10}}{\binom{60}{10}} = \frac{(1)\left(\frac{40!}{10!30!}\right)}{\frac{60!}{10!50!}}$$

$$= \left(\frac{40!}{10!30!}\right)\left(\frac{10!50!}{60!}\right)$$

$$= \frac{40 \cdot 39 \cdot 38 \cdot 37 \cdot 36 \cdot 35 \cdot 34 \cdot 33 \cdot 32 \cdot 31}{60 \cdot 59 \cdot 58 \cdot 57 \cdot 56 \cdot 55 \cdot 54 \cdot 53 \cdot 52 \cdot 51}$$

$= .0112$

b. $r = 20$, $x = 1$

$$f(1) = \frac{\binom{20}{1}\binom{40}{9}}{\binom{60}{10}} = 20\left(\frac{40!}{9!31!}\right)\left(\frac{10!50!}{60!}\right)$$

$= .0725$

c. $1 - f(0) - f(1) = 1 - .0112 - .0725 = .9163$
d. Same as the probability one will be from Hawaii; .0725

52. a. .2917
b. .0083
c. .5250, .1750; 1 bank
d. .7083
e. .90, .49, .70

54. a.

x	1	2	3	4	5	6	7	8	9	10
$f(x)$	.150	.050	.075	.050	.125	.050	.100	.125	.125	.150

b. .275
c. 5.925; 9.6694
d. Not much difference

56. a. .0005
b. .4952
c. 980
d. 720, 460.8, 21.4663

58. a. .9510
b. .0480
c. .0490

60. a. 47
b. 5.9962
c. 5.9962

62. .1912

64. a. .2240
b. .5767

66. a. .4667
b. .4667
c. .0667

Chapter 6

1. a.

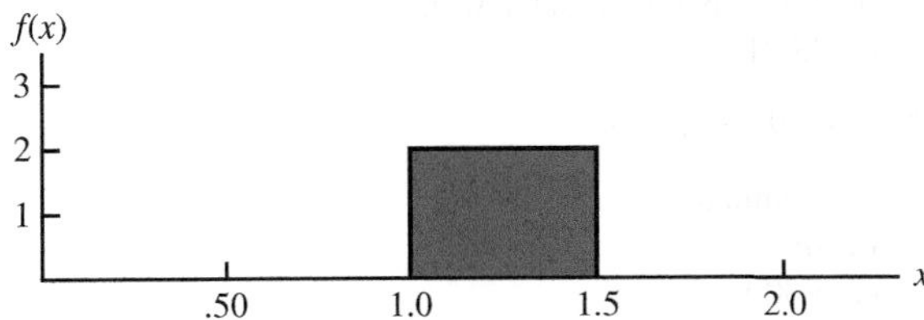

b. $P(x = 1.25) = 0$; the probability of any single point is zero because the area under the curve above any single point is zero
c. $P(1.0 \leq x \leq 1.25) = 2(.25) = .50$
d. $P(1.20 < x < 1.5) = 2(.30) = .60$

2. b. .50
c. .60
d. 15
e. 8.33

4. a.

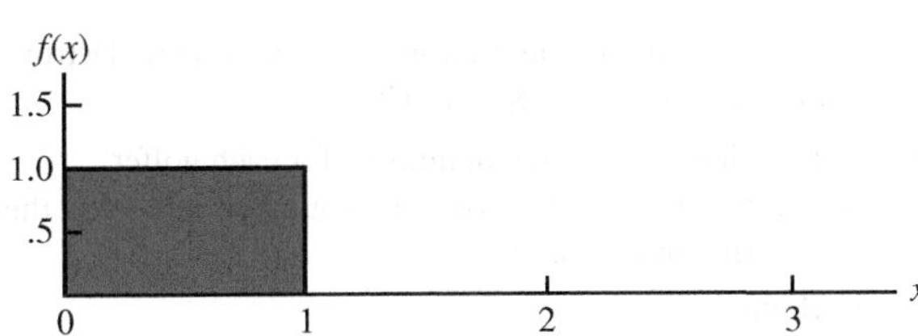

b. $P(.25 < x < .75) = 1(.50) = .50$
c. $P(x \leq .30) = 1(.30) = .30$
d. $P(x > .60) = 1(.40) = .40$

6. a. 56, 216
b. .6250
c. .4125
d. .1500

10. a. .9332
b. .8413
c. .0919
d. .4938

12. a. .2967
b. .4418
c. .3300
d. .5910
e. .8849
f. .2389

13. a. $P(-1.98 \leq z \leq .49) = P(z \leq .49) - P(z < -1.98)$ $= .6879 - .0239 = .6640$
b. $P(.52 \leq z \leq 1.22) = P(z \leq 1.22) - P(z < .52)$ $= .8888 - .6985 = .1903$
c. $P(-1.75 \leq z \leq -1.04) = P(z \leq -1.04) - P(z < -1.75) = .1492 - .0401 = .1091$

14. a. $z = 1.96$
b. $z = 1.96$
c. $z = .61$
d. $z = 1.12$
e. $z = .44$
f. $z = .44$

15. a. The z value corresponding to a cumulative probability of .2119 is $z = -.80$
b. Compute .9030/2 = .4515; the cumulative probability of .5000 + .4515 = .9515 corresponds to $z = 1.66$
c. Compute .2052/2 = .1026; z corresponds to a cumulative probability of .5000 + .1026 = .6026, so $z = .26$
d. The z value corresponding to a cumulative probability of .9948 is $z = 2.56$
e. The area to the left of z is 1 − .6915 = .3085, so $z = -.50$

16. a. $z = 2.33$
b. $z = 1.96$
c. $z = 1.645$
d. $z = 1.28$

18. $\mu = 14.4$ and $\sigma = 4.4$

a. At $x = 20$, $z = \dfrac{20 - 14.4}{4.4} = 1.27$

$P(z \leq 1.27) = .8980$
$P(x \geq 20) = 1 - .8980 = .1020$
Using Excel: 1-NORM.DIST(20,14.4,4.4,TRUE) = .1016

b. At $x = 10$, $z = \dfrac{10 - 14.4}{4.4} = -1.00$

$P(z \leq -1.00) = .1587$
So, $P(x \leq 10) = .1587$
Using Excel: NORM.DIST(10,14.4,4.4,TRUE) = .1587

c. A z-value of 1.28 cuts off an area of approximately 10% in the upper tail
$x = 14.4 + 4.4(1.28) = 20.03$
A return of 20.03% or higher will put a domestic stock fund in the top 10%
Using Excel: NORM.INV(.9,14.4,4.4) = 20.0388

20. a. Using Excel: NORM.DIST(3.5,3.73,.25,TRUE) = .1788
b. Using Excel: NORM.DIST(3.5,3.40,.20,TRUE) = .6915
c. Using Excel: 1-NORM.DIST (3.73,3.40,.20,TRUE) = .0495

22. a. Using Excel: NORM.DIST(10,8.35,2.5,TRUE) − NORM.DIST(5,8.35,2.5,TRUE) = .6553
b. Using Excel: NORM.INV (.97,8.35,2.5) = 13.0530
c. Using Excel: 1-NORM.DIST(3,8.35,2.5) = .9838

24. a. Using Excel: NORM.DIST(400,749,225, TRUE) = .0604
b. Using Excel: 1-NORM.DIST(800,749,225,TRUE) = .4103
c. Using Excel: NORM.DIST(1000,749,225,TRUE) − NORM.DIST(500,749,225,TRUE) = .7335
d. Using Excel: NORM.INV(.95,749,225) = 1119.0921

26. a. .5276
b. .3935
c. .4724
d. .1341

27. a. $P(x \leq x_0) = 1 - e^{-x_0/3}$
b. $P(x \leq 2) = 1 - e^{-2/3} = 1 - .5134 = .4866$
c. $P(x \geq 3) = 1 - P(x \leq 3) = 1 - (1 - e^{-3/3})$
$= e^{-1} = .3679$
d. $P(x \leq 5) = 1 - e^{-5/3} = 1 - .1889 = .8111$
e. $P(2 \leq x \leq 5) = P(x \leq 5) - P(x \leq 2)$
$= .8111 - .4866 = .3245$

28. a. $f(x) = \frac{1}{20}e^{-x/20}$
b. .5276
c. .3679
d. .5105

29. a.

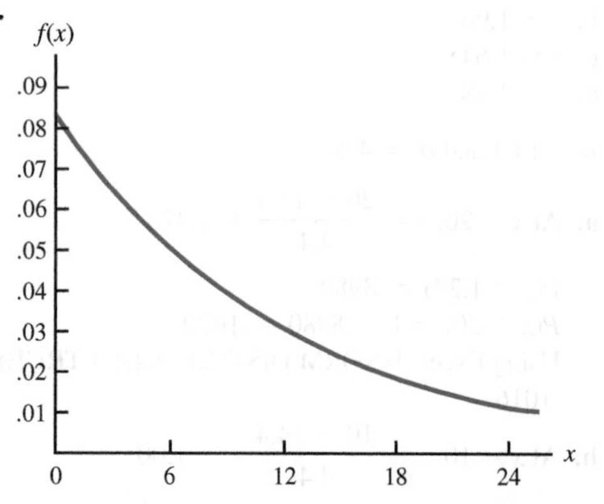

b. $P(x \leq 12) = 1 - e^{-12/12} = 1 - .3679 = .6321$
c. $P(x \leq 6) = 1 - e^{-6/12} = 1 - .6065 = .3935$
d. $P(x \geq 30) = 1 - P(x < 30)$
$= 1 - (1 - e^{-30/12})$
$= .0821$

30. a. .3935
b. .2386
c. .1353

32. a. 37.5 minutes
b. $f(x) = \frac{1}{37.5}e^{-x/37.5}$
c. .7981
d. .4493
e. .2886

34. a. Using Excel: NORM.INV(.90,19000,2100) = 16,308
b. Using Excel: 1-NORM.DIST(22000,19000,2100) = .0766
c. Using Excel: NORM.INV(.97,19000,2100) = 22,949.6666

36. a. 25.5319
b. .9401
c. 706 or more

38. a. .0228
b. $50

40. a. 38.3%
b. 3.59% better, 96.41% worse
c. 38.21%

42. $\mu = 19.23$ ounces

44. a. 1/7 minute
b. $7e^{-7x}$
c. .0009
d. .2466

46. a. 2 minutes
b. .2212
c. .3935
d. .0821

Chapter 7

1. a. AB, AC, AD, AE, BC, BD, BE, CD, CE, DE
b. With 10 samples, each has a 1/10 probability
c. B and D because the two smallest random numbers are .0476 and .0957

2. Elements 2, 3, 5, and 10

3. The simple random sample consists of New York, Detroit, Oakland, Boston, and Kansas City

4. Step 1. Generate a random number for each golfer
Step 2. Sort with respect to random numbers and select the first three golfers

6. a. finite
b. infinite

c. infinite
d. finite
e. infinite

7. **a.** $\bar{x} = \frac{\Sigma x_i}{n} = \frac{54}{6} = 9$

b. $s = \sqrt{\frac{\Sigma(x_i - \bar{x})^2}{n - 1}}$

$$\Sigma(x_i - \bar{x})^2 = (-4)^2 + (-1)^2 + 1^2 + (-2)^2 + 1^2 + 5^2 = 48$$

$$s = \sqrt{\frac{48}{6 - 1}} = 3.1$$

8. **a.** .50
b. .3667

9. **a.** $\bar{x} = \frac{\Sigma x_i}{n} = \frac{465}{5} = 93$

b.

	x_i	$(x_i - \bar{x})$	$(x_i - \bar{x})^2$
	94	+1	1
	100	+7	49
	85	−8	64
	94	+1	1
	92	−1	1
Totals	465	0	116

$$s = \sqrt{\frac{\Sigma(x_i - \bar{x})^2}{n - 1}} = \sqrt{\frac{116}{4}} = 5.39$$

10. **a.** .05
b. .425
c. .20

12. **a.** U.S. adults age 50 and over
b. .8216
c. 315
d. .8310
e. U.S. adults age 50 and over

15. **a.** The sampling distribution is normal with:

$$E(\bar{x}) = \mu = 200$$

$$\sigma_{\bar{x}} = \frac{\sigma}{\sqrt{n}} = \frac{50}{\sqrt{100}} = 5$$

For +5, $(\bar{x} - \mu) = 5$,

$$z = \frac{\bar{x} - \mu}{\sigma_{\bar{x}}} = \frac{5}{5} = 1$$

Area = .8413 − .1587 = .6826

b. For ±10, $(\bar{x} - \mu) = 10$,

$$z = \frac{\bar{x} - \mu}{\sigma_{\bar{x}}} = \frac{10}{5} = 2$$

Area = .9772 − .0228= .9544

16. 3.54, 2.50, 2.04, 1.77
$\sigma_{\bar{x}}$ decreases as n increases

18. **a.** Normal with $E(\bar{x}) = 51{,}800$ and $\sigma_{\bar{x}} = 516.40$
b. $\sigma_{\bar{x}}$ decreases to 365.15
c. $\sigma_{\bar{x}}$ decreases as n increases

19. **a.**

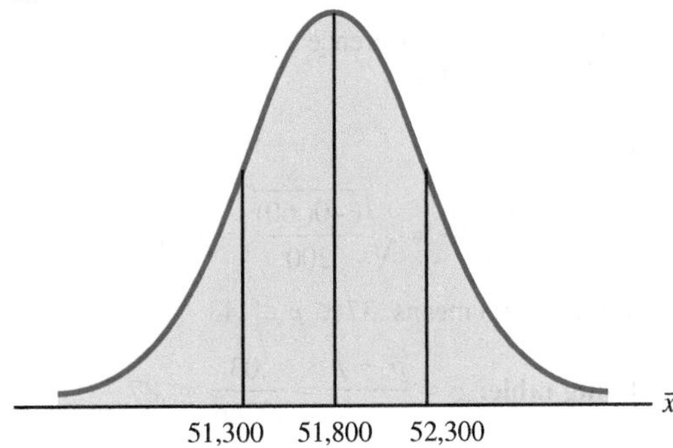

$$\sigma_{\bar{x}} = \frac{\sigma}{\sqrt{n}} = \frac{4000}{\sqrt{60}} = 516.40$$

$$\text{At } \bar{x} = 52{,}300,\ z = \frac{52{,}300 - 51{,}800}{516.40} = .97$$

$$P(\bar{x} \le 52{,}300) = P(z \le .97) = .8340$$

$$\text{At } \bar{x} = 51{,}300,\ z = \frac{51{,}300 - 51{,}800}{516.40} = -.97$$

$$P(\bar{x} \le 51{,}300) = P(z < -.97) = .1660$$
$$P(51{,}300 \le \bar{x} \le 52{,}300) = .8340 - .1660 = .6680$$

Using Excel:
NORM.DIST(52300,51800,516.40,TRUE)−
NORM.DIST(51300,51800,516.40,TRUE) = .6671

b. $\sigma_{\bar{x}} = \frac{\sigma}{\sqrt{n}} = \frac{4000}{\sqrt{120}} = 365.15$

$$\text{At } \bar{x} = 52{,}300,\ z = \frac{52{,}300 - 51{,}800}{365.15} = 1.37$$

$$P(\bar{x} \le 52{,}300) = P(z \le 1.37) = .9147$$

$$\text{At } \bar{x} = 51{,}300,\ z = \frac{51{,}300 - 51{,}800}{365.15} = -1.37$$

$$P(\bar{x} < 51{,}300) = P(z < -1.37) = .0853$$
$$P(51{,}300 \le \bar{x} \le 52{,}300) = .9147 - .0853 = .8294$$

Using Excel:
NORM.DIST(52300,51800,365.15,TRUE)−
NORM.DIST(51300,51800,365.15,TRUE) = .8291

20. **a.** Normal with $E(\bar{x}) = 17.5$ and $\sigma_{\bar{x}} = .57$
b. .9198
c. .6212

22. a. Using table: .3544, .4448, .5934, .9050
b. Higher probability with a larger sample size

24. a. Normal with $E(\bar{x}) = 22$ and $\sigma_{\bar{x}} = .7303$
b. Using table: .8294; using NORM.DIST: .8291
c. Using table: .9070; using NORM.DIST: .9065
d. Part (c) because of the larger sample size

26. a. $n/N = .01$; no
b. 1.29, 1.30; little difference
c. Using table: .8764

28. a. $E(\bar{p}) = .40$

$$\sigma_{\bar{p}} = \sqrt{\frac{p(1-p)}{n}} = \sqrt{\frac{(.40(.60)}{200}} = .0346$$

Within ±.03 means $.37 \leq \bar{p} \leq .43$

Using table: $z = \dfrac{\bar{p} - p}{\sigma_{\bar{p}}} = \dfrac{.03}{.0346} = .87$

$$\begin{aligned} P(.37 \leq \bar{p} \leq .43) &= P(-.87 \leq z \leq .87) \\ &= .8078 - .1922 \\ &= .6156 \end{aligned}$$

Using Excel:
NORM.DIST(.43,.40,.0346,TRUE)−
NORM.DIST(.37,.40,.0346,TRUE) = .6141

b. Using table: $z = \dfrac{\bar{p} - p}{\sigma_{\bar{p}}} = \dfrac{.05}{.0346} = 1.44$

$$\begin{aligned} P(.35 \leq \bar{p} \leq .45) &= P(-1.44 \leq z \leq 1.44) \\ &= .9251 - .0749 \\ &= .8502 \end{aligned}$$

Using Excel:
NORM.DIST(.45,.40,.0346,TRUE)−
NORM.DIST(.35,.40,.0346,TRUE) = .8516

30. a. Using table: .6156; using NORM.DIST: .6175
b. Using table: .7814; using NORM.DIST: .7830
c. Using table: .9488; using NORM.DIST: .9490
d. Using table: .9942; using NORM.DIST: .9942
e. Higher probability with larger n

31. a.

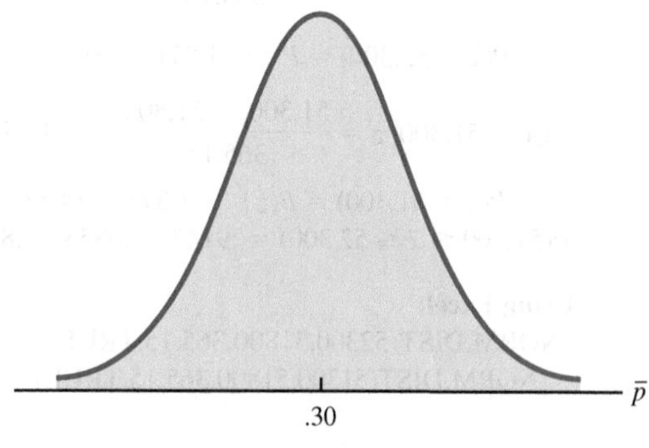

$$\sigma_{\bar{p}} = \sqrt{\frac{p(1-p)}{n}} = \sqrt{\frac{.30(.70)}{100}} = .0458$$

The normal distribution is appropriate because $np = 100(.30) = 30$ and $n(1 - p) = 100(.70) = 70$ are both greater than 5

b. $P(.20 \leq \bar{p} \leq .40) = ?$

$$z = \frac{.40 - .30}{.0458} = 2.18$$

$$\begin{aligned} P(.20 \leq \bar{p} \leq .40) &= P(-2.18 \leq z \leq 2.18) \\ &= .9854 - .0146 \\ &= .9708 \end{aligned}$$

Using Excel:
NORM.DIST(.40,.30,.0458,TRUE)−
NORM.DIST(.20,.30,.0458,TRUE) = .9710

c. $P(.25 \leq \bar{p} \leq .35) = ?$

$$z = \frac{.35 - .30}{.0458} = 1.09$$

$$\begin{aligned} P(.25 \leq \bar{p} \leq .35) &= P(-1.09 \leq z \leq 1.09) \\ &= .8621 - .1379 \\ &= .7242 \end{aligned}$$

Using Excel:
NORM.DIST(.35,.30,.0458,TRUE)−
NORM.DIST(.25,.30,.0458,TRUE) = .7250

32. a. Normal with $E(\bar{p}) = .55$ and $\sigma_{\bar{p}} = .0352$
b. Using table: .8444; using NORM.DIST: .8445
c. Normal with $E(\bar{p}) = .45$ and $\sigma_{\bar{p}} = .0352$
d. Using table: .8444; using NORM.DIST: .8445
e. No, $\sigma_{\bar{p}}$ is the same in both cases
f. Using table: .9556; using NORM.DIST: .9554

34. a. Normal with $E(\bar{p}) = .42$ and $\sigma_{\bar{p}} = .0285$
b. Using table: .7062; using NORM.DIST: .7075
c. Using table: .9198; using NORM.DIST: .9206
d. Probabilities would increase

36. a. Normal with $E(\bar{p}) = .76$ and $\sigma_{\bar{p}} = .0214$
b. Using table: .8384; using NORM.DIST: .8390
c. Using table: .9452; using NORM.DIST: .9455

38. a. LMI Aerospace, Alpha & Omega, Olympic Steel, Kimball International, International Shipholding
b. Different companies

40. a. Normal with $E(\bar{x}) = 406$ and $\sigma_{\bar{x}} = 10$
b. Using table: .8664; using NORM.DIST: .8664
c. Using table: $z = -2.60$, .0047

42. a. 955
b. .50
c. Using table: $z = \pm 1.05$, .7062; using NORM.DIST: .7050
d. .8230
using NORM.DIST: .8234

44. a. 625
b. .7888

46. a. Normal with $E(\bar{p}) = .15$ and $\sigma_{\bar{p}} = .0230$
b. Using table: .9182; using NORM.DIST: .9180
c. Using table: .6156; using NORM.DIST: .6155

48. a. Using table: $z = \pm 1.59$, .8882; using NORM.DIST: .8900
b. Using table: $z = +1.99$, .0233; using NORM.DIST: .0232

50. a. 48
b. Normal, $E(\bar{p}) = .25$ and $\sigma_{\bar{p}} = .0625$
c. .2119

Chapter 8

2. Use $\bar{x} \pm z_{\alpha/2}(\sigma/\sqrt{n})$
a. $32 \pm 1.645(6/\sqrt{50})$
32 ± 1.4; 30.6 to 33.4
b. $32 \pm 1.96(6/\sqrt{50})$
32 ± 1.66; 30.34 to 33.66
c. $32 \pm 2.576(6/\sqrt{50})$
32 ± 2.19; 29.81 to 34.19

4. 54

5. a. $1.96\sigma/\sqrt{n} = 1.96(5/\sqrt{49}) = 1.40$
b. 24.80 ± 1.40; 23.40 to 26.20

6. 39.13 to 41.49

8. a. Population is at least approximately normal
b. 3.41
c. 4.48

10. a. \$3388 to \$3584
b. \$3370 to \$3602
c. \$3333 to \$3639
d. Width increases as confidence level increases

12. a. 2.179
b. −1.676
c. 2.457
d. −1.708 and 1.708
e. −2.014 and 2.014

13. a. $\bar{x} = \frac{\Sigma x_i}{n} = \frac{80}{8} = 10$

b. $s = \sqrt{\frac{\Sigma(x_i - \bar{x})^2}{n - 1}} = \sqrt{\frac{84}{7}} = 3.46$

c. $t_{.025}\left(\frac{s}{\sqrt{n}}\right) = 2.365\left(\frac{3.46}{\sqrt{8}}\right) = 2.9$

d. $\bar{x} \pm t_{.025}\left(\frac{s}{\sqrt{n}}\right)$

10 ± 2.9 (7.1 to 12.9)

14. a. 21.5 to 23.5
b. 21.3 to 23.7
c. 20.9 to 24.1
d. A larger margin of error and a wider interval

15. $\bar{x} \pm t_{\alpha/2}(s/\sqrt{n})$
90% confidence: $df = 64$ and $t_{.05} = 1.669$

$19.5 \pm 1.669\left(\frac{5.2}{\sqrt{65}}\right)$

19.5 ± 1.08 (18.42 to 20.58)
95% confidence: $df = 64$ and $t_{.025} = 1.998$

$19.5 \pm 1.998\left(\frac{5.2}{\sqrt{65}}\right)$

19.5 ± 1.29 (18.21 to 20.79)

16. a. 9.7063, 7.9805
b. 7.1536 to 12.2590
c. 3.8854 to 1.6194
d. 3.3674 to 4.4034

18. a. 22
b. 3.8014
c. 18.20 to 25.80
d. Larger n next time

20. a. 2551
b \$2409.99 to \$2692.01
c. Interval does not include national average. Be confident that premiums in Michigan are above the national average

22. a. \$9269.52 to \$12,540.48
b. 1523
c. 4,748,714; 434 million

24. a. Planning value of $\sigma = \frac{\text{Range}}{4} = \frac{36}{4} = 9$

b. $n = \frac{z^2_{.025}\sigma^2}{E^2} = \frac{(1.96)^2(9)^2}{(3)^2} = 34.57$; use $n = 35$

c. $n = \frac{(1.96)^2(9)^2}{(2)^2} = 77.79$; use $n = 78$

25. a. Use $n = \frac{z^2_{\alpha/2}\sigma^2}{E^2}$

$n = \frac{(1.96)^2(6.84)^2}{(1.5)^2} = 79.88$; use $n = 80$

b. $n = \frac{(1.645)^2(6.84)^2}{(2)^2} = 31.65$; use $n = 32$

26. a. 25
b. 49
c. 97

28. a. $n = 188$
b. $n = 267$
c. $n = 461$
d. Sample size gets larger

30. 1537

31. a. $\bar{p} = \frac{100}{400} = .25$

b. $\sqrt{\frac{\bar{p}(1 - \bar{p})}{n}} = \sqrt{\frac{.25(.75)}{400}} = .0217$

c. $\bar{p} \pm z_{.025}\sqrt{\frac{\bar{p}(1 - \bar{p})}{n}}$

$.25 \pm 1.96(.0217)$
$.25 \pm .0424$; .2076 to .2924

32. a. .6733 to .7267
b. .6682 to .7318

34. 1068

35. a. $\bar{p} = \frac{1760}{2000} = .88$
b. Margin of error

$$z_{.05}\sqrt{\frac{\bar{p}(1-\bar{p})}{n}} = 1.645\sqrt{\frac{.88(1-.88)}{2000}} = .0120$$

c. Confidence interval:
.88 ± .0120
or .868 to .892

d. Margin of error

$$z_{.025}\sqrt{\frac{\bar{p}(1-\bar{p})}{n}} = 1.96\sqrt{\frac{.88(1-.88)}{2000}} = .0142$$

95% confidence interval
.88 ± .0142 or .8658 to .8942

36. a. .23
b. .1716 to .2884

38. a. .1790
b. .0738, .5682 to .7158
c. 354

39. a. $n = \frac{1.96^2 p^*(1-p^*)}{E^2}$

$$n = \frac{1.96^2(.156)(1-.156)}{(.03)^2} = 562$$

b. $n = \frac{2.576^2(.156)(1-.156)}{(.03)^2} = 970.77$; use $n = 971$

40. .0346; .4854 to .5546

42. a. .0442
b. 601, 1068, 2401, 9604

44. a. 4.00
b. 29.77 to 37.77

46. a. 122
b. $1751 to $1995
c. $172.316 billion
d. Less than $1873

48. a. $712.27 to $833.73
b. $172.31 to $201.69
c. .34
d. part (a)

50. 37

52. 176

54. a. .5420
b. .0508
c. .4912 to .5928

56. a. .22
b. .1904 to .2496
c. .3847 to .4553
d. part (c)

58. a. 1267
b. 1509

60. a. .3101
b. .2898 to .3304
c. 8219; no, this sample size is unnecessarily large

Chapter 9

2. a. $H_0: \mu \leq 14$
$H_a: \mu > 14$
b. No evidence that the new plan increases sales
c. The research hypothesis $\mu > 14$ is supported; the new plan increases sales

4. a. $H_0: \mu \geq 220$
$H_a: \mu < 220$

5. a. Rejecting $H_0: \mu \leq 56.2$ when it is true
b. Accepting $H_0: \mu \leq 56.2$ when it is false

6. a. $H_0: \mu \leq 1$
$H_a: \mu > 1$
b. Claiming $\mu > 1$ when it is not true
c. Claiming $\mu \leq 1$ when it is not true

8. a. $H_0: \mu \geq 220$
$H_a: \mu < 220$
b. Claiming $\mu < 220$ when it is not true
c. Claiming $\mu \geq 220$ when it is not true

10. a. $z = \frac{\bar{x} - \mu_0}{\sigma/\sqrt{n}} = \frac{26.4 - 25}{6/\sqrt{40}} = 1.48$
b. Using normal table with $z = 1.48$: p-value = 1.0000 − .9306 = .0694
Using Excel: p-value
= 1 − NORM.S.DIST(1.48,TRUE)
= .0694
c. p-value > .01, do not reject H_0
d. Reject H_0 if $z \geq 2.33$
1.48 < 2.33, do not reject H_0

11. a. $z = \frac{\bar{x} - \mu_0}{\sigma/\sqrt{n}} = \frac{14.15 - 15}{3/\sqrt{50}} = -2.00$
b. p-value = 2(.0228) = .0456
c. p-value ≤ .05, reject H_0
d. Reject H_0 if $z \leq -1.96$ or $z \geq 1.96$
$-2.00 \leq -1.96$, reject H_0

12. a. .1056; do not reject H_0
b. .0062; reject H_0
c. ≈0; reject H_0
d. .7967; do not reject H_0

14. a. .3844; do not reject H_0
b. .0074; reject H_0
c. .0836; do not reject H_0

15. a. $H_0: \mu \geq 1056$
$H_a: \mu < 1056$

b. $z = \dfrac{\bar{x} - \mu_0}{\sigma/\sqrt{n}} = \dfrac{910 - 1056}{1600/\sqrt{400}} = -1.83$
p-value = .0336
c. p-value $\leq$ .05, reject H_0; the mean refund of "last-minute" filers is less than \$1056
d. Reject H_0 if $z \leq -1.645$
$-1.83 \leq -1.645$; reject H_0

16. a. H_0: $\mu \leq 3173$
H_a: $\mu > 3173$
b. .0207
c. Reject H_0; the mean credit card balance has increased

18. a. H_0: $\mu = 192$
H_a: $\mu \neq 192$
b. -2.23; using Excel: p-value = 2*NORM.S.DIST(−2.23,TRUE) = .0257
c. Reject H_0; conclude the mean number of restaurant meals eaten by millennials has changed in 2012

20. a. H_0: $\mu \geq 838$
H_a: $\mu < 838$
b. -2.40
c. Using Excel: p-value = NORM.S.DIST(−2.40,TRUE) = .0082
d. Reject H_0; the annual expenditure per person on presciption drugs is less in the Midwest than in the Northeast

22. a. H_0: $\mu = 8$
H_a: $\mu \neq 8$
b. .1706
c. Do not reject H_0
d. 7.83 to 8.97; yes

24. a. $t = \dfrac{\bar{x} - \mu_0}{s/\sqrt{n}} = \dfrac{17 - 18}{4.5/\sqrt{48}} = -1.54$
b. Degrees of freedom = $n - 1 = 47$
Area in lower tail is between .05 and .10
p-value (two-tail) is between .10 and .20
Using Excel p-value = 2*T.DIST(−1.54,47,TRUE) = .1303
c. p-value > .05; do not reject H_0
d. With $df = 47$, $t_{.025} = 2.012$
Reject H_0 if $t \leq -2.012$ or $t \geq 2.012$
$t = -1.54$; do not reject H_0

26. a. Between .02 and .05; using Excel: p-value = 2*[1−T.DIST(2.10,64,TRUE)] = .0397; reject H_0
b. Between .01 and .02; using Excel: p-value = 2*T.DIST(−2.57,64,TRUE) = .0125; reject H_0
c. Between .10 and .20; using Excel: p-value = 2*[1−T.DIST(1.54,64,TRUE)] = .1285; do not reject H_0

27. a. H_0: $\mu \geq 238$
H_a: $\mu < 238$
b. $t = \dfrac{\bar{x} - \mu_0}{s/\sqrt{n}} = \dfrac{231 - 238}{80/\sqrt{100}} = -.88$
Degrees of freedom = $n - 1 = 99$
p-value is between .10 and .20
Using Excel: p-value = T.DIST(−.88,99,TRUE)=.1905
c. p-value > .05; do not reject H_0
Cannot conclude mean weekly benefit in Virginia is less than the national mean
d. $df = 99$, $t_{.05} = -1.66$
Reject H_0 if $t \leq -1.66$
$-.88 > -1.66$; do not reject H_0

28. a. H_0: $\mu \geq 9$
H_a: $\mu < 9$
b. Between .005 and .01
Using Excel: p-value = T.DIST(−2.50,84,TRUE) = .0072
c. Reject H_0

30. a. H_0: $\mu = 6.4$
H_a: $\mu \neq 6.4$
b. $\bar{x} = 7.0$
Using Excel: p-value = 2*(1−T.DIST(1.56,39,TRUE)) = .1268
c. With $\alpha > .1268$, we cannot reject H_0

32. a. H_0: $\mu = 10{,}192$
H_a: $\mu \neq 10{,}192$
b. Between .02 and .05
Using Excel: p-value = T.DIST(−2.23,49,TRUE) = .0304
c. Reject H_0

34. a. H_0: $\mu = 2$
H_a: $\mu \neq 2$
b. 2.2
c. .52
d. Between .20 and .40
Using Excel: p-value = 2*[1−T.DIST(1.22,9,TRUE)] = .2535
e. Do not reject H_0

36. a. $z = \dfrac{\bar{p} - p_0}{\sqrt{\dfrac{p_0(1 - p_0)}{n}}} = \dfrac{.68 - .75}{\sqrt{\dfrac{.75(1 - .75)}{300}}} = -2.80$
p-value = .0026
p-value $\leq$ .05; reject H_0
b. $z = \dfrac{.72 - .75}{\sqrt{\dfrac{.75(1 - .75)}{300}}} = -1.20$
p-value = .1151
p-value > .05; do not reject H_0
c. $z = \dfrac{.70 - .75}{\sqrt{\dfrac{.75(1 - .75)}{300}}} = -2.00$
p-value = .0228
p-value $\leq$ .05; reject H_0

d. $z = \dfrac{.77 - .75}{\sqrt{\dfrac{.75(1 - .75)}{300}}} = .80$

p-value $= .7881$

p-value $> .05$; do not reject H_0

38. a. H_0: $p = .64$

H_a: $p \neq .64$

b. $\bar{p} = 52/100 = .52$

$$z = \frac{\bar{p} - p_0}{\sqrt{\dfrac{p_0(1 - p_0)}{n}}} = \frac{.52 - .64}{\sqrt{\dfrac{.64(1 - .64)}{100}}} = -2.50$$

Area $= .4938$

p-value $= 2(.0062) = .0124$

c. p-value $\leq .05$; reject H_0

Proportion differs from the reported .64

d. Yes, because $\bar{p} = .52$ indicates that fewer believe the supermarket brand is as good as the name brand

40. a. .35

b. H_0: $p \geq .46$

H_a: $p < .46$

p-value $= .0436$

c. Proportion providing gifts has decreased

42. a. $\bar{p} = .15$

b. .0718 to .2218

c. Houston proportion is different

44. a. H_0: $p \leq .50$

H_a: $p > .50$

b. Using Excel: p-value = 1−NORM.S.DIST(2.78,TRUE) = .0027

c. Reject H_0; conclude the number of physicians over the age of 50 who have been sued at least once is greater than 50%

46. a. H_0: $\mu = 16$

H_a: $\mu \neq 16$

b. .0286; reject H_0

Readjust line

c. .2186; do not reject H_0

Continue operation

d. $z = 2.19$; reject H_0

$z = -1.23$; do not reject H_0

Yes, same conclusion

48. a. H_0: $\mu \leq 4$

H_a: $\mu > 4$

b. Using Excel: p-value = 1−NORM.S.DIST(2.58,TRUE) = .0049

c. Reject H_0; conclude that the mean daily background television children from low-income families are exposed to is greater than 4 hours

50. $t = -.93$

p-value between .20 and .40

Using Excel: p-value = 2*T.DIST(−1.05,41,TRUE) = .2999

Do not reject H_0

52. $t = 2.26$

p-value between .01 and .025

Using Excel: p-value = 1−T.DIST(2.26,31,TRUE) = .0155

Reject H_0

54. a. H_0: $p \leq .80$

H_a: $p > .80$

p-value $= .0099$

Over 80% feel body scanners will improve security

b. H_0: $p \leq .75$

H_a: $p > .75$

p-value $= .0537$

Cannot conclude that over 75% approve using

56. a. H_0: $p \leq .30$

H_a: $p > .30$

b. .34

c. .0401

d. p-value $\leq .05$; reject H_0. Conclude that more than 30% of the millennials either live at home with their parents or are otherwise dependent on their parents

58. H_0: $p \geq .90$

H_a: $p < .90$

p-value $= .0808$

Do not reject H_0

Chapter 10

1. a. $\bar{x}_1 - \bar{x}_2 = 13.6 - 11.6 = 2$

b. $z_{\alpha/2} = z_{.05} = 1.645$

$$\bar{x}_1 - \bar{x}_2 \pm 1.645\sqrt{\frac{\sigma_1^2}{n_1} + \frac{\sigma_2^2}{n_2}}$$

$$2 \pm 1.645\sqrt{\frac{(2.2)^2}{50} + \frac{(3)^2}{35}}$$

$2 \pm .98$ (1.02 to 2.98)

c. $z_{\alpha/2} = z_{.05} = 1.96$

$$2 \pm 1.96\sqrt{\frac{(2.2)^2}{50} + \frac{(3)^2}{35}}$$

2 ± 1.17 (.83 to 3.17)

2. a. $z = \dfrac{(\bar{x}_1 - \bar{x}_2) - D_0}{\sqrt{\dfrac{\sigma_1^2}{n_1} + \dfrac{\sigma_2^2}{n_2}}} = \dfrac{(25.2 - 22.8) - 0}{\sqrt{\dfrac{(5.2)^2}{40} + \dfrac{(6)^2}{50}}} = 2.03$

b. p-value $= 1.0000 - .9788 = .0212$

c. p-value $\leq .05$; reject H_0

4. a. $\bar{x}_1 - \bar{x}_2 = 85.36 - 81.40 = 3.96$

b. $z_{.025}\sqrt{\dfrac{\sigma_1^2}{n_1} + \dfrac{\sigma_2^2}{n_2}} = 1.96\sqrt{\dfrac{(4.55)^2}{37} + \dfrac{(3.97)^2}{44}} = 1.88$

c. 3.96 ± 1.88 (2.08 to 5.84)

6. p-value $= .0351$
Reject H_0; mean price in Atlanta lower than mean price in Houston

8. a. Reject H_0; customer service has improved for Rite Aid
b. Do not reject H_0; the difference is not statistically significant
c. p-value $= .0336$; reject H_0; customer service has improved for Expedia
d. 1.80
e. The increase for J.C. Penney is not statistically significant

9. a. $\bar{x}_1 - \bar{x}_2 = 22.5 - 20.1 = 2.4$

b. $$df = \frac{\left(\frac{s_1^2}{n_1} + \frac{s_2^2}{n_2}\right)^2}{\frac{1}{n_1 - 1}\left(\frac{s_1^2}{n_1}\right)^2 + \frac{1}{n_2 - 1}\left(\frac{s_2^2}{n_2}\right)^2}$$

$$= \frac{\left(\frac{2.5^2}{20} + \frac{4.8^2}{30}\right)^2}{\frac{1}{19}\left(\frac{2.5^2}{20}\right)^2 + \frac{1}{29}\left(\frac{4.8^2}{30}\right)^2} = 45.8$$

c. $df = 45$, $t_{.025} = 2.014$

$$t_{.025}\sqrt{\frac{s_1^2}{n_1} + \frac{s_2^2}{n_2}} = 2.014\sqrt{\frac{2.5^2}{20} + \frac{4.8^2}{30}} = 2.1$$

d. 2.4 ± 2.1 (.3 to 4.5)

10. a. $$t = \frac{(\bar{x}_1 - \bar{x}_2) - 0}{\sqrt{\frac{s_1^2}{n_1} + \frac{s_2^2}{n_2}}} = \frac{(13.6 - 10.1) - 0}{\sqrt{\frac{5.2^2}{35} + \frac{8.5^2}{40}}} = 2.18$$

b. $$df = \frac{\left(\frac{s_1^2}{n_1} + \frac{s_2^2}{n_2}\right)^2}{\frac{1}{n_1 - 1}\left(\frac{s_1^2}{n_1}\right)^2 + \frac{1}{n_2 - 1}\left(\frac{s_2^2}{n_2}\right)^2}$$

$$= \frac{\left(\frac{5.2^2}{35} + \frac{8.5^2}{40}\right)^2}{\frac{1}{34}\left(\frac{5.2^2}{35}\right)^2 + \frac{1}{39}\left(\frac{8.5^2}{40}\right)^2} = 65.7$$

Use $df = 65$
c. $df = 65$, area in tail is between .01 and .025; two-tailed p-value is between .02 and .05
Exact p-value $= .0329$
d. p-value $\leq .05$; reject H_0

12. a. $\bar{x}_1 - \bar{x}_2 = 22.5 - 18.6 = 3.9$ miles

b. $$df = \frac{\left(\frac{s_1^2}{n_1} + \frac{s_2^2}{n_2}\right)^2}{\frac{1}{n_1 - 1}\left(\frac{s_1^2}{n_1}\right)^2 + \frac{1}{n_2 - 1}\left(\frac{s_2^2}{n_2}\right)^2}$$

$$= \frac{\left(\frac{8.4^2}{50} + \frac{7.4^2}{40}\right)^2}{\frac{1}{49}\left(\frac{8.4^2}{50}\right)^2 + \frac{1}{39}\left(\frac{7.4^2}{40}\right)^2} = 87.1$$

Use $df = 87$, $t_{.025} = 1.988$

$$3.9 \pm 1.988\sqrt{\frac{8.4^2}{50} + \frac{7.4^2}{40}}$$

3.9 ± 3.3 (.6 to 7.2)

14. a. H_0: $\mu_1 - \mu_2 \geq 0$
H_a: $\mu_1 - \mu_2 < 0$
b. -2.41
c. Using t table, p-value is between .005 and .01
Exact p-value $= .009$
d. Reject H_0; nursing salaries are lower in Tampa

16. a. H_0: $\mu_1 - \mu_2 \leq 0$
H_a: $\mu_1 - \mu_2 > 0$
b. 38
c. $t = 1.80$, $df = 25$
Using t table, p-value is between .025 and .05
Exact p-value $= .0420$
d. Reject H_0; conclude higher mean score if college grad

18. a. H_0: $\mu_1 - \mu_2 = 0$
H_a: $\mu_1 - \mu_2 \neq 0$
b. 50.6 and 52.8 minutes
c. p-value greater than .40
Do not reject H_0; cannot conclude population mean delay times differ

19. a. 1, 2, 0, 0, 2
b. $\bar{d} = \Sigma d_i/n = 5/5 = 1$
c. $$s_d = \sqrt{\frac{\Sigma(d_i - \bar{d})^2}{n - 1}} = \sqrt{\frac{4}{5 - 1}} = 1$$
d. $$t = \frac{\bar{d} - \mu}{s_d/\sqrt{n}} = \frac{1 - 0}{1/\sqrt{5}} = 2.24$$
$df = n - 1 = 4$
Using t table, p-value is between .025 and .05
Exact p-value $= .0443$
p-value $\leq .05$; reject H_0

20. a. 3, −1, 3, 5, 3, 0, 1
b. 2
c. 2.08
d. 2
e. .07 to 3.93

21. H_0: $\mu_d \leq 0$
H_a: $\mu_d > 0$
$\bar{d} = .625$
$s_d = 1.30$
$$t = \frac{\bar{d} - \mu_d}{s_d/\sqrt{n}} = \frac{.625 - 0}{1.30/\sqrt{8}} = 1.36$$

$df = n - 1 = 7$
Using t table, p-value is between .10 and .20
Exact p-value = .1080
p-value > .05; do not reject H_0; cannot conclude commercial improves mean potential to purchase

22. a. \$3.41
b. \$1.67 to \$5.15
Very nice increase

24. a. $H_0: \mu_d \leq 0$
$H_a: \mu_d > 0$
$\bar{d} = 23, t = 2.05$
p-value between .05 and .025
Reject H_0; conclude airfares have increased
b. \$487, \$464
c. 5% increase in airfares

26. a. $t = -1.42$
Using t table, p-value is between .10 and .20
Exact p-value = .1718
Do not reject H_0; no difference in mean scores
b. −1.05
c. 1.28; yes

28. a. $\bar{\bar{x}} = (156 + 142 + 134)/3 = 144$

$$\text{SSTR} = \sum_{j=1}^{k} n_j(\bar{x}_j - \bar{\bar{x}})^2 = 6(156 - 144)^2 + 6(142 - 144)^2 + 6(134 - 144)^2 = 1488$$

b. $\text{MSTR} = \text{SSTR}/(k - 1) = 1488/2 = 744$
c. $s_1^2 = 164.4 \quad s_2^2 = 131.2 \quad s_3^2 = 110.4$

$$\text{SSE} = \sum_{j=1}^{k}(n_j - 1)s_j^2 = 5(164.4) + 5(131.2) + 5(110.4) = 2030$$

d. $\text{MSE} = \text{SSE}/(n_T - k) = 2030/(12 - 3) = 135.3$
e.

Source of Variation	Sum of Squares	Degrees of Freedom	Mean Square	F	p-value
Treatments	1488	2	744	5.50	.0162
Error	2030	15	135.3		
Total	3518	17			

f. $F = \text{MSTR/MSE} = 744/135.3 = 5.50$
Using F table (2 degrees of freedom numerator and 15 denominator), p-value is between .01 and .025
Using Excel, the p-value corresponding to $F = 5.50$ is .0162
Because p-value $\leq \alpha = .05$, we reject the hypothesis that the means for the three treatments are equal

30. a. $H_0: u_1 = u_2 = u_3 = u_4 = u_5$
H_a: Not all the population means are equal
b. Using Excel, the p-value corresponding to $F = 14.07$ is .0000
Because p-value $\leq \alpha = .05$, we reject H_0

32.

Source of Variation	Sum of Squares	Degrees of Freedom	Mean Square	F	p-value
Treatments	1200	2	600	43.99	.0000
Error	600	44	13.64		
Total	1800	46			

Using F table (2 degrees of freedom numerator and 44 denominator), p-value is less than .01
Using Excel, the p-value corresponding to $F = 43.99$ is .0000
Because p-value $\leq \alpha = .05$, we reject the hypothesis that the treatment means are equal

34. a.

Source of Variation	Sum of Squares	Degrees of Freedom	Mean Square	F	p-value
Treatments	4560	2	2280	9.87	.0006
Error	6240	27	231.11		
Total	10,800	29			

b. Using F table (2 degrees of freedom numerator and 27 denominator), p-value is less than .01
Using Excel, the p-value corresponding to $F = 9.87$ is .0006
Because p-value $\leq \alpha = .05$, we reject the null hypothesis that the means of the three assembly methods are equal

36. SSTR = 70, MSTR = 35, SSE = 236, MSE = 19.67
$F = 1.78$
Using F table (2 degrees of freedom numerator and 12 denominator), p-value is greater than .10
Using Excel, the p-value corresponding to $F = 1.78$ is .2104
Because p-value $> \alpha = .05$, we cannot reject the null hypothesis that the mean yields for the three temperatures are equal

38. SSTR = 330, MSTR = 110, SSE = 692, MSE = 43.25
$F = 2.54$
Using F table (3 degrees of freedom numerator and 16 denominator), p-value is between .05 and .10
Using Excel, the p-value corresponding to $F = 2.54$ is .0931
Because p-value $> \alpha = .05$, we cannot reject the null hypothesis that the mean drying times for the four paints are equal

40. a. $H_0: \mu_1 - \mu_2 = 0$
$H_a: \mu_1 - \mu_2 \neq 0$
$z = 2.79$
p-value = .0052
Reject H_0; a significant difference between systems exists

42. **a.** H_0: $\mu_1 - \mu_2 \leq 0$
H_a: $\mu_1 - \mu_2 > 0$
b. $t = .60$, $df = 57$
Using t table, p-value is greater than .20
Exact p-value = .2754
Do not reject H_0

44. **a.** $\bar{d} = 2.45$
b. \$.30 to \$4.60
c. 8% decrease
d. \$23.93

46. Significant relationship; p-value = .0061

48. Significant difference; p-value = .0002

50. Significant relationship; p-value = .0340

Chapter 11

1. **a.** $\bar{p}_1 - \bar{p}_2 = .48 - .36 = .12$

b. $$\bar{p}_1 - \bar{p}_2 \pm z_{.05}\sqrt{\frac{\bar{p}_1(1-\bar{p}_1)}{n_1} + \frac{\bar{p}_2(1-\bar{p}_2)}{n_2}}$$

$$.12 \pm 1.645\sqrt{\frac{.48(1-.48)}{400} + \frac{.36(1-.36)}{300}}$$

$.12 \pm .0614$ (.0586 to .1814)

c. $$.12 \pm 1.96\sqrt{\frac{.48(1-.48)}{400} + \frac{.36(1-.36)}{300}}$$

$.12 \pm .0731$ (.0469 to .1931)

2. **a.** .2333
b. .1498
c. Do not reject H_0; cannot conclude population proportions differ

3. **a.** $$\bar{p} = \frac{n_1\bar{p}_1 + n_2\bar{p}_2}{n_1 + n_2} = \frac{200(.22) + 300(.16)}{200 + 300} = .1840$$

$$z = \frac{\bar{p}_1 - \bar{p}_2}{\sqrt{\bar{p}(1-\bar{p})\left(\frac{1}{n_1} + \frac{1}{n_2}\right)}}$$

$$= \frac{.22 - .16}{\sqrt{.1840(1-.1840)\left(\frac{1}{200} + \frac{1}{300}\right)}} = 1.70$$

p-value = 1.0000 − .9554 = .0446

b. p-value $\leq .05$; reject H_0; conclude p_1 is greater than p_2

4. $\bar{p}_1 = 220/400 = .55$ $\bar{p}_2 = 192/400 = .48$

$$\bar{p}_1 - \bar{p}_2 \pm z_{.025}\sqrt{\frac{\bar{p}_1(1-\bar{p}_1)}{n_1} + \frac{\bar{p}_2(1-\bar{p}_2)}{n_2}}$$

$$.55 - .48 \pm 1.96\sqrt{\frac{.55(1-.55)}{400} + \frac{.48(1-.48)}{400}}$$

$.07 \pm .0691$ (.0009 to .1391)

6. **a.** .45
b. .35
c. $.10 \pm .0989$ or (.0011 to .1989)

8. **a.** H_0: $p_1 \leq p_2$
H_a: $p_1 > p_2$
b. .2017
c. .1111
d. $z = 2.10$; p-value = .0179
Reject H_0; higher proportion of dry wells were drilled in 2005

10. **a.** H_0: $p_1 - p_2 \leq 0$
H_a: $p_1 - p_2 > 0$
b. .84, .81
c. p-value = .0094
Reject H_0; conclude an increase
d. .005 to .055; yes due to increase

11. H_0: $p_1 = p_2 = p_3$
H_a: Not all population proportions are equal
Expected frequencies (e_{ij}):

	1	2	3	Total
Yes	132.0	158.4	105.6	396
No	118.0	141.6	94.4	354
Total	250	300	200	750

Chi-square calculations $(f_{ij} - e_{ij})^2/e_{ij}$:

	1	2	3	Total
Yes	2.45	.45	.87	3.77
No	2.75	.50	.98	4.22
				$\chi^2 = 7.99$

$df = k - 1 = (3 - 1) = 2$
χ^2 table with $\chi^2 = 7.99$ shows p-value between .025 and .01
p-value $\leq .05$, reject H_0; not all population proportions are equal

12. **a.** $\bar{p}_1 = 150/250 = .60$
$\bar{p}_2 = 150/300 = .50$
$\bar{p}_3 = 96/200 = .48$
b. Population 1 has the largest proportion of Yes responses

14. **a.** H_0: $p_1 = p_2 = p_3$
H_a: Not all population proportions are equal
b. Expected frequencies (e_{ij}):

Component	A	B	C	Total
Defective	25	25	25	75
Good	475	475	475	1425
Total	500	500	500	1500

Chi-square calculations $(f_{ij} - e_{ij})^2/e_{ij}$:

Component	A	B	C	Total
Defective	4.00	1.00	9.00	14.00
Good	.21	.05	.47	0.74
				$\chi^2 = 14.74$

$df = k - 1 = (3 - 1) = 2$
χ^2 table, $\chi^2 = 14.74$, p-value is less than .01
p-value $\leq .05$, reject H_0; three suppliers do not provide equal proportions of defective components

16. a. .14, .09
b. $\chi^2 = 3.41$, $df = 1$
p-value between .10 and .05
Reject H_0; conclude two offices do not have equal error rates
c. z provides options for one-tailed tests

18. $\chi^2 = 5.70$, $df = 4$
p-value greater than .10
Do no reject H_0; no evidence suppliers differ in quality

19. H_0: The column variable is independent of the row variable
H_a: The column variable is not independent of the row variable
Expected frequencies (e_{ij}):

	A	B	C	Total
P	28.5	39.9	45.6	114
Q	21.5	30.1	34.4	86
Total	50	70	80	200

Chi-square calculations $(f_{ij} - e_{ij})^2 / e_{ij}$:

	A	B	C	Total
P	2.54	.42	.42	3.38
Q	3.36	.56	.56	4.48
				$\chi^2 = 7.86$

$df = (2 - 1)(3 - 1) = 2$
Using the χ^2 table, p-value between .01 and .025
p-value $\leq .05$, reject H_0; conclude variables are not independent

20. $\chi^2 = 19.77$, $df = 4$
p-value less than .005
Reject H_0; conclude variables are not independent

21. a. H_0: Ticket purchased is independent of flight
H_a: Ticket purchased is not independent of flight
Expected frequencies:

$e_{11} = 35.59$ $e_{12} = 15.41$
$e_{21} = 150.73$ $e_{22} = 65.27$
$e_{31} = 455.68$ $e_{32} = 197.32$

Observed Frequency (f_i)	Expected Frequency (e_i)	Chi-square $(f_i - e_i)^2 / e_i$
29	35.59	1.22
22	15.41	2.82
95	150.73	20.61
121	65.27	47.59
518	455.68	8.52
135	197.32	19.68
920		$\chi^2 = 100.43$

$df = (r - 1)(c - 1) = (3 - 1)(2 - 1) = 2$
Using the χ^2 table, p-value is less than .005
p-value $\leq .05$, reject H_0; conclude ticket purchased is not independent of the type of flight
b. Column Percentages

	Type of Flight	
Type of Ticket	Domestic	International
First Class	4.5%	7.9%
Business Class	14.8%	43.5%
Economy Class	80.7%	48.6%

A higher percentage of first-class and business-class tickets are purchased for international flights

22. a. $\chi^2 = 9.44$, $df = 2$
p-value is less than .01
Reject H_0; plan not independent of type of company
b.

Employment Plan	Private	Public
Add Employees	.5139	.2963
No Change	.2639	.3148
Lay Off Employees	.2222	.3889

Employment opportunities better for private companies

24. a. $\chi^2 = 6.57$, $df = 6$
p-value greater than .10
Do not reject H_0; cannot reject assumption of independence
b. 29%, 46%, and 25%
Outstanding is most frequent owner rating

26. a. 900
b. .2044, .2278, .2100, .1400, .2178
The movie fans favored Jennifer Lawrence, but three other nominees (Jessica Chastain, Emmanuelle Riva, and Naomi Watts) were each favored by almost as many of the fans
c. $\chi^2 = 77.74$; p-value is approximately 0
Reject H_0; actress and respondent age are not independent

28. $\chi^2 = 45.36$, $df = 4$
p-value less than .05
Reject H_0; conclude that the ratings of the hosts are not independent

30. a. p-value ≈ 0, reject H_0
b. .0468 to .1332

32. a. .35 and .47
b. $.12 \pm .1037$ (.0163 to .2237)
c. Yes, we would expect occupancy rates to be higher

34. a. 8.8%, 11.7%, 9.0%, 8.5%
b. $\chi^2 = 2.48$, $df = 3$
p-value greater than .10
Do not reject H_0; cannot reject assumption that the population proportions are equal

36. Let
p_1 = population proportion of on-time arrivals for American Airlines
p_2 = population proportion of on-time arrivals for Continental Airlines
p_3 = population proportion of on-time arrivals for Delta Air Lines
p_4 = population proportion of on-time arrivals for JetBlue Airways
p_5 = population proportion of on-time arrivals for Southwest Airlines
p_6 = population proportion of on-time arrivals for United Airlines
p_7 = population proportion of on-time arrivals for US Airways
a. .8384, .75, .8205, .7317, .75, .8148, .85
b. $\chi^2 = 7.370$
Degrees of freedom $= k - 1 = 7 - 1 = 6$
p-value = .2880

Do not reject H_0; no significant differences in proportion of on-time arrivals

38. Let
p_1 = population proportion of truck drivers who rate Rochester, New York, as satisfactory in keeping its streets clear of snow
p_2 = population proportion of truck drivers who rate Salt Lake City, Utah, as satisfactory in keeping its streets clear of snow
p_3 = population proportion of truck drivers who rate Madison, Wisconsin, as satisfactory in keeping its streets clear of snow
p_4 = population proportion of truck drivers who rate Bridgeport, Connecticut, as satisfactory in keeping its streets clear of snow

a. .5625, .625, .617, .5333
b. $\chi^2 = 1.16$
Degrees of freedom $= k - 1 = 4 - 1 = 3$
p-value = .7623
Do not reject H_0; no significant differences in the proportions who rate job as satisfactory

40. $\chi^2 = 23.37$, $df = 3$
p-value is less than .005
Reject H_0; employment status is not independent of region

42. a. 71%, 22%, slower preferred
b. $\chi^2 = 2.99$, $df = 2$
p-value greater than .10
Do not reject H_0; cannot conclude men and women differ in preference

44. $\chi^2 = 7.75$, $df = 3$
p-value is between .05 and .10
Do not reject H_0; cannot conclude office vacancies differ by metropolitan area

Appendix E: Microsoft Excel 2013 and Tools for Statistical Analysis

Microsoft Excel 2013, part of the Microsoft Office 2013 system, is a spreadsheet program that can be used to organize and analyze data, perform complex calculations, and create a wide variety of graphical displays. We assume that readers are familiar with basic Excel operations such as selecting cells, entering formulas, copying, and so on. But we do not assume readers are familiar with Excel 2013 or the use of Excel for statistical analysis.

The purpose of this appendix is twofold. First, we provide an overview of Excel 2013 and discuss the basic operations needed to work with Excel 2013 workbooks and worksheets. Second, we provide an overview of the tools that are available for conducting statistical analysis with Excel. These include Excel functions and formulas which allow users to conduct their own analyses and add-ins that provide more comprehensive analysis tools.

Excel's Data Analysis add-in, included with the basic Excel system, is a valuable tool for conducting statistical analysis. In the last section of this appendix we provide instruction for installing the Data Analysis add-in. Other add-ins have been developed by outside suppliers to supplement the basic statistical capabilities provided by Excel. In the last section we also discuss StatTools, a commercially available add-in developed by Palisade Corporation.

Overview of Microsoft Excel 2013

A workbook is a file containing one or more worksheets.

When using Excel for statistical analysis, data is displayed in workbooks, each of which contains a series of worksheets that typically include the original data as well as any resulting analysis, including charts. Figure E.1 shows the layout of a blank workbook created each time Excel is opened. The workbook is named Book1, and contains one worksheet named Sheet1. Excel highlights the worksheet currently displayed (Sheet1) by setting the name on the worksheet tab in bold. Note that cell A1 is initially selected.

The wide bar located across the top of the workbook is referred to as the Ribbon. Tabs, located at the top of the Ribbon, provide quick access to groups of related commands. There are eight tabs shown on the workbook in Figure E.1: FILE; HOME; INSERT; PAGE LAYOUT; FORMULAS; DATA; REVIEW; and VIEW. Each tab contains a series of groups of related commands. Note that the HOME tab is selected when Excel is opened. Figure E.2 displays the groups available when the HOME tab is selected. Under the HOME tab there are seven groups: Clipboard; Font; Alignment; Number; Styles; Cells; and Editing. Commands are arranged within each group. For example, to change selected text to boldface, click the HOME tab and click the Bold **B** button in the Font group.

Figure E.3 illustrates the location of the Quick Access Toolbar and the Formula Bar. The Quick Access Toolbar allows you to quickly access workbook options. To add or remove features on the Quick Access Toolbar, click the Customize Quick Access Toolbar button at the end of the Quick Access Toolbar.

The Formula Bar (see Figure E.3) contains a Name box, the Insert Function button *fx*, and a Formula box. In Figure E.3, "A1" appears in the name box because cell A1 is selected. You can select any other cell in the worksheet by using the mouse to move the cursor to another cell and clicking or by typing the new cell location in the Name box. The Formula box is used to display the formula in the currently selected cell. For instance, if you enter =A1+A2 into cell A3, whenever you select cell A3 the formula =A1+A2 will be shown in the Formula box. This feature makes it very easy to see and edit a formula in

FIGURE E.1 BLANK WORKBOOK CREATED WHEN EXCEL IS OPENED

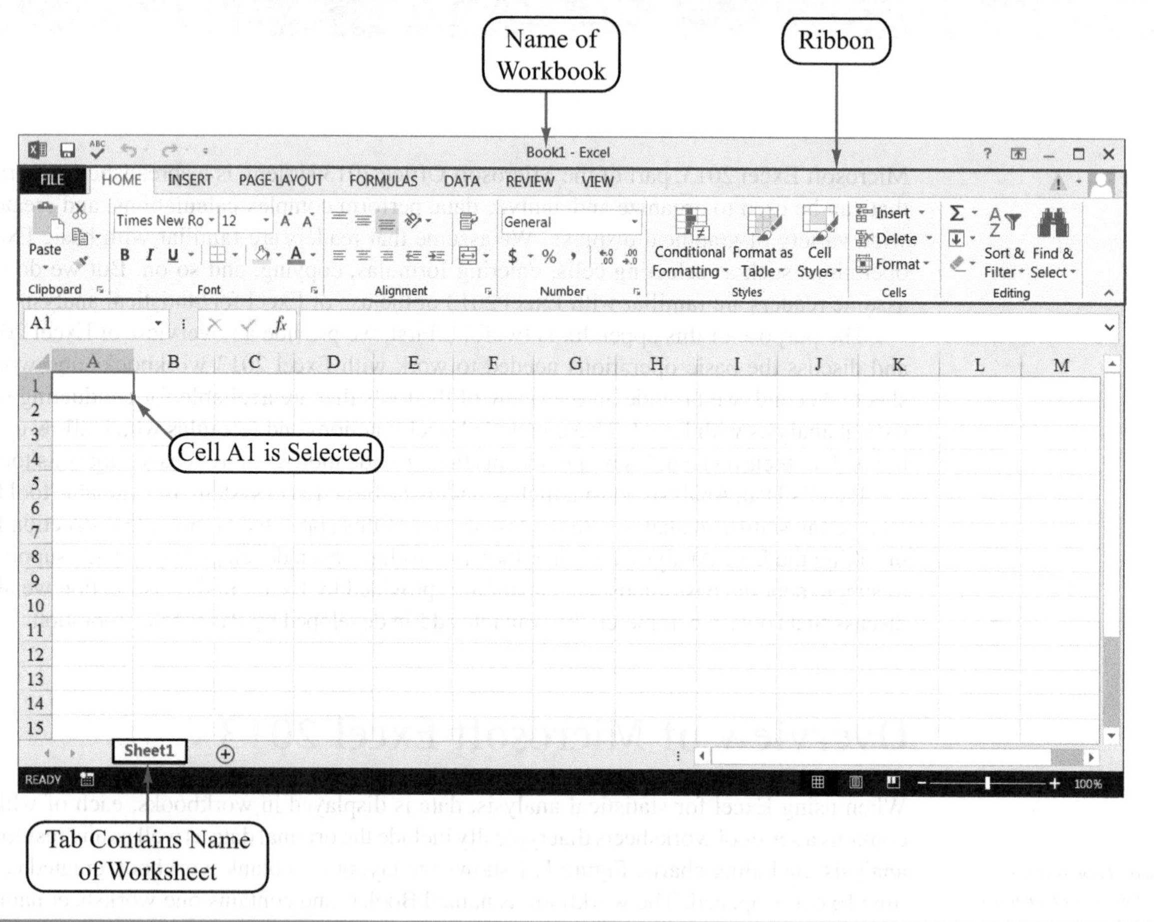

a particular cell. The Insert Function button allows you to quickly access all the functions available in Excel. Later we show how to find and use a particular function.

Basic Workbook Operations

Figure E.4 illustrates the worksheet options that can be performed after right-clicking on a worksheet tab. For instance, to change the name of the current worksheet from "Sheet1" to "Data," right-click the worksheet tab named "Sheet1" and select the Rename option. The current worksheet name (Sheet1) will be highlighted. Then, simply type the new name (Data) and press the Enter key to rename the worksheet.

Suppose that you wanted to create a copy of "Sheet1." After right-clicking the tab named "Sheet1," select the Move or Copy option. When the Move or Copy dialog box appears, select Create a Copy and click OK. The name of the copied worksheet will appear as "Sheet1 (2)." You can then rename it, if desired.

To add a new worksheet to the workbook, right-click any worksheet tab and select the Insert option; when the Insert dialog box appears, select Worksheet and click OK. An additional blank worksheet will appear in the workbook. You can also insert a new worksheet by clicking the New sheet button + that appears to the right of the last worksheet tab displayed. Worksheets can be deleted by right-clicking the worksheet tab and choosing

FIGURE E.2 PORTION OF THE HOME TAB

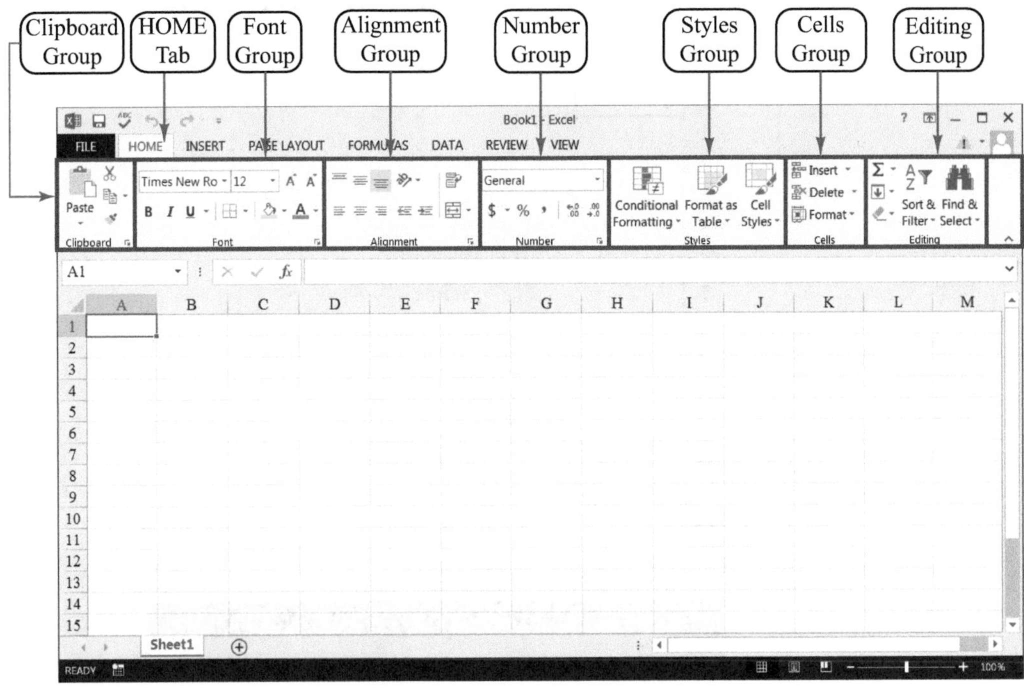

FIGURE E.3 EXCEL 2013 QUICK ACCESS TOOLBAR AND FORMULA BAR

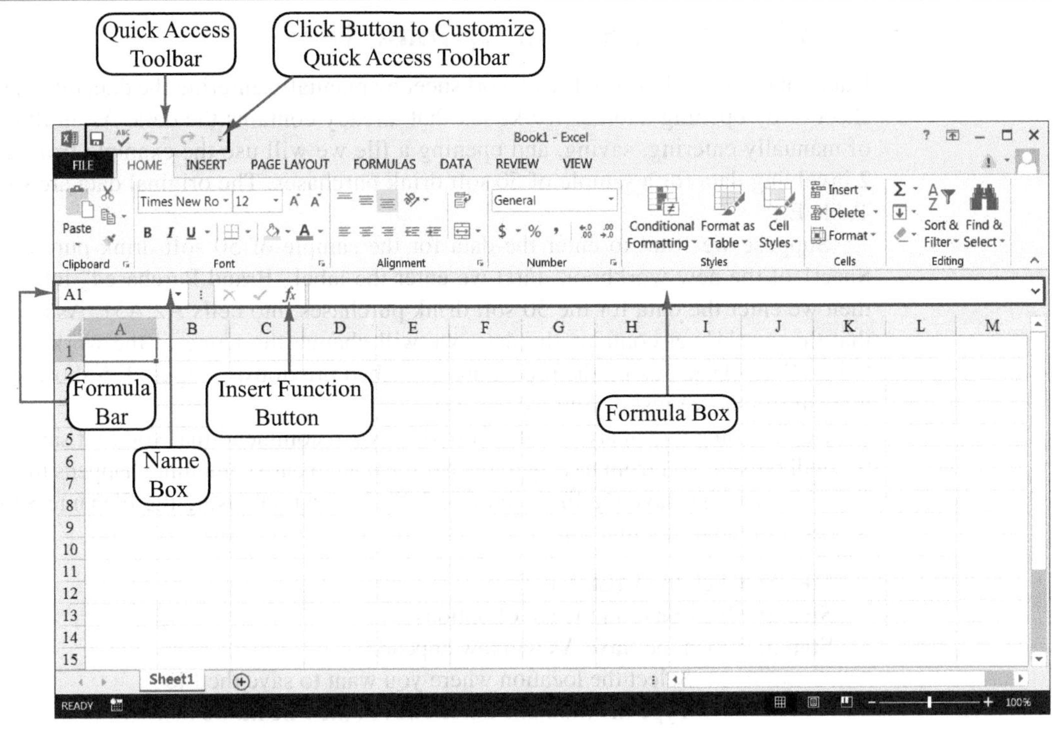

FIGURE E.4 WORKSHEET OPTIONS OBTAINED AFTER RIGHT-CLICKING ON A WORKSHEET TAB

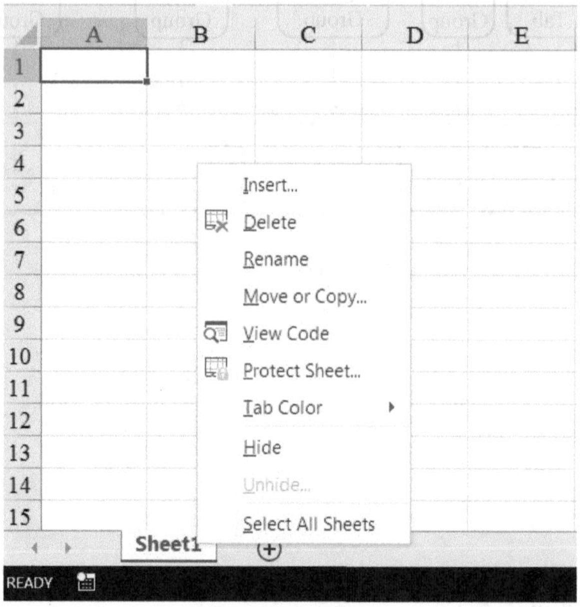

Delete. Worksheets can also be moved to other workbooks or a different position in the current workbook by using the Move or Copy option.

Creating, Saving, and Opening Files

Data can be entered into an Excel worksheet by manually entering the data into the worksheet or by opening another workbook that already contains the data. As an illustration of manually entering, saving, and opening a file we will use the example from Chapter 2 involving data for a sample of 50 soft drink purchases. The original data are shown in Table E.1.

Suppose we want to enter the data for the sample of 50 soft drink purchases into Sheet1 of the new workbook. First we enter the label "Brand Purchased" into cell A1; then we enter the data for the 50 soft drink purchases into cells A2:A51. As a reminder that this worksheet contains the data, we will change the name of the worksheet from "Sheet1" to "Data" using the procedure described previously. Figure E.5 shows the data worksheet that we just developed.

Before doing any analysis with these data, we recommend that you first save the file; this will prevent you from having to reenter the data in case something happens that causes Excel to close. To save the file as an Excel 2013 workbook using the filename SoftDrink we perform the following steps:

Step 1: Click the **FILE** tab
Step 2: Click **Save** in the list of options
Step 3: When the **Save As** window appears:
Select the location where you want to save the file
Type the filename **SoftDrink** in the **File name** box
Click **Save**

TABLE E.1 DATA FROM A SAMPLE OF 50 SOFT DRINK PURCHASES

Coca-Cola	Sprite	Pepsi
Diet Coke	Coca-Cola	Coca-Cola
Pepsi	Diet Coke	Coca-Cola
Diet Coke	Coca-Cola	Coca-Cola
Coca-Cola	Diet Coke	Pepsi
Coca-Cola	Coca-Cola	Dr. Pepper
Dr. Pepper	Sprite	Coca-Cola
Diet Coke	Pepsi	Diet Coke
Pepsi	Coca-Cola	Pepsi
Pepsi	Coca-Cola	Pepsi
Coca-Cola	Coca-Cola	Pepsi
Dr. Pepper	Pepsi	Pepsi
Sprite	Coca-Cola	Coca-Cola
Coca-Cola	Sprite	Dr. Pepper
Diet Coke	Dr. Pepper	Pepsi
Coca-Cola	Pepsi	Sprite
Coca-Cola	Diet Coke	

FIGURE E.5 WORKSHEET CONTAINING THE SOFT DRINK DATA

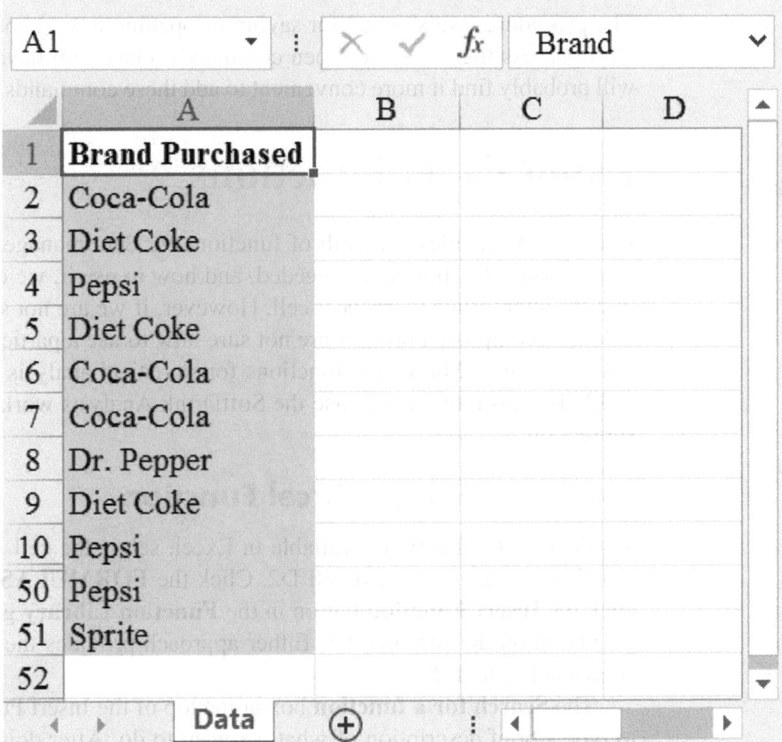

Note: Rows 11–49 are hidden.

Keyboard shortcut: To save the file, press CTRL+S.

Excel's Save command is designed to save the file as an Excel 2013 workbook. As you work with the file to do statistical analysis you should follow the practice of periodically saving the file so you will not lose any statistical analysis you may have performed. Simply click the File tab and select Save in the list of options.

Sometimes you may want to create a copy of an existing file. For instance, suppose you would like to save the soft drink data and any resulting statistical analysis in a new file named "SoftDrink Analysis." The following steps show how to create a copy of the SoftDrink workbook and analysis with the new filename, "SoftDrink Analysis."

Step 1: Click the **FILE** tab
Step 2: Click **Save As**
Step 3: When the Save As window appears:
Select the location where you want to save the file
Type the filename **SoftDrink Analysis** in the **File name** box
Click **Save**

Once the workbook has been saved, you can continue to work with the data to perform whatever type of statistical analysis is appropriate. When you are finished working with the file simply click the FILE tab and then click close in the list of options. To access the SoftDrink Analysis file at another point in time you can open the file by performing the following steps:

Step 1: Click the **FILE** tab
Step 2: Click **Open**
Step 3: When the Open window appears:
Select the location where you previously saved the file
Enter the filename **SoftDrink Analysis** in the **File name** box
Click **Open**

The procedures we showed for saving or opening a workbook begin by clicking the File tab to access the Save and Open commands. Once you have used Excel for a while you will probably find it more convenient to add these commands to the Quick Access Toolbar.

Using Excel Functions

Excel 2013 provides a wealth of functions for data management and statistical analysis. If we know what function is needed, and how to use it, we can simply enter the function into the appropriate worksheet cell. However, if we are not sure what functions are available to accomplish a task, or are not sure how to use a particular function, Excel can provide assistance. Many new functions for statistical analysis have been added with Excel 2013. To illustrate we will use the SoftDrink Analysis workbook created in the previous subsection.

Finding the Right Excel Function

To identify the functions available in Excel, select the cell where you want to insert the function; we have selected cell D2. Click the **FORMULAS** tab on the Ribbon and then click the **Insert Function** button in the **Function Library** group. Alternatively, click the *fx* button on the formula bar. Either approach provides the **Insert Function** dialog box shown in Figure E.6.

The **Search for a function** box at the top of the Insert Function dialog box enables us to type a brief description of what we want to do. After doing so and clicking **Go**, Excel will search for and display, in the **Select a function** box, the functions that may accomplish our task. In many situations, however, we may want to browse through an entire category of functions to see what is available. For this task, the **Or select a category** box is helpful.

FIGURE E.6 INSERT FUNCTION DIALOG BOX

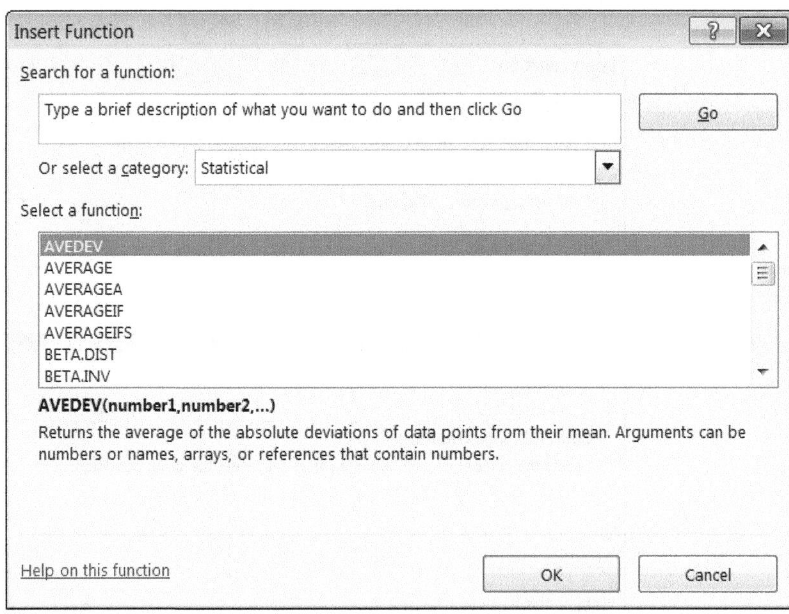

It contains a drop-down list of several categories of functions provided by Excel. Figure E.6 shows that we selected the **Statistical** category. As a result, Excel's statistical functions appear in alphabetic order in the Select a function box. We see the AVEDEV function listed first, followed by the AVERAGE function, and so on.

The AVEDEV function is highlighted in Figure E.6, indicating it is the function currently selected. The proper syntax for the function and a brief description of the function appear below the Select a function box. We can scroll through the list in the Select a function box to display the syntax and a brief description for each of the statistical functions that are available. For instance, scrolling down farther, we select the COUNTIF function as shown in Figure E.7. Note that COUNTIF is now highlighted, and that immediately below the Select a function box we see **COUNTIF(range,criteria)**, which indicates that the COUNTIF function contains two inputs, range and criteria. In addition, we see that the description of the COUNTIF function is "Counts the number of cells within a range that meet the given condition."

If the function selected (highlighted) is the one we want to use, we click **OK**; the **Function Arguments** dialog box then appears. The Function Arguments dialog box for the COUNTIF function is shown in Figure E.8. This dialog box assists in creating the appropriate arguments (inputs) for the function selected. When finished entering the arguments, we click OK; Excel then inserts the function into a worksheet cell.

Using Excel Add-Ins

Excel's Data Analysis Add-In

Excel's Data Analysis add-in, included with the basic Excel package, is a valuable tool for conducting statistical analysis. Before you can use the Data Analysis add-in it must be installed. To see if the Data Analysis add-in has already been installed, click the DATA tab on the Ribbon. In the Analysis group you should see the Data Analysis command. If you

FIGURE E.7 DESCRIPTION OF THE COUNTIF FUNCTION IN THE INSERT FUNCTION DIALOG BOX

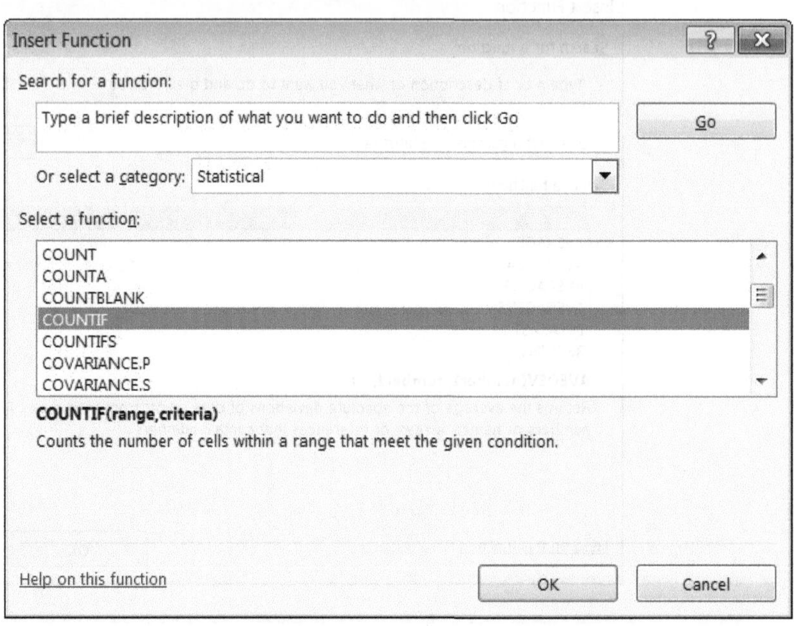

do not have an Analysis group and/or the Data Analysis command does not appear in the Analysis group, you will need to install the Data Analysis add-in. The steps needed to install the Data Analysis add-in are as follows:

Step 1. Click the **FILE** tab
Step 2. Click **Options**
Step 3. When the Excel Options dialog box appears:
    Select **Add-Ins** from the list of options (on the pane on the left)
    In the **Manage** box, select **Excel Add-Ins**
    Click **Go**
Step 4. When the Add-Ins dialog box appears:
    Select **Analysis ToolPak**
    Click **OK**

FIGURE E.8 FUNCTION ARGUMENTS DIALOG BOX FOR THE COUNTIF FUNCTION

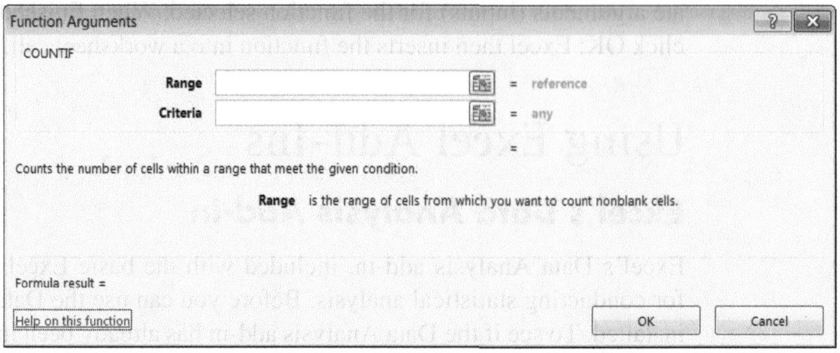

Function Arguments
COUNTIF
Range = reference
Criteria = any
=
Counts the number of cells within a range that meet the given condition.
Range is the range of cells from which you want to count nonblank cells.
Formula result =
Help on this function
OK Cancel

Outside Vendor Add-Ins

One of the leading companies in the development of Excel add-ins for statistical analysis is Palisade Corporation. In this text we use StatTools, an Excel add-in developed by Palisade. StatTools provides a powerful statistics toolset that enables users to perform statistical analysis in the familiar Microsoft Office environment.

In the appendix to Chapter 1 we describe how to download and install the StatTools add-in and provide a brief introduction to using the software. In several appendices throughout the text we show how StatTools can be used when no corresponding basic Excel procedure is available or when additional statistical capabilities would be useful.

Typically the add-ins offered with textbooks are designed primarily for classroom use. StatTools, however, was developed for commercial applications. As a result, students who learn how to use StatTools will be able to continue using StatTools throughout their professional career.